NORTH CAROLI

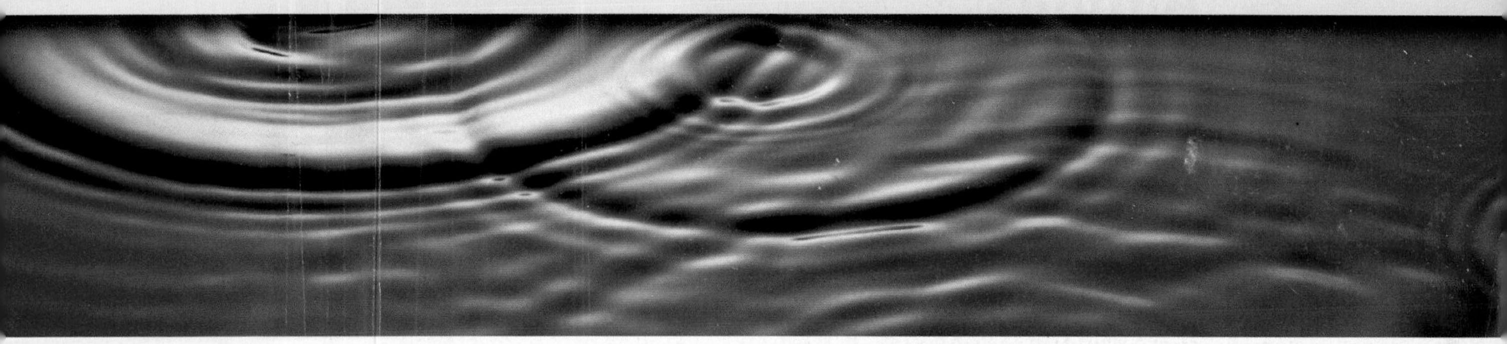

PRENTICE HALL MATHEMATICS

ALGEBRA 2

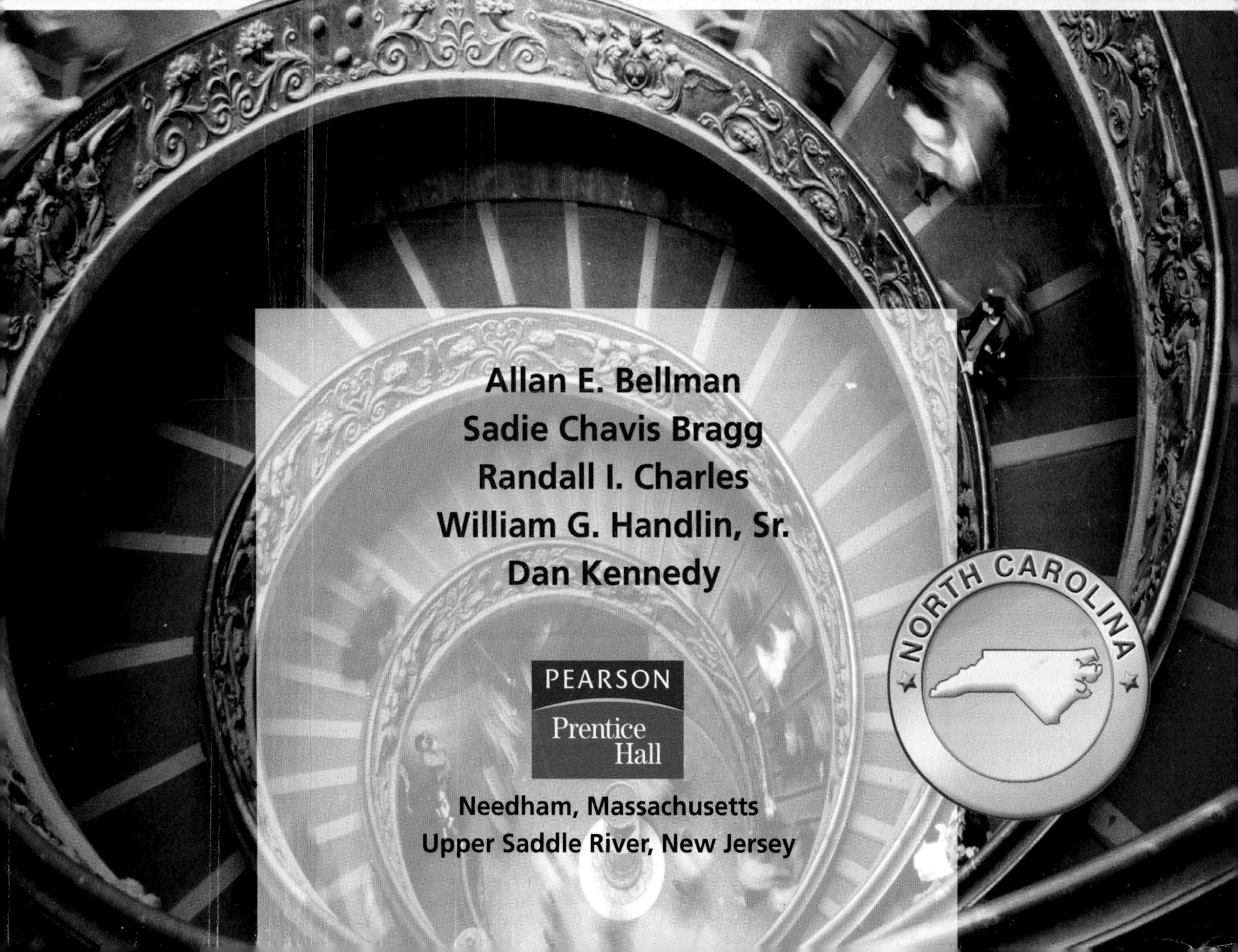

Allan E. Bellman
Sadie Chavis Bragg
Randall I. Charles
William G. Handlin, Sr.
Dan Kennedy

PEARSON
Prentice Hall

Needham, Massachusetts
Upper Saddle River, New Jersey

Authors

Series Authors

Dan Kennedy, Ph.D., is a classroom teacher and the Lupton Distinguished Professor of Mathematics at the Baylor School in Chattanooga, Tennessee. A frequent speaker at professional meetings on the subject of mathematics education reform, Dr. Kennedy has conducted more than 50 workshops and institutes for high school teachers. He is co-author of textbooks in calculus and precalculus, and from 1990 to 1994 he chaired the College Board's AP Calculus Development Committee. He is a 1992 Tandy Technology Scholar and a 1995 Presidential Award winner.

Randall I. Charles, Ph.D., is Professor Emeritus in the Department of Mathematics and Computer Science at San Jose State University, San Jose, California. He began his career as a high school mathematics teacher, and he was a mathematics supervisor for five years. Dr. Charles has been a member of several NCTM committees and is the former Vice President of the National Council of Supervisors of Mathematics. Much of his writing and research has been in the area of problem solving. He has authored more than 75 mathematics textbooks for kindergarten through college.

Dorling Kindersley (DK) is an international publishing company that specializes in the creation of high-quality, illustrated information books for children and adults. Dorling Kindersley's unique graphic presentation style is used in this program to motivate students in learning about real-world applications of mathematics. DK is part of the Pearson family of companies.

ISBN 0-13-180865-6

3 4 5 6 7 8 9 10   07 06 05 04

Algebra 1 and Algebra 2 Authors

Allan E. Bellman is a Lecturer/Supervisor in the School of Education at the University of California, Davis. Before coming to Davis, he was a mathematics teacher for 31 years in Montgomery County, Maryland. He has been an instructor for both the Woodrow Wilson National Fellowship Foundation and the T^3 program. Mr. Bellman has a particular expertise in the use of technology in education and speaks frequently on this topic. He was a 1992 Tandy Technology Scholar.

Sadie Chavis Bragg, Ed.D., is Professor of Mathematics and Vice President of Academic Affairs at the Borough of Manhattan Community College of the City University of New York. Dr. Bragg is a past president of the American Mathematical Association of Two-Year Colleges (AMATYC), is co-director of the AMATYC project to revise the standards for introductory college mathematics before calculus, and is an active member of the Benjamin Banneker Association. Since 1976, she has co-authored more than 50 mathematics textbooks from kindergarten through college.

William G. Handlin, Sr., is a classroom teacher and Department Chairman of Technology Applications at Spring Woods High School in Houston, Texas. Awarded Life Membership in the Texas Congress of Parent and Teachers Association for his contributions to the well-being of children, Mr. Handlin is also a frequent workshop and seminar leader in professional meetings throughout the world.

Geometry Authors

Laurie E. Bass
Fieldston, the Grades 7–12 Division of
the Ethical Culture Fieldston School
Riverdale, New York

Art Johnson, Ed.D.
Professor of Mathematics
Boston University
Boston, Massachusetts

Reviewers

North Carolina Math Program Advisors

Kelly S. Crisp
Mathematics Teacher
Buncombe County Schools
Arden, North Carolina

Don McGurrin
Educational Math Consultant
Clayton, North Carolina

Sheila S. Brookshire
Mathematics Teacher
AC Reynolds Middle School
Asheville, North Carolina

Dr. Ann R. Crawford
University of North Carolina at Wilmington
Wilmington, North Carolina

Cynthia Hanner Davis
Mathematics Teacher
Northeast High School
Greensboro, North Carolina

Judy Porter
Leesville Road High School
Raleigh, North Carolina

Algebra 1 Reviewers

Mary Lou Beasley
Southside Fundamental Middle School
St. Petersburg, Florida

Blanche Smith Brownley
Washington, D.C., Public Schools
Washington, D.C.

Joseph Caruso
Somerville High School
Somerville, Massachusetts

Belinda Craig
Highland West Junior High School
Moore, Oklahoma

Jane E. Damaske
Lakeshore Public Schools
Stevensville, Michigan

Stacy A. Ego
Warren Central High School
Indianapolis, Indiana

Earl R. Jones
Formerly, Kansas City Public Schools
Kansas City, Missouri

Jeanne Lorenson
James H. Blake High School
Silver Spring, Maryland

John T. Mace
Hibbett Middle School
Florence, Alabama

Ann Marie Palmieri-Monahan
Director of Mathematics
Bayonne Board of Education
Bayonne, New Jersey

Marie Schalke
Woodlawn Middle School
Long Grove, Illinois

Julie Welling
LaPorte High School
LaPorte, Indiana

Sharon Zguzenski
Naugatuck High School
Naugatuck, Connecticut

Geometry Reviewers

Marian Avery
Great Valley High School
Malvern, Pennsylvania

Mary Emma Bunch
Farragut High School
Knoxville, Tennessee

Karen A. Cannon
K–12 Mathematics Coordinator
Rockwood School District
Eureka, Missouri

Johnnie Ebbert
Department Chairman
DeLand High School
DeLand, Florida

Russ Forrer
Math Department Chairman
East Aurora High School
Aurora, Illinois

Andrea Kopco
Midpark High School
Middleburg Heights, Ohio

Gordon E. Maroney III
Camden Fairview High School
Camden, Arkansas

Charlotte Phillips
Math Coordinator
Wichita USD 259
Wichita, Kansas

Richard P. Strausz
Farmington Public Schools
Farmington, Michigan

Jane Tanner
Jefferson County International Baccalaureate School
Birmingham, Alabama

Karen D. Vaughan
Pitt County Schools
Greenville, North Carolina

Robin Washam
Math Specialist
Puget Sound Educational Service District
Burien, Washington

Algebra 2 Reviewers

Josiane Fouarge
Landry High School
New Orleans, Louisiana

Susan Hvizdos
Math Department Chair
Wheeling Park High School
Wheeling, West Virginia

Kathleen Kohler
Kearny High School
Kearny, New Jersey

Julia Kolb
Leesville Road High School
Raleigh, North Carolina

Deborah R. Kula
Sacred Hearts Academy
Honolulu, Hawaii

Betty Mayberry
Gallatin High School
Gallatin, Tennessee

John L. Pitt
Formerly, Prince William County Schools
Manassas, Virginia

Margaret Plouvier
Billings West High School
Billings, Montana

Sandra Sikorski
Berea High School
Berea, Ohio

Tim Visser
Grandview High School
Cherry Creek School District
Aurora, Colorado

Mathematics Content Consultants

Courtney Lewis
Prentice Hall Senior National Consultant
Baltimore, Maryland

Deana Cerroni
Prentice Hall National Consultant
Las Vegas, Nevada

Kim Margel
Prentice Hall National Consultant
Scottsdale, Arizona

Sandra Mosteller
Prentice Hall National Consultant
Anderson, South Carolina

Rita Corbett
Prentice Hall Consultant
Elgin, Illinois

Cathy Davies
Prentice Hall Consultant
Laguna Niguel, California

Sally Marsh
Prentice Hall Consultant
Baltimore, Maryland

Dr. Barbara Rogers
Prentice Hall Consultant
Raleigh, North Carolina

Rose Primiani
Prentice Hall Consultant
Brick, New Jersey

Loretta Rector
Prentice Hall Consultant
Foresthill, California

Charlotte Samuels
Prentice Hall Consultant
Lafayette Hill, Pennsylvania

Margaret Thomas
Prentice Hall Consultant
Indianapolis, Indiana

Contents in Brief

Chapter 1

Tools of Algebra

Student Support

Chapter 2

Functions, Equations, and Graphs

Student Support

Chapter 3

Linear Systems

Student Support

Chapter 4

Matrices

Student Support

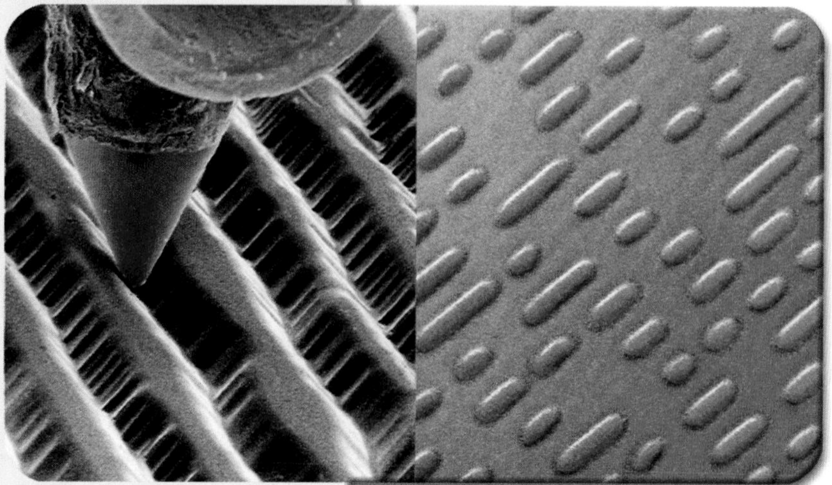

Chapter 5

Quadratic Equations and Functions

Student Support

Chapter 6

Polynomials and Polynomial Functions

Student Support

Instant Check System

Diagnosing Readiness, 298

Check Skills You'll Need, 300, 307, 314, 321, 329, 335, 339, 347

Check Understanding, 301, 302, 303, 307, 308, 309, 310, 315, 316, 317, 321, 322, 323, 324, 330, 331, 332, 336, 337, 339, 340, 341, 348, 349

Checkpoint Quiz, 320, 345

Reading Math

Reading Math, 301, 304, 310, 316, 325, 329, 336

Reading for Problem Solving, 327

Understanding Vocabulary, 353

Standardized Test Prep

305, 313, 319, 326, 334, 338, 344, 351

Test-Taking Strategies, 352

Standardized Test Prep, 357

Real-World Connections

Gold, 302
Algebra at Work, 320
Design, 325
Boating, 340
Consumer Issues, 343
Genetics, 350
Soccer, 358–359
. . . and more!

Chapter 7

Radical Functions and Rational Exponents

Student Support

Chapter 8

Exponential and Logarithmic Functions

Student Support

Instant Check System

Reading Math

Standardized Test Prep

Real-World Connections

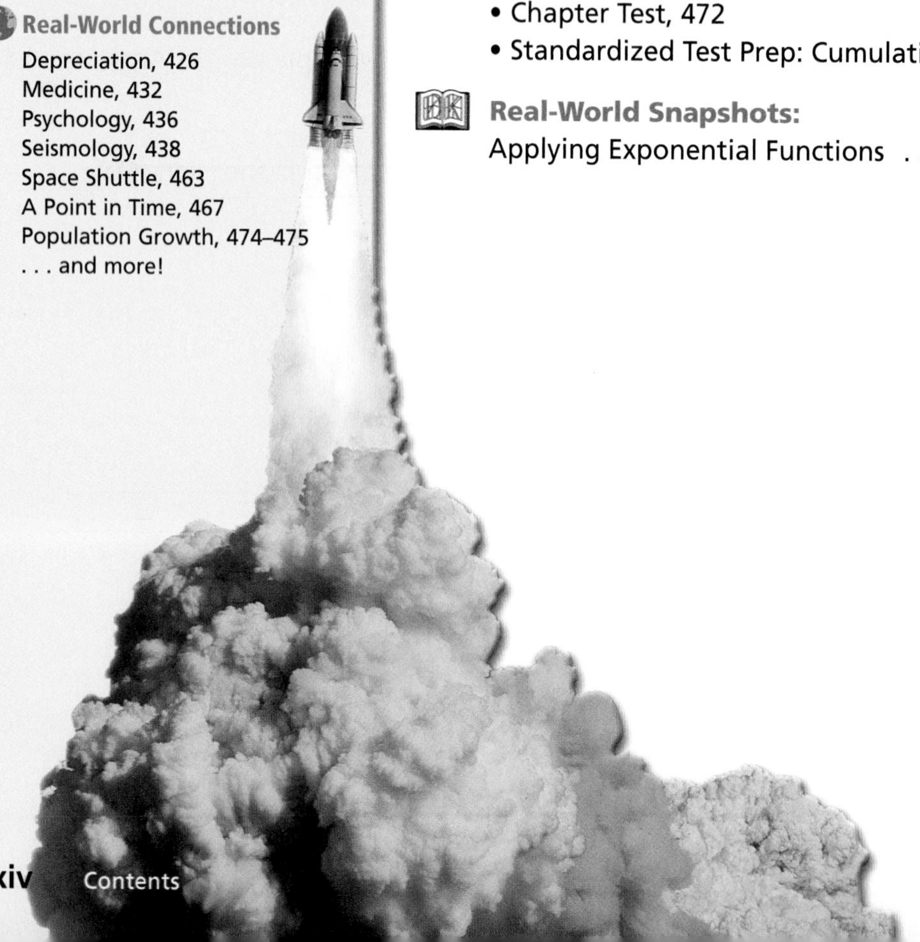

Chapter 9

Rational Functions

Student Support

Chapter 10

Quadratic Relations

Student Support

Chapter 11

Sequences and Series

Student Support

Chapter 12

Probability and Statistics

Student Support

Chapter 13

Periodic Functions and Trigonometry

Student Support

Instant Check System

Reading Math

Standardized Test Prep

Real-World Connections

Chapter 14

Trigonometric Identities and Equations

Student Support

Take It to the Net

Throughout this book you will find links to the Prentice Hall Web site for *Algebra 2*. Use the Web Code provided with each link to gain direct access to online material.

For a complete list of online features, use Web Code agk-0099

Here's how to **Take It to the Net:**

- Go to **PHSchool.com**.
- Enter the Web Code.
- Click Go!

Lesson Quiz Web Codes

There is an online quiz for each lesson. Access these quizzes with Web Codes aga-0101 through aga-1407 for Lesson 1-1 through Lesson 14-7. See page 8.

88 Lesson Quizzes
Web Code format: aga-0204 02 = Chapter 2 04 = Lesson 4

Chapter Resource Web Codes

Chapter	Vocabulary Quizzes *See page 47.*	Chapter Tests *See page 50.*	Dorling Kindersley Real-World Snapshots *See pages 112–113.*	Chapter Projects
1	agj-0151	aga-0152		agd-0161
2	agj-0251	aga-0252	age-0253	agd-0261
3	agj-0351	aga-0352		agd-0361
4	agj-0451	aga-0452	age-0453	agd-0461
5	agj-0551	aga-0552		agd-0561
6	agj-0651	aga-0652	age-0653	agd-0661
7	agj-0751	aga-0752		agd-0761
8	agj-0851	aga-0852	age-0853	agd-0861
9	agj-0951	aga-0952		agd-0961
10	agj-1051	aga-1052	age-1053	agd-1061
11	agj-1151	aga-1152		agd-1161
12	agj-1251	aga-1252	age-1253	agd-1261
13	agj-1351	aga-1352		agd-1361
14	agj-1451	aga-1452	age-1453	agd-1461
End-of-Course		aga-1454		

Additional Resource Web Codes

Data Updates Use Web Code agg-2041 to get up-to-date government data for use in examples and exercises. *See page 83.*

Algebra at Work For information about each Algebra at Work feature, use Web Code agb-2031. *See page 24.*

A Point in Time For information about each A Point in Time feature, use Web Code age-2032. *See page 207.*

Graphing Calculator Procedures There are 27 procedures available online. Use Web Code age-2100 for an index of all the procedures, or Web Codes age-2101 through age-2127 to access individual procedures. *See page 85.*

Using Your Book for Success

Welcome to Prentice Hall *Algebra 2*. There are many features built into the daily lessons of this text that will help you learn the important skills and concepts you will need to be successful in this course. Look through the following pages for some study tips that you will find useful as you complete each lesson.

Instant Check System
An *Instant Check System*, built into the text and marked with a ✓, allows you to check your understanding of skills before moving on to the next topic.

✓ Diagnosing Readiness
Complete the *Diagnosing Readiness* exercises to see what topics you may need to review before you begin the chapter.

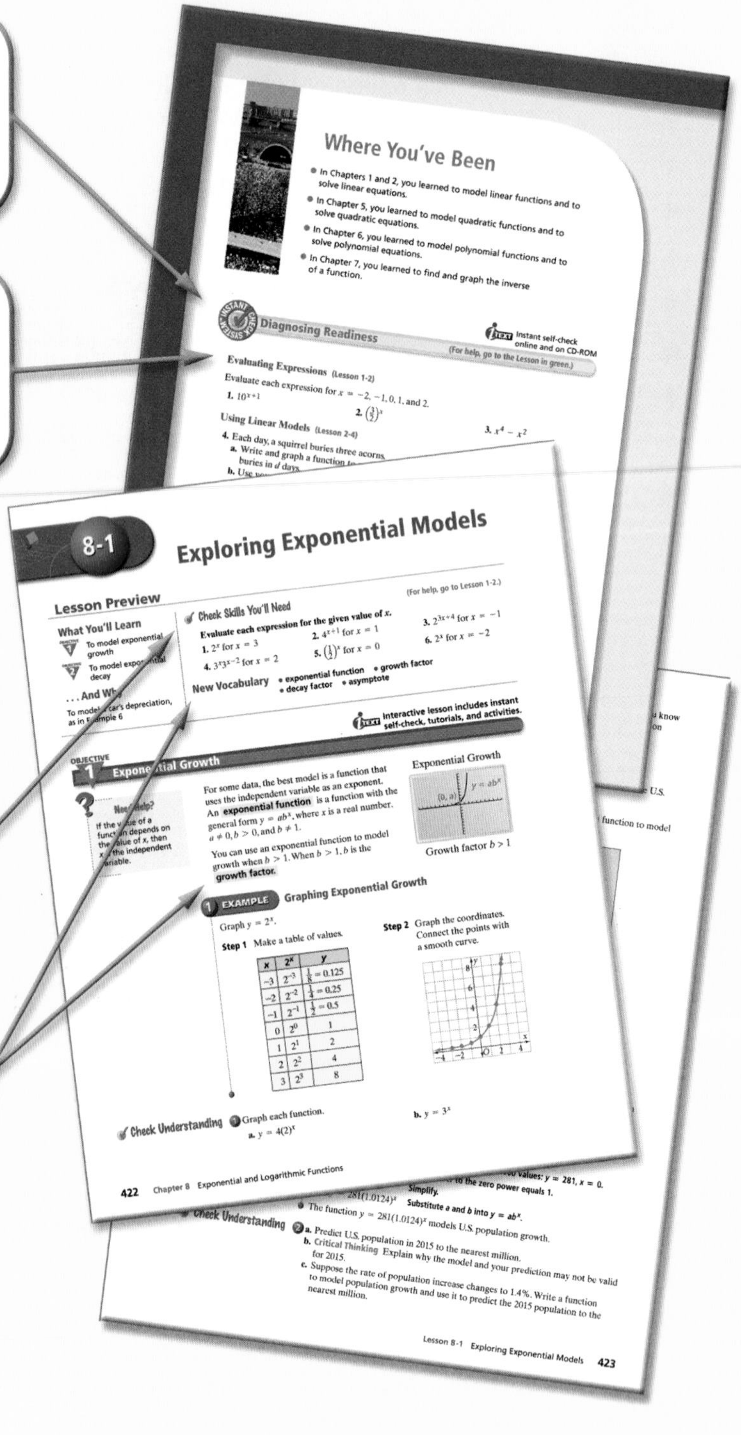

✓ Check Skills You'll Need
Complete the *Check Skills You'll Need* exercises to make sure you have the skills needed to successfully learn the concepts in the lesson.

New Vocabulary
New Vocabulary is listed for each lesson so you can pre-read the text. As each term is introduced, it is highlighted in yellow.

Need Help?
Need Help? notes provide a quick review of a concept you need to understand the topic being presented. Look for the green labels throughout the text that tell you where to "Go" for help.

Check Understanding
Every lesson includes numerous *Examples,* each followed by a *Check Understanding* question that you can do on your own to see if you understand the skill being introduced. Check your progress with the answers at the back of the book.

Reading Math
The *Reading Math* hints help you to use mathematical notation correctly, understand new mathematical vocabulary, and translate mathematical symbols into everyday English so you can talk about what you've learned.

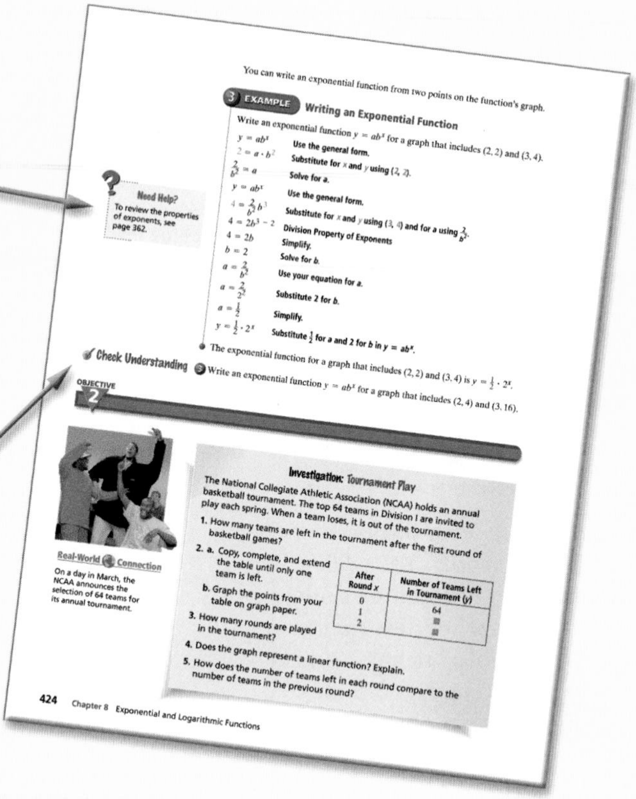
You can write an exponential function from two points on the function's graph.

3 EXAMPLE Writing an Exponential Function

Write an exponential function $y = ab^x$ for a graph that includes (2, 2) and (3, 4).

Need Help? To review the properties of exponents, see page 362.

The exponential function for a graph that includes (2, 2) and (3, 4) is $y = \frac{1}{2} \cdot 2^x$.

Check Understanding 3 Write an exponential function $y = ab^x$ for a graph that includes (2, 4) and (3, 16).

OBJECTIVE 2

Real-World Connection: On a day in March, the NCAA announces the selection of 64 teams for its annual tournament.

Investigation: Tournament Play

The National Collegiate Athletic Association (NCAA) holds an annual basketball tournament. The top 64 teams in Division I are invited to play each spring. When a team loses, it is out of the tournament.

1. How many teams are left in the tournament after the first round of basketball games?
2. a. Copy, complete, and extend the table until only one team is left.
   b. Graph the points from your table on graph paper.
3. How many rounds are played in the tournament?
4. Does the graph represent a linear function? Explain.
5. How does the number of teams left in each round compare to the number of teams in the previous round?

After Round x	Number of Teams Left in Tournament (y)
0	64
1	■
2	■

424 Chapter 8 Exponential and Logarithmic Functions

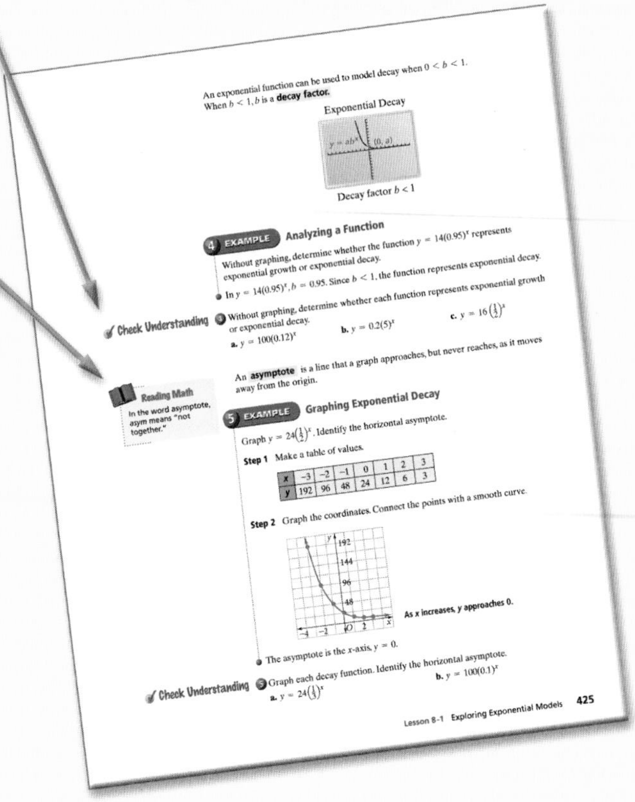
An exponential function can be used to model decay when $0 < b < 1$. When $b < 1$, b is a **decay factor.**

Exponential Decay

Decay factor $b < 1$

4 EXAMPLE Analyzing a Function

Without graphing, determine whether the function $y = 14(0.95)^x$ represents exponential growth or exponential decay.

In $y = 14(0.95)^x$, $b = 0.95$. Since $b < 1$, the function represents exponential decay.

Check Understanding 4 Without graphing, determine whether each function represents exponential growth or exponential decay.
a. $y = 100(0.12)^x$ b. $y = 0.2(5)^x$ c. $y = 16\left(\frac{1}{2}\right)^x$

An **asymptote** is a line that a graph approaches, but never reaches, as it moves away from the origin.

Reading Math: In the word asymptote, asym means "not together."

5 EXAMPLE Graphing Exponential Decay

Graph $y = 24\left(\frac{1}{2}\right)^x$. Identify the horizontal asymptote.

Step 1 Make a table of values.

x	−3	−2	−1	0	1	2	3
y	192	96	48	24	12	6	3

Step 2 Graph the coordinates. Connect the points with a smooth curve.

As x increases, y approaches 0.

The asymptote is the x-axis, $y = 0$.

Check Understanding 5 Graph each decay function. Identify the horizontal asymptote.
a. $y = 24\left(\frac{1}{3}\right)^x$ b. $y = 100(0.1)^x$

Lesson 8-1 Exploring Exponential Models 425

Exercises
There are numerous *Exercises* in each lesson that give you the practice you need to master the concepts in the lesson. Each practice set includes the following sections.

A: Practice by Example
The *A: Practice by Example* exercises refer you back to the Examples in the lesson, in case you need help with completing these exercises.

B: Apply Your Skills
The *B: Apply Your Skills* exercises combine skills from earlier lessons to offer you richer skill exercises and multi-step application problems.

C: Challenge
The *C: Challenge* exercises give you an opportunity to solve problems that extend and stretch your thinking.

Standardized Test Prep
Standardized Test Prep exercises give you daily practice with the types of test question formats that you will encounter on state and national tests.

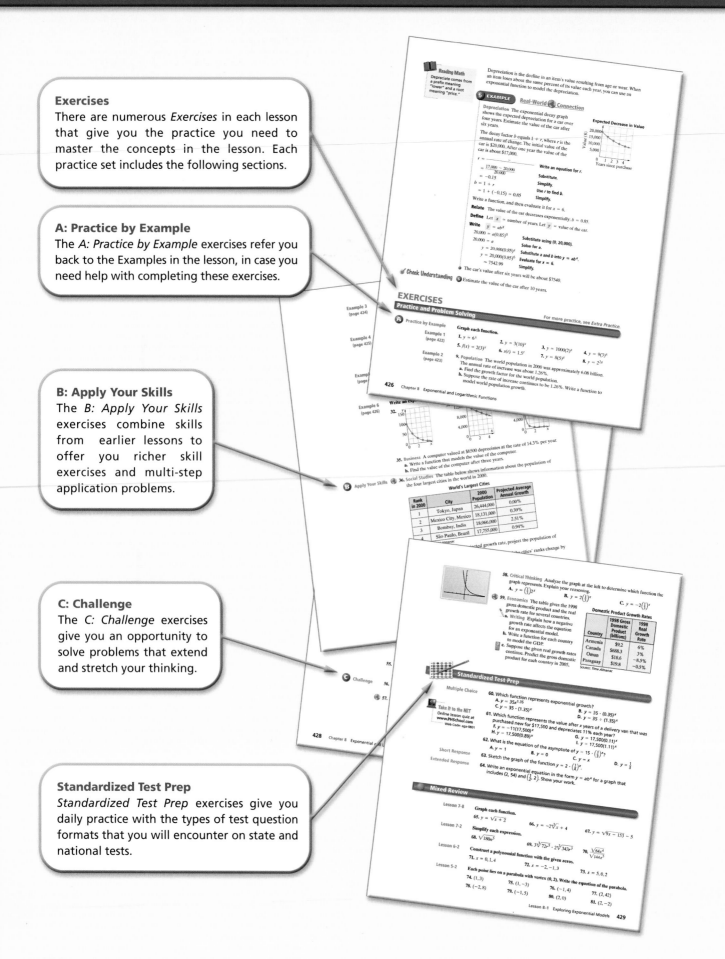

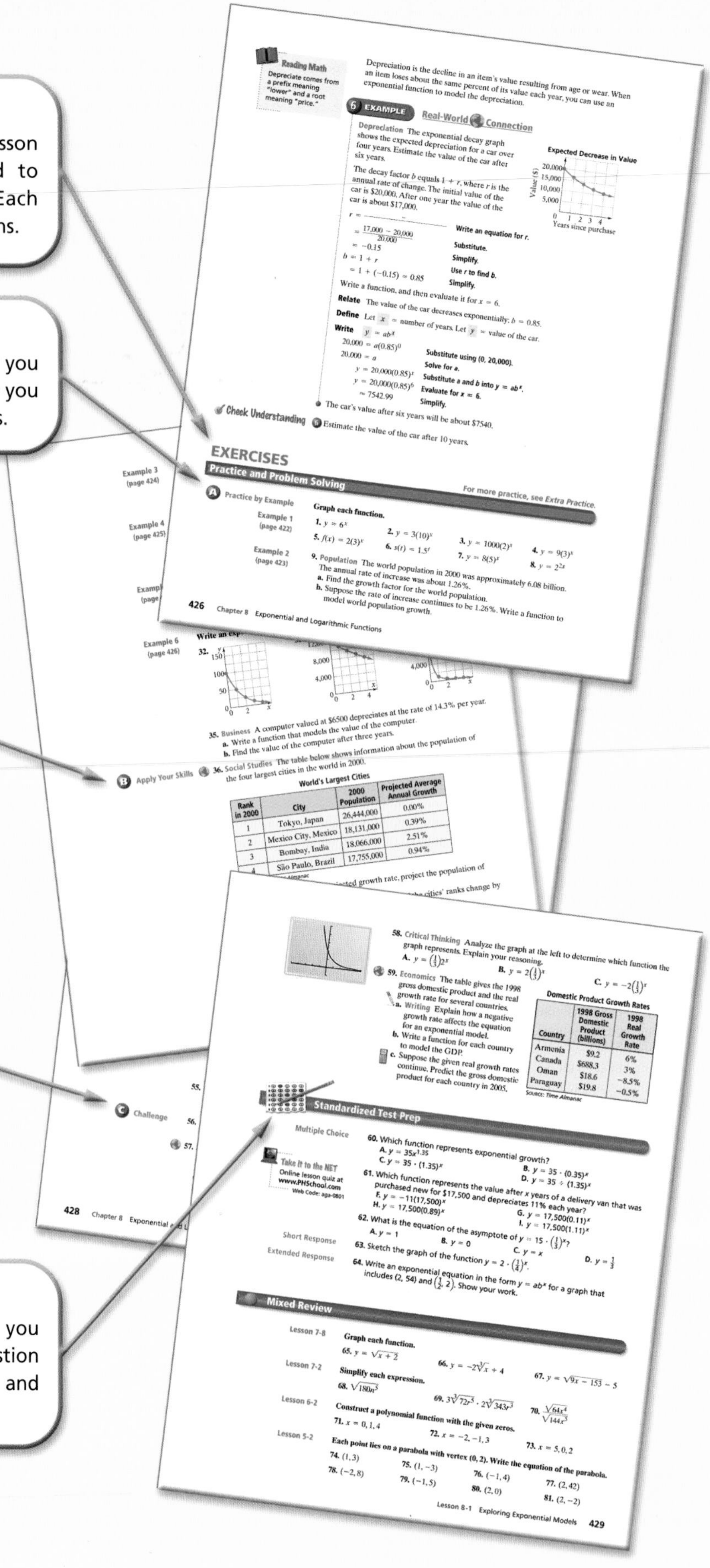

Preparing for Tests

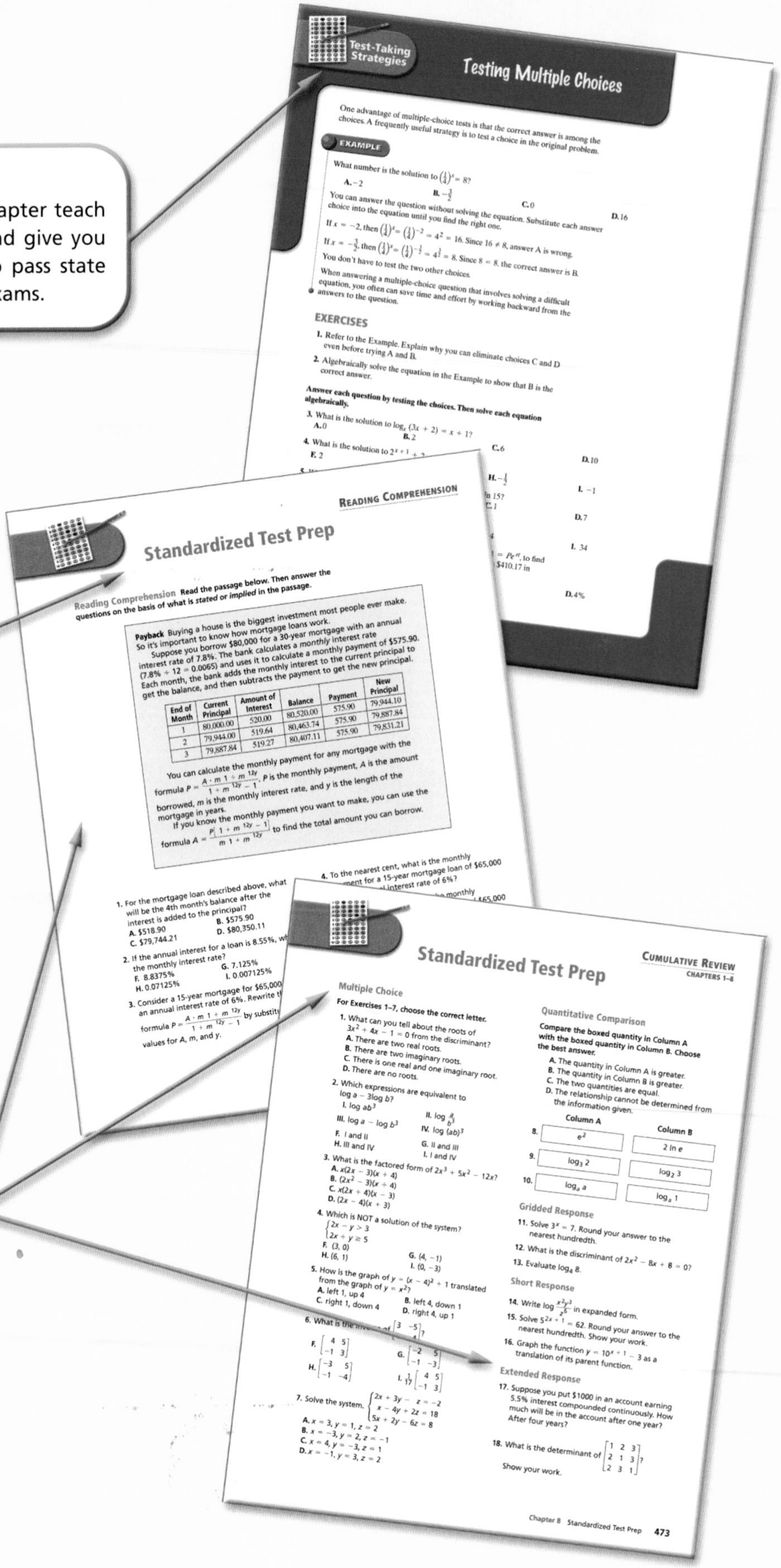

Test-Taking Strategies
Test-Taking Strategies in every chapter teach you strategies to be successful and give you practice in the skills you need to pass state tests and standardized national exams.

Standardized Test Prep
Standardized Test Prep pages in every chapter give you more opportunities to prepare for the tests you will have to take.

Test Item Formats
The *Standardized Test Prep* exercises in your book give you the practice you need to answer all types of test questions.

- *Multiple Choice*
- *Quantitative Comparison*
- *Gridded Response*, for which you write your answer in a grid
- *Short Response*, which are scored using a rubric
- *Extended Response*, which are scored using a rubric
- *Reading Comprehension*

Reading to Learn

In addition to the Reading Math hints shown on page xxiii, your *Algebra 2* text provides even more ways for you to develop your ability to read mathematically so that you are successful in this course and on state tests.

Reading Math lessons
Reading Math lessons focus on a variety of topics to help you read more effectively, so that you can write, speak, and think mathematically.

Reading Math exercises
Reading Math exercises in the Chapter Review help you to understand and correctly use the vocabulary presented in the chapter.

English/Spanish Illustrated Glossary
While you are learning, use your *English/Spanish Illustrated Glossary* as a handy reference for all the vocabulary in the book. Not only is there a written explanation, but you will also find an illustrated example of each term to help you understand and remember.

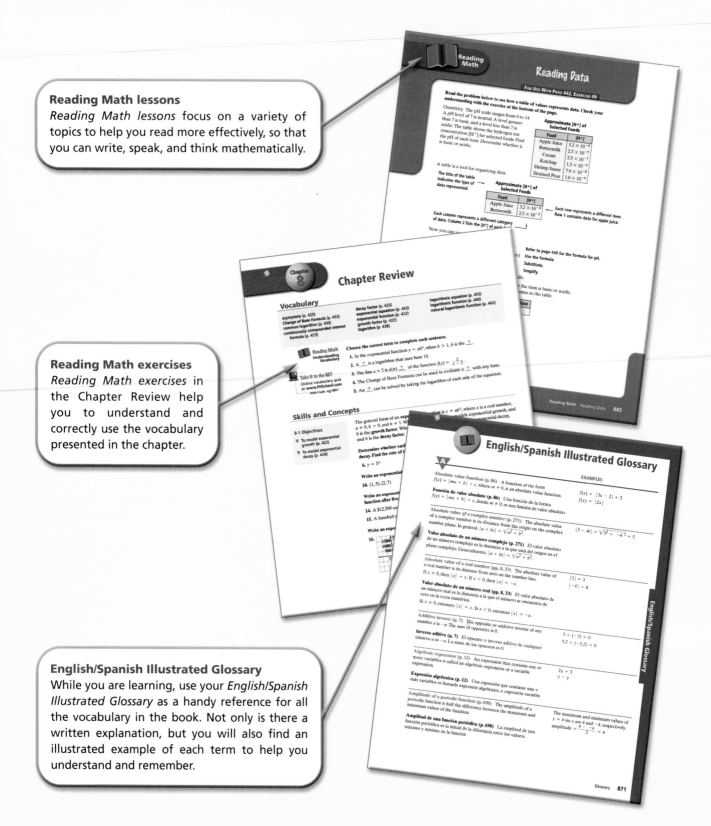

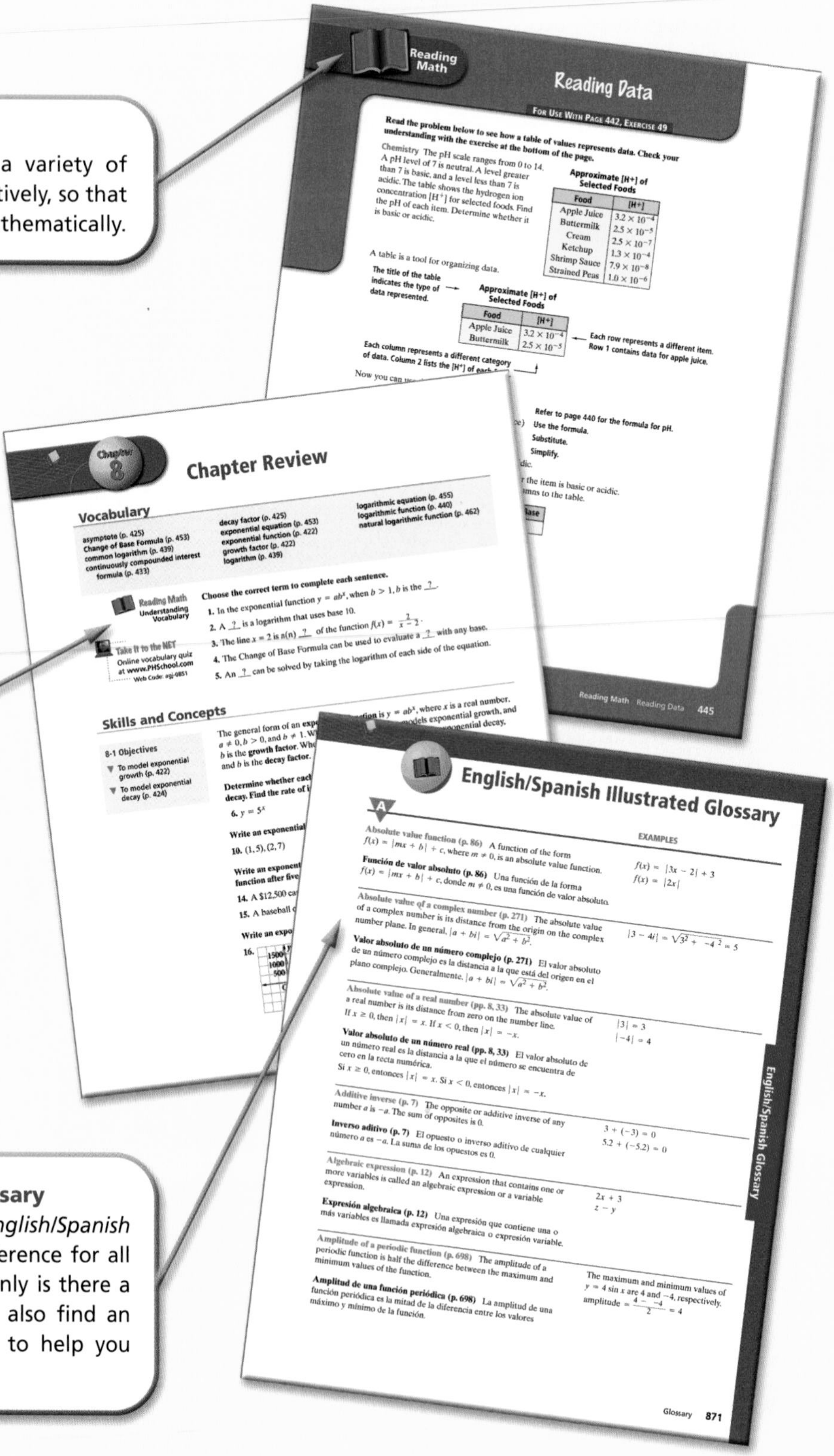

Dorling Kindersley (DK) is an international publishing company that specializes in the creation of high-quality, illustrated information books for children and adults. DK is part of the Pearson family of companies.

Real-World Snapshots
The *Real-World Snapshots* feature applies the exciting and unique graphic presentation style found in Dorling Kindersley books to show you how mathematics is used in real life.

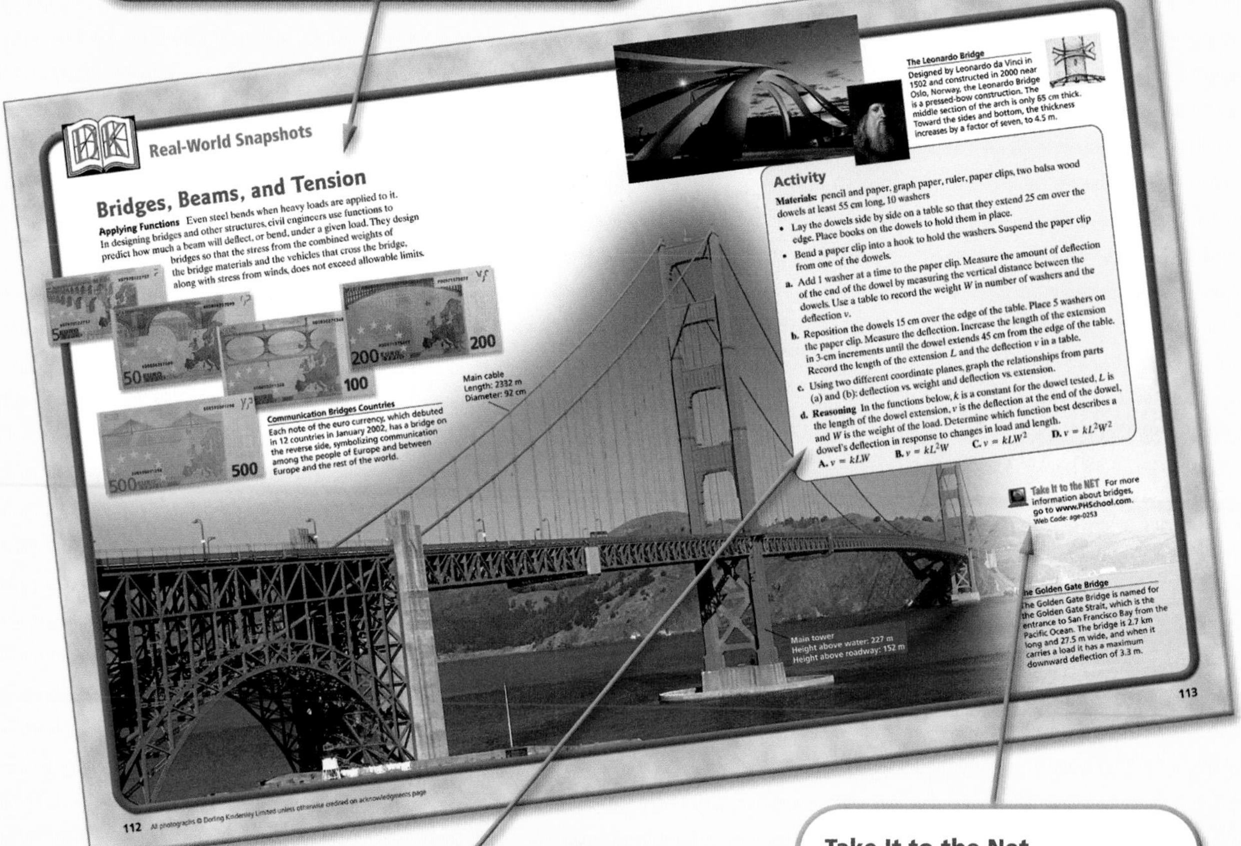

Real-World Snapshots

Bridges, Beams, and Tension

Applying Functions Even steel bends when heavy loads are applied to it. In designing bridges and other structures, civil engineers use functions to predict how much a beam will deflect, or bend, under a given load. They design bridges so that the stress from the combined weights of the bridge materials and the vehicles that cross the bridge, along with stress from winds, does not exceed allowable limits.

Communication Bridges Countries
Each note of the euro currency, which debuted in 12 countries in January 2002, has a bridge on the reverse side, symbolizing communication among the people of Europe and between Europe and the rest of the world.

Main cable
Length: 2332 m
Diameter: 92 cm

The Leonardo Bridge
Designed by Leonardo da Vinci in 1502 and constructed in 2000 near Oslo, Norway, the Leonardo Bridge is a pressed-bow construction. The middle section of the arch is only 65 cm thick. Toward the sides and bottom, the thickness increases by a factor of seven, to 4.5 m.

Activity
Materials: pencil and paper, graph paper, ruler, paper clips, two balsa wood dowels at least 55 cm long, 10 washers

- Lay the dowels side by side on a table so that they extend 25 cm over the edge. Place books on the dowels to hold them in place.
- Bend a paper clip into a hook to hold the washers. Suspend the paper clip from one of the dowels.

a. Add 1 washer at a time to the paper clip. Measure the amount of deflection of the end of the dowel by measuring the vertical distance between the dowels. Use a table to record the weight W in number of washers and the deflection v.
b. Reposition the dowels 15 cm over the edge of the table. Place 5 washers on the paper clip. Measure the deflection. Increase the length of the extension in 3-cm increments until the dowel extends 45 cm from the edge of the table. Record the length of the extension L and the deflection v in a table.
c. Using two different coordinate planes, graph the relationships from parts (a) and (b): deflection vs. weight and deflection vs. extension.
d. Reasoning In the functions below, k is a constant for the dowel tested, L is the length of the dowel extension, v is the deflection at the end of the dowel, and W is the weight of the load. Determine which function best describes a dowel's deflection in response to changes in load and length.
A. $v = kLW$ **B.** $v = kL^2W$ **C.** $v = kLW^2$ **D.** $v = kL^2W^2$

Take It to the NET For more information about bridges, go to www.PHSchool.com.
Web Code: age-0253

Main tower
Height above water: 227 m
Height above roadway: 152 m

The Golden Gate Bridge
The Golden Gate Bridge is named for the Golden Gate Strait, which is the entrance to San Francisco Bay from the Pacific Ocean. The bridge is 2.7 km long and 27.5 m wide, and when it carries a load it has a maximum downward deflection of 3.3 m.

112 All photographs © Dorling Kindersley Limited unless otherwise credited on acknowledgements page

113

Activities
Using data from these pages and data that you gather, complete the hands-on *Activities* to apply the mathematics you are learning in real-world situations.

Take It to the Net
Enter the Web Code for online information you can use to learn more about the topic of the feature.

North Carolina Algebra 2 Standard Course of Study Handbook

North Carolina High School Standard Course of Study, Algebra 2

These pages introduce you to the state standards which you will be learning this year. You will see the wording from the state documents, a short explanation of what the standard means to you, as well as an example of how the standard might be tested. Don't worry if you don't understand the concepts and the vocabulary yet. This book will guide you through all of the standards using skills and concepts that you *do* know.

North Carolina Course of Study

Here is a complete list of the objectives of the North Carolina Standard Mathematics Course of Study for Algebra 2. These are provided so that you will know what you are expected to learn this year.

Following each objective is an example of how you might see that objective tested. These test questions will become more meaningful to you as the year unfolds. You might want to check back to this section of the book from time to time to check that you understand how to answer the questions.

NUMBER & OPERATION

1.01 Simplify and perform operations with rational exponents and logarithms (common and natural) to solve problems.

What It Means to You

Radical signs, rational exponents and logarithms are ways of writing expressions that include numbers or variables raised to another power. A rational exponent looks like a fraction or a decimal. You may have seen them in science formulas, such as the formulas used to calculate the age of an artifact using carbon dating. The National Weather Service uses rational exponents to calculate wind chill in the formula $35.74 + 0.6215T - 35.75V^{0.16} + 0.4275TV^{0.16} = I$, where T is the temperature, V is the wind velocity, and I is the wind chill index. You will learn that the rules that you used to simplify expressions with integer exponents can also be used with rational exponents.

You may have seen *log* or *ln* in formulas used in discussions of the Richter scale (used to measure earthquakes) and the pH scale (used to measure acidity). The formula $L = 10\log\frac{I}{I_0}$ is used to measure the apparent loudness of sound using measures of intensity.

Logarithms are often written in the form $\log_b x = y$. You can rewrite a logarithmic expression using exponents. For example, $\log_2 8 = 3$ can also be written as $2^3 = 8$. Because of their relationship to exponents, logarithms are often used to simplify expressions with exponents containing variables, rather than calculating a root directly. Two of the most common bases for logarithms are 10—written as $\log_{10} x$ or more commonly as $\log x$—and the irrational number e—written as $\log_e x$ or more commonly as $\ln x$. You will learn how to simplify, add, subtract, multiply, and divide expressions with rational exponents and logarithms this year.

Where You'll Learn This

You will study this in Chapters 7 and 8.

What is the logarithmic form of the exponential equation $3^4 = 81$?

A $\log_4 81 = 3$
B $\log_4 3 = 81$
C $\log_3 81 = 4$
D $\log_{81} 3 = 4$

Answer: C

Evaluate $\log_5 125$.

A $\frac{1}{3}$
B 3
C 5
D 25

Answer: B

NUMBER & OPERATION

1.02 Define and compute with complex numbers.

What It Means to You

As you have seen, there are many different types of numbers in mathematics. So far, you have studied types of numbers found in the real numbers, which include integers, rational numbers, and irrational numbers.

You may wonder if there is another type of number not included in the real numbers. Where on a number line do you find $\sqrt{-4}$? Working only in real numbers, you may think $\sqrt{-4}$ does not exist. It is, however, part of another set of numbers called *imaginary numbers*. The imaginary numbers use the symbol i to mean $\sqrt{-1}$, and in the imaginary number system $\sqrt{-4} = 2i$. Real numbers and imaginary numbers together make up a new set of numbers called *complex numbers*. You will learn how to graph complex numbers and use them in calculations.

Where You'll Learn This

You will study this in Chapters 1, 5, and 6.

Find $(2i)(-3i)$. Show your wo

First, multiply the real numbe
$(2i)(-3i) = -6i^2$

Then, substitute -1 for i^2:
$(2i)(-3i) = -6(-1)$
$(2i)(-3i) = 6$

The correct answer is 6.

NU

1.04

W

1.03 Operate with algebraic expressions (polynomial, rational, complex fractions) to solve problems.

What It Means to You

Sentences often contain a phrase or two. For example, in the sentence "Joe is the student with the highest grade.", "with the highest grade" is a phrase. A phrase in algebra is an algebraic expression. It includes numbers, variables (usually letters), and operation symbols, for example, $4n$, $5x^3$, and $2x^2 + y$. Some may even involve fractions or have more than one variable. One algebraic expression you may be familiar with is the formula for counting permutations, ${}_nP_r = \frac{n!}{(n-r)!}$. You can also combine expressions and evaluate an expression if you know the value of the variable or variables. You will learn how to add, subtract, multiply, and divide the parts of algebraic expressions in order to solve problems.

Where You'll Learn This

You will study this in Chapters 1, 5, 6, and 9.

Seven students compete in a track meet. First, second, and third place ribbons will be awarded to the three fastest runners. How many arrangements of first, second, and third places are possible? Explain your answer.

One way to approach this problem is to use the permutation formula:

$${}_nP_r = \frac{n!}{(n-r)!}$$

There are seven runners arranged three at a time, so $n = 7$ and $r = 3$.

Plug in the numbers and compute:

$${}_7P_3 = \frac{7!}{(7-3)!}$$
$$= \frac{7!}{(4)!} = \frac{5{,}040}{24} = 210$$

The correct answer is 210.

MBER & OPERATION

Operate with matrices to model and solve problems.

hat It Means to You

hen you use a data table, you organize your data nto columns and rows. Like data tables, you can use a matrix to organize data and solve algebra problems.

For example, the number of books sold at two bookstores can be represented as:

	Store 1	Store 2
May	412	902
June	518	321
July	612	602
August	781	819

You can also perform operations with matrices similar to the operations you perform on numbers. For example, suppose you find out that Store 1 and Store 2 each have stores in another town. You can represent the books sold at Store 1b and Store 2b in a matrix. By adding the matrices together, you can find the total number of books sold in both locations for each store.

Store 1, Store 2 + Store 1b, Store 2b = Store 1 and 1b, Store 2 and 2b

$$\begin{bmatrix} 412 & 902 \\ 518 & 321 \\ 612 & 602 \\ 781 & 819 \end{bmatrix} + \begin{bmatrix} 504 & 615 \\ 320 & 475 \\ 600 & 620 \\ 756 & 750 \end{bmatrix} = \begin{bmatrix} 916 & 1{,}517 \\ 838 & 796 \\ 1{,}212 & 1{,}222 \\ 1{,}537 & 1{,}569 \end{bmatrix}$$

You will learn how to use matrices to represent real-world situations and solve problems. You will also be learning how to use operations, such as addition and multiplication, to develop new matrices and solve problems.

Where You'll Learn This

You will study this in Chapter 4.

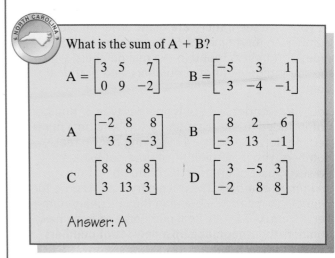

What is the sum of A + B?

$$A = \begin{bmatrix} 3 & 5 & 7 \\ 0 & 9 & -2 \end{bmatrix} \qquad B = \begin{bmatrix} -5 & 3 & 1 \\ 3 & -4 & -1 \end{bmatrix}$$

A $\begin{bmatrix} -2 & 8 & 8 \\ 3 & 5 & -3 \end{bmatrix}$

B $\begin{bmatrix} 8 & 2 & 6 \\ -3 & 13 & -1 \end{bmatrix}$

C $\begin{bmatrix} 8 & 8 & 8 \\ 3 & 13 & 3 \end{bmatrix}$

D $\begin{bmatrix} 3 & -5 & 3 \\ -2 & 8 & 8 \end{bmatrix}$

Answer: A

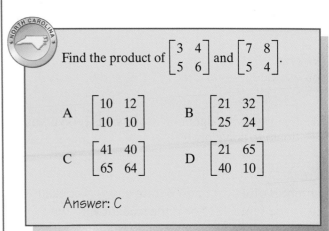

Find the product of $\begin{bmatrix} 3 & 4 \\ 5 & 6 \end{bmatrix}$ and $\begin{bmatrix} 7 & 8 \\ 5 & 4 \end{bmatrix}$.

A $\begin{bmatrix} 10 & 12 \\ 10 & 10 \end{bmatrix}$

B $\begin{bmatrix} 21 & 32 \\ 25 & 24 \end{bmatrix}$

C $\begin{bmatrix} 41 & 40 \\ 65 & 64 \end{bmatrix}$

D $\begin{bmatrix} 21 & 65 \\ 40 & 10 \end{bmatrix}$

Answer: C

NUMBER & OPERATION

1.05 Model and solve problems using direct, inverse, combined and joint variation.

What It Means to You

You will be learning different ways that variables in algebraic expressions relate to one another. For example, you have worked with direct variation. This is a relationship between two variables in which changing one variable changes the other one at a constant rate. In many situations, however, variables in a problem will change at different rates. For example, suppose you have $40 to buy some CDs. One store sells CDs for $12 each. A second store sells CDs for $14 each. You could buy three $12 CDs or two $14 CDs. As the cost of the CDs increases, the number you can buy decreases. This relationship is an example of *inverse variation*. The two variables—the cost of CDs and the number you can buy—do not change at a constant rate.

Other types of variation combine direct variation and inverse variation to make more complicated relationships. In some cases with multiple variables, a variable will vary directly with one variable and inversely with another. If you decide to spend your $40 on CDs and books, you will want to consider the relationship between the cost of books and the new variable, the number of books you can buy for a certain price. You will apply what you've learned about direct variation to inverse, combined, and joint variations to model and solve real-world problems. This will involve identifying when variables vary directly and when they vary inversely and representing each in algebraic expressions.

Where You'll Learn This

You will study this in Chapter 9.

North Carolina Fact

On December 17, 1903, former bicycle mechanics Wilbur and Orville Wright made the first sustained airplane flight when Wilbur kept their fragile plane in the air for 12 seconds.

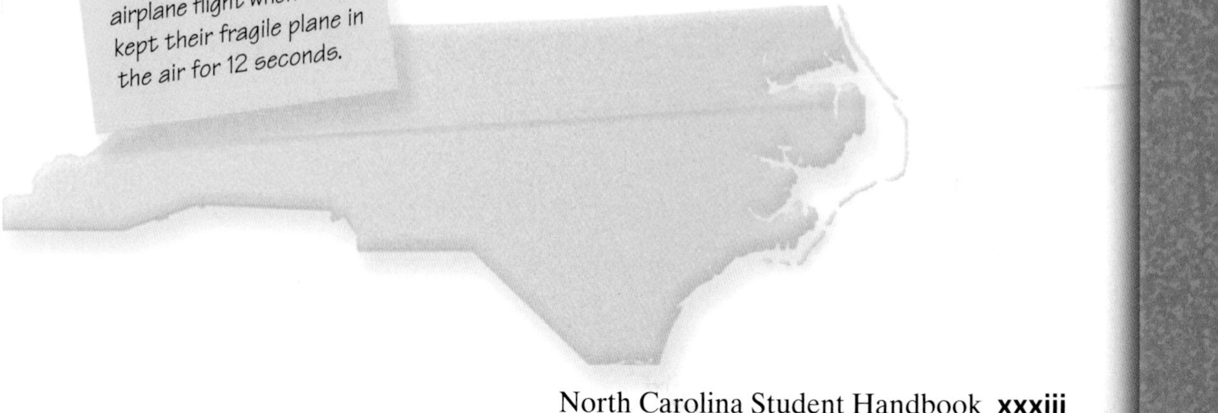

Which equation does not represent inverse variation between x and y?

A $y = -\frac{2b}{x}$
B $xy = 3n$
C $x = \frac{y}{n}$
D $x = -\frac{19t}{y}$

Answer: C

How does y vary in relation to z and x in the equation below?

$$y = \frac{kxz}{w}$$

A jointly
B inversely
C indirectly
D There is no relationship.

Answer: A

ALGEBRA

2.01 Use the composition and inverse of functions to model and solve problems; justify results.

What It Means to You

In miniature golf, you often have a two-tiered hole. When you play this hole, your ball goes down one of many chutes and ends up below for you to continue play. Where you continue play depends on where the ball comes out. In a similar fashion, you will encounter situations in which you can combine two functions. In this case, the output of the first function becomes the input for the second function to form a *composite* function. What you put in the first function (which chute your ball goes through) determines what will go in the second function (where you continue to play).

When solving equations, you have explored operations that undo other operations. For example, you can use division to undo multiplication. These are called *inverse operations*. Similarly, you may want to undo an entire function. When you interchange the x and y values in a function, you get its *inverse*. For a function $f(x)$, you write that its inverse is $f^{-1}(x)$. If you combine a function and its inverse, you will see that they undo each other. For example, if $f(x) = x + 4$, then $f^{-1}(x) = x - 4$. You can use composition to see that these two functions undo each other. You can use the composition and inverse of functions to model and solve problems. These are the types of things you will be learning to do this year.

Where You'll Learn This

You will study this in Chapter 7.

Find f^{-1} for the following function.
$f(x) = \sqrt{x - 1}$

Show your work.

Rewrite the equation using y:
$y = \sqrt{x - 1}$

Then, interchange x and y:
$x = \sqrt{y - 1}$

Square both sides:
$x^2 = y - 1$

Solve for y:
$y = x^2 + 1$

The correct answer is $f^{-1}(x) = x^2 + 1$, $x \geq 0$.

Find $(f \circ g)(x)$ where:

$f(x) = \frac{1}{x}$ $\quad g(x) = x^2$

A $\sqrt{x}$ $\qquad$ B $\frac{1}{x^2}$

C $\frac{1}{2}x$ $\qquad$ D $-2x$

Answer: B

North Carolina Fact

Did you know that the first recorded discovery of gold in the U.S. took place in Carrabus County, North Carolina? John Reed found this treasure in Little Meadow Creek in 1799.

ALGEBRA

2.02 Use quadratic functions and inequalities to model and solve problems; justify results.
a) Solve using tables, graphs, and algebraic properties.
b) Interpret the constants and coefficients in the context of the problem.

What It Means to You

You're on a trip and you are traveling at an average speed of 60 mi/h. You can write a function $f(t) = 60t$ to determine how far you'll travel in a given amount of time. If you were to graph this function you would get a straight line. Therefore, $f(t) = 60t$ is a linear function. But what about functions whose graph is not a line?

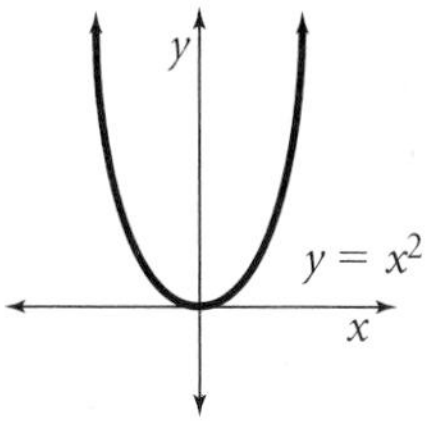

Quadratic equations contain a squared variable (x^2) and their graphs are U-shaped. The function used to model the distance an object falls is $d = -16t^2 + h$, where d is the distance the object falls, t is the time it falls, and h is the height from which it is dropped. Many area formulas, such as the area of a circle ($A = \pi r^2$) or a square ($A = s^2$) are quadratic equations.

As with linear functions, each constant and coefficient in a quadratic function has meaning. The number -16 tells you that the U-shape will open downward. The constant, h, is the y-intercept of the graph.

You will learn how to graph these curves and work with their equations in order to solve problems, such as the time it takes a ball to hit the ground when dropped from a specific height. You will also be learning how to use quadratic functions and inequalities to model and solve real-world problems.

Where You'll Learn This

You will study this in Chapter 5.

Sky divers are in free fall from the time they leave the plane until their parachute opens. A diver's height y in feet after t seconds can be modeled with this quadratic function: $y = -16t^2 + 1500$ for a jump from 1,500 feet. How long is the diver in free fall if the parachute opens at 1,000 feet? Show your work.

First, replace y with 1,000:
$1{,}000 = -16t^2 + 1500$

Solve for t:
$-500 = -16t^2$
$31.25 = t^2$
$5.6 \approx t$

The answer is about 5.6 seconds.

Graph the equation $y = 3x^2 + 1$.

Answer:

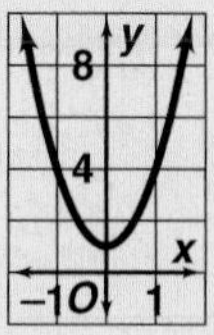

ALGEBRA

2.03 Use exponential functions to model and solve problems; justify results.

a) Solve using tables, graphs, and algebraic properties.

b) Interpret the constants, coefficients, and bases in the context of the problem.

What It Means to You

In the expression 4^2, the 2 is known as an exponent. You are familiar with evaluating exponents and solving equations with exponents. In some equations, however, the exponent is a variable. For example, a population of bacteria doubles every hour. If you start with a single cell, you can write a function for the population, $y = 2^x$, where x is the number of hours. If you plot the population's growth over time the result is a J-shaped curve.

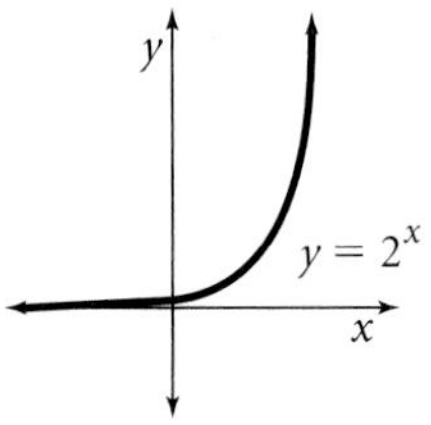

Functions that contain a number raised to another power (a^x) are called exponential functions. Their graphs are steep curves, looking almost like a "j". These functions are used to model rapid growth, such as that of a bacterial population.

As with other functions, the constants and coefficients can help you draw the graph of the function. If the base is greater than 1—as in the model of bacteria population, where the base is 2—the function models growth. If the base is between 0 and 1, the function models decay. For example, a quantity that is halved every hour might be represented with the function $y = \left(\frac{1}{2}\right)^x$.

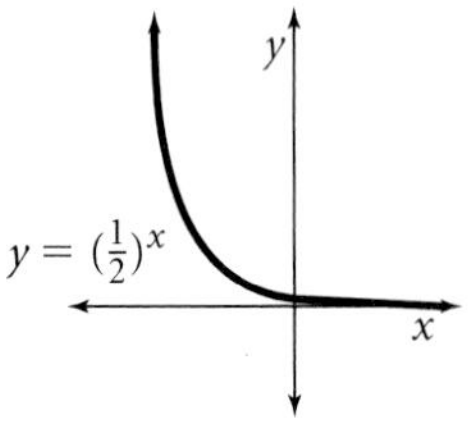

You will learn how to use exponential functions to model data. You will also learn to graph exponential functions and solve exponential equations in order to solve problems.

Where You'll Learn This

You will study this in Chapter 8.

Which function represents exponential growth?

A $y = -\left(\frac{1}{25^x}\right)$

B $y = 25^x$

C $y = -(25^x)$

D $y = \left(\frac{1}{25}\right)^x$

Answer: B

Graph $y = 2^x + 4$.

Answer:

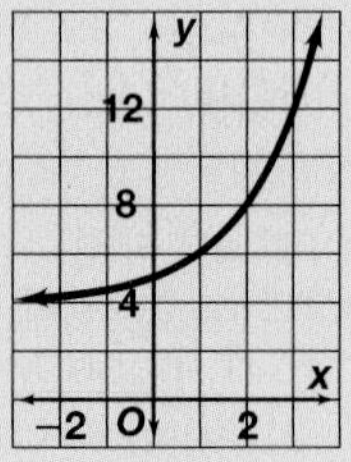

ALGEBRA

2.04 Create and use best-fit mathematical models of linear, exponential, and quadratic functions to solve problems involving sets of data.

a) Interpret the constants, coefficients, and bases in the context of the data.

b) Check the model for goodness-of-fit and use the model, where appropriate, to draw conclusions or make predictions.

What It Means to You

Sometimes when you plot data on a graph you can't easily "connect the dots." For example, if you conduct a survey, you may create a scatterplot to display your data. Frequently, the data will not form a straight line. Sometimes, you can identify a trend in data. For example, if you compare time spent studying to grades on an exam, you will see that grades increase as time spent studying increases. You can use the trend to draw a *line of best fit* and use it to estimate what a grade will be given a certain amount of time spent studying.

In some cases, the line of best fit will be a curve or an exponential function, depending on the data you are studying. That's because real-world problems don't always follow a simple equation exactly. However, you can examine data for patterns that look similar to the linear, exponential, and quadratic functions you will be learning about and find a best-fit model. The model you choose will depend on your data and how exact your approximations need to be. Once you have a model to base the data on, you can use the model to draw conclusions or make predictions about the data.

Where You'll Learn This

You will study this in Chapters 2, 6, and 8.

A candle is 10 cm tall after burning for 1 h. After burning for 3 h, it is 9 cm tall. Write a linear equation to model the height *y* of the candle after burning for *x* hours. Then use your equation to predict how tall the candle will be after burning for 10 hours.

First, find the slope of the model line:

$$m = \frac{10 - 9}{1 - 3} = -\frac{1}{2}$$

Then write a linear equation:

$$y - y_1 = m(x - x_1)$$

$$y - 9 = -\frac{1}{2}(x - 3)$$

$$y = -\frac{1}{2}x + 10.5$$

Finally, use the equation to predict the height of the candle after 10 hours of burning: $x = 10$

$$y = -\frac{1}{2}(10) + 10.5$$

$$y = 5.5$$

The candle will be about 5.5 cm tall after burning for 10 h.

North Carolina Fact

North Carolina's Cape Hatteras National Seashore is one of the longest stretches of undeveloped shoreline along the Atlantic seaboard.

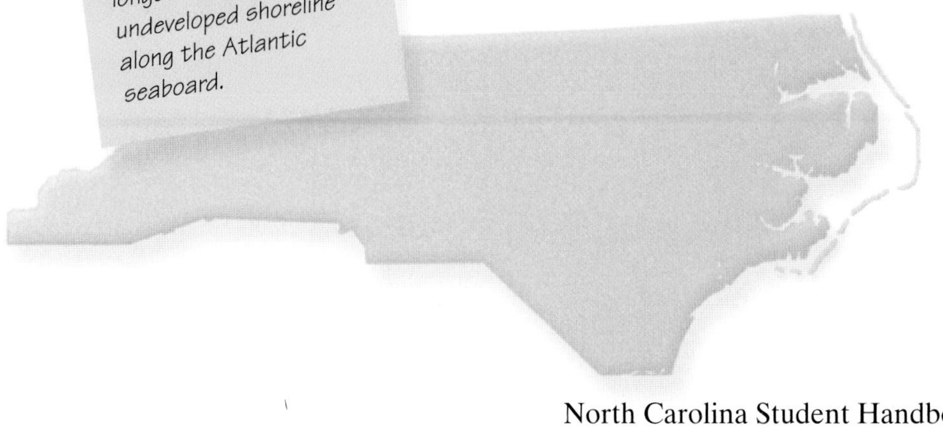

ALGEBRA

2.05 Use rational equations to model and solve problems; justify results.

a) Solve using tables, graphs, and algebraic properties.
b) Interpret the constants and coefficients in the context of the problem.
c) Identify the asymptotes and intercepts graphically and algebraically.

What It Means to You

When you write a fraction, such as $\frac{2}{3}$, you are writing a type of rational number. A rational expression is similar in that it is a fraction. It is different in that the numerator and denominator are polynomials. An inverse variation is one example of a rational equation. In an inverse relationship, as one variable decreases, the other increases proportionally. For example, if you squeeze a balloon the volume will decrease and the pressure exerted will increase. A simple way to write this relationship is $y = \frac{k}{x}$. Many proportions are also forms of rational equations. For example, the relationship $\frac{2}{x+3} = \frac{x+1}{x^2}$ is an example of a proportion that is also a rational equation.

Rational equations also have unique characteristics. Think of the equation $y = \frac{1}{x}$. What will happen to the graph when x is 0?

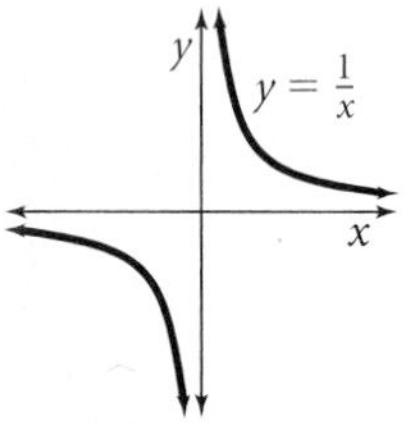

Since $\frac{1}{0}$ is undefined, in this case there will be no y-values for $x = 0$. We call this break a *discontinuity* in the graph. You will learn to identify different types of discontinuities and other properties of graphs of rational equations. You will also be learning how to simplify rational expressions and solve rational equations.

Where You'll Learn This

You will study this in Chapter 9.

Marty has 5,000 summer camp packets to staple. He can staple the packets twice as fast as his sister Maria can. Working together, Marty and Maria can complete the job in 5 hours. How long will it take each of them to do the job alone? Show your work.

Begin by writing down what you know from the problem:

Marty's rate + Maria's rate = combined rate

	Time in hours	Rate (packets per hour)
Marty	x	$\frac{5{,}000}{x}$
Maria	2x	$\frac{5{,}000}{2x}$

Then, write an equation to model the situation:

$$5\left(\frac{5{,}000}{x}\right) + 5\left(\frac{5{,}000}{2x}\right) = 5{,}000$$

$$\frac{5{,}000}{x} + \frac{5{,}000}{2x} = 1{,}000$$

Multiply by 2x:

$$10{,}000 + 5{,}000 = 2{,}000x$$
$$15{,}000 = 2{,}000x$$
$$7.5 = x$$

Marty could complete the job in 7.5 hours. Maria could do it in about 15 hours.

ALGEBRA

2.06 Use cubic equations to model and solve problems.
a) Solve using tables and graphs.
b) Interpret constants and coefficients in the context of the problem.

What It Means to You

Many real-world situations can be modeled using different kinds of functions. You can use a linear function (whose graph is a line) to model how far you'll travel going a certain rate, an exponential function (whose graph is J-shaped) to model population growth, and quadratic functions (whose graph is U-shaped) to model the flight of a ball thrown in the air. Sometimes, you can fit data more closely if you use a model with a variable raised to a degree of three (x^3). The graph of $y = x^3$ is similar to a quadratic equation that has been turned at the vertex.

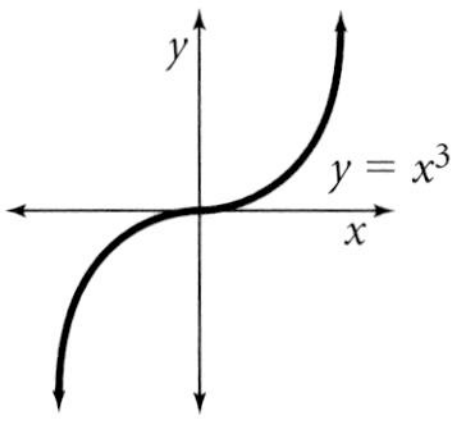

The volume of a rectangular prism with dimensions x, $x + 5$, and $10 - x$ can be modeled with a polynomial of degree three. The equation $y = x(x + 5)(10 - x)$ can be simplified $y = -x^3 + 5x^2 + 50x$. These types of equations are called cubic equations.

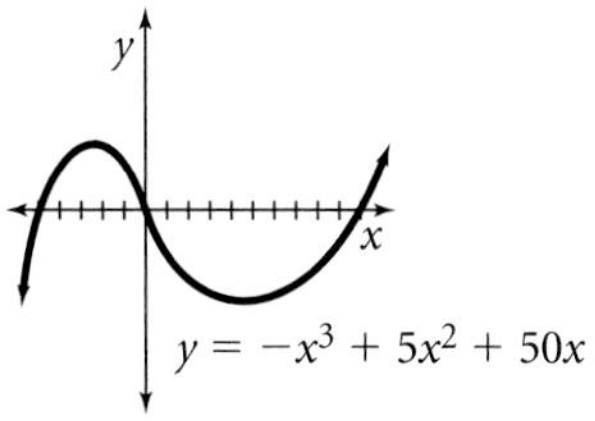

Looking at the shape of this type of cubic equation, you might want to use a cubic equation to find maximum and minimum values. In a cubic equation, however, you will find a *relative* maximum or minimum. This means that the point is the greatest (or least) y-value when compared to other points near it, but it is not the greatest point in the graph. You will learn to use cubic equations to model and solve real-world problems.

Where You'll Learn This

You will study this in Chapter 6.

Which model best fits the data in the table?

Data Table

x	y
-2	$-2\frac{2}{3}$
-1	$-\frac{1}{3}$
0	0
1	$\frac{1}{3}$
2	$2\frac{2}{3}$

A $y = x^3$

B $y = 3x^3$

C $y = \frac{1}{3}x^3$

D $y = -\frac{1}{3}x^3$

Answer: C

ALGEBRA

2.07 Use equations with radical expressions to model and solve problems; justify results.

a) Solve using tables, graphs, and algebraic properties.

b) Interpret the degree, constants, and coefficients in the context of the problem.

What It Means to You

When you multiply a number by itself, you square the number. The inverse of squaring a number is finding its square root. For example, $4^2 = 16$, and the square root of 16 is 4, or $\sqrt{16} = 4$. Now you will apply what you know to radical expressions and equations.

A radical equation is one that contains a variable under a radical symbol, such as $2 + \sqrt{x} = 12$, or $x^{\frac{2}{3}} = 200$. You often see radical expressions in geometry formulas. For example, the formula for the length of the side of a square given its area is $s = \sqrt{A}$.

You can solve equations with radical expressions using exponents. For example, if $\sqrt{x} = 4$, you can write $(\sqrt{x})^2 = 4^2$, or $x = 16$. You will see that sometimes when you use exponents to solve an equation, *extraneous solutions*, or solutions that fit the squared equation but not the original equation, will appear. In such cases, you will need to check all solutions to eliminate extraneous solutions. This year, you will learn how to work with equations with radical expressions in order to model and solve problems. You will also learn how to transform radical functions using methods similar to those used in linear equations.

Where You'll Learn This

You will study this in Chapter 7.

Solve $5(x - 1)^{\frac{2}{3}} = 125$. Show your work.

First, divide both sides by 5:

$(x - 1)^{\frac{2}{3}} = 25$

Raise both sides to the $\frac{3}{2}$ power:

$(x - 1)^1 = \pm 25^{\frac{3}{2}}$

Simplify:

$x - 1 = \pm 25^{\frac{3}{2}}$

$x - 1 = \pm 125$

$x = 126$ or $x = -124$

The correct answer is -124 or 126.

When designing a sailboat, an engineer uses the following formula to determine the maximum possible speed that the hull can attain where m is speed in knots and L is the length of the waterline in feet.

$m = 1.35 \cdot \sqrt{L}$

Rounded to the nearest hundredth, what is the length of the waterline of a boat with a maximum speed of 7.9 knots?

A 3.79 ft

B 32.15 ft

C 34.24 ft

D 46.23 ft

Answer: C

ALGEBRA

2.08 Use equations and inequalities with absolute value to model and solve problems; justify results.

a) Solve using tables, graphs, and algebraic properties.

b) Interpret the constants and coefficients in the context of the problem.

What It Means to You

You're traveling from your home to your cousin's house. Regardless of the direction in which you go, the distance you travel will be a positive value. Just like distance traveled, the absolute value represents distance on the number line. Because distance traveled cannot be a negative number, the absolute value of a number cannot be a negative number. A number's absolute value is never negative, it is always positive or 0.

You can think of the graph of an absolute value as being the combination of two graphs. Because of this, an absolute value equation is V-shaped. To graph $y = |x|$, you will combine the graphs of $y = x$ (for the right part of the graph) and $y = -x$ (for the left part of the graph).

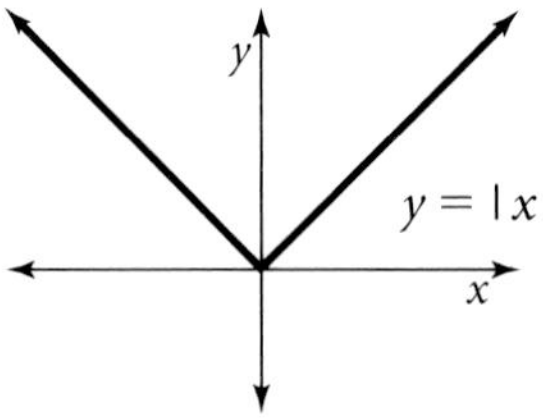

Just as you can use two equations to draw the graph of an absolute value equation, you can use two equations to solve an absolute value equation. Suppose $|x + 2| = 5$. Since $|5| = 5$ and $|-5| = 5$, you know that $x + 2 = 5$ or $x + 2 = -5$ will solve the equation. You can solve the two simpler equations to find solutions for the original equation. You will learn how to solve equations with absolute value to model and solve problems.

Where You'll Learn This

You will study this in Chapter 1.

Solve $2|4x - 1| - 2 = 18$. Show your work.

First, add 2 to each side:
$2|4x - 1| = 20$

Then, divide each side by 2:
$|4x - 1| = 10$

Rewrite as two equations:
$4x - 1 = 10$ or $4x - 1 = -10$

Solve both equations:
$4x = 11$ or $4x = -9$
$x = \frac{11}{4}$ or $x = -\frac{9}{4}$

The correct answer is $x = \frac{11}{4}$ or $-\frac{9}{4}$.

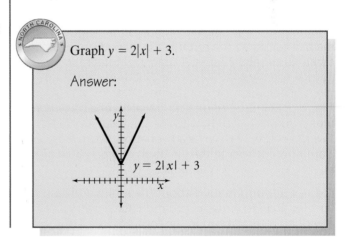

Graph $y = 2|x| + 3$.

Answer:

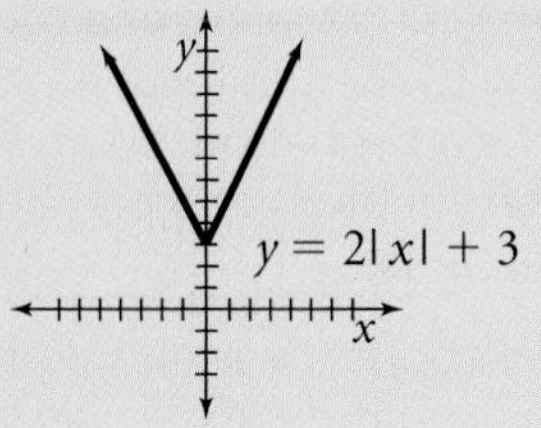

ALGEBRA

2.09 Use the equations of parabolas and circles to model and solve problems; justify results.

a) Solve using tables, graphs, and algebraic properties.

b) Interpret the constants and coefficients in the context of the problem.

What It Means to You

You are familiar with thinking of circles as the set of points in a plane a given distance from a single point. The term *radius* describes the given distance. A parabola, on the other hand, is a set of points in a plane where each point is a given distance from a single line and a fixed point not on that line. The term *focus* describes the fixed point, and the term *directrix* describes the line.

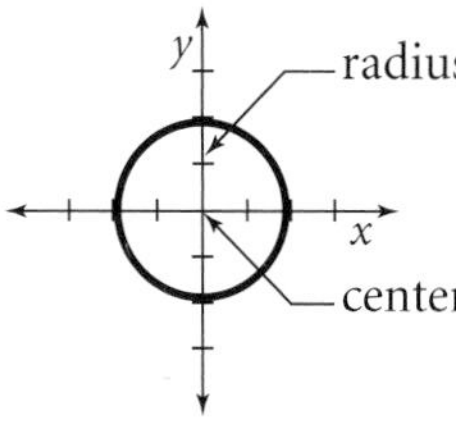

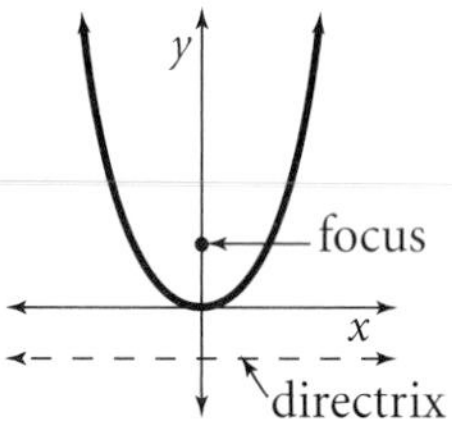

If you toss a ball in the air and graph the height of the ball over time the result is a U-shaped curve, or parabola. Parabolas are the graphs of quadratic functions, written $y = ax^2 + bx + c$. Quadratic functions can describe many other real-life situations, such as the stopping distance of a car traveling at a certain speed. You will learn how to use the focus and directrix of a parabola to write an equation. You will also learn how changes to the equation of a parabola affect the graph of the parabola.

You can use information about the radius and center of a circle to write its equation. Circles are described by equations in the form $x^2 + y^2 = r^2$, where r is the radius. You will learn how changes to the equation of a circle can change its size or shape, resulting in larger or smaller circles and ellipses. You will work with equations of parabolas and circles in order to solve problems.

Where You'll Learn This

You will study this in Chapter 10.

Which of the following is the equation of a circle with center $(-2, 3)$ and radius 5?

A $(x - 3)^2 + (y - 2)^2 = 5$

B $(x - 2)^2 + (y - 3)^2 = 25$

C $(x + 2)^2 + (y - 3)^2 = 25$

D $(x + 2)^2 + (y + 3)^2 = 25$

Answer: C

Find the equation of the parabola described by the following information.

Focus: $(3, 0)$

Vertex: $(0, 0)$

A $x = \left(\frac{1}{12}\right)y^2$

B $x = 12y^2$

C $y = \left(\frac{1}{12}\right)x^2$

D $y = 12x^2$

Answer: A

ALGEBRA

2.10 Use systems of two or more equations or inequalities to model and solve problems; justify results. Solve using tables, graphs, matrix operations, and algebraic properties.

What It Means to You

You may have seen ads for competing phone services. But which is the better plan? If you model each plan then you have created a system of equations. A system of equations is a set of two or more equations that use the same variables. You will learn how to solve these systems of equations by finding any or all points where the equations intersect.

You have seen how to solve equations by graphing to find where equations or inequalities intersect. In some cases, you will not have the tools to create a graph, or the graphs will be too complex to help determine the solution. In these cases, you may want to solve a single equation for a variable and then substitute that expression into other equations. This is called the *substitution method.*

At other times, you will find that equations are too complex to solve for a single variable. Sometimes you will be able to use algebraic properties to convert two or more equations into one equation with one variable. You will learn a method called *elimination*, in which you combine the equations to eliminate a variable.

In situations that involve more than two equations and more than two variables, you may even want to use a matrix to model the equations. You can then perform matrix operations to find solutions for the equations.

You will learn a variety of methods for solving groups (or *systems*) of equations and inequalities in multiple variables. You will then be able to decide which method is appropriate for each problem you encounter.

Where You'll Learn This

You will study this in Chapters 3 and 4.

In order to take swim fitness classes at the pool, you must join the Pool Club and pay a monthly class fee. Two months of classes cost \$115. Five months of classes cost \$175. What is the cost of joining the Pool Club?

A \$20 B \$25
C \$50 D \$75

Answer: D

Solve the system of equations by elimination.

$x^2 + y^2 = 4$

$x^2 + 4y^2 = 16$

A $\{(0, 2), (0, -2)\}$
B $\{(0, 4), (0, -4)\}$
C $\{(2, 0), (-2, 0)\}$
D $\{(4, 0), (-4, 0)\}$

Answer: A

Where You've Been

- In your first course in algebra, you learned to add, subtract, multiply, and divide rational numbers. Rational numbers are the quotients of integers, and they include integers, positive and negative fractions, and positive and negative decimals.
- You have also learned to use the order of operations, which tells how to simplify expressions with grouping symbols, exponents, and operations.
- You have also learned to use algebraic expressions.

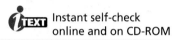

Instant self-check online and on CD-ROM

Diagnosing Readiness

(For help, go to the Skills Handbook.)

Adding Rational Numbers (Skills Handbook page 845)

Find each sum.

1. $6 + (-6)$ **2.** $-8 + 6$ **3.** $5.31 + (-7.40)$ **4.** $-1.95 + 10$

5. $7\frac{3}{4} + \left(-8\frac{1}{2}\right)$ **6.** $-2\frac{1}{3} + 3\frac{1}{4}$ **7.** $6\frac{2}{5} + \left(4\frac{3}{10}\right)$ **8.** $-1\frac{5}{6} + 5\frac{1}{3}$

Subtracting Rational Numbers (Skills Handbook page 845)

Find each difference.

9. $-28 - 14$ **10.** $61 - (-11)$ **11.** $-16 - (-25)$ **12.** $-6.2 - 3.6$

13. $-5\frac{2}{3} - \left(-2\frac{1}{3}\right)$ **14.** $-2\frac{1}{4} - 3\frac{1}{4}$ **15.** $2\frac{2}{3} - 7\frac{1}{3}$ **16.** $\frac{5}{2} - \frac{13}{4}$

Multiplying and Dividing Rational Numbers (Skills Handbook page 845)

Find each product or quotient.

17. $-3 \cdot 7$ **18.** $-2.1 \cdot (-3.5)$ **19.** $-\frac{2}{3} \div 4$ **20.** $-\frac{3}{8} \div \frac{5}{8}$

Using the Order of Operations (Skills Handbook page 845)

Simplify each expression.

21. $8 \cdot (-3) + 4$ **22.** $3 \cdot 4 - 8 \div 2$ **23.** $1 \div 2^2 - 0.54 + 1.26$

24. $9 \div (-3) - 2$ **25.** $5(3 \cdot 5 - 4)$ **26.** $1 - (1 - 5)^2 \div (-8)$

Tools of Algebra

Chapter 1

LESSONS

- **1-1** Properties of Real Numbers
- **1-2** Algebraic Expressions
- **1-3** Solving Equations
- **1-4** Solving Inequalities
- **1-5** Absolute Value Equations and Inequalities
- **1-6** Probability

Key Vocabulary

- absolute value (p. 33)
- absolute value of a real number (p. 8)
- additive inverse (p. 7)
- algebraic expression (p. 12)
- coefficient (p. 13)
- compound inequality (p. 28)
- evaluate (p. 12)
- experimental probability (p. 40)
- extraneous solution (p. 34)
- multiplicative inverse (p. 7)
- opposite (p. 7)
- reciprocal (p. 7)
- sample space (p. 41)
- simulation (p. 40)
- solution of an equation (p. 18)
- term (p. 13)
- theoretical probability (p. 41)
- tolerance (p. 36)
- variable (p. 12)
- variable expression (p. 12)

Where You're Going

- In Chapter 1, you will review and extend your knowledge of algebraic expressions and your skill in solving equations and inequalities.
- You will solve absolute value equations and inequalities by changing them to compound equations and inequalities.
- You will apply theoretical and experimental probabilities to real-world situations such as genetic inheritance.

Real-World Connection Applying what you learn, you will use algebraic expressions on page 13 to solve a problem involving elections.

1-1

Properties of Real Numbers

North Carolina Objectives

1.02 Define and compute with complex numbers.

Lesson Preview

What You'll Learn

OBJECTIVE 1 To graph and order real numbers

OBJECTIVE 2 To identify and use properties of real numbers

. . . And Why

To classify the numbers used in managing an amusement park, as in Example 1

Check Skills You'll Need

(For help, go to Skills Handbook page 845.)

Simplify.

1. $-(-7.2)$
2. $1 - (-3)$
3. $-9 + (-4.5)$
4. $(-3.4)(-2)$
5. $-15 \div 3$
6. $\frac{-2}{5} + \frac{3}{-5}$

New Vocabulary

- opposite
- additive inverse
- reciprocal
- multiplicative inverse
- absolute value of a real number

Interactive lesson includes instant self-check, tutorials, and activities.

OBJECTIVE 1

Graphing and Ordering Real Numbers

Real-World Connection

Artists frequently use geometric figures in their work. Juan Gris (1887–1927) used right triangles in this portrait of Picasso.

Investigation: Estimating Square Roots

1. Use the Pythagorean Theorem to calculate *PB, PC, PD,* and so on, in the figure below.

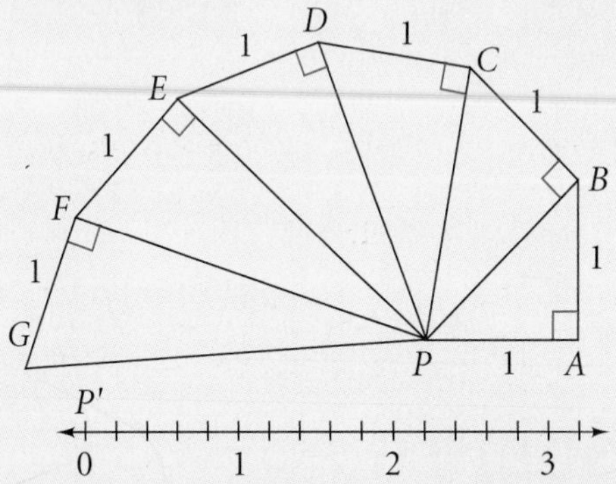

2. Copy the number line above. Mark point B' so that $P'B' = PB$. Similarly mark points C', D', and so on, on your number line.

3. Estimate the decimal coordinates of B', C', D', and so on. Copy and complete the table below.

Leg 1	1	$\sqrt{2}$	■	■	■	■
Leg 2	1	1	1	1	1	1
Hypotenuse	$\sqrt{2} \approx ?$	■	■	■	■	■

4. Evaluate each square root in the table using your calculator. Does the calculator give you exact answers? How do you know?

Algebra deals with operations and relations among numbers, including real numbers and imaginary numbers. Listed below are some of the subsets of the real numbers. Imaginary numbers will be introduced in Chapter 5.

Key Concepts

Summary **Subsets of Real Numbers**

Natural numbers 1, 2, 3, 4, . . .
- Natural numbers are the numbers used for counting.

Whole numbers 0, 1, 2, 3, 4, . . .
- Whole numbers are the natural numbers and 0.

Integers . . . −3, −2, −1, 0, 1, 2, 3, 4, . . .
- The integers are the natural numbers (positive integers), zero, and the negative integers.
- Each negative integer is the opposite, or additive inverse, of a positive integer.

Rational numbers Examples: $\frac{7}{5}, \frac{-3}{2}, -\frac{4}{5}, 0, 0.3, -1.2, 9$
- Rational numbers are all the numbers that can be written as quotients of integers. Each quotient must have a nonzero denominator.
- Some rational numbers can be written as terminating decimals. For example, $\frac{1}{8} = 0.125$.
- All other rational numbers can be written as repeating decimals. For example, $\frac{1}{3} = 0.\overline{3}$.

Irrational numbers Examples: $\sqrt{2}, \sqrt{7}, \sqrt{\frac{2}{3}}, \pi, 1.011011101111011111\ldots$
- Irrational numbers are numbers that cannot be written as quotients of integers.
- Their decimal representations neither terminate nor repeat.
- If a positive rational number is not a perfect square such as 25 or $\frac{4}{9}$, then its square root is irrational.

Reading Math

$\sqrt{2}$ refers to the principal or positive square root of 2. The negative square root of 2 is written as $-\sqrt{2}$.

This diagram shows how the above sets of numbers are related.

Real Numbers examples: $-5, -\sqrt{3}, -\frac{1}{2}, 1, \sqrt{5}, \frac{8}{3}$

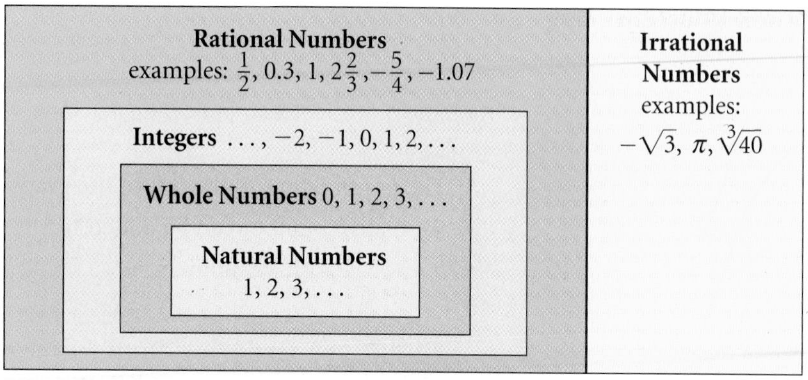

For example, the diagram shows the following:
- The set of whole numbers is a subset of the set of integers, the set of rational numbers, and the set of real numbers.
- The set of rational numbers and the set of irrational numbers do not intersect.
- The rational numbers and irrational numbers form the set of real numbers.

Real-World Connection

The maximum speed of a roller coaster is given by the formula $s = \frac{1200}{\sqrt{h}}$.

1 EXAMPLE Real-World Connection

Recreation Many mathematical relationships involving variables are related to amusement parks. Which set of numbers best describes the values for each variable?

a. the cost C in dollars of admission for n people

The cost C of admission is a rational number (such as \$7.25), and the number n of people is a whole number.

b. the maximum speed s in meters per second on a roller coaster of height h in meters (Use the formula in the caption of the photograph.)

The height h is measured in rational numbers. Since the speed s is calculated using a formula with a square root, s is an irrational number unless h is the square of a rational number.

c. the park's profit (or loss) P in dollars for each week w of the year

The week number w is one of the first 52 natural numbers, and the profit (or loss) P is a rational number.

Check Understanding **1** The number r is the ratio of the number of adult tickets sold to the number of children's tickets sold. Which set of numbers best describes the values of r? Which set of numbers best describes the average cost c per family for tickets?

Real numbers are graphed as points on the number line.

2 EXAMPLE Graphing Numbers on the Number Line

Graph the numbers $-\frac{3}{2}$, $1.\overline{7}$, and $\sqrt{5}$.

Since $-\frac{3}{2} = -1\frac{1}{2}$, $-\frac{3}{2}$ is between -1 and -2. Round $1.\overline{7}$ to 1.8.
Use a calculator to find that $\sqrt{5} \approx 2.2$.

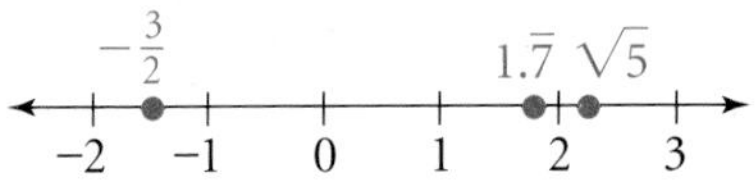

Check Understanding **2** Graph the numbers $-\sqrt{2}$, $0.\overline{3}$, and $-2\frac{1}{4}$.

If a and b are real numbers, then $a = b$, $a < b$, or $a > b$. There are several ways to prove that $a < b$:

- The graph of a is to the left of the graph of b on a number line.
- A positive number can be added to a to get b.
- $b - a$ is a positive number.

3 EXAMPLE Ordering Real Numbers

Compare $-\sqrt{0.25}$ and $-\sqrt{0.01}$. Use the symbols $<$ and $>$.

$-\sqrt{0.25} = -0.5$, and $-\sqrt{0.01} = -0.1$. Since $-0.1 - (-0.5)$ is positive, $-0.5 < -0.1$. So $-\sqrt{0.25} < -\sqrt{0.01}$ and $-\sqrt{0.01} > -\sqrt{0.25}$.

Check Understanding **3** Compare $-\sqrt{0.08}$ and $-\sqrt{0.1}$ using the symbols $<$ and $>$.

OBJECTIVE 2

Properties of Real Numbers

The **opposite** or **additive inverse** of any number a is $-a$. The sum of opposites is 0.

The **reciprocal** or **multiplicative inverse** of any nonzero number a is $\frac{1}{a}$. The product of reciprocals is 1.

Reading Math

Read $-(-3.2)$ as "the opposite of negative 3.2."

Read $\frac{1}{-3.2}$ as "the reciprocal of negative 3.2" or as "1 divided by negative 3.2."

4 EXAMPLE Finding Inverses

Find the opposite and the reciprocal of each number.

a. -3.2

Opposite $-(-3.2) = 3.2$

Reciprocal $\frac{1}{-3.2} = \frac{10}{-32}$

$= -\frac{5}{16}$, or -0.3125

b. $\frac{3}{5}$

Opposite $-\left(\frac{3}{5}\right) = -\frac{3}{5}$

Reciprocal $\frac{1}{\frac{3}{5}} = 1 \cdot \frac{5}{3} = \frac{5}{3}$

Check Understanding 4 Find the opposite and the reciprocal of each number.

a. 400 **b.** $4\frac{1}{5}$ **c.** -0.002 **d.** $-\frac{4}{9}$

You can summarize the properties of real numbers in terms of addition and multiplication.

Key Concepts

Summary **Properties of Real Numbers**

Let a, b, and c represent real numbers.

Property	Addition	Multiplication
Closure	$a + b$ is a real number.	ab is a real number.
Commutative	$a + b = b + a$	$ab = ba$
Associative	$(a + b) + c = a + (b + c)$	$(ab)c = a(bc)$
Identity	$a + 0 = a, 0 + a = a$	$a \cdot 1 = a, 1 \cdot a = a$
Inverse	$a + (-a) = 0$	$a \cdot \frac{1}{a} = 1, a \neq 0$
Distributive	$a(b + c) = ab + ac$	

5 EXAMPLE Identifying Properties of Real Numbers

Which property is illustrated?

a. $6 + (-6) = 0$

Inverse Property of Addition

b. $(-4 \cdot 1) - 2 = -4 - 2$

Identity Property of Multiplication

Check Understanding 5 Which property is illustrated?

a. $(3 + 0) - 5 = 3 - 5$ **b.** $-5 + [2 + (-3)] = (-5 + 2) + (-3)$

The **absolute value of a real number** is its distance from zero on the number line.

Reading Math

Read $|3|$ as "the absolute value of 3."

6 EXAMPLE Finding Absolute Value

Find $|-4|$, $|0|$, and $|-1 \cdot (-2)|$.

$|-1 \cdot (-2)| = |2|$ **Simplify within absolute symbols first**

Graph -4, 0, and 2 on a number line.

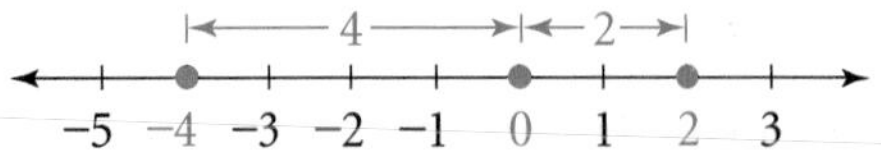

The distances from the origin are 4, 0, and 2. So,

$|-4| = 4$ $\quad |0| = 0$ $\quad |-1 \cdot (-2)| = |2| = 2$

Check Understanding 6 **a.** Simplify $|-10|$, $|1.5|$, and $|0 - 3|$.

b. **Critical Thinking** For what values of x does $|x| = -x$?

EXERCISES

For more practice, see *Extra Practice.*

Practice and Problem Solving

A Practice by Example

Example 1 (page 6)

To which sets of numbers does each number belong?

1. 4 **2.** $\sqrt{6}$ **3.** π **4.** -6

5. 0 **6.** $0.\overline{6}$ **7.** $-\sqrt{0.04}$ **8.** $\sqrt{0.4}$

Which set of numbers best describes the value of each variable?

9. the number of times n a cricket chirps; the outdoor temperature T in tenths of a degree

10. the year y; the median selling price p for a house that year

11. the time t in seconds an object takes to fall d feet, where $t = \frac{\sqrt{d}}{4}$

Example 2 (page 6)

Graph each number on a number line.

12. 0 **13.** $-\sqrt{24}$ **14.** -2 **15.** $2\frac{1}{2}$ **16.** $-4\frac{2}{3}$

Example 3 (page 6)

Replace each ■ with the symbol <, >, or = to make the sentence true.

17. -7 ■ -9 **18.** 3 ■ 3 **19.** 14 ■ $\sqrt{14}$

20. $\sqrt{6}$ ■ $\sqrt{10}$ **21.** 0 ■ $0.\overline{3}$ **22.** 0.8 ■ $\frac{4}{5}$

23. -18 ■ -82 **24.** 0.72737475 . . . ■ 0.73737373 . . .

Compare each pair of numbers. Use < and >.

25. $-\frac{1}{4}, -\frac{1}{3}$ **26.** 0.075, 0.39 **27.** $-2.\overline{3}, 2.\overline{1}$

28. $-5.2, -4.8$ **29.** $3.0\overline{4}, 3.4$ **30.** $0.4, \sqrt{0.4}$

31. $-4, -\sqrt{4}$ **32.** $\sqrt{5}, \sqrt{7}$ **33.** $-\sqrt{3}, -\sqrt{5}$

Example 4 (page 7)

Find the opposite and the reciprocal of each number.

34. 200 **35.** $3\frac{3}{5}$ **36.** -0.01 **37.** $-\frac{7}{2}$

38. $\sqrt{3}$ **39.** 2π **40.** -2.34 **41.** $\pi - 3$

Example 5 (page 7)

Name the property of real numbers illustrated by each equation.

42. $92.5(1) = 92.5$

43. $\pi(a + b) = \pi a + \pi b$

44. $-7 + 4 = 4 + (-7)$

45. $(2\sqrt{10}) \cdot \sqrt{3} = 2(\sqrt{10} \cdot \sqrt{3})$

46. $29\pi = \pi \cdot 29$

47. $-\sqrt{5} + 0 = -\sqrt{5}$

48. $(-8) + [-(-8)] = 0$

49. $\frac{4}{7} \cdot \frac{7}{4} = 1$

50. $25(2x + 5y) = 50x + 125y$

51. $(-2)(-3) = (-3)(-2)$

52. $(0.5 + 0.25) + (-0.25) = 0.5 + [0.25 + (-0.25)]$

Example 6 (page 8)

Simplify each expression.

53. $|10.3|$ **54.** $|-0.06|$ **55.** $-|-25|$ **56.** $0.2|-8|$

57. $\left|-\frac{1}{3}\right|$ **58.** $|7 - 10|$ **59.** $|10 - 7|$ **60.** $|5| - |-7|$

B Apply Your Skills

Estimate the numbers graphed at the labeled points.

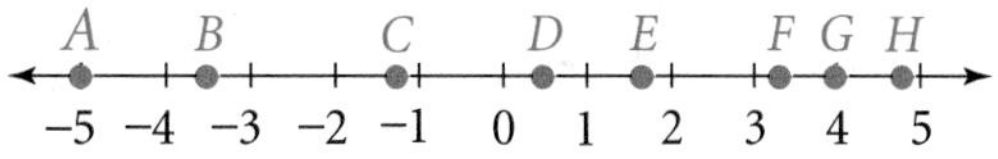

61. point A **62.** point B **63.** point C **64.** point D

65. point E **66.** point F **67.** point G **68.** point H

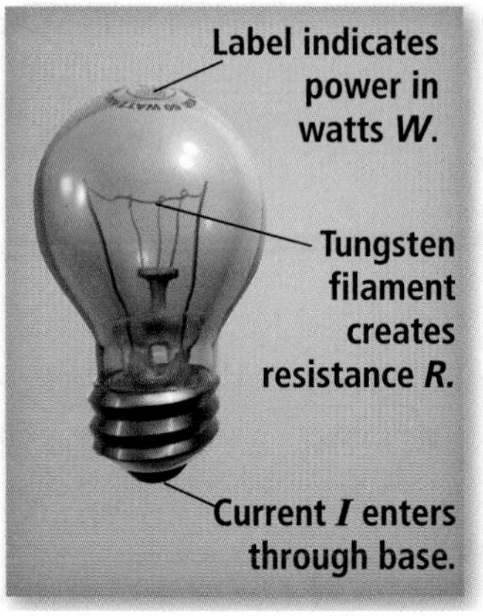

Electric Circuits **The electric current I in amperes that flows through an appliance is given by the formula $I = \sqrt{\frac{W}{R}}$, where W is the power in watts and R is the resistance in ohms. Which sets of numbers contain the value of I for the given values of W and R?**

69. $W = 100, R = 25$ **70.** $W = 100, R = 50$ **71.** $W = 500, R = 100$

72. $W = 50, R = 200$ **73.** $W = 250, R = 100$ **74.** $W = 240, R = 100$

Replace each ■ with the symbol $<, >,$ or $=$ to make the sentence true.

75. 0 ■ -4 **76.** -4 ■ -9 **77.** -5.2 ■ -4.8 **78.** $|-8|$ ■ $|3|$

79. $|2|$ ■ $|-6|$ **80.** $|7|$ ■ $|-8|$ **81.** $-|6|$ ■ $|6|$ **82.** $-|-6|$ ■ $|-6|$

Reasoning **Show that each statement is false by finding a counterexample (an example that makes the statement false).**

83. The reciprocal of each whole number is a whole number.

84. The opposite of each natural number is a natural number.

85. There is no whole number that has an opposite that is a whole number.

86. There is no integer that has a reciprocal that is an integer.

87. The product of two irrational numbers is an irrational number.

88. Open-Ended Write an example of each of the eleven properties of real numbers listed on page 7.

C Challenge

Critical Thinking **Review the eleven properties on page 7. Which ones still hold true if *real numbers* is replaced by each of the following?**

89. natural numbers **90.** whole numbers **91.** integers

92. rational numbers **93.** irrational numbers

94. Writing Are there two integers with a product of −12 and a sum of −3? Explain.

Standardized Test Prep

Multiple Choice

95. Which of the following is NOT a rational number?
A. $\frac{\pi}{2\pi}$ **B.** $-\sqrt{144}$ **C.** 3.14 **D.** $\sqrt{8}$

96. If p is a multiple of 3 and q is a multiple of 5, which of the following is true?
F. $p + q$ is even. **G.** pq is odd.
H. $5p + 3q$ is a multiple of 15. **I.** $3p + 5q$ is a multiple of 15.

97. The number 8.09 belongs to which sets of numbers?
A. natural numbers, real numbers
B. irrational numbers, real numbers
C. rational numbers, real numbers
D. whole numbers, integers, rational numbers, real numbers

Take It to the NET
Online lesson quiz at
www.PHSchool.com
Web Code: aga-0101

98. Which shows the numbers −3.5, −4.60, and $-3\frac{1}{4}$ in order from greatest to least?
F. $-4.60, -3\frac{1}{4}, -3.5$ **G.** $-4.60, -3.5, -3\frac{1}{4}$
H. $-3\frac{1}{4}, -4.60, -3.5$ **I.** $-3\frac{1}{4}, -3.5, -4.60$

99. What is the value of $|3 - 7| - |-11 + 3|$?
A. −4 **B.** 4 **C.** 12 **D.** 24

Short Response

100. Explain why the *opposite of the reciprocal of 5* is the same as the *reciprocal of the opposite of 5.*

101. Are there any numbers that are their own reciprocals? Explain.

Mixed Review

Previous Course

Simplify each expression.

102. $3.6 + (-1.7)$ **103.** $1.2 - 5$ **104.** $(-3)(-9)$

105. $0(-8)$ **106.** $-2.8 \div 7$ **107.** $-35 \div (-5)$

Previous Course

Use the order of operations to simplify each expression.

108. $3 \div 4 + 6 \div 4$ **109.** $5[(2 + 5) \div 3]$

110. $\frac{8 + 5 \cdot 2}{12}$ **111.** $(40 + 24) \div 8 - (2^2 - 1)$

112. $40 + 24 \div 8 - 2^2 - 1$ **113.** $40 + 24 \div (8 - 2^2) - 1$

Investigation

Exploring Pi

For Use With Lesson 1-1

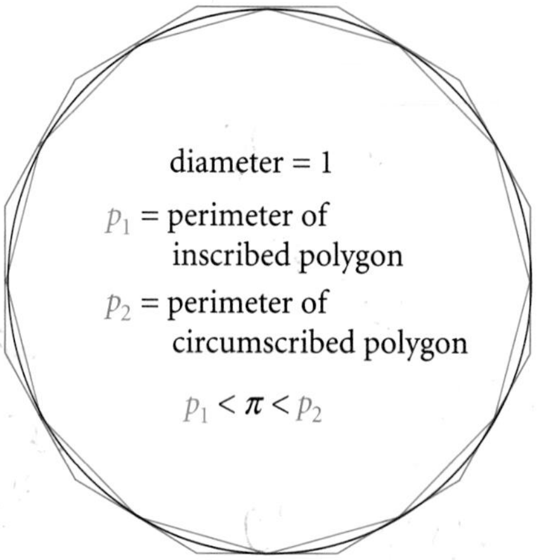

The number π, the ratio of the circumference of a circle to its diameter, has fascinated mathematicians for thousands of years.

Archimedes (about 287–212 B.C.) considered the perimeters of inscribed and circumscribed regular polygons of 96 sides. He found that $\frac{223}{71} < \pi < \frac{22}{7}$.

Seven hundred years later, the Chinese mathematician Tsu Ch'ung-Chi calculated the more precise value $\frac{355}{113}$.

English mathematicians introduced the notation π about 1700. π is the first letter of the Greek word for perimeter.

In 1761, the German mathematician Johann Lambert proved that π is an irrational number.

Although there is no finite formula for calculating π, mathematicians have found many formulas that involve infinite numbers of additions, subtractions, multiplications, or divisions.

More than 500 years ago, the Indian mathematician Madhava discovered this formula.

$$\frac{\pi}{4} = \frac{1}{1} - \frac{1}{3} + \frac{1}{5} - \frac{1}{7} + \frac{1}{9} - \frac{1}{11} + \dots$$

This formula has an infinite number of products.

$$\frac{\pi}{2} = \frac{2}{1} \cdot \frac{2}{3} \cdot \frac{4}{3} \cdot \frac{4}{5} \cdot \frac{6}{5} \cdot \frac{6}{7} \cdot \frac{8}{7} \cdot \frac{8}{9} \cdot \frac{10}{9} \cdot \frac{10}{11} \cdot \dots$$

And this formula is a continued fraction.

$$\frac{4}{\pi} = 1 + \cfrac{1^2}{3 + \cfrac{2^2}{5 + \cfrac{3^2}{7 + \cfrac{4^2}{9 + \cfrac{5^2}{11 + \dots}}}}}$$

Now mathematicians have computed π to millions of decimal places using efficient computer algorithms. Here are the first 100 digits.

3.14159265358979323846264338327950288419716939937510
5820974944592307816406286208998628034825342117067

EXERCISES

1. **a.** Find the average of Archimedes' two approximations.
   b. Compare that average with the computer-generated value of π given above. To which decimal place are they the same?
2. Make the same comparison for Tsu Ch'ung-Chi's approximation.
3. Compute the value of π using 6 terms, 8 terms, and 10 terms of Madhava's formula. Compare these values with the computer-generated value.
4. **Writing** Compute approximations of π using the other two formulas. Which formula do you prefer for calculating approximations of π? Explain.

1-2

Algebraic Expressions

North Carolina Objectives

1.03 Operate with algebraic expressions (polynomial, rational, complex fractions) to solve problems.

Lesson Preview

What You'll Learn

OBJECTIVE 1 To evaluate algebraic expressions

OBJECTIVE 2 To simplify algebraic expressions

. . . And Why

To use an expression for the number of voters in U.S. elections, as in Example 3

Check Skills You'll Need

(For help, go to Skills Handbook page 845.)

Use the order of operations to simplify each expression.

1. $8 \cdot 3 - 2 \cdot 4$

2. $8 - 4 + 6 \div 3$

3. $24 \div 12 \cdot 4 \div 3$

4. $3 \cdot 8^2 + 12 \div 4$

5. $27 + 18 \div 9 - 3^2 + 1$

6. $(40 + 24) \div 8 - (2^3 + 1)$

New Vocabulary • variable • algebraic expression • variable expression • evaluate • term • coefficient

Interactive lesson includes instant self-check, tutorials, and activities.

OBJECTIVE 1 Evaluating Algebraic Expressions

A **variable** is a symbol, usually a letter, that represents one or more numbers. An expression that contains one or more variables is an **algebraic expression** or a **variable expression.** When you substitute numbers for the variables in an expression and follow the order of operations, you **evaluate** the expression.

Need Help?

To review the order of operations, go to page 845.

1 EXAMPLE Evaluating an Algebraic Expression

Evaluate $a - 2b + ab$ for $a = 3$ and $b = -1$.

$a - 2b + ab = 3 - 2(-1) + 3(-1)$	Substitute 3 for a and -1 for b.
$= 3 - (-2) + (-3)$	Multiply first.
$= 3 + 2 + (-3)$	To subtract, add the opposite.
$= 5 + (-3)$	Add from left to right.
$= 2$	Add.

Check Understanding 1 Evaluate each expression for $x = 4$ and $y = -2$.

a. $x + y \div x$ **b.** $3x - 4y + x - y$ **c.** $x + 2x \div y - 2y$

2 EXAMPLE Evaluating an Algebraic Expression with Exponents

Evaluate $-x^2 - 2(x + 1)$ for $x = 3$.

$-x^2 - 2(x + 1) = -3^2 - 2(3 + 1)$	Substitute 3 for x.
$= -9 - 2(4)$	Simplify the power 3^2. Add within the parentheses.
$= -9 - 8$	Multiply.
$= -17$	Subtract.

Reading Math

Note that $-3^2 \neq (-3)^2$.

$-3^2 = -(3 \cdot 3) = -9$

$(-3)^2 = (-3)(-3) = 9$

Check Understanding 2 Evaluate each expression for $c = -3$ and $d = 5$.

a. $c^2 - d^2$ **b.** $c(3 - d) - c^2$ **c.** $-d^2 - 4(d - 2c)$

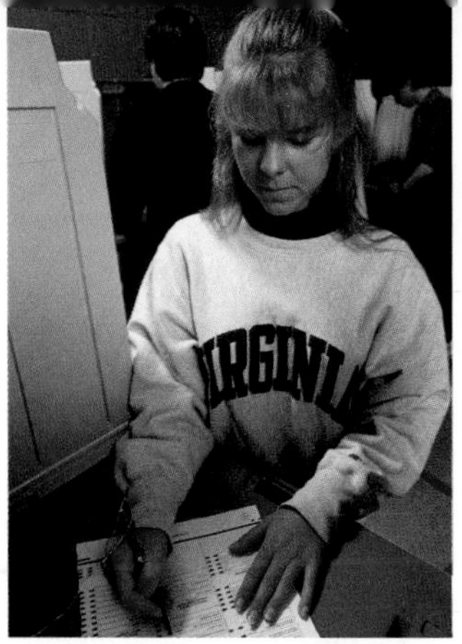

In 1971, the U.S. voting age was lowered from 21 to 18.

3 EXAMPLE Real-World Connection

Elections The expression $-0.3y + 61$ models the percent of eligible voters who voted in presidential elections from 1960 to 2000. In the expression, y represents the number of years since 1960. Find the approximate percent of eligible voters who voted in 1988.

Since $1988 - 1960 = 28$, $y = 28$ represents the year 1988.

$-0.3y + 61 = -0.3(28) + 61$ **Substitute 28 for *y*.**

≈ 53

About 53% of the eligible voters voted in the 1988 presidential election.

Check Understanding 3 **a.** Assume that the model in Example 3 holds for future years. What percent of the eligible voters will vote in 2012? In 2020?

b. Critical Thinking Give some reasons that the model may not hold in future years.

OBJECTIVE

2 Simplifying Algebraic Expressions

In an algebraic expression such as $-4x + 10$, the parts that are added are called terms. A **term** is a number, a variable, or the product of a number and one or more variables. The numerical factor in a term is the **coefficient.** Think of an expression such as $a - 2b$ as the sum $a + (-2b)$ to determine that the coefficient of b is -2.

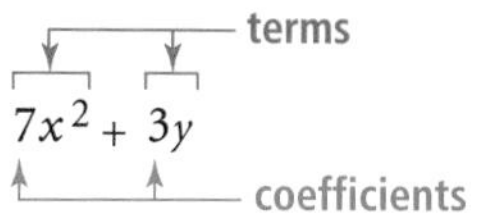

Like terms have the same variables raised to the same powers.

Like terms: $3r^2$ and $-r^2$ $\quad -2xy^3$ and $3xy^3$

You can simplify expressions by combining like terms using the basic properties on page 7 and other properties that can be derived from them. The simplified expressions are equivalent to the original expressions; that is, their values are equal for any replacement of the variables.

Key Concepts

Summary **Properties for Simplifying Algebraic Expressions**

Let a, b, and c represent real numbers.

Definition of Subtraction	$a - b = a + (-b)$
Definition of Division	$a \div b = \frac{a}{b} = a \cdot \frac{1}{b}, b \neq 0$
Distributive Property for Subtraction	$a(b - c) = ab - ac$
Multiplication by 0	$0 \cdot a = 0$
Multiplication by −1	$-1 \cdot a = -a$
Opposite of a Sum	$-(a + b) = -a + (-b)$
Opposite of a Difference	$-(a - b) = b - a$
Opposite of a Product	$-(ab) = -a \cdot b = a \cdot (-b)$
Opposite of an Opposite	$-(-a) = a$

4 EXAMPLE Combining Like Terms

Simplify by combining like terms.

a. $3k - k$

$3k - k = 3k - 1k$ **Identity Property of Multiplication**

$= (3 - 1)k$ **Distributive Property**

$= 2k$

b. $5z^2 - 10z - 8z^2 + z$

$5z^2 - 10z - 8z^2 + z = 5z^2 - 8z^2 + (-10z) + z$ **Commutative Property of Addition**

$= (5 - 8)z^2 + (-10 + 1)z$ **Distributive Property**

$= -3z^2 - 9z$

c. $-(m - n) + 2(m - 3n)$

$-(m + n) + 2(m - 3n)$

$= -m + (-n) + 2m + (-6n)$ **Opposite of a Sum, Distributive Property**

$= -m + 2m + (-n) + (-6n)$ **Commutative Property of Addition**

$= -1 \cdot m + 2m + (-1 \cdot n) + (-6n)$ **Multiplication by −1**

$= (-1 + 2)m + [-1 + (-6)]\,n$ **Distributive Property**

$= m - 7n$

Need Help?

When collecting like terms in an algebraic expression, think of it as a sum. For example,

$x^2 - 2 - 3x^2$
$= x^2 + (-2) + (-3x^2)$
$= x^2 + (-3x^2) + (-2)$
$= -2x^2 + (-2)$
$= -2x^2 - 2$

Check Understanding **4** Simplify by combining like terms.

a. $2x^2 + 5x - 4x^2 + x - x^2$

b. $-2(r + s) - (2r + 2s)$

c. $y(1 + y) - 3y^2 - (y + 1)$

5 EXAMPLE Finding Perimeter

Geometry Find the perimeter of this figure. Simplify the answer.

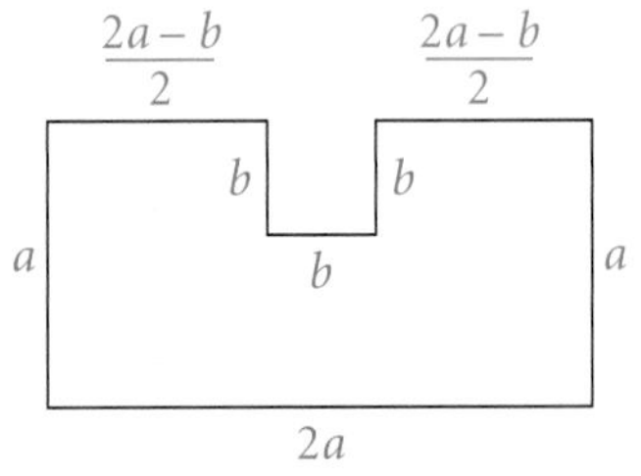

$\frac{2a - b}{2} + b + b + b + \frac{2a - b}{2} + a + 2a + a$

$= \frac{2a - b}{2} + \frac{2a - b}{2} + 3b + 4a$

$= \frac{2(2a - b)}{2} + 3b + 4a$

$= 2a - b + 3b + 4a$

$= 6a + 2b$

Check Understanding **5** Find the perimeter of each figure. Simplify the answer.

a.

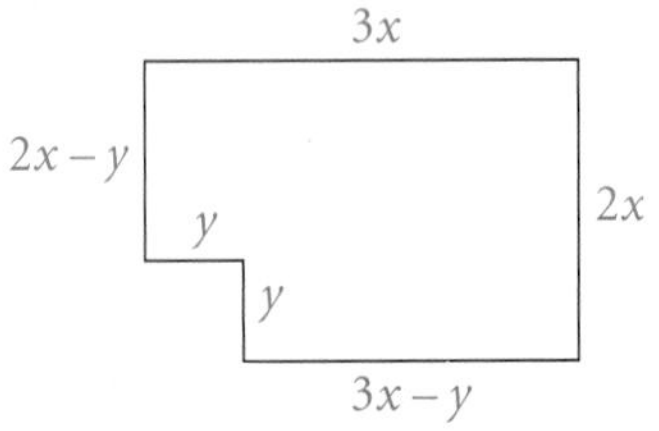

b.

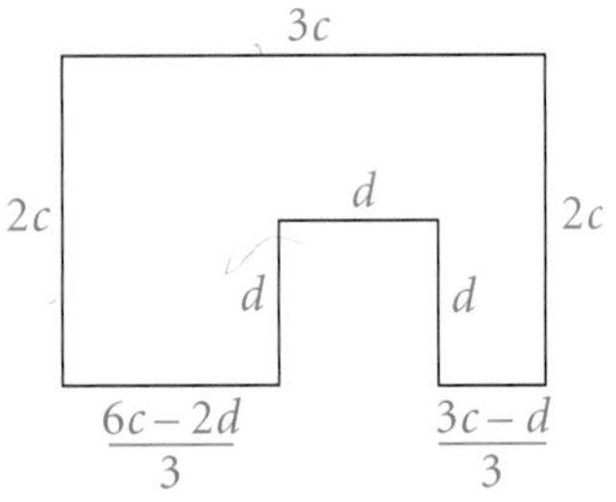

c. Critical Thinking The figure in part (b) is a rectangle with an indention. By how much does the indention increase the perimeter of the rectangle?

EXERCISES

For more practice, see *Extra Practice*.

Practice and Problem Solving

A Practice by Example

Examples 1 and 2 (page 12)

Evaluate each expression for the given values of the variables.

1. $4a + 7b + 3a - 2b + 2a; a = -5$ and $b = 3$
2. $5y - 3z + 4y - 1z - 3y; y = 3$ and $z = -2$
3. $12a^2 - 3ab + 2b; a = -5$ and $b = 4$
4. $-k^2 - (3k - 5n) + 4n; k = -1$ and $n = -2$
5. $3y - (4y + 6x); x = 3$ and $y = -2$
6. $3(2c + d) - d; c = 5$ and $d = -1$
7. $-5(x + 2y) + 15(x + 2y); x = 7$ and $y = -7$
8. $4(2m - n) - 3(2m - n); m = -15$ and $n = -18$

Example 3 (page 13)

Physics **The expression $16t^2$ models the distance in feet that an object falls during t seconds after being dropped. Find the distance an object falls during each time.**

9. 0.25 second
10. 0.5 second
11. 2 seconds
12. 10 seconds

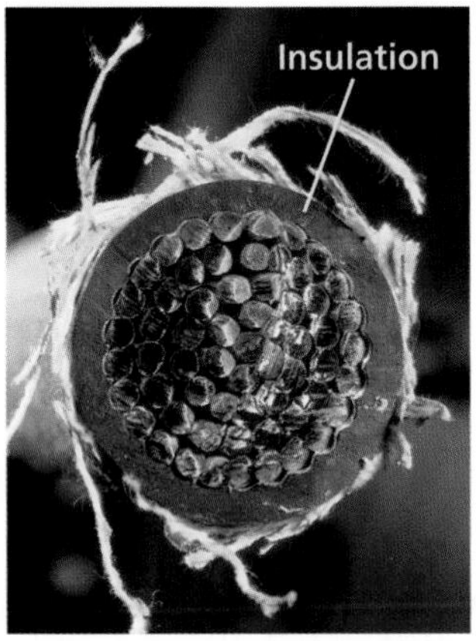

Electrical Engineering **The expression $0.01E + 0.003E^2$ gives the thickness in millimeters of the insulation needed for the high voltage cable shown at the left. E is the number of kilovolts carried by the cable. Find the thickness of insulation material needed for each voltage.**

13. 1 kilovolt
14. 2 kilovolts
15. 10 kilovolts
16. 20 kilovolts

Investing **The expression $1000(1.1)^t$ represents the value of a \$1000 investment that earns 10% interest per year, compounded annually for t years. Find the value of a \$1000 investment at the end of each period.**

17. 2 years
18. 3 years
19. 4 years
20. 5 years

Example 4 (page 14)

Simplify by combining like terms.

21. $5a - a$
22. $5 + 10s - 8s$
23. $-5a - 4a + b$
24. $2a + 3b + 4a$
25. $6r + 3s + 2s + 4r$
26. $w + 3z + 5w + 2z$
27. $x^2 + x^2 + x$
28. $xy + 2x + x$
29. $0.5x - x$
30. $3(2x + 1) - 8$
31. $2(5y - 2) + x$
32. $3y - (4y + 6x)$
33. $7b - (3a - 8b)$
34. $5 + (4g - 7)$
35. $-(3x - 4y + z)$

Example 5 (page 14)

Geometry **Find the perimeter of each figure. Simplify the answer.**

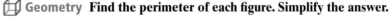

36.

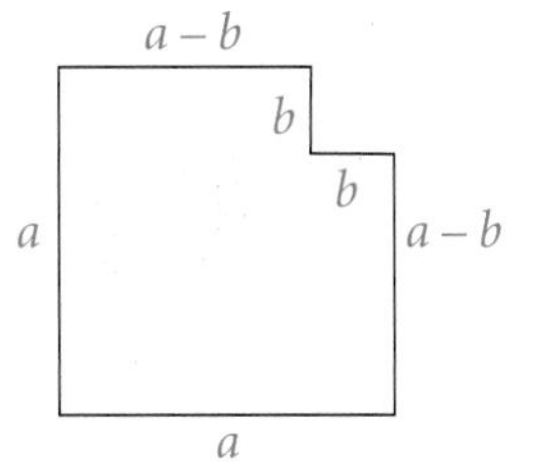

37.

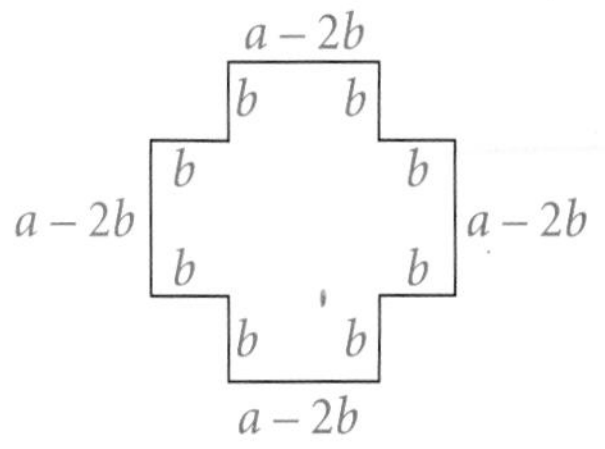

B Apply Your Skills

Evaluate each expression for the given value of the variable.

38. $|x| + |2x| - |x - 1|; x = 2$

39. $|2z + 3| + |5 - 3z|; z = -3$

40. $3|2a + 5| + 2|3 - a|; a = 4$

41. $6|4b - 5| + 3|2 - 2b|; b = -1$

42. $\frac{3(2x + 1) - 2(x - 3)}{x + 6}; x = -3$

43. $\frac{5(2k - 3) - 3(k + 4)}{3k + 2}; k = -2$

44. $y^2 + 3; y = \sqrt{7}$

45. $5c^3 - 6c^2 - 2c; c = -5$

Real-World Connection

Each year, millions of U.S. citizens turn 18 and become eligible to vote. Unfortunately, fewer than half of them register.

46. Elections The expression $2.6y + 107$ models the number of eligible voters in millions in the United States from 1960 to 2000. In the expression, y represents the number of years since 1960.

a. Find the approximate number of eligible voters in 1988.

b. Assume that the model continues to hold for future years. How many eligible voters will there be in 2012? In 2020?

c. The expression $-0.3y + 61$ models the *percent* of eligible voters who voted in presidential elections from 1960 to 2000. (See Example 3.) Write an expression that models the *number* of voters in presidential elections from 1960 to 2000.

d. Use your model from (c) to find the approximate number of voters who voted for president in 1980.

Simplify by combining like terms.

47. $-a^2 + 2b^2 + \frac{1}{4}a^2$

48. $x + \frac{x^2}{2} + 2x^2 - x$

49. $\frac{y^2}{4} + \frac{y}{3} + \frac{y^2}{3} - \frac{y}{5}$

50. $-(2x + y) - 2(-x - y)$

51. $x(3 - y) + y(x + 6)$

52. $4(2x + y) - 2(2x + y)$

53. $\frac{1}{2}(x^2 - y^2) - \frac{5}{2}(x^2 - y^2)$

Match the property name with the appropriate equation.

54. Definition of Subtraction

55. Definition of Division

56. Distributive Property

57. Multiplication by 0

58. Multiplication by -1

59. Opposite of a Sum

60. Opposite of a Difference

61. Opposite of a Product

62. Opposite of an Opposite

A. $2(s - t) = 2s - 2t$

B. $-(a - b) = (-1)(a - b)$

C. $(7 - y) \div (2y) = \frac{7 - y}{2y}$

D. $-[-(x - 10)] = x - 10$

E. $-(2t - 11) = 11 - 2t$

F. $2t - 11 = 2t + (-11)$

G. $(4a^2 - 9a)(0) + 5a = 0 + 5a$

H. $-[3 + (-y)] = -3 + [-(-y)]$

I. $-(4z^2) = 4(-z^2)$

Justifying Steps **Name the property used in each step of simplification.**

63.
$$\begin{aligned}(3x + y) + x &= 3x + (y + x)\\ &= 3x + (x + y)\\ &= (3x + x) + y\\ &= (3x + 1x) + y\\ &= (3 + 1)x + y\\ &= 4x + y\end{aligned}$$

64.
$$\begin{aligned}2(5 + x) + 4(5 + x) &= (2 + 4)(5 + x)\\ &= 6(5 + x)\\ &= 30 + 6x\end{aligned}$$

C Challenge

65. Open-Ended Write four different expressions that simplify to $x^2 - x$. Each expression must have five terms.

66. Simplify $2(b - a) + 5(b - a)$ and explain each step in your simplification.

67. a. Evaluate the expression $2(2x^2 - x) - 3(x^2 - x) + x^2 - x$ for $x = 3$. Do *not* simplify the expression before evaluating it.

b. Simplify the expression in (a) and then evaluate your answer for $x = 3$.

c. **Writing** Explain why the values in (a) and (b) should be the same.

d. **Error Analysis** A student simplified $2x(x - 6)$ to $2x^2 - 6x$. Should the student check his work by evaluating both expressions for $x = 0$? Explain.

Standardized Test Prep

Multiple Choice

68. Which of the following expressions is NOT equivalent to the others?

A. $3x - y - x - y$ B. $-2(x - y)$
C. $2(x - y)$ D. $2x - 2y$

69. If xy is negative, which one of the following is possible?

F. $x < y < 0$ G. $x < 0 < y$
H. $x = y$ I. $0 \le x \le y$

Short Response

70. For which values of x does $6x(x - 3) = 0$? Explain your answer.

Quantitative Comparison

Compare the boxed quantity in Column A with the boxed quantity in Column B. Choose the best answer.

A. The quantity in Column A is greater.
B. The quantity in Column B is greater.
C. The two quantities are equal.
D. The relationship cannot be determined from the information given.

	Column A	Column B
71.	the perimeter of a square with side 17 in.	the perimeter of an equilateral triangle with side 19 in.
72.	the area of a rectangle with perimeter 24 cm	the area of a rectangle with perimeter 26 cm
73.	the perimeter of a square with area $100a^2b^2$ in.^{2}	the total perimeter of two squares, each with area $25a^2b^2$ in.^{2}

Take It to the NET
Online lesson quiz at
www.PHSchool.com
Web Code: aga-0102

Mixed Review

Lesson 1-1

Order the numbers from least to greatest.

74. $-1.5, -0.5, -\sqrt{2}, -1.4$

75. $|-4.3|, -4.3, -|3.4|, |-3.4|$

76. $-\frac{3}{8}, \frac{1}{2}, -\frac{3}{4}, -\frac{5}{6}$

77. $\sqrt{\frac{1}{4}}, \sqrt{\frac{1}{16}}, -\sqrt{\frac{1}{8}}, -\sqrt{\frac{1}{10}}$

Lesson 1-1

Replace each ■ with the symbol <, >, or = to make the sentence true.

78. $|-11|$ ■ $|9|$

79. $|11|$ ■ $|9|$

80. $|-11|$ ■ $|-9|$

81. $-|-7|$ ■ $|7|$

82. $-|7|$ ■ $|-7|$

83. $-|-7|$ ■ $-|7|$

1-3 Solving Equations

North Carolina Objectives

1.03 Operate with algebraic expressions (polynomial, rational, complex fractions) to solve problems.

Lesson Preview

What You'll Learn

OBJECTIVE 1 To solve equations

OBJECTIVE 2 To solve problems by writing equations

. . . And Why

To solve a problem about aeronautics, as in Example 7

Check Skills You'll Need

(For help, go to Lesson 1-2.)

Simplify each expression.

1. $5x - 9x + 3$

2. $2y + 7x + y - 1$

3. $10h + 12g - 8h - 4g$

4. $\frac{x}{3} + \frac{y}{3} + \frac{2y}{3} - y$

5. $(x + y) - (x - y)$

6. $-(3 - c) - 4(c - 1)$

New Vocabulary • solution of an equation

Interactive lesson includes instant self-check, tutorials, and activities.

OBJECTIVE 1 Solving Equations

An equation that contains a variable may be true for some replacements of the variable and false for others. A number that makes the equation true is a **solution of the equation.** You can use the properties of equality to solve equations.

Key Concepts

Summary **Properties of Equality**

Let a, b, and c represent real numbers.

Reflexive Property	$a = a$
Symmetric Property	If $a = b$, then $b = a$.
Transitive Property	If $a = b$ and $b = c$, then $a = c$.
Addition Property	If $a = b$, then $a + c = b + c$.
Subtraction Property	If $a = b$, then $a - c = b - c$.
Multiplication Property	If $a = b$, then $ac = bc$.
Division Property	If $a = b$ and $c \neq 0$, then $\frac{a}{c} = \frac{b}{c}$.
Substitution Property	If $a = b$, then b may be substituted for a in any expression to obtain an equivalent expression.

Reading Math

Literally, to solve means "to set apart." Think of solving an equation as setting apart the variable.

1 EXAMPLE Solving an Equation with a Variable on Both Sides

Solve $13y + 48 = 8y - 47$.

$13y + 48 = 8y - 47$

$5y + 48 = -47$ **Subtract 8y from each side.**

$5y = -95$ **Subtract 48 from each side.**

$y = -19$ **Divide each side by 5.**

Check $13y + 48 = 8y - 47$

$13(-19) + 48 \stackrel{?}{=} 8(-19) - 47$

$-199 = -199$ ✓

Check Understanding 1 Solve each equation. Check your answers.

a. $8z + 12 = 5z - 21$ **b.** $2t - 3 = 9 - 4t$

2 EXAMPLE Using the Distributive Property

Solve $3x - 7(2x - 13) = 3(-2x + 9)$.

$3x - 7(2x - 13) = 3(-2x + 9)$

$3x - 14x + 91 = -6x + 27$ **Distributive Property**

$-11x + 91 = -6x + 27$ **Combine like terms.**

$-5x + 91 = 27$ **Add 6x to each side.**

$-5x = -64$ **Subtract 91 from each side.**

$x = \frac{64}{5}$, or 12.8 **Divide each side by −5.**

Check Understanding 2 Solve each equation. Check your answers.

a. $2(y - 3) + 6 = 70$ **b.** $6(t - 2) = 2(9 - 2t)$

When you have a formula or equation that has more than one variable, you can solve for any one of the variables.

3 EXAMPLE Solving a Formula for One of Its Variables

Geometry The formula for the area of a trapezoid is $A = \frac{1}{2}h(b_1 + b_2)$. Solve the formula for h.

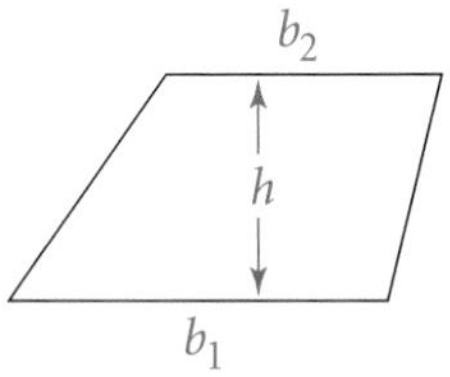

$A = \frac{1}{2}h(b_1 + b_2)$

$2A = h(b_1 + b_2)$ **Multiply each side by 2.**

$\frac{2A}{b_1 + b_2} = h$ **Divide each side by $b_1 + b_2$.**

Check Understanding 3 Solve the formula for the area of a trapezoid for b_1.

4 EXAMPLE Solving an Equation for One of Its Variables

Solve $\frac{x}{a} + 1 = \frac{x}{b}$ for x. Find any restrictions on a and b.

$\frac{x}{a} + 1 = \frac{x}{b}$

$ab\left(\frac{x}{a}\right) + ab(1) = ab\left(\frac{x}{b}\right)$ **Multiply each side by the least common denominator (LCD).**

$bx + ab = ax$ **Simplify.**

$ab = ax - bx$ **Collect terms with x on one side.**

$ab = (a - b)x$ **Distributive Property**

$x = \frac{ab}{a - b}$ **Divide each side by $a - b$.**

The denominators cannot be 0, so $a \neq 0$ and $b \neq 0$. Also $a - b \neq 0$, so $a \neq b$.

Check Understanding 4 Solve each equation for x. Find any restrictions.

a. $ax + bx - 15 = 0$ **b.** $d = \frac{2x}{a} + b$

OBJECTIVE 2

Writing Equations To Solve Problems

You can write an equation to model and solve a real-world problem.

5 EXAMPLE Real-World Connection

Real-World Connection

Some states regulate the minimum amount of floor space for animals in kennels.

Construction A dog kennel owner has 100 ft of fencing to enclose a rectangular dog run. She wants it to be 5 times as long as it is wide. Find the dimensions of the dog run.

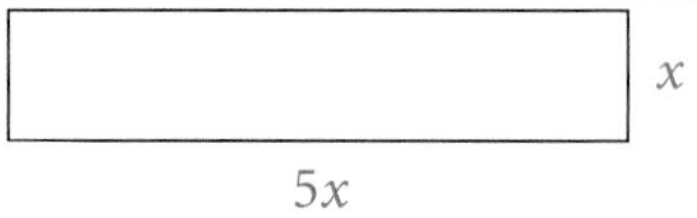

Relate $2 \cdot$ width $+ 2 \cdot$ length $=$ perimeter

Define Let x = the width.

Then $5x$ = the length.

Write $2x + 2(5x) = 100$

$2x + 10x = 100$ **Multiply.**

$12x = 100$ **Combine like terms.**

$x = 8\frac{1}{3}$ **Divide each side by 12.**

$5x = 41\frac{2}{3}$ **Find the length.**

The width is $8\frac{1}{3}$ ft and the length is $41\frac{2}{3}$ ft.

Check Is the answer reasonable? Since the dimensions are about 8 ft and 42 ft, and $2 \cdot 8 + 2 \cdot 42 = 100$, the answer is reasonable.

Check Understanding 5 A rectangle is twice as long as it is wide. Its perimeter is 48 cm. Find its dimensions.

Many geometry problems require writing and solving equations.

6 EXAMPLE Using Ratios

Geometry The lengths of the sides of a triangle are in the ratio 3 : 4 : 5. The perimeter of the triangle is 18 in. Find the lengths of the sides.

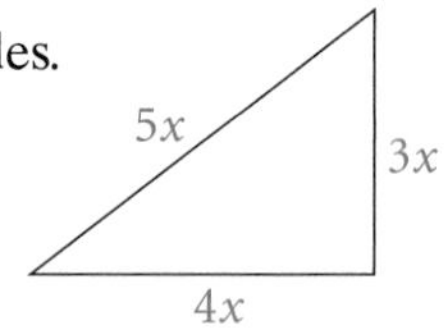

Relate Perimeter equals the sum of the lengths of the three sides.

Define Let $3x$ = the length of the shortest side.
Then $4x$ = the length of the second side.
Then $5x$ = the length of the third side.

Write $18 = 3x + 4x + 5x$

$18 = 12x$ **Combine like terms.**

$1.5 = x$

$3x = 3(1.5) = 4.5$ $\quad 4x = 4(1.5) = 6$ $\quad 5x = 5(1.5) = 7.5$ **Find the length of each side.**

The lengths of the sides are 4.5 in., 6 in., and 7.5 in.

Check Is the answer reasonable? Since $5 + 6 + 8 = 19$, the answer is reasonable.

Check Understanding 6 The sides of a triangle are in the ratio 12 : 13 : 15. The perimeter is 120 cm. Find the lengths of the sides of the triangle.

Real-World Connection

The F-117 is nearly invisible to radar. The faceted construction deflects most radar energy away from the radar receiver.

7 EXAMPLE **Real-World Connection**

Aeronautics Radar detected an unidentified plane 5000 mi away, approaching at 700 mi/h. Fifteen minutes later an interceptor plane was dispatched, traveling at 800 mi/h. How long did the interceptor take to reach the approaching plane?

Relate distance for interceptor + distance for approaching plane = 5000 mi

Define Let t = the time in hours for the interceptor.
Then $t + 0.25$ = the time in hours for the approaching plane.

Write $800t + 700(t + 0.25) = 5000$

$800t + 700t + 175 = 5000$ **Distributive Property**

$1500t = 4825$ **Solve for *t*.**

$t \approx 3.217$ or about 3 h 13 min

Check Is the answer reasonable? In $3\frac{1}{4}$ h, the interceptor flies 2600 mi. In $3\frac{1}{2}$ h, the approaching plane flies 2450 mi. $2600 + 2450 \approx 5000$, so the answer is reasonable.

Check Understanding **7** A space probe leaves Earth at the rate of 3 km/s. After 100 days, a radio signal is sent to the probe. Radio signals travel at the speed of light, about 3×10^5 km/s. About how long does the signal take to reach the probe?

EXERCISES

For more practice, see *Extra Practice*.

Practice and Problem Solving

A Practice by Example

Example 1 (page 18)

Solve each equation. Check your answers.

1. $7w + 2 = 3w + 94$
2. $15 - g = 23 - 2g$
3. $43 - 3d = d + 9$
4. $5y + 1.8 = 4y - 3.2$
5. $6a - 5 = 4a + 2$
6. $7y + 4 = 3 - 2y$
7. $5c - 9 = 8 - 2c$
8. $4y - 8 - 2y + 5 = 0$

Example 2 (page 19)

9. $6(n - 4) = 3n$
10. $2 - 3(x + 4) = 8$
11. $5(2 - g) = 0$
12. $2(x + 4) = 8$
13. $6(t - 2) = 2(9t - 2)$
14. $4w - 2(1 - w) = -38$
15. $4(k + 5) = 2(9k - 4)$
16. $10(1 - 2y) = -5(2y - 1)$

Example 3 (page 19)

Solve each formula for the indicated variable.

17. $A = \frac{1}{2}bh$, for h
18. $s = \frac{1}{2}gt^2$, for g
19. $V = \ell wh$, for w
20. $I = prt$, for r
21. $S = 2\pi rh$, for r
22. $V = \pi r^2 h$, for h

Example 4 (page 19)

Solve each equation for *x*. Find any restrictions.

23. $ax + bx = c$
24. $bx - cx = -c$
25. $\frac{x}{a} + b = c$
26. $\frac{x}{a} - 5 = b$
27. $\frac{x - 2}{2} = m + n$
28. $\frac{2}{5}(x + 1) = g$

Examples 5–7 (pages 20, 21)

Write an equation to solve each problem.

29. Two buses leave Houston at the same time and travel in opposite directions. One bus averages 55 mi/h and the other bus averages 45 mi/h. When will they be 400 mi apart?

30. Two planes left an airport at noon. One flew east at a certain speed and the other flew west at twice the speed. The planes were 2700 mi apart in 3 h. How fast was each plane flying?

31. Geometry The length of a rectangle is 3 cm greater than its width. The perimeter is 24 cm. Find the dimensions of the rectangle.

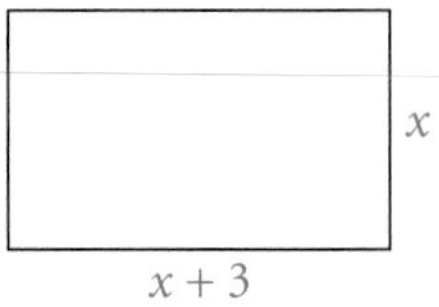

32. Geometry One side of a triangle is 1 in. longer than the shortest side and is 1 in. shorter than the longest side. The perimeter is 17 in. Find the dimensions of the triangle.

33. Geometry The sides of a rectangle are in the ratio 3 : 2. What is the length of each side if the perimeter of the rectangle is 55 cm?

34. Geometry The sides of a triangle are in the ratio 3 : 4 : 5. What is the length of each side if the perimeter of the triangle is 30 cm?

35. The sum of three consecutive integers is 90.
a. Find the three numbers by letting x represent the first integer.
b. Find the three numbers by letting x represent the second integer.

B Apply Your Skills

Solve each equation.

36. $0.2(x + 3) - 4(2x - 3) = 3.4$

37. $12 - 3(2w + 1) = 7w - 3(7 + w)$

38. $3(m - 2) - 5 = 8 - 2(m - 4)$

39. $7(a + 1) - 3a = 5 + 4(2a - 1)$

40. $\frac{x}{2} + \frac{x}{5} + \frac{x}{3} = 31$

41. $0.5\left(2x + \frac{3}{4}\right) - \frac{1}{3}(0.1 + x) = 1$

Solve each formula for the indicated variable.

42. $R(r_1 + r_2) = r_1r_2$, for R

43. $R(r_1 + r_2) = r_1r_2$, for r_2

44. $S = 2\pi r^2 + 2\pi rh$, for h

45. $h = vt - 5t^2$, for v

46. $v = s^2 + \frac{1}{2}sh$, for h

47. $A = \frac{1}{2}h(b_1 + b_2)$, for b_2

48. Geometry The measure of the supplement of an angle is 20° more than three times the measure of the original angle. Find the measures of the angles.

49. Geometry The measures of an angle and its complement differ by 22°. Find the measures of the angles.

Real-World Connection

In the 2000 Olympics, Marion Jones won three gold and two bronze medals.

50. Michael drove to a friend's house at a rate of 40 mi/h. He returned by the same route at a rate of 45 mi/h. The driving time for the round trip was 4 h. What is the distance Michael traveled?

51. Sports In the 2000 Olympics, Marion Jones of the United States won the gold medal in the 100-meter race with a time of 10.75 seconds. In the 1968 Olympics, Wyomia Tyus, also of the United States, won the gold medal in the 100-meter race in 11.08 seconds. If they ran in the same race repeating their respective times, by how many meters would Jones beat Tyus?

52. Investments Suppose you have \$5000 to invest. A certificate of deposit (CD) earns 6% annual interest, while bonds, which are more risky, earn 8% annual interest. You decide to invest \$2000 in a CD and the rest in bonds. How much interest will you have earned at the end of one year? Of two years?

53. Find 4 consecutive odd integers with a sum of 184.

54. Find 4 consecutive even integers such that the sum of the second and fourth is 76.

Solve for x. State any restrictions on the variables.

55. $\frac{x + a}{b} + b = a$

56. $bx + a = dx + c$

57. $cx - b = ax + d$

58. $a(x - 3) + 8 = b(x - 1)$

59. $c(x + 2) - 5 = b(x - 3)$

60. $a(3tx - 2b) = c(dx - 2)$

61. $b(5px - 3c) = a(qx - 4)$

62. $\frac{a}{b}(2x - 12) = \frac{c}{d}$

63. $\frac{3ax}{5} - 4c = \frac{ax}{5}$

64. $\frac{a - c}{x - a} = m$

C Challenge

65. **a.** The speed of sound in air s, in ft/s, is given by the formula $s = 1055 + 1.1t$, where t is the temperature in degrees Fahrenheit. Solve the formula for t.
b. Find the Fahrenheit temperature at which the speed of sound is 1100 ft/s.
c. The relationship between the temperature in degrees Fahrenheit F and degrees Celsius C is given by the formula $F = \frac{9}{5}C + 32$. Solve the formula for C.
d. Find the Celsius temperature at which the speed of sound is 1100 ft/s.

66. There are 40 cows and chickens in the farmyard. One quiet afternoon, Jack counted and found that there were 100 legs in all. How many cows and how many chickens are there?
a. Solve this problem by writing and solving an equation.
b. **Critical Thinking** This problem can also be solved by reasoning. Suppose all 40 animals are chickens. How many legs would there be? How many too few legs is that? If one chicken is replaced by one cow, by how many would the number of legs be increased? How many cows would have to replace chickens to get the required 100 legs?
c. **Open-Ended** Write a problem about the number of wheels in a group of bicycles and tricycles. Solve your problem.

67. Assume that a, b, and c are integers and $a \neq 0$.
a. **Proof** Prove that the solution of the linear equation $ax - b = c$ must be a rational number.
b. **Writing** Describe the values of a, b, and c for which the solutions of $ax^2 + b = c$ are rational.

68. A tortoise crawling at the rate of 0.1 mi/h passes a resting hare. The hare wants to rest another 30 min before chasing the tortoise at the rate of 5 mi/h. How many feet must the hare run to catch the tortoise?

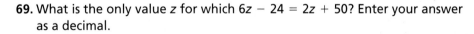

Standardized Test Prep

Gridded Response

69. What is the only value z for which $6z - 24 = 2z + 50$? Enter your answer as a decimal.

70. If 16 less than four times a number is 64, what is the number?

71. The measure of the supplement of an angle is 25° more than 7 times the measure of the angle. To the nearest hundredth, what is the measure of the angle?

72. The sides of a rectangle are in the ratio 5 : 7 and the perimeter of the rectangle is 96 cm. What is the area of the rectangle?

Take It to the NET
Online lesson quiz at **www.PHSchool.com**
Web Code: aga-0103

Mixed Review

Lesson 1-2 **Evaluate each expression for $x = -4$ and $y = 3$.**

73. $x - 2y + 3$ **74.** $x + x \div y$ **75.** $3x - 4y - x$ **76.** $x + 2y \div x$

Lesson 1-2 **Simplify each expression.**

77. $2x^2 + x + 5x^2 - 3x$ **78.** $ab - a - 5a$ **79.** $-(3x - y + 4x - y)$

80. $2(5x - 3) + x$ **81.** $5 - 2(3x + 5)$ **82.** $4r + 2s - (6r + 7s)$

Checkpoint Quiz 1 — Lessons 1-1 through 1-3

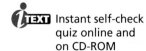

iTEXT Instant self-check quiz online and on CD-ROM

1. Simplify the numbers and arrange them in order from least to greatest.
$|4 - 11|$ $0.1|-3|$ $|1 - \frac{1}{3}|$ $|3| - |4|$

2. What three properties of real numbers are needed to simplify $3x + (2 + 5x)$?

Simplify each expression.

3. $-(a + 2b) + 4(a + 2b) - 2(a + 2b)$ **4.** $-3(a^2 + a + 1) - 4(-a^2 - a + 1)$

Solve each equation.

5. $2(4x + 1) = 3(4 + 2x)$ **6.** $12 - 2(3x + 1) = 4x - 5$

7. $\frac{1}{2}(4b + 1) = 7 - \frac{1}{4}(6b - 2)$

Solve for the indicated variable. Find any restrictions.

8. $A = p(1 + rt)$, for r **9.** $8ax - b = 3b + ax$, for x

10. The perimeter of Sportsland Park is 624 yd. The length of the rectangular park is 8 yd more than 3 times the width. Find the dimensions of the park.

Algebra at Work

Wildlife Biologist

Wildlife biologists can model changes in an animal population. An animal population increases rapidly when conditions are good. However, as the number of animals increases, the food supplies decrease. Hunger and disease then lower the population.

Wildlife biologists take a special interest in extremes of animal populations. If the population of one species becomes too large, it may reduce the population of another species. A continuing decrease may result in an endangered or extinct species.

Take It to the NET For more information about wildlife biology, go to **www.PHSchool.com**.
Web Code: agb-2031

Technology

Spreadsheets

FOR USE WITH LESSON 1-3

Suppose that you buy an electronic keyboard and sound system for $500 using a credit card. When you get your first monthly statement, the minimum payment is $25. The minimum payment is either 5% of your balance or $15, whichever is greater. Interest is calculated at 1.8% per month. You pay the minimum each month.

EXAMPLE

You can examine the situation described above with a spreadsheet. Write cell formulas for row 3 of the spreadsheet.

	A	B	C	D	E	F	G
1	Month	Balance	Interest	Payment	New Balance	Total Interest	Total Paid
2	1	$500.00	$9.00	$25.00	$484.00	$9.00	$25.00
3	2	$484.00	$8.71	$24.20	$468.51	$17.71	$49.20
4	3	$468.51	$8.43	$23.43	$453.52	$26.15	$72.63

Month	A3 = A2 + 1	**Increase the month by 1.**
Balance	B3 = E2	**balance from the previous month**
Interest	$C3 = B3 \cdot 0.018$	**1.8% of the month's balance**
Payment	$D3 = B3 \cdot 0.05$	**5% of the month's balance**
New Balance	E3 = B3 + C3 − D3	**Add the interest and subtract the payment.**
Total Interest	F3 = F2 + C3	**Add the month's interest to the previous total interest.**
Total Paid	G3 = G2 + D3	**Add the month's payment to the previous total.**

EXERCISES

1. Create a spreadsheet for the situation in the Example.
  a. In which month will the minimum payment first be $15?
  b. After how many months will the balance reach zero?
  c. What is the total interest paid?
  d. What is the total amount you will pay?
  e. How many payments are required to reduce the balance to $400?
  f. Rewrite the right side of E3 = B3 + C3 − D3 in terms of B3.

2. Create a new spreadsheet for an account that charges 14.9% annual interest. Use a minimum payment of 10% or $20, whichever is greater. What is the total interest paid for the keyboard and sound system?

3. Writing Why is it better to pay off a credit card debt as soon as you can rather than pay just the minimum each month?

1-4 Solving Inequalities

North Carolina Objectives

1.03 Operate with algebraic expressions (polynomial, rational, complex fractions) to solve problems.

Lesson Preview

What You'll Learn

OBJECTIVE 1 To solve and graph inequalities

OBJECTIVE 2 To solve and write compound inequalities

. . . And Why

To analyze quality control, as in Example 6

✓ Check Skills You'll Need

(For help, go to Lessons 1-1 and 1-3.)

State whether each inequality is true or false.

1. $5 < 12$ **2.** $5 < -12$ **3.** $5 \geq 12$

4. $5 \leq -12$ **5.** $5 \leq 5$ **6.** $5 \geq 5$

Solve each equation.

7. $3x + 3 = 2x - 3$ **8.** $5x = 9(x - 8) + 12$

New Vocabulary • compound inequality

Interactive lesson includes instant self-check, tutorials, and activities.

OBJECTIVE 1 Solving and Graphing Inequalities

As with an equation, the solutions of an inequality are the numbers that make it true.

An equation such as $-2x = 10$ has only one solution, -5. On the other hand, the inequality $-2x < 10$ is true for many values of x, such as -4.99, -1, and 100. The solutions of $-2x < 10$ are all the numbers x such that $x > -5$, as shown in the graph at the right.

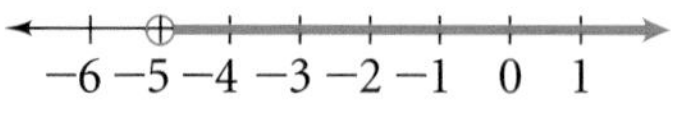

$x > -5$

Need Help?

To review the properties of equality, go to p. 18.

The properties for solving inequalities are similar to the properties for solving equations. The exception occurs when you multiply or divide each side by a negative quantity. Notice that you can obtain $x > -5$ from $-2x < 10$ by dividing each side by -2 and *reversing* the inequality.

The following properties are for $\leq$. There are similar properties for $<$, $>$, and $\geq$.

Key Concepts

Property **Properties of Inequalities**

Let a, b, and c represent real numbers.

Transitive Property	If $a \leq b$ and $b \leq c$, then $a \leq c$.
Addition Property	If $a \leq b$, then $a + c \leq b + c$.
Subtraction Property	If $a \leq b$, then $a - c \leq b - c$.
Multiplication Property	If $a \leq b$ and $c > 0$, then $ac \leq bc$. If $a \leq b$ and $c < 0$, then $ac \geq bc$.
Division Property	If $a \leq b$ and $c > 0$, then $\frac{a}{c} \leq \frac{b}{c}$. If $a \leq b$ and $c < 0$, then $\frac{a}{c} \geq \frac{b}{c}$.

←Notice that the inequality is reversed ←when c is negative.

1 EXAMPLE Solving and Graphing Inequalities

Reading Math

For help with reading and solving Example 1b, see page 32.

Solve each inequality. Graph the solution.

a. $3x - 12 < 3$

$3x - 12 < 3$

$3x < 15$ **Add 12 to each side.**

$x < 5$ **Divide each side by 3.**

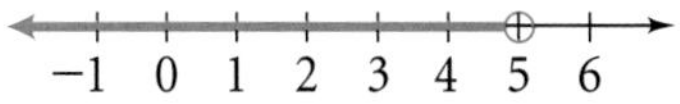

Graph the solution.

Check First check the boundary point: $3(5) - 12 = 3$. ✓
Then check another point on the graph, such as 4: $3(4) - 12 < 3$. ✓

b. $6 + 5(2 - x) \leq 41$

$6 + 10 - 5x \leq 41$ **Distributive Property**

$16 - 5x \leq 41$ **Simplify.**

$-5x \leq 25$ **Subtract 16 from each side.**

$x \geq -5$ **Divide each side by −5 and reverse the inequality.**

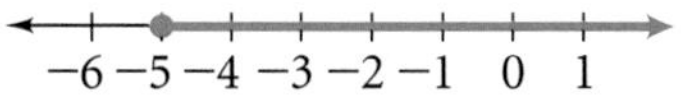

Graph the solution.

Check First check the boundary point: $6 + 5[2 - (-5)] = 41$. ✓
Then check another point, such as −4: $6 + 5[2 - (-4)] \leq 41$. ✓

Check Understanding **1** Solve each inequality. Graph the solution.

a. $3x - 6 < 27$ **b.** $12 \geq 2(3n + 1) + 22$

Some inequalities have no solution, and some are true for all real numbers.

2 EXAMPLE No Solutions or All Real Numbers as Solutions

Solve each inequality. Graph the solution.

a. $2x - 3 > 2(x - 5)$

$2x - 3 > 2x - 10$ **Distributive Property**

$2x > 2x - 7$ **Add 3 to each side.**

$0 > -7$ **Subtract 2x from each side.**

The last inequality is always true, so $2x - 3 > 2(x - 5)$ is always true. All real numbers are solutions.

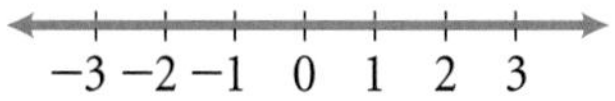

b. $7x + 6 < 7(x - 4)$

$7x + 6 < 7x - 28$ **Distributive Property**

$6 < -28$ **Subtract 7x from each side.**

The last inequality is always false, so $7x + 6 < 7(x - 4)$ is always false. It has no solution.

Check Understanding **2** **a.** Solve $2x < 2(x + 1) + 3$. Graph the solution.
b. Solve $4(x - 3) + 7 \geq 4x + 1$. Graph the solution.
c. **Critical Thinking** If possible, find values of a such that $2x + a > 2x$ has no solution. Then find values of a such that all real numbers are solutions.

3 EXAMPLE Real-World Connection

Revenue The band shown at the left agrees to play for \$200 plus 25% of the ticket sales. Find the ticket sales needed for the band to receive at least \$500.

Relate \$200 + 25% of ticket sales $\geq$ \$500

Define Let x = ticket sales (in dollars).

Write $200 + 0.25x \geq 500$

$0.25x \geq 300$ **Subtract 200 from each side.**

$x \geq 1200$ **Divide each side by 0.25.**

The ticket sales must be greater than or equal to \$1200.

Check Understanding **3** A salesperson earns a salary of \$700 per month plus 2% of the sales. What must the sales be if the salesperson is to have a monthly income of at least \$1800?

OBJECTIVE

2 Compound Inequalities

A **compound inequality** is a pair of inequalities joined by *and* or *or*.

Examples:
- $-1 < x$ and $x \leq 3$, which you can also write as $-1 < x \leq 3$
- $x < -1$ or $x \geq 3$

To solve a compound inequality containing *and*, find all values of the variable that make both inequalities true.

4 EXAMPLE Compound Inequality Containing *And*

Graph the solution of $3x - 1 > -28$ and $2x + 7 < 19$.

$3x - 1 > -28$ and $2x + 7 < 19$

$3x > -27$ | $2x < 12$

$x > -9$ and $x < 6$

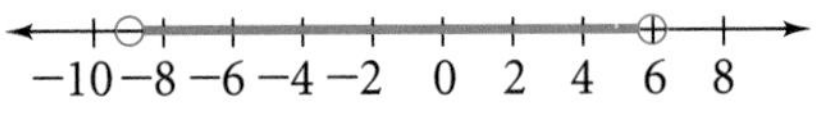

This compound inequality can be rewritten as $-9 < x < 6$.

Check Understanding **4** Graph the solution of $2x > x + 6$ and $x - 7 < 2$.

To solve a compound inequality containing *or*, find all values of the variable that make at least one of the inequalities true.

5 EXAMPLE Compound Inequality Containing *Or*

Graph the solution of $4y - 2 \geq 14$ or $3y - 4 \leq -13$.

$4y - 2 \geq 14$ or $3y - 4 \leq -13$

$4y \geq 16$ | $3y \leq -9$

$y \geq 4$ or $y \leq -3$

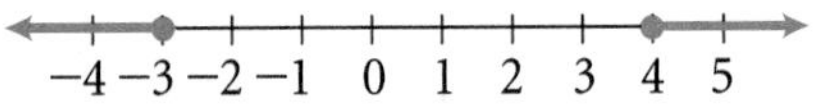

Check Understanding **5** Solve the compound inequality $x - 1 < 3$ or $x + 3 > 8$. Graph the solution.

Real-World Connection

When engineers design a part, they specify the allowable variation, or tolerance, in the size of the part.

6 EXAMPLE Real-World Connection

Quality Control The plans for a gear assembly specify a length of 13.48 cm with a tolerance of ±0.03 cm. A machinist finds that the part is now 13.67 cm long. By how much should the machinist decrease the length?

Relate minimum length $\le$ final length $\le$ maximum length

Define Let x = number of centimeters to remove.

Write $13.48 - 0.03 \le 13.67 - x \le 13.48 + 0.03$

$13.45 \le 13.67 - x \le 13.51$ **Simplify.**

$-0.22 \le -x \le -0.16$ **Subtract 13.67.**

$0.22 \ge x \ge 0.16$ **Multiply by −1.**

The machinist must remove at least 0.16 cm and no more than 0.22 cm.

Check Understanding 6 The plans for a circular plastic part in a medical instrument require a diameter of 1.5 in. with a tolerance of ±0.2 in. A machinist finds that the diameter is now 1.73 in. By how much should the machinist decrease the diameter?

EXERCISES

For more practice, see *Extra Practice*.

Practice and Problem Solving

A Practice by Example

Examples 1 and 2 (page 27)

Solve each inequality. Graph the solution.

1. $-12 \ge 24x$ **2.** $-7k < 63$ **3.** $8a - 15 > 73$

4. $57 - 4t \ge 13$ **5.** $-18 - 5y \ge 52$

6. $14 - 4y \ge 38$ **7.** $4(x + 3) \le 44$

8. $2(m - 3) + 7 < 21$ **9.** $4(n - 2) - 6 > 18$

10. $9(x + 2) > 9(x - 3)$ **11.** $6x - 13 < 6(x - 2)$

12. $-6(2x - 10) + 12x \le 180$ **13.** $-7(3x - 7) + 21x \ge 50$

Example 3 (page 28)

Solve each problem by writing an inequality.

14. The length of a picture frame is 3 in. greater than the width. The perimeter is less than 52 in. Describe the dimensions of the frame.

15. The lengths of the sides of a triangle are in the ratio 5 : 6 : 7. Describe the length of the longest side if the perimeter is not more than 54 cm.

16. Find the lesser of two consecutive integers with a sum greater than 16.

17. A company estimates that 1% of the computer chips produced in its plant are defective. How many chips must the company make and test in order to be able to ship at least 4500 nondefective chips?

Example 4 (page 28)

Solve each compound inequality. Graph the solution.

18. $2x > -10$ and $9x < 18$ **19.** $3x \ge -12$ and $8x \le 16$

20. $6x \ge -24$ and $9x < 54$ **21.** $7x > -35$ and $5x \le 30$

Example 5 (page 28)

Solve each compound inequality. Graph the solution.

22. $4x < 16$ or $12x > 144$

23. $3x \geq 3$ or $9x < 54$

24. $8x > -32$ or $-6x \leq 48$

25. $9x \leq -27$ or $4x \geq 36$

Example 6 (page 29)

Solve each problem by writing a compound inequality.

26. A baker needs between 40 lb and 50 lb of a flour-sugar mixture that contains ten times as much flour as sugar. What are the possible weights of flour the baker can use?

27. Between 15,000 yd^3 and 16,000 yd^3 of earth must be trucked away from a construction site. The trucks can remove 1000 yd^3 per day, and 10,500 yd^3 has already been removed. How many days are needed?

28. By how much should a machinist decrease the length of a rod that is 4.78 cm long if the length must be 4.5 ± 0.02 cm?

B Apply Your Skills

Solve each inequality. Graph the solution.

29. $2 - 3z \geq 7(8 - 2z) + 12$

30. $17 - 2y \leq 5(7 - 3y) - 15$

31. $\frac{2}{3}(x - 12) \leq x + 8$

32. $\frac{3}{5}(x - 12) > x - 24$

33. $3[4x - (2x - 7)] < 2(3x - 5)$

34. $6[5y - (3y - 1)] \geq 4(3y - 7)$

35. Writing Write a problem that can be solved using the inequality $x + 0.5x \leq 60$.

36. Geometry The sum of the lengths of any two sides of a triangle is greater than the length of the third side. In $\triangle ABC$, $BC = 4$ and $AC = 8 - AB$. Write an inequality for AB.

37. Construction A contractor estimated that her expenses for a construction project would be between \$700,000 and \$750,000. She has already spent \$496,000. How much more can she spend and remain within her estimate?

Real-World Connection

Careers To bid on a job, a construction contractor must consider all the costs of running a business as well as the costs of materials and labor.

38. a. Error Analysis Suppose a classmate writes $y \leq 20$ as the solution of $\frac{1}{2}(y - 16) \geq y + 2$. Prove that your classmate's answer is wrong by checking a number that is less than 20. Choose a number that makes the computation easy.

b. Solve $\frac{1}{2}(y - 16) \geq y + 2$.

Justifying Steps **Justify each step by identifying the property used.**

39.
$$3x \leq 4(x - 1) - 8$$
$$3x \leq 4x - 4 - 8$$
$$3x \leq 4x - 12$$
$$-x \leq -12$$
$$x \geq 12$$

40.
$$\frac{1}{2}(y + 3) > \frac{1}{3}(4 - y)$$
$$3(y + 3) > 2(4 - y)$$
$$3y + 9 > 8 - 2y$$
$$5y + 9 > 8$$
$$5y > -1$$
$$y > -0.2$$

Solve each compound inequality. Graph the solutions.

41. $-6 < 2x - 4 < 12$

42. $11 < 3y + 2 < 20$

43. $-18 > 4x - 3 > -15$

44. $36 \geq 1 - 5z > -21$

45. $5a - 4 > 16$ or $3a + 2 < 17$

46. $6b + 3 < 15$ or $4b - 2 > 18$

47. $6c \leq 18$ or $-5c \leq 15$

48. $8d < -64$ and $5d > 25$

49. $4x \leq 12$ or $-7x \leq 21$

50. $15x > 30$ and $18x < -36$

Challenge

Open-Ended **Write an inequality with a solution that matches the graph. At least two steps should be needed to solve your inequality.**

51. 

52. 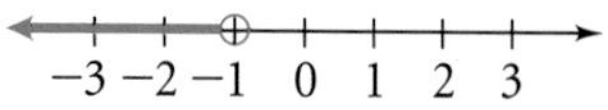

53. 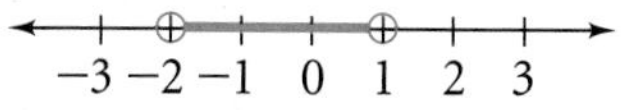

54. 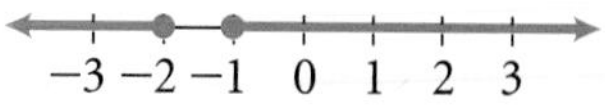

55. **Critical Thinking** Consider the compound inequality $x < 8$ and $x > a$.
  a. Are there any values of a such that all real numbers are solutions of the compound inequality? If so, what are they?
  b. Are there any values of a such that no real numbers are solutions of the compound inequality? If so, what are they?
  c. Repeat parts (a) and (b) for the compound inequality $x < 8$ or $x > a$.

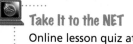

Standardized Test Prep

Multiple Choice

56. Which of the following statements are true?

I. $-(-6) = 6$ and $-(-4) > -4$
II. $-(-4) < 4$ or $-10 > 10 - 10$
III. $5 + 6 = 11$ or $9 - 2 = 11$
IV. $17 > 2$ or $6 < 9$

A. I and II only
B. I, II, and III only
C. I, III, and IV only
D. III and IV only

57. What is the solution of the inequality $8 - 3x < -3(1 + x) + 1$?
A. all real numbers **B.** no real numbers **C.** $x > \frac{2}{3}$ **D.** $x < -\frac{11}{6}$

58. What is the solution of the compound inequality $2 < 2(x + 4) < 18$?
F. all real numbers **G.** no real numbers **H.** $-3 < x < 5$ **I.** $-4 < x < 5$

59. What is the solution of the compound inequality $\frac{x}{2} - 4 > 0$ or $\frac{x}{2} + 1 < 0$?
A. all real numbers
B. no real numbers
C. $x > 6$ or $x < 0$
D. $x > 8$ or $x < -2$

Take It to the NET
Online lesson quiz at **www.PHSchool.com**
Web Code: aga-0104

Short Response

60. What is the maximum number of 3- to 5-min songs that fill a 90-min CD? What is the minimum number? Explain your reasoning.

Extended Response

61. Fill each box with the word *and* or *or*, so that the solution of one compound inequality is *all real numbers* and the solution of the other is *no real numbers.* Justify each step of your solution.

$x + 5 > 0$ ☐ $x - 3 < 0$ $x + 5 < 0$ ☐ $x + 5 > 0$

Mixed Review

Lesson 1-3 **Solve each equation. Check your answers.**

62. $7x - 6(11 - 2x) = 10$
63. $10x - 7 = 2(13 + 5x)$
64. $4y - \frac{1}{10} = 3y + \frac{4}{5}$
65. $0.4x + 1.18 = -3.1(2 - 0.01x)$

Lesson 1-2 **Simplify each expression.**

66. $(2a - 4) + (5a + 9)$
67. $3(x + 3y) - 5(x - y)$
68. $\frac{1}{3}(b + 12) - \frac{1}{4}(b + 12)$
69. $0.4(k - 0.1) + 0.5(3.3 - k)$

Reading Math

Reading an Example

FOR USE WITH PAGE 27, EXAMPLE 1b

Examples show you how to use and apply the concepts taught in each lesson. As you read the example, check your understanding by doing the work yourself.

Before reading an example, read the preceding paragraph for information about the concept. The box on page 26 lists the properties you can use to solve inequalities.

Many examples have two or more parts. Part (b) of Example 1 is examined below.

EXAMPLE **Solving and Graphing Inequalities**

These are the instructions. Read the problem and think about how to solve it. Remember that the goal when solving an equation or inequality is to get the variable by itself.

Solve the inequality. Graph the solution.

$6 + 5(2 - x) \leq 41$

This is the first step in the solution. The text at the right explains what was done. Follow along by doing the calculations yourself.

$6 + 10 - 5x \leq 41$ **Distributive Property**

These are the next steps in the solution. Verify that the work was done correctly.

$16 - 5x \leq 41$ **Simplify.**

$-5x \leq 25$ **Subtract 16 from each side.**

This is the last step.

$x \geq -5$ **Divide each side by −5 and reverse the inequality.**

Example 1 shows the graph of the inequality. Graph it yourself to check your understanding.

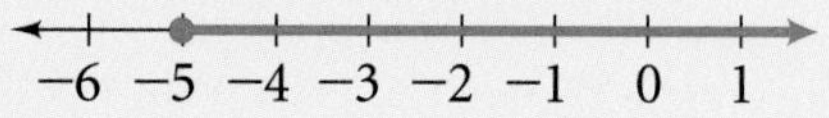

Always check your work.

Check First check the boundary point.
$6 + 5[2 - (-5)] = 41$ ✓
Then check another point on the graph, such as −4.
$6 + 5[2 - (-4)] \leq 41$ ✓

Questions to check your understanding follow each example. Try the problems that follow this example.

EXERCISE

Solve each inequality. Graph the solution.

a. $3x - 6 < 27$

b. $12 \geq 2(3n + 1) + 22$

1-5 Absolute Value Equations and Inequalities

North Carolina Objectives

2.08 Use equations and inequalities with absolute value to model and solve problems; justify results. a) Solve using tables, graphs, and algebraic properties.

Lesson Preview

What You'll Learn

OBJECTIVE 1 To solve absolute value equations

OBJECTIVE 2 To solve absolute value inequalities

. . . And Why

To write specifications for a basketball, as in Example 6

Check Skills You'll Need

(For help, go to Lessons 1-3 and 1-4.)

Solve each equation.

1. $5(x - 6) = 40$ **2.** $5b = 2(3b - 8)$ **3.** $2y + 6y = 15 - 2y + 8$

Solve each inequality.

4. $4x + 8 > 20$ **5.** $3a - 2 \geq a + 6$ **6.** $4(t - 1) < 3t + 5$

New Vocabulary • absolute value • extraneous solution • tolerance

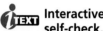

Interactive lesson includes instant self-check, tutorials, and activities.

OBJECTIVE 1 Absolute Value Equations

The **absolute value** of a number is its distance from zero on the number line and distance is nonnegative. So the absolute value of a negative number such as -5 is its opposite, $-(-5)$. For $x < 0$, $|x| = -x$.

Key Concepts

Definition — **Algebraic Definition of Absolute Value**

- If $x \geq 0$, then $|x| = x$.
- If $x < 0$, then $|x| = -x$.

An absolute value equation such as $|2y - 4| = 12$ has two solutions, since the expression $2y - 4$ can equal 12 or -12.

1 EXAMPLE Solving Absolute Value Equations

Solve $|2y - 4| = 12$.

$|2y - 4| = 12$

$2y - 4 = 12$ or $2y - 4 = -12$ — **The value of $2y - 4$ can be 12 or -12 since $|12|$ and $|-12|$ both equal 12.**

$2y = 16$ | $2y = -8$ — **Add 4 to each side of both equations.**

$y = 8$ or $y = -4$ — **Divide each side of both equations by 2.**

Check $|2y - 4| = 12$

$|2(8) - 4| \stackrel{?}{=} 12$ $|2(-4) - 4| \stackrel{?}{=} 12$

$|12| = 12$ ✓ $|-12| = 12$ ✓

Check Understanding **1** Solve $|3x + 2| = 7$. Check your answer.

You will find it easier to solve a multi-step absolute value equation if you first isolate the absolute value expression on one side of the equation.

2 EXAMPLE Solving Multi-Step Absolute Value Equations

Solve $3|4w - 1| - 5 = 10$.

$3|4w - 1| - 5 = 10$

$3|4w - 1| = 15$ **Add 5 to each side.**

$|4w - 1| = 5$ **Divide each side by 3.**

$4w - 1 = 5$ or $4w - 1 = -5$ **Rewrite as two equations.**

$4w = 6$ | $4w = -4$ **Add 1 to each side of both equations.**

$w = \frac{3}{2}$ or $w = -1$ **Divide each side of both equations by 4.**

Check $3|4w - 1| - 5 = 10$ $\quad$ $3|4w - 1| - 5 = 10$

$3|4(\frac{3}{2}) - 1| - 5 \stackrel{?}{=} 10$ $\quad$ $3|4(-1) - 1| - 5 \stackrel{?}{=} 10$

$3|5| - 5 \stackrel{?}{=} 10$ $\quad$ $3|-5| - 5 \stackrel{?}{=} 10$

$10 = 10$ ✓ $\quad$ $10 = 10$ ✓

Check Understanding **2** Solve $2|3x - 1| + 5 = 33$. Check your answer.

The equation $|2x + 7| = -2$ has no solution because $|2x + 7|$ cannot be negative. It is important to check possible solutions in the original equation. One or more may be extraneous solutions.

Key Concepts

Definition	Extraneous Solution
An **extraneous solution** is a solution of an equation derived from an original equation that is not a solution of the original equation.	

Reading Math

Extraneous is pronounced ek-STRAY-nee-us.

3 EXAMPLE Checking for Extraneous Solutions

Solve $|2x + 5| = 3x + 4$.

$|2x + 5| = 3x + 4$

$2x + 5 = 3x + 4$ or $2x + 5 = -(3x + 4)$ **Rewrite as two equations.**

$-x = -1$ | $2x + 5 = -3x - 4$ **Solve each equation.**

$x = 1$ | $5x = -9$

$x = 1$ or $x = -\frac{9}{5}$

Check $|2x + 5| = 3x + 4$ $\quad$ $|2x + 5| = 3x + 4$

$|2(1) + 5| \stackrel{?}{=} 3(1) + 4$ $\quad$ $\left|2\left(-\frac{9}{5}\right) + 5\right| \stackrel{?}{=} 3\left(-\frac{9}{5}\right) + 4$

$|7| \stackrel{?}{=} 7$ $\quad$ $\left|\frac{7}{5}\right| \stackrel{?}{=} -\frac{7}{5}$

$7 = 7$ ✓ $\quad$ $\frac{7}{5} \neq -\frac{7}{5}$

The only solution is 1. $-\frac{9}{5}$ is an extraneous solution.

Check Understanding **3** **a.** Solve $|2x + 3| = 3x + 2$. Check for extraneous solutions.
b. Solve $|x| = x - 1$. Check for extraneous solutions.
c. **Critical Thinking** Find a value for a such that $|x| = x + a$ has exactly one solution.

OBJECTIVE

2 Absolute Value Inequalites

If $|x| > 3$, then x is more than 3 units from 0 on the number line.

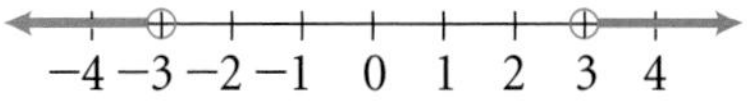

This is also the graph of $x < -3$ or $x > 3$. So the absolute value inequality $|x| > 3$ can be rewritten as the compound inequality $x < -3$ or $x > 3$.

4 EXAMPLE Solving Inequalities of the Form $|A| \geq b$

Solve $|3x + 6| \geq 12$. Graph the solution.

$|3x + 6| \geq 12$

$3x + 6 \leq -12$ or $3x + 6 \geq 12$ **Rewrite as a compound inequality.**

$3x \leq -18$ or $3x \geq 6$

$x \leq -6$ or $x \geq 2$

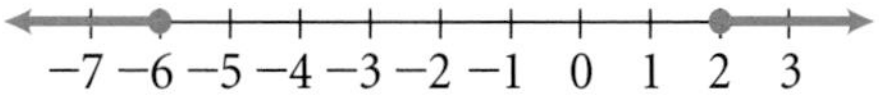

Graph the solution.

Check Understanding 4 Solve $|2x - 3| > 7$. Graph the solution.

If $|x| < 2$, then x is less than 2 units from 0 on the number line.

This is also the graph of $-2 < x < 2$. So the absolute value inequality $|x| < 2$ can be written as the compound inequality $-2 < x < 2$.

Key Concepts

Properties	Absolute Value Inequalities	
Let k represent a positive real number.		
$\|x\| \geq k$	is equivalent to	$x \leq -k$ or $x \geq k$.
$\|x\| \leq k$	is equivalent to	$-k \leq x \leq k$.

When an absolute value is combined with other operations, first isolate the absolute value expression on one side of the inequality.

Need Help?

To review the properties of inequalities, go to p. 26.

5 EXAMPLE Solving Inequalities of the Form $|A| < b$

Solve $3|2x + 6| - 9 < 15$. Graph the solution.

$3|2x + 6| - 9 < 15$

$3|2x + 6| < 24$ **Isolate the absolute value expression. Add 9 to each side.**

$|2x + 6| < 8$ **Divide each side by 3.**

$-8 < 2x + 6 < 8$ **Rewrite as a compound inequality.**

$-14 < 2x < 2$ **Solve for *x*.**

$-7 < x < 1$

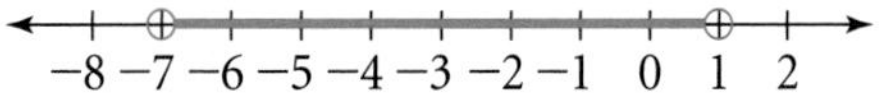

Check Understanding 5 Solve $|5z + 3| - 7 < 34$. Graph the solution.

You can use absolute value inequalities and compound inequalities to specify allowable ranges in measurements. The difference between a desired measurement and its maximum and minimum allowable values is the tolerance. The **tolerance** equals one half of the difference between the maximum and the minimum values.

For example, if a manufacturing specification calls for a dimension d of 10 cm with a tolerance of 0.1 cm, then the allowable difference between d and 10 is less than or equal to 0.1. This specification can be expressed in the following ways.

$\lvert d - 10 \rvert \leq 0.1$	**absolute value inequality**
$d - 10 \leq 0.1$ and $d - 10 \geq -0.1$	**equivalent compound inequality**
$-0.1 \leq d - 10 \leq 0.1$	**equivalent compound inequality**
$9.9 \leq d \leq 10.1$	**simplified compound inequality**

6 EXAMPLE Real-World Connection

Basketball The specification for the circumference C in inches of a basketball for men is $29.5 \leq C \leq 30$. Write the specification as an absolute value inequality.

$\frac{30 - 29.5}{2} = \frac{0.5}{2} = 0.25$	**Find the tolerance.**
$\frac{29.5 + 30}{2} = 29.75$	**Find the average of the maximim and minimum values.**
$-0.25 \leq C - 29.75 \leq 0.25$	**Write an inequality.**
$\lvert C - 29.75 \rvert \leq 0.25$	**Rewrite as an absolute value inequality.**

Check Understanding 6 The specification for the circumference C in inches of a basketball for junior high school is $27.75 \leq C \leq 28.5$. Write the specification as an absolute value inequality.

EXERCISES

For more practice, see *Extra Practice*.

Practice and Problem Solving

A Practice by Example

Examples 1 and 2 (pages 33, 34)

Solve each equation. Check your answers.

1. $\lvert 3x \rvert = 18$ **2.** $\lvert -4x \rvert = 32$ **3.** $\lvert x - 3 \rvert = 9$

4. $2\lvert 3x - 2 \rvert = 14$ **5.** $\lvert 3x + 4 \rvert = -3$ **6.** $\lvert 2x - 3 \rvert = -1$

7. $\lvert x + 4 \rvert + 3 = 17$ **8.** $\lvert y - 5 \rvert - 2 = 10$ **9.** $\lvert 4 - z \rvert - 10 = 1$

Example 3 (page 34)

Solve each equation. Check for extraneous solutions.

10. $\lvert x - 1 \rvert = 5x + 10$ **11.** $\lvert 2z - 3 \rvert = 4z - 1$ **12.** $\lvert 3x + 5 \rvert = 5x + 2$

13. $\lvert 2y - 4 \rvert = 12$ **14.** $3\lvert 4w - 1 \rvert - 5 = 10$ **15.** $\lvert 2x + 5 \rvert = 3x + 4$

Example 4 (page 35)

Solve each inequality. Graph the solution.

16. $\lvert x + 3 \rvert > 9$ **17.** $\lvert x - 5 \rvert \geq 8$ **18.** $\lvert y - 3 \rvert \geq 12$

19. $\lvert 2x + 1 \rvert \geq -9$ **20.** $3\lvert 2x - 1 \rvert \geq 21$ **21.** $\lvert 3z \rvert - 4 > 8$

Example 5 (page 35)

22. $3\lvert y - 9 \rvert < 27$ **23.** $\lvert 6y - 2 \rvert + 4 < 22$ **24.** $\lvert 3x - 6 \rvert + 3 < 15$

25. $\frac{1}{4}\lvert x - 3 \rvert + 2 < 1$ **26.** $4\lvert 2w + 3 \rvert - 7 \leq 9$ **27.** $3\lvert 5t - 1 \rvert + 9 \leq 23$

Example 6 (page 36)

Write each specification as an absolute value inequality.

28. $1.3 \le h \le 1.5$ **29.** $50 \le k \le 51$ **30.** $27.25 \le C \le 27.75$

31. $50 \le b \le 55$ **32.** $1200 \le m \le 1300$ **33.** $0.1187 \le d \le 0.1190$

B Apply Your Skills

Solve each equation.

34. $-|4 - 8b| = 12$ **35.** $4|3x + 4| = 4x + 8$

36. $|3x - 1| + 10 = 25$ **37.** $\frac{1}{2}|3c + 5| = 6c + 4$

38. $5|6 - 5x| = 15x - 35$ **39.** $7|8 - 3h| = 21h - 49$

40. $2|3x - 7| = 10x - 8$ **41.** $6|2x + 5| = 6x + 24$

42. $\frac{1}{4}|4x + 7| = 8x + 16$ **43.** $\frac{2}{3}|3x - 6| = 4(x - 2)$

Solve each inequality. Graph the solutions.

44. $|3x - 4| + 5 \le 27$ **45.** $|2x + 3| - 6 \ge 7$

46. $-2|x + 4| > 22$ **47.** $2|4t - 1| + 6 > 20$

48. $|3z + 15| \ge 0$ **49.** $|-2x + 1| > 2$

50. $\frac{1}{9}|5x - 3| - 3 \ge 2$ **51.** $\frac{1}{11}|2x - 4| + 10 \le 11$

52. $\left|\frac{x - 3}{2}\right| + 2 < 6$ **53.** $\left|\frac{x + 5}{3}\right| - 3 > 6$

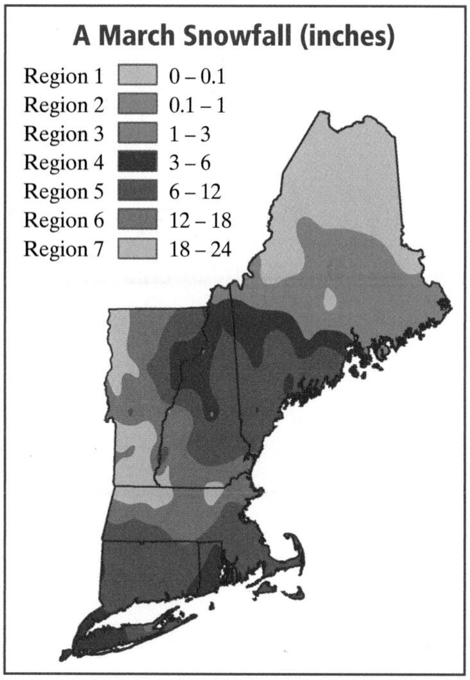

Source: Northeast River Forecast Center/NOAA

54. Meteorology Write a compound inequality and an absolute value inequality for the snowfall in regions 1, 2, 3, and 4 in the figure at the left.

55. Basketball The circumference of a basketball for women must be from 28.5 in. to 29.0 in. Write an absolute value inequality and a compound inequality for the circumference.

56. Writing Describe the differences in the graphs of $|x| < a$ and $|x| > a$, where a is a positive real number.

57. Open-Ended Write an absolute value inequality for which every real number is a solution. Write an absolute value inequality that has no solution.

Write an absolute value inequality and a compound inequality for each length x with the given tolerance.

58. a length of 36.80 mm with a tolerance of 0.05 mm

59. a length of 9.55 mm with a tolerance of 0.02 mm

60. a length of 100 yd with a tolerance of 4 in.

C Challenge

Solve each equation for x. Assume that a, b, c, and d represent positive real numbers.

61. $|ax| - b = c$ **62.** $|cx - d| = ab$ **63.** $a|bx - c| = d$

Graph each solution.

64. $|x| \ge 5$ and $|x| \le 6$ **65.** $|x| \ge 6$ or $|x| < 5$ **66.** $|x - 5| \le x$

Standardized Test Prep

Multiple Choice

67. Which number is a solution of $|x - 3| = x - 3$?

A. -3 B. 0 C. 1 D. 3

68. What is the solution of the inequality $\left|\frac{3 - x}{2}\right| < 4$?

F. $-5 < x < 11$ G. $-11 > x > -5$ H. $5 < x < 11$ I. $11 > x > -1$

69. Which of the following inequalities have the same solutions?

I. $|5x - 7| \leq 8$ II. $-8 \leq 5x - 7$ or $5x - 7 \leq 8$

III. $8 \leq 5x - 7$ and $5x - 7 \geq -8$ IV. $-8 \leq 5x - 7$ and $5x - 7 \leq 8$

A. I and II B. I and III C. I and IV D. I, III, and IV

Take It to the NET
Online lesson quiz at www.PHSchool.com
Web Code: aga-0105

70. Which number is a solution of $|9 - x| = 9 + x$?

F. -3 G. 0 H. 3 I. 6

Short Response

71. Find all the integers that are solutions of $|x - 3| \leq 5$. Show your work.

Extended Response

72. Solve $3|2x - 4| + 5 < 41$. Justify each step of your solution.

Mixed Review

Lesson 1-4

Solve each inequality. Graph the solution.

73. $5y - 10 < 20$ **74.** $-5(4s + 1) < 23$ **75.** $4a + 6 \geq 2a + 14$

76. $0.5x + 5 \geq x - 1$ **77.** $3(4x - 1) \geq 2(4 - x)$ **78.** $4(3t + 2) \leq 43 + 7t$

Lesson 1-2

Evaluate each expression for the given value.

79. $3|4x - 6| - 2x^2$, for $x = -3$ **80.** $\frac{5r - r^2}{1 - 4r}$, for $r = 4$

Lesson 1-1

Name the property of real numbers illustrated by each of the following.

81. $16x + (-16x) = 0$ **82.** 5π is a real number. **83.** $4(x - 9) = (x - 9)4$

Checkpoint Quiz 2 — Lessons 1-4 through 1-5

iTEXT Instant self-check quiz online and on CD-ROM

Solve each inequality. Graph the solution.

1. $3x + 10 \leq 25$ **2.** $8x + 15 > 15x - 24$

3. $5z > 2z - 18$ and $3 - 9z < 12$ **4.** $4w > 1 + 3w$ or $12w + 18 < 11w + 15$

5. $2|x + 4| \leq 22$ **6.** $|2x| + 8 > 12$

Solve each equation.

7. $7|3 - 2y| = 56$ **8.** $\frac{1}{4}|4x + 2| = 1 - 2x$

9. Write and solve an inequality to find three consecutive whole numbers with a sum between 13 and 16.

10. Geometry The length of a side of any triangle is less than the sum of the lengths of the other two sides. In $\triangle PQR$, $PR = RQ + 4$ and $RQ < 11$. Write and solve an inequality for PQ.

1-6 Probability

Lesson Preview

What You'll Learn

OBJECTIVE 1 To find experimental probabilities

OBJECTIVE 2 To find theoretical probabilities

. . . And Why

To find the probabilities of inherited traits, as in Example 4

✓ Check Skills You'll Need

(For help, go to Skills Handbook page 842.)

Write each number as a percent.

1. $\frac{3}{8}$ **2.** $1\frac{5}{6}$ **3.** 0.0043

4. $\frac{1}{400}$ **5.** 1.04 **6.** 3

New Vocabulary

- **experimental probability**
- **simulation**
- **sample space**
- **theoretical probability**

Interactive lesson includes instant self-check, tutorials, and activities.

OBJECTIVE 1 Experimental Probability

Investigation: Experimental Probability

Fold an index card slightly off center, as shown at the left. When you drop the card from a height of several feet, how will it land?

1. Drop the card 50 times. Record the number of times the card lands in each position.
2. What percent of the time does the card land on its short side? Find the percents for the other positions.
3. In what position is the card most likely to land? Least likely to land?
4. Suppose that you drop the card another 20 times. Predict how many times it will land in each position.
5. **a.** Drop the card another 20 times. Record your results.
   b. Compare the results with your prediction from Question 4. Are they close? How could you improve your prediction?

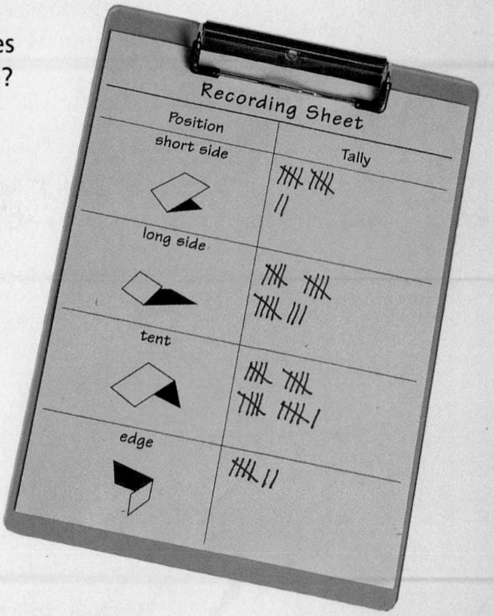

Probability measures how likely to occur an event is. You can express probabilities as percents (0% through 100%) or as real numbers (0 through 1).

The probability of an impossible event is 0 or 0%. The probability of a certain event, which must happen, is 1 or 100%.

When you gather data from observations, you can calculate an experimental probability. Each observation is called an experiment or a trial.

Key Concepts

Definition | **Experimental Probability**

experimental probability of event $= P(\text{event})$

$$= \frac{\text{number of times the event occurs}}{\text{number of trials}}$$

1 EXAMPLE Finding Experimental Probability

Reading Math

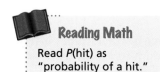

Read $P(\text{hit})$ as "probability of a hit."

A baseball player got a hit 21 times in 60 at-bats. Find the experimental probability of his getting a hit.

$P(\text{hit}) = \frac{21}{60} = 0.35$, or 35%

Check Understanding

1. A basketball player has made 32 free throws in 50 tries. What is the experimental probability of her making a free throw?

When actual trials are difficult to conduct, you can find experimental probabilities by using a **simulation,** which is a model of one or more events.

2 EXAMPLE Using a Simulation

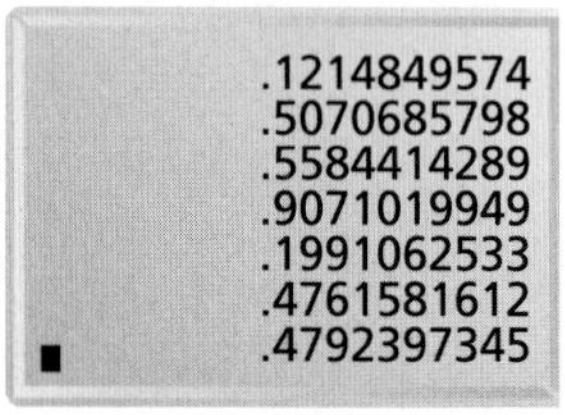

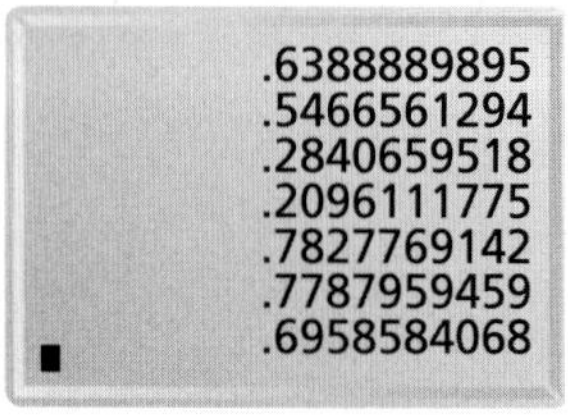

Suppose you take a four-question true-or-false quiz and guess the answers at random. What is the probability that you will get at least three questions correct?

Step 1 Define how you will do the simulation.

- Generate random numbers on a calculator.
- Since you answer true or false at random, you have a 50% chance of guessing correctly on each question. So let half of the digits represent correct answers. For example, let even digits represent correct answers.
- Since there are four questions, group the random digits in groups of four. List 50 groups to represent taking the test 50 times.

Step 2 Conduct the simulation. Underline groups with at least three even digits.

8767	0447	4672	0872	8315	6495	8778	8634	6243	5756
8958	2295	6246	1520	8491	1214	8495	7450	7068	5798
5584	4142	8990	7101	9949	1991	0625	3347	6158	1612
4792	3973	4563	8888	9895	5466	5612	9428	4065	9518
2096	1117	7578	2776	9142	7787	9594	5969	5858	4068

Step 3 Interpret the simulation. Since 15 of the 50 groups represent at least three correct answers, $P(\text{at least 3 correct}) = \frac{15}{50} = 0.3$.

The probability that you will get at least three questions correct is 30%.

Check Understanding

2. What is the experimental probability of getting all four answers correct?

OBJECTIVE

2 Theoretical Probability

When you roll a number cube, the possible outcomes are 1, 2, 3, 4, 5, and 6. The set of all possible outcomes is called the **sample space.** You can calculate theoretical probability as a ratio of outcomes.

Key Concepts

Definition **Theoretical Probability**

If a sample space has n equally likely outcomes and an event A occurs in m of these outcomes, then the **theoretical probablilty** of event A is $P(A) = \frac{m}{n}$.

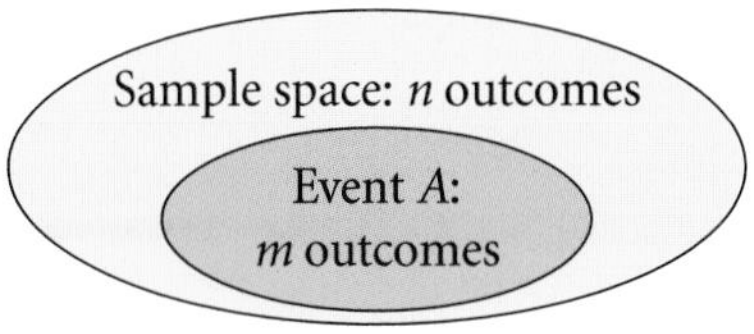

3 EXAMPLE Finding Theoretical Probability

Find the theoretical probability of getting an even number when you roll a number cube.

The even outcomes are 2, 4, and 6.

3 outcomes result in an even number. → $\frac{3}{6}$ ← **6 equally likely outcomes are in the sample space.**

$= \frac{1}{2}$

Check Understanding 3 Find the theoretical probability of getting a prime number when you roll a number cube.

4 EXAMPLE Real-World Connection

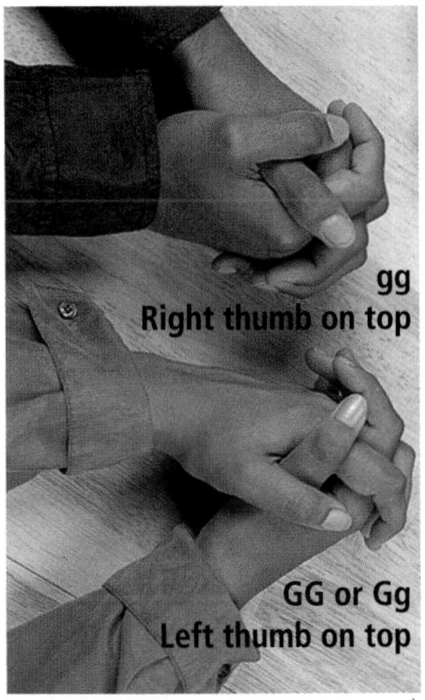

Biology Fold your hands so your fingers interlace. Do you naturally place your left or right thumb on top? Placing your left thumb on top is a dominant genetic trait.

When a parent has both a dominant and a recessive gene, then the two genes are equally likely to be passed to a child. If you have one or two dominant genes, you normally place your left thumb on top.

Suppose a child has parents who both have just one dominant gene. What is the theoretical probability that the child will naturally place the left thumb on top?

Make a table. Let G represent the dominant gene (left thumb on top). Let g represent the recessive gene (right thumb on top).

		Gene from Mother	
		G	g
Gene from Father	G	GG	Gg
	g	Gg	gg

The sample space {GG, Gg, Gg, gg} contains four equally likely outcomes. Three outcomes have at least one Gg gene. So $P(\text{left thumb on top}) = \frac{3}{4}$.

The theoretical probability that the child will naturally place the left thumb on top is $\frac{3}{4}$, or 75%.

Check Understanding 4 What is the theoretical probability that a child of the parents in Example 4 places the right thumb on top?

Sometimes you can use areas to find theoretical probability.

5 EXAMPLE Finding Geometric Probability

Geometry Suppose that all the points on the circular dartboard shown at the right are equally likely to be hit by a dart you have thrown. Find the probability of scoring at least ten points.

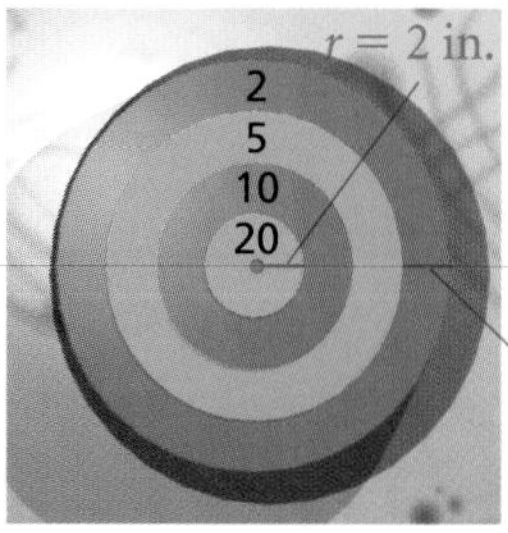

$P(\text{at least 10 points})$

$$= \frac{\text{area of circle with radius } 2r}{\text{area of circle with radius } 4r}$$

$$= \frac{\pi(2r)^2}{\pi(4r)^2}$$

$$= \frac{4\pi r^2}{16\pi r^2} = \frac{1}{4}$$

The theoretical probability of scoring at least ten points is $\frac{1}{4}$, or 25%.

Check Understanding 5 Use the dartboard from Example 5. Find each probability.

a. P(scoring 20 points) **b.** P(scoring 5 points)

EXERCISES

For more practice, see *Extra Practice*.

Practice and Problem Solving

A Practice by Example

Example 1 (page 40)

1. A class tossed coins and recorded 161 heads and 179 tails. What is the experimental probability of heads? Of tails?

2. Another class rolled number cubes. Their results are shown in the table. What is the experimental probability of rolling each number?

Number	1	2	3	4	5	6
Occurrences	42	44	45	44	47	46

Example 2 (page 40)

For Exercises 3–5, define a simulation by telling how you represent correct answers, incorrect answers, and the quiz. Use your simulation to find each experimental probability.

Graphing Calculator Hint

To generate random numbers, press MATH ◄ 1 ENTER.

3. If you guess the answers at random, what is the probability of getting at least two correct answers on a five-question true-or-false quiz?

4. If you guess the answers at random, what is the probability of getting at least three correct answers on a five-question true-or-false quiz ?

5. A five-question multiple-choice quiz has five choices for each answer. What is the probability of correctly guessing at random exactly one correct answer? Exactly two correct answers? Exactly three correct answers? (*Hint:* You could let any two digits represent correct answers, and the other digits represent wrong answers.)

Example 3 (page 41)

A jar contains 30 red marbles, 50 blue marbles, and 20 white marbles. You pick one marble from the jar at random. Find each theoretical probability.

6. P(red) 7. P(blue) 8. P(not white) 9. P(red or blue)

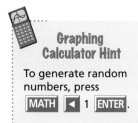

A bag contains 36 red, 48 green, 22 yellow, and 19 purple blocks. You pick one block from the bag at random. Find each theoretical probability.

10. *P*(green) **11.** *P*(purple) **12.** *P*(not yellow)

13. *P*(green or yellow) **14.** *P*(yellow or not green)

Example 4 (page 41)

For each situation, find the sample space and the theoretical probability that a child will naturally place the left thumb on top.

15. The father has gene pair gg and the mother has Gg.

16. The father has gene pair gg and the mother has GG.

Example 5 (page 42)

Geometry **Suppose that a dart lands at random on the dartboard shown at the right. Find each theoretical probability.**

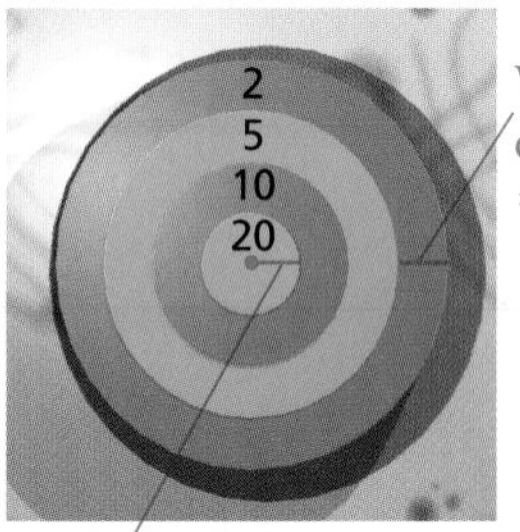

17. The dart lands in the bull's-eye.

18. The dart lands in a green region.

19. The dart scores at least 10 points.

20. The dart scores less than 10 points.

B Apply Your Skills

21. The common interpretation of Murphy's Law is, If something can go wrong, it will. Assume that Murphy's Law applies to the following situations, and estimate each probability as either 0 or 1.
a. *P*(your dog chews up your homework after you've finished it)
b. *P*(your teacher accepts your excuse for not having your homework)

22. Quality Control Suppose the experimental probability is $\frac{1}{3}$ that a carton of eggs contains at least one broken egg. Use a simulation of 20 trials to find the experimental probability that three cartons selected at random contain only unbroken eggs. (*Hint:* Use any three digits to represent cartons with broken eggs and six other digits to represent cartons with unbroken eggs. Discard the tenth digit.)

23. Use the random number table at the left to simulate tossing a coin 50 times. Find the experimental probability that the outcome of a coin toss is heads.

Random Number Table

31504	51648	40613
79321	80927	42404
15594	84675	68591
34178	00460	31754
49676	58733	00884
85400	72294	22551
22547	86066	93114
85211	07790	20890
21339	09414	51549
13843	18407	87043
34990	16214	46849
11390	01322	82656
45950	37521	77417

In a class of 147 students, 95 are taking math (M), 73 are taking science (S), and 52 are taking both math and science. One student is picked at random. Find each probability.

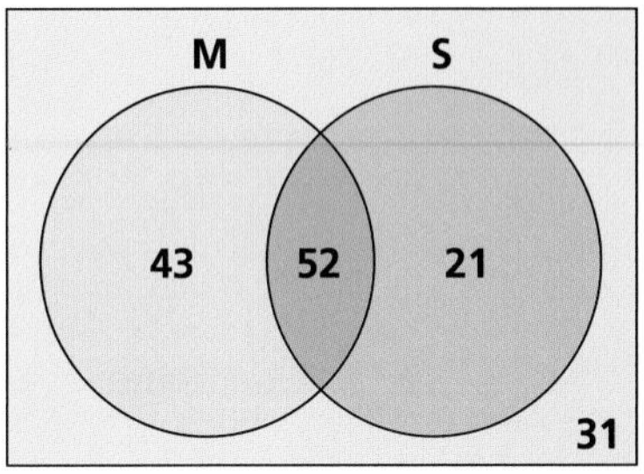

24. *P*(taking math or science or both)

25. *P*(not taking math)

26. *P*(taking math but not science)

27. *P*(taking neither math nor science)

Suppose you roll a number cube. Find each theoretical probability.

28. *P*(5) **29.** *P*(an even number)

30. *P*(a number less than 5) **31.** *P*(8)

32. *P*(a number greater than 5) **33.** *P*(a number less than 8)

Suppose you select a number at random from the sample space {1, 2, 3, 4, 5, 6, 7, 8, 9}. Find each theoretical probability.

34. P(the number is a multiple of 3)

35. P(the number is less than 5)

36. P(the number is prime)

37. P(the number is even)

38. Suppose you roll two number cubes.
a. What is the sample space?
b. How many outcomes are there?
c. What is the theoretical probability of getting a sum of 12?
d. What is the theoretical probability of getting a sum of 7?

39. **Sports** The batter's strike zone depends on the height and stance of the batter. Find the geometric probability that a baseball thrown at random within the batter's strike zone as shown in the figure below will be "high and inside." This is one of the harder pitches to hit!

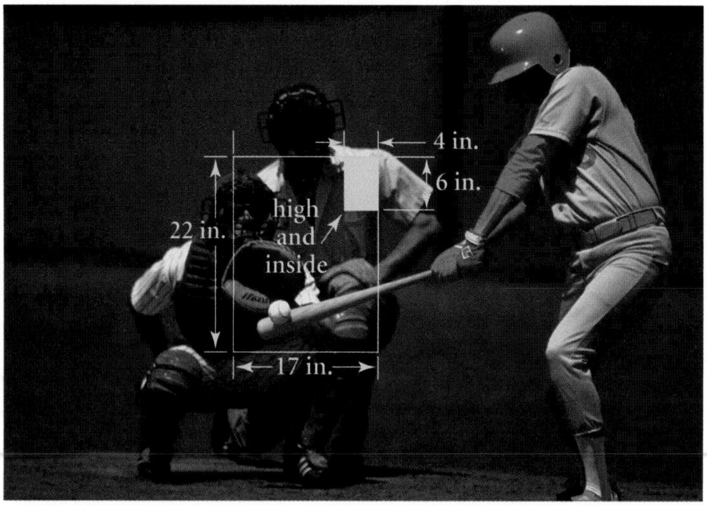

40. a. **Sports** Team A has won one game and team B has won three games in a World Series. What is the experimental probability that team A wins the next game? That team B wins the next game?
b. **Critical Thinking** Do you think that experimental probability is a good predictor of the winner of the next game? Explain.

41. **Writing** Explain what you would need to know to determine the theoretical probability that a five-digit postal ZIP code ends in 1.

42. Suppose you choose a two-digit number at random. What is the theoretical probability that its square root is an integer?

C Challenge

43. The odds in favor of an event are the ratio of the number of favorable outcomes to the number of unfavorable outcomes.
a. If the odds in favor of an event are a to b or $\frac{a}{b}$, what is the probability of the event?
b. If the probability of an event is $\frac{a}{b}$, what are the odds in favor of the event?
c. Would you rather play a game where your odds of winning are $\frac{1}{2}$, or a game where your probability of winning is $\frac{1}{2}$? Explain.

44. **Open-Ended** Use a telephone book. Select 50 telephone numbers at random and record the first three digits (the "exchange") of each number. Summarize your results using probability statements.

45. On a TV game show, you want to win a prize that is hidden behind one of three doors. You choose one door, but before it is opened the host opens another door and shows that the prize is not there. Now you can switch to the other unopened door or stick with your original choice.
   a. Find the experimental probability of winning the prize if you stick with your original choice. (*Hint:* Simulate the doors with index cards and the prize with a mark on one side of one card. One person can act as the host and another as the contestant.)
   b. Find the experimental probability of winning if you switch to the other door.

Standardized Test Prep

Multiple Choice

46. What is the theoretical probability of getting a 2 or a 3 when rolling a number cube?

A. $\frac{1}{2}$ **B.** $\frac{1}{3}$ **C.** $\frac{1}{4}$ **D.** $\frac{1}{6}$

47. How many outcomes are in the sample space for rolling a number cube and tossing a coin?

F. 2 **G.** 6 **H.** 12 **I.** 24

Short Response

48. What is the sample space for spinning the spinner at the right twice? Are all the outcomes equally likely?

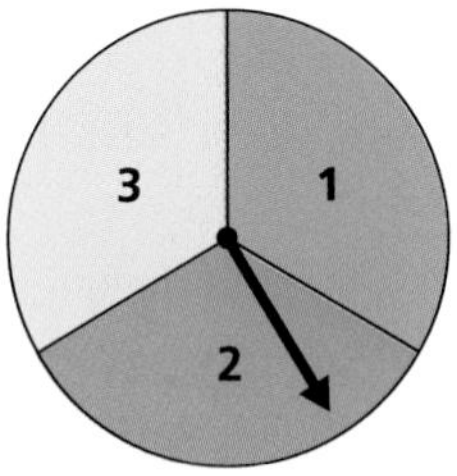

49. What is the probability of spinning a 1 on both of two spins? Explain.

Extended Response

50. Which is more likely on two spins, an even sum or a sum that is not prime? Include all the steps of your solution.

Reading Comprehension

51. Read the passage below. Do you agree with the statement in the last sentence? Explain.

> The chances of the chromosomes being defective are 1 in 250, which sounds like reasonable odds. Except that all odds are, in reality, 50-50: it may happen and it may not.

Take It to the NET
Online lesson quiz at
www.PHSchool.com
Web Code: aga-0106

Mixed Review

Lesson 1-5 **Solve each absolute value equation. Check your answers.**

52. $|x + 3| = 9$ **53.** $|3x - 5| = 10$ **54.** $|2x + 7| + 3 = 22$

55. $|3x - 6| - 7 = 14$ **56.** $|2x + 3| - 9 = 14$ **57.** $|6 - 5x| = 18$

Lesson 1-5 **Solve each absolute value inequality.**

58. $2|x| - 3 \geq 5$ **59.** $|2x - 4| + 16 \leq 24$ **60.** $|3x - 5| - 2 > 0$

61. $|2x + 4| - 6 < 0$ **62.** $2|x + 3| \geq 10$ **63.** $6|x + 9| \leq 36$

Test-Taking Strategies

Writing Gridded Responses

Some tests require that you enter numerical answers in a grid. After finding an answer, write it in the top row of the grid. Then fill in the corresponding bubbles below.

EXAMPLE

A rabbit weighs one pound less than eight times the weight of a guinea pig. The rabbit weighs nine pounds. What is the weight in pounds of the guinea pig?

First find the answer by writing and solving an equation.

$8x - 1 = 9$

$8x = 10$

$x = \frac{10}{8}$ or $\frac{5}{4}$ or 1.25

Enter the answer in the grid. You could write it as $\frac{10}{8}$, as $\frac{5}{4}$, or as 1.25. Do not enter the answer as a mixed number. If you enter 1 1/4, it may be interpreted as $\frac{11}{4}$.

Note how to enter fraction bars and decimal points.

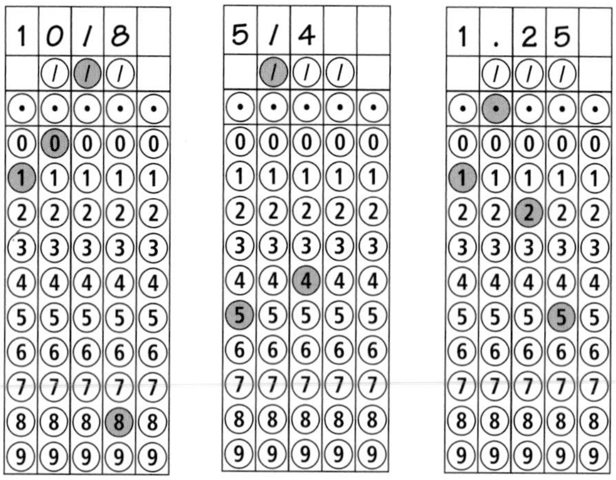

EXERCISES

Use a response grid to answer each question.

1. What is the value of $\frac{x^2 + 1}{2.5}$ when $x = 1.5$?
2. A music tape costs a dollar more than half the price of a CD. The music tape costs \$9.49. What is the cost in dollars of the CD?
3. What is the solution of the equation $3(x - 1) - (x + 2) = 9$?
4. A number is selected at random from the sample space {10, 11, 12, 13, 14, 15}. What is the probability that the number is a multiple of 3?
5. Write a 4-digit number that is a multiple of both 5 and 6.
6. Write a rational number between $\sqrt{5}$ and $\sqrt{6}$.
7. 44.8 is what percent of 128?
8. The length of a picture frame must be at least 4.25 cm greater than the frame's width. The width is 19.5 cm. What is the minimum perimeter, in centimeters, of the picture frame?

Chapter Review

Chapter 1

Vocabulary

absolute value (p. 33)
absolute value of a real number (p. 8)
additive inverse (p. 7)
algebraic expression (p. 12)
coefficient (p. 13)
compound inequality (p. 28)
evaluate (p. 12)
experimental probability (p. 40)
extraneous solution (p. 34)
multiplicative inverse (p. 7)
opposite (p. 7)
reciprocal (p. 7)
sample space (p. 41)
simulation (p. 40)
solution of an equation (p. 18)
term (p. 13)
theoretical probability (p. 41)
tolerance (p. 36)
variable (p. 12)
variable expression (p. 12)

Reading Math
Understanding Vocabulary

Take It to the NET
Online vocabulary quiz at www.PHSchool.com
Web Code: agj-0151

Choose the correct vocabulary term to complete each sentence.

1. The opposite of a number is also called its __?__.
2. The __?__ is the set of all possible outcomes of an experiment.
3. The __?__ makes an equation true.
4. A pair of inequalities joined by *and* or *or* is called a(n) __?__.
5. __?__ is another name for a multiplicative inverse of a number.
6. The __?__ of an event is the ratio of occurrences to trials.
7. The __?__ of an event is the ratio of possible event outcomes to total possible outcomes.
8. A possible solution that does not satisfy the original equation is a(n) __?__.
9. You can use a(n) __?__ to find experimental probabilities.
10. A number's distance from zero on the number line is its __?__.

Skills and Concepts

1-1 Objectives

- To graph and order real numbers (p. 4)
- To identify and use properties of real numbers (p. 7)

The natural numbers, whole numbers, integers, rational numbers, and irrational numbers are all subsets of the real numbers. Each real number corresponds to a point on the number line. A real number's distance from zero on the number line is its absolute value.

For both addition and multiplication, real numbers satisfy the properties of closure, associativity, and commutativity. Real numbers have **additive inverses (opposites)** and **multiplicative inverses (reciprocals)**. They also have additive and multiplicative identities. Real numbers satisfy the Distributive Property.

To which sets of numbers does each number belong?

11. 8.1π **12.** -79 **13.** $\sqrt{121}$ **14.** $\sqrt{200}$ **15.** $12\frac{7}{8}$

Compare each pair of numbers. Use < or >.

16. $-\frac{2}{3}, -\frac{3}{2}$ **17.** $\sqrt{6}, 2.\overline{3}$ **18.** $0.45, 0.405$ **19.** $-7, |-7|$

Find the opposite and reciprocal of each number. Then graph all three numbers on a number line.

20. -3.4 **21.** $4 + \pi$ **22.** $1\frac{7}{8}$ **23.** $\sqrt{12}$

Open-Ended Write an equation that illustrates each property of real numbers.

24. The Identity Property of Multiplication

25. The Associative Property of Addition

26. The Distributive Property

27. The Commutative Property of Multiplication

28. The Identity Property of Addition

1-2 and 1-3 Objectives

- To evaluate algebraic expressions (p. 12)
- To simplify algebraic expressions (p. 13)
- To solve equations (p. 18)
- To solve problems by writing equations (p. 20)

You **evaluate** an **algebraic expression** by substituting numbers for the **variables**. You simplify an algebraic expression by combining like **terms**, using the appropriate properties. To find the **solutions of an equation**, use the properties of equality. To check for **extraneous solutions**, substitute in the original equation. Some equations may have no solutions. Some equations are true for all real numbers.

29. Evaluate $-x^2 + |x - 10|$ for $x = 2$.

30. Evaluate $3t(t + 2) - (3t^2 + 5t)$ for $t = 19$.

31. Simplify $-(3a - 2b) - 3(-a - b)$.

Solve each equation for x. State any restrictions.

32. $2x - 5 = 17$ **33.** $8 - \frac{1}{2}x = 3$

34. $3x = 4x - 5$ **35.** $0.1x + 1.4 = 1.2x - 3$

36. $\frac{7 - x}{3} = 5$ **37.** $\frac{x + a}{b} = \frac{1}{a}$

Write an equation to solve each problem.

38. Geometry The lengths of the sides of a rectangle are in the ratio 5 : 3. The perimeter of the rectangle is 32 cm. Find the length of each side.

39. Two planes left St. Louis for Los Angeles at the same time. After 4 h they were 700 mi apart. The slower plane traveled at 350 mi/h. What was the speed of the faster plane?

40. Geometry The measures of an angle and its supplement differ by 40°. Find the measures of the angles.

1-4 Objectives

- To solve and graph inequalities (p. 26)
- To solve and write compound inequalities (p. 28)

You can solve inequalities using properties that are similar to the properties for equations. An important difference is that multiplying or dividing each side of an inequality by a negative number reverses the inequality. Just as with equations, some inequalities are true for all real numbers, and some have no solutions. If a **compound inequality** uses *and*, the solutions must satisfy both inequalities. If a compound inequality uses *or*, the solutions may satisfy either or both of the inequalities.

Solve each inequality. Graph the solution.

41. $4 - 5z \geq 2$ **42.** $2(5 - 3x) < x - 4(3 - x)$ **43.** $0.3(y - 2) > \frac{1}{2}(6 - y)$

Solve each compound inequality. Graph the solution.

44. $5 \leq 9 - 4x \leq 13$ **45.** $3 \geq 2x$ or $x - 4 > 2$ **46.** $6y > 2$ and $y - 5 \geq -2y$

47. A publisher estimates that the cost of publishing a book is from \$980,000 to \$1,240,000. So far, \$824,150 has been spent. Use a compound inequality to describe the amount A that the publisher can still spend while remaining within the estimate.

1-5 Objectives

- To solve absolute value equations (p. 33)
- To solve absolute value inequalities (p. 35)

You can rewrite an equation or inequality that involves the absolute value of an **algebraic expression** as a compound sentence. You must consider both cases of the definition of absolute value. Check for **extraneous solutions.**

Solve each equation. Check for extraneous solutions.

48. $|2x + 8| = 3x + 7$ **49.** $|3x - 5| = 4 + 2x$ **50.** $|x - 4| + 3 = 1$

Solve each inequality. Graph the solution.

51. $|3x - 2| + 4 \leq 7$ **52.** $4|y - 9| > 36$ **53.** $\frac{2}{5}|3x - 3| - 4 > 2$

54. The specification for a length x is 43.6 cm with a tolerance of 0.1 cm. Write the specification as an absolute value inequality.

1-6 Objectives

- To find experimental probabilities (p. 39)
- To find theoretical probabilities (p. 41)

The probability of an event can be expressed as a number from 0%(impossible) to 100% (certain).

Experimental probability is the ratio of two numbers. The first is the observed number of times an experiment results in a particular event. The second is the number of trials. **Simulation** uses random numbers or other models to determine an experimental probability.

Theoretical probability in a sample space of equally likely outcomes is also the ratio of two numbers. The first is the number of outcomes corresponding to the particular event. The second is the number of elements in the sample space, which is the set of all possible outcomes. Geometric probability is computed as a ratio of areas.

Suppose you select a number at random from the sample space $\{-3, -2, -1, 0, 1, 2, 3, 4\}$. Find each probability.

55. P(the number is positive) **56.** P(the number is less than 2)

57. P(the number is even) **58.** P(the number is a multiple of 3)

59. Games You have won five games of checkers and your opponent has won three. What is the experimental probability of your winning?

60. Tests A five-question multiple-choice quiz has four choices for each answer. Find the experimental probability of getting exactly three correct answers if you guess the answers at random. Define a simulation using the random number table on page 43. Use your simulation to find the experimental probability.

Chapter 1

Chapter Test

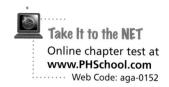

Take It to the NET
Online chapter test at
www.PHSchool.com
Web Code: aga-0152

1. **Writing** Describe the relationships among these sets of numbers: natural numbers, whole numbers, integers, rational numbers, irrational numbers, and real numbers.

2. **Justifying Steps** Justify each step by identifying the property used.

$$\begin{aligned} t + 5(t + 1) &= t + (5t + 5) \\ &= (t + 5t) + 5 \\ &= (1t + 5t) + 5 \\ &= (1 + 5)t + 5 \\ &= 6t + 5 \end{aligned}$$

Evaluate each expression for $x = 5$.

3. $\frac{5}{3}(3x - 6) - (6 - 4x)$
4. $3(x^2 - 4) + 7(x - 2)$
5. $x - 2x + 3x - 4x + 5x$

Simplify each expression.

6. $a^2 + a + a^2$
7. $2x + 3y - 5x + 2y$
8. $5(a - 2b) - 3(a - 2b)$
9. $3[2(x - 3) + 2] + 5(x - 3)$

Solve each equation.

10. $4y - 6 = 2y + 8$
11. $3(2z + 1) = 35$
12. $5(3w - 2) - 7 = 23$
13. $t - 2(3 - 2t) = 2t + 9$
14. $5(s - 12) - 24 = 3(s + 2)$
15. $7(3 - 0.5k) = 3k - 5$

Solve each equation for x. State any restrictions.

16. $ax - bx = 2a$
17. $\frac{x}{c} + c = 4c$
18. $\frac{x - 5}{a} + 1 = b$
19. $ax + 2 = bx + c$

20. The lateral surface area of a cylinder is given by the formula $S = 2\pi rh$. Solve this equation for r.

Write an equation to solve each problem.

21. **Savings** Briana and her sister Molly both want to buy the same model bicycle. Briana needs \$73 more before she can afford the bike. Molly needs \$65 more. If they combine their money, they will have just enough to buy one bicycle that they could share. What is the cost of the bicycle?

22. **Musical** There is only one freshman in the cast of the high school musical. There are 6 sophomores and 11 juniors. One third of the cast are seniors. How many seniors are in the musical?

Solve each inequality or equation. Graph the solution.

23. $3x + 17 \geq 5$
24. $25 - 2x < 11$
25. $7t > 4t + 3(1 - t)$
26. $\frac{3}{8}x < -6$ or $5x > 2$
27. $2 < 10 - 4d < 6$
28. $4 - x = |2 - 3x|$
29. $|4x + 4| = 8x + 16$
30. $|5 - p| \leq 2$
31. $5|3w + 2| - 3 > 7$

Suppose you select a number at random from the sample space {5, 6, 7, 8, 9, 10, 11, 12, 13, 14}. Find each probability.

32. P(greater than 10)
33. P(multiple of 30)
34. P(less than 7 or greater than 10)
35. P(integer)

36. **Open-Ended** Your teacher selects at random two days out of every five days to give a "pop" quiz. Define a simulation to find the experimental probability that you will get a pop quiz on two consecutive days. Then use your simulation to find the probability.

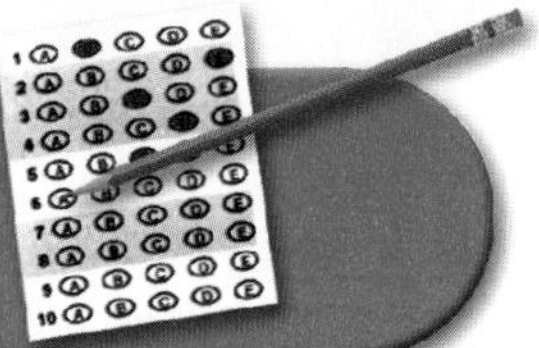

Standardized Test Prep

Reading Comprehension **Read the passage below. Then answer the questions on the basis of what is *stated* or *implied* in the passage.**

A-Frame Bookshelf Do-it-yourselfers can build large-capacity, self-supporting bookshelves that are easy to set up and break down. They are called A-frame bookshelves, because the frame and shelves form an A.

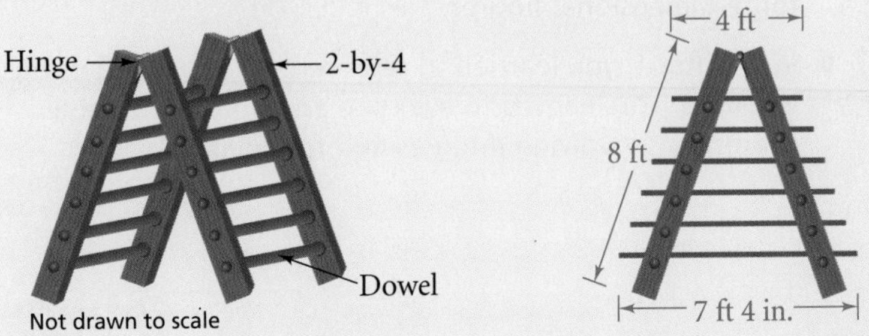

Not drawn to scale

The frame uses four 2-by-4's, each 8 feet long. They are joined in pairs by a hinge. Holes are drilled through the 2-by-4's at 1-foot intervals. Round dowels, $\frac{3}{4}$ of an inch in diameter, connect the two parts of the frame.

The shelves are fastened to the dowels. Each shelf is a constant length longer than the shelf above it. In the six-shelf unit shown above, the top shelf is 4 feet long and the bottom shelf is 7 feet 4 inches long.

1. What is the difference in length between each shelf and the one directly below it?
   A. 4 in. **B.** 6 in. **C.** 8 in. **D.** $14\frac{2}{3}$in.

2. How far beyond each edge of the top shelf does each edge of the bottom shelf extend?
   F. 4 in. **G.** 8 in.
   H. 1 ft 8 in. **I.** 3 ft 6 in.

3. What is the total length of the shelves?
   A. 29 ft 8 in. **B.** 32 ft
   C. 33 ft 4 in. **D.** 34 ft

4. Suppose you can buy 2-by-4's in any length for $.29 per foot. About how much will you pay for the 2-by-4's for the bookcase?
   F. $5 **G.** $10 **H.** $15 **I.** $20

5. Suppose the 2-by-4's are 2 in. thick, the shelves are 8 in. deep, and the dowels are cut flush with the front and back faces of the bookshelf. If the dowels are sold in 4-ft lengths, how many lengths would you have to buy for the bookcase?
   A. 2 **B.** 3 **C.** 4 **D.** 12

For Questions 6–10, use the information below. Show your work.

A shorter bookshelf uses 2-by-4's that are 6 ft long, and has five shelves. The top shelf is 3 ft long and the bottom shelf is 6 ft 8 in. long.

6. What is the difference in length from each shelf to the one below it?

7. How much does the bottom shelf extend to the right beyond the right-most edge of the top shelf?

8. What is the total length of shelving in the bookshelf?

9. In a four-shelf bookshelf, the bottom shelf is 8 ft long. The top shelf is 5 ft $1\frac{1}{2}$ in. long. How long are the other two shelves?

10. Which is greater, the average length of the shelves in Questions 6–8 or the average length of the shelves in Question 9? How much greater is it?

Where You've Been

- In first-year algebra, you learned to interpret and solve problems algebraically.
- In geometry, you learned to analyze and manipulate two- and three-dimensional figures.
- In Chapter 1, you learned to represent relationships using variables. You learned to evaluate and simplify variable expressions involving integers and fractions.

Instant self-check online and on CD-ROM

Diagnosing Readiness

(For help, go to the Lesson in green.)

Graphing Numbers on the Number Line (Lesson 1-1)

Graph each group of numbers on a number line.

1. $2, -\frac{7}{4}, -1, \frac{15}{2}$ **2.** $0, \frac{2}{3}, -\sqrt{2}, -3$ **3.** $-\frac{5}{4}, \sqrt{7}, 2.\overline{6}, 4$

Simplifying Expressions (Lesson 1-2)

Simplify by combining like terms.

4. $7s - s$ **5.** $3a + b + a$ **6.** $xy - y + x$

7. $0.5g + g$ **8.** $4t - (t + 3t)$ **9.** $b - 2(1 + c - b)$

10. $5f - (5d - f)$ **11.** $2(h + 2g) - (g - h)$ **12.** $-(3z - 5) + z$

13. $(2 - d)g - 3d(4 + g)$ **14.** $5v - 3(2 - v)$ **15.** $7t - 3s(2 + t) + s$

Solving Absolute-Value Inequalities (Lesson 1-5)

Solve each absolute-value inequality. Graph the solution.

16. $|x - 3| < 5$ **17.** $|2a - 1| \geq 2a + 1$ **18.** $|3x + 4| > -4x - 3$

19. $|3x + 1| + 1 > 12$ **20.** $3|d - 4| \leq 13 - d$ **21.** $-\frac{1}{3}|f + 3| + 2 \geq -5$

Probability (Lesson 1-6)

A bag contains 12 red, 15 green, 10 yellow, 25 purple, and 2 black blocks. Find each theoretical probability for one block selected at random.

22. P(green) **23.** P(black) **24.** P(red or yellow)

25. P(not red) **26.** P(not yellow) **27.** P(black or not red)

Functions, Equations, and Graphs

Chapter 2

Where You're Going

- In Chapter 2, you will move from simplifying variable expressions and solving one-variable equations and inequalities to working with two-variable equations and inequalities.
- You will learn how to represent function relationships by writing and graphing linear equations and inequalities.
- By graphing data and trend lines, you will understand how the slope of a line can be interpreted in real-world situations.

Real-World Snapshots Applying what you learn, on pages 112–113 you will do activities involving bridges.

LESSONS

Key Vocabulary

- absolute value function (p. 86)
- constant of variation (p. 72)
- dependent variable (p. 62)
- direct variation (p. 72)
- domain (p. 56)
- function (p. 57)
- independent variable (p. 62)
- linear equation (p. 62)
- linear function (p. 62)
- linear inequality (p. 99)
- parent function (p. 91)
- point-slope form (p. 65)
- range (p. 56)
- relation (p. 55)
- slope (p. 64)
- slope-intercept form (p. 65)
- standard form (p. 63)
- translation (p. 91)
- vertical-line test (p. 57)
- x-intercept (p. 63)
- y-intercept (p. 63)

Algebra Review

The Coordinate Plane

FOR USE WITH LESSON 2-1

There is a one-to-one correspondence between the points in the coordinate plane and the set of ordered pairs (x, y), where x and y are real numbers. The first number is the x-coordinate, or abscissa. The abscissa gives the horizontal position of a point. The second number is the y-coordinate, or ordinate. The ordinate gives the vertical position of a point.

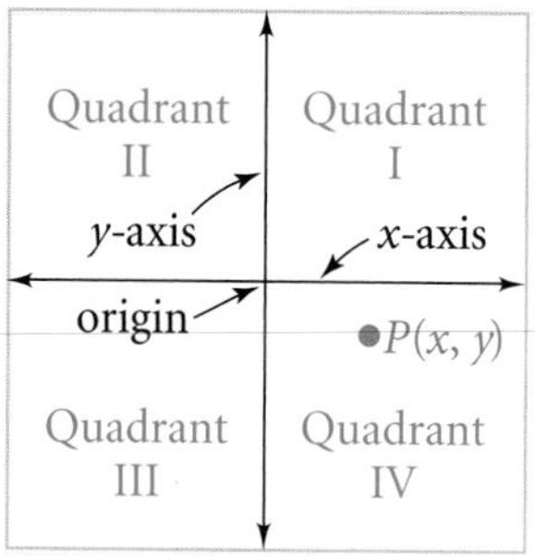

1 EXAMPLE Graphing Points

Graph $(4, 3)$ and $(-4, -3)$.

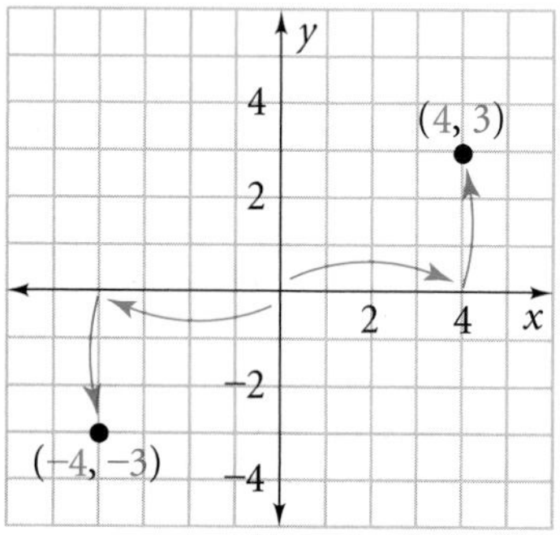

Graph and label each ordered pair.

You can write the coordinates of a point if you are given its graph.

2 EXAMPLE Writing Coordinates

Write the coordinates of each point in the graph.

The points are $A(2, 4)$, $B(3, 0)$, $C(-4, 0)$, $D(0, -3)$, $E(-5, 4)$, $F\left(4, \frac{1}{2}\right)$, $G(0, 0)$, and $H\left(-3, -3\frac{1}{2}\right)$.

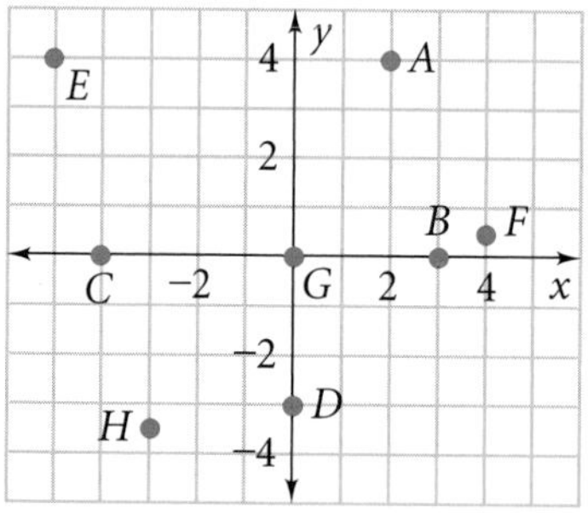

EXERCISES

Graph and label each ordered pair. Name the quadrant or axis where each point lies.

1. $(5, -2)$ **2.** $(-3, 4)$ **3.** $(-4, -2)$

4. $(5, 0)$ **5.** $(5, 2)$ **6.** $(0, -3)$

Write the coordinates of each point in the graph at the right.

7. C **8.** G **9.** J **10.** A

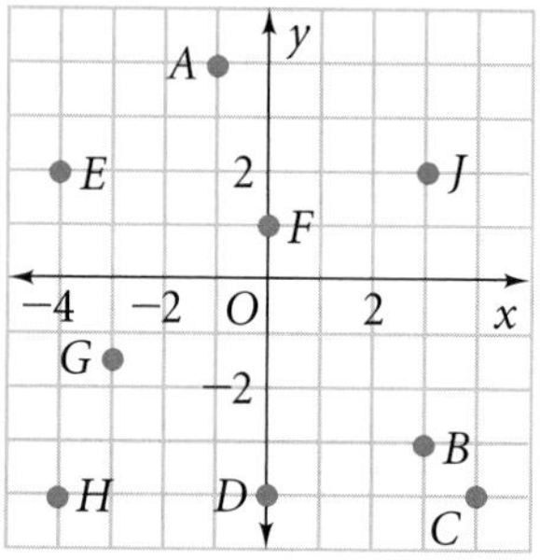

2-1 Relations and Functions

Lesson Preview

What You'll Learn

OBJECTIVE 1 To graph relations

OBJECTIVE 2 To identify functions

. . . And Why

To write a function for the area of a square, as in Example 6

Check Skills You'll Need (For help, go to Skills Handbook page 848 and Lesson 1-2.)

Graph each ordered pair on the coordinate plane.

1. $(-4, -8)$ **2.** $(3, 6)$ **3.** $(0, 0)$ **4.** $(-1, 3)$ **5.** $(-6, 5)$

Evaluate each expression for $x = -1, 0, 2,$ and 5.

6. $x + 2$ **7.** $-2x + 3$ **8.** $2x^2 + 1$ **9.** $|x - 3|$

New Vocabulary • relation • domain • range • mapping diagram • function • vertical-line test • function notation

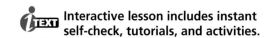

Interactive lesson includes instant self-check, tutorials, and activities.

OBJECTIVE

1 Graphing Relations

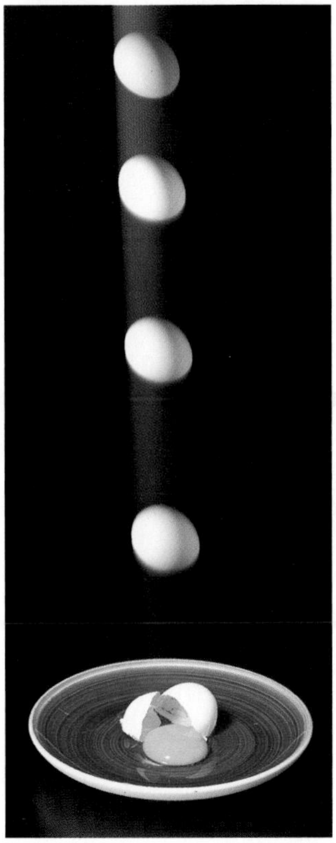

A camera recorded the egg's height at various times during its fall.

Suppose you use a motion detector to track an egg as it drops from 10 ft above the ground. The motion detector stores input values (times) and output values (heights). A **relation** is a set of pairs of input and output values. You can write a relation as a set of ordered pairs.

input (time in seconds) → {0 0.1 0.2 0.3 0.4}

relation → {(0, 10), (0.1, 9.8), (0.2, 9.4), (0.3, 8.6), (0.4, 7.4)}

output (height in feet) → {10 9.8 9.4 8.6 7.4}

You can graph a relation on a coordinate plane.

1 EXAMPLE Graphing a Relation

Graph the relation $\{(-2, 4), (3, -2), (-1, 0), (1, 5)\}$.

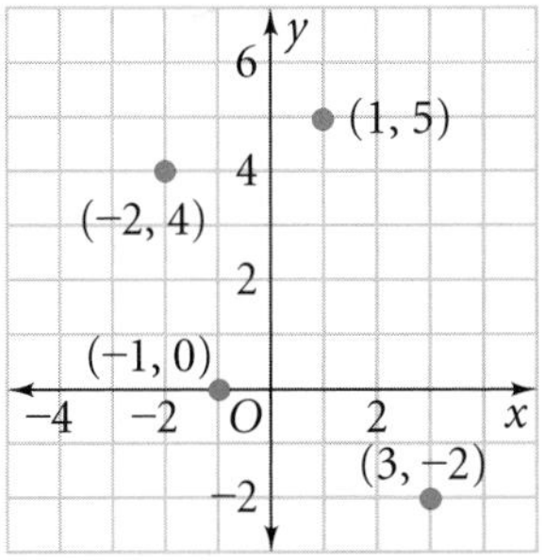

Graph and label each ordered pair.

Check Understanding **1** Graph each relation.

a. $\{(0, 4), (-2, 3), (-1, 3), (-2, 2), (1, -3)\}$

b. $\{(-2, 1), (-1, 0), (0, 1), (1, 2)\}$

The **domain** of a relation is the set of all inputs, or x-coordinates, of the ordered pairs. The **range** of a relation is the set of all outputs, or y-coordinates, of the ordered pairs.

You can sometimes find the domain and range of a relation from its graph.

Backpacks or bookbags are used by 93% of students.

2 EXAMPLE Finding Domain and Range

Write the ordered pairs for the relation shown in the graph. Find the domain and range.

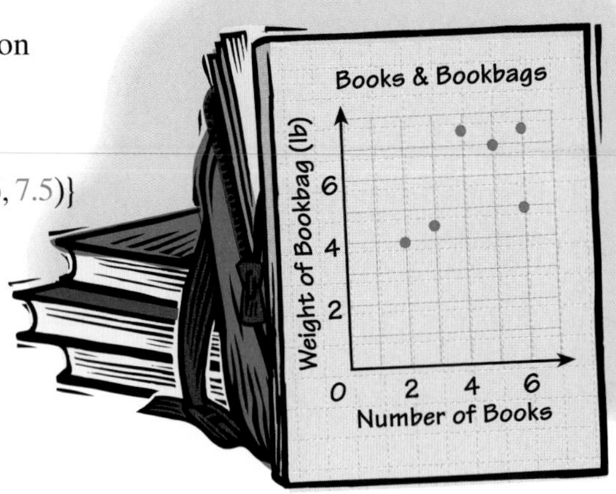

$\{(2, 4), (3, 4.5), (4, 7.5), (5, 7), (6, 5), (6, 7.5)\}$

The domain is $\{2, 3, 4, 5, 6\}$.

The range is $\{4, 4.5, 5, 7, 7.5\}$.

Check Understanding 2 Find the domain and range of each relation.

a.

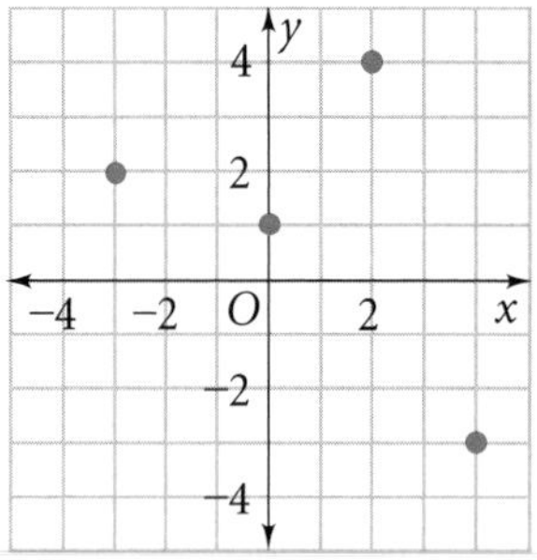

b.

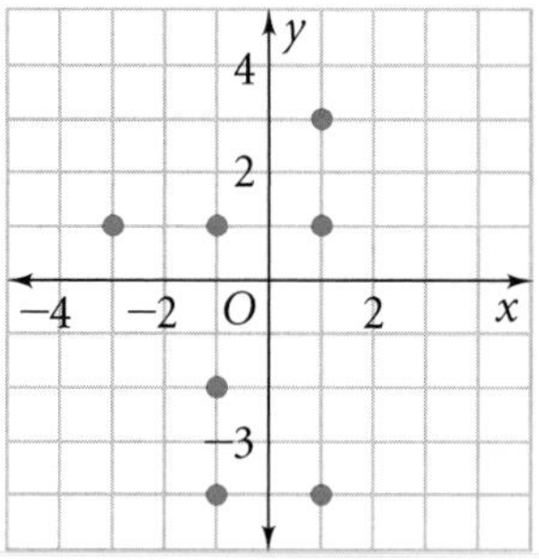

Another way to show a relation is to use a **mapping diagram,** which links elements of the domain with corresponding elements of the range. Write the elements of the domain in one region and the elements of the range in another. Draw arrows to show how each element from the domain is paired with elements from the range.

3 EXAMPLE Making a Mapping Diagram

Make a mapping diagram for the relation $\{(-1, -2), (3, 6), (-5, -10), (3, 2)\}$.

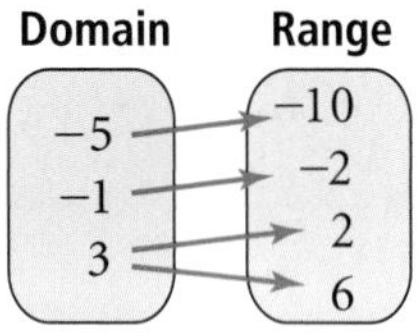

Pair the domain elements with the range elements.

Check Understanding 3 Make a mapping diagram for each relation.

a. $\{(0, 2), (1, 3), (2, 4)\}$

b. $\{(2, 8), (-1, 5), (0, 8), (-1, 3), (-2, 3)\}$

OBJECTIVE 2

Identifying Functions

A **function** is a relation in which each element of the domain is paired with exactly one element in the range.

4 EXAMPLE Identifying Functions

Determine whether each relation is a function.

a.

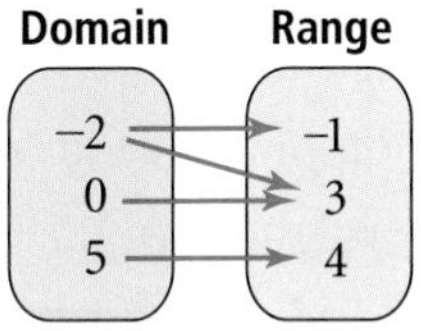

The element −2 of the domain is paired with both −1 and 3 of the range. The relation is *not* a function.

b.

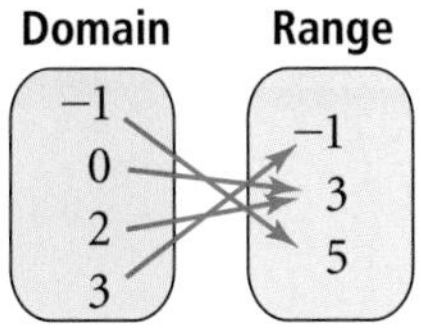

Each element of the domain is paired with exactly one element of the range. The relation is a function.

Check Understanding 4 Determine whether each relation is a function.

a.

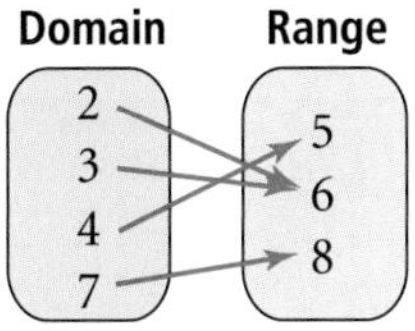

b.

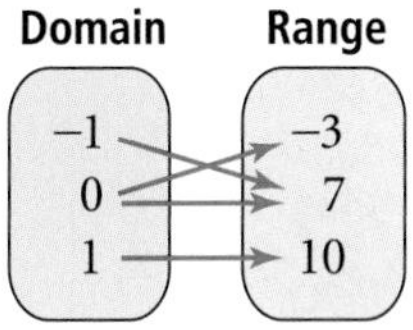

Reading Math

The word *discrete* means separate. The word *discreet* means careful about what one says or does.

As you saw earlier in this lesson, relations can be represented as discrete data points that may or may not follow a pattern. Relations can also be shown as two-dimensional figures, such as lines or curves.

Graphing a relation on a coordinate plane gives you a visual way to tell whether it is a function. You can use the **vertical-line test** to determine whether the relation has at least one element of the domain paired with more than one element of the range. If a vertical line passes through two or more points on the graph, then the relation is *not* a function.

5 EXAMPLE Using the Vertical-Line Test

Use the vertical-line test to determine whether each graph represents a function.

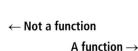

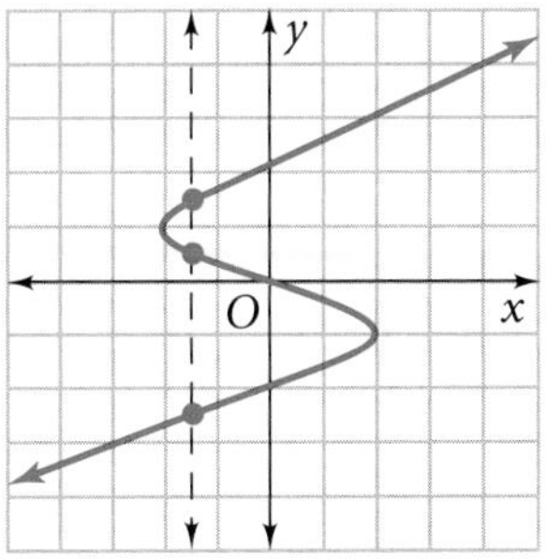

Vertical line passes through

← 3 points 1 point →

← Not a function

A function →

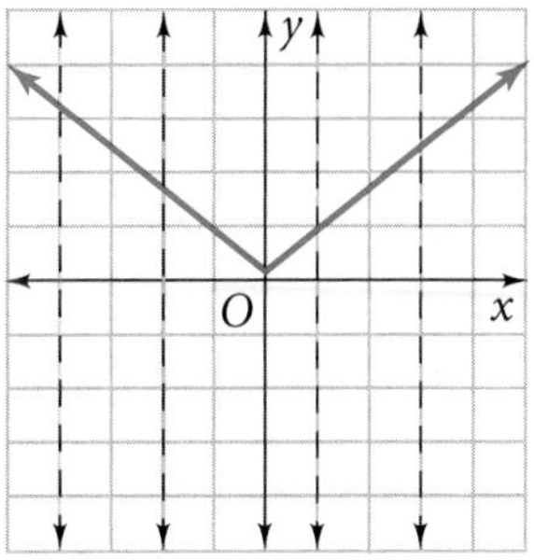

Check Understanding **5** Use the vertical-line test to determine whether each graph represents a function.

a.

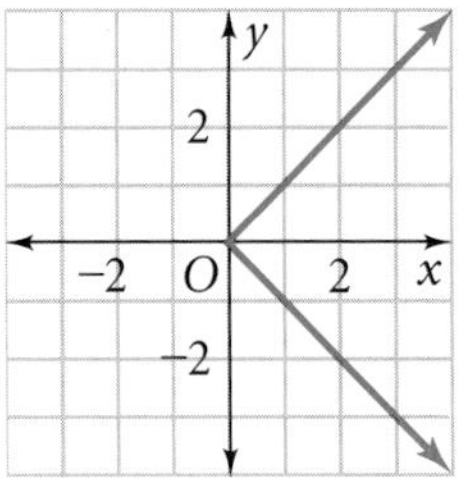

b.

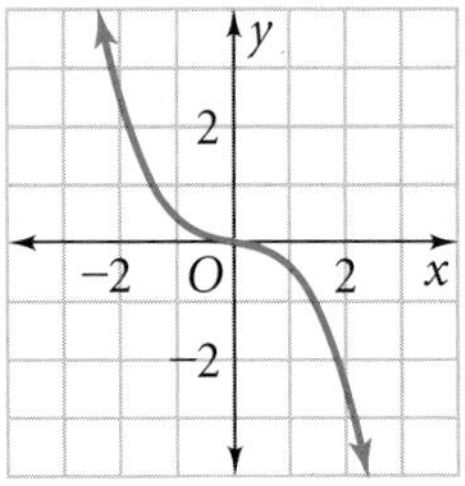

c.

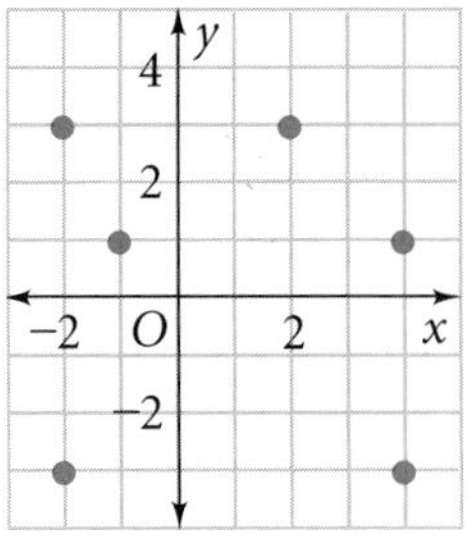

A function rule expresses an output value in terms of an input value.

Examples of Function Rules

Input ↓	Input ↓	Input ↓
$y = 2x$	$f(x) = x + 5$	$C = \pi d$
↑ Output	↑ Output	↑ Output

Reading Math

You can use $g(x)$, $h(t)$, and so on to represent functions. You read the notation $g(x)$ as "g of x," and the notation $h(t)$ as "h of t."

You read the **function notation** $f(x)$ as "f of x" or "a function of x." Note that $f(x)$ does *not* mean "f times x." When the value of x is 3, $f(3)$, read "f of 3," represents the value of the function at $x = 3$.

Input		Function		Output	Ordered Pair
5	⟶	Subtract 1	⟶	4	(5, 4)
a	⟶	Add 2	⟶	$a + 2$	$(a, a + 2)$
3	⟶	g	⟶	$g(3)$	$(3, g(3))$
x	⟶	f	⟶	$f(x)$	$(x, f(x))$

6 EXAMPLE Real-World Connection

Real-World Connection

Square tiles are used as decorative wall and floor coverings.

Art The area of a square tile is a function of the length of a side of the square. Write a function rule for the area of a square. Evaluate the function for a square tile with side length 3.5 in.

Relate area of a square is (side length)^2

Define Let s = the length of one side of the square tile.

Then $A(s)$ = the area of the square tile.

Write $A(s) = s^2$

$A(3.5) = (3.5)^2$ **Substitute 3.5 for s.**

$= 12.25$ **Simplify.**

The area of a square tile with side length 3.5 in. is 12.25 in.^{2}.

Check Understanding **6** Find $f(-3)$, $f(0)$, and $f(5)$ for each function.

a. $f(x) = 3x - 5$ **b.** $f(a) = \frac{3}{4}a - 1$ **c.** $f(y) = -\frac{1}{5}y + \frac{3}{5}$

EXERCISES

For more practice, see *Extra Practice.*

Practice and Problem Solving

A Practice by Example

Example 1 (page 55)

Graph each relation.

1. $\{(-1, 3), (-2, 1), (-3, -3), (-4, -5)\}$ **2.** $\{(0, -2), (2, 0), (3, 1), (5, 3)\}$

3. $\left\{(-1, 0), \left(\frac{1}{2}, -1\right), \left(0, \frac{1}{2}\right), \left(-1, -\frac{1}{2}\right)\right\}$ **4.** $\left\{\left(2\frac{1}{2}, 0\right), \left(-\frac{1}{2}, 0\right), (2, 0), (0, 0)\right\}$

Example 2 (page 56)

Write the ordered pairs for each relation. Find the domain and range.

5.

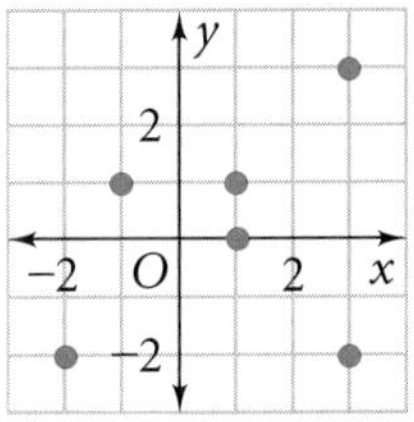

6.

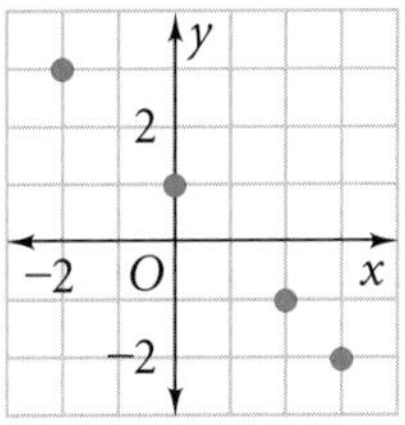

7.

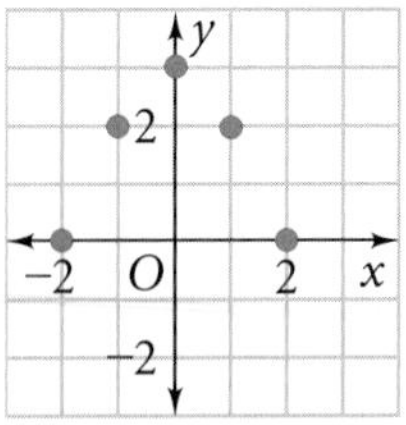

Example 3 (page 56)

Make a mapping diagram for each relation.

8. $\{(0, 0), (-1, -1), (-2, -8), (-3, -27)\}$ **9.** $\{(-2, 8), (-1, 1), (0, 0), (1, 1), (2, 8)\}$

10. $\{(-\frac{1}{2}, 11), (0, 10), \left(\frac{1}{2}, 5\right), (1, 12)\}$ **11.** $\{(5, 10), (10, 5), (15, 20), (20, 15)\}$

Example 4 (page 57)

Determine whether each relation is a function.

12. $\{(1, -2), (-2, 0), (-1, 2), (1, 3)\}$ **13.** $\{(1, 1), (2, 2), (3, 5), (4, 10), (5, 15)\}$

14. $\left\{\left(17, \frac{15}{4}\right), \left(\frac{15}{4}, 17\right), \left(15, \frac{17}{4}\right), \left(\frac{17}{4}, 15\right)\right\}$ **15.** $\left\{\left(-3, \frac{2}{5}\right), \left(-2, \frac{3}{5}\right), \left(\frac{3}{2}, -5\right), \left(5, \frac{2}{5}\right)\right\}$

Example 5 (page 57)

Use the vertical-line test to determine whether each graph represents a function.

16.

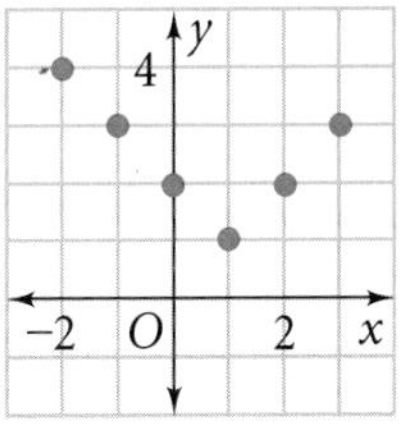

17.

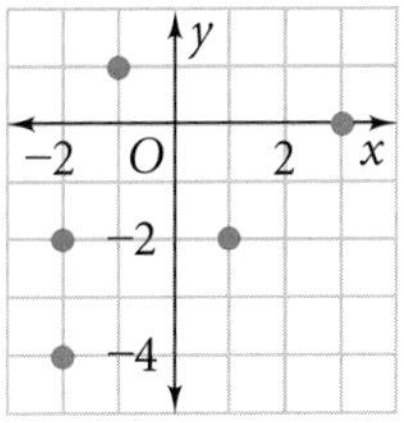

18.

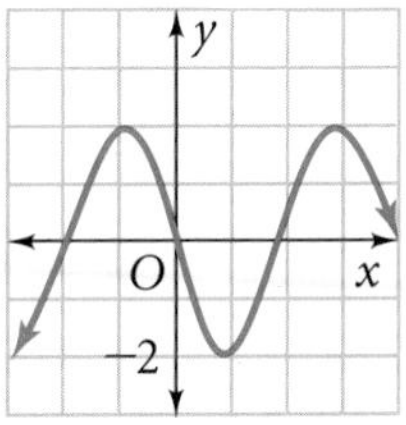

19.

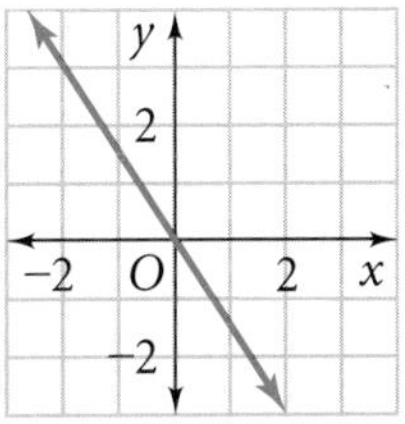

20.

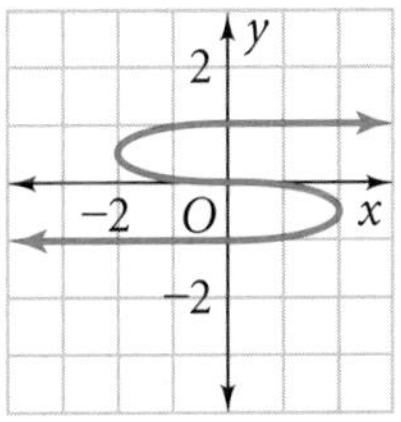

21.

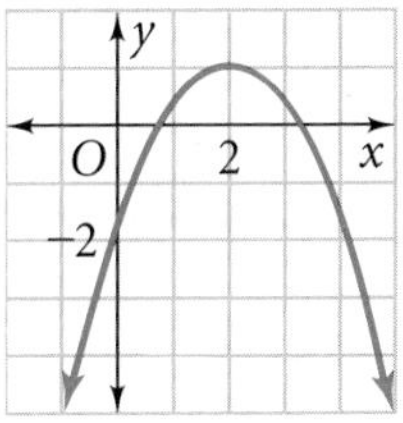

Example 6 (page 58)

For each function, find $f(-5)$, $f(-3)$, $f\left(\frac{1}{2}\right)$, and $f(4)$.

22. $f(a) = 2a + 3$ **23.** $f(y) = -3y - 2$ **24.** $f(z) = z + 9.5$

25. $f(x) = -x - 7$ **26.** $f(d) = 1 - 4d$ **27.** $f(x) = 2x - 3$

28. $f(h) = -6h - \frac{2}{3}$ **29.** $f(x) = \frac{5}{6}x + \frac{1}{3}$ **30.** $f(t) = \frac{1}{2}t - 2$

31. Measurement One meter equals about 39.37 in. Write a function rule for converting inches to meters. Evaluate the function for 59 in.

B Apply Your Skills

Graph each relation. Find the domain and range.

32. $\{(2,4),(3,5),(4,6),(5,7)\}$

33. $\{(-1,1),(-2,2),(-3,3),(-4,4)\}$

34. $\left\{\left(-\frac{1}{2},2\right),\left(2,\frac{1}{2}\right),\left(0,-\frac{1}{2}\right),\left(-\frac{1}{2},-2\right)\right\}$

35. $\left\{\left(\frac{3}{2},-\frac{1}{2}\right),\left(\frac{5}{2},\frac{1}{2}\right),\left(\frac{1}{2},\frac{1}{2}\right),\left(-\frac{3}{2},\frac{1}{2}\right)\right\}$

Find the domain and range of each relation and determine whether it is a function.

36. $\{(2,4),(4,8),(8,16)\}$

37. $\{(-1,2),(-2,5),(-2,7),(0,2),(9,2)\}$

38.

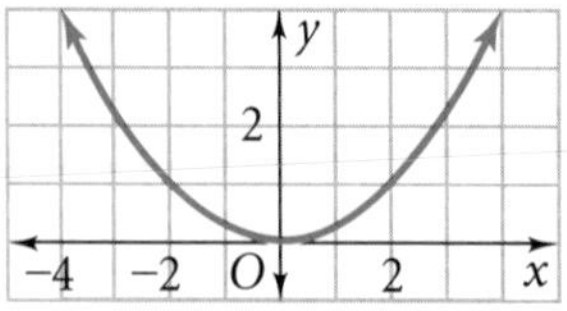

39.

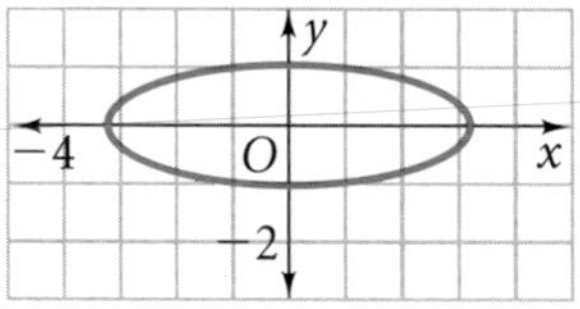

Match each relation with a model.

40. $\{(1,2),(-1,-2),(2,-1)\}$

41. $\{(2,1),(1,2),(1,-2)\}$

42. $\{(-1,2),(-2,1),(-1,-2)\}$

A.

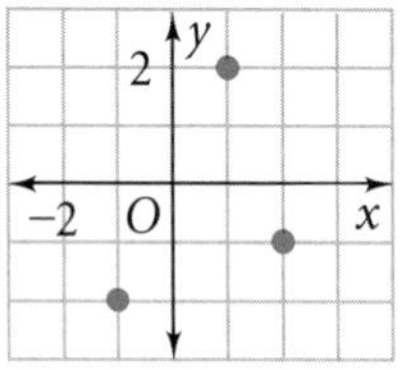

B.

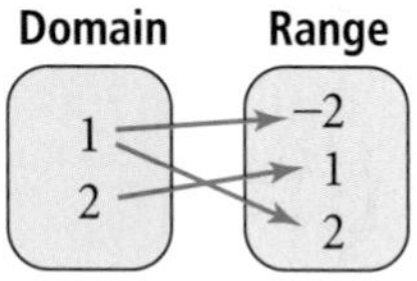

C.

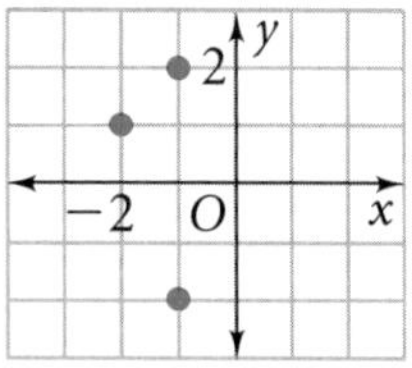

Determine whether each graph represents *y* as a function of *x*.

43.

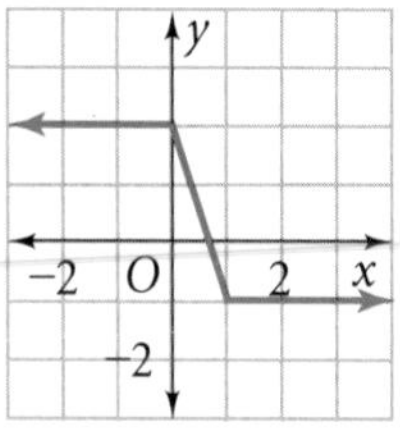

44.

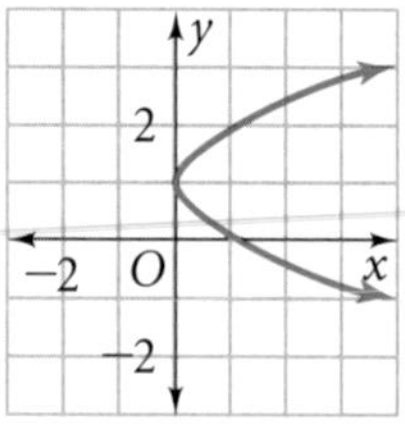

45.

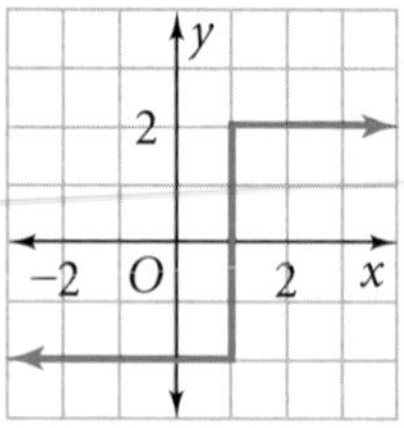

46. Geometry The volume of a cube is a function of the length of a side of the cube. Write a function for the volume of a cube. Find the volume of a cube with a side 13.5 cm long.

47. Sports The volume of a sphere is a function of the radius of the sphere. Write a function for the volume of a ball. Evaluate the function for a volleyball of radius 10.5 cm.

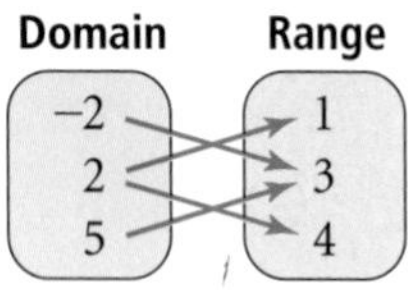

48. Writing Does the mapping diagram at the left represent a function? Explain.

49. Data Collection Draw a graph to show the relationship between the weight of a letter and the cost of postage. Is it a graph of a function? Explain.

Suppose $f(x) = 2x + 5$ and $g(x) = -\frac{1}{3}x + 2$. Find each value. (*Hint:* For $2g(x)$, find $g(x)$ first, and then multiply the result by 2.)

50. $f(-4)$

51. $2g(7)$

52. $-2f(x+1)$

53. $\frac{f(1)}{g(3)}$

54. $\frac{f(-2)}{g(f(-2)+1)}$

C Challenge

For each relation, determine whether *y* is a function of *x*. Explain why or why not.

55. $y = 2x - 3$

56. $y^2 = x$

57. $x^2 = y - 3$

Real-World Connection

Careers Chemists use math to predict chemical reactions.

58. Chemistry The time required for a certain chemical reaction is related to the amount of catalyst present during the reaction. The domain of the relation is the number of grams of catalyst, and the range is the number of seconds required for a fixed amount of the chemical to react. The following relation is the data from several reactions: $\{(2, 180), (2.5, 6), (2.7, 0.05), (2.9, 0.001), (3.0, 6), (3.1, 15), (3.2, 37), (3.3, 176)\}$. Is the relation a function? If the domain and range were interchanged, would the relation be a function? Explain.

Suppose *a* and *b* are variables representing integers. Find the domain and range of each relation and determine whether it is a function. Justify your reasoning.

59. Domain Range

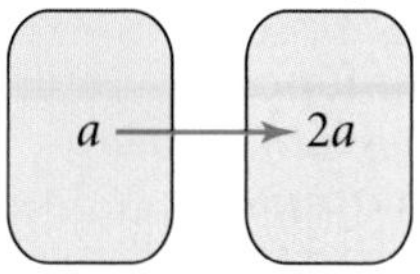

60. Domain Range

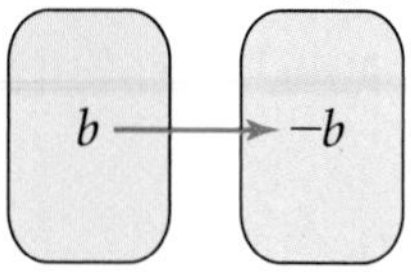

61. Domain Range

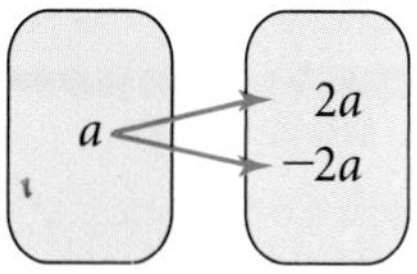

Standardized Test Prep

Multiple Choice

62. Which graph models the relation $\{(-3, -1), (3, 1), (-3, 1), (3, -1)\}$?

A.

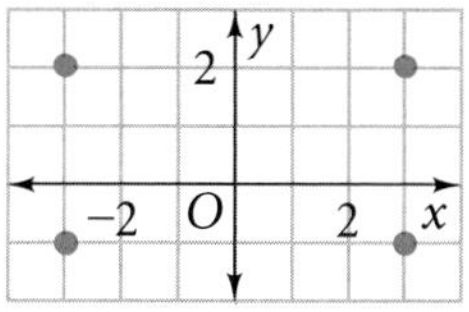

B.

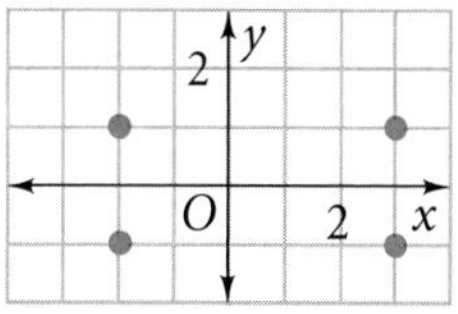

C.

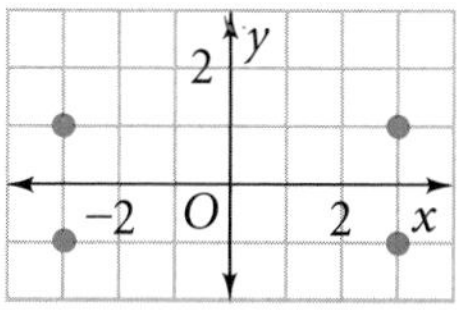

Take It to the NET
Online lesson quiz at **www.PHSchool.com**
Web Code: aga-0201

63. Which relation is *not* a function?

F. $\{(0, 9), (2, 3), (3, 2), (4, 1)\}$
G. $\{(3, 2), (4, 1), (0, 9), (3, 3)\}$
H. $\{(0, 3), (2, 3), (3, 3), (4, 3)\}$
I. $\{(0, 3), (3, 2), (2, 4), (4, 6)\}$

Short Response

64. If $f(x) = -2x + 3$ and $g(x) = 4x - 3$, which is greater, $f(5)$ or $g(-2)$? Show your work.

Extended Response

65. Is the total surface area *A* of a cube a function of the edge *c* of the cube? If it is not a function, explain why not. If it is a function, write the function rule and then evaluate the function for a cube with edge 2.5 cm.

Mixed Review

Lesson 1-6

Find each probability for choosing a letter at random from the word *mathematics*.

66. P(e) **67.** P(m) **68.** P(vowel) **69.** P(n)

70. P(a letter that occurs more than once) **71.** P(consonant) **72.** P(s or t)

Lesson 1-5

Solve each equation or inequality. Graph the solution on a number line.

73. $|x - 4| = 10$ **74.** $3 + |b| \leq 5$ **75.** $|6 - y| > 0$

Previous Course

Find each percent of increase or decrease.

76. from 9 m to 10 m **77.** from 1 gal to 1.5 gal **78.** from 2 km to 1.5 km

2-2 Linear Equations

Lesson Preview

What You'll Learn

OBJECTIVE 1 To graph linear equations

OBJECTIVE 2 To write equations of lines

. . . And Why

To solve a transportation problem, as in Example 2

✓ Check Skills You'll Need

(For help, go to Lesson 1-2.)

Evaluate each expression for $x = -2, 0, 1$, and 4.

1. $\frac{2}{3}x + 7$ **2.** $\frac{3}{5}x - 2$ **3.** $3x + 1$ **4.** $\frac{1}{2}x - 8$

New Vocabulary

- linear function
- linear equation
- dependent variable
- independent variable
- *x*-intercept
- *y*-intercept
- standard form of a linear equation
- slope
- point-slope form
- slope-intercept form

Interactive lesson includes instant self-check, tutorials, and activities.

OBJECTIVE 1 Graphing Linear Equations

A function whose graph is a line is a **linear function**. You can represent a linear function with a **linear equation**, such as $y = 3x + 2$. A solution of a linear equation is any ordered pair (x, y) that makes the equation true.

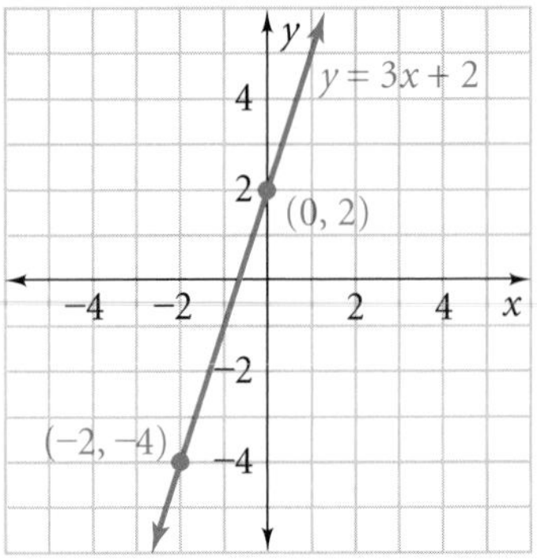

You can write the solutions of the equation using set notation as $\{(x, y) \mid y = 3x + 2\}$. Read the notation as "the set of ordered pairs x, y such that $y = 3x + 2$." Because the value of y depends on the value of x, y is called the **dependent variable** and x is called the **independent variable.**

1 EXAMPLE Graphing a Linear Equation

Graph the equation $y = \frac{2}{3}x + 3$.

Choose two values for x and find the corresponding values of y. Plot the point for each ordered pair and complete the graph by drawing a line through the points.

x	$\frac{2}{3}x + 3$	y	(x, y)
−3	$\frac{2}{3}(-3) + 3$	1	(−3, 1)
3	$\frac{2}{3}(3) + 3$	5	(3, 5)

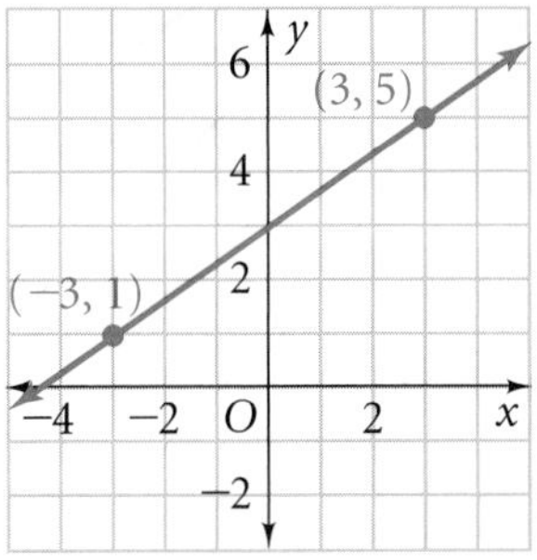

Check Choose a third point on the line and check that its ordered pair satisfies the equation. Since (0, 3) is a point on the line, and $\frac{2}{3}(0) + 3 = 3$, the graph is correct.

Need Help?

Geometry Since two points determine a line, you can use two points to graph a line. Check your line by finding a third point.

Check Understanding **1** Graph each equation. Check your work.

a. $y = \frac{3}{4}x$ **b.** $x + y = -2$ **c.** $y = -\frac{1}{2}x + \frac{1}{2}$

The **y-intercept** of a line is the point at which the line crosses the y-axis. You can use the same term to identify the y-coordinate of this point.

The **x-intercept** of a line is the point at which the line crosses the x-axis. You can use the same term to identify the x-coordinate of this point.

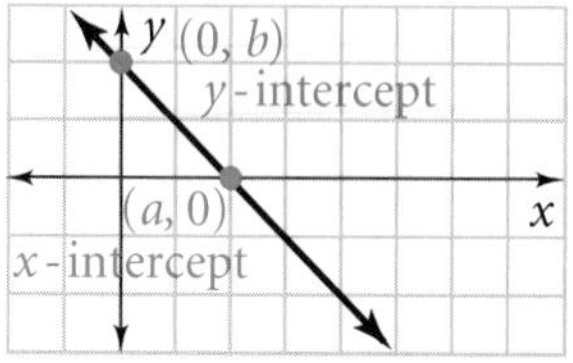

The **standard form of a linear equation** is $Ax + By = C$, where A, B, and C are real numbers, and A and B are not both zero. You can graph a linear equation in standard form by finding the x- and y-intercepts.

2 EXAMPLE Real-World Connection

Transportation The equation $3x + 2y = 120$ models the number of passengers who can sit in a train car, where x is the number of adults and y is the number of children. Graph the equation. Describe the domain and the range. Explain what the x- and y-intercepts represent.

Set x or y equal to zero to find each intercept.

$$\begin{aligned} 3x + 2y &= 120 \\ 3x + 2(0) &= 120 \\ 3x &= 120 \\ x &= 40 \end{aligned} \qquad \begin{aligned} 3x + 2y &= 120 \\ 3(0) + 2y &= 120 \\ 2y &= 120 \\ y &= 60 \end{aligned}$$

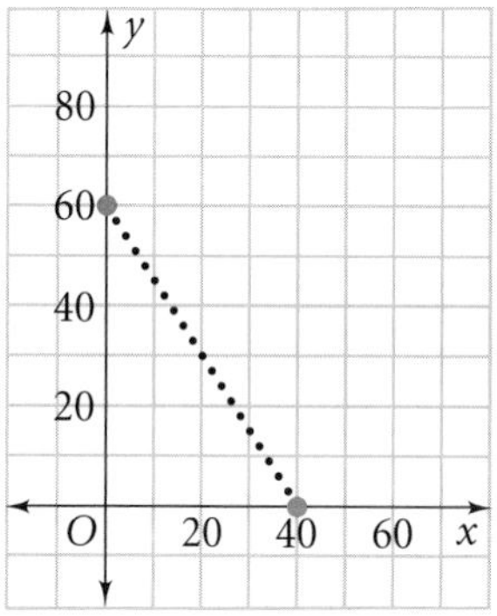

Use the intercepts to graph the equation. The x-intercept is (40, 0). When 40 adults are seated, no children are seated. The y-intercept is (0, 60). When 60 children are seated, no adults are seated.

The number of people is both discrete and non-negative. Both the domain and the range of the graph are limited to the whole numbers.

Check Understanding **2** **a.** Suppose the train system buys new train cars with molded plastic seats. The model changes to $x + y = 40$. Graph the equation and interpret the x- and y-intercepts.

b. Explain how using molded seats changes the number of seated passengers.

Real-World Connection

In Japan, so many people ride public transportation that they need help getting into the trains.

Reading Math

The slope of a line is also the rate of change between two points on the line.

The **slope** of a nonvertical line is the ratio of the vertical change to a corresponding horizontal change. You can calculate slope by subtracting the corresponding coordinates of two points on the line.

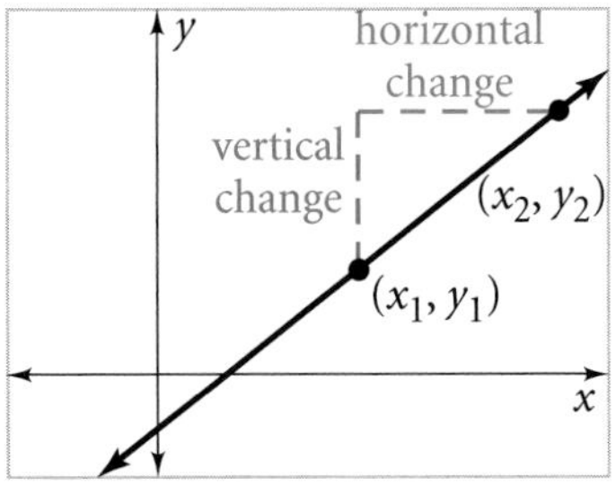

Key Concepts

Definition	Slope Formula

$$\text{slope} = \frac{\text{vertical change (rise)}}{\text{horizontal change (run)}} = \frac{y_2 - y_1}{x_2 - x_1}, \text{ where } x_2 - x_1 \neq 0$$

3 EXAMPLE Finding Slope

Find the slope of the line through the points (3, 2) and (−9, 6).

$\text{slope} = \frac{y_2 - y_1}{x_2 - x_1}$ **Use the slope formula.**

$= \frac{6 - 2}{-9 - 3}$ **Substitute (3, 2) for (x_1, y_1) and (−9, 6) for (x_2, y_2).**

$= \frac{4}{-12}$ **Subtract.**

$= -\frac{1}{3}$ **Simplify.**

The slope of the line is $-\frac{1}{3}$.

Check Understanding 3 Find the slope of the line through each pair of points.

a. (−2, −2) and (4, 2) **b.** (0, −3) and (7, −9)

OBJECTIVE 2

Writing Equations of Lines

Investigation: Point-Slope Form

1. Make a table of values to graph each line.

   a. $y - 1 = -2(x - 2)$ b. $y - 2 = \frac{1}{3}(x - 1)$ c. $y - 5 = 3(x - 4)$

2. Find the slope of each line. Compare the slope of the line to the red number in the equation of the line. What do you notice?

3. Find the point on the graph of each line with an *x*-coordinate that is equal to the green number in the equation line. Then compare the *y*-coordinate of the point to the blue number in the equation of the line. What do you notice?

4. **Make a Conjecture** All three equations in Question 1 are in the form $y - y_1 = m(x - x_1)$. Make a conjecture about how you can use that form to help you graph an equation.

When you know the slope and a point on a line, you can use the **point-slope form** to write the equation of the line.

Key Concepts

Definition	Point-Slope Form
The line through point (x_1, y_1) with slope m has the equation below. $y - y_1 = m(x - x_1)$	

4 EXAMPLE Writing an Equation Given the Slope and a Point

Write in standard form an equation of the line with slope $-\frac{1}{2}$ through the point $(8, -1)$.

$y - y_1 = m(x - x_1)$	**Use the point-slope equation.**
$y - (-1) = -\frac{1}{2}(x - 8)$	**Substitute $-\frac{1}{2}$ for m, -1 for y_1, and 8 for x_1.**
$y - (-1) = -\frac{1}{2}x - \left(-\frac{1}{2}\right)(8)$	**Distributive Property**
$y + 1 = -\frac{1}{2}x + 4$	**Simplify.**
$\frac{1}{2}x + y = 3$	**Write in standard form.**

Check Understanding 4 Write in standard form the equation of each line.

a. slope 2, through $(4, -2)$ **b.** slope $\frac{5}{6}$, through $(5, 6)$

When you know two points on a line, you can write an equation by using the point-slope equation combined with the slope formula.

5 EXAMPLE Writing an Equation Given Two Points

Write in point-slope form the equation of the line through $(1, 5)$ and $(4, -1)$.

$y - y_1 = m(x - x_1)$	**Write the point-slope equation.**
$y - y_1 = \frac{y_2 - y_1}{x_2 - x_1}(x - x_1)$	**Substitute the slope formula for m.**
$y - 5 = \frac{-1 - 5}{4 - 1}(x - 1)$	**Substitute: $x_1 = 1, y_1 = 5, x_2 = 4, y_2 = -1$.**
$y - 5 = \frac{-6}{3}(x - 1)$	**Simplify.**
$y - 5 = -2(x - 1)$	**Write in point-slope form.**

Check Understanding 5 Write in point-slope form the equation of the line through each pair of points.

a. $(5, 0)$ and $(-3, 2)$ **b.** $(-2, -1)$ and $(-10, 17)$ **c.** $(5, 1)$ and $(-4, -3)$

Another form of the equation of a line is **slope-intercept form,** which you can use to find slope by examining the equation.

Key Concepts

Definition	Slope-Intercept Form
slope → m, y-intercept → b: $y = mx + b$	

6 EXAMPLE Finding Slope Using Slope-Intercept Form

Find the slope of $4x + 3y = 7$.

$4x + 3y = 7$

$3y = -4x + 7$ **Subtract 4x from each side.**

$y = -\frac{4}{3}x + \frac{7}{3}$ **Write in slope-intercept form.**

The slope of the line is $-\frac{4}{3}$.

Check Understanding 6 Find the slope of each line.

a. $3x + 2y = 1$ **b.** $\frac{2}{3}x + \frac{1}{2}y = 1$ **c.** $Ax + By = C$

Key Concepts

Summary	Equations of a Line	
Point-Slope Form	Standard Form	Slope-Intercept Form
$y - 2 = -3(x + 4)$	$3x + y = -10$	$y = -3x - 10$

The slopes of horizontal, vertical, perpendicular, and parallel lines have special properties.

Horizontal Line

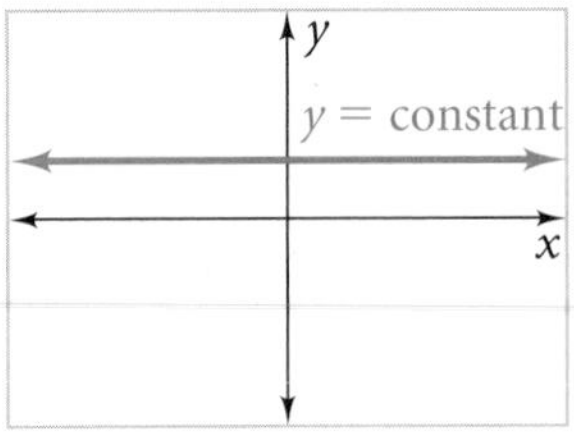

$m = 0$
$y =$ constant

Vertical Line

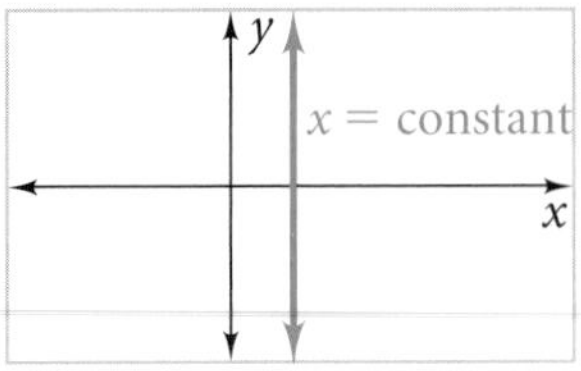

m is undefined.
$x =$ constant

Perpendicular Lines

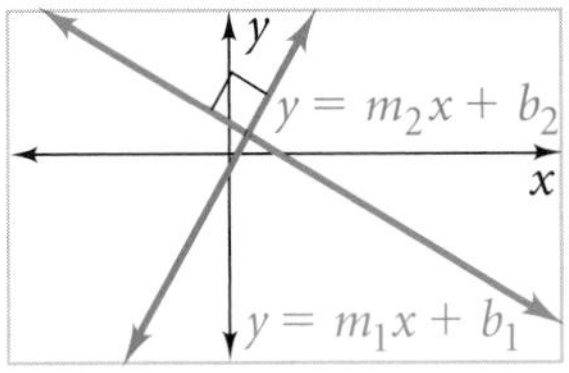

$m_1 \cdot m_2 = -1$
(In other words, m_2 is the negative reciprocal of m_1.)

Parallel Lines

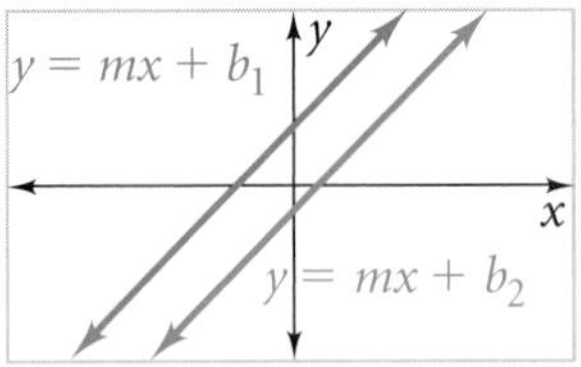

$m = m$
$b_1 \neq b_2$

Real-World Connection

The steel girders of the Eiffel Tower model horizontal, vertical, perpendicular, and parallel lines.

7 EXAMPLE Writing an Equation of a Perpendicular Line

Write an equation of the line through each point and perpendicular to $y = \frac{3}{4}x + 2$. Graph all three lines.

a. (0, 4)

$m = -\left(\frac{1}{\frac{3}{4}}\right) = -\frac{4}{3}$ **Find the negative reciprocal of $\frac{3}{4}$.**

$y = mx + b$ **Use slope-intercept form.**

$y = -\frac{4}{3}x + 4$ **Substitute: $m = -\frac{4}{3}$ and $b = 4$.**

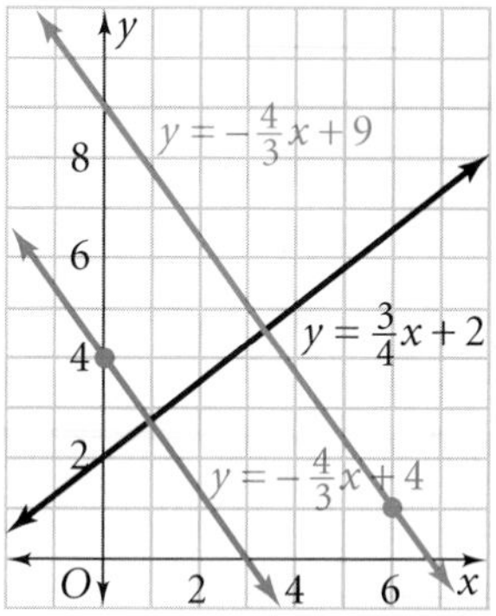

b. (6, 1)

$y = -\frac{4}{3}x + b$ **Slope is $-\frac{4}{3}$.**

$1 = -\frac{4}{3}(6) + b$ **Substitute (6, 1) for (x, y).**

$1 = -8 + b$ **Simplify.**

$9 = b$ **Solve for b.**

$y = -\frac{4}{3}x + 9$ **Write the equation.**

Check Understanding 7 Write an equation for each line. Then graph the line.

a. through (−1, 3) and perpendicular to the line $y = 5x - 3$

b. through (2, 1) and parallel to the line $y = \frac{2}{3}x + \frac{5}{8}$

c. vertical and through (5, −3)

EXERCISES

For more practice, see *Extra Practice*.

Practice and Problem Solving

A Practice by Example

Example 1 (page 62)

Graph each equation. Check your work.

1. $y = 2x$ **2.** $y = -3x - 1$ **3.** $y = 3x - 2$ **4.** $y = -4x + 5$

5. $5x - 2y = -4$ **6.** $-2x + 5y = -10$ **7.** $y - 3 = -2x$ **8.** $y + 4 = -3x$

Example 2 (page 63)

9. Cost Analysis The equation $y - 0.23x = 0$ relates the cost of operating a car to the number of miles driven, where x is the number of miles driven and y is the cost.

a. Graph the equation and determine the domain and range.

b. Explain what the x- and y-intercepts represent.

c. Explain what 0.23 represents.

10. Fund-Raising The school glee club needs a total of \$4500 for a trip to Omaha, Nebraska. To make money, members are selling baseball caps for \$4.50 and sweatshirts for \$12.50.

a. Graph the equation $4.5x + 12.5y = 4500$, where x is the number of baseball caps and y is the number of sweatshirts sold.

b. Explain the meaning of the x- and y-intercepts in terms of the fund-raising.

Example 3 (page 64)

Find the slope of the line through each pair of points.

11. (1, 6) and (8, −1) **12.** (−3, 9) and (0, 3) **13.** (0, 0) and (2, 6)

14. (−4, −3) and (7, 1) **15.** (−2, −1) and (8, −3) **16.** (1, 2) and (2, 3)

17. $\left(\frac{2}{3}, \frac{4}{7}\right)$ and $\left(\frac{2}{3}, \frac{11}{7}\right)$ **18.** (−3, 5) and (4, 5) **19.** (−5, −7) and (0, 10)

Example 4 (page 65)

Write in standard form the equation of each line.

20. slope $= 3; (1, 5)$ **21.** slope $= \frac{5}{6}; (22, 12)$ **22.** slope $= -\frac{3}{5}; (-4, 0)$

23. slope $= 0; (4, -2)$ **24.** slope $= -1; (-3, 5)$ **25.** slope $= 5; (0, 2)$

Example 5 (page 65)

Write in point-slope form the equation of the line through each pair of points.

26. $(-10, 3)$ and $(-2, -5)$ **27.** $(1, 0)$ and $(5, 5)$ **28.** $(-4, 10)$ and $(-6, 15)$

29. $(0, -1)$ and $(3, -5)$ **30.** $(7, 11)$ and $(13, 17)$ **31.** $(1, 9)$ and $(6, 2)$

Example 6 (page 66)

Find the slope of each line.

32. $5x + y = 4$ **33.** $-3x + 2y = 7$ **34.** $-\frac{1}{2}x - y = \frac{3}{4}$

35. $Ax + By = C$ **36.** $Ax - By = C$ **37.** $y = 7$

Example 7 (page 67)

Write an equation for each line. Then graph the line.

38. through $(-2, 1)$ and parallel to $y = -3x + 1$

39. through $(-3, -1)$ and perpendicular to $y = -\frac{2}{5}x - 4$

40. through $(-7, 10)$ and horizontal

41. through $\left(1, -\frac{2}{7}\right)$ and vertical

B Apply Your Skills

Graph each equation.

42. $y = -\frac{3}{5}x - \frac{12}{5}$ **43.** $y = -2x + 3$ **44.** $y = -x + 7$

45. $3y - 2x = -12$ **46.** $4x + 5y = 20$ **47.** $4x - 3y = -6$

48. $\frac{2}{3}x + \frac{y}{3} = -\frac{1}{3}$ **49.** $\frac{3}{5}y - \frac{x}{5} = -\frac{6}{5}$ **50.** $\frac{4}{5} = -\frac{1}{3}x - \frac{3}{4}y$

Find the slope of each line.

51.
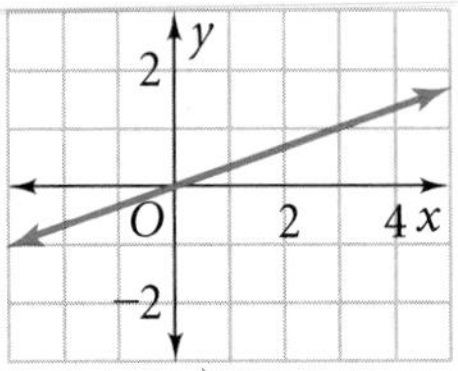

52.
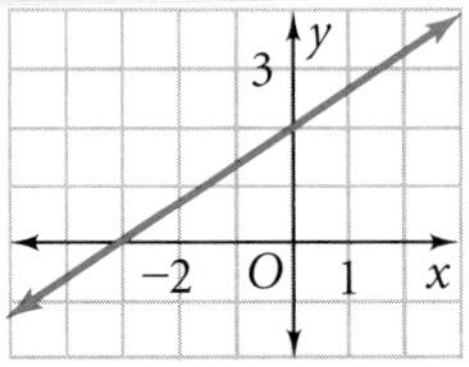

53.
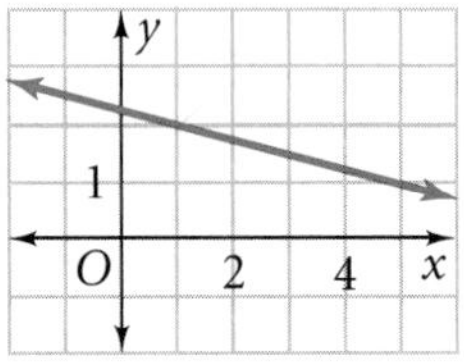

Find the slope and the intercepts of each line.

54. $f(x) = \frac{2}{3}x + 4$ **55.** $y = -x + 1000$ **56.** $-Rx + Sy = -T$

57. $g(x) = 54x - 1$ **58.** $x = -3$ **59.** $y = 0$

60. $-\frac{1}{3}x - \frac{2}{3}y = \frac{5}{3}$ **61.** $y = 0.4 - 0.8x$ **62.** $\frac{A}{D}x + \frac{B}{D}y = \frac{C}{D}$

Find the slope of the line through each pair of points.

63. $\left(\frac{3}{2}, -\frac{1}{2}\right)$ and $\left(-\frac{2}{3}, \frac{1}{3}\right)$ **64.** $\left(-\frac{1}{2}, -\frac{1}{2}\right)$ and $(-3, -4)$ **65.** $\left(0, \frac{1}{2}\right)$ and $\left(\frac{5}{7}, 0\right)$

Write an equation for each line. Each interval is 1 unit.

66.
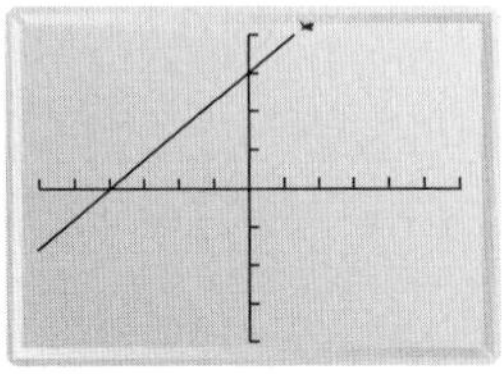

67.
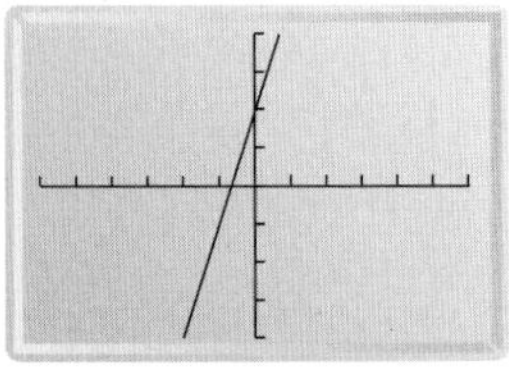

68.
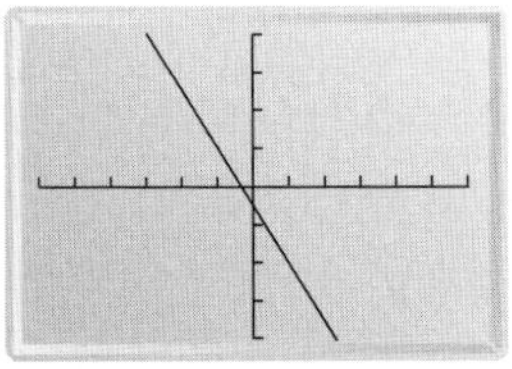

Real-World Connection

You can download data from a motion detector to a computer to produce graphs of distance versus time.

69. Data Analysis Three students moved away from or toward a motion detector, one at a time. Each graph shows distance from the detector as a function of time.

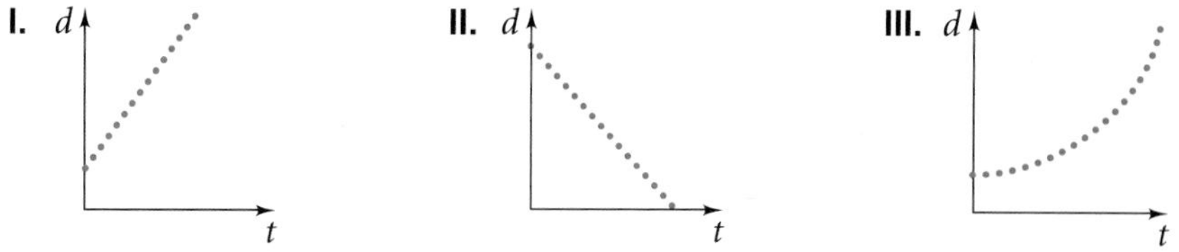

a. Which student(s) moved at a constant rate? Which student(s) did not? Justify your reasoning.
b. Which student(s) moved away from the motion detector?
c. Which student started farthest from the motion detector?

70. Critical Thinking Most graphing calculators are designed to graph equations that are solved for y. What lines could not be graphed with this method?

Write an equation for each line. Then graph the line.

71. $m = 0$, through $(5, -1)$

72. $m = 2$, through $(1, 3)$

73. $m = \frac{5}{6}$, through $(-4, 0)$

74. $m = -\frac{3}{2}$, through $(0, -1)$

Write each equation in standard form.

75. $y = \frac{3}{2}x - 1$

76. $x + \frac{1}{3}y = \frac{2}{9}$

77. $-\left(\frac{1}{2}x + 2y\right) = \frac{2}{3}$

78. a. Open-Ended Write an equation of a line.
b. Write an equation of the line parallel to the line you wrote in part (a) passing through the point $(0.5, 0.6)$.
c. Write an equation of the line perpendicular to the line you wrote in part (a) passing through the point $\left(\frac{5}{3}, 2\right)$.
d. Write an equation of the line parallel to the line you wrote in part (c) passing through the point $(-3, 1)$.
e. **Geometry** Graph the lines from parts (a), (b), (c), and (d). If they form a polygon, describe it.

C Challenge

Points that are on the same line are *collinear*. Use the definition of slope to determine whether the given points are collinear.

79. $(-2, 6), (0, 2), (1, 0)$

80. $(3, -5), (-3, 3), (0, 2)$

Need Help?

The slopes of parallel lines are equal. The slopes of perpendicular lines are negative reciprocals.

81. a. Graph $y = 3x + 1$.
b. Write an equation of the line through point $(-1, 3)$ that is parallel to the line from part (a). Graph the line on the same set of axes.
c. Write an equation of the line through point $(-1, 3)$ that is perpendicular to the line from part (a). Graph the line on the same set of axes.
d. What is true about the lines from parts (b) and (c)? Explain.

82. Geometry Prove that the triangle with vertices $(3, 5), (-2, 6)$, and $(1, 3)$ is a right triangle.

83. Geometry Prove that the quadrilateral with vertices $(2, 5), (4, 8), (7, 6)$, and $(5, 3)$ is a rectangle.

84. Critical Thinking Lines p, q, and r all pass through point $(-3, 4)$. Line p has slope 4 and is perpendicular to line q. Line r passes through Quadrants I and II only. Write an equation for each line. Then graph the three lines on the same coordinate plane.

Standardized Test Prep

Multiple Choice

85. Which equation represents a line through (3, 5) that is perpendicular to $y = 2x - 5$?

A. $2y = -x + 13$ **B.** $2y = x + 13$
C. $2y - x = 13$ **D.** $2y + x = -13$

86. For the equation $3x - 2y = 12$, which has value -6?

F. the x-intercept **G.** the y-intercept
H. the slope **I.** the origin

Quantitative Comparison

Compare the boxed quantity in Column A with the boxed quantity in Column B. Choose the best answer.

A. The quantity in Column A is greater.
B. The quantity in Column B is greater.
C. The two quantities are equal.
D. The relationship cannot be determined from the information given.

	Column A	Column B
87.	the slope of $3y + 2x = 4$	the slope of $-3y - 2x = 4$
88.	the slope of the line through $(-1, 3)$ and $(5, -1)$	the slope of a horizontal line
89.	the slope of a line perpendicular to $y = -3x + 5$	the slope of a line parallel to $9y = 3x - 20$
90.	the value of c if the line $2x - 5y = 4$ contains $(-3, c)$	the value of a if the line $\frac{x}{3} - 2y = 10$ contains $(a, -3)$

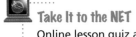

Take It to the NET
Online lesson quiz at
www.PHSchool.com
Web Code: aga-0202

Mixed Review

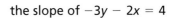

Lesson 2-1 **Find the domain and range of each relation. Then decide whether it is a function.**

91.

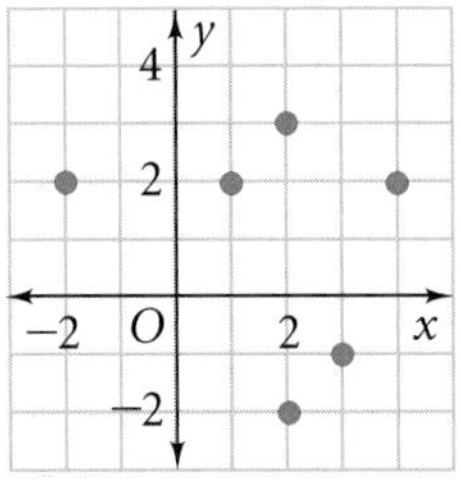

92.

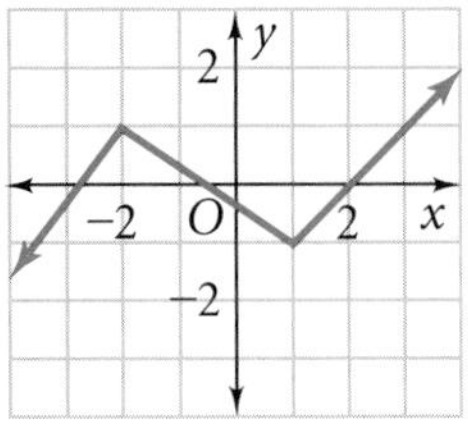

93.

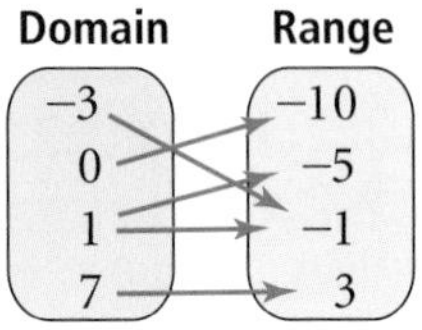

Lesson 1-1 **Identify each demonstrated property (or properties) of real numbers.**

94. $7.4 - 3.4 + 2.6 = 7.4 + 2.6 - 3.4$ **95.** $\frac{2}{5} + \frac{27}{5} \cdot \frac{5}{27} = \frac{2}{5} \cdot 1$

96. $97(7) = 100(7) - 3(7)$ **97.** $21 + 19.7 - 19.7 = 21$

Previous Course **98. Commission** A fabric designer earns a 60% commission for works sold in a textile studio. The studio receives the other 40%. How much does the studio receive for selling a length of fabric that costs $15.65? How much does the designer receive?

Extension Piecewise Functions

FOR USE WITH LESSON 2-2

A piecewise function has different rules for different parts of its domain.

1 EXAMPLE Writing a Piecewise Function

Write a piecewise function to represent the graph at the right.

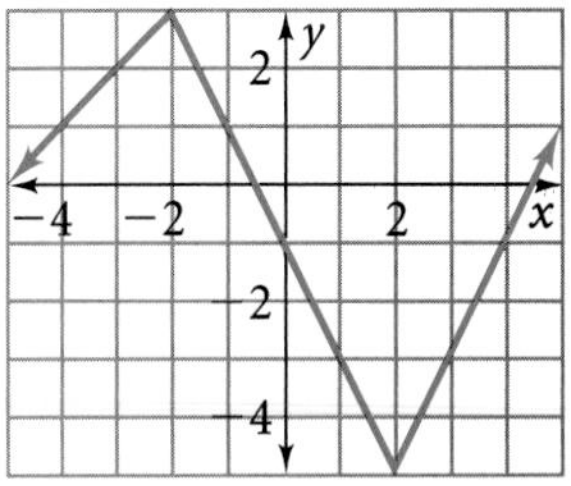

There are three sections on the graph, so there will be three parts to the function. Since $(-2, 3)$ and $(2, -5)$ both lie on two sections of the graph, arbitrarily assign each point to just one section.

When $x \le -2$, the function is $f(x) = x + 5$. When $-2 < x \le 2$, the function is $f(x) = -2x - 1$. When $x > 2$, the function is $f(x) = 2x - 9$.

The piecewise function has three parts. $f(x) = \begin{cases} x + 5, \text{ if } x \le -2 \\ -2x - 1, \text{ if } -2 < x \le 2 \\ 2x - 9, \text{ if } x > 2 \end{cases}$

Some piecewise functions are step functions. Their graphs look like the steps of a staircase. One step function is the greatest integer function $f(x) = [x]$, where $[x]$ means the greatest integer less than or equal to x.

2 EXAMPLE Graphing a Piecewise Function

Graph the function $f(x) = [x]$.

Step 1 Choose an interval bounded by two consecutive integers. Make a table of values for the interval $0 \le x \le 1$.

x	0	0.25	0.5	0.75	1
f(x)	0	0	0	0	1

Each section of the graph ends at the y-value at which it starts. The left endpoint of each "step" is a closed circle. The right endpoint is an open circle.

Step 2 Graph the function.

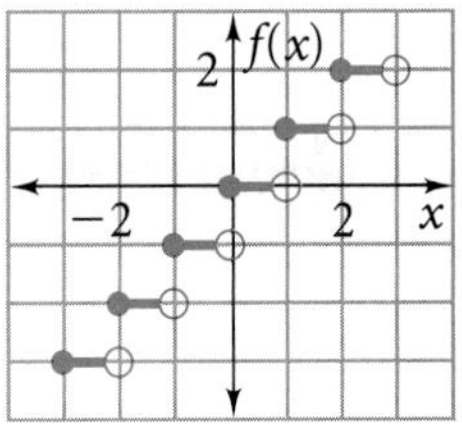

Use closed circles for included endpoints; use open circles for excluded endpoints.

EXERCISES

Graph each piecewise function.

1. $y = [x] + 2$
2. $f(x) = 3[x]$
3. $y = \begin{cases} x + 4, \text{ if } x \le -2 \\ -x, \text{ if } x > -2 \end{cases}$
4. $f(x) = \begin{cases} -2x + 1, \text{ if } x < 3 \\ x - 8, \text{ if } x \ge 3 \end{cases}$
5. Write a piecewise function to represent the graph at the right.
6. **Writing** Explain how to graph a piecewise function.

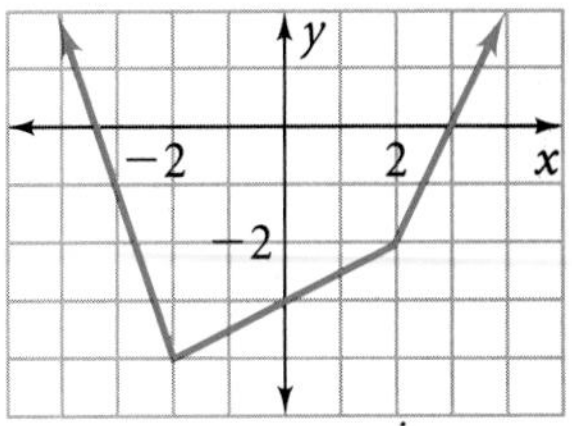

2-3 Direct Variation

North Carolina Objectives

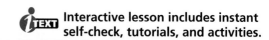

1.05 Model and solve problems using direct, inverse, combined and joint variation.

Lesson Preview

What You'll Learn

OBJECTIVE 1 To write and interpret direct variation equations

. . . And Why

To model a dripping faucet, as in Example 3

Check Skills You'll Need

(For help, go to Lesson 1-3 and Skills Handbook page 844.)

Solve each equation for *y*.

1. $12y = 3x$ **2.** $12y = 5x$ **3.** $\frac{3}{4}y = 15$ **4.** $0.9y = 27x$ **5.** $5y = 35$

Tell whether each equation is true.

6. $\frac{1}{4} \stackrel{?}{=} \frac{2}{8}$ **7.** $\frac{2}{5} \stackrel{?}{=} \frac{6}{15}$ **8.** $\frac{9}{24} \stackrel{?}{=} \frac{12}{36}$ **9.** $\frac{20}{24} \stackrel{?}{=} \frac{30}{36}$

New Vocabulary • direct variation • constant of variation

Interactive lesson includes instant self-check, tutorials, and activities.

OBJECTIVE 1 Writing and Interpreting a Direct Variation

A linear function defined by an equation of the form $y = kx$, where $k \neq 0$, represents **direct variation.** As with any line, the slope k is constant.

When x and y are variables, you can write $k = \frac{y}{x}$, so the ratio $y : x$ equals the constant k, the **constant of variation.**

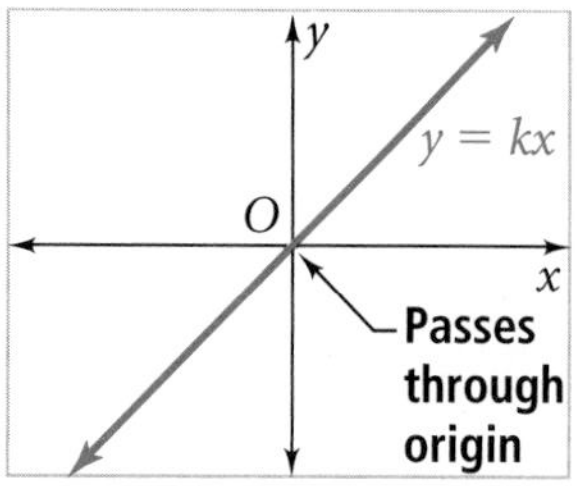

1 EXAMPLE Identifying Direct Variation from a Table

Reading Math

You can describe direct variation as "*y* varies directly as *x*" or "*y* varies directly with *x*."

For each function, determine whether y varies directly with x. If so, find the constant of variation and write the equation.

a.

x	y
2	8
3	12
5	20

$\frac{y}{x} = \frac{8}{2} = \frac{12}{3} = \frac{20}{5} = 4$,

so y varies directly with x.

The constant of variation is 4.

The equation is $y = 4x$.

b.

x	y
1	4
2	7
5	16

Since $\frac{4}{1}$, $\frac{7}{2}$, and $\frac{16}{5}$ are not equal,

$\frac{y}{x}$ is not a constant.

y does *not* vary directly with x.

Check Understanding

1 For each function, determine whether y varies directly with x. If so, find the constant of variation and write the equation.

a.

x	y
−6	−2
3	1
12	4

b.

x	y
−1	−2
3	4
6	7

c.

x	y
−9	5
3	$-1\frac{2}{3}$
6	$3\frac{5}{8}$

You can analyze an equation to determine whether it represents direct variation.

2 EXAMPLE Identifying Direct Variation from an Equation

For each function, determine whether y varies directly with x. If so, find the constant of variation.

a. $3y = 2x$
$3y = 2x$ is equivalent to $y = \frac{2}{3}x$, so y varies directly with x.
The constant of variation is $\frac{2}{3}$.

b. $y = 2x + 3$
Since you cannot write the equation in the form $y = kx$, y does *not* vary directly with x.

Check Understanding **2** For each function, determine whether y varies directly with x. If so, find the constant of variation.

a. $y = \frac{x}{2}$ **b.** $2y - 1 = x$ **c.** $\frac{5}{6}x = \frac{1}{3}y$ **d.** $7x + 4y = 10$

You can write an equation to solve a direct variation problem.

3 EXAMPLE Real-World Connection

Water Conservation A dripping faucet wastes a cup of water if it drips for three minutes. The amount of water wasted varies directly with the amount of time the faucet drips.

a. Find the constant of variation k and write an equation to model the direct variation.

Relate water wasted — varies directly — with time

Define Let w = number of cups of water wasted.
Let t = time in minutes the faucet drips.

Write $w = k \cdot t$

$1 = k(3)$ **Substitute 1 for w and 3 for t.**
$\frac{1}{3} = k$ **Solve for k.**

The constant of variation k is $\frac{1}{3}$. The equation $w = \frac{1}{3}t$ models the direct variation.

b. Find how long the faucet must drip to waste $4\frac{1}{2}$ c of water.

$w = \frac{1}{3}t$ **Use the direct variation.**
$4\frac{1}{2} = \frac{1}{3}t$ **Substitute $4\frac{1}{2}$ for w.**
$\frac{9}{2}(3) = t$ **Solve for t.**
$13\frac{1}{2} = t$ **Simplify.**

The faucet must drip for $13\frac{1}{2}$ min to waste $4\frac{1}{2}$ c of water.

Check Understanding **3** **Geometry** The circumference of a circle varies directly with the diameter of the circle. The formula $C = \pi d$ relates the circumference to the diameter.
a. What is the constant of variation?
b. Find the diameter of a circle with circumference 105 cm to the nearest tenth.

You can use proportions to solve some direct variation problems. This can save time when the problem does not ask for the constant of variation.

Need Help?

In direct variation, $k = \frac{y}{x}$, so the ratio $y : x$ is constant.

4 EXAMPLE Using a Proportion

Suppose y varies directly with x, and $x = 27$ when $y = -51$. Find x when $y = -17$.

Let $(x_1, y_1) = (27, -51)$ and let $(x_2, y_2) = (x_2, -17)$.

$\frac{y_1}{x_1} = \frac{y_2}{x_2}$ **Write a proportion.**

$\frac{-51}{27} = \frac{-17}{x_2}$ **Substitute.**

$-51(x_2) = 27(-17)$ **Write the cross products.**

$x_2 = \frac{27(-17)}{-51}$ **Solve for x_2.**

$x_2 = 9$ **Simplify.**

Check Understanding 4 Find the missing value for each direct variation.

a. If $y = 4$ when $x = 3$, find y when $x = 6$.
b. If $y = 7$ when $x = 2$, find y when $x = 8$.
c. If $y = 10$ when $x = -3$, find x when $y = 2$.
d. If $y = 1$ when $x = 10$, find y when $x = 2$.

EXERCISES

For more practice, see *Extra Practice.*

Practice and Problem Solving

A Practice by Example

Example 1 (page 72)

For each function, determine whether y varies directly with x. If so, find the constant of variation and write the equation.

1.

x	y
2	4
4	8
16	32

2.

x	y
2	−6
4	−12
5	−15

3.

x	y
11	22
16	32
7	42

4.

x	y
27	9
30	10
60	20

5.

x	y
2	14
3	21
5	35

6.

x	y
3	9
4	13
7	23

7.

x	y
−2	4
−3	6
−5	10

8.

x	y
1	−2
3	−8
5	14

Example 2 (page 73)

Determine whether y varies directly with x. If so, find the constant of variation.

9. $y = 12x$ **10.** $y = 6x$ **11.** $y = -2x$ **12.** $y = 4x + 1$

13. $y = 4x - 3$ **14.** $y = -5x$ **15.** $y - 6x = 0$ **16.** $y + 3 = -3x$

Example 3 (page 73)

For each direct variation, find the constant of variation. Then find the value of y when $x = -5$.

17. $y = 2$ when $x = 7$ **18.** $y = -5$ when $x = 3$

19. $y = -2$ when $x = 2$ **20.** $y = -\frac{2}{3}$ when $x = -\frac{1}{3}$

21. $y = 17$ when $x = -4$ **22.** $y = \frac{1}{2}$ when $x = -2$

23. **Environment** Suppose you work on a tree farm and you need to find the height of each tree. You know that the length of an object's shadow varies directly with its height. Refer to the diagram.

a. Find the constant of variation.

b. Write an equation to calculate the height of the tree.

c. Find the height of a tree with a shadow 8 ft 4 in. long.

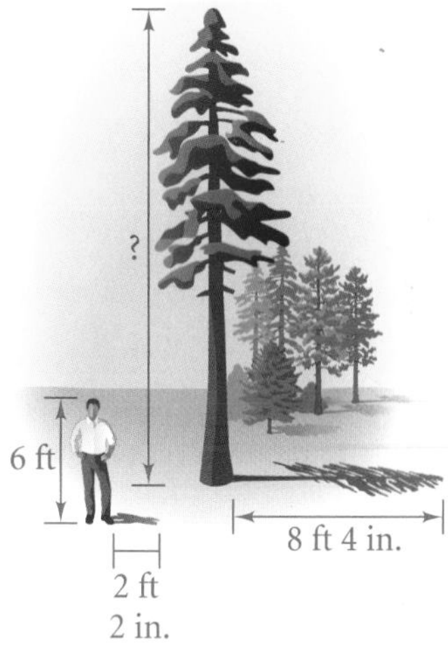

Example 4 (page 74)

For Exercises 24–27, y varies directly with x.

24. If $y = 4$ when $x = -2$, find x when $y = 6$.

25. If $y = 6$ when $x = 2$, find x when $y = 12$.

26. If $y = 7$ when $x = 2$, find y when $x = 3$.

27. If $y = 5$ when $x = -3$, find y when $x = -1$.

28. Aviation A speed of 60 mi/h is equal to a speed of 88 ft/s. Find the speed in miles per hour of an aircraft travelling 1000 ft/s.

B Apply Your Skills

For each function, determine whether y varies directly with x. If so, find the constant of variation and write the equation.

29.

x	y
9	6
12	8
15	10

30.

x	y
4	1
6	2
8	3

31.

x	y
23	24
55	56
66	67

32.

x	y
2	2.6
3	3.9
4	5.2

Write an equation for a direct variation with a graph that passes through each point.

33. $(1, 2)$ **34.** $(-3, -7)$ **35.** $(2, -9)$ **36.** $(-0.1, 50)$

37. $(-5, -3)$ **38.** $(9, -1)$ **39.** $(7, 2)$ **40.** $(-3, 14)$

In Exercises 41–45, y varies directly with x.

41. If $y = 7$ when $x = 3$, find x when $y = 21$.

42. If $y = 25$ when $x = 15$, find x when $y = 10$.

43. If $y = 30$ when $x = -3$, find y when $x = -9$.

44. If $y = -20$ when $x = 2$, find y when $x = 14$.

45. If $y = 0.9$ when $x = 4.8$, find y when $x = 6.4$.

Determine whether a line with the given slope through the given point represents a direct variation. Explain.

46. $m = -1.7, (9, -9)$ **47.** $m = -\frac{5}{6}, \left(15, -12\frac{1}{2}\right)$ **48.** $m = \frac{7}{2}, \left(6\frac{1}{2}, 22\frac{3}{4}\right)$

Open-Ended **In Exercises 49–51, choose a value of k within the given range. Then write and graph a direct variation using your value for k.**

49. $0 < k < 1$ **50.** $3 < k < 4.5$ **51.** $-1 < k < -\frac{1}{2}$

It takes more effort for an engine to propel a car with underinflated tires. Cars with properly inflated tires get better gas mileage.

52. Gas Mileage Suppose you drive a car 392 mi on one tank of gas. The tank holds 14 gallons. The number of miles traveled varies directly with the number of gallons of gas you use.

a. Write an equation that relates miles traveled to gallons of gas used.

b. You only have enough money to buy 3.7 gallons of gas. How far can you drive before refueling?

c. Last year you drove 11,700 mi. About how many gallons of gas did you use?

d. Suppose the price of gas averaged $1.57 per gallon last year. Find the cost per mile.

53. Writing Suppose you use the origin to test whether a linear equation is a direct variation. Does this method work? Support your answer with an example.

54. Error Analysis Find the error in the following computation: If y varies directly with x^2, and $y = 2$ when $x = 4$, then $y = 3$ when $x = 9$.

C Challenge

In Exercises 55–58, y varies directly with x.

55. If x is doubled, what happens to y?

56. If x is halved, what happens to y?

57. If x is divided by 7, what happens to y?

58. If x is multiplied by 10, what happens to y?

59. If z varies directly with the product of x and y ($z = kxy$), then z is said to vary jointly with x and y.

a. Geometry The area of a triangle varies jointly with its base and height. What is the constant of variation?

b. Suppose q varies jointly with v and s, and $q = 24$ when $v = 2$ and $s = 3$. Find q when $v = 4$ and $s = 2$.

c. Critical Thinking Suppose z varies jointly with x and y, and x varies directly with w. Show that z varies jointly with w and y.

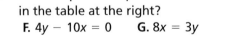

Standardized Test Prep

Multiple Choice

60. Which equation does NOT represent a direct variation?

A. $y - 3x = 0$ B. $y + 2 = \frac{1}{2}x$ C. $\frac{y}{x} = \frac{2}{3}$ D. $y = \frac{x}{17}$

61. Suppose y varies directly with x. If x is 30 when y is 10, what is x when y is 9?

F. 3 G. 27 H. 29 I. $\frac{300}{9}$

62. Suppose y varies directly with x. If x is -7 when y is 3, what is x when y is -5?

A. $-11\frac{2}{3}$ B. $-4\frac{1}{5}$ C. $4\frac{1}{5}$ D. $11\frac{2}{3}$

63. Which equation represents the direct variation in the table at the right?

x	3	4	9
y	8.1	10.8	24.3

F. $4y - 10x = 0$ G. $8x = 3y$
H. $y + 8.1x = 0$ I. $10y = 27x$

Take It to the NET
Online lesson quiz at www.PHSchool.com
Web Code: aga-0203

Short Response

64. Do the values in the table below represent a direct variation? Explain.

x	4	5	7
y	13.1	16.3	22.6

Mixed Review

Lesson 2-2 **Use the given information to graph each line.**

65. slope $= -\frac{3}{5}$, through $(-2, 5)$

66. slope $= -\frac{3}{2}$, through $(1, -4)$

67. slope $= -4$, through $(0, -1)$

68. slope $= -2, (-1, 6)$

Lesson 2-1 **Graph each relation. Find the domain and range.**

69. $\{(0, 1), (1, -3), (-2, -3), (3, -3)\}$

70. $\{(4, 0), (7, 0), (4, -1), (7, -1)\}$

71. $\{(1, -2), (2, -1), (4, 1), (5, 2)\}$

72. $\{(1, 7), (2, 8), (3, 9), (4, 10)\}$

Previous Course **73. Aviation** In 1995, an aircraft set the around-the-world record time for a passenger jet at 31 h, 27 min, 49 s. Six refueling stops took a total of 8 h, 48 min, 8 s. What percent of the time was spent in the air?

Checkpoint Quiz 1 — Lessons 2-1 through 2-3

Instant self-check quiz online and on CD-ROM

Find the *x*- and *y*-intercepts of each line.

1. $x - 3y = 9$ **2.** $y = 7x + 5$ **3.** $y = 6x$ **4.** $-4x + y = 10$

Write the equation of each line in slope-intercept form.

5. $2x - y = 9$ **6.** $4x = 2 + y$ **7.** $5y = -3x - 10$ **8.** $4x + 6y = 12$

9. a. A group of friends is going to the movies. Each ticket costs $7.00. Write an equation to model the total cost of the group's tickets.

b. Graph the equation. Explain what the *x*- and *y*-intercepts represent.

c. Writing Could the domain include fractions? Explain.

10. Which line is perpendicular to $3x + 2y = 6$?

A. $4x - 6y = 3$ **B.** $y = -\frac{3}{2}x + 4$ **C.** $2x + 3y = 12$ **D.** $y = \frac{3}{2}x + 1$

Algebra at Work

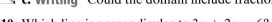

Miniaturist

People who make a career out of designing and creating miniature models of an actual object are called miniaturists. They apply direct variations to reproduce realistic models of items such as houses, stores, or scenes. Common scales used to create miniatures are the following.

- the one-inch scale (1 in. : 1 ft or 1 : 12)
- the half-inch scale (0.5 in. : 1 ft or 1 : 24)
- the quarter-inch scale (0.25 in. : 1 ft or 1 : 48)

Take It to the NET For more information about careers in model design, go to **www.PHSchool.com.**
Web Code: agb-2031

2-4 Using Linear Models

North Carolina Objectives

2.04 Create and use best-fit mathematical models of linear functions to solve problems involving sets of data. b) Check the model for goodness-of-fit and use it to draw conclusions or make predictions.

Lesson Preview

What You'll Learn

OBJECTIVE 1 To write linear equations that model real-world data

OBJECTIVE 2 To make predictions from linear models

. . . And Why

To model a burning candle, as in Example 2

Check Skills You'll Need

(For help, go to Lessons 2-1 and 2-2.)

Find the change in *x* and the change in *y* between each pair of points.

1. $(-0.2, 9)$ and $(3.4, 7.3)$ **2.** $(10, 17)$ and $(11.5, 13.5)$ **3.** $\left(0, \frac{3}{10}\right)$ and $\left(-1, \frac{2}{5}\right)$

Evaluate each function for the given values.

4. $f(x) = \frac{4}{3}x - 2$ for $x = -3, 0, \frac{1}{2}$ **5.** $g(x) = 3(2 - x)$ for $x = 0, \frac{1}{6}, 1$

New Vocabulary • scatter plot • trend line

Interactive lesson includes instant self-check, tutorials, and activities.

OBJECTIVE 1

Modeling Real-World Data

You can write linear equations to model real-world problems.

1 EXAMPLE Real-World Connection

Transportation Jacksonville, Florida has an elevation of 12 ft above sea level. A hot-air balloon taking off from Jacksonville rises 50 ft/min. Write an equation to model the balloon's elevation as a function of time. Graph the equation. Interpret the intercept at which the graph intersects the vertical axis.

Real-World Connection

Careers Hot-air balloonists use mathematics to plot courses, calculate wind speed, and determine their air speed.

Relate balloon's elevation = rate · time + starting elevation

Define Let h = the balloon's elevation.

Let t = time (in minutes) since the hot-air balloon lifted off.

Write $h = 50 \cdot t + 12$

An equation that models the balloon's elevation is $h = 50t + 12$.

The h-intercept is $(0, 12)$.

The t-coordinate, 0, represents the time at the start of the trip.

The h-coordinate, 12, represents the elevation of the balloon at the start of the trip.

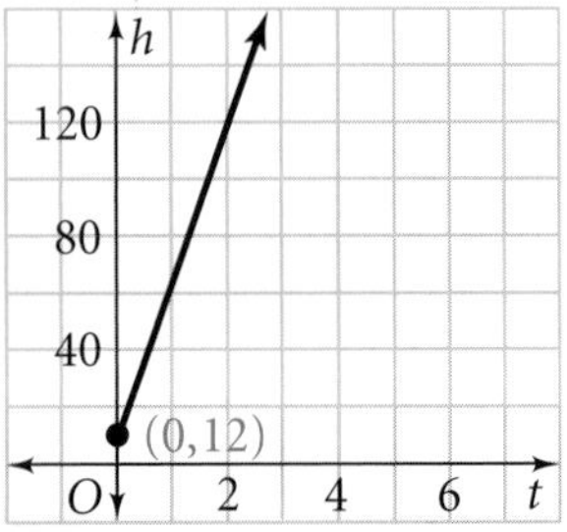

Check Understanding

1 Suppose a balloon begins descending at a rate of 20 ft/min from an elevation of 1350 ft.

a. Write an equation to model the balloon's elevation as a function of time. What is true about the slope of this line?

b. Graph the equation. Interpret the h-intercept.

You can use two data points from a linear relationship to write a model.

2 EXAMPLE Real-World Connection

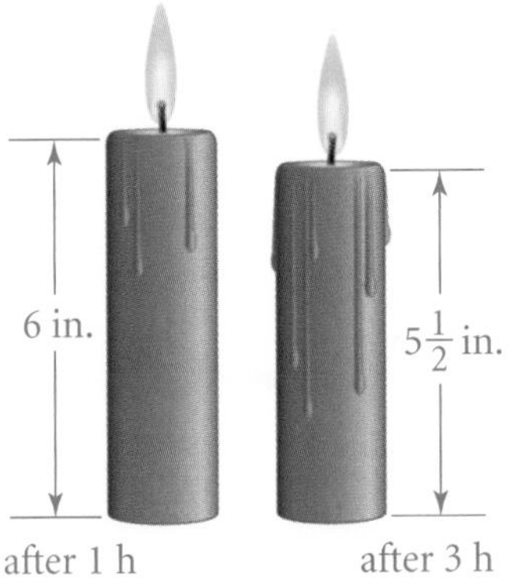

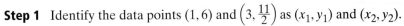

Science A candle is 6 in. tall after burning for 1 h. After 3 h, it is $5\frac{1}{2}$ in. tall. Write a linear equation to model the height y of the candle after burning x hours.

Step 1 Identify the data points $(1, 6)$ and $\left(3, \frac{11}{2}\right)$ as (x_1, y_1) and (x_2, y_2).

Step 2 Find the slope of the line.

$m = \frac{y_2 - y_1}{x_2 - x_1}$ **Use the slope formula.**

$m = \frac{\frac{11}{2} - 6}{3 - 1}$ **Substitute.**

$m = \frac{-\frac{1}{2}}{2}$ **Simplify the numerator and denominator.**

$m = -\frac{1}{4}$ **Simplify.**

Step 3 Use one of the points and the point-slope form to write an equation for the line.

$y - y_1 = m(x - x_1)$ **Use point-slope form.**

$y - 6 = -\frac{1}{4}(x - 1)$ **Substitute.**

$y = -\frac{1}{4}x + 6\frac{1}{4}$ **Solve for *y*.**

An equation of the line that models the height of the candle is $y = -\frac{1}{4}x + 6\frac{1}{4}$.

Check Understanding 2 **a. Reasoning** What does the slope $-\frac{1}{4}$ represent?

b. What does the y-intercept $6\frac{1}{4}$ represent?

c. Another candle is 7 in. tall after burning for 1 h and 5 in. tall after burning for 2 h. Write a linear equation to model the height of the candle.

OBJECTIVE 2 Predicting With Linear Models

You can use a linear model to make predictions.

3 EXAMPLE Using a Linear Model

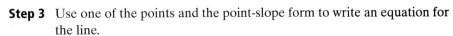

Use the equation from Example 2. When will the candle be 4 in. tall?

$y = -\frac{1}{4}x + 6\frac{1}{4}$ **Write the equation.**

$4 = -\frac{1}{4}x + 6\frac{1}{4}$ **Substitute 4 for *y*.**

$-4\left(4 - 6\frac{1}{4}\right) = x$ **Solve for *x*.**

$9 = x$ **Simplify.**

The candle will be 4 in. tall after burning for 9 h.

Check Understanding 3 **a.** How tall will the candle be after burning for 11 h?

b. What was the original height of the candle?

c. When will the candle burn out?

A **scatter plot** is a graph that relates two different sets of data by plotting the data as ordered pairs. You can use a scatter plot to determine a relationship between the data sets.

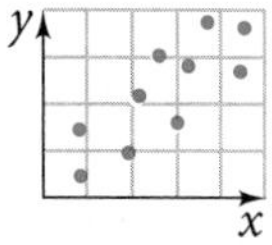

Weak, positive correlation

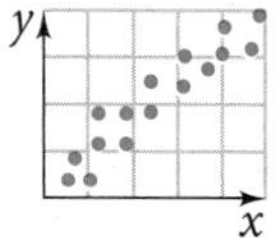

Strong, positive correlation

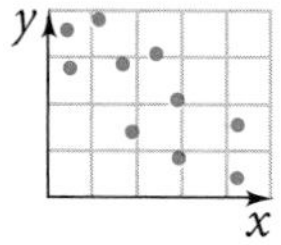

Weak, negative correlation

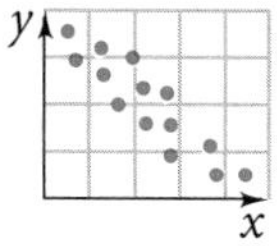

Strong, negative correlation

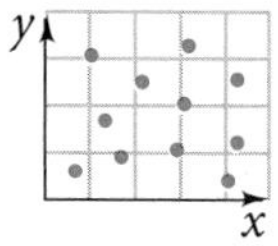

No correlation

A **trend line** is a line that approximates the relationship between the data sets of a scatter plot. You can use a trend line to make predictions.

4 EXAMPLE Real-World Connection

Automobiles A woman is considering buying the 1993 car shown in the photo. She researches prices for various years of the same model and records the data in a table.

Model Year	1994	1995	1996	1997	1998
Prices	\$5784	\$6810	\$8237	\$9660	\$10,948
	\$5435	\$6207	\$7751	\$9127	\$10,455

a. Let x represent the model year. (Use 4 for 1994, 5 for 1995, and so forth.) Let y be the price of the car. Draw a scatter plot. Decide whether a linear model is reasonable.

A linear model seems reasonable, since the points fall close to a line.

Used Car Prices

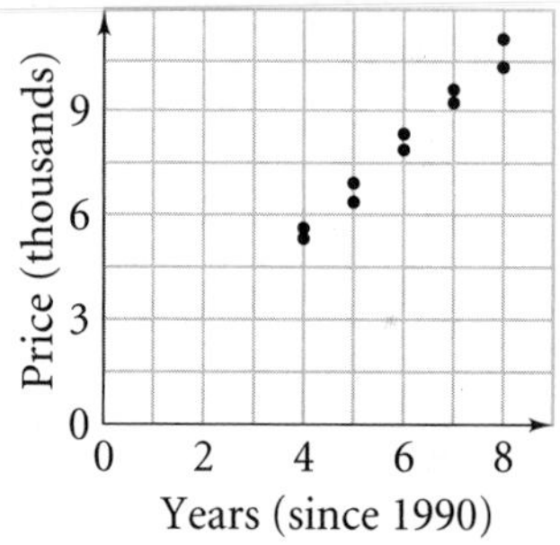

b. Draw a trend line. Write the equation of the line. Determine whether the asking price is reasonable.

Draw a line that has about the same number of data points above and below it. Use the slope and the y-intercept to find the equation of the line. Plot the data point for the asking price.

The equation of the trend line in the graph is $y = 1.3x + 0.2$. A fair price would be the value of y for $x = 3$, or about \$4100.

The asking price of \$4200 is reasonable.

Used Car Prices

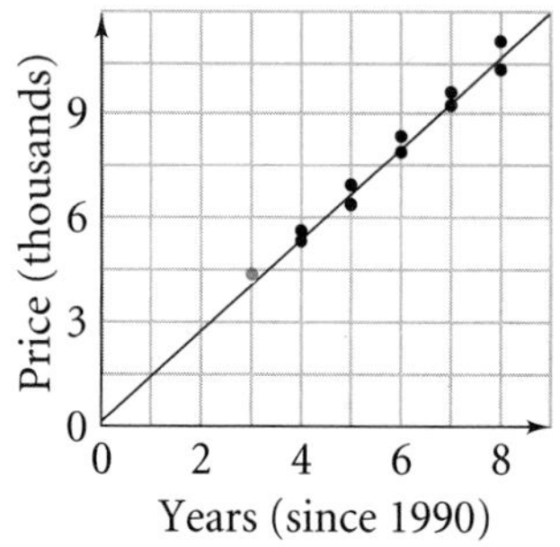

Check Understanding 4 Graph each set of data. Decide whether a linear model is reasonable. If so, draw a trend line and write its equation.

a. $\{(-7.5, 19.75), (-2, 9), (0, 6.5), (1.5, 3), (4, -1.5)\}$

b. $\{(0, -3), (0.5, -2.5), (1, -1), (3.5, 21.5), (6, 69), (7, 35)\}$

EXERCISES

For more practice, see *Extra Practice*.

Practice and Problem Solving

A Practice by Example

Example 1 (page 78)

1. A car enters an interstate highway 15 mi north of a city. The car travels due north at an average speed of 62.5 mi/h. Write an equation to model the car's distance d from the city after traveling for h hours. Graph the equation.

2. A pump removes 1000 gal of water from a pool at a constant rate of 50 gal/min.
a. Write an equation to find the amount of water y in the pool after t minutes.
b. Graph the equation and interpret the t- and y-intercepts.

3. A tree 5 ft tall grows an average of 8 in. each year. Write and graph an equation to model the tree's height h after x years.

Examples 2 and 3 (page 79)

For each situation, find a linear model and use it to make a prediction.

4. There are 2 leaves along 3 in. of an ivy vine. There are 14 leaves along 15 in. of the same vine. How many leaves are there along 6 in. of the vine?

5. An empty 5-gal water jug weighs 0.75 lb. With 3 c of water inside, the jug weighs 2.25 lb. Predict the weight of the jug with 5 c of water inside.

6. There are 55 blades of grass in 1 in.^{2} of lawn. There are 230 blades of grass in 4 in.^{2} of the same lawn. How many blades of grass are in 3 in.^{2} of lawn?

7. A 2-mi cab ride costs \$5.25. A 5-mi cab ride costs \$10.50. How much does a 3.8-mi cab ride cost?

Example 4 (page 80)

Graph each set of data. Decide whether a linear model is reasonable. If so, draw a trend line and write its equation.

8. $\{(0, 11), (2, 8), (3, 7), (7, 2), (8, 0)\}$

9. $\{(1.2, 1), (2.5, 6), (2.5, 7.5), (4.1, 11), (7.9, 19)\}$

10. $\left\{\left(-10, 3\frac{1}{2}\right), \left(-5\frac{1}{2}, 1\frac{1}{2}\right), \left(-\frac{1}{10}, -4\right), \left(3\frac{1}{2}, -7\frac{1}{2}\right), (12, -12)\right\}$

11. $\{(-15, 8), (-8, -7), (-3, 0), (0, 5), (7, -3)\}$

B Apply Your Skills

12. Measurement The numbering system used in Europe for shoe sizes is different from the system used in the United States. Use the data in the table at the right to create a model for converting between systems.
a. Graph the data. Is a linear model reasonable?
b. Find the European equivalent of U.S. size 8.
c. Writing Explain how to use a model to convert European sizes to U.S. sizes.

Women's Shoe Sizes

U.S. Size	European Size
1	31
3	34
5	36
7	39
9	41
11	44

SOURCE: *Sizes*

13. Nutrition The table at the left shows the average daily energy requirements for male children and adolescents.
a. Graph the data. Model the data with a linear equation.
b. Estimate the daily energy requirements for a male 16 years old.
c. Reasoning Do you think your model also applies to adult males? Explain.

Daily Energy Requirements for Males

Age (years)	Energy Needed (Calories)
1	1100
2	1300
5	1800
8	2200
11	2500
14	2800
17	3000

SOURCE: *Go Figure: The Numbers You Need for Everyday Life*

14. Sales Suppose you manufacture and sell tarps. The table displays your current sizes and prices.

Tarps

Size	Price	Size	Price
5 × 7 ft	\$1.39	18 × 20 ft	\$14.39
6 × 8 ft	\$1.99	15 × 30 ft	\$17.99
8 × 10 ft	\$3.19	20 × 30 ft	\$23.99
10 × 12 ft	\$4.79	20 × 40 ft	\$31.99
12 × 16 ft	\$7.69	25 × 45 ft	\$44.99
10 × 20 ft	\$7.99	30 × 50 ft	\$59.99
16 × 20 ft	\$12.79	30 × 60 ft	\$71.99

a. Draw a scatter plot showing the relationship between a tarp's area and its cost. Use area as the independent variable.
b. Use your scatter plot to develop a model relating the area of a tarp to its cost.
c. How good a model do you feel you have? Explain.
d. Is \$7.00 a reasonable price for a tarp that measures 10 ft by 15 ft? Explain.
e. Using your model and the prices in the table, determine which tarp size varies the most from your predicted price. How great is the discrepancy between your model and the actual price?

Write an equation for each line.

15. through $(2, 2)$, y-intercept 10

16. x-intercept -2, y-intercept -6

17. y-intercept $-\frac{5}{2}$, x-intercept $-\frac{1}{3}$

18. through $(3.5, -2.3)$, x-intercept 5.1

19. Entertainment Refer to the diagram below. Suppose you are trying to decide whether to subscribe to cable service or just rent videos.

a. Write an equation to model the cost y of the cable service for 1 month.
b. Write a second equation to model the cost y of renting x movies from the video store. What is the slope? What is the y-intercept?
c. Open-Ended Suppose you currently rent 8 to 12 movies each month. Graph the two equations from parts (a) and (b). Interpret the graph. Use your interpretation to choose between the alternatives. Explain your reasoning.

20. Nutrition The table below shows the relationship between Calories and fat in various fast-food hamburgers.

Hamburger	A	B	C	D	E	F	G	H	I
Calories	720	530	510	500	305	410	440	320	598
Fat (g)	46	30	27	26	13	20	25	13	26

SOURCE: *The Fat Counter*

a. Develop a model for the relationship between Calories and fat.
b. How much fat would you expect a 330–Calorie hamburger to have?
c. Error Analysis A student reports these estimates: 10 g of fat for a 200-Calorie hamburger and 36 g of fat for a 660-Calorie hamburger. Which estimate is *not* reasonable? Explain.

21. **Data Analysis** Is the population of a state related to the number of licensed drivers in that state? The table shows population and licensed-driver statistics from a recent year.

a. Which variable should be the independent variable?

b. Draw a scatter plot.

c. Draw a trend line.

d. The population of Oregon was approximately 3 million that year. About how many licensed drivers lived in Oregon that year?

e. **Writing** Is the correlation between population and number of licensed drivers strong or weak? Explain.

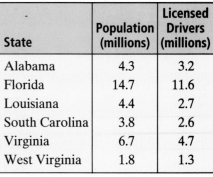

State	Population (millions)	Licensed Drivers (millions)
Alabama	4.3	3.2
Florida	14.7	11.6
Louisiana	4.4	2.7
South Carolina	3.8	2.6
Virginia	6.7	4.7
West Virginia	1.8	1.3

SOURCE: U.S. Census Bureau, National Highway Administration. Go to **www.PHSchool.com** for a data update.
Web Code: agg-2041

A linear model for each situation passes through the origin. Find each missing value. Round your answer to the nearest tenth.

22. 47.5 min to jog 5 mi, ■ min to jog 11 mi

23. 8.5 gal of gas to drive 243.1 mi, 3 gal of gas to drive ■ mi

24. 336 words keyboarded in 3.5 min, 624 words keyboarded in ■ min

25. \$9.45 to buy 7 lb of apples, \$17.55 to buy ■ lb

26. 567 bricks in a wall 9 ft long, ■ bricks in a wall 14 ft long

C Challenge

27. **Social Studies** The table at the right shows per capita revenues and expenditures for selected states from a recent year.

a. Show the data on a scatter plot. Draw a trend line.

b. If a state collected revenue of \$2000 per capita in taxes, how much would you expect it to spend per capita?

c. Virginia spent \$2654 per capita during that year. According to your model, how much did it collect in taxes per capita?

d. In that same year, Alaska collected \$2503 per capita in taxes and spent \$9274 per capita. Does this information follow the trend? Explain.

State	Per Capita Revenue (\$)	Per Capita Expenditure (\$)
Delaware	2329	4480
Florida	1368	2532
Hawaii	2601	5023
Indiana	1444	2631
Kentucky	1671	3049
Massachusetts	2045	4095
North Carolina	1623	2898
Oklahoma	1399	2807
Tennessee	1163	2599

SOURCE: U.S. Census Bureau. Go to **www.PHSchool.com** for a data update.
Web Code: agg-2041

Reading Math

Per capita means "for each person". Capita is a form of the Latin word for head.

28. a. Use the first and last data points to find a linear model for the data in the table at the right.

x	−5	−2	−1	1	3	6
y	22	15	12	8	7	5

b. Use the middle two data points to find a linear model for the data.

c. Which model better represents the data? Can you find a third model that you think best represents the data? Explain.

29. **Geometry** Write the equation of the perpendicular bisector of the segment with endpoints $(-3, 5)$ and $(7, 1)$.

Standardized Test Prep

Gridded Response

Each set of three points is collinear. Find each missing x- or y-value. Enter each answer to the nearest hundredth.

30. $(2, 3.37)$, $(10, 23.37)$, $(6, y)$

31. $(6, 10.2)$, $(1.5, 3.45)$, $(x, 2.85)$

32. $(0.5, 1)$, $(2.2, y)$, $(1.6, 4.3)$

33. $(x, 0.8)$, $(15, -0.4)$, $(-4, 2.9)$

Reading Comprehension

Use the newspaper article below for Exercises 34 and 35.

What's Harming Japan's Oysters?

A 1994 red tide killed off thousands of *akoya* oysters in Japan's Ago Bay. For years following the red tide, oysters continued to die, confounding pearl farmers and scientists alike. Scientists have suggested many possible causes, from a virus to pollutants.

Whatever the reason, in 1996, Japanese pearl farmers harvested only 56.6 tons of pearls from *akoya* oysters, down from 72.6 tons in 1993.

Source: *NOVA*, "The Perfect Pearl"

Take It to the NET
Online lesson quiz at www.PHSchool.com
Web Code: aga-0204

34. a. Write a linear model for the tons of pearls harvested from *akoya* oysters.
b. Use your model to estimate the number of tons of pearls harvested in 2000.

35. a. Count the number of words in one line of the article. Then count the number of words in four lines. Write a linear model.
b. Use your linear model to estimate the number of words in the entire article.

Mixed Review

Lesson 2-3

Find each constant of variation. Then find the value of y when $x = -5$.

36. $y = 27$ when $x = -10$

37. $y = -36$ when $x = 12$

38. $y = -\frac{2}{5}$ when $x = \frac{1}{3}$

39. $y = -\frac{21}{4}$ when $x = -\frac{5}{8}$

Lesson 2-1

Find the range of each function when the domain is $\{-3, -1, 0, 1.5, 4\}$.

40. $f(x) = 2x - 1$

41. $y = -(x - 5)$

42. $y = x^2 + 3$

43. $g(x) = \frac{x-4}{2}$

44. $y = 100x + 1$

45. $y = 9 - 2x$

Previous Course

46. Track Svetlana Masterkova of Russia set a record for running the mile, in 4 minutes 12.56 seconds.
a. Find Svetlana's rate in feet per second. How far did she run in 100 seconds?
b. Write an equation that relates the distance she ran to time. Use feet per second as the unit.
c. Calculate Svetlana's speed in miles per hour.

Technology

Finding a Line of Best Fit

FOR USE WITH LESSON 2-4

You can use your graphing calculator to display data sets, draw scatter plots, and draw a line to fit the data. The line is the linear regression line, or line of best fit. The LinReg feature on your calculator fits data to the model $y = ax + b$.

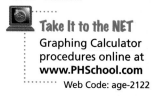

Take It to the NET
Graphing Calculator procedures online at **www.PHSchool.com**
Web Code: age-2122

EXAMPLE Using the LinReg Feature

The table shows the number of bicycles produced in the United States from 1993 to 1996. Enter the given data on your calculator. Generate a scatter plot of the data and a line of best fit. Then sketch the graph.

Year	Number of Bicycles Produced (millions)
1993	9.9
1994	9.7
1995	8.8
1996	8.0

SOURCE: Bicycle Manufacturers Association of America, Inc.

Step 1 Clear any existing lists or stored equations.

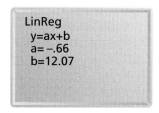

L1	L2	L3
3	9.9	
4	9.7	
5	8.8	
6	8.0	
------	------	

L2(5)=

LinReg
y=ax+b
a=–.66
b=12.07

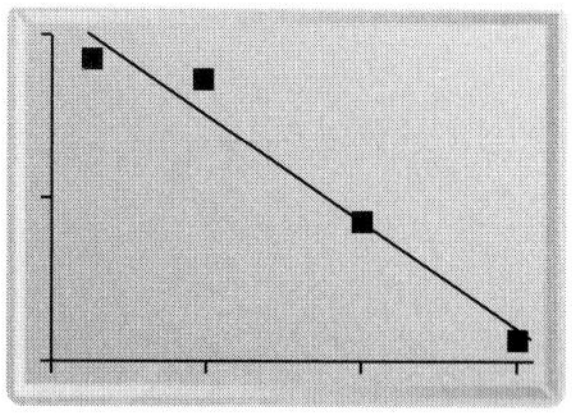

Step 2 Enter data. Press STAT ENTER. Enter the x-values in L_1 and the y-values in L_2. Let 1990 correspond to $x = 0$.

Step 3 Find the line of best fit. Press STAT ▶ 4 ENTER to select LinReg (ax+b). Press Y= VARS 5 ▶ ▶ ENTER to enter the regression equation to Y1.

Step 4 Draw the graph. Use the STAT PLOT feature and press 1 ENTER to turn on Plot 1.

Use the ▼ key to move down the rows to select a scatter plot using L1 and L2. Then press ZOOM 9 to get the scatter plot and the line of best fit.

EXERCISES

Find a line of best fit for each set of data. Round to the nearest hundredth.

1. $\{(-5, 6.3), (-4, 5.6), (-3, 4.8), (-2, 3.1), (-1, 2.5), (0, 1.0), (1, -1.4)\}$

2.

Year	1992	1993	1994	1995	1996	1997
National Health Expenditures (billions of dollars)	836.5	898.5	947.7	993.7	1042.5	1092.4

3.

State	AL	FL	IN	KY	LA	NC	OK	SC	TN	VA
Population (millions)	4.0	12.9	5.5	3.7	4.2	6.6	3.1	3.5	4.9	6.2
Representatives	7	23	10	6	7	12	6	6	9	11

4. Writing Describe the advantages of using a graphing calculator to draw a line of best fit.

2-5 Absolute Value Functions and Graphs

North Carolina Objectives

2.08 Use equations and inequalities with absolute value to model and solve problems; justify results. a) Solve using tables, graphs, and algebraic properties.

Lesson Preview

What You'll Learn

OBJECTIVE 1 To graph absolute value functions

. . . And Why

To model distance, as in Example 4

Check Skills You'll Need

(For help, go to Lesson 2-2 and Skills Handbook page 851.)

Graph each equation for the given domain and range.

1. $y = x$ for real numbers x and $y \geq 0$

2. $y = 2x - 4$ for real numbers x and $y \geq 0$

3. $y = -x + 6$ for real numbers x and $y \leq 3$

New Vocabulary • absolute value function • vertex

Interactive lesson includes instant self-check, tutorials, and activities.

OBJECTIVE

1 Graphing Absolute Value Functions

A function of the form $f(x) = |mx + b| + c$, where $m \neq 0$, is an **absolute value function.** An equation of the form $y = |mx + b| + c$ is an absolute value equation in two variables. Graphs of absolute value equations in two variables look like angles.

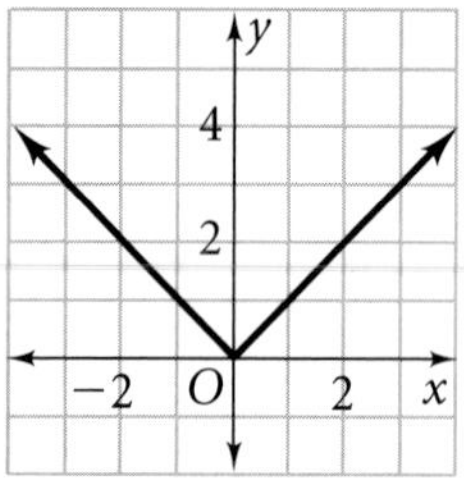

$y = |x|$

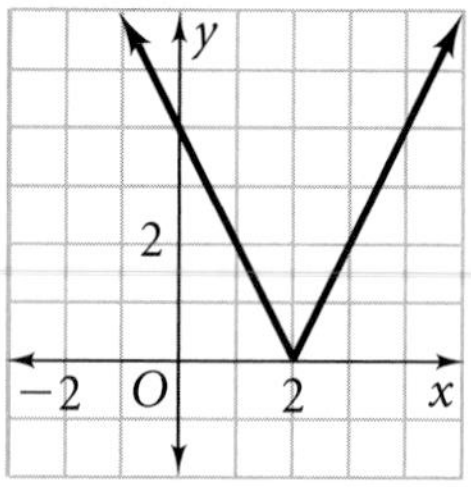

$y = |2x - 4|$

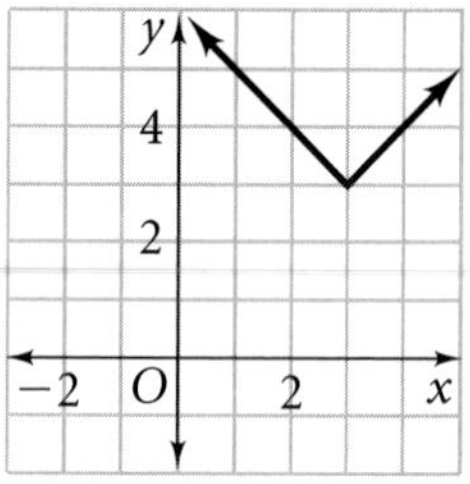

$y = |x - 3| + 3$

Reading Math

Vertex means "turning point."

The **vertex** of a function is a point where the function reaches a maximum or minimum. In general, the vertex of $y = |mx + b| + c$ is located at $\left(-\frac{b}{m}, c\right)$. In the middle graph above, the x-coordinate of the vertex is $-\left(\frac{-4}{2}\right) = 2$.

Note that the graph of $y = -|x|$ is a reflection over the x-axis of the graph of $y = |x|$.

1 EXAMPLE Graphing an Absolute Value Function

Graph $y = |3x + 12|$.

Evaluate the equation for several values of x, beginning with $x = -\frac{b}{m} = -\frac{12}{3} = -4$.

Make a table of values.

x	−6	−4	−3	−2
y	6	0	3	6

Graph the function.

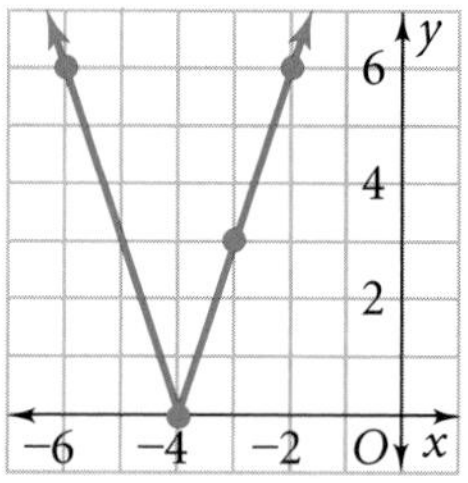

Check Understanding 1 Graph each equation.

a. $y = |2x - 5|$ **b.** $y = -|x + 1| - 2$

You can use a graphing calculator to graph an absolute value equation.

Graphing Calculator Hint

For a calculator screen that shows x- and y-intervals of equal width, press ZOOM, and then select ZSquare.

2 EXAMPLE Using a Graphing Calculator

Graph $y = -|3x + 4| + 6$ on a graphing calculator.

Use the absolute value key. Graph the equation $Y_1 = -\text{abs}(3X+4)+6$.

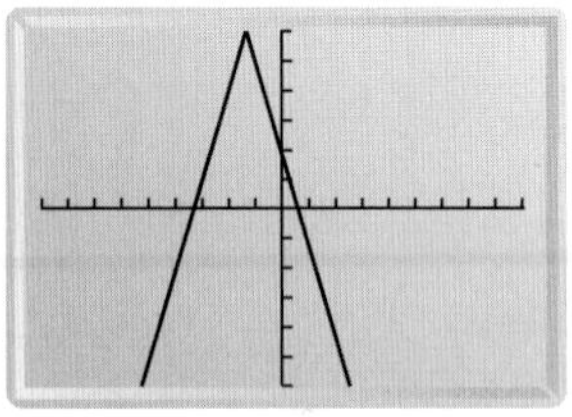

Check Understanding 2 Graph each equation on a graphing calculator. Then sketch the graph.

a. $y = -|-x| + 5$ **b.** $y = 3 - \left|\frac{x}{2}\right|$

You can also graph an absolute value equation by first writing it as two linear equations.

3 EXAMPLE Writing Two Linear Equations

Graph $y = |x - 3| + 5$.

Step 1 Isolate the absolute value.

$$y = |x - 3| + 5$$
$$y - 5 = |x - 3|$$

Need Help?

If $x \geq 0$, then $|x| = x$.
If $x < 0$, then $|x| = -x$.

Step 2 Use the definition of absolute value. Write one equation for $x - 3 \geq 0$ and a second equation for $x - 3 < 0$.

when $x - 3 \geq 0$	**when $x - 3 < 0$**
$y - 5 = x - 3$	$y - 5 = -(x - 3)$
$y = x + 2$	$y = -x + 8$

Step 3 Graph each equation for the appropriate domain.

When $x - 3 \geq 0$, or $x \geq 3$, $y = x + 2$.

When $x - 3 < 0$, or $x < 3$, $y = -x + 8$.

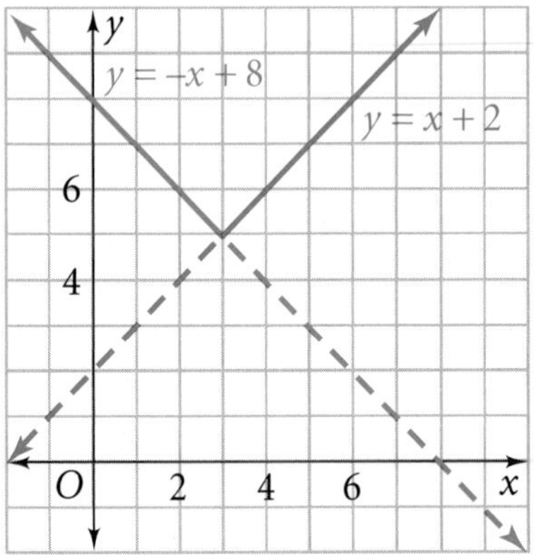

Check Understanding 3 Graph each equation by writing two equations.

a. $y = \left|\frac{3}{2}x + 4\right| - 3$ **b.** $y = 2 - |x + 1|$

You can use absolute value functions to model time-and-distance problems. You can consider the time before you arrive at a destination to be negative.

4 EXAMPLE **Real-World Connection**

Travel Suppose you pass the Betsy Ross House halfway along your trip to school each morning. You walk at a rate of one city block per minute. Sketch a graph of your trip to school based on your distance and time from the Besty Ross House.

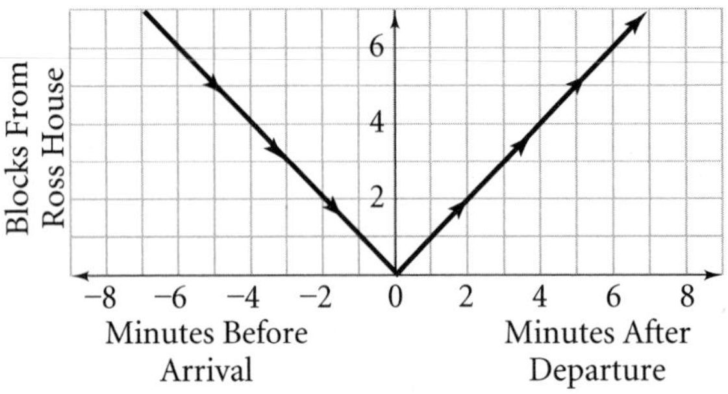

The equation $d = |t|$ models your distance from the Betsy Ross House.

Real-World Connection

According to legend, Betsy Ross made the first flag of the United States in her house in Philadelphia, Pennsylvania.

Check Understanding 4 **a.** **Critical Thinking** Suppose you ride your bicycle to school at a rate of three city blocks per minute. How would the graph of your trip to school change?

b. Sketch a new graph.

EXERCISES

For more practice, see *Extra Practice.*

Practice and Problem Solving

A Practice by Example

Example 1 (page 86)

Make a table of values for each equation. Then graph the equation.

1. $y = |4x|$ **2.** $y = |4x| - 1$ **3.** $y = |4x - 1|$

4. $y = |-3x|$ **5.** $y = |-3x| + 2$ **6.** $y = |-3x + 2|$

7. $y = -|2x|$ **8.** $y = -|2x| + 5$ **9.** $y = -|2x + 5|$

Example 2 (page 87)

Graph each equation on a graphing calculator. Then sketch the graph.

10. $y = |x + 2| - 4$ **11.** $y = 4 - |x + 2|$ **12.** $y = 4|x + 2|$

13. $y = \frac{1}{3}|3 - 3x|$ **14.** $y = 3\left|\frac{1}{3} - \frac{1}{3}x\right|$ **15.** $y = \frac{3}{2}|x| - \frac{5}{2}$

16. $y = |x| + \frac{1}{2}|x|$ **17.** $y = \frac{1}{2}|x| - |x|$ **18.** $y = \frac{1}{2}\left|x - \frac{1}{2}\right|$

Example 3 (page 87)

Graph each equation by writing two linear equations.

19. $y = |x + 6|$ **20.** $y = |3x + 6|$ **21.** $y = |3x - 6|$

22. $y = -|x - 5|$ **23.** $y = |2x + 1|$ **24.** $y = \frac{3}{2}|3x - 1|$

25. $y = |x - 2| - 6$ **26.** $y = \left|\frac{1}{2}x - 4\right| + 4$ **27.** $y = \frac{1}{2}\left|\frac{1}{2}x + 2\right| - 2$

Example 4 (page 88)

28. **Manufacturing** The conveyor belt at a factory operates continuously 24 hours a day, carrying vitamin bottles and moving two feet each minute. Sketch a graph showing the distance in feet from the filling arm of one bottle on the conveyor belt before and after it is filled. Use the x-axis for time before and after the bottle is filled and the y-axis for distance from the filling arm.

B Apply Your Skills

Match each equation with its graph. Each interval is 1 unit.

29. $y = |3x| - 4$ **30.** $y = |3x - 4|$ **31.** $y = 3|x - 4|$ **32.** $y = |3x + 12|$

A.

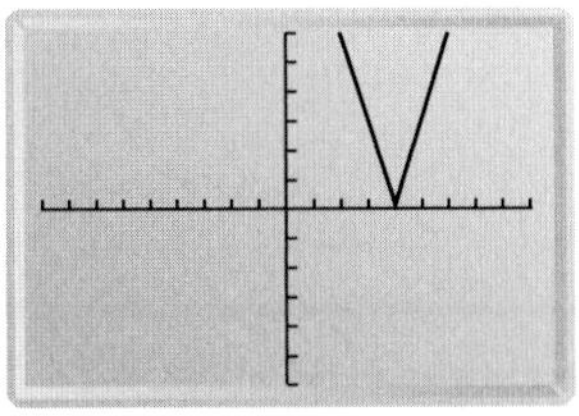

B.

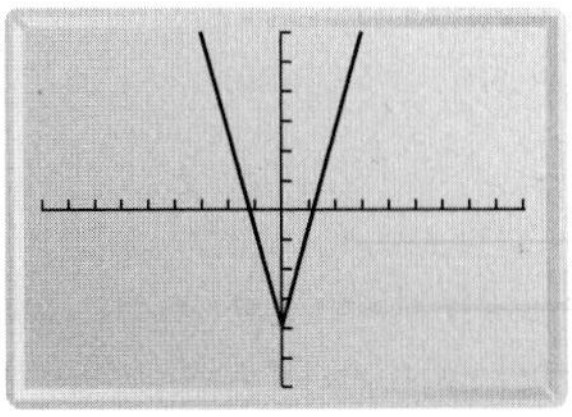

C.

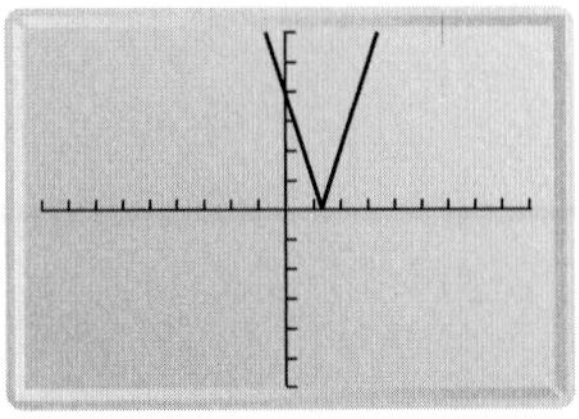

D.

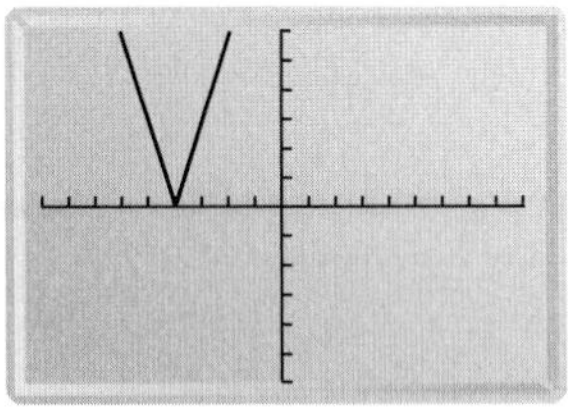

Need Help?
Before graphing, rewrite each equation as two equations.

Graph each absolute value equation.

33. $y = |4x + 2|$ **34.** $y = |-3x + 5|$ **35.** $y = |4 - 2x|$

36. $y = \left|-\frac{1}{4}x - 1\right|$ **37.** $y = \left|\frac{5}{2}x - 2\right|$ **38.** $y = \left|\frac{3}{2}x + 2\right|$

39. $y = |3x - 6| + 1$ **40.** $y = -|x - 3|$ **41.** $y = |2x + 6|$

42. $y = 2|x + 2| - 3$ **43.** $y = 6 - |3x|$ **44.** $y = 6 - |3x + 1|$

45. $y = -|-2x - 1| + 1$ **46.** $y = 2|x - 3|$ **47.** $y = -\frac{3}{2}\left|\frac{1}{2}x\right|$

48. $2y = \frac{1}{2}|x + 2|$ **49.** $\frac{1}{3}y - 3 = -|x + 2|$ **50.** $-3y = |3x - 6|$

51. Travel The graph at the right models a car traveling at a constant speed.

a. Describe the relation shown in the graph.

b. Which equation best represents the relation?

A. $y = |60x|$
B. $y = |x + 60|$
C. $y = |60 - x|$
D. $y = |x| + 60$

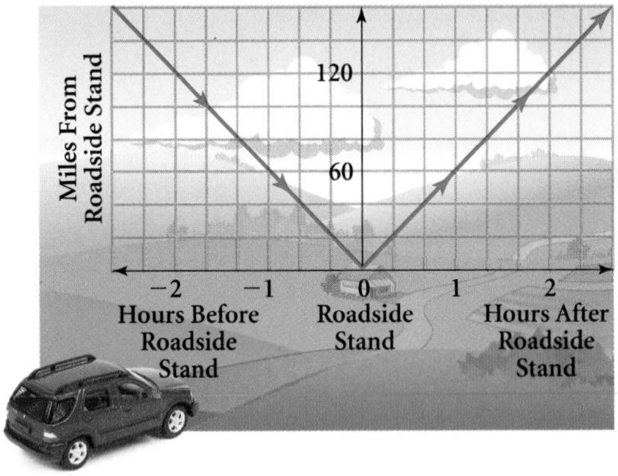

52. a. Graph the equations $y = \left|\frac{1}{2}x - 6\right| + 3$ and $y = -\left|\frac{1}{2}x + 6\right| - 3$ on the same set of axes.

b. Writing Describe the similarities and differences in the graphs.

C Challenge

Graph each absolute value equation.

53. $y = |3x| - x\left|\frac{1}{3}\right|$ **54.** $y = x - |2x|$ **55.** $y = |2x| - x$

56. $y = \frac{1}{2}|x - 3| + 5$ **57.** $y = \frac{1}{2}|x| + 4|x - 1|$ **58.** $y = |x + 1| + |x|$

59. a. Open-Ended Find two absolute value equations with graphs that share a vertex.

b. Find two absolute value equations with graphs that share part of a ray.

Standardized Test Prep

Multiple Choice

60. The graph at the right models which equation?
A. $y = |3x - 1| + 2$ **B.** $y = |x - 1| - 2$
C. $y = |x - 1| + 2$ **D.** $y = |3x - 3| - 2$

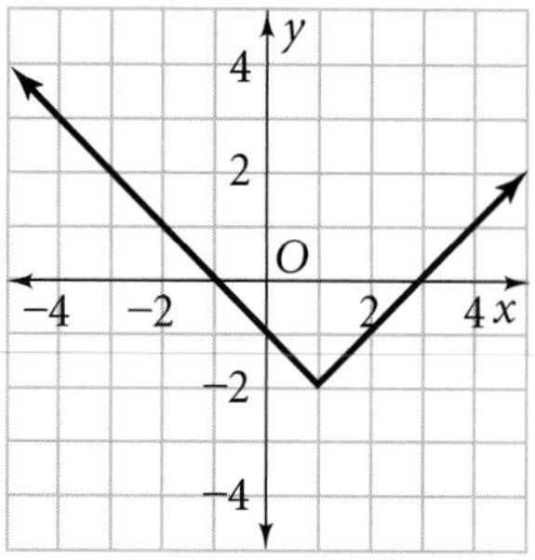

61. What is the vertex of $y = |x| - 5$?
F. (5, 0) **G.** (−5, 0)
H. (0, 5) **I.** (0, −5)

62. What is the vertex of $y = -|x| - 2$?
A. (0, −2) **B.** (0, 2)
C. (2, 0) **D.** (2, −2)

Take It to the NET
Online lesson quiz at
www.PHSchool.com
Web Code: aga-0205

63. What is the vertex of $y = |x - 3| + 5$?
F. (−3, 5) **G.** (−3, 11) **H.** (0, 5) **I.** (3, 5)

64. Which pair of linear equations represents the equation $y = |x + 3| - 4$?
A. $y = x + 1$ for $x \geq 3$
$y = x - 1$ for $x < 3$
B. $y = x - 1$ for $x \geq 3$
$y = -x - 1$ for $x < 3$
C. $y = x - 1$ for $x \geq -3$
$y = -x - 7$ for $x < -3$
D. $y = -x - 1$ for $x \geq -3$
$y = -x + 7$ for $x < -3$

Short Response

65. Explain how to find the *x*-coordinate of the vertex of $y = |3x - 6|$.

Extended Response

66. How can you graph the equation $y = -|5x + 1|$ by writing two linear equations? Show both equations, and label the coordinates of the vertex in your graph.

Mixed Review

Lesson 2-4

Graph each set of data. Decide whether a linear model is reasonable. If so, draw a trend line and write its equation.

67. $\{(0, -5), (5, 25), (7, 44), (9, 70), (11, 90)\}$

68. $\{(-10, 0), (-4, 4), (-1, 6), (2, 8), (5, 10)\}$

69. $\{(-5, 6), (-1, 4), (0, 5), (3, 8), (4, 7)\}$

70. $\{(0, 7), (2, 6), (5, 4.5), (6, 4), (9, 2.5)\}$

Lesson 2-4

Find the slope of each line.

71. $3x + y = 1$ **72.** $5y - 20x = 6$ **73.** $y = \frac{-x}{9}$

74. $12x = 3y - 2$ **75.** $\frac{x}{2} + \frac{y}{3} = 1$ **76.** $0.1y = 0.5x + 0.1$

77. A tutor earns \$18 per hour. Write a function to model the tutor's earnings after *h* hours. What kind of function is this?

Lesson 1-3

Solve each equation.

78. $17x = 187$ **79.** $13c - 26 = 91$ **80.** $2(a - 6) + 11 = 25$

81. $7(b + 3) - 18(1 - b) = 103$ **82.** $6(m + 3) = 3(5 - m) + 66$

2-6 Vertical and Horizontal Translations

North Carolina Objectives

2.08 Use equations and inequalities with absolute value to model and solve problems; justify results. b) Interpret the constants and coefficients in the context of the problem.

Lesson Preview

What You'll Learn

OBJECTIVE 1 To analyze vertical translations

OBJECTIVE 2 To analyze horizontal translations

. . . And Why

To analyze a fabric design, as in Example 6

Check Skills You'll Need

(For help, go to Lessons 2-2 and 2-5.)

Graph each pair of functions on the same coordinate plane.

1. $y = x, y = x + 4$

2. $y = -2x, y = -2x - 3$

3. $y = |x|, y = |x| - 2$

4. $y = -|2x|, y = -|2x| + 1$

5. $y = |x|, y = |x - 1|$

6. $y = -\left|\frac{1}{2}x\right|, y = -\left|\frac{1}{2}x + 2\right|$

New Vocabulary • translation • parent function

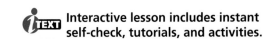

Interactive lesson includes instant self-check, tutorials, and activities.

OBJECTIVE 1 Translating Graphs Vertically

Reading Math

Translate is a synonym for transfer.

A **translation** is an operation that shifts a graph horizontally, vertically, or both. It results in a graph of the same shape and size, in a different position.

1 EXAMPLE Comparing Graphs

Compare the graphs of $y = |x|$ and $y = |x| - 3$. Describe how the graph of $y = |x| - 3$ relates to the graph of $y = |x|$.

x	$y = \lvert x \rvert$	$y = \lvert x \rvert - 3$
−6	6	3
−3	3	0
0	0	−3
3	3	0
6	6	3

Make a table of values and graph the equations.

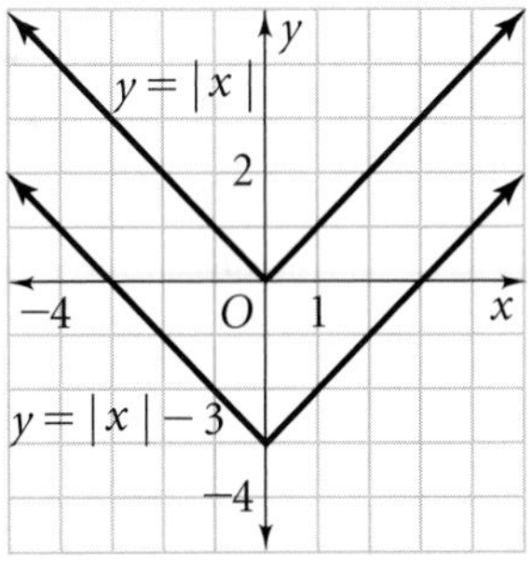

For each value of x, $y = |x| - 3$ is 3 less than the value of $y = |x|$. The graph of $y = |x| - 3$ is the graph of $y = |x|$ shifted 3 units down.

Check Understanding

1 Compare the graphs of each pair of functions. Describe how the graph of the second function relates to the graph of the first function.

a. $y = x$ and $y = x + 5$

b. $f(x) = -|x|$ and $f(x) = -|x| + 2$

A family of functions is a group of functions with common characteristics. A **parent function** is the simplest function with these characteristics. A parent function and one or more translations make up a family of functions.

Let k be a positive real number. To graph the functions $y = x + k$ and $y = |x| + k$, translate the graph of the parent function up k units. To graph the functions $y = x - k$ and $y = |x| - k$, translate the graph down k units.

Real-World Connection

Translations of two lines result in the diamond shapes in this window.

2 EXAMPLE Graphing a Vertical Translation

For each function, identify the parent function and the value of k. Then graph the function by translating the parent function.

a. $y = x - 2$

The parent function is $y = x$, and $k = 2$. Translate the graph of $y = x$ *down* 2 units.

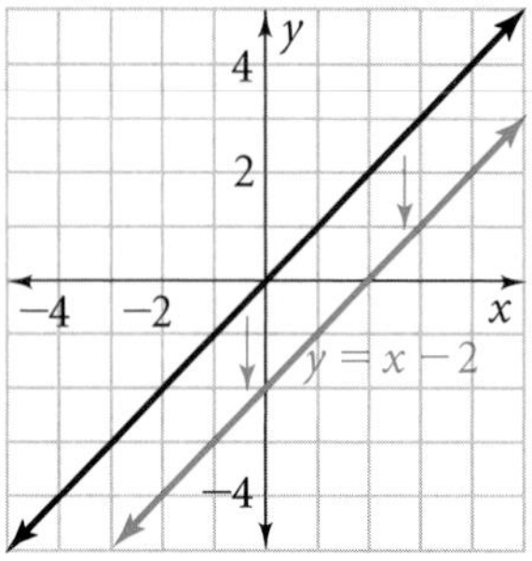

b. $y = -|x| + 3$

The parent function is $y = -|x|$, and $k = 3$. Translate the graph of $y = -|x|$ *up* 3 units.

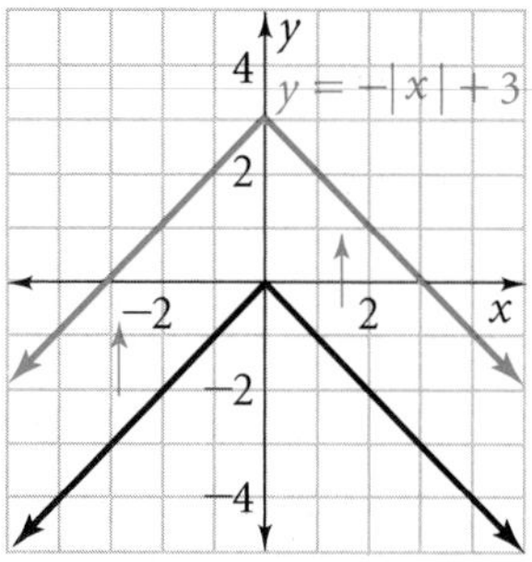

Check Understanding **2** Identify each parent function and the value of k. Then graph each function by translating the parent function.

a. $y = |x| - 1$ **b.** $y = 3x + 5$

You can write an equation for a translation.

3 EXAMPLE Writing Equations for Vertical Translations

Write an equation for each translation.

a. $y = 2x$, 4 units down

The graph of $y = 2x$,

shifted 4 units down,

means $k = 4$.

An equation is $y = 2x - 4$.

b. $y = \left|\frac{1}{4}x\right|$, $\frac{1}{2}$ unit up

The graph of $y = \left|\frac{1}{4}x\right|$,

shifted $\frac{1}{2}$ unit up,

means $k = \frac{1}{2}$.

An equation is $y = \left|\frac{1}{4}x\right| + \frac{1}{2}$.

Check Understanding **3** Write an equation for each translation.

a. $y = |3x|$, 2 units down **b.** $y = \frac{1}{3}x$, 3 units up

OBJECTIVE 2 Translating Graphs Horizontally

Horizontal translations share some of the characteristics of vertical translations.

Let h be a positive real number. Then $y = |x + h|$ translates the graph of $y = |x|$ h units to the left, and $y = |x - h|$ translates the graph h units to the right.

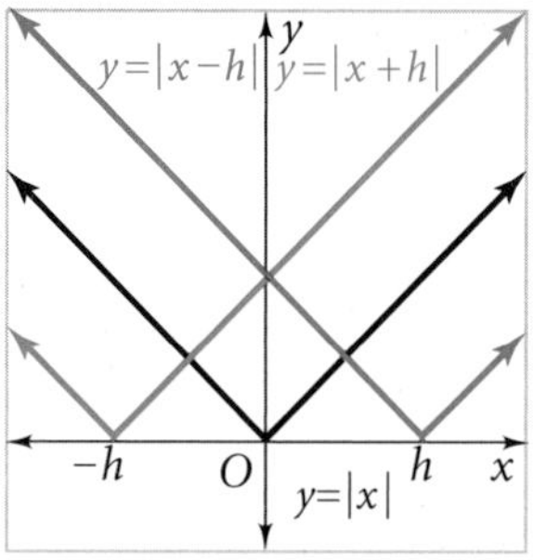

4 EXAMPLE Graphing Horizontal Translations

For each function, identify the parent function and the value of h. Then graph the function by translating the parent function.

a. $y = |x + 3|$

The parent function is $y = |x|$, and $h = 3$. The plus sign means translate to the left.
Translate the graph of $y = |x|$ *left* 3 units.

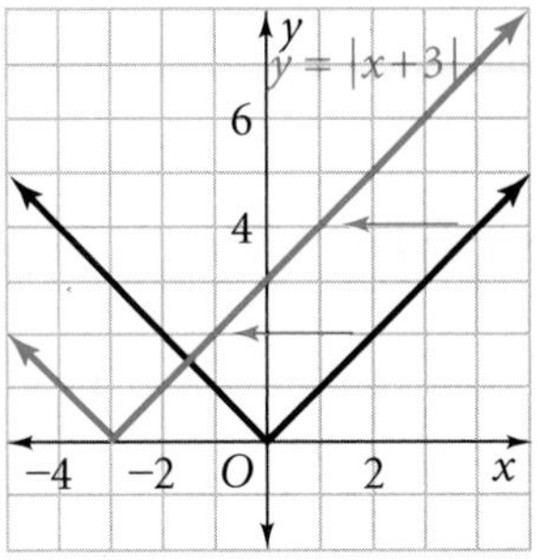

b. $y = -|x - 2|$

The parent function is $y = -|x|$, and $h = 2$. The minus sign means translate to the right.
Translate the graph of $y = -|x|$ *right* 2 units.

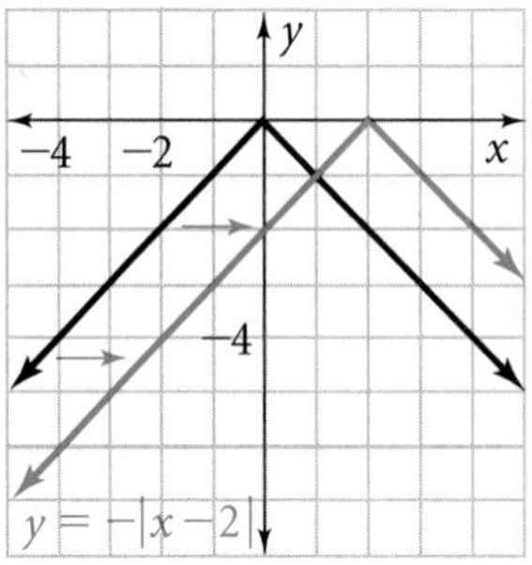

Check Understanding **4** Identify each parent function and the value of h. Then graph each function by translating the parent function.

a. $y = |x - 1|$ **b.** $y = -\left|x + \frac{5}{2}\right|$

Need Help?
Graph the parent function before you graph the translation.

You can write a horizontal translation from a graph of a function.

5 EXAMPLE Writing Equations for Horizontal Translations

The blue graph at the right is a translation of $y = |x|$. Write an equation for the graph.

This is the graph of $y = |x|$ translated 5 units to the right. A shift to the right calls for an equation of the form $y = |x - h|$. An equation for the graph is $y = |x - 5|$.

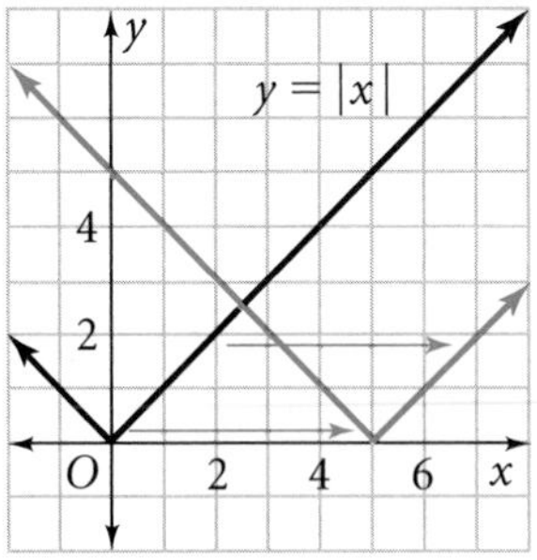

Check Understanding **5** Each graph is a translation of $y = |x|$. Write an equation for each graph.

a.

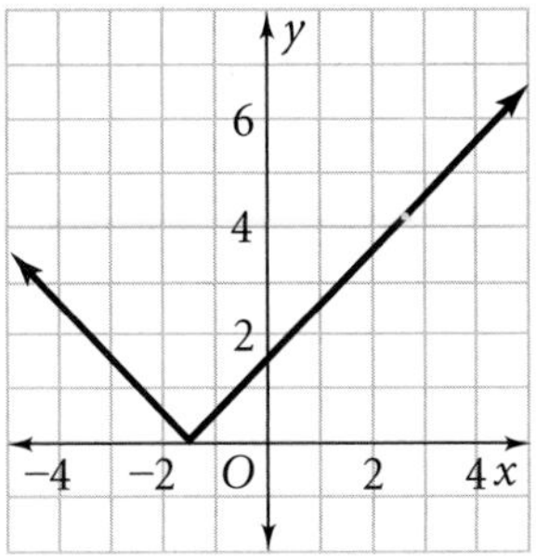

b.

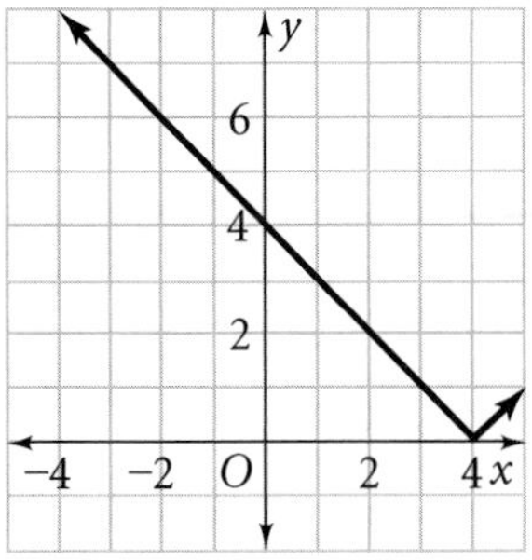

You can combine vertical and horizontal translations to produce diagonal translations.

6 EXAMPLE Real-World Connection

Fabric Design Describe a possible translation of Figures A and B in the Nigerian textile design below.

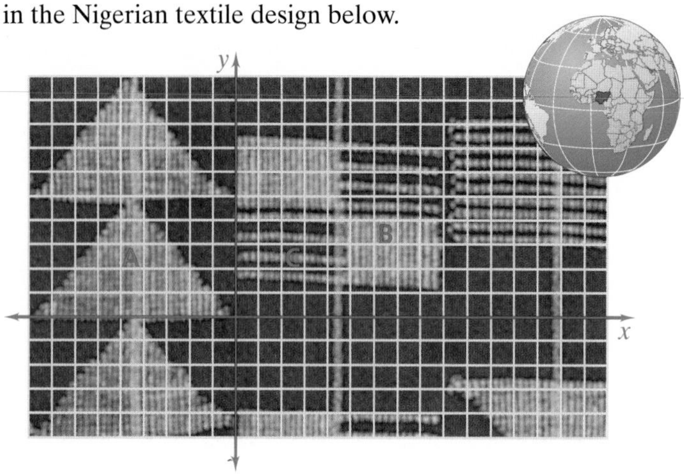

A translation of Figure A: 5 units up or 5 units down

A translation of Figure B: about 5 units left and about 3 units up

Check Understanding **6** Describe a possible translation of Figure C in the textile design.

You can use a parent function to graph a diagonal translation.

7 EXAMPLE Graphing Diagonal Translations

Graph each function.

a. $y = |x - 3| + 1$

The parent function is $y = |x|$, so $h = 3$, and $k = 1$.

The minus sign means move h units to the right. The plus sign means move k units up.

Place the vertex at (3, 1), and draw the graph opening upward.

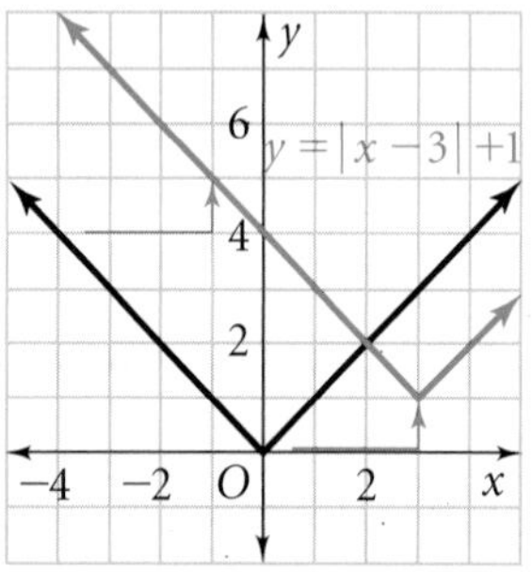

b. $f(x) = -|x + 2| - 4$

The parent function is $f(x) = -|x|$, so $h = 2$, and $k = 4$.

The plus sign means move h units to the left. The minus sign means move k units down.

Place the vertex at (−2, −4), and draw the graph opening downward.

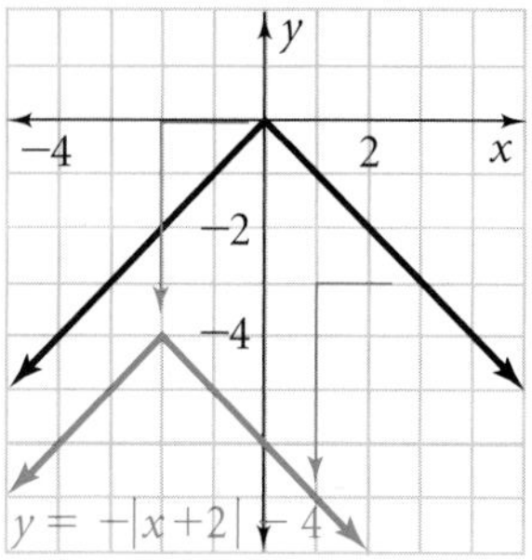

Check Understanding **7** Graph the function $f(x) = |x + 5| + 3$.

You can write an equation to describe a diagonal translation.

8 EXAMPLE Writing Diagonal Translations

Write an equation for each translation.

a. $y = |x|$, 2 units down, 3 units left

3 units left $\rightarrow h = 3$; plus sign

2 units down $\rightarrow k = 2$; minus sign

An equation is $y = |x + 3| - 2$.

b. $f(x) = -|x|$, 1 unit up, $\frac{1}{2}$ unit right

$\frac{1}{2}$ unit right $\rightarrow h = \frac{1}{2}$; minus sign

1 unit up $\rightarrow k = 1$; plus sign

An equation is $f(x) = -\left|x - \frac{1}{2}\right| + 1$.

Check Understanding 8 Write an equation for each translation.

a. $g(x) = |x|$, 1 unit down, 7 units right **b.** $y = -|x|$, 4 units up, 3 units right

EXERCISES

For more practice, see *Extra Practice.*

Practice and Problem Solving

A Practice by Example

Example 1 (page 91)

Compare the graphs of each pair of functions. Describe how the graph of the second function relates to the graph of the first function.

1. $y = -|x|, y = -|x| + 3$

2. $f(x) = |x|, f(x) = |x| - 1$

3. $g(x) = |3x|, g(x) = |3x| + 2$

4. $y = \frac{1}{2}|x|, y = \frac{1}{2}|x| - \frac{2}{3}$

Example 2 (page 92)

For each function, identify the parent function and the value of *k*. Then graph the function by translating the parent function.

5. $y = x - 3$

6. $y = -x + 4$

7. $y = |x| + 2$

8. $y = -|x| - 6$

Example 3 (page 92)

Write an equation for each vertical translation.

9. $y = x$, $\frac{2}{3}$ units down

10. $y = |x|$, 4 units up

11. $y = -|x|$, 2 units up

Example 4 (page 93)

For each function, identify the parent function and the value of *h*. Then graph the function by translating the parent function.

12. $y = |x - 4|$

13. $y = |x + 5|$

14. $y = -|x - 1|$

15. $y = -|x + 2|$

Example 5 (page 93)

Write an equation for each horizontal translation of $y = |x|$ or $y = -|x|$.

16.

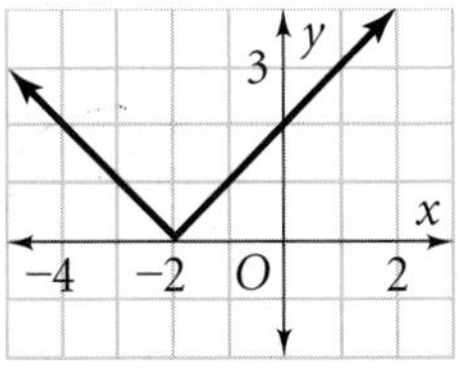

17.

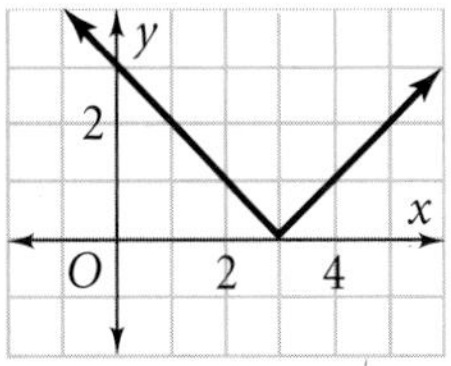

18.

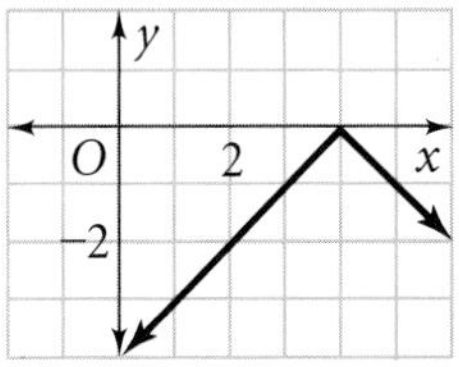

Example 6 (page 94)

Describe a possible translation for each figure.

19.

20.

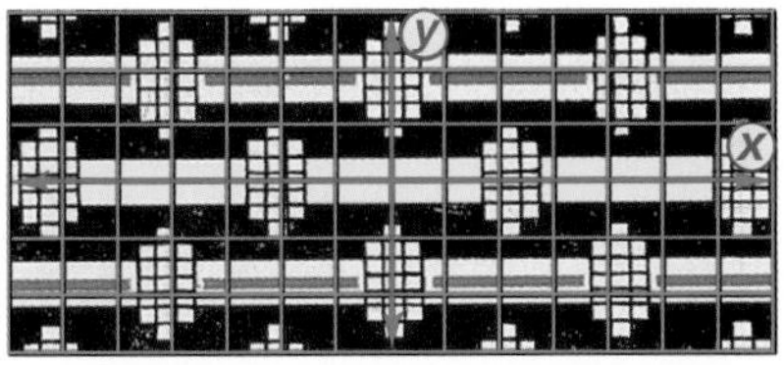

Example 7 (page 94)

Graph each function.

21. $y = |x + 2| - 3$ **22.** $y = |x - 4| + 2$ **23.** $y = |x + 2| + 1$

24. $y = |x - 1| - 2$ **25.** $y = -|x + 1| - 2$ **26.** $y = |-x - 2| - 3$

Example 8 (page 95)

Write an equation for each translation.

27. $y = |x|$, 1 unit down, 3 units right **28.** $y = -|x|$, 2 units up, 1 unit left

29. $y = -|x|$, $\frac{1}{2}$ unit up, $2\frac{1}{2}$ units right **30.** $y = |x|$, 3 units up, 7 units right

B Apply Your Skills

Describe each translation of $f(x) = x$ or $f(x) = |x|$ as *vertical, horizontal,* or *diagonal.* Then graph each translation.

31. $f(x) = x - 5$ **32.** $f(x) = |x - 5| + 3$ **33.** $f(x) = |x + 1|$

34. $f(x) = |x| + 1$ **35.** $f(x) = x + \frac{1}{2}$ **36.** $f(x) = |x| - 3$

37. $f(x) = |x - 2| + 3$ **38.** $f(x) = |x + 4| - 2$ **39.** $f(x) = |x - 3| - 6$

Write the equation of each translation of $y = x$ or $y = |x|$. Each interval is 1 unit.

40.

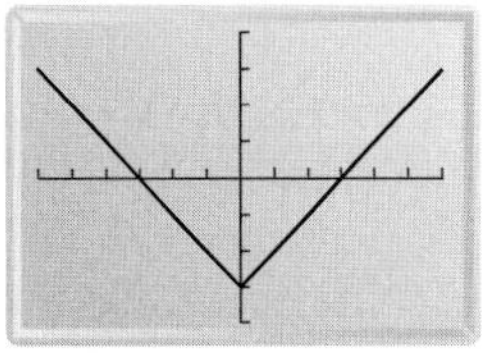

41.

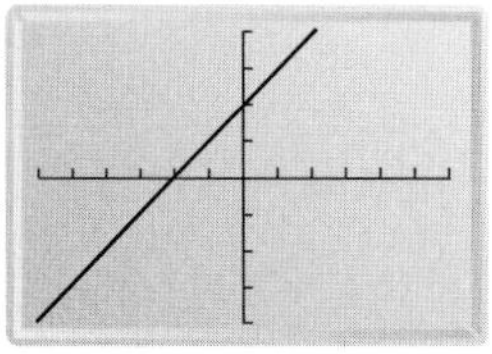

42.

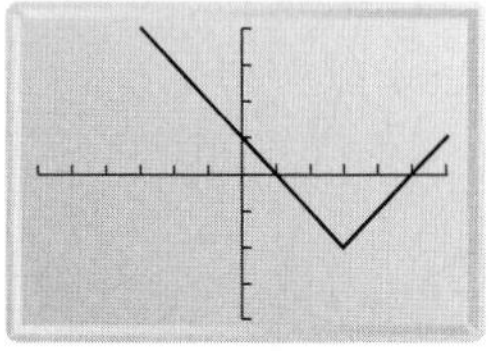

Each graph shows a translation of $y = -|x|$. State the values of h and k.

43.

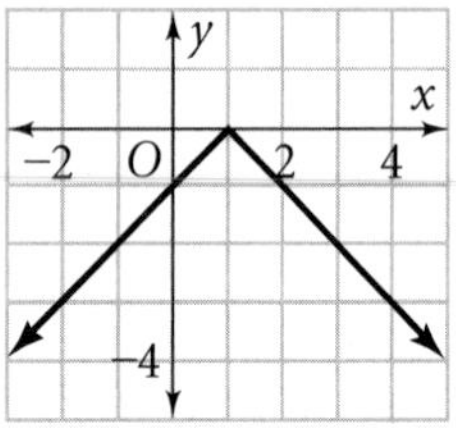

44.

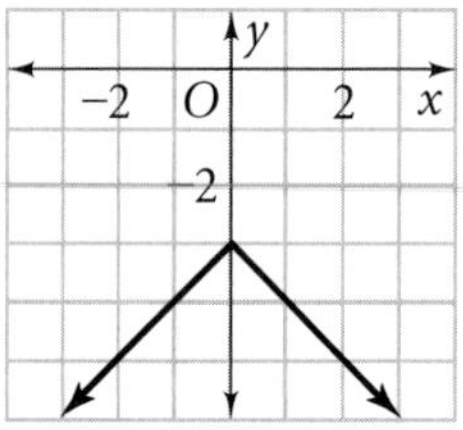

45.

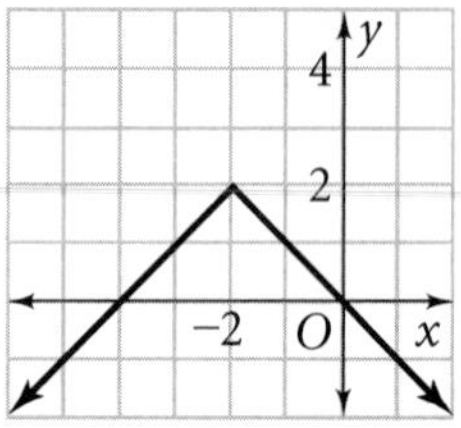

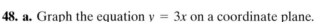

46. Data Analysis Suppose you plot data with years as the independent variable. What type of translation are you making when you start with $x = 0$ rather than a year such as 1998? Explain.

47. Writing Explain why applying a vertical translation and then a horizontal translation produces the same result as applying a horizontal translation and then a vertical translation.

48. a. Graph the equation $y = 3x$ on a coordinate plane.

b. Translate the graph 5 units up. Write an equation for the new line.

c. Translate the graph from part (b) 2 units right. Write an equation for the new line.

d. Which equation describes the line you graphed in part (c)?

A. $y = 3x + 5$ **B.** $y = 3x + 2$ **C.** $y = 3x - 2$

D. $y = 3(x - 5) + 2$ **E.** $y = 3(x - 2) + 5$

e. Critical Thinking Write the equation of the translation of $y = mx$ that has a graph passing through point (h, k).

49. Open-Ended Draw a figure in Quadrant I. Use a translation to move your figure into Quadrant III. Describe your translation.

Need Help?

Use the form $y = |x \pm h| \pm k$ for diagonal translations of absolute value functions.

Each graph shows an absolute value function after a translation 4 units up and 3 units left. Write the equation of the original function.

50.

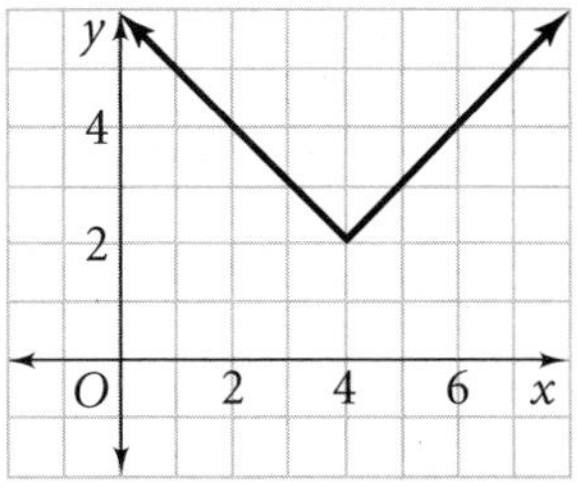

51.

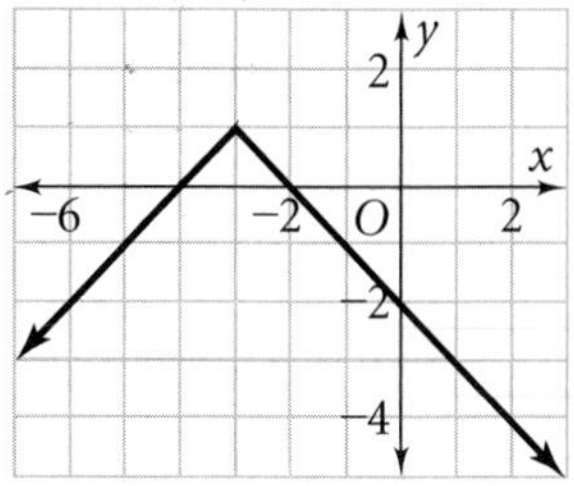

Write an equation for each translation.

52. $y = -|x|$; vertex $(-5, 0)$

53. $y = x$; through $(-4, 3)$

54. $y = |x|$; vertex (a, b)

55. $y = x$; through (p, q)

C Challenge

Graph each pair of functions on the same coordinate plane. Describe the translation that takes the first function to the second function.

56. $y = |x + 1|, y = |x - 5|$

57. $y = |x| + 3, y = |x - 4|$

58. $y = |x - 3|, y = |x| + 1$

59. $y = |x + 1| - 1, y = |x - 2| + 2$

60. Suppose you are playing with a yo-yo, as shown at the right.

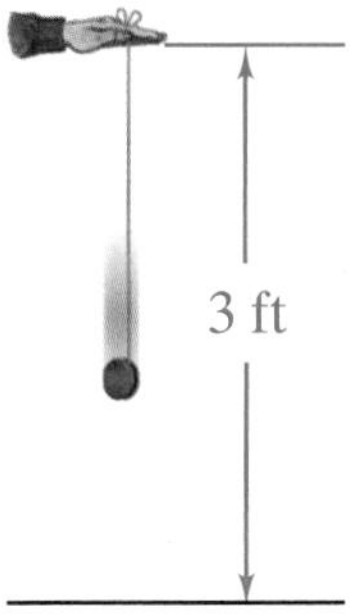

a. Sketch a graph of $h(t)$ to show the height h of the yo-yo above the floor over time t. At $t = 0$, the yo-yo leaves your hand.

b. Critical Thinking Should your graph be that of a function? Explain.

c. Suppose you demonstrate your yo-yo ability on an auditorium stage that is 5 ft above the floor. Describe the translation of the graph of $h(t)$ that represents the height of the yo-yo above the auditorium floor.

d. Choose a function $g(t)$ that represents the height of the yo-yo above the auditorium floor when you are on stage.

A. $g(t) = h(t + 5)$ **B.** $g(t) = h(t - 5)$

C. $g(t) = h(t) + 5$ **D.** $g(t) = h(t) - 5$

61. Use the graph of the function $y = f(x)$ at the right. Sketch the graph of each function.

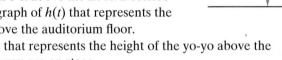

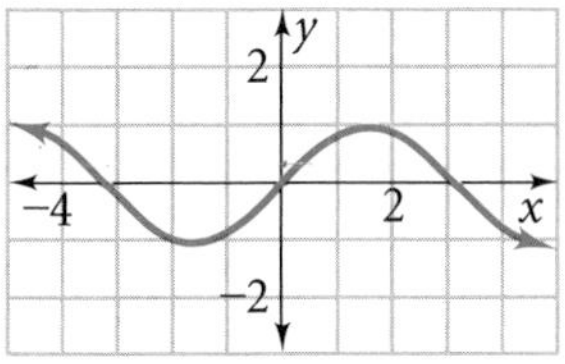

a. $f(x + 1)$

b. $f(x) - 2$

c. $f(x + 2) + 1$

Standardized Test Prep

Multiple Choice

62. Which translation takes $y = |x + 2| - 1$ to $y = |x| + 2$?

A. 2 units right, 3 units down **B.** 2 units left, 3 units up

C. 2 units right, 3 units up **D.** 2 units left, 3 units down

63. The graph of which equation will NOT have a y-intercept of 5?

F. $y = |x| + 5$ **G.** $y = |x - 5|$ **H.** $y = |x - 5| + 5$ **I.** $y = |x + 5|$

Take It to the NET
Online lesson quiz at **www.PHSchool.com**
Web Code: aga-0206

64. The graph of $y = |x - 1|$ is translated 3 units left and 2 units down. What is the equation of the new graph?
A. $y = |x + 2| - 2$ B. $y = |x - 4| - 2$
C. $y = |x + 4| + 2$ D. $y = |x - 4| + 2$

Extended Response

65. Start with the parent function of $y = |x + 3| - 2$. Explain how to describe the graph of $y = |x + 3| - 2$ as two consecutive translations of the parent function. Include graphs of the parent function and each translation.

Mixed Review

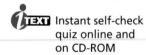

Lesson 2-5 **Evaluate each function for five values of x. Then graph each function.**

66. $f(x) = |x - 3| + 2$ **67.** $f(x) = |2x + 1| - 3$ **68.** $f(x) = \frac{1}{3}\left|\frac{1}{3}x - 3\right|$

Lesson 1-4 **Solve each inequality. Graph each solution on a number line.**

69. $x + 7 \leq -3$ **70.** $2a + 6 > 15$ **71.** $7.5 - 3b < 12$

Lesson 1-3 **72. Geometry** Keiko, an orca whale who starred in a number of movies, moved into an outdoor pool with a volume of 281,250 cubic feet. The pool's surface is 150 ft by 75 ft. Write and solve an equation to find the depth of the pool.

Checkpoint Quiz 2 — Lessons 2-4 through 2-6

iTEXT Instant self-check quiz online and on CD-ROM

Graph each function.

1. $y = x - 5$ **2.** $y = |x + 1| + 4$ **3.** $f(x) = \frac{2}{3}x - 2$

4. $f(x) = |x| - 4$ **5.** $y = |2x - 1| - 2$ **6.** $y = 3x + 3$

Write an equation for each graph.

7.

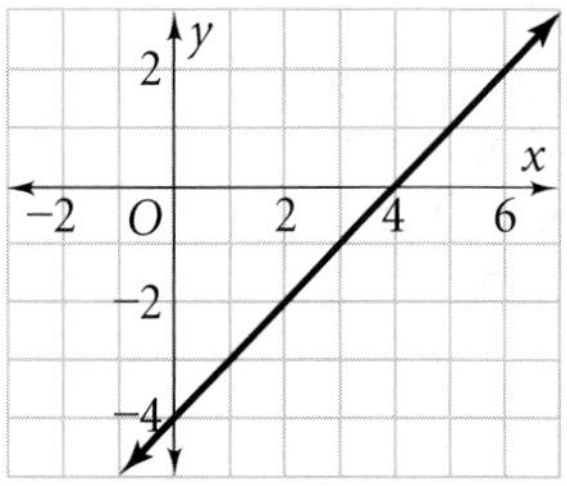

8.

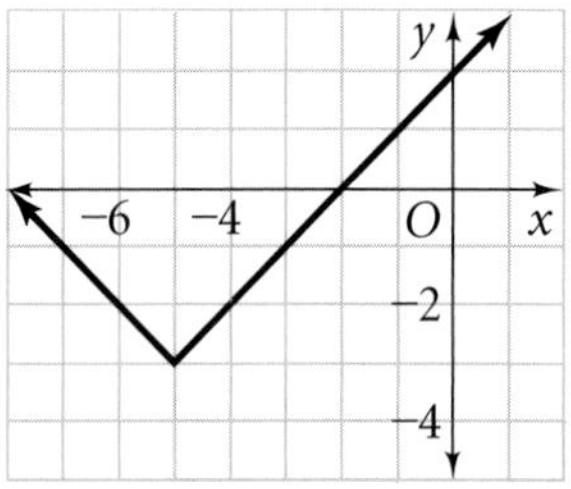

9. a. Use the table below. Model the relation with a scatter plot and a trend line.
b. Predict the value of y when $x = 10$.

x	1.0	2.0	3.0	4.0	5.0	6.0	7.0
y	−1.5	0.0	1.5	2.0	2.5	3.5	4.0

10. The graph of $y = |x|$ is translated down 5 units and right 4 units. What is the equation of the new graph?
A. $y = |x + 4| + 5$ **B.** $y = |x + 4| - 5$
C. $y = |x - 4| + 5$ **D.** $y = |x - 4| - 5$

2-7 Two-Variable Inequalities

North Carolina Objectives

2.08 Use equations and inequalities with absolute value to model and solve problems; justify results. a) Solve using tables, graphs, and algebraic properties.

Lesson Preview

What You'll Learn

OBJECTIVE 1 To graph linear inequalities

OBJECTIVE 2 To graph absolute value inequalities

. . . And Why

To solve problems involving combinations, as in Example 2

✓ Check Skills You'll Need

(For help, go to Lessons 1-4 and 1-5.)

Solve each inequality. Graph the solution on a number line.

1. $12p \leq 15$ **2.** $4 + t > 17$ **3.** $5 - 2t \geq 11$

Solve and graph each absolute value equation or inequality.

4. $|4c| = 18$ **5.** $|5 - b| = 3$ **6.** $|2h| \geq 7$

New Vocabulary • linear inequality

Interactive lesson includes instant self-check, tutorials, and activities.

OBJECTIVE

1 Graphing Linear Inequalities

Investigation: Linear Inequalities

1. Graph the line $y = 2x + 3$ on graph paper.
2. a. Plot each point listed below.
   $(-2, -3), (-2, -1), (-1, -1), (-1, 5), (0, 4), (0, 5), (1, 6), (2, 3), (2, 7)$
   b. Classify each point as *on the line*, *above the line*, or *below the line*.
3. Are all the points that satisfy the inequality $y > 2x + 3$ *above*, *below*, or *on* the line?

Need Help?

- $<$ less than
- $\leq$ less than or equal to
- $>$ greater than
- $\geq$ greater than or equal to
- $\neq$ not equal to

A **linear inequality** is an inequality in two variables whose graph is a region of the coordinate plane that is bounded by a line. To graph a linear inequality, first graph the boundary line. Then decide which side of the line contains solutions to the inequality and whether the boundary line is included.

$y > \frac{1}{2}x - 1$

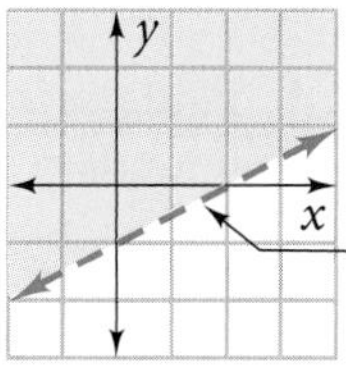

For an inequality with $y <$ or $y \leq$, shade below the line. For an inequality with $y >$ or $y \geq$, shade above the line.

A *dashed* boundary line indicates that the line is not part of the solution.

$2x + 3y \leq 6$

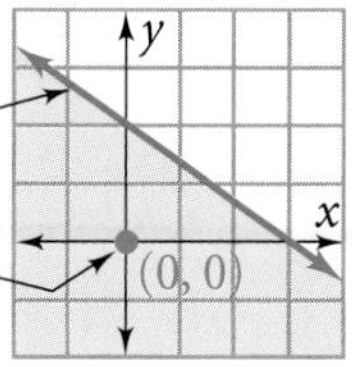

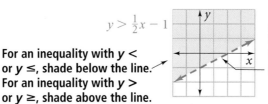

A *solid* boundary line indicates that the line is part of the solution.

Choose a test point above or below the boundary line. The test point (0, 0) makes the inequality true. Shade the region containing this point.

1 EXAMPLE Graphing a Linear Inequality

Graph the inequality $y < \frac{1}{2}x - 3$.

Step 1 Graph the boundary line $y = \frac{1}{2}x - 3$. Since the inequality is *less than,* not *less than or equal to,* use a dashed boundary line.

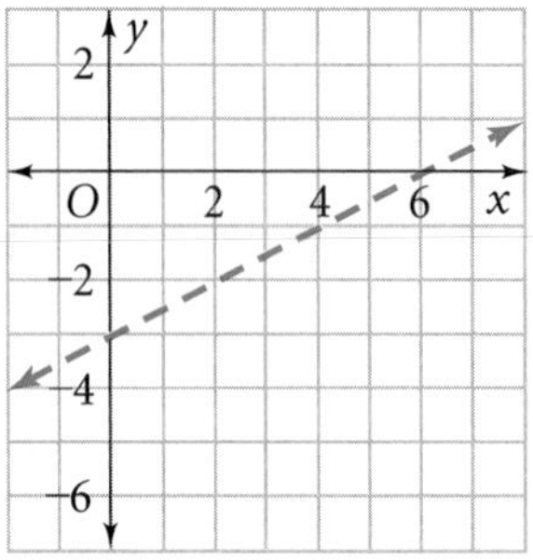

Step 2 Since the inequality is *less than*, y-values must be less than those on the boundary line. Shade the region *below* the boundary line.

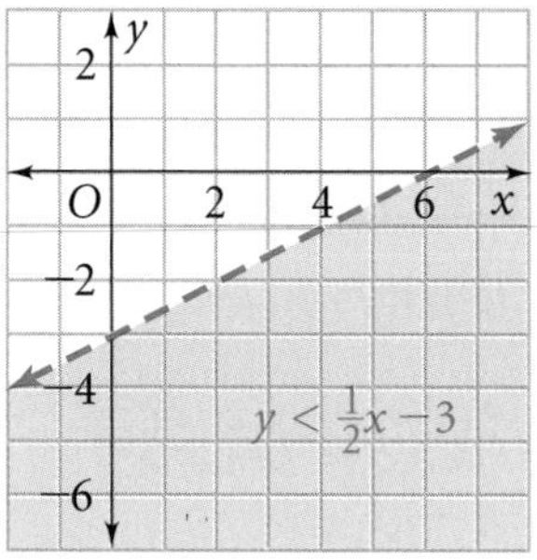

Check Understanding **1** Graph each inequality.

a. $4x + 2y \le 4$ **b.** $y \ge 3x$ **c.** $\frac{x}{3} < -y + 2$

You can use linear inequalities to solve problems.

2 EXAMPLE Real-World Connection

Entertainment At least 35 performers of the Big Tent Circus are in the grand finale. Some pile into cars, while others balance on bicycles. Seven performers are in each car, and five performers are on each bicycle. Draw a graph showing all the possible combinations of cars and bicycles that could be used in the finale.

Relate	the number of performers in cars	plus	the number of performers on bicycles	is greater than or equal to	35

Define Let x = the number of cars.

Let y = the number of bicycles.

Write $7x + 5y \ge 35$

Step 1 Find the intercepts of the boundary line. Use the intercepts to graph the boundary line.

When $y = 0$, $7x + 5(0) = 35$.
$7x = 35$
$x = 5$

When $x = 0$, $7(0) + 5y = 35$.
$5y = 35$
$y = 7$

Graph the intercepts (5, 0) and (0, 7). Since the inequality is *greater than or equal to,* use a solid boundary line.

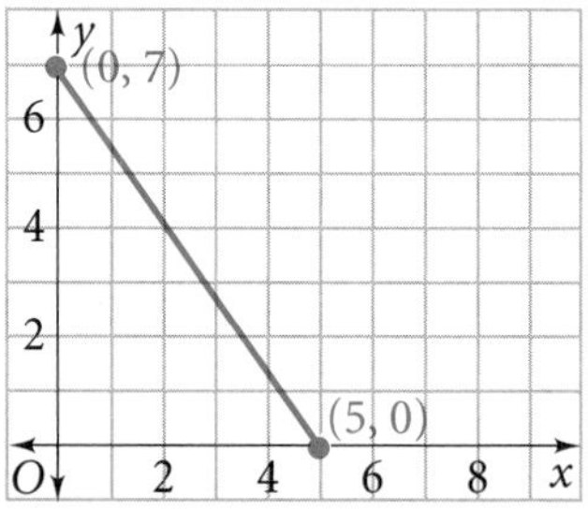

Step 2 Choose a test point not on the boundary line. The test point (6, 4) makes the inequality true. Shade the region containing (6, 4).

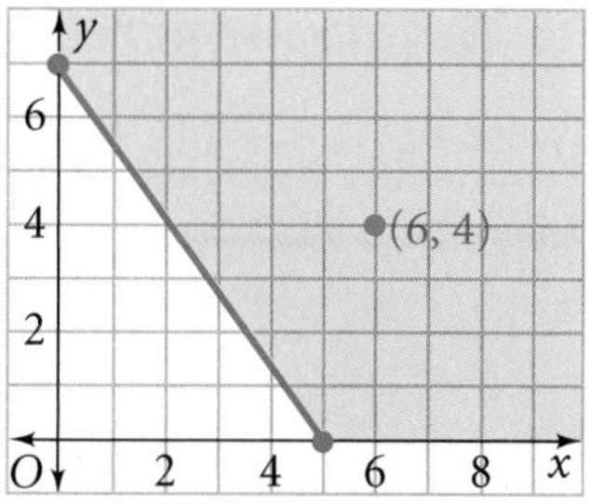

All ordered pairs with whole-number coordinates that are in the shaded area represent a combination of cars x and bicycles y that could be used in the grand finale.

Check Understanding **2** **a.** Find the minimum number of bicycles that will be needed if three cars are available. Then determine three other possible combinations of bicycles and cars.

b. **Critical Thinking** Give the domain and range for Example 2. Justify your reasoning.

OBJECTIVE 2

Graphing Two-Variable Absolute Value Inequalities

You can graph two-variable absolute value inequalities the same way you graph linear inequalities.

Need Help?
To review graphing absolute value functions, go to Lesson 2-5.

3 EXAMPLE Graphing Absolute Value Inequalities

Graph each absolute value inequality.

a. $y \leq |x - 4| + 5$

Graph $y = |x - 4| + 5$.

Since the inequality is *less than or equal to,* the boundary is solid and the shaded region is below the boundary.

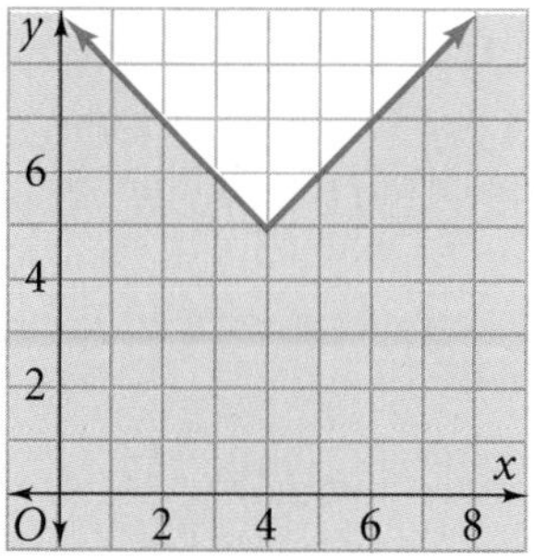

b. $-y + 3 > |x + 1|$

$$-y > |x + 1| - 3$$
$$y < -|x + 1| + 3$$

Graph $y = -|x + 1| + 3$.

Since the inequality is *less than,* the boundary is dashed and the shaded region is below the boundary.

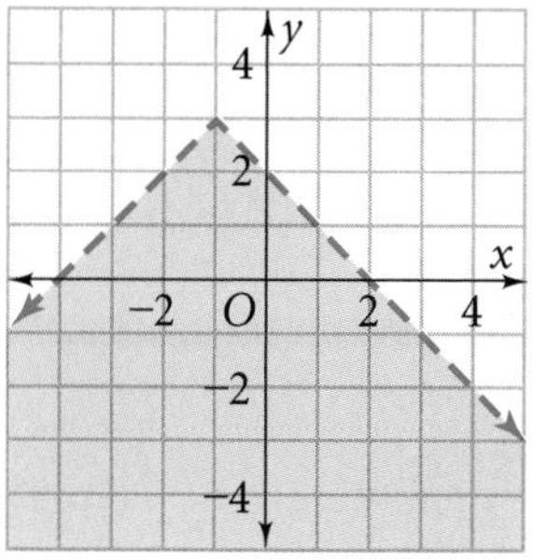

Check Understanding **3** Graph each absolute value inequality.

a. $y > -|x + 2| - 3$

b. $2y + 3 \leq -|x - 5|$

You can write an inequality by examining a graph.

4 EXAMPLE Writing Inequalities

Write an inequality for each graph. The boundary line is given.

a.

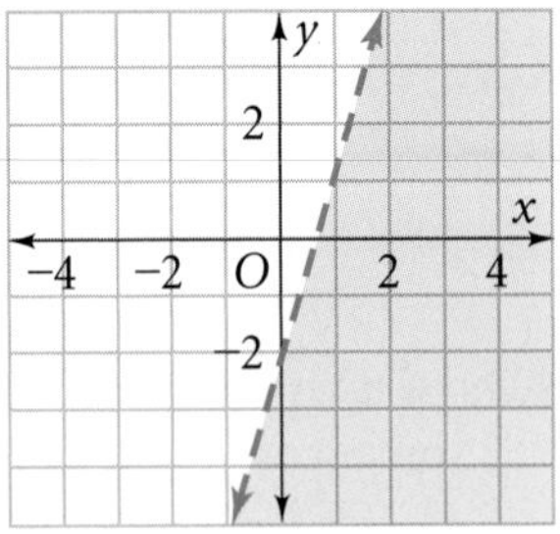

boundary: $y = 3x - 2$

The boundary line is dashed. The shaded region is below the boundary. This is the graph of $y < 3x - 2$.

b.

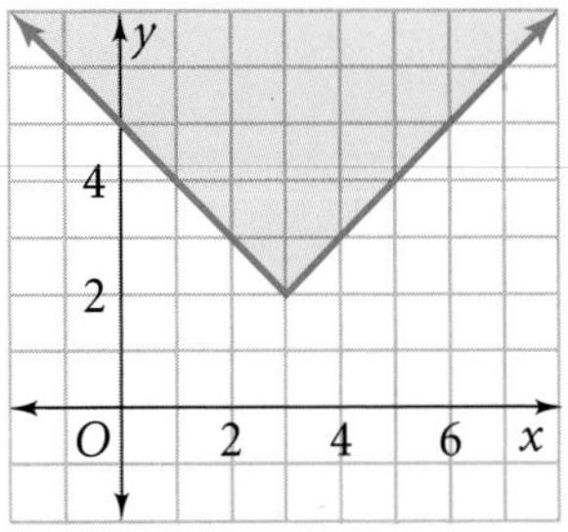

boundary: $y = |x - 3| + 2$

The boundary is solid. The shaded region is above the boundary. This is the graph of $y \geq |x - 3| + 2$.

Check Understanding **4** Write an inequality for each graph.

a.

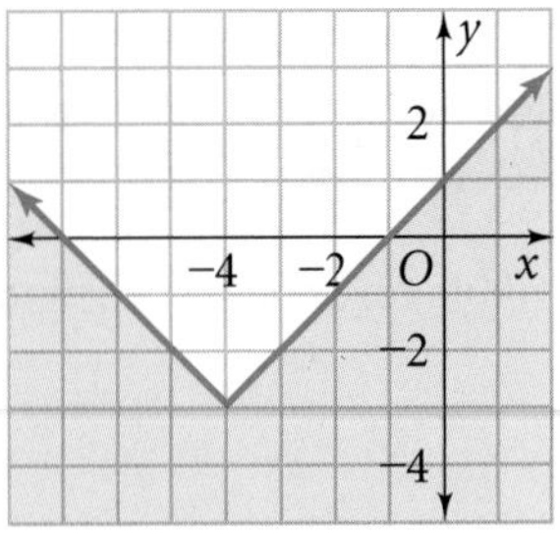

b.

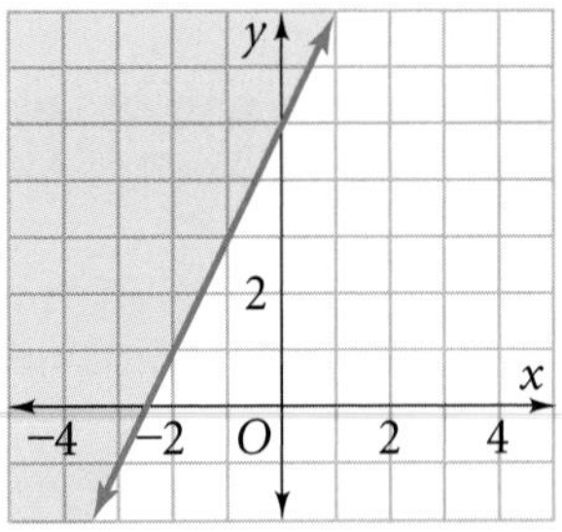

EXERCISES

For more practice, see *Extra Practice.*

Practice and Problem Solving

A Practice by Example

Example 1 (page 100)

Graph each inequality.

1. $y > 2x + 1$ **2.** $y < 3$ **3.** $x \leq 0$

4. $y \leq x - 5$ **5.** $2x + 3y \geq 12$ **6.** $2y \geq 4x - 6$

7. $y > \frac{2}{3}x + \frac{1}{3}$ **8.** $3x - 2y \leq 9$ **9.** $5x > -y + 3$

Example 2 (pages 100–101)

10. Cooking The time needed to roast a chicken depends on its weight. Allow at least 20 min/lb for a chicken weighing up to 6 lb. Allow at least 15 min/lb for a chicken weighing more than 6 lb.

a. Write two inequalities to represent the time needed to roast a chicken.

b. Graph the inequalities.

Example 3 (page 101)

Graph each absolute value inequality.

11. $y \geq |2x - 1|$ **12.** $y \leq |3x| + 1$ **13.** $y \leq |4 - x|$

14. $y > |-x + 4| + 1$ **15.** $y - 7 > |x + 2|$ **16.** $y + 2 \leq \left|\frac{1}{2}x\right|$

17. $3 - y \geq -|x - 4|$ **18.** $1 - y < |2x - 1|$ **19.** $y + 3 \leq |3x| - 1$

Example 4 (page 102)

Write an inequality for each graph. In each case, the equation for the boundary line is given.

20. $y = -x - 2$

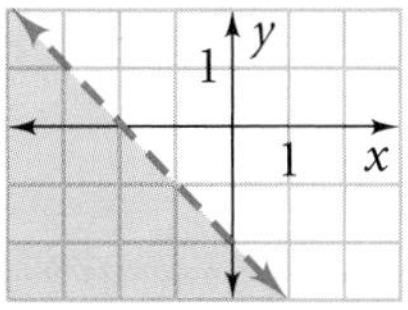

21. $5x + 3y = 9$

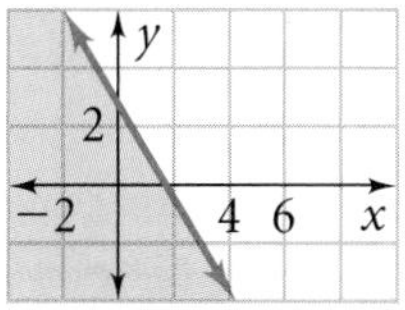

22. $2y = |2x + 6|$

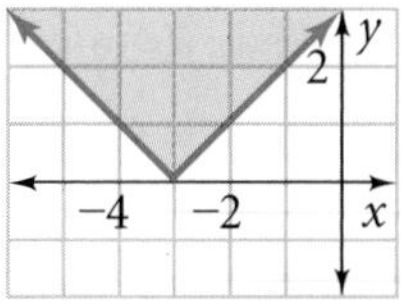

B Apply Your Skills

Graph each inequality on a coordinate plane.

23. $5x - 2y \geq -10$

24. $2x - 5y < -10$

25. $\frac{3}{4}x + \frac{2}{3}y > \frac{5}{2}$

26. $3(x - 2) + 2y \leq 6$

27. $0.5x + 1.2y < 6$

28. $-3x + 4y > -6$

29. $\frac{1}{2}x + \frac{2}{3}y \geq 1$

30. $|x - 1| > y + 7$

31. $y - |2x| \leq 21$

32. $2(x + 3) + y \geq 2$

33. $\frac{1}{4}x - \frac{1}{2}y > 1$

34. $|x + 2| - 3 < y$

35. $\frac{2}{3}x + 2 \leq \frac{2}{9}y$

36. $0.25y - 1.5x \geq -4$

37. $8x - 4y \geq -3$

Write an inequality for each graph.

38.

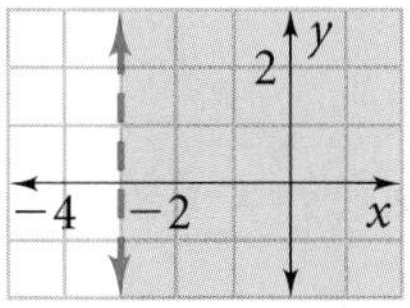

39.

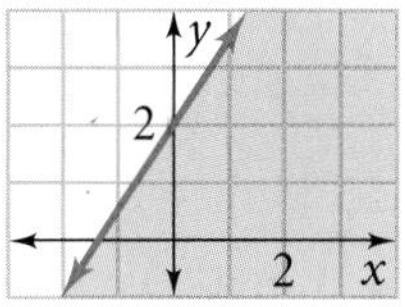

40.

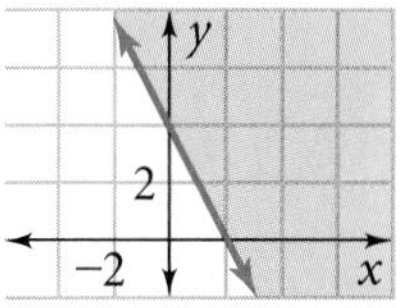

41.

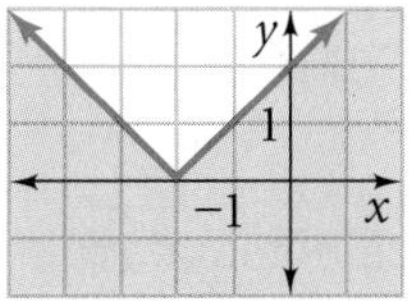

42.

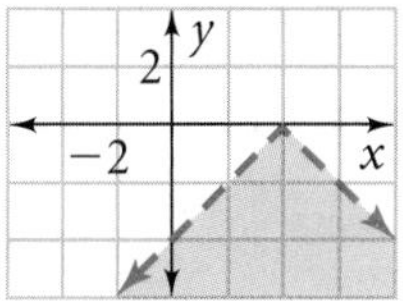

43.

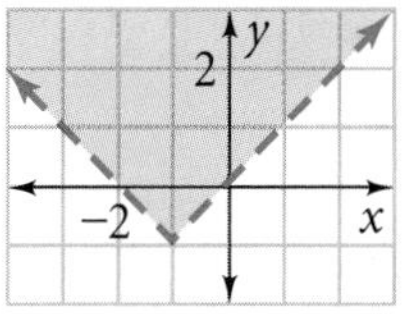

Reading Math

For help with reading and solving Exercise 44, see p. 105.

44. Open-Ended Write an inequality that has (10, 15), (−10, 20), (−20, −25), and (25, −10) as solutions.

45. Business To raise funds, the junior class plans to sell frozen yogurt cones and sundaes. Each dessert contains one scoop of yogurt.

a. Write an expression to represent the number of scoops of yogurt used in making c cones and s sundaes.

b. Suppose you have enough yogurt for 200 scoops. Write an inequality to represent all the possible combinations of cones and sundaes.

c. Graph the inequality. Is the point (20, 50) a solution?

d. On your graph, find the point representing 60 cones and as many sundaes as possible. What does the s-value of this point represent?

C Challenge

46. Writing When you graph an inequality, you can often use the point (0, 0) to test which side of the boundary line to shade. Describe a situation in which you could *not* use (0, 0) as a test point.

Graph each inequality on a graphing calculator. Then sketch the graph.

47. $y \leq |x + 1| - |x - 1|$

48. $y > |x| + |x + 3|$

49. $y < |x - 3| - |x + 3|$

50. $y < 7 - |x - 4| + |x|$

Standardized Test Prep

Multiple Choice

51. The graph at the right shows which inequality?

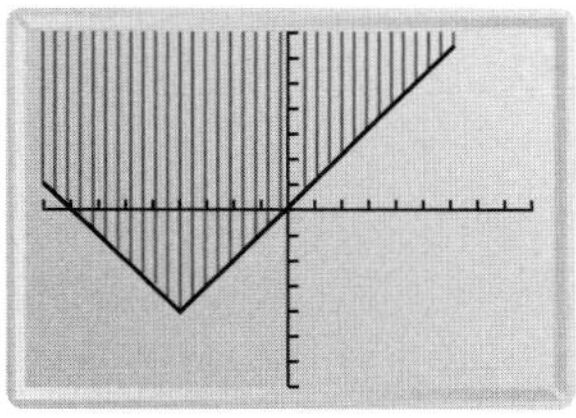

A. $y > |x + 4| - 4$
B. $y > |x - 4| + 4$
C. $y < |x + 4| - 4$
D. $y < |x - 4| + 4$

52. The graph of which inequality has its vertex at $\left(2\frac{1}{2}, -5\right)$?

F. $y < |2x - 5| + 5$ **G.** $y < |2x + 5| - 5$
H. $y > |2x + 5| - 5$ **I.** $y > |2x - 5| - 5$

Take It to the NET
Online lesson quiz at **www.PHSchool.com**
Web Code: aga-0207

53. Which inequality is NOT equivalent to the others?

A. $y \le \frac{2}{3}x - 3$ **B.** $3y \le 2x - 9$
C. $2x - 3y \ge 9$ **D.** $2x - 3y \le 9$

54. The graph at the right shows which inequality?

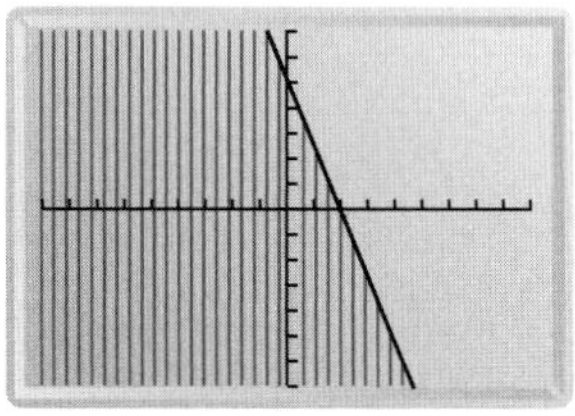

F. $y \le -2.5x + 5$
G. $2.5x + y \ge 5$
H. $2.5x + y < 5$
I. $5x + 2y \le 5$

55. Which point(s) are solutions of the inequality $5x + 3y \ge 2$?

I. (0, 0) **II.** $(-1, 0)$ and $\left(0, -\frac{2}{3}\right)$ **III.** $\left(0, \frac{2}{3}\right)$ and $\left(1, -\frac{2}{3}\right)$

A. I only **B.** I and II **C.** III only **D.** II and III

Short Response

56. At least 300 tornadoes occur in the United States each year. Write an inequality to model the number of tornadoes that could occur during the next x years. Describe the domain and range of the inequality.

Mixed Review

Lesson 2-6 **Graph each function by translating its parent function.**

57. $y = 2x + 5$ **58.** $y = |x| - 3$ **59.** $f(x) = |x + 6|$

60. $f(x) = x - 2$ **61.** $y = |x + 2|$ **62.** $y = |x - 1| + 5$

Lesson 2-3 **Determine whether y varies directly with x. If so, find the constant of variation.**

63. $y = x + 1$ **64.** $y = 100x$ **65.** $5x + y = 0$ **66.** $y - 2 = 2x$

67. $x = \frac{y}{3}$ **68.** $-4 = y - x$ **69.** $y = -10x$ **70.** $xy = 1$

71. Commissions The amount of a commission is directly proportional to the amount of a sale. A realtor received a commission of \$13,500 on the sale of a \$225,000 house. How much would the commission be on a \$130,000 house?

Lesson 2-2 **Graph each pair of equations on the same coordinate plane.**

72. $y = x, y = -x + 5$ **73.** $y = -2x + 1, y = 2x$ **74.** $y = 4x - 1, y = x$

Reading Math

Reading for Problem Solving

For Use With Page 103, Exercise 44

Read the problem below. Then follow along with Carmen as she solves the problem. Check your understanding with the exercise at the bottom of the page.

Open-Ended Write an inequality that has (10, 15), (−10, 20), (−20, −25), and (25, −10) as solutions.

What Carmen Thinks

These points are not necessarily on the same line. I'll plot the points and see where they lie on the coordinate plane.

The problem asks me to write an inequality with these points as solutions. But the graph of a linear inequality has a boundary line with shading on one side. So, I'll have to choose a boundary line.

There are so many possibilities! I need only two points to draw a line, so I'll use (−20, −25) and (25, −10).

The boundary line is solid since the points lie on it. I can include the other two points in the solution set by shading above the boundary line.

Since I have two points, I can use point-slope form to write the equation of the boundary line.

I can substitute the values of *m*, *x*, and *y* into my equation and simplify.

I need to write an inequality. I shaded above the line toward greater *y*-values, so the inequality includes "greater than." Since I used a solid boundary line, the inequality is "greater than or equal to."

What Carmen Writes

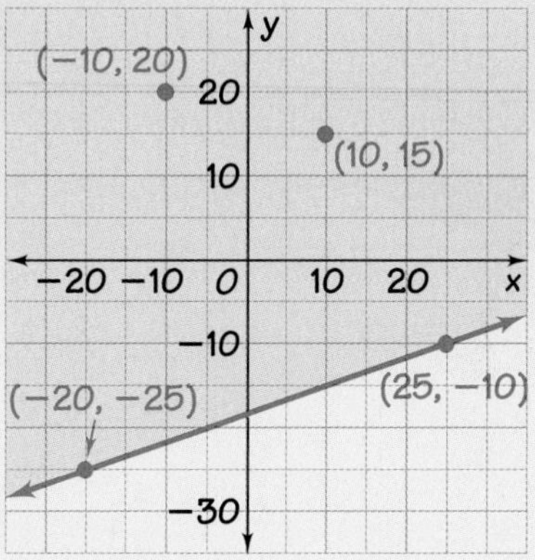

Boundary line through (−20, −25) and (25, −10) has slope $m = \dfrac{-10 - (-25)}{25 - (-20)}$.

$$y - y_1 = m(x - x_1)$$

$$y - (-25) = \frac{-10 - (-25)}{25 - (-20)}(x - (-20))$$

$$y + 25 = \frac{15}{45}(x + 20)$$

$$y = \frac{1}{3}(x + 20) - 25$$

$$y = \frac{1}{3}x - \frac{55}{3} \quad \text{equation of boundary line}$$

$$y \geq \frac{1}{3}x - \frac{55}{3} \quad \text{inequality}$$

EXERCISE

Write a different inequality that has (10, 15), (−10, 20), (−20, −25), and (25, −10) as solutions.

Test-Taking Strategies

Writing Short Responses

Short-response questions are usually worth two points. To get full credit you must not only give the correct answer, but also show your work or justify your reasoning.

EXAMPLE

A line parallel to $4x - 2y = 5$ passes through the point $(2, -3)$. Write the equation of the line in standard form, $Ax + By = C$.

Study the three responses below. Each received a different score.

2 points	1 point	0 points
$4x - 2y = 5$ $4x - 5 = 2y$ $y = 2x - \frac{5}{2}$ Slope is 2. $y + 3 = 2(x - 2)$ $y + 3 = 2x - 4$ $y = 2x - 7$ $2x - y = 7$	$4x - 2y = 5$ $-2y = 5 + 4x$ $y = -2x - \frac{5}{2}$ Slope is -2. $y = -2x + b$ $-3 = -4 + b$ $1 = b$ $y = -2x + 1$ $2x + y = 1$	$4x - 2y = -3$

In the 2-point response, the student found the correct answer and showed all the work.

In the 1-point response, the student made a computational error in the second line. The final answer is wrong, but still the student received a point because the rest of the work is correct.

In the 0-point response, the student gave an incorrect answer without showing any work. The answer is not far off, so the student probably would have received a point if some work had been shown.

EXERCISES

1. At the right is another response to the Example above. How many points does the response deserve? Explain your reasoning.

> The equation is
> $4x - 2y = k$
> $4(2) - 2(-3) = k$
> $14 = k$
> $4x - 2y = 14$

Answer each question. Show your work.

2. As an orange grows over a five-week period, there is a linear relationship between the volume of the orange and time. At the beginning of the period, the volume is about 34 cm^3. Four weeks later, the volume is about 50 cm^3. What is the volume at the end of the five-week period?

3. A line perpendicular to $x + 3y = 5$ passes through $(1, -1)$. What is the equation of the line in standard form?

Chapter 2

Chapter Review

Vocabulary

absolute value function (p. 86)
constant of variation (p. 72)
dependent variable (p. 62)
direct variation (p. 72)
domain (p. 56)
function (p. 57)
function notation (p. 58)
independent variable (p. 62)
linear equation (p. 62)
linear function (p. 62)
linear inequality (p. 99)
mapping diagram (p. 56)
parent function (p. 91)
point-slope form (p. 65)
range (p. 56)
relation (p. 55)
scatter plot (p. 80)
slope (p. 64)
slope-intercept form (p. 65)
standard form (p. 63)
translation (p. 91)
trend line (p. 80)
vertex (p. 86)
vertical-line test (p. 57)
***x*-intercept** (p. 63)
***y*-intercept** (p. 63)

Reading Math
Understanding Vocabulary

Take It to the NET
Online vocabulary quiz at **www.PHSchool.com**
Web Code: agj-0251

Choose the correct term to complete each sentence.

1. In the function $y = f(x)$, y is the (*dependent, independent*) variable.
2. All functions are (*relations, domains*).
3. The graph of a function is (*always, sometimes*) a line.
4. An equation of the form $y - y_1 = m(x - x_1)$ is in (*point-slope, slope-intercept*) form.
5. The vertex of the graph of an absolute value function is (*always, sometimes*) the lowest point on the graph.

Skills and Concepts

2-1 Objectives

- To graph relations (p. 55)
- To identify functions (p. 57)

A **relation** is a set of ordered pairs that can be represented by points in the coordinate plane or by a **mapping diagram.** The **domain** of a relation is the set of x-coordinates. The **range** is the set of y-coordinates.

When each element of the domain of a relation is paired with exactly one element of the range, the relation is a **function.** You can write a function using the notation $f(x)$, called **function notation.**

Determine whether each relation is a function. Find the domain and range.

6. $\{(5, 0), (8, 1), (1, 3), (5, 2), (3, 8)\}$

7. $\{(10, 2), (-10, 2), (6, 4), (5, 3), (-6, 7)\}$

8.

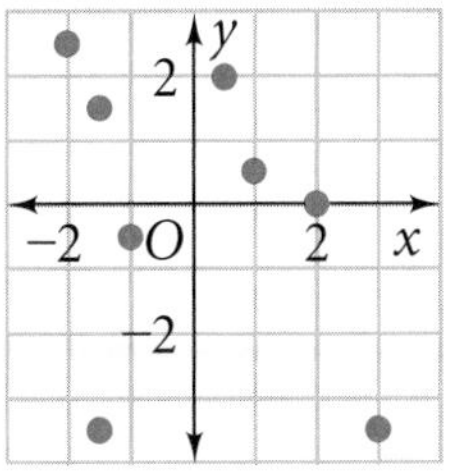

9. Domain Range

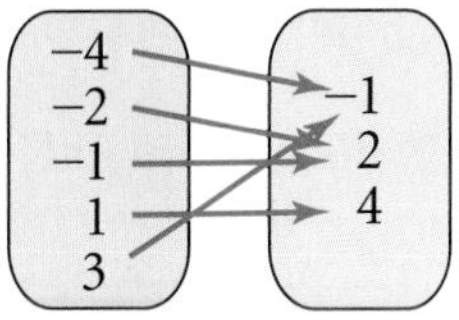

10. Domain Range

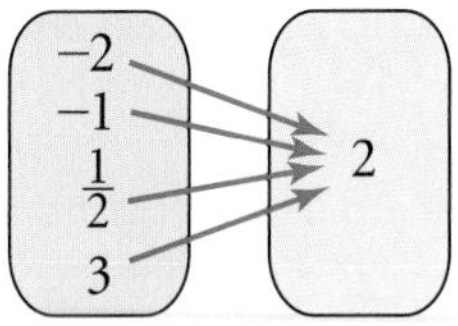

For each function, find $f(-2)$, $f(-0.5)$, and $f(3)$.

11. $f(x) = -x + 4$

12. $f(x) = \frac{3}{8}x - 3$

13. $f(x) = -\frac{5}{12}x + 2$

2-2 Objectives

- To graph linear equations (p. 62)
- To write equations of lines (p. 64)

The graph of a **linear function** is a line. You can represent a linear function with a **linear equation.** In a function, the value of y depends on the value of x, so y is the **dependent variable** and x is the **independent variable.**

Given two points on a line, the **slope** of the line is the ratio of the difference of the y-coordinates to the corresponding difference of the x-coordinates. The slope equals the coefficient of x when you write a linear equation in **slope-intercept form.** You can also write a linear equation in **point-slope form** or **standard form.** You can use the slopes of lines to determine whether or not they are parallel, perpendicular, or horizontal. A vertical line has no slope.

Write in standard form an equation for each line.

14. slope $= -3$, through $(4, 0)$

15. through $(2, 3)$ and $(3, 5)$

Find the slope, x-intercept, and y-intercept of each line.

16. $4x - 2y = 3$

17. $Mx = Ny + P$

18. $5 - x = y$

19. a. Write an equation of the line parallel to $x + 2y = 6$ through $(8, 3)$.
b. Write an equation of the line perpendicular to $x + 2y = 6$ through $(8, 3)$.
c. Graph the three lines on the same coordinate plane.

2-3 Objectives

- To write and interpret direct variation equations (p. 72)

A linear equation of the form $y = kx$ represents a **direct variation.** The **constant of variation** is k. You can use proportions to solve some direct variation problems.

For each function, determine whether y varies directly with x. If so, find the constant of variation and write the equation.

20.

x	y
−2	3
0	4
2	7

21.

x	y
4	5
6	9
10	17

22.

x	y
0	0
1	1
5	5

Find each constant of variation. Then find the value of y when $x = -0.3$.

23. $y = 2$ when $x = -\frac{1}{2}$

24. $y = \frac{2}{3}$ when $x = 0.2$

25. $y = 7$ when $x = 2$

2-4 Objectives

- To write linear equations that model real-world data (p. 78)
- To make predictions from linear models (p. 79)

You can use mathematical models such as **scatter plots** to show relationships between data sets. You can use the models to make predictions about the data set. Sometimes you can draw a **trend line** to model the relation and make predictions.

26. a. Data Analysis Draw a scatter plot of the data below.
b. Draw a trend line. Write its equation.
c. Estimate the number of cable TV subscribers in 2005.

Cable TV Subscribers

Year	1980	1985	1990	1995
Millions of Subscribers	17.7	39.9	54.9	63.0

SOURCE: Television Bureau of Advertising

Draw a scatter plot of each set of data. Decide whether a linear model is reasonable. If so, draw a trend line and write its equation. Then predict the value of y when x is 15.

27.

x	3	4	5	7	8	9	10
y	5	7	9	10	10	11	13

28.

x	6	7	8	9	10	11	12
y	15.5	14.0	13.0	12.5	12.0	11.5	10.0

2-5 and 2-6 Objectives

- To graph absolute value functions (p. 86)
- To analyze vertical translations (p. 91)
- To analyze horizontal translations (p. 92)

The **absolute value function** $y = |x|$ has a graph in the shape of a V. It is the **parent function** for the family of functions of the form $y = |x + h| + k$. The maximum or minimum point of the V is the **vertex** of the graph.

The value of h represents a horizontal translation of the parent graph by h units left (h is positive) or right (h is negative). The k represents a vertical translation of the graph by k units up (k is positive) or down (k is negative). A combination of a horizontal and a vertical translation is a diagonal translation.

Graph each equation by writing two linear equations.

29. $y = |x - 7|$ **30.** $y = -|x + 10|$ **31.** $y = \frac{1}{3}|2x + 6| + 2$

Describe each translation of $f(x) = |x|$ as vertical, horizontal, or diagonal. Then graph each translation.

32. $f(x) = |x| - 8$ **33.** $f(x) = |x - 5|$ **34.** $f(x) = |x - 3| + 3$

Write an equation for each translation.

35. $y = x$, 2 units down
36. $y = x$, through $(-3, 2)$
37. $y = |x|$, 4 units up, 2 units right
38. $y = |x|$, vertex $(-3, 0)$
39. $y = -|x|$, vertex $(5, 2)$
40. $y = -x$, through $(4, 1)$

2-7 Objectives

- To graph linear inequalities (p. 99)
- To graph absolute value inequalities (p. 101)

A **linear inequality** describes a region of the coordinate plane that has a boundary. To graph an inequality involving two variables, first graph the boundary. Then decide which side of the boundary contains solutions. Points on a dashed boundary are not solutions. Points on a solid boundary are solutions.

Graph each inequality.

41. $y \geq -2$ **42.** $y < 3x + 1$ **43.** $y \leq -|x - 5|$ **44.** $y > |2x + 1|$

45. Transportation An air cargo plane can transport as many as 15 regular shipping containers. One super-size container takes up the space of 3 regular containers.
a. Write an inequality to model the situation.
b. Describe the domain and range.
c. Graph the inequality you wrote in part (a).

46. Open-Ended Write an absolute value inequality with a solid boundary that has solutions below the x-axis only.

Chapter 2

Chapter Test

Take It to the NET
Online chapter test at
www.PHSchool.com
Web Code: aga-0252

Find the domain and range. Graph each relation.

1. $\{(0,0), (1,-1), (2,-4), (3,-9), (4,-16)\}$

2. $\{(3,2), (4,3), (5,4), (6,5), (7,6)\}$

3. Domain Range

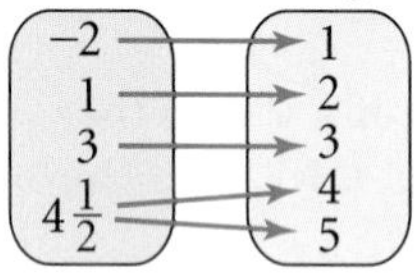

4. Domain Range

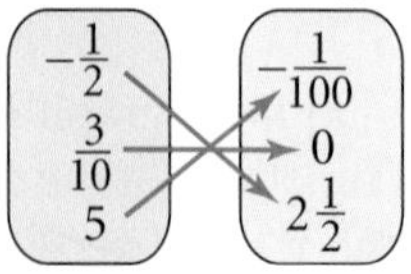

Suppose $f(x) = 2x - 5$ and $g(x) = |-3x - 1|$. Find each value.

5. $f(3)$
6. $f(1) + g(2)$
7. $g(0)$
8. $g(2) - f(0)$
9. $f(-1) - g(3)$
10. $2g(-4)$

11. **Open-Ended** Graph a relation that is *not* a function. Find its domain and range.

Find the slope of each line.

12. through (3, 5) and (1, 1)

13. $4x + 3y = 2$

14. through $(-0.5, 0.5)$, perpendicular to $y = -2x - 4$

Write in standard form an equation of the line with the given slope through the given point.

15. slope $= -3$, (0, 0)
16. slope $= \frac{2}{5}$, (6, 7)
17. slope $= 4$, $(-2, -5)$
18. slope $= -0.5$, (0, 6)

Write in point-slope form an equation of the line through each pair of points.

19. (0, 0) and $(-4, 7)$
20. $(-1, -6)$ and $(-2, 10)$
21. (3, 0) and $(-1, -2)$
22. (9, 5) and (8, 2)

23. a. **Open-Ended** Write an equation of a line with negative slope.
  b. Write an equation of the line perpendicular to the line from part (a) passing through $(-6, 9)$.
  c. Write an equation of the line parallel to the line from part (b) passing through (12, 12).
  d. Write an equation of the line perpendicular to the line from part (c) passing through $(-1, -4)$.
  e. Graph the lines from parts (a), (b), (c), and (d). If they form a polygon, describe it.

For each direct variation, find the constant of variation. Then find the value of y when $x = -0.5$.

24. $y = 4$ when $x = 0.5$
25. $y = 2$ when $x = 3$

26. **Transportation** The number of minutes a freight train takes to pass an intersection varies directly with the number of cars in the train. A 150-car train passes in 3 min. How long will a 210-car train take to pass?

Graph each function.

27. $y = 3x + 4$
28. $y = |5x - 3| + 1$
29. $y = -|x - 3| + 1$
30. $y = 3 - \frac{2}{5}x$

31. **Recreation** The table displays the amounts the Jackson family spent on vacations during the years 1993–2003.

Jackson Family Vacation Costs

Year	Cost	Year	Cost
1993	\$1000	1999	\$2750
1994	\$1750	2000	\$3200
1995	\$1750	2001	\$2900
1996	\$2000	2002	\$3100
1997	\$2200	2003	\$3300
1998	\$2700		

  a. Make a scatter plot of the data.
  b. Draw a trend line. Write its equation.
  c. Estimate the cost to the Jackson family of vacations in 2005.
  d. **Writing** Explain how to use a trend line with a scatter plot.

Describe each translation as vertical, horizontal, or diagonal. Then graph each function.

32. $y = x - 4$
33. $y = |x - 1| - 5$
34. $y = -|x + 4| + 3$
35. $y = x + 1$
36. $y = |x| + 5$
37. $y = -|x + 2| - 3$

Graph each inequality.

38. $y \geq x + 7$
39. $y > |2x + 3| - 3$
40. $4x + 3y < 2$
41. $y \leq -|x + 1| - 2$

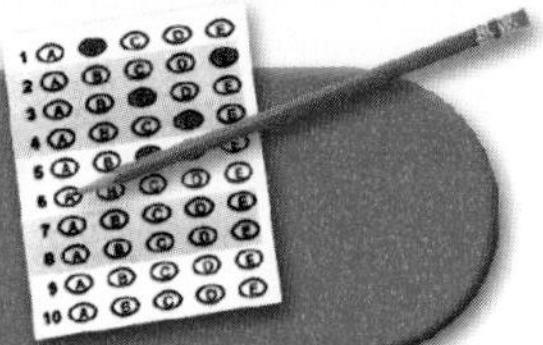

Standardized Test Prep

Multiple Choice

For Exercises 1–8, choose the correct letter.

1. Which phrase could NOT describe $\sqrt{625}$?
A. whole number **B.** irrational number
C. integer **D.** rational number

2. Which value is in the solution set of
$4 < -4x - 2 < 8$ and $3 > 4x + 2 > -10$?
F. -2 **G.** 0 **H.** 2 **I.** 4

3. Which point could NOT be on the graph of a function that includes (5, 4), (8, −1), (7, 3), (0, 5), and (10, −2)?
A. (6, 4) **B.** (10, 1) **C.** (11, −1) **D.** (9, 3)

4. Which relations are functions?

I.
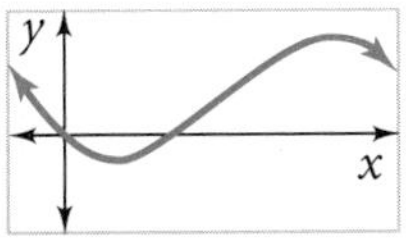

II.
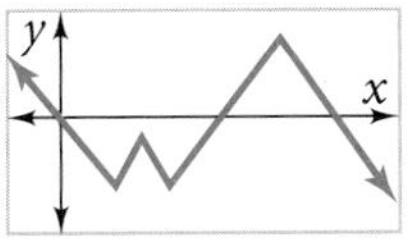

III.

IV.
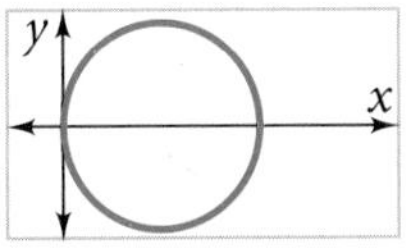

F. I and II **G.** I and III
H. II and III **I.** II and IV

5. Which lines are parallel?
I. $y = -2x + 1$ **II.** $y = x - 4$
III. $y = -x + 5$ **IV.** $y = 3 - 2x$
A. I and II **B.** I and III
C. I and IV **D.** II and IV

6. Which values are solutions of $y < 2x + 3$?
I. (0, 2) **II.** (−1, 1) **III.** (2, 0)
F. I only **G.** II only
H. I and III **I.** II and III

7. Which line is perpendicular to $y = 2x - 4$?
A. $y = -2x + 4$ **B.** $y = -4 - 2x$
C. $y = -x - 2$ **D.** $y = -\frac{1}{2}x + 4$

8. Which equation is in standard form?
F. $x - y = 7$ **G.** $y = 3x - 1$
H. $x = 4y + 2$ **I.** $10 - 5x = 2y$

Quantitative Comparison

Compare the boxed quantity in Column A with the boxed quantity in Column B. Choose the best answer.

A. The quantity in Column A is greater.
B. The quantity in Column B is greater.
C. The two quantities are equal.
D. The relationship cannot be determined from the information given.

	Column A	Column B
9.	$\sqrt{27}$	5^2
10.	$\sqrt{36}$	6^2
11.	the *x*-intercept of $3x + 4y = 12$	the *y*-intercept of $3x + 4y = 12$
12.	the slope of $y = 3x - 4$	the slope of $2y - 6x = 7$

Gridded Response

13. What is the *y*-coordinate of the point through which the graph of every direct variation passes?

14. In one roll of two number cubes, what is the probability that the product of the faces is 12?

Short Response

15. Graph $y < |x + 3|$. Identify the parent function of the boundary and describe the translation.

16. Suppose *y* varies directly as *x*, and $y = 2$ when $x = -2$. Find the constant of variation. Then find the value of *x* when $y = 3$.

Extended Response

17. a. Write an equation of the line through (−2, 6) with slope 2.
b. Write an equation of the line through (1, 1) perpendicular to the line in part (a).
c. Graph the two lines on the same set of axes.

Bridges, Beams, and Tension

Applying Functions Even steel bends when heavy loads are applied to it. In designing bridges and other structures, civil engineers use functions to predict how much a beam will deflect, or bend, under a given load. They design bridges so that the stress from the combined weights of the bridge materials and the vehicles that cross the bridge, along with stress from winds, does not exceed allowable limits.

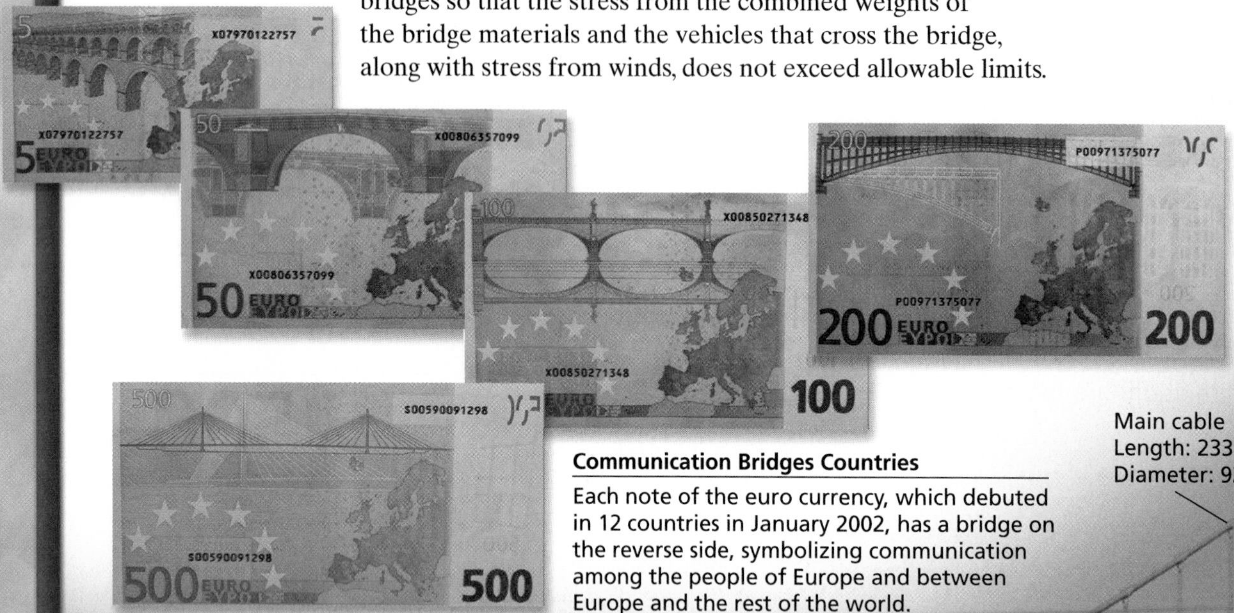

Communication Bridges Countries

Each note of the euro currency, which debuted in 12 countries in January 2002, has a bridge on the reverse side, symbolizing communication among the people of Europe and between Europe and the rest of the world.

The Leonardo Bridge

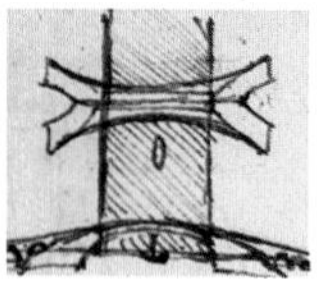

Designed by Leonardo da Vinci in 1502 and constructed in 2000 near Oslo, Norway, the Leonardo Bridge is a pressed-bow construction. The middle section of the arch is only 65 cm thick. Toward the sides and bottom, the thickness increases by a factor of seven, to 4.5 m.

Activity

Materials: pencil and paper, graph paper, ruler, paper clips, two balsa wood dowels at least 55 cm long, 10 washers

- Lay the dowels side by side on a table so that they extend 25 cm over the edge. Place books on the dowels to hold them in place.
- Bend a paper clip into a hook to hold the washers. Suspend the paper clip from one of the dowels.

a. Add 1 washer at a time to the paper clip. Measure the amount of deflection of the end of the dowel by measuring the vertical distance between the dowels. Use a table to record the weight W in number of washers and the deflection v.

b. Reposition the dowels 15 cm over the edge of the table. Place 5 washers on the paper clip. Measure the deflection. Increase the length of the extension in 3-cm increments until the dowel extends 45 cm from the edge of the table. Record the length of the extension L and the deflection v in a table.

c. Using two different coordinate planes, graph the relationships from parts (a) and (b): deflection vs. weight and deflection vs. extension.

d. **Reasoning** In the functions below, k is a constant for the dowel tested, L is the length of the dowel extension, v is the deflection at the end of the dowel, and W is the weight of the load. Determine which function best describes a dowel's deflection in response to changes in load and length.

A. $v = kLW$ **B.** $v = kL^2W$ **C.** $v = kLW^2$ **D.** $v = kL^2W^2$

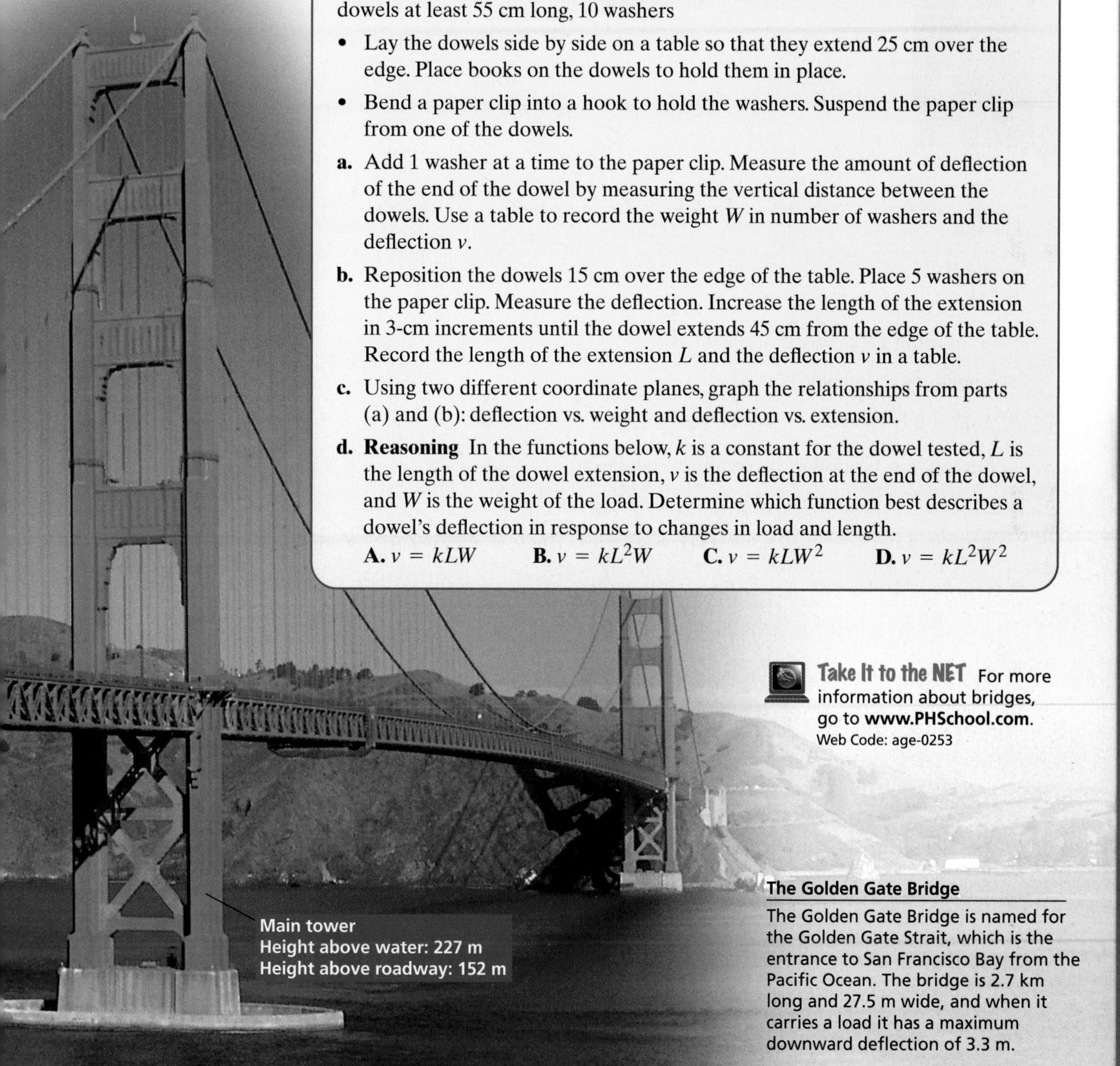

Take It to the NET For more information about bridges, go to **www.PHSchool.com**.
Web Code: age-0253

The Golden Gate Bridge

The Golden Gate Bridge is named for the Golden Gate Strait, which is the entrance to San Francisco Bay from the Pacific Ocean. The bridge is 2.7 km long and 27.5 m wide, and when it carries a load it has a maximum downward deflection of 3.3 m.

Where You've Been

- In Chapter 1, you learned to write and solve equations and inequalities in one variable.
- In Chapter 2, you learned to write and solve equations and inequalities in two variables.
- In Chapter 2, you learned to graph points and equations in two dimensions.

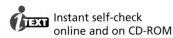

Instant self-check online and on CD-ROM

Diagnosing Readiness

(For help, go to the Lesson in green.)

Combining Like Terms (Lesson 1-2)

Simplify by combining like terms.

1. $3x + (4x - 1)$ **2.** $12 - (p + 7)$ **3.** $(2z + 10) - 8z$ **4.** $(r - 1) - 3$

Solving and Graphing Inequalities (Lesson 1-4)

Solve each inequality. Graph the solutions on a number line.

5. $6a \leq 9$ **6.** $8b + 11 > 27$ **7.** $3(24 + 2c) < 0$ **8.** $5(0.2 + d) \leq -4$

Graphing Relations (Lesson 2-1)

Graph each relation on a coordinate plane.

9. $\{(0, 4), (-2, 1), (2, 7), (-4, 4), (4, 4)\}$ **10.** $\left\{\left(0, \frac{1}{2}\right), \left(1, \frac{5}{2}\right), \left(2, \frac{9}{2}\right), \left(3, \frac{13}{2}\right), \left(4, \frac{17}{2}\right)\right\}$

Graphing Equations (Lesson 2-2)

Graph each equation on a coordinate plane.

11. $y = 4x + 1$ **12.** $-6y + x = 3$ **13.** $15x - 3y = 5$ **14.** $x = 2y - 7$

Writing a Linear Model (Lesson 2-4)

15. Each minute, a toll collector serves an average of six motorists. Write an equation to model the number of motorists this toll collector assists as a function of time. Graph the equation.

Graphing Inequalities (Lesson 2-7)

Graph each inequality on a coordinate plane.

16. $y > 8x + 3$ **17.** $2y + x \leq -10$ **18.** $18x - 9y < 2$ **19.** $x \geq 4y - 5$

Linear Systems

Chapter 3

LESSONS

Key Vocabulary

- constraints (p. 135)
- coordinate space (p. 142)
- dependent system (p. 118)
- equivalent systems (p. 125)
- feasible region (p. 136)
- inconsistent system (p. 118)
- independent system (p. 118)
- linear programming (p. 135)
- linear system (p. 116)
- objective function (p. 135)
- ordered triples (p. 142)
- system of equations (p. 116)
- trace (p. 144)

Where You're Going

- In Chapter 3, you will learn to solve systems of equations and inequalities in two variables algebraically and by graphing.
- You will learn to graph points and equations in three dimensions.
- You will learn to solve systems of equations in three variables.

Real-World Connection Applying what you learn, on page 139 you will solve a problem about planting trees.

3-1 Graphing Systems of Equations

North Carolina Objectives

2.10 Use systems of two or more equations or inequalities to model and solve problems; justify results. Solve using tables, graphs, matrix operations, and algebraic properties.

Lesson Preview

What You'll Learn

OBJECTIVE 1 To solve a system by graphing

. . . And Why

To predict sports records, as in Example 2

Check Skills You'll Need

(For help, go to Lesson 2-2.)

Graph each equation.

1. $y = 3x - 2$ **2.** $y = -x$ **3.** $y = -\frac{1}{2}x + 4$

Graph each equation. Use one coordinate plane for all three graphs.

4. $2x - y = 1$ **5.** $2x - y = -1$ **6.** $x + 2y = 2$

New Vocabulary
- system of equations
- linear system
- independent system
- dependent system
- inconsistent system

Interactive lesson includes instant self-check, tutorials, and activities.

OBJECTIVE 1

Systems of Linear Equations

Investigation: Analyzing Graphs

1. Use a graphing calculator to graph each pair of equations.

   a. $y = x + 5$, $y = -2x + 5$ **b.** $y = 3x + 2$, $y = 3x - 1$ **c.** $y = -4x - 2$, $y = \frac{8x + 4}{-2}$

2. For each pair, answer the following questions.
   a. Do the graphs have any points in common; if so, how many?
   b. Compare the slopes of the graphs. What is the relationship between the slopes and the number of points in common?

3. Copy and complete the table for the graphs of two linear equations.

Description of Lines	How Many Points of Intersection?	Equal Slopes? (yes/no)	Same y-intercepts? (yes/no)
intersecting	■	■	either
parallel	■	■	■
coinciding	■	■	■

Need Help?

If the equation of a line is in the form $y = mx + b$, then the slope is m.

A **system of equations** is a set of two or more equations that use the same variables. If the graph of each equation in a system of two variables is a line, then the system is a **linear system.**

A brace is used to keep the equations of a system together.

$$\begin{cases} y = x + 3 \\ y = -2x + 3 \end{cases}$$

A solution of a system of equations is a set of values for the variables that makes all the equations true. You can solve some linear systems by graphing the equations. The points where both (or all) the graphs intersect represent solutions.

1 EXAMPLE Solving by Graphing

Solve the system by graphing. $\begin{cases} x + 2y = -7 \\ 2x - 3y = 0 \end{cases}$

Graph the equations and find the intersection. The solution appears to be $(-3, -2)$.

Check Show that $(-3, -2)$ makes both equations true.

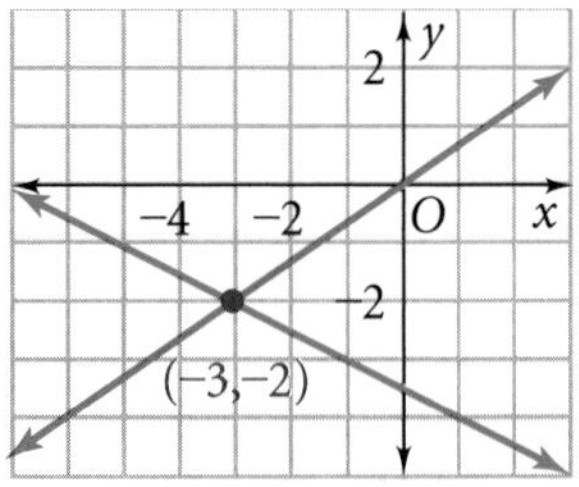

$$\begin{aligned} x + 2y &= -7 \\ -3 + 2(-2) &\stackrel{?}{=} -7 \\ -3 - 4 &\stackrel{?}{=} -7 \\ -7 &= -7 \ \checkmark \end{aligned} \qquad \begin{aligned} 2x - 3y &= 0 \\ 2(-3) - 3(-2) &\stackrel{?}{=} 0 \\ -6 + 6 &\stackrel{?}{=} 0 \\ 0 &= 0 \ \checkmark \end{aligned}$$

Check Understanding **1** Solve $\begin{cases} 2x + y = 5 \\ -x + y = 2 \end{cases}$ by graphing. Check your solution.

2 EXAMPLE Real-World Connection

Real-World Connection

Cathy Freeman won the 400-m run in the 2000 Olympics.

Sports Winning times for the Olympic 400-m run have been decreasing more rapidly for women than for men. Use the data in the table to find linear models for women's and men's times. Predict the year in which the women's winning time could equal that of the men, assuming that current trends continue.

Winning Times for the Olympic 400-Meter Dash (seconds)

Year	1968	1972	1976	1980	1984	1988	1992	1996	2000
Men's Time	43.86	44.66	44.26	44.60	44.27	43.87	43.50	43.49	43.84
Women's Time	52.03	51.08	49.29	48.88	48.83	48.65	48.83	48.25	49.11

SOURCE: *The World Almanac*

Step 1 Let x = number of years since 1968.
Let y = winning times in seconds.

Use the **LinReg** feature of a graphing calculator to find linear models.

Men's time: $y \approx -0.02433x + 44.43$
Women's time: $y \approx -0.08883x + 50.86$

Step 2 Graph each model. Use the Intersect feature on the graphing calculator. The two lines meet at about (99.7, 42.0).

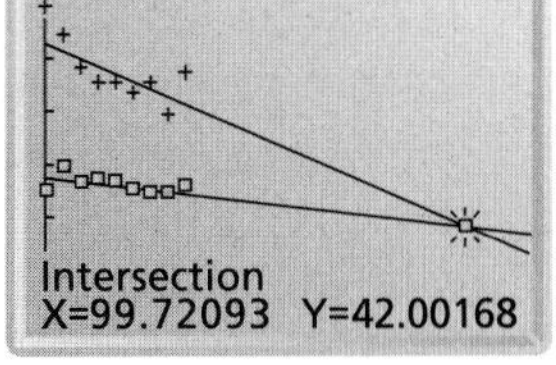

If the trends continue, the times for men and women will be equal about 100 years from 1968, in 2068.

Check Understanding **2** **a.** Use the models in Example 2 to predict the winning times for the 400-m run at the Olympics in 2008 and in 2024.

b. Critical Thinking Example 2 assumes that current trends will continue. Explain why that assumption may not be valid.

Reading Math

Unique means "exactly one."

You can classify a system of two linear equations by the number of solutions. A system that has a unique solution, as in Examples 1 and 2, is an **independent system.** However, not every system has a unique solution.

A **dependent system** does not have a unique solution. An **inconsistent system** is a system that has no solution.

Key Concepts

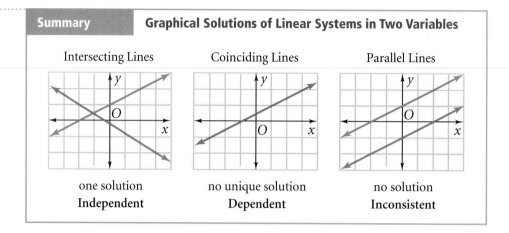

Summary **Graphical Solutions of Linear Systems in Two Variables**

Intersecting Lines

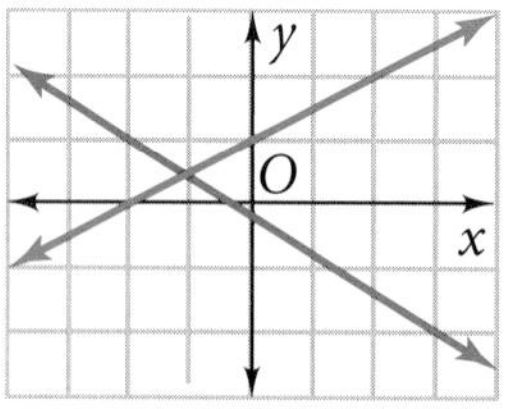

one solution
Independent

Coinciding Lines

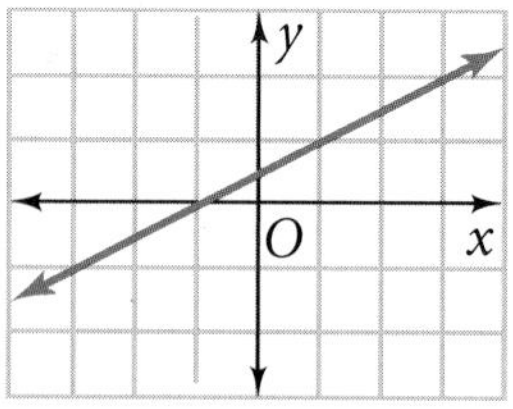

no unique solution
Dependent

Parallel Lines

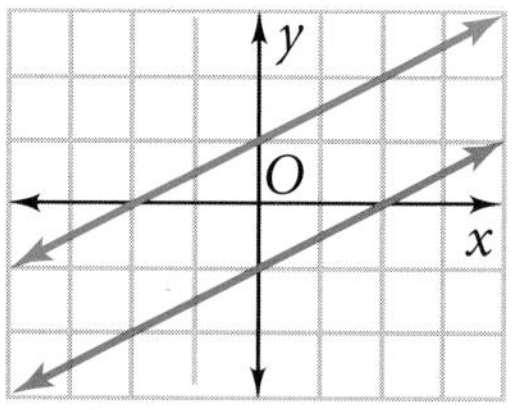

no solution
Inconsistent

You can also classify a system of equations without graphing. By comparing the slopes and y-intercepts of the equations, you can find the number of solutions.

3 EXAMPLE Classifying Systems Without Graphing

Classify the system without graphing. $\begin{cases} y = 2x + 3 \\ -2x + y = 1 \end{cases}$

$y = 2x + 3$	**Rewrite in slope-intercept form.** →	$y = 2x + 1$
$m = 2, b = 3$	← **Find the slope and y-intercept.** →	$m = 2, b = 1$

Since the slopes are the same, the lines could coincide. Compare the y-intercepts. Since the y-intercepts are different, the lines are parallel. There is no solution. The system is an inconsistent system.

Check Understanding **3** Without graphing, classify each system as *independent*, *dependent*, or *inconsistent*.

a. $\begin{cases} 3x + y = 5 \\ 15x + 5y = 2 \end{cases}$ **b.** $\begin{cases} y = 2x + 3 \\ -4x + 2y = 6 \end{cases}$ **c.** $\begin{cases} x - y = 5 \\ y + 3 = 2x \end{cases}$

EXERCISES

For more practice, see *Extra Practice.*

Practice and Problem Solving

A Practice by Example

Example 1 (page 117)

Solve each system by graphing. Check your answers.

1. $\begin{cases} y = x - 2 \\ y = -2x + 7 \end{cases}$ **2.** $\begin{cases} y = -x + 3 \\ y = \frac{3}{2}x - 2 \end{cases}$ **3.** $\begin{cases} 2x + 4y = 12 \\ x + y = 2 \end{cases}$

4. $\begin{cases} x = -3 \\ y = 5 \end{cases}$ **5.** $\begin{cases} 2x - 2y = 4 \\ y - x = 6 \end{cases}$ **6.** $\begin{cases} 3x + y = 5 \\ x - y = 7 \end{cases}$

7. $\begin{cases} -5x + y = -9 \\ x + 3y = 21 \end{cases}$ **8.** $\begin{cases} y = x \\ y - 5x = 0 \end{cases}$ **9.** $\begin{cases} x = 10 \\ x = y - 10 \end{cases}$

Example 2 (page 117)

For Exercises 10–11, use your graphing calculator. Find linear models for each set of data. Use each model to predict the year in which the quantities will be equal.

10. **Annual U.S. Consumption of Vegetables**

Year	Broccoli (lb/person)	Cucumbers (lb/person)
1970	0.5	2.6
1975	1.0	2.6
1980	1.4	3.6
1985	2.6	4.0
1990	3.4	4.3
1995	4.4	5.2
2000	5.7	5.8

SOURCE: *Statistical Abstract of the United States.*
Go to **www.PHSchool.com** for a data update.
Web Code: agg-2041

11. **U.S. Life Expectancy at Birth**

Year	Men (years)	Women (years)
1970	67.1	74.7
1975	68.8	76.6
1980	70.0	77.4
1985	71.1	78.2
1990	71.8	78.8
1995	72.5	78.9
1997	73.6	79.4

SOURCE: U.S. Census Bureau.
Go to **www.PHSchool.com** for a data update.
Web Code: agg-2041

12. a. **Business** The spreadsheet shows the monthly revenue and monthly expenses for a new business. Find a linear model for monthly revenue and a linear model for monthly expenses.

b. Use the models to predict the month in which revenue will equal expenses.

	A	B	C
1	Month	Revenue	Expenses
2	Feb	8000	35000
3	Mar	12000	33000
4	Apr	13000	34000
5	May	18000	32000
6	Jun	20000	31000

Example 3 (page 118)

Without graphing, classify each system as *independent*, *dependent*, or *inconsistent*.

13. $\begin{cases} 7x - y = 6 \\ -7x + y = -6 \end{cases}$

14. $\begin{cases} -3x + y = 4 \\ x - \frac{1}{3}y = 1 \end{cases}$

15. $\begin{cases} 4x + 8y = 12 \\ x + 2y = -3 \end{cases}$

16. $\begin{cases} y = 2x - 1 \\ y = -2x + 5 \end{cases}$

17. $\begin{cases} x = 6 \\ x = -2 \end{cases}$

18. $\begin{cases} 2y = 5x + 6 \\ -10x + 4y = 8 \end{cases}$

19. $\begin{cases} x - 3y = 2 \\ 4x - 12y = 8 \end{cases}$

20. $\begin{cases} x + 4y = 12 \\ 2x - 8y = 4 \end{cases}$

21. $\begin{cases} 4x + 8y = -6 \\ 6x + 12y = -9 \end{cases}$

22. $\begin{cases} 4y - 2x = 6 \\ 8y = 4x - 12 \end{cases}$

23. $\begin{cases} y - x = 0 \\ y = -x \end{cases}$

24. $\begin{cases} 2y - x = 4 \\ \frac{1}{2}x - y = 2 \end{cases}$

B Apply Your Skills

Graph and solve each system. Where necessary, estimate the solution.

25. $\begin{cases} 3 = 4y + x \\ 4y = -x + 3 \end{cases}$

26. $\begin{cases} x - 2y + 1 = 0 \\ x + 4y - 6 = 0 \end{cases}$

27. $\begin{cases} 3x + 6y - 12 = 0 \\ x + 2y = 8 \end{cases}$

28. $\begin{cases} -x + 3y = 6 \\ 2x - y = 8 \end{cases}$

29. $\begin{cases} 3x + y = 3 \\ 2x - y = 7 \end{cases}$

30. $\begin{cases} 2x + 3y = 6 \\ 4x = 6y + 3 \end{cases}$

31. $\begin{cases} 10 - 3x = -3y \\ 2 = 2x + y \end{cases}$

32. $\begin{cases} 3x = -5y + 4 \\ 250 + 150x = 300 \end{cases}$

33. $\begin{cases} x + 3y = 6 \\ 6y + 2x = 12 \end{cases}$

34. $\begin{cases} 2y + x = 8 \\ y - 2x = -6 \end{cases}$

35. $\begin{cases} y = -2x + 6 \\ x - 3y = -6 \end{cases}$

36. $\begin{cases} -x - 2 = -2y \\ 2x - 4y - 4 = 0 \end{cases}$

37. **Banking** To pay your monthly bills, you can either open a checking account or use an online banking service. A local bank charges \$3 per month and \$.40 per check, while an online services charges a flat fee of \$9 per month.

  a. Write and graph a system of linear equations to model the cost c of each service for b bills that you need to pay monthly.

  b. Find the point of intersection of the two linear models. What does this answer represent?

  c. If you pay about 12 bills per month, which service should you choose? Explain.

Classify each system without graphing.

38. $\begin{cases} 3x - 2y = 8 \\ 4y = 6x - 5 \end{cases}$ **39.** $\begin{cases} 2x + 8y = 6 \\ x = -4y + 3 \end{cases}$ **40.** $\begin{cases} 3a + 6b = 14 \\ -a + 2b = 3 \end{cases}$

41. $\begin{cases} 3m = -5n + 4 \\ n - \frac{6}{5} = -\frac{3}{5}m \end{cases}$ **42.** $\begin{cases} -12x + 4y = 8 \\ y - 4 = 3x \end{cases}$ **43.** $\begin{cases} -6y + 18 = 12x \\ 3y + 6x = 9 \end{cases}$

Real-World Connection

Groomers must be able to handle dogs of every breed and temperament.

44. **Fees** Suppose you are going on vacation and leaving your dog in a kennel. The Bowowery charges \$25 per day, which includes a one-time grooming treatment. The Poochpad charges \$20 per day and a one-time fee of \$30 for grooming.

  a. Write a system of equations to represent the cost c for d days that your dog will stay at a kennel.

  b. Using a graphing calculator, find the number of days for which the costs are the same.

  c. If your vacation is a week long, which kennel should you choose? Explain.

45. **Advertising** You and your business partner are mailing advertising flyers to your customers. You address 6 flyers each minute and have already done 80. Your partner addresses 4 flyers each minute and has already done 100. Graph and solve a system of equations to find when the two of you will have addressed equal numbers of flyers.

Open-Ended Write a second equation for each system so that the system will have the indicated number of solutions.

46. one $\begin{cases} y = -3x + 2 \\ \underline{\quad ? \quad} \end{cases}$ **47.** none $\begin{cases} y = -4x - 6 \\ \underline{\quad ? \quad} \end{cases}$ **48.** an infinite number $\begin{cases} 3y = 6x + 7 \\ \underline{\quad ? \quad} \end{cases}$

49. **Reasoning** Is it possible for an inconsistent linear system to consist of two lines with the same y-intercept? Explain.

50. **Writing** Summarize the possible relationships for the y-intercepts, slopes, and number of solutions in a system of two linear equations of two variables.

C Challenge

Open-Ended Write a second equation for each system so that the system will have the indicated number of solutions.

51. infinite number of solutions $\begin{cases} \frac{x}{4} + \frac{y}{3} = 1 \\ \underline{\quad ? \quad} \end{cases}$ **52.** no solutions $\begin{cases} 5x + 2y = 10 \\ \underline{\quad ? \quad} \end{cases}$

53. Write a system of linear equations with the solution set $\{(x, y) \mid y = 5x + 2\}$.

54. **Critical Thinking** Look back through the exercises on the previous two pages to find several dependent systems. What relationship exists between the equations in each system?

Reading Math

A widget is a small, unspecified gadget.

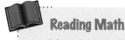

55. Economics Research shows that in a certain market only 2000 widgets can be sold at \$8 each, but if the price is reduced to \$3, then 10,000 can be sold.

a. Let p represent price and n represent the number of widgets. Identify the independent variable and the dependent variable.

b. Use the information above to write a linear *demand* equation.

c. A shop can make 2000 widgets for \$5 each and 20,000 widgets for \$2 each. Use this information to write a linear *supply* equation.

d. Find the equilibrium point where supply is equal to demand and profit is a maximum. Explain the meaning of the coordinates of this point within the context of the exercise.

Standardized Test Prep

Multiple Choice

56. Which is an equation for Line 2?

A. $3x - 5y = 15$ **B.** $3x + 5y = 3$

C. $3x + 5y = 15$ **D.** $5x + 3y = 15$

57. Which is NOT an equation for Line 1?

F. $y = x$ **G.** $x + y = 0$

H. $x - y = 0$ **I.** $y - x = 0$

58. Which point lies on both Line 1 and Line 2?

A. (0, 0) **B.** (1.875, 1.875)

C. (1.95, 1.95) **D.** (2, 2)

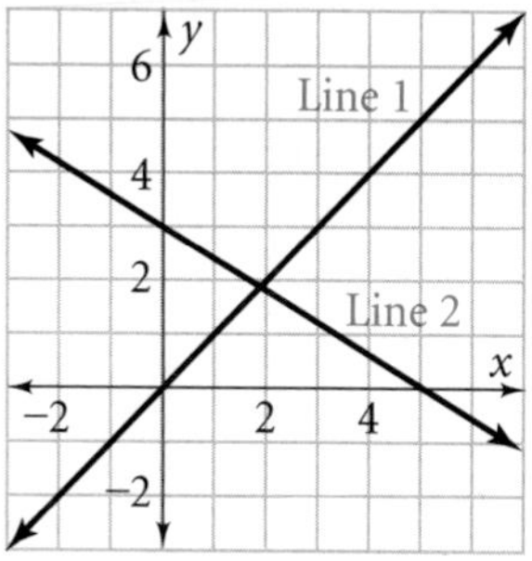

Exercises 56–58.

Take It to the NET

Online lesson quiz at **www.PHSchool.com**

Web Code: aga-0301

59. What is the solution of the system? $\begin{cases} 5x + 6y = -24 \\ -2x + 3y = 15 \end{cases}$

F. (6, −1) **G.** (6, 1) **H.** (−6, 1) **I.** (−6, −1)

Short Response

60. Explain how you can use slopes to show that the system $\begin{cases} 2x - 5y = 23 \\ 3y - 7x = -8 \end{cases}$ is NOT inconsistent.

Extended Response

61. One equation of a system of equations is $2x - 3y = 5$.

a. Find a second equation such that the system is dependent.

b. Find a second equation such that the system is inconsistent.

Mixed Review

Lesson 2-7 **Graph each inequality on a coordinate plane.**

62. $3x - 4y \geq 16$ **63.** $-5x > 8y + 4$ **64.** $x < -4$

Lesson 2-2 **Write an equation for each line.**

65. $m = -\frac{2}{3}$; contains $(-9, 4)$ **66.** $m = 0$; contains $(3, 4)$

67. $m = 2$; contains $(-2, -3)$ **68.** $m = -\frac{1}{2}$; contains $(2, -6)$

Lesson 1-3 **Solve each equation and check the solution.**

69. $3n = -4(2 + n)$ **70.** $-4a + a = 7a - 6$ **71.** $\frac{x}{3} + 5 = \frac{1}{6}$

72. $4x - 2 = \frac{1}{2}x$ **73.** $\frac{r}{5} + 5 = r - 3$ **74.** $2(m - 3) = -4$

Technology

Parametric Equations

For Use With Lesson 3-2

Parametric equations are equations that express the coordinates x and y as separate functions of a common third variable, called the parameter. You can use parametric equations to determine the position of an object over time.

EXAMPLE

Starting from a birdbath 3 ft above the ground, a bird takes flight. Let t equal time in seconds, x equal horizontal distance in feet, and y equal vertical distance in feet. The equations $x(t) = 5t$ and $y(t) = 8t + 3$ model the bird's distance from the base of the birdbath. Graph the equations. Describe the position of the bird at time $t = 3$.

Step 1 Press MODE. Change the function mode to Parametric.

```
Normal  Sci  Eng
Float  0123456789
Radian  Degree
Func  Par  Pol  Seq
Connected  Dot
Sequential  Simul
Real  a+bi  re^θi
Full  Horiz  G-T
```

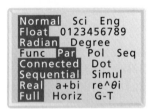

Step 2 Enter the equations.
(When you press Y= you will see a list of pairs of equations.)

```
  Plot1 Plot2 Plot3
\X1T=5T
 Y1T=8T+3
\X2T=
 Y2T=
\X3T=
 Y3T=
\X4T=
```

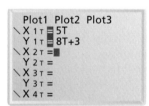

Step 3 Set the window values as shown.

```
WINDOW
 Tmin = 0
 Tmax = 6
 Tstep = .1
 Xmin = 0
 Xmax = 50
 Xscl = 2
↓Ymin = 0
```

```
WINDOW
↑Tstep = .1
 Xmin = 0
 Xmax = 50
 Xscl = 2
 Ymin = 0
 Ymax = 50
 Yscl = 2
```

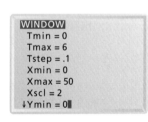

Step 4 Graph the equations.
Press TRACE to find $t = 3$.

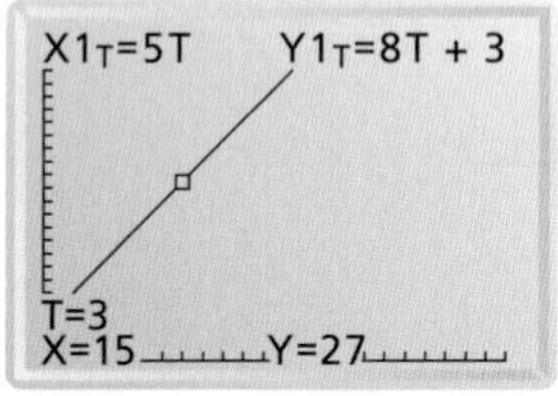

Three seconds after taking flight, the bird is 15 ft horizontally and 27 ft vertically from the base of the birdbath.

EXERCISES

Graph each pair of parametric equations. Set the window with the t-values at the right. Find the values of x and y at time $t = 3$.

```
WINDOW
 Tmin = -10
 Tmax = 10
 Tstep = .1
 Xmin = -10
 Xmax = 10
 Xscl = 1
↓Ymin = -10
```

1. $x(t) = t$
$y(t) = -t + 6$

2. $x(t) = -3t$
$y(t) = t - 6$

3. $x(t) = |t - 2|$
$y(t) = t + 2$

4. Writing Write a word problem involving the graph of $x(t) = 3t$ and $y(t) = 10t$. Interpret the x- and y-values at times $t = 0$, $t = 5$, and $t = -2$.

3-2 Solving Systems Algebraically

North Carolina Objectives

2.10 Use systems of two or more equations or inequalities to model and solve problems; justify results. Solve using tables, graphs, matrix operations, and algebraic properties.

Lesson Preview

What You'll Learn

OBJECTIVE 1 To solve a system by substitution

OBJECTIVE 2 To solve a system by elimination

. . . And Why

To find the cost of joining a health club, as in Example 2

Check Skills You'll Need

(For help, go to Lessons 1-1 and 1-3.)

Find the additive inverse of each term.

1. 4 **2.** $-x$ **3.** $5x$ **4.** $8y$

Substitute $2y - 1$ for x in each equation. Solve for y.

5. $x + 2y = 3$ **6.** $y - 2x = 8$ **7.** $2y + 3x = -5$

New Vocabulary

- equivalent systems

Interactive lesson includes instant self-check, tutorials, and activities.

OBJECTIVE 1 Solving Systems by Substitution

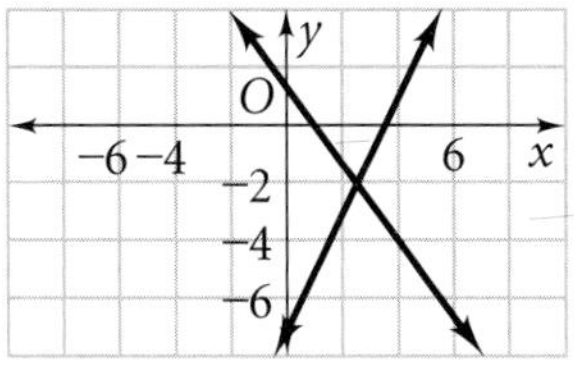

$$\begin{cases} 4x + 3y = 4 \\ 2x - y = 7 \end{cases}$$

Not every system can be solved easily by graphing. Consider the system at the left. Although you can graph each line easily, the exact point of intersection is not obvious. Substitution allows you to find exact solutions without using a graphing calculator.

1 EXAMPLE Solving by Substitution

Solve the system by substitution. $\begin{cases} 4x + 3y = 4 \\ 2x - y = 7 \end{cases}$

Step 1 Solve for one of the variables. Solving the second equation for y is easiest.

$$2x - y = 7$$
$$y = 2x - 7$$

Step 2 Substitute the expression for y into the other equation. Solve for x.

$$4x + 3y = 4$$
$$4x + 3(2x - 7) = 4 \quad \text{Substitute for } y.$$
$$4x + 6x - 21 = 4 \quad \text{Distributive Property}$$
$$4x + 6x = 25$$
$$x = 2.5$$

Step 3 Substitute the value of x into either equation. Solve for y.

$$y = 2x - 7$$
$$y = 2(2.5) - 7 \quad \text{Substitute for } x.$$
$$y = -2$$

The solution is $(2.5, -2)$.

Check Understanding

1 Solve each system by substitution. Check your answers.

a. $\begin{cases} 2x - 3y = 6 \\ x + y = -12 \end{cases}$ **b.** $\begin{cases} 3x - y = 0 \\ 4x + 3y = 26 \end{cases}$

2 EXAMPLE **Real-World Connection**

Health Club Membership Fees

2 months: \$100
6 months: \$200

Fees Refer to the photo at the left. The cost of membership in a health club includes a monthly charge and a one-time initiation fee. Find the monthly charge and the initiation fee.

Relate 2 · monthly charge + initiation fee = \$100

6 · monthly charge + initiation fee = \$200

Define Let m = the monthly charge. Let f = the initiation fee.

Write $\begin{cases} 2m + f = 100 \\ 6m + f = 200 \end{cases}$

$2m + f = 100$ **Solve for one of the variables.**

$f = -2m + 100$

$6m + (-2m + 100) = 200$ **Substitute the expression for f into the other equation. Solve for m.**

$m = 25$

$2(25) + f = 100$ **Substitute the value of m into one of the equations. Solve for f.**

$f = 50$

The monthly charge is \$25, and the initiation fee is \$50.

Check Understanding 2 **Shopping** You can buy CDs at a local store for \$15.49 each. You can buy them at an online store for \$13.99 each plus \$6 for shipping. Solve a system of equations to find the number of CDs that you can buy for the same amount at the two stores.

OBJECTIVE 2

Solving Systems by Elimination

You can solve a system of equations using the Addition Property of Equality. If the quantities you add contain a pair of additive inverses, you can eliminate a variable. You can also eliminate a variable by subtracting like terms.

3 EXAMPLE **Solving by Elimination**

Use the elimination method to solve the system. $\begin{cases} 4x - 2y = 7 \\ x + 2y = 3 \end{cases}$

$4x - 2y = 7$

$x + 2y = 3$ **Two terms are additive inverses, so add.**

$5x = 10$

$x = 2$ **Solve for x.**

$x + 2y = 3$ **Choose one of the original equations.**

$2 + 2y = 3$ **Substitute for x.**

$y = \frac{1}{2}$ **Solve for y.**

The solution is $\left(2, \frac{1}{2}\right)$.

Check Understanding 3 Solve each system by elimination.

a. $\begin{cases} 3x - 2y = 14 \\ 2x + 2y = 6 \end{cases}$

b. $\begin{cases} 4x + 9y = 1 \\ 4x + 6y = -2 \end{cases}$

Need Help?

The Multiplication Property of Equality states that if $a = b$ then $ac = bc$.

To make two terms additive inverses, you may need to multiply one or both equations in a system by a nonzero number. In doing so, you create a system equivalent to the original one. **Equivalent systems** are systems that have the same solution(s).

4 EXAMPLE Solving an Equivalent System

Solve the system below by elimination.

$$\begin{cases} 3x + 7y = 15 \\ 5x + 2y = -4 \end{cases}$$

To eliminate the y terms, make them additive inverses by multiplying.

① $3x + 7y = 15$	$6x + 14y = 30$	**Multiply ① by 2.**
② $5x + 2y = -4$	$-35x - 14y = 28$	**Multiply ② by −7.**
	$-29x = 58$	**Add.**
	$x = -2$	**Solve for x.**
	$3x + 7y = 15$	**Choose an original equation.**
	$3(-2) + 7y = 15$	**Substitute the value of x.**
	$-6 + 7y = 15$	**Simplify.**
	$7y = 21$	
	$y = 3$	**Solve for y.**

The solution is $(-2, 3)$.

Check Understanding **4** Explain how to solve the system in Example 4 by eliminating x.

Solving a system algebraically does not always result in a unique solution, as in Examples 3 and 4. You may get an equation that is always true, or one that is never true.

5 EXAMPLE Solving a System Without a Unique Solution

Solve each system by elimination.

a. $\begin{cases} 2x - y = 3 \\ -2x + y = -3 \end{cases}$

$0 = 0$

Elimination gives an equation that is always true. The two equations in the system represent the same line. The system has an infinite number of solutions: $\{(x, y) \mid y = 2x - 3\}$.

b. $\begin{cases} 2x - 3y = 18 \\ -2x + 3y = -6 \end{cases}$

$0 = 12$

Elimination gives an equation that is always false. The two equations in the system represent parallel lines. The system has no solution.

Check Understanding **5** Solve each system by substitution or elimination.

a. $\begin{cases} -3x + 5y = 7 \\ 6x - 10y = -14 \end{cases}$

b. $\begin{cases} -2x + 4y = 6 \\ -3x + 6y = 8 \end{cases}$

EXERCISES

For more practice, see *Extra Practice.*

Practice and Problem Solving

A Practice by Example

Solve each system by substitution. Check your answers.

Example 1 (page 123)

1. $\begin{cases} 4x + 2y = 7 \\ y = 5x \end{cases}$

2. $\begin{cases} 3c + 2d = 2 \\ d = 4 \end{cases}$

3. $\begin{cases} x + 12y = 68 \\ x = 8y - 12 \end{cases}$

4. $\begin{cases} 4p + 2q = 8 \\ q = 2p + 1 \end{cases}$

5. $\begin{cases} x + 3y = 7 \\ 2x - 4y = 24 \end{cases}$

6. $\begin{cases} x + 6y = 2 \\ 5x + 4y = 36 \end{cases}$

7. $\begin{cases} 3a + b = 3 \\ 2a - 5b = -15 \end{cases}$

8. $\begin{cases} t = 2r + 3 \\ 5r - 4t = 6 \end{cases}$

9. $\begin{cases} y = 2x - 1 \\ 3x - y = -1 \end{cases}$

10. $\begin{cases} 2m + 4n = 10 \\ 3m + 5n = 11 \end{cases}$

11. $\begin{cases} -6 = 3x - 6y \\ 4x = 4 + 5y \end{cases}$

12. $\begin{cases} r + s = -12 \\ 2r - 3s = 6 \end{cases}$

Example 2 (page 124)

13. **Fund-Raising** Suppose you have signed up for a bike-a-thon to raise money for charity. One person is sponsoring you at a rate of \$.50 per mile. Each of the other sponsors plans to donate \$15 no matter how far you bike.
    a. Write a system of equations to model the donation d for m miles biked.
    b. For how many miles will all sponsors donate the same amount?

14. **Transportation** A youth group with 26 members is going skiing. Each of the five chaperones will drive a van or a sedan. The vans can seat seven people, and the sedans can seat five people. How many of each type of vehicle could transport all 31 people to the ski area in one trip?

15. Suppose you have a part-time job delivering packages. Your employer pays you at a flat rate of \$7 per hour. You discover that a competitor pays employees \$2 per hour plus \$.35 per delivery.
    a. Write a system of equations to model the pay p for d deliveries. Assume a four-hour shift.
    b. How many deliveries would the competitor's employees have to make in four hours to earn the same pay you earn in a four-hour shift?

16. A boat can travel 24 mi in 3 h when traveling with a current. Against the same current, it can travel only 16 mi in 4 h. Find the rate of the current and the rate of the boat in still water.

17. **Geometry** The measure of one acute angle of a right triangle is 30° more than twice the measure of the other acute angle. Find the measures of the angles.

Example 3 (page 124)

Solve each system by elimination.

18. $\begin{cases} x + y = 12 \\ x - y = 2 \end{cases}$

19. $\begin{cases} x + 2y = 10 \\ x + y = 6 \end{cases}$

20. $\begin{cases} 3a + 4b = 9 \\ -3a - 2b = -3 \end{cases}$

21. $\begin{cases} 4x + 2y = 4 \\ 6x + 2y = 8 \end{cases}$

22. $\begin{cases} 2w + 5y = -24 \\ 3w - 5y = 14 \end{cases}$

23. $\begin{cases} 3u + 3v = 15 \\ -2u + 3v = -5 \end{cases}$

24. $\begin{cases} x + 3y = 11 \\ x + 4y = 14 \end{cases}$

25. $\begin{cases} 5x + 3y = 30 \\ 3x + 3y = 18 \end{cases}$

26. $\begin{cases} x - 14 = -y \\ x - y = 2 \end{cases}$

27. $\begin{cases} 3x + 2y = 6 \\ 3x + 3 = y \end{cases}$

28. $\begin{cases} 5x - y = 4 \\ 2x - y = 1 \end{cases}$

29. $\begin{cases} 2r + s = 3 \\ 4r - s = 9 \end{cases}$

Examples 4, 5 (page 125)

Solve each system by elimination.

30. $\begin{cases} 4x - 6y = -26 \\ -2x + 3y = 13 \end{cases}$

31. $\begin{cases} 9a - 3d = 3 \\ -3a + d = -1 \end{cases}$

32. $\begin{cases} 2a + 3b = 12 \\ 5a - b = 13 \end{cases}$

33. $\begin{cases} 2x - 3y = 6 \\ 6x - 9y = 9 \end{cases}$

34. $\begin{cases} 20x + 5y = 120 \\ 10x + 7.5y = 80 \end{cases}$

35. $\begin{cases} 6x - 2y = 11 \\ -9x + 3y = 16 \end{cases}$

36. $\begin{cases} 2x - 3y = -1 \\ 3x + 4y = 8 \end{cases}$

37. $\begin{cases} 5x - 2y = -19 \\ 2x + 3y = 0 \end{cases}$

38. $\begin{cases} r + 3s = 7 \\ 2r - s = 7 \end{cases}$

39. $\begin{cases} y = 4 - x \\ 3x + y = 6 \end{cases}$

40. $\begin{cases} 3x + 2y = 10 \\ 6x + 4y = 15 \end{cases}$

41. $\begin{cases} 3m + 4n = -13 \\ 5m + 6n = -19 \end{cases}$

Reading Math

For help with reading and solving Exercise 42, see p. 129.

42. **Elections** In a mayoral election, the incumbent received 25% more votes than the opponent. Altogether, 5175 votes were cast for the two candidates. How many votes did the incumbent mayor receive?

43. **Writing** Explain how you decide whether to use substitution or elimination to solve a system.

B Apply Your Skills

Solve each system.

44. $\begin{cases} 5x + y = 0 \\ 5x + 2y = 30 \end{cases}$

45. $\begin{cases} 2m = -4n - 4 \\ 3m + 5n = -3 \end{cases}$

46. $\begin{cases} 7x + 2y = -8 \\ 8y = 4x \end{cases}$

47. $\begin{cases} v = 9t + 300 \\ v = 7t + 400 \end{cases}$

48. $\begin{cases} 80x + 60y = 85 \\ 100x - 40y = 20 \end{cases}$

49. $\begin{cases} 2x + 3y = 0 \\ 7x = 3(2y) + 3 \end{cases}$

50. $\begin{cases} \frac{x}{3} + \frac{4y}{3} = 300 \\ 3x - 4y = 300 \end{cases}$

51. $\begin{cases} 0.02a - 1.5b = 4 \\ 0.5b - 0.02a = 1.8 \end{cases}$

52. $\begin{cases} 4y = 2x \\ 2x + y = \frac{x}{2} + 1 \end{cases}$

53. $\begin{cases} -x + y = 4 \\ 3x - y = 6 \end{cases}$

54. $\begin{cases} \frac{1}{2}x + y = 7 \\ 2x - 3y = 7 \end{cases}$

55. $\begin{cases} 0.4x + 0.1y = 0.6 \\ 0.5x - 0.3y = -0.1 \end{cases}$

For each system, choose the method of solving that seems easier to use. Explain why you made each choice.

56. $\begin{cases} 3x - 5y = 26 \\ -2x - 3y = -11 \end{cases}$

57. $\begin{cases} y = \frac{2}{3}x - 3 \\ -x + 3y = 18 \end{cases}$

58. $\begin{cases} 2m + 3n = 12 \\ -5m + n = -13 \end{cases}$

59. $\begin{cases} 3x - y = 5 \\ y = 4x + 2 \end{cases}$

60. $\begin{cases} 2x - 3y = 4 \\ 2x - 5y = -6 \end{cases}$

61. $\begin{cases} 6x - 3y = 3 \\ 5x - 5y = 10 \end{cases}$

62. **Open-Ended** Write a system of equations in which both equations must be multiplied by a nonzero number before using elimination. Solve your system.

63. **Critical Thinking** Give an example of a system of equations that would be easier to solve graphically than algebraically.

64. **Internet Access** The ads at the left show the costs of Internet access for two companies.

a. Write a system of equations to represent the cost c for t hours of access in one month for each company.
b. Graph the system from part (a). Label each line.
c. For how many hours of use will the costs for the companies be the same? How is this information represented on the graph?
d. If you use the Internet about 20 hours each month, which company should you choose? Explain how you reached an answer.

65. **Break-Even Point** A theater production costs \$40,000 plus \$2800 per performance. A sold-out performance brings in \$3675. How many sold-out performances will the production need to break even?

C Challenge

66. **Weather** The equation $F = \frac{9}{5}C + 32$ relates temperatures on the Celsius and Fahrenheit scales. Does any temperature have the same number reading on both scales? If so, what is the number?

Find the value of *a* that makes each system a dependent system.

67. $\begin{cases} y = 3x + a \\ 3x - y = 2 \end{cases}$

68. $\begin{cases} 3y = 2x \\ 6y - a - 4x = 0 \end{cases}$

69. $\begin{cases} y = \frac{x}{2} + 4 \\ 2y - x = a \end{cases}$

Standardized Test Prep

Gridded Response

Use the following system of equations for Exercises 70–73.

$\begin{cases} 5x - 3y = 11 \\ -x + 12y = 3.5 \end{cases}$

70. If you want to solve the system by eliminating the x terms (with addition), by what would you multiply the second equation?

71. If you want to solve the system by eliminating the y terms (with addition), by what would you multiply the first equation?

72. What is the value of x in the solution? Enter your answer as a decimal.

73. What is the value of y in the solution? Enter your answer as a decimal.

Take It to the NET
Online lesson quiz at
www.PHSchool.com
Web Code: aga-0302

Use the following system of equations for Exercises 74–75.

$\begin{cases} 4x - 10y = -3 \\ 12x + 5y = 12 \end{cases}$

74. What is the value of x in the solution? Enter your answer as a fraction in simplest form.

75. What is the value of y in the solution? Enter your answer as a decimal.

Mixed Review

Lesson 3-1

Solve each system of equations by graphing.

76. $\begin{cases} y = 3x + 4 \\ 2y = 6x - 2 \end{cases}$

77. $\begin{cases} -3y = 9x + 1 \\ 6y = -18x - 2 \end{cases}$

78. $\begin{cases} 4x - y = -5 \\ -8x + 2y = 15 \end{cases}$

Lesson 2-6

Write an equation for each diagonal translation.

79. $y = x$, 4 units down, 3 units left

80. $y = |x|$, $\frac{1}{2}$ unit up, 2 units right

81. $y = 2x - 3$, 1 unit down, 1 unit right

82. $y = |x| + 2$, 4 units up, 2 units left

Lesson 1-1

83. What subset(s) of real numbers contain(s) 6?

84. The sum of the first and last of four consecutive odd integers is 48. What are the four integers?

Reading Math

Reading For Problem Solving

FOR USE WITH PAGE 127 EXERCISE 42

Read the problem below. Then follow along with David as he solves the problem. Check your understanding with the exercise at the bottom of the page.

Elections In a mayoral election, the incumbent received 25% more votes than the opponent. Altogether, 5175 votes were cast for the two candidates. How many votes did the incumbent mayor receive?

What David Thinks	What David Writes
I'll restate the important information. In the first sentence, 25% more means the greater number is 1.25 times the lesser number.	Incumbent received 25% more votes than opponent. $\text{incumbent's votes} = 1.25(\text{opponent's votes})$
The second sentence gives me the total number of votes.	5175 votes total for both candidates. $\text{incumbent's votes} + \text{opponent's votes} = 5175$
What quantities are being used in the problem? I'll assign variables to the number of votes each received.	n = number of incumbent's votes p = number of opponent's votes
Now I can write a system of equations.	$\begin{cases} n = 1.25p \\ n + p = 5175 \end{cases}$
Great! The first equation defines the value of *n*. I'll solve the system by substituting 1.25*p* from the first equation into the second equation.	$n + p = 5175$ $1.25p + p = 5175$ $2.25p = 5175$ $p = 2300$
The problem asks me to find the number of incumbent votes. That's *n*. I'll use one of the original equations and substitute.	$n = 1.25p$ $n = 1.25(2300)$ $n = 2875$
Now I'll write my answer as a sentence.	The incumbent mayor received 2875 votes.

EXERCISE

Two baseball cards together are worth $30. One card is worth 40% more than the other card. How much is the more expensive card worth?

3-3

Systems of Inequalities

North Carolina Objectives

2.10 Use systems of two or more equations or inequalities to model and solve problems; justify results. Solve using tables, graphs, matrix operations, and algebraic properties.

Lesson Preview

What You'll Learn

OBJECTIVE 1 To solve systems of linear inequalities

. . . And Why

To model college entrance requirements, as in Example 2

✓ Check Skills You'll Need

(For help, go to Lessons 1-4, 2-5, amd 2-7.)

Solve each inequality.

1. $5x - 6 > 27$ **2.** $-18 - 5y \geq 52$ **3.** $-5(4x + 1) < 23$

Graph each inequality.

4. $y \leq 4x - 1$ **5.** $3y \geq 6x + 3$ **6.** $-5y + 2x > -5$

7. $y \leq |x|$ **8.** $y \geq |x + 3|$ **9.** $y < |x - 2| + 4$

Interactive lesson includes instant self-check, tutorials, and activities.

OBJECTIVE 1

Solving Systems of Inequalities

You can solve a system of linear inequalities by graphing. Every point in the region of overlap is a solution of both inequalities and is therefore a solution of the system.

1 EXAMPLE Solving a System of Inequalities

Solve the system of inequalities. $\begin{cases} x - 2y < 6 \\ y \leq -\frac{3}{2}x + 5 \end{cases}$

Need Help?

After graphing a boundary line, test whether (0, 0) satisfies the inequality. If it does, shade the side of the line containing (0, 0)

Graph each inequality. First graph the boundary lines. Then decide which side of each boundary line contains solutions and whether the boundary line is included.

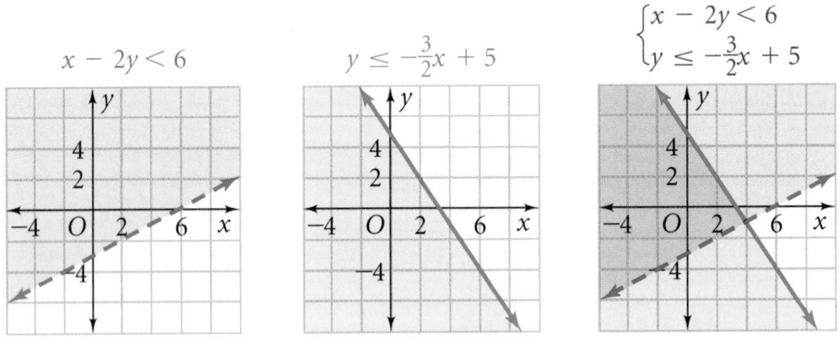

Every point in the red region above the dashed line is a solution of $x - 2y < 6$.

Every point in the blue region or on the solid line is a solution of $y \leq -\frac{3}{2}x + 5$.

Every point in the purple region where the red and blue regions intersect is a solution of the system. For example, (1,1) is a solution.

Check Check (1,1) in both inequalities of the system.

$$x - 2y < 6 \qquad y \leq -\tfrac{3}{2}x + 5$$

$$1 - 2(1) < 6 \qquad 1 \leq -\tfrac{3}{2}(1) + 5$$

$$-1 < 6 \checkmark \qquad 1 \leq \tfrac{7}{2} \checkmark$$

✓ Check Understanding 1 Solve each system of inequalities.

a. $\begin{cases} y \leq -2x + 4 \\ x > -3 \end{cases}$ b. $\begin{cases} y \leq 3x - 6 \\ y > -4x + 2 \end{cases}$

2 EXAMPLE Real-World Connection

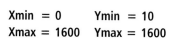

Real-World Connection

Most college admission requirements include standardized test scores.

College Admissions An entrance exam has two parts, a verbal part and a mathematics part. You can score a maximum total of 1600 points. For admission, the school of your choice requires a math score of at least 600. Write and solve a system of inequalities to model scores that meet the school's requirements.

Relate verbal score + math score $\leq$ 1600

math score $\geq$ 600

Define Let x = the verbal score.

Let y = the mathematics score.

Write $x + y \leq 1600$, or $y \leq 1600 - x$

$y \geq 600$

The system of inequalities is $\begin{cases} y \leq 1600 - x \\ y \geq 600 \end{cases}$.

Xmin = 0 Ymin = 10
Xmax = 1600 Ymax = 1600

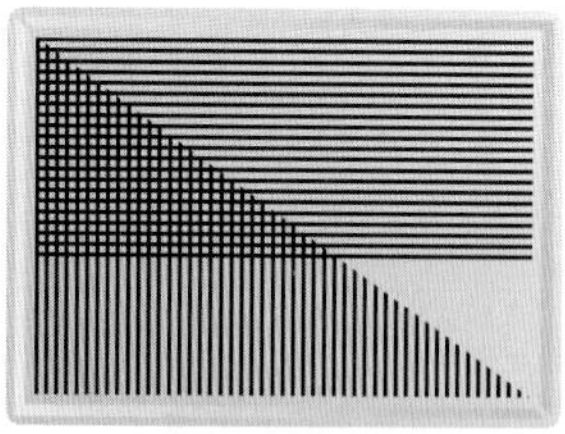

Use a graphing calculator. Graph the corresponding equations $y = 1600 - x$ and $y = 600$. Since the first inequality is $\leq$, shade below the first line. Since the second inequality is $\geq$, shade above the second line. The region of overlap is a graph of the solution.

✓ Check Understanding 2 Another school requires a math score of at least 550 points and a total score of at least 1100 points. You can score up to 800 points on each part. Write and solve a system of inequalities to model scores that meet the school's requirements.

Some systems consist of linear and absolute value inequalities.

3 EXAMPLE Solving a Linear Absolute Value System

Solve the system of inequalities. $\begin{cases} y < 4 \\ y \geq |x - 3| \end{cases}$

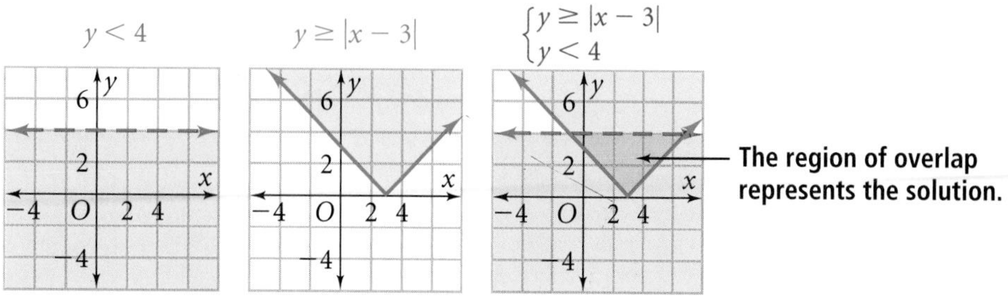

✓ Check Understanding 3 Solve each system of inequalities.

a. $\begin{cases} y \geq x \\ y \leq |x + 5| - 2 \end{cases}$ b. $\begin{cases} y \geq -2x + 4 \\ y \leq |x - 4| \end{cases}$

EXERCISES

For more practice, see *Extra Practice*.

Practice and Problem Solving

A Practice by Example

Example 1 (page 130)

Tell whether $(-3, 3)$ is a solution of each system.

1. $\begin{cases} y \geq x + 2 \\ 3y < -6x + 6 \end{cases}$ **2.** $\begin{cases} y - 2x \leq 1 \\ y < -2x - 2 \end{cases}$ **3.** $\begin{cases} -2y + x \leq 4 \\ 3y < -9x + 3 \end{cases}$

Solve each system of inequalities by graphing.

4. $\begin{cases} y \leq 2x + 2 \\ y < -x + 1 \end{cases}$ **5.** $\begin{cases} y > -2 \\ x < 1 \end{cases}$ **6.** $\begin{cases} y \leq 3 \\ y \leq \frac{1}{2}x + 1 \end{cases}$

7. $\begin{cases} y < 2x \\ y \geq -x + 3 \end{cases}$ **8.** $\begin{cases} -2y < 4x + 2 \\ y > x + 2 \end{cases}$ **9.** $\begin{cases} y > x - 5 \\ 3x + y < -2 \end{cases}$

10. $\begin{cases} y \leq 3x + 1 \\ -6x + 2y > 5 \end{cases}$ **11.** $\begin{cases} x + 2y \leq 10 \\ x + y \leq 3 \end{cases}$ **12.** $\begin{cases} -x - y \leq 2 \\ y - 2x > 1 \end{cases}$

13. $\begin{cases} y > -2x \\ 2x - y \geq 2 \end{cases}$ **14.** $\begin{cases} c \geq d - 3 \\ c < \frac{1}{2}d + 3 \end{cases}$ **15.** $\begin{cases} 2x + y < 1 \\ -y + 3x < 1 \end{cases}$

Example 2 (page 131)

16. Fund-Raising You want to bake at least 6 and at most 11 loaves of bread for a bake sale. You want at least twice as many loaves of banana bread as nut bread.
a. Write a system of inequalities to model the situation.
b. Graph the system.

17. Psychology A psychologist needs at least 40 subjects for her experiment. She cannot use more than 30 children. Write and graph a system of inequalities.

Example 3 (page 131)

Solve each system of inequalities by graphing.

18. $\begin{cases} y > 4 \\ y < |x - 1| \end{cases}$ **19.** $\begin{cases} y < -\frac{1}{3}x + 1 \\ y > |2x - 1| \end{cases}$ **20.** $\begin{cases} y > x - 2 \\ y \geq |x + 2| \end{cases}$

21. $\begin{cases} y \leq -\frac{4}{3}x \\ y \geq -|x| \end{cases}$ **22.** $\begin{cases} 3y < -x - 1 \\ y \leq |x + 1| \end{cases}$ **23.** $\begin{cases} y > -2 \\ y \leq -|x - 3| \end{cases}$

24. $\begin{cases} -2x + y > 3 \\ y \leq -|x + 4| \end{cases}$ **25.** $\begin{cases} 5y \geq 2x - 5 \\ y < |x + 3| \end{cases}$ **26.** $\begin{cases} y \geq -3x + 3 \\ y > |x + 2| \end{cases}$

27. $\begin{cases} -2y < 4x + 2 \\ y > |2x + 1| \end{cases}$ **28.** $\begin{cases} -x \geq 4 - y \\ y \geq |3x - 6| \end{cases}$ **29.** $\begin{cases} y \leq x - 4 \\ y > |x - 6| \end{cases}$

B Apply Your Skills

In Exercises 30–39, identify the inequalities A, B, and C for which the given ordered pair is a solution.

A. $x + y \leq 2$

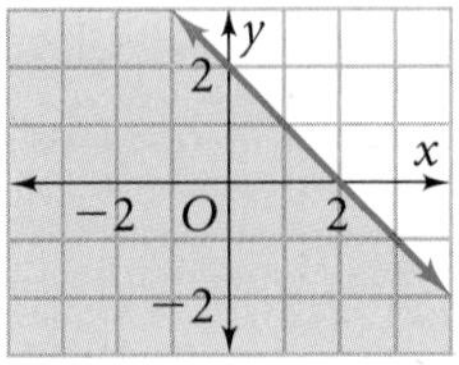

B. $y \leq \frac{3}{2}x - 1$

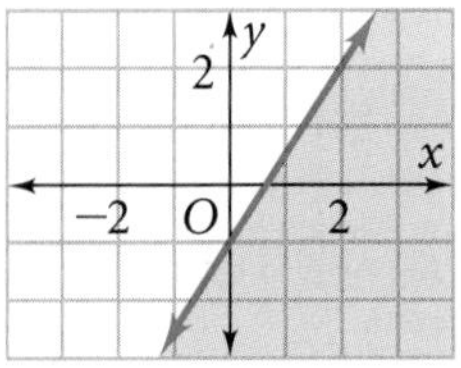

C. $y > -\frac{1}{3}x - 2$

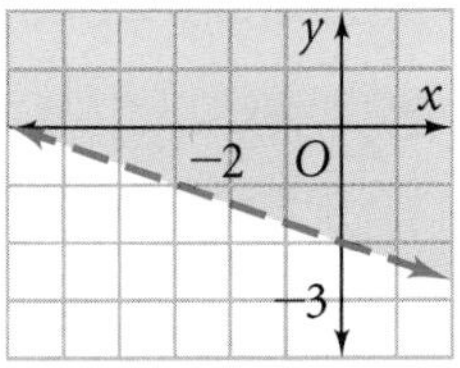

30. $(0, 0)$ **31.** $(-2, -5)$ **32.** $(-2, 0)$ **33.** $(0, -2)$ **34.** $(-15, 15)$

35. $(3, 2)$ **36.** $(2, 0)$ **37.** $(-6, 0)$ **38.** $(4, -1)$ **39.** $(-8, -11)$

Real-World Connection

Bake sales are a popular way to raise money.

40. Fund-Raising Suppose the Student Council has asked you to form a committee to run a bake sale. The committee needs from 7 to 10 members. The number of seniors should be greater than the number of juniors.

a. Write a system of inequalities to model the problem.

b. Graph the system and list the combinations of juniors and seniors that may participate in the committee.

c. **Critical Thinking** Explain why your list in part (b) is finite.

41. Open-Ended Write and graph a system of inequalities for which the solution is bounded by a dashed vertical line and a solid horizontal line.

42. Writing Explain how you determine where to shade when solving a system of inequalities.

Solve each system of inequalities by graphing.

43. $\begin{cases} x + y < 8 \\ x \geq 0 \\ y \geq 0 \end{cases}$

44. $\begin{cases} 2y - 4x \leq 0 \\ x \geq 0 \\ y \geq 0 \end{cases}$

45. $\begin{cases} y \geq -2x + 4 \\ x > -3 \\ y \geq 1 \end{cases}$

46. $\begin{cases} y \leq \frac{2}{3}x + 2 \\ y \geq |x| + 2 \end{cases}$

47. $\begin{cases} y < x - 1 \\ y > -|x - 2| + 1 \end{cases}$

48. $\begin{cases} 2x + y \leq 3 \\ y > |x + 3| - 2 \end{cases}$

C Challenge **Geometry** **Write a system of inequalities to describe each shaded figure.**

49.

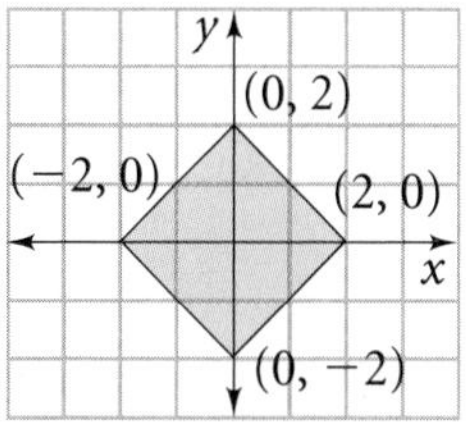

50.

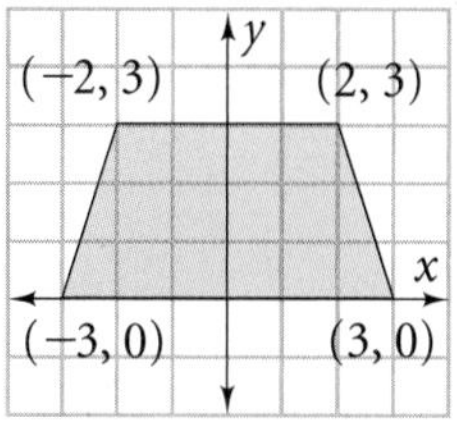

51.

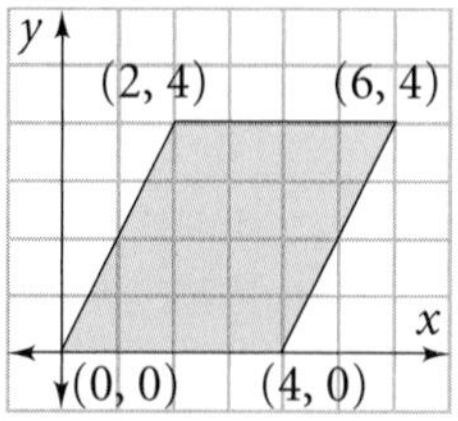

52. a. Graph the "bowtie" inequality, $|y| \leq |x|$.

b. Write a system of inequalities to describe the graph shown at the right.

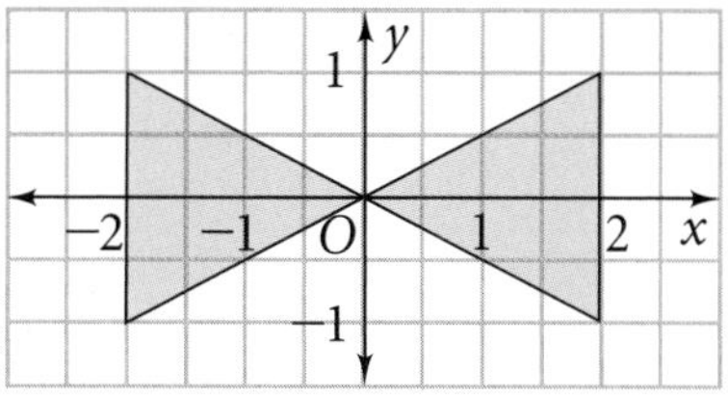

Standardized Test Prep

Multiple Choice

53. When you graph Inequality ① at the right, the boundary line should be __?__ and the shading should be __?__ the line.

① $\begin{cases} y < -2x + 3 \\ y \geq x - 4 \end{cases}$ ②

A. dashed, above B. dashed, below C. solid, above D. solid, below

Take It to the NET
Online lesson quiz at www.PHSchool.com
Web Code: aga-0303

54. When you graph Inequality ②, the boundary line should be __?__ and the shading should be __?__ the line.

F. dashed, above G. dashed, below H. solid, above I. solid, below

55. What is the x-value of the intersection of the boundary lines?

A. $\frac{-7}{3}$ B. $\frac{-3}{7}$ C. $\frac{3}{7}$ D. $\frac{7}{3}$

Short Response

56. How would you test whether $(2, -2)$ is a solution of the system?

Mixed Review

Lesson 3-2 **Solve each system by elimination or substitution.**

57. $\begin{cases} y = 3x + 1 \\ 2x - y = 8 \end{cases}$

58. $\begin{cases} 3x + y = 4 \\ 2x - 4y = 7 \end{cases}$

59. $\begin{cases} -x + 5y = 3 \\ 2x - 10y = 4 \end{cases}$

60. $\begin{cases} 2x + 4y = -8 \\ -5x + 4y = 6 \end{cases}$

61. $\begin{cases} y - 3 = x \\ 4x + y = -2 \end{cases}$

62. $\begin{cases} 2 = 4y - 3x \\ 5x = 2y - 3 \end{cases}$

Lesson 2-3 **For each function, *y* varies directly as *x*.**

63. If $y = -6$ when $x = -2$, find y when $x = 3$.

64. If $y = -8$ when $x = 2$, find x when $y = 2$.

65. If $y = 4$ when $x = 7$, find y when $x = -14$.

66. If $y = 9$ when $x = 15$, find x when $y = 6$.

Lesson 1-5 **Solve each equation. Check your answers.**

67. $|2x + 5| = 6$

68. $|x + 7| = -2$

69. $3|x - 4| + 1 = 13$

70. $-2|x + 1| - 5 = -7$

71. $\frac{1}{2}|3x + 2| - 3 = 4$

72. $-|2x + 5| = -3$

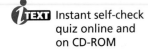

Checkpoint Quiz 1 — Lessons 3-1 through 3-3

iTEXT Instant self-check quiz online and on CD-ROM

Solve each system of equations.

1. $\begin{cases} 3x + 2y = 6 \\ x - 2y = 10 \end{cases}$

2. $\begin{cases} 4x + 7y = 28 \\ y = 2x - 14 \end{cases}$

3. $\begin{cases} 4x + 5y = -12 \\ 3x - 4y = 22 \end{cases}$

4. $\begin{cases} 3y - 2x = 7 \\ 2y - 2 = 4x \end{cases}$

5. The Village Inn offers two special packages. For two nights and three meals the cost is $158. For two nights and five meals the cost is $181. Write and solve a system of linear equations to find the costs per night and per meal.

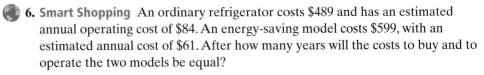

6. **Smart Shopping** An ordinary refrigerator costs $489 and has an estimated annual operating cost of $84. An energy-saving model costs $599, with an estimated annual cost of $61. After how many years will the costs to buy and to operate the two models be equal?

7. Each week you must do a minimum of 18 hours of homework. Participation in sports requires at least 12 hours per week. You have no more than 35 hours per week in total to devote to these activities.

a. Write a system of inequalities to model the situation.

b. Graph and solve the system.

Solve each system of inequalities by graphing.

8. $\begin{cases} y \le -2 \\ y > |x + 1| \end{cases}$

9. $\begin{cases} 8x + 2y > 5 \\ x + 2y \le -3 \end{cases}$

10. $\begin{cases} 4y < 3x - 1 \\ y > 2|x| - 3 \end{cases}$

3-4 Linear Programming

North Carolina Objectives

2.10 Use systems of two or more equations or inequalities to model and solve problems; justify results. Solve using tables, graphs, matrix operations, and algebraic properties.

Lesson Preview

What You'll Learn

OBJECTIVE 1 To find maximum and minimum values

OBJECTIVE 2 To solve problems with linear programming

. . . And Why

To maximize profit, as in Example 2

Check Skills You'll Need

(For help, go to Lessons 3-2 and 3-3.)

Solve each system of equations.

1. $\begin{cases} y = -3x + 3 \\ y = 2x - 7 \end{cases}$
2. $\begin{cases} x + 2y = 5 \\ x - y = -1 \end{cases}$
3. $\begin{cases} 4x + 3y = 7 \\ 2x - 5y = -3 \end{cases}$

Solve each system of inequalities by graphing.

4. $\begin{cases} x \geq 5 \\ y > -3x + 6 \end{cases}$
5. $\begin{cases} 3y > 5x + 2 \\ y \leq -x + 7 \end{cases}$
6. $\begin{cases} x + 3y < -6 \\ 2x - 3y \leq 4 \end{cases}$

New Vocabulary

- linear programming
- objective function
- constraints
- feasible region

Interactive lesson includes instant self-check, tutorials, and activities.

OBJECTIVE 1 Finding Maximum and Minimum Values

Investigation: Finding a Minimum Value

Music Suppose you want to buy some tapes and CDs. You can afford as many as 10 tapes or 7 CDs. You want at least 4 CDs and at least 10 hours of recorded music. Each tape holds about 45 minutes of music, and each CD holds about an hour.

1. Write a system of inequalities to model the problem.
   Let x represent the number of tapes purchased.
   Let y represent the number of CDs purchased.
2. Graph your system of inequalities.
3. Does each ordered pair satisfy the system you have graphed?
   a. (4, 7) b. (12, 7) c. (7, 6) d. (9, 4) e. (10, 4)

Reading Math

Constraints are sometimes referred to as restrictions.

Linear programming is a technique that identifies the minimum or maximum value of some quantity. This quantity is modeled with an **objective function.** Limits on the variables in the objective function are **constraints,** written as linear inequalities.

The first paragraph of the Investigation describes the constraints on buying tapes and CDs. Suppose you buy x tapes and y CDs. The constraints on x and y can be modeled with inequalities as follows.

as many as 10 tapes	$x \leq 10$	at least 4 CDs	$y \geq 4$
as many as 7 CDs	$y \leq 7$	at least 10 hours	$\frac{3}{4}x + y \geq 10$

The constraints form the system of inequalities at the right. The red region in the graph, the **feasible region,** contains all the points that satisfy all the constraints.

$$\begin{cases} x \leq 10 \\ y \leq 7 \\ y \geq 4 \\ \frac{3}{4}x + y \geq 10 \end{cases}$$

If you buy tapes at \$8 each and CDs at \$12 each, then the objective function for the total cost C is $C = 8x + 12y$. The blue line is the graph for the total cost \$140. The green line is for the total cost \$112.

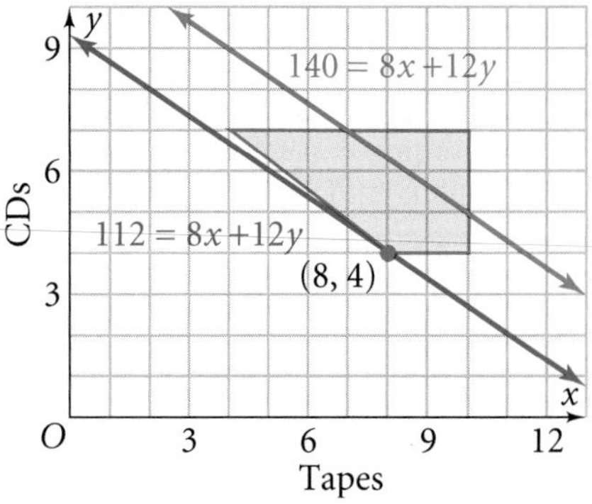

Graphs of the objective function for various values of C are parallel lines. Lines closer to the origin represent lower costs. The graph closest to the origin that intersects the feasible region intersects it at the vertex (8, 4). The graph of the objective function farthest from the origin that intersects the feasible region intersects it at the vertex (10, 7). Graphs of an objective function that represent a maximum or minimum value intersect a feasible region at a vertex.

Key Concepts

Property	Vertex Principle of Linear Programming
If there is a maximum or a minimum value of the linear objective function, it occurs at one or more vertices of the feasible region.	

1 EXAMPLE Testing Vertices

Find the values of x and y that maximize and minimize P for the objective function $P = 3x + 2y$. What is the value of P at each vertex?

Constraints $\begin{cases} y \geq \frac{3}{2}x - 3 \\ y \leq -x + 7 \\ x \geq 0, y \geq 0 \end{cases}$

Step 1
Graph the constraints.

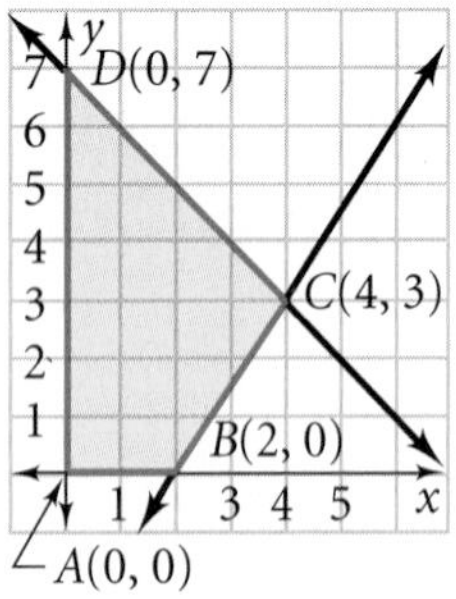

Step 2
Find coordinates for each vertex.

Vertex
$A(0, 0)$
$B(2, 0)$
$C(4, 3)$
$D(0, 7)$

Step 3
Evaluate P at each vertex.

$\mathbf{P = 3x + 2y}$
$P = 3(0) + 2(0) = 0$
$P = 3(2) + 2(0) = 6$
$P = 3(4) + 2(3) = 18$
$P = 3(0) + 2(7) = 14$

When $x = 4$ and $y = 3$, P has its maximum value of 18. When $x = 0$ and $y = 0$, P has its minimum value of 0.

Check Understanding 1 Use the constraints in Example 1 with the objective function $P = 2x + 3y$. Find the values of x and y that maximize and minimize P. Find the value of P at each point.

OBJECTIVE

2 Writing Linear Programs

You can use linear programming to solve many real-world problems.

Reading Math

Linear programming got its name because it provides a plan, or a program, that uses linear equations and inequalities.

2 EXAMPLE **Real-World Connection**

Profit Suppose you are selling cases of mixed nuts and roasted peanuts. You can order no more than a total of 500 cans and packages and spend no more than \$600. How can you maximize your profit? How much is the maximum profit?

Define Let x = number of cases of mixed nuts ordered.
Let y = number of cases of roasted peanuts ordered.
Let P = total profit.

Relate Organize the information in a table.

	Mixed Nuts	Roasted Peanuts	Total	
Number of Cases	x	y	$x+y$	
Number of Units	$12x$	$20y$	500	constraint
Cost	$24x$	$15y$	600	constraint
Profit	$18x$	$15y$	$18x+15y$	objective

Write Write and simplify the constraints. Write the objective function.

$$\begin{cases} 12x + 20y \leq 500 \\ 24x + 15y \leq 600 \\ x \geq 0,\ y \geq 0 \end{cases} \Rightarrow \begin{cases} 3x + 5y \leq 125 \\ 8x + 5y \leq 200 \\ x \geq 0,\ y \geq 0 \end{cases} \qquad P = 18x + 15y$$

Step 1
Graph the constraints.

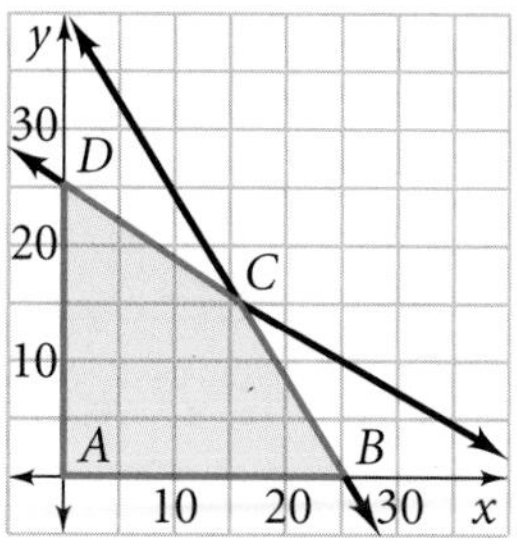

Step 2
Find the coordinates of each vertex.

Vertex
$A(0, 0)$
$B(25, 0)$
$C(15, 16)$
$D(0, 25)$

Step 3
Evaluate P at each vertex.

$\mathbf{P = 18x + 15y}$
$P = 18(0) + 15(0) = 0$
$P = 18(25) + 15(0) = 450$
$P = 18(15) + 15(16) = 510$
$P = 18(0) + 15(25) = 375$

You can maximize your profit by selling 15 cases of mixed nuts and 16 cases of roasted peanuts. The maximum profit is \$510.

Check Understanding **2** If you sell mixed nuts for \$4.25 per can, what should you order to maximize profit?

EXERCISES

For more practice, see *Extra Practice.*

Practice and Problem Solving

A Practice by Example

Find the values of x and y that maximize or minimize the objective function for each graph.

Example 1 (page 136)

1.

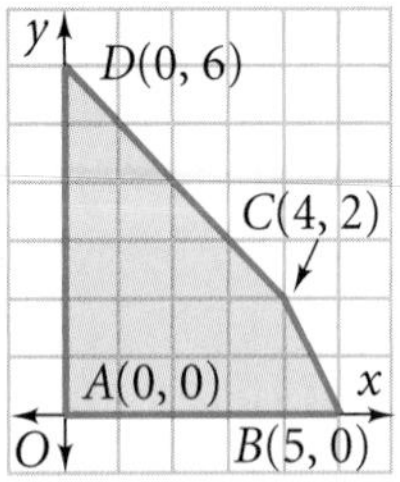

Maximum for $P = 3x + 2y$

2.

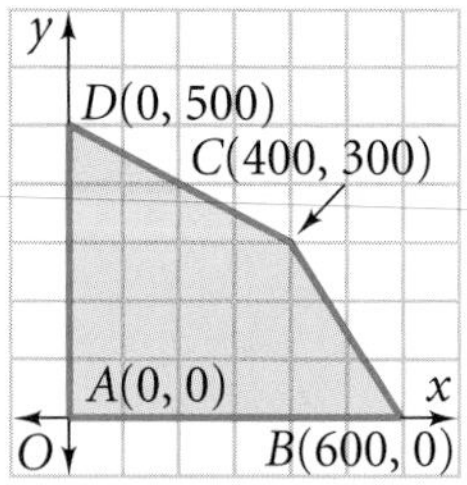

Maximum for $P = 7x + 4y$

3.

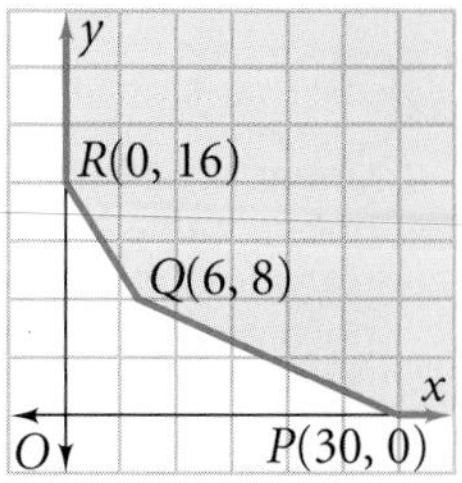

Minimum for $C = 2x + 3y$

Graph each system of constraints. Name all vertices. Then find the values of x and y that maximize or minimize the objective function.

4. $\begin{cases} x \le 5 \\ y \le 4 \\ x \ge 0, y \ge 0 \end{cases}$

Maximum for $P = 3x + 2y$

5. $\begin{cases} x + y \ge 8 \\ y \ge 5 \\ x \ge 0 \end{cases}$

Minimum for $P = 3x + 2y$

6. $\begin{cases} x + y \le 8 \\ 2x + y \le 10 \\ x \ge 0, y \ge 0 \end{cases}$

Maximum for $N = 100x + 40y$

7. $\begin{cases} x + y \ge 6 \\ x \le 8 \\ y \le 5 \end{cases}$

Minimum for $C = x + 3y$

8. $\begin{cases} x + 2y \ge 8 \\ x \ge 2 \\ y \ge 0 \end{cases}$

Minimum for $C = x + 3y$

9. $\begin{cases} 2 \le x \le 6 \\ 1 \le y \le 5 \\ x + y \le 8 \end{cases}$

Maximum for $P = 3x + 2y$

Example 2 (page 137)

10. Ecology Teams chosen from 30 forest rangers and 16 trainees are planting trees. An experienced team consisting of two rangers can plant 500 trees per week. A training team consisting of one ranger and two trainees can plant 200 trees per week.

	Experienced Teams	Training Teams	Total
Number of Teams	x	y	$x+y$
Number of Rangers	$2x$	y	30
Number of Trainees	0	$2y$	16
Number of Trees Planted	$500x$	$200y$	$500x+200y$

a. Write an objective function and constraints for a linear program that models the problem.

b. How many of each type of team should be formed to maximize the number of trees planted? How many trainees are used in this solution? How many trees are planted?

c. Find a solution that uses all the trainees. How many trees will be planted in this case?

11. **Air Quality** Trees in urban areas help keep air fresh by absorbing carbon dioxide. A city has \$2100 to spend on planting spruce and maple trees. The land available for planting is 45,000 ft^2. How many of each tree should the city plant to maximize carbon dioxide absorption?

Facts for a Single Tree

	Spruce	Maple
Planting Cost	\$30	\$40
Area Required	600 ft^2	900 ft^2
Carbon Dioxide Absorption	650 lb/yr	300 lb/yr

SOURCES: Auburn University and Anderson & Associates

B Apply Your Skills

12. **Writing** Explain why solving a system of linear equations is a necessary skill for linear programming.

13. **Microbiology** A biologist is developing two new strains of bacteria. Each sample of Type I bacteria produces four new viable bacteria, and each sample of Type II produces three new viable bacteria. Altogether, at least 240 new viable bacteria must be produced. At least 30, but not more than 60, of the original samples must be Type I. Not more than 70 of the samples can be Type II. A sample of Type I costs \$5 and a sample of Type II costs \$7. How many samples of each should be used to minimize cost?

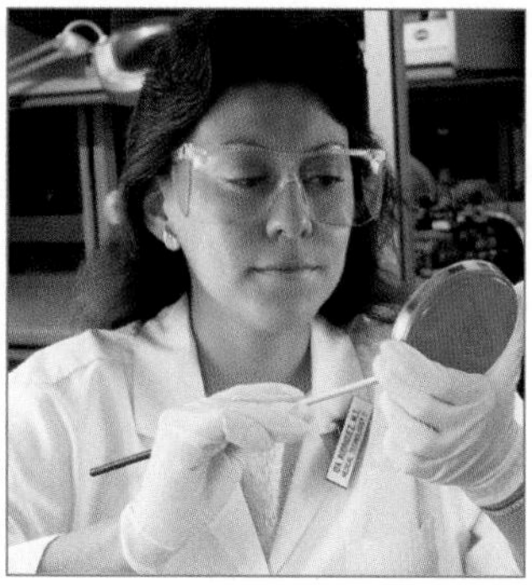

Real-World Connection

Careers A microbiologist studies microorganisms, such as bacteria and viruses, to determine their structure and function.

Graph each system of constraints. Name all vertices. Then find the values of x and y that maximize or minimize the objective function. Find the maximum or minimum value.

14. $\begin{cases} 3x + y \le 7 \\ x + 2y \le 9 \\ x \ge 0, y \ge 0 \end{cases}$

Maximum for $P = 2x + y$

15. $\begin{cases} 25 \le x \le 75 \\ y \le 110 \\ 8x + 6y \ge 720 \end{cases}$

Minimum for $C = 8x + 5y$

16. $\begin{cases} x + y \le 11 \\ 2y \ge x \\ x \ge 0, y \ge 0 \end{cases}$

Maximum for $P = 3x + 2y$

17. $\begin{cases} 2x + y \le 300 \\ x + y \le 200 \\ x \ge 0, y \ge 0 \end{cases}$

Maximum for $P = x + 2y$

18. $\begin{cases} 5x + y \ge 10 \\ x + y \ge 6 \\ x + 4y \ge 12 \\ x \ge 0, y \ge 0 \end{cases}$

Minimum for $C = 10{,}000x + 20{,}000y$

19. $\begin{cases} 6 \le x + y \le 13 \\ x \ge 3 \\ y \ge 1 \end{cases}$

Maximum for $P = 4x + 3y$

20. **Cooking** Baking a tray of corn muffins takes 4 c milk and 3 c wheat flour. A tray of bran muffins takes 2 c milk and 3 c wheat flour. A baker has 16 c milk and 15 c wheat flour. He makes \$3 profit per tray of corn muffins and \$2 profit per tray of bran muffins. How many trays of each type of muffin should the baker make to maximize his profit?

C Challenge

21. A vertex of a feasible region does not always have whole-number coordinates. Sometimes you may need to round coordinates to find the solution. Using the objective function and the constraints at the right, find the whole-number values of x and y that minimize C. Then find C for those values of x and y.

$C = 6x + 9y$

$\begin{cases} x + 2y \ge 50 \\ 2x + y \ge 60 \\ x \ge 0, y \ge 0 \end{cases}$

Reading Math

Feasible means "doable" or "suitable."

22. **Open-Ended** Write a system of constraints whose graphs determine a trapezoid. Write an objective function and evaluate it at each vertex.

23. Critical Thinking Sometimes two corners of a graph both yield the maximum profit. In this case, many other points may also yield the maximum profit. Evaluate the profit formula $P = x + 2y$ for the graph shown. Find four points that yield the maximum profit.

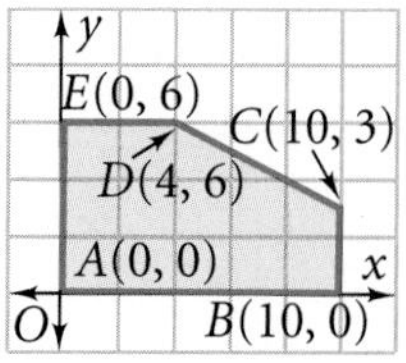

Standardized Test Prep

Multiple Choice

24. Which point maximizes $N = 4x + 3y$ and lies within the feasible region of the constraints at the right?

$$\begin{cases} y \leq 9 \\ 2x + 2y \leq 18 \\ x \leq 3 \end{cases}$$

A. (0, 0) **B.** (9, 0) **C.** (3, 6) **D.** (0, 9)

Take It to the NET
Online lesson quiz at
www.PHSchool.com
Web Code: aga-0304

25. The vertices of a feasible region are (0, 0), (0, 2), (5, 2), and (4, 0). For which objective function is the maximum cost C found at the vertex (4, 0)?

E. $C = -2x + 3y$ **F.** $C = 2x + 7y$
G. $C = 4x - 3y$ **H.** $C = 5x + 3y$

Short Response

26. The figure at the right shows the feasible region for a system of constraints. This system includes $x \geq 0$ and $y \geq 0$. Find the remaining constraint(s).

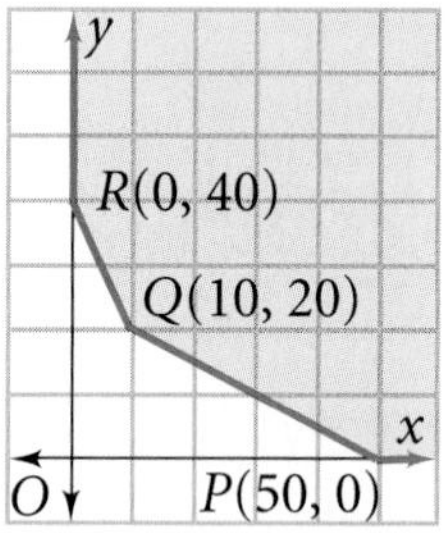

Extended Response

27. What are the vertices of the feasible region bounded by the constraints at the right?

$$\begin{cases} x + y \leq 3 \\ 2x + y \leq 4 \\ x \geq 0,\ y \geq 0 \end{cases}$$

Mixed Review

Lesson 3-3 **Graph each system of inequalities. Indicate any region containing solutions.**

28. $\begin{cases} y < -2x + 8 \\ 3y \geq 4x - 6 \end{cases}$ **29.** $\begin{cases} x - 2y \geq 11 \\ 5x + 4y < 27 \end{cases}$ **30.** $\begin{cases} 2x + 6y > 12 \\ 3x + 9y \leq 27 \end{cases}$

31. $\begin{cases} 2y + x < 4 \\ y - 2x \geq 4 \end{cases}$ **32.** $\begin{cases} y + 5 \geq -2x \\ y - x \geq -2 \end{cases}$ **33.** $\begin{cases} 2y - 4x < 6 \\ 6x < 3y + 12 \end{cases}$

Lesson 2-4 **34. Data Analysis** Use the data below.

Take It to the NET
Graphing Calculator procedures online at
www.PHSchool.com
Web Code: age-2109

A Survey of Paperback Books: How Long and How Much?

Pages	326	450	246	427	208	339	367	445	404	465	378	265
Price ($)	7.50	7.99	6.99	7.99	6.99	7.95	7.50	7.95	7.95	7.99	7.99	6.99

a. Make a scatter plot of the data.
b. What kind of correlation do you see?
c. Find a linear model.
d. What price would you predict for a paperback containing 100 pages?

Lesson 1-2 **Evaluate each expression for $a = 3$ and $b = -5$.**

35. $2a + b$ **36.** $a - b$ **37.** $-4 + 2ab$ **38.** $a + \frac{3b}{a}$

39. $3(a - b)$ **40.** $4a - 2 + 3b$ **41.** $\frac{a - b}{2a}$ **42.** $b(2b - a)$

Technology

Linear Programming

For Use With Lesson 3-4

You can solve linear programming problems with your graphing calculator.

EXAMPLE

Find the values of x and y that will maximize the objective function $P = 13x + 2y$ for the constraints at the right. What is the value of P at this maximum point?

$$\begin{cases} -3x + 2y \leq 8 \\ -8x + y \geq -48 \\ x \geq 0,\ y \geq 0 \end{cases}$$

Step 1 Rewrite the first two inequalities to isolate y. Enter the inequalities.

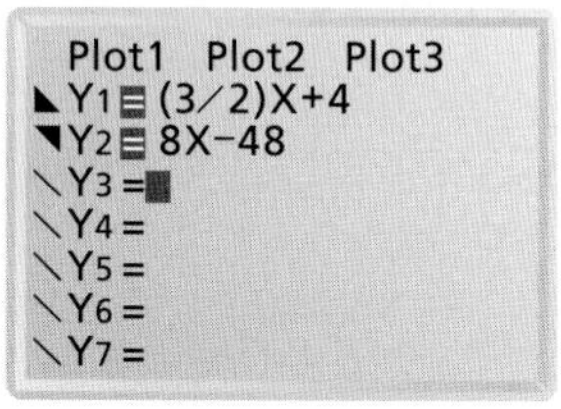

Step 2 Graph, using the window $0 \leq x \leq 12$, $0 \leq y \leq 20$.

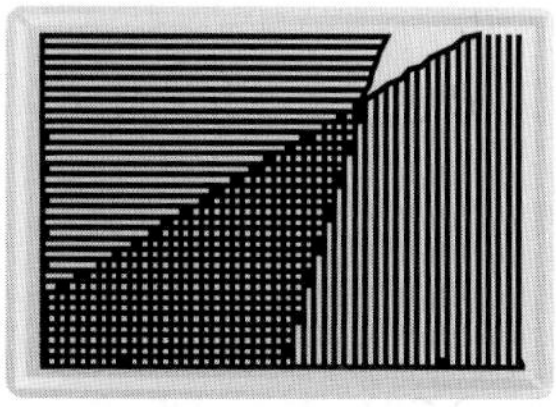

Step 3 Use the value option of **CALC** to find the upper left vertex. Press 0 ENTER.

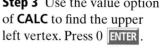

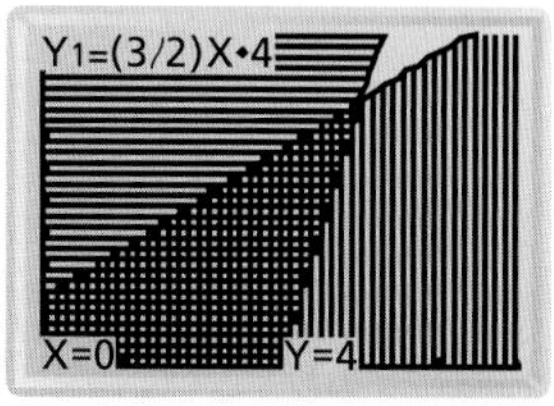

Step 4 Enter the expression for the objective function on the home screen. Press ENTER for the value of P at the vertex.

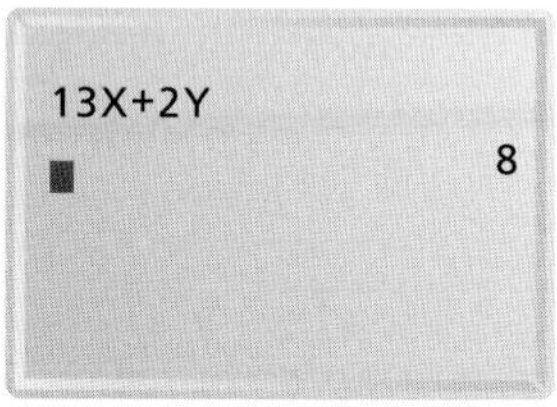

Step 5 Use the intersect option of **CALC** to find the upper right vertex. Go to the home screen and press ENTER for the value of P.

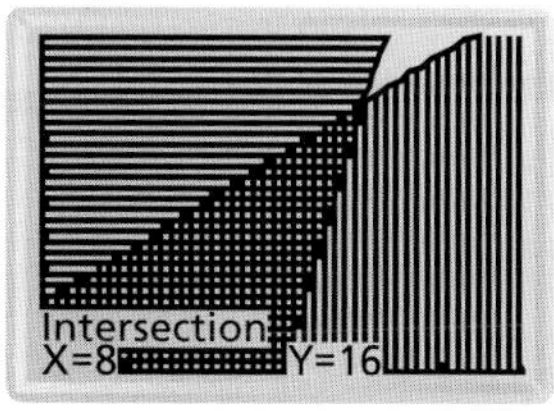

Step 6 Use the zero option of **CALC** to find the lower right vertex. Go to the home screen and press ENTER for the value of P.

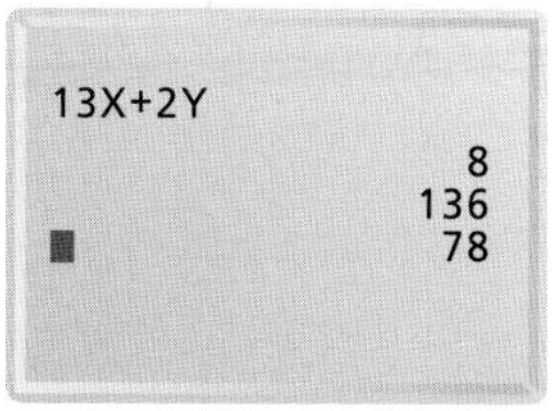

Compare the values of P for the coordinates of the three vertices you found. The objective function has a value of 0 for the vertex located at the origin. The maximum value 136 occurs when $x = 8$ and $y = 16$.

EXERCISES

Find the values of x and y that maximize or minimize the objective function.

1. $\begin{cases} 4x + 3y \geq 30 \\ x + 3y \geq 21 \\ x \geq 0, y \geq 0 \end{cases}$

Minimum for $C = 5x + 8y$

2. $\begin{cases} 3x + 5y \leq 35 \\ 2x + y \leq 14 \\ x \geq 0, y \geq 0 \end{cases}$

Maximum for $P = 3x + 2y$

3. $\begin{cases} x + y \geq 8 \\ x + 5y \geq 20 \\ x \geq 0, y \geq 2 \end{cases}$

Minimum for $C = 3x + 4y$

4. $\begin{cases} x + 2y \leq 24 \\ 3x + 2y \leq 34 \\ 3x + y \leq 29 \\ x \geq 0 \end{cases}$

Maximum for $P = 2x + 3y$

3-5 Graphs in Three Dimensions

Lesson Preview

What You'll Learn

OBJECTIVE 1 To graph points in three dimensions

OBJECTIVE 2 To graph equations in three dimensions

. . . And Why

To locate points on a virtual bicycle helmet, as in Example 2

✓ Check Skills You'll Need

(For help, go to Lesson 2-2.)

Find the *x*- and *y*-intercepts of the graph of each linear equation.

1. $y = 2x + 6$

2. $2x + 9y = 36$

3. $3x - 8y = -24$

4. $4x - 5y = 40$

Graph each linear equation.

5. $y = 3x$

6. $y = -2x + 4$

7. $4y = 3x - 8$

8. $-3x - 2y = 7$

New Vocabulary • coordinate space • ordered triples • trace

Interactive lesson includes instant self-check, tutorials, and activities.

OBJECTIVE 1 Graphing Points in Three Dimensions

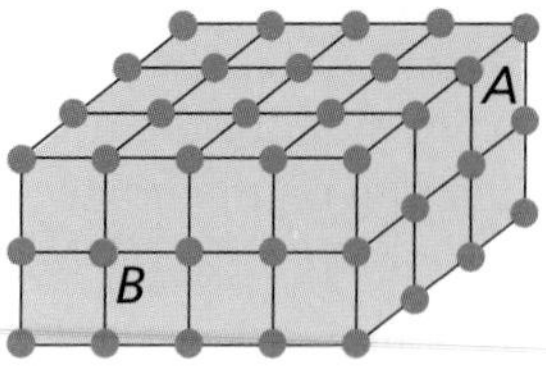

Suppose you want to describe how to get from point *A* to point *B* along the grid shown at the right. You could say "Move down one unit, forward two units, and left three units," or "Move left three units, forward two units, and down one unit."

To describe positions in space, you need a three-dimensional coordinate system.

You have learned to graph on an *xy*-coordinate plane using ordered pairs. Adding a third axis, the *z*-axis, to the *xy*-coordinate plane creates **coordinate space.** In coordinate space you graph points using **ordered triples** of the form (x, y, z).

Points in a Plane

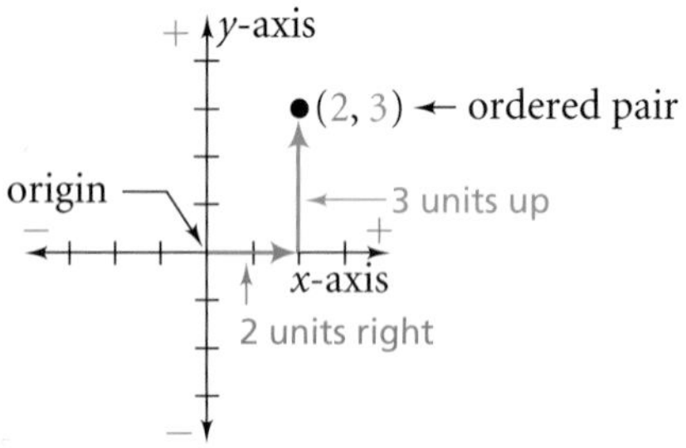

A two-dimensional coordinate system allows you to graph points in a plane.

Points in Space

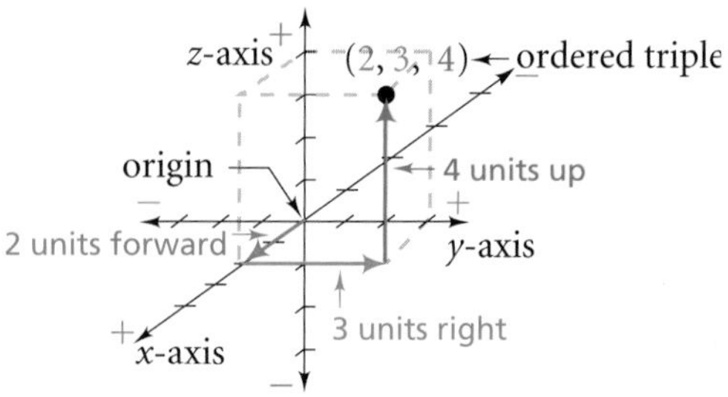

A three-dimensional coordinate system allows you to graph points in space.

Real-World Connection

The global positioning system locates persons or objects in three dimensions.

In the coordinate plane, point (2, 3) is two units right and three units up from the origin. In coordinate space, point (2, 3, 4) is two units forward, three units right, and four units up.

1 EXAMPLE Graphing in Coordinate Space

Graph each point in coordinate space.

a. (0, 3, −2)
Sketch the axes. From the origin, move right 3 units and down 2 units.

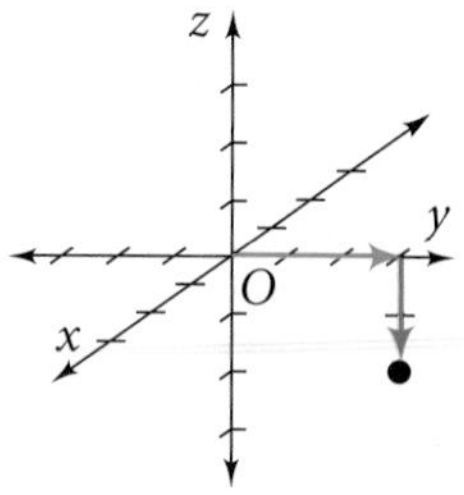

b. (−2, −1, 3)
Sketch the axes. From the origin, move back 2 units, left 1 unit, and up 3 units.

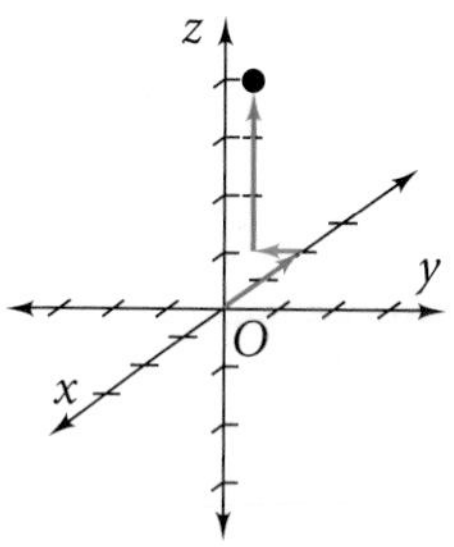

Check Understanding **1** Graph each point in coordinate space.

a. (0, −4, −2) **b.** (−1, 1, 3) **c.** (3, −5, 2) **d.** (3, 3, −3)

2 EXAMPLE Real-World Connection

Product Design Computers are used to design three-dimensional objects. Programs allow the designer to view the object from different perspectives. Find coordinates for points A, B, and C in the diagram below.

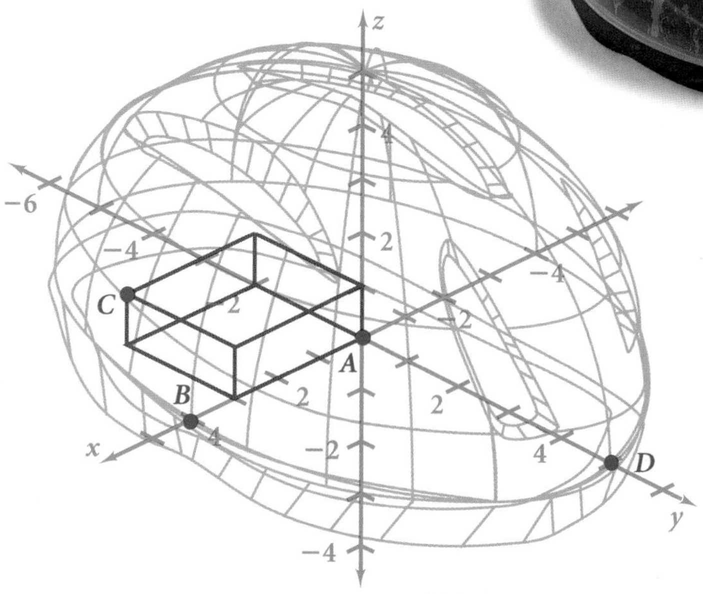

$A(0, 0, 0)$, $B(4, 0, 0)$, $C(3, -2, 1)$

Check Understanding **2** **a.** Find coordinates for point D in the diagram.
b. Does the point (−3, 2, 4) lie inside or outside the helmet? Explain.

OBJECTIVE 2

Graphing Equations in Three Dimensions

The graph of an equation is a picture of all the solutions to the equation. In two dimensions, the graph of $3x - 2y = 6$ is a line. In three dimensions, the graph of $3x - 2y + z = 6$ is a plane, as shown at the right.

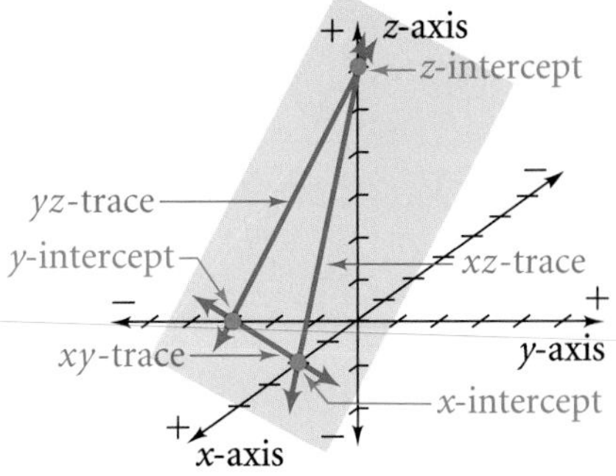

If the graph of a plane intersects one of the coordinate planes in a line, then the line is called a **trace.** For example, the *xy*-trace is the line in the *xy*-plane that contains the *x*- and the *y*-intercepts. The *xz*-trace and the *yz*-trace are defined similarly.

> **Need Help?**
> The *x*-intercept of a line or plane is the point of intersection with the *x*-axis.

To sketch a plane, find the *x*-, *y*-, and *z*- intercepts. Then draw the traces and show the plane with shading.

3 EXAMPLE Sketching a Plane

Sketch the graph of $2x + 3y + 4z = 12$.

Step 1 Find the intercepts.

$$2x + 3y + 4z = 12$$

$$2x + 3(0) + 4(0) = 12$$ **To find the *x*-intercept, substitute 0 for *y* and *z*.**

$$2x = 12$$

$$x = 6$$ **The *x*-intercept is 6.**

$$2(0) + 3y + 4(0) = 12$$ **To find the *y*-intercept, substitute 0 for *x* and *z*.**

$$3y = 12$$

$$y = 4$$ **The *y*-intercept is 4.**

$$2(0) + 3(0) + 4z = 12$$ **To find the *z*-intercept, substitute 0 for *x* and *y*.**

$$4z = 12$$

$$z = 3$$ **The *z*-intercept is 3.**

Step 2 Graph the intercepts.

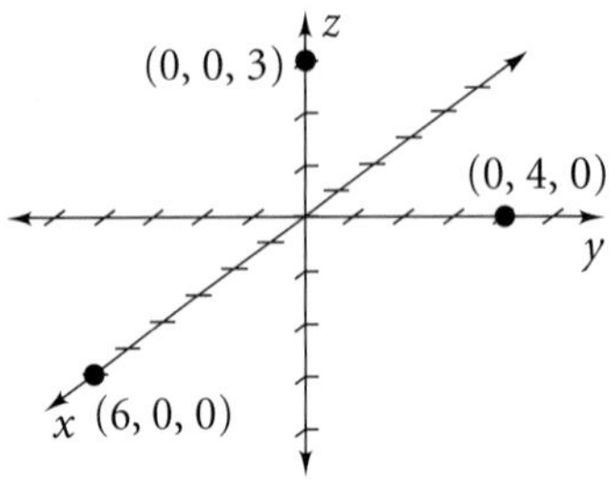

Step 3 Draw the traces. Shade the plane.

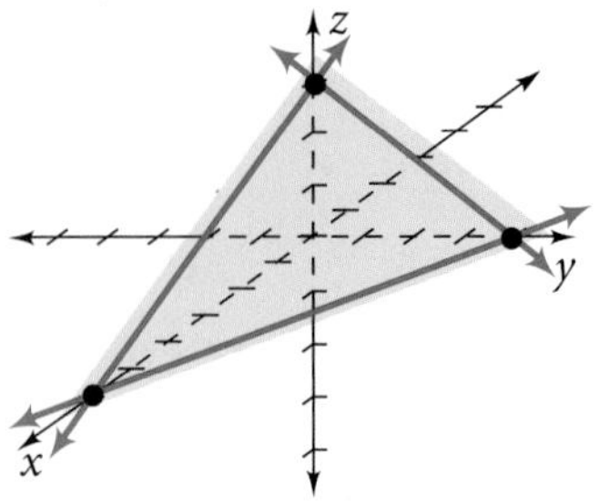

Each point on the plane represents a solution to $2x + 3y + 4z = 12$.

Check Understanding 3 Sketch the graph of each equation.

a. $x + y + z = 5$ **b.** $2x - y + 3z = 6$ **c.** $x + 2y - z = -4$

EXERCISES

For more practice, see *Extra Practice.*

Practice and Problem Solving

A Practice by Example

Example 1 (page 143)

Describe the location of each point in coordinate space.

1. $(-1, 5, 0)$ **2.** $(3, -3, 4)$

3. $(2, 0, 5)$ **4.** $(-4, -7, -1)$

Graph each point in coordinate space.

5. $(5, 0, -2)$ **6.** $(0, 0, 4)$

7. $(10, -2, -5)$ **8.** $(-1, -1, -1)$

9. $(-4, -5, 3)$ **10.** $(25, 40, -30)$

11. $(1, 1, 0)$ **12.** $(0, -2, 2)$

Example 2 (page 143)

Find the coordinates of each point in the diagram.

13. *A* **14.** *B* **15.** *C*

16. *D* **17.** *E* **18.** *F*

Example 3 (page 144)

Sketch the graph of each equation.

19. $x + y + 2z = 4$ **20.** $x + y + z = 2$ **21.** $2x + 6y + z = 6$

22. $x - y - 4z = 8$ **23.** $-x + 3y + z = 6$ **24.** $2x - y - 5z = 10$

B Apply Your Skills

25. Writing While visiting friends in New York, you go to a concert. Explain how the seat information on your ticket at the right represents a point in three-dimensional coordinate space.

26. a. Party Planning Suppose you have \$20 to spend on party decorations. Balloons are \$.05 each, streamers are \$.25 each, and noisemakers are \$.40 each. Write and graph an equation in three variables for the numbers of decorations you can buy.

b. Open-Ended Find two solutions for your equation.

c. Critical Thinking Is the number of solutions to your equation finite or infinite? Explain.

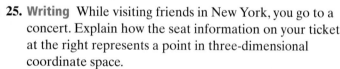

Sketch the graph of each equation.

27. $7x + 14y - z = 7$ **28.** $-3x + 5y + 10z = 15$

29. $32x + 16y - 8z = 32$ **30.** $-25x + 30y + 50z = 75$

31. $50x + 25y + 100z = 200$ **32.** $14x - 8y + 28z = 28$

Sketch the graph of each equation and find the equation of each trace.

33. $6x + 6y - 12z = 36$ **34.** $-20x + 10y + 50z = 100$

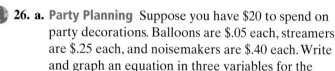

35. $-12x - 32y - 48z = 96$ **36.** $25x + 125y - 25z = 125$

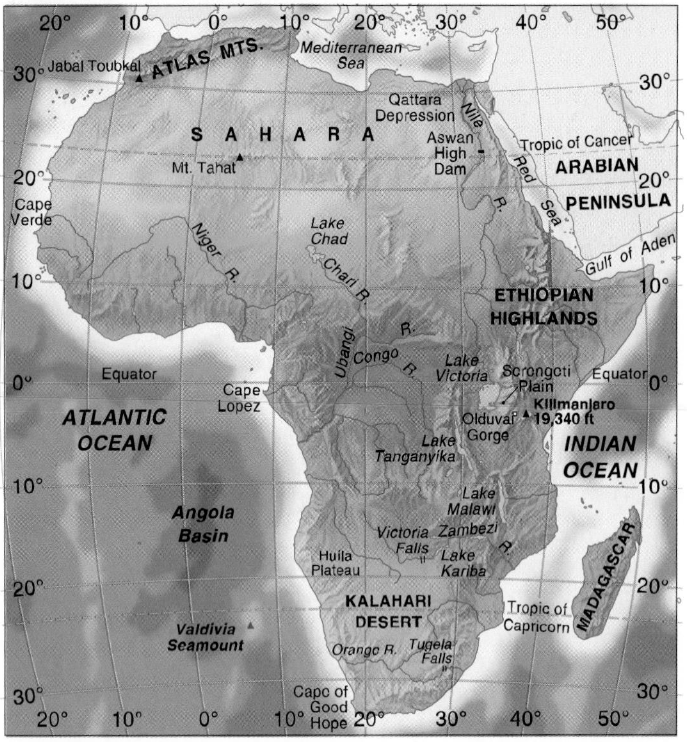

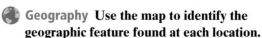

Geography **Use the map to identify the geographic feature found at each location.**

37. latitude 3° S
longitude 37° E
elevation 19,340 ft

38. latitude 23° N
longitude 5° E
elevation 9,573 ft

39. latitude 25° S
longitude 6° E
elevation −3,072 ft

40. latitude 15° N
longitude 18° W
elevation 0 ft

41. latitude 30° N
longitude 27° E
elevation −440 ft

42. latitude 13° N
longitude 14° E
elevation 919 ft

43. latitude 31° N
longitude 8° W
elevation 49,212 ft

44. latitude 18° S
longitude 25° E
elevation 2,927 ft

45. latitude 22° N
longitude 31° E
elevation 600 ft

46. latitude 1° S
longitude 33° E
elevation 3,720 ft

47. **Error Analysis** A student claims to find the x-intercept of a plane by substituting 0 for x in the equation of the plane. Explain the student's error.

C **Challenge**

48. a. **Geometry** Use the Pythagorean Theorem to find the distance between $(1, 2, 4)$ and $(3, -2, 7)$. (*Hint:* Recall the Distance Formula.)

b. **Make a Conjecture** Make a conjecture about how to find the coordinates of the midpoint of a segment in coordinate space.

49. a. **Critical Thinking** Does every plane have three traces? Explain.

b. Must any two traces of a plane intersect? Explain.

Graph each equation in three-dimensional coordinate space.

50. $x = 3$ **51.** $2x + 3y = 6$ **52.** $y = 0$

Standardized Test Prep

Multiple Choice

53. Which point is NOT on the graph of $2x + 3y - z - 12 = 0$?
A. (6, 0, 0) B. (3, 3, 3) C. (0, 4, 0) D. (1, 1, 7)

54. Which point is NOT on the plane with equation $-2x - 3y + 5z = 7$?
F. (1, 2, 3) G. (−2, −3, 5) H. (−2, 4, 3) I. (−4, 2, 1)

Take It to the NET
Online lesson quiz at www.PHSchool.com
Web Code: aga-0305

55. What are the intercepts of $-3x + 5y - 2z = 60$?
A. $x = -180, y = 300, z = -120$ B. $x = -20, y = 12, z = -30$
C. $x = -3, y = 5, z = -2$ D. $x = -60, y = 60, z = -60$

56. What is the xy-trace of $2x - 4y + z = 8$?
F. $-4y + z = 8$ G. $x - 2y = 4$ H. $2x + z = 8$ I. $z = 8$

Short Response

57. What is the intersection of the xz-traces for the two planes $2x - 3y - 4z = -4$ and $x + 3y + z = 7$? Explain each step of your answer.

Mixed Review

Lesson 3-4

58. Maximize the objective function $P = x + 3y$ under the given constraints. At what vertex does this maximum value occur?
$$\begin{cases} x + y \le 5 \\ x + 2y \le 8 \\ x \ge 0, y \ge 0 \end{cases}$$

Lesson 2-7

Graph each inequality.

59. $y \le x - 3$ **60.** $3y - x > -4$ **61.** $2x - y \ge 0$

Lesson 1-6

62. **Probability** Your town has a drawing for 50 summer jobs. Including you, 150 students apply.
a. What is the probability that you will get one of the jobs?
b. You and a friend apply. What is the probability that you both get jobs?

Checkpoint Quiz 2

Lessons 3-4 through 3-5

TEXT Instant self-check quiz online and on CD-ROM

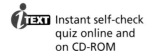

1. Find the values of x and y that minimize the objective function $C = 2x + 3y$ for the constraints at the right.
$$\begin{cases} y \ge x \\ x + y \le 32 \\ x \ge 5, y \ge 3 \end{cases}$$

2. **Agriculture** A farmer has at most 400 acres and \$45,000 available to grow corn and soybeans. Use the cost and profit information at the right to decide how many acres of each crop will maximize profit.

Cost and Profit for Corn and Soybeans

	Corn	Soybeans
Number of Acres	x	y
Cost	$100x$	$150y$
Profit	$60x$	$75y$

Graph each equation. Use traces and intercepts.

3. $3x + 2y + z = 6$ **4.** $x - y + z = 4$ **5.** $4x + z = 8$

Algebra at Work

Radiologist

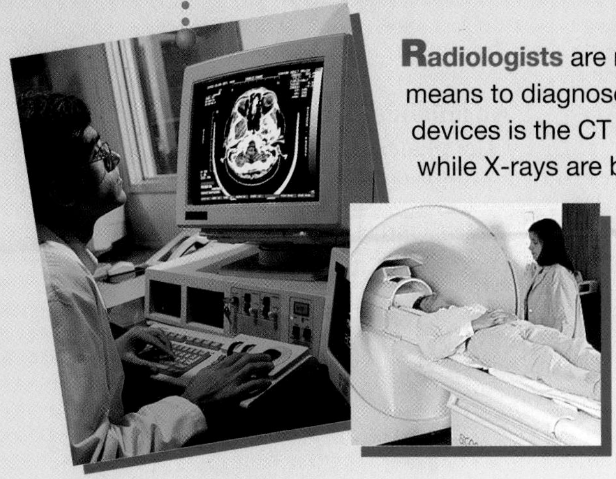

Radiologists are medical doctors who use X-rays, sound waves, and other means to diagnose diseases. Among the radiologist's most powerful diagnostic devices is the CT (computerized tomography) scan. The patient lies on a table while X-rays are beamed through the patient's body from different angles. Images are recorded and fed into a computer. The computer uses a three-dimensional coordinate system to record information and then to produce images of a cross section of the patient's body.

Take It to the NET For more information about radiology, go to **www.PHSchool.com**.
Web Code: agb-2031

3-6 Systems With Three Variables

North Carolina Objectives

2.10 Use systems of two or more equations or inequalities to model and solve problems; justify results. Solve using tables, graphs, matrix operations, and algebraic properties.

Lesson Preview

What You'll Learn

OBJECTIVE 1 To solve systems in three variables by elimination

OBJECTIVE 2 To solve systems in three variables by substitution

. . . And Why

To choose an investment strategy, as in Example 4

✓ Check Skills You'll Need

(For help, go to Lessons 3-1 and 3-2.)

Solve each system.

1. $\begin{cases} 2x - y = 11 \\ x + 2y = -7 \end{cases}$ **2.** $\begin{cases} -x + 6y = 8 \\ 2x - 12y = -14 \end{cases}$ **3.** $\begin{cases} 3x + 2y = -5 \\ 4x + 3y = -8 \end{cases}$

Let $y = 4x - 2$. Solve each equation for x.

4. $3x + y = 5$ **5.** $x - 2y = -3$ **6.** $4x + 3y = 2$

Determine whether the given ordered pair is a solution of each equation in the system.

7. $(1, 3)$ $\begin{cases} 2x + 5y = 17 \\ -4x + 3y = 5 \end{cases}$ **8.** $(-4, 2)$ $\begin{cases} x + 2y = 0 \\ 3x - 2y = -16 \end{cases}$

Interactive lesson includes instant self-check, tutorials, and activities.

OBJECTIVE 1 Solving Three-Variable Systems by Elimination

You can represent systems of equations in three variables as graphs in three dimensions. As you learned in Lesson 3-5, the graph of any equation of the form $Ax + By + Cz = D$, where A, B, and C are not all zero, is a plane. The solutions of a three-variable system can be shown graphically as the intersections of planes.

Need Help?

To review solving systems by graphing, go to Lesson 3-1.

No solution
No point lies in all three planes.

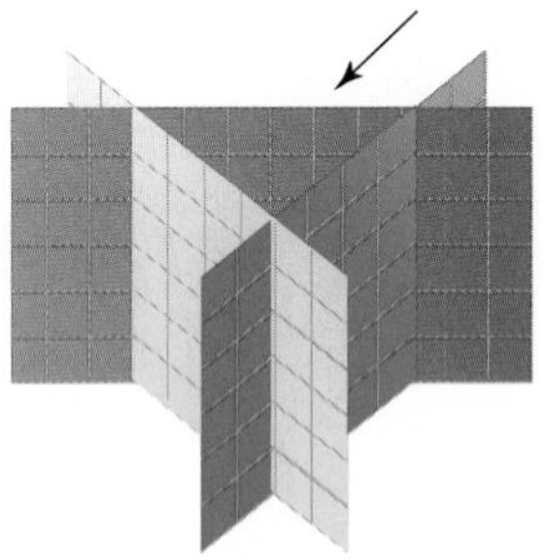

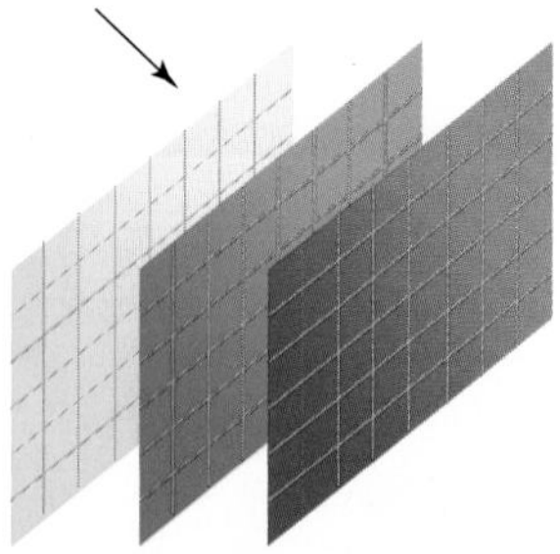

One solution
The planes intersect at one common point.

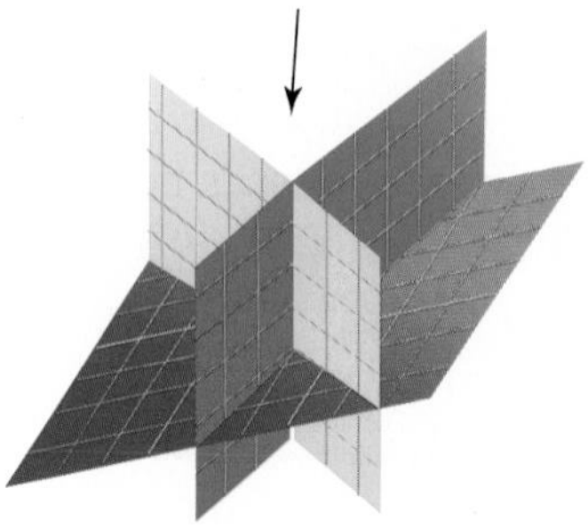

An infinite number of solutions
The planes intersect at all the points along a common line.

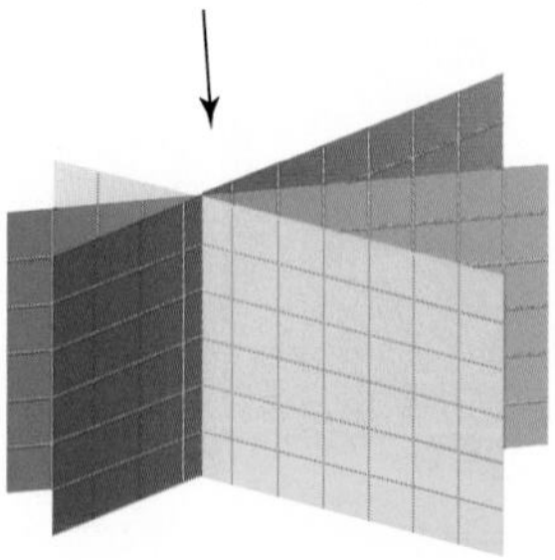

When the solution of a system of equations in three variables is represented by one point, you can write it as an ordered triple (x, y, z).

You can solve a system of three equations in three variables by working with the equations in pairs. You will use one of the equations *twice*.

Real-World Connection

You can use a system in three variables to model the amounts of vitamin C, potassium, and beta carotene in this three-fruit salad.

1 EXAMPLE Solving by Elimination

Solve the system by elimination. The equations are numbered to make the procedure easy to follow.

$$\begin{cases} x - 3y + 3z = -4 & ① \\ 2x + 3y - z = 15 & ② \\ 4x - 3y - z = 19 & ③ \end{cases}$$

Step 1 Pair the equations to eliminate y, because the y terms are already additive inverses.

$$\begin{array}{ll} ① & x - 3y + 3z = -4 \\ ② & 2x + 3y - z = 15 \\ \hline ④ & 3x \qquad + 2z = 11 \end{array} \quad \textbf{Add.} \quad \begin{array}{ll} ② & 2x + 3y - z = 15 \\ ③ & 4x - 3y - z = 19 \\ \hline ⑤ & 6x \qquad - 2z = 34 \end{array}$$

Step 2 Write the two new equations as a system. Solve for x and z.

$$\begin{array}{ll} ④ & 3x + 2z = 11 \\ ⑤ & 6x - 2z = 34 \\ \hline & 9x = 45 \\ & x = 5 \end{array} \qquad \begin{array}{rl} ④ \quad 3x + 2z &= 11 \\ 3(5) + 2z &= 11 \\ 2z &= -4 \\ z &= -2 \end{array}$$

Substitute the value of *x*.

Step 3 Substitute the values for x and z into one of the original equations (①, ②, or ③) and solve for y.

$$\begin{aligned} ① \quad x - 3y + 3z &= -4 \\ 5 - 3y + 3(-2) &= -4 \\ 5 - 3y - 6 &= -4 \\ -3y &= -3 \\ y &= 1 \end{aligned}$$

The solution of the system is $(5, 1, -2)$.

Check Show that $(5, 1, -2)$ makes each equation true.

$$\begin{aligned} x - 3y + 3z &= -4 \\ 5 - 3(1) + 3(-2) &\stackrel{?}{=} -4 \\ 5 - 3 - 6 &\stackrel{?}{=} -4 \\ -4 &= -4 ✓ \end{aligned} \qquad \begin{aligned} 2x + 3y - z &= 15 \\ 2(5) + 3(1) - (-2) &\stackrel{?}{=} 15 \\ 10 + 3 + 2 &\stackrel{?}{=} 15 \\ 15 &= 15 ✓ \end{aligned} \qquad \begin{aligned} 4x - 3y - z &= 19 \\ 4(5) - 3(1) - (-2) &\stackrel{?}{=} 19 \\ 20 - 3 + 2 &\stackrel{?}{=} 19 \\ 19 &= 19 ✓ \end{aligned}$$

Check Understanding

1. Solve each system by elimination. Check your answers.

a. $\begin{cases} 2x + y - z = 5 \\ 3x - y + 2z = -1 \\ x - y - z = 0 \end{cases}$ **b.** $\begin{cases} 2x - y + z = 4 \\ x + 3y - z = 11 \\ 4x + y - z = 14 \end{cases}$

c. **Critical Thinking** Suppose one of the equations in a system contains a variable with a coefficient of zero. When pairing the equations to solve the system, would you use that equation twice? Explain.

You can apply the method in Example 1 to any system of three equations in three variables. You may need to multiply one or more of the equations by a nonzero number to create an equivalent system.

2 EXAMPLE Solving an Equivalent System

Solve the system by elimination.
$$\begin{cases} ① & 2x + y - z = 5 \\ ② & x + 4y + 2z = 16 \\ ③ & 15x + 6y - 2z = 12 \end{cases}$$

Step 1 Pair the equations to eliminate z.

$$\begin{cases} ① & 2x + y - z = 5 \\ ② & x + 4y + 2z = 16 \end{cases} \qquad \begin{aligned} 4x + 2y - 2z &= 10 \\ x + 4y + 2z &= 16 \\ \hline ④\ 5x + 6y \quad &= 26 \end{aligned}$$ **Multiply by 2.**

$$\begin{aligned} ② \quad x + 4y + 2z &= 16 \\ ③ \quad 15x + 6y - 2z &= 12 \\ \hline ⑤ \quad 16x + 10y \quad &= 28 \end{aligned}$$

Step 2 Write the two new equations as a system. Solve for x and y.

$$\begin{cases} ④ & 5x + 6y = 26 \\ ⑤ & 16x + 10y = 28 \end{cases} \qquad \begin{aligned} 25x + 30y &= 130 \\ -48x - 30y &= -84 \\ \hline -23x \quad &= 46 \\ x &= -2 \end{aligned}$$ **Multiply by 5.** **Multiply by −3.**

$$\begin{aligned} ④ \quad 5x + 6y &= 26 \\ 5(-2) + 6y &= 26 \quad \textbf{Substitute the value of } x. \\ y &= 6 \end{aligned}$$

Step 3 Substitute the values for x and y into one of the original equations (①, ②, or ③). Solve for z.

$$\begin{aligned} ① \quad 2x + y - z &= 5 \\ 2(-2) + 6 - z &= 5 \\ z &= -3 \end{aligned}$$

The solution of the system is $(-2, 6, -3)$.

Check Understanding ② Solve the system by elimination. Check your answers.
$$\begin{cases} x + 4y - 5z = -7 \\ 3x + 2y + 3z = 7 \\ 2x + y + 5z = 8 \end{cases}$$

The graph illustrates the solution to Example 2. Each equation in the system represents a tilted plane. The graph of ① is red, the graph of ② is blue, and the graph of ③ is green. The three planes intersect at $(-2, 6, -3)$.

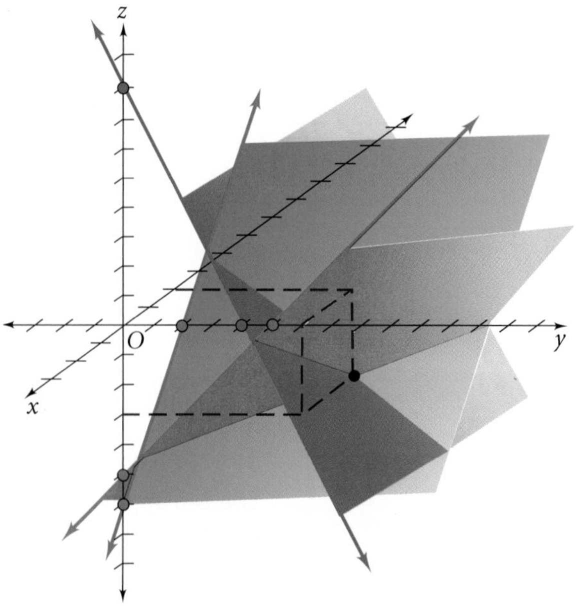

OBJECTIVE 2

Solving Three-Variable Systems by Substitution

You can also use the substitution method to solve a system of three equations. Substitution is the best method to use when one of the equations can be solved easily for one variable.

3 EXAMPLE Solving by Substitution

Need Help?
To review the substitution method, go to Lesson 3-2.

Solve the system by substitution. $\begin{cases} x - 2y + z = -4 & ① \\ -4x + y - 2z = 1 & ② \\ 2x + 2y - z = 10 & ③ \end{cases}$

Step 1 Choose one equation to solve for one of its variables.

$$① \; x - 2y + z = -4 \quad \textbf{Solve the first equation for x.}$$
$$x - 2y = -z - 4$$
$$x = 2y - z - 4$$

Step 2 Substitute the expression for x into each of the other two equations.

$$②\quad -4x + y - 2z = 1$$
$$-4(2y - z - 4) + y - 2z = 1 \quad \textbf{Simplify.}$$
$$-8y + 4z + 16 + y - 2z = 1$$
$$-7y + 2z + 16 = 1$$
$$④\quad -7y + 2z = -15$$

$$③\quad 2x + 2y - z = 10$$
$$2(2y - z - 4) + 2y - z = 10$$
$$4y - 2z - 8 + 2y - z = 10$$
$$6y - 3z - 8 = 10$$
$$⑤\quad 6y - 3z = 18$$

Step 3 Write the two new equations as a system. Solve for y and z.

$$\begin{cases} -7y + 2z = -15 & ④ \\ 6y - 3z = 18 & ⑤ \end{cases}$$

$$-21y + 6z = -45 \quad \textbf{Multiply by 3.}$$
$$12y - 6z = 36 \quad \textbf{Multiply by 2.}$$
$$-9y = -9$$
$$y = 1$$

$$④\quad -7y + 2z = -15$$
$$-7(1) + 2z = -15 \quad \textbf{Substitute the value of y.}$$
$$-7 + 2z = -15$$
$$2z = -8$$
$$z = -4$$

Step 4 Substitute the values for y and z into one of the original equations (①, ②, or ③). Solve for x.

$$①\quad x - 2y + z = -4$$
$$x - 2(1) + (-4) = -4$$
$$x - 2 - 4 = -4$$
$$x - 6 = -4$$
$$x = 2$$

The solution of the system is $(2, 1, -4)$.

Check Understanding 3 Solve each system by substitution. Check your answers.

a. $\begin{cases} x - 3y + z = 6 \\ 2x - 5y - z = -2 \\ -x + y + 2z = 7 \end{cases}$

b. $\begin{cases} 3x + 2y - z = 12 \\ -4x + y - 2z = 4 \\ x - 3y + z = -4 \end{cases}$

Investment Options

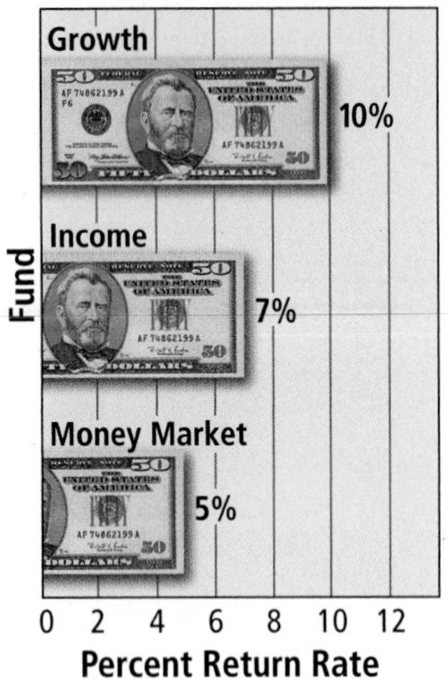

4 EXAMPLE Real-World Connection

Money Management Suppose you have saved \$3200 from a part-time job and you want to invest your savings in a growth fund, an income fund, and a money market fund. Refer to the graph. To maximize your return, you decide to put twice as much money in the growth fund as in the money market fund. How should you invest the \$3200 to get a return of \$250 in one year?

Relate growth fund + income fund + money market fund = 3200

growth fund = 2 times money market fund

10% of growth + 7% of income + 5% of money market = 250

Define Let g = amount invested in a growth fund.

Let i = amount invested in an income fund.

Let m = amount invested in a money market fund.

Write

$$\begin{cases} g + i + m = 3200 & ① \\ g = 2m & ② \\ 0.10g + 0.07i + 0.05m = 250 & ③ \end{cases}$$

Step 1 Substitute $2m$ for g in equations ① and ③. Simplify.

① $g + i + m = 3200$ ③ $0.10g + 0.07i + 0.05m = 250$

$2m + i + m = 3200$ $0.10(2m) + 0.07i + 0.05m = 250$

④ $3m + i = 3200$ ⑤ $0.25m + 0.07i = 250$

Step 2 Write the two new equations as a system. Solve for m and i.

$$\begin{cases} 3m + i = 3200 & ④ \\ 0.25m + 0.07i = 250 & ⑤ \end{cases}$$

$3m + i = 3200$

$3m + 0.84i = 3000$ **Multiply by 12.**

$0.16i = 200$

$i = 1250$

④ $3m + i = 3200$

$3m + 1250 = 3200$ **Substitute the value of *i*.**

$3m = 1950$

$m = 650$

Step 3 Substitute the value of m into equation 2 and solve for g.

② $g = 2m$

$g = 2(650)$

$g = 1300$

You should invest \$1300 in the growth fund, \$1250 in the income fund, and \$650 in the money market fund to get a return of \$250 in one year.

Check Understanding 4 Suppose you discover that your growth fund, income fund, and money market fund return rates are better estimated at 12%, 6%, and 3% per year respectively. How should you invest the \$3200 to get a return of \$255 in one year?

You have learned how to solve systems of equations using the methods of graphing, elimination, and substitution. In Chapter 4, you will learn how to use matrices to solve systems of equations.

EXERCISES

For more practice, see *Extra Practice.*

Practice and Problem Solving

A Practice by Example

Examples 1 and 2 (pages 149 and 150)

Solve each system by elimination. Check your answers.

1. $\begin{cases} x - y + z = -1 \\ x + y + 3z = -3 \\ 2x - y + 2z = 0 \end{cases}$ **2.** $\begin{cases} x - y - 2z = 4 \\ -x + 2y + z = 1 \\ -x + y - 3z = 11 \end{cases}$ **3.** $\begin{cases} 2x - y + z = -2 \\ x + 3y - z = 10 \\ x + 2z = -8 \end{cases}$

4. $\begin{cases} a + b + c = -3 \\ 3b - c = 4 \\ 2a - b - 2c = -5 \end{cases}$ **5.** $\begin{cases} 6q - r + 2s = 8 \\ 2q + 3r - s = -9 \\ 4q + 2r + 5s = 1 \end{cases}$ **6.** $\begin{cases} x - y + 2z = -7 \\ y + z = 1 \\ x = 2y + 3z \end{cases}$

7. $\begin{cases} x + y + 2z = 3 \\ 2x + y + 3z = 7 \\ -x - 2y + z = 10 \end{cases}$ **8.** $\begin{cases} 3x - y + z = 3 \\ x + y + 2z = 4 \\ x + 2y + z = 4 \end{cases}$ **9.** $\begin{cases} x - 2y + 3z = 12 \\ 2x - y - 2z = 5 \\ 2x + 2y - z = 4 \end{cases}$

Examples 3 and 4 (pages 151 and 152)

Solve each system by substitution. Check your answers.

10. $\begin{cases} x + 2y + 3z = 6 \\ y + 2z = 0 \\ z = 2 \end{cases}$ **11.** $\begin{cases} 3a + b + c = 7 \\ a + 3b - c = 13 \\ b = 2a - 1 \end{cases}$ **12.** $\begin{cases} 5r - 4s - 3t = 3 \\ t = s + r \\ r = 3s + 1 \end{cases}$

13. $\begin{cases} 13 = 3x - y \\ 4y - 3x + 2z = -3 \\ z = 2x - 4y \end{cases}$ **14.** $\begin{cases} x + 3y - z = -4 \\ 2x - y + 2z = 13 \\ 3x - 2y - z = -9 \end{cases}$ **15.** $\begin{cases} x - 4y + z = 6 \\ 2x + 5y - z = 7 \\ 2x - y - z = 1 \end{cases}$

16. $\begin{cases} x - y + 2z = 7 \\ 2x + y + z = 8 \\ x - z = 5 \end{cases}$ **17.** $\begin{cases} x + y + z = 2 \\ x + 2z = 5 \\ 2x + y - z = -1 \end{cases}$ **18.** $\begin{cases} 5x - y + z = 4 \\ x + 2y - z = 5 \\ 2x + 3y - 3z = 5 \end{cases}$

Real-World Connection

Careers Stadium designers must take into account the profitability of different types of seating.

19. **Finance** A company placed \$1,000,000 in three different accounts. It placed part in short-term notes paying 4.5% per year, twice as much in government bonds paying 5%, and the rest in utility bonds paying 4%. The income after one year was \$45,500. How much did the company place in each account?

20. **Sports** A stadium has 49,000 seats. Seats sell for \$25 in Section A, \$20 in section B, and \$15 in Section C. The number of seats in Section A equals the total number of seats in Sections B and C. Suppose the stadium takes in \$1,052,000 from each sold-out event. How many seats does each section hold?

21. A change machine contains nickels, dimes, and quarters. There are 75 coins in the machine, and the value of the coins is \$7.25. There are 5 times as many nickels as dimes. Find the number of coins of each type in the machine.

B Apply Your Skills

Find the number of solutions of each system.

22.

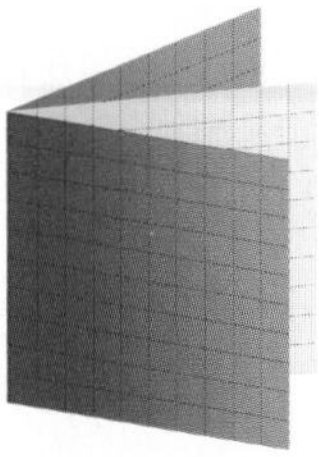

23.

24.

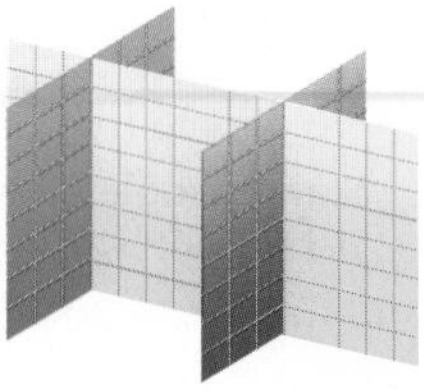

Solve each system.

25. $\begin{cases} x - 3y + 2z = 11 \\ -x + 4y + 3z = 5 \\ 2x - 2y - 4z = 2 \end{cases}$

26. $\begin{cases} x + 2y + z = 4 \\ 2x - y + 4z = -8 \\ -3x + y - 2z = -1 \end{cases}$

27. $\begin{cases} 4x - y + 2z = -6 \\ -2x + 3y - z = 8 \\ 2y + 3z = -5 \end{cases}$

28. $\begin{cases} 4A + 2U + I = 2 \\ 5A - 3U + 2I = 17 \\ A - 5U = 3 \end{cases}$

29. $\begin{cases} 4x - 2y + 5z = 6 \\ 3x + 3y + 8z = 4 \\ x - 5y - 3z = 5 \end{cases}$

30. $\begin{cases} 2\ell + 2w + h = 72 \\ \ell = 3w \\ h = 2w \end{cases}$

31. $\begin{cases} 3x + 2y - z = 17.8 \\ x - 3y + 2z = 7.9 \\ 2x + y - 3z = 3.9 \end{cases}$

32. $\begin{cases} x + 2y = 2 \\ 2x + 3y - z = -9 \\ 4x + 2y + 5z = 1 \end{cases}$

33. $\begin{cases} 3x + 2y + 2z = -2 \\ 2x + y - z = -2 \\ x - 3y + z = 0 \end{cases}$

34. $\begin{cases} 6x + y - 4z = -8 \\ \frac{y}{4} - \frac{z}{6} = 0 \\ 2x - z = -2 \end{cases}$

35. $\begin{cases} 4y + 2x = 6 - 3z \\ x + z - 2y = -5 \\ x - 2z = 3y - 7 \end{cases}$

36. $\begin{cases} 5z + 4y = 4 \\ 3x - 2y = 0 \\ x + 3z = -8 \end{cases}$

37. $\begin{cases} x + 6z = 12 \\ -2x + 3y = 6 \\ y - \frac{z}{2} = \frac{5}{2} \end{cases}$

38. $\begin{cases} 4x - y + z = -5 \\ -x + y - z = 5 \\ 2x - z - 1 = y \end{cases}$

History Exercises 39 and 40 appeared in the book *Algebraical Problems*, published in 1824. Write and solve a system for each problem.

39. Ten apples cost a penny, and 25 pears cost two pennies. Suppose I buy 100 apples and pears for $9\frac{1}{2}$ pennies. How many of each shall I have?

40. A fish was caught whose tail weighed 9 lb. Its head weighed as much as its tail plus half its body. Its body weighed as much as its head and tail. What did the fish weigh?

41. **Writing** How do you decide whether substitution is the best method to solve a system in three variables?

C Challenge

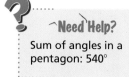

42. **Error Analysis** A student says that the system consisting of $x = 0$, $y = 0$, and $z = 0$ has no solutions. Explain the student's error.

Need Help?
Sum of angles in a pentagon: 540°

43. **Geometry** Refer to the regular five-pointed star at the right. Write and solve a system of three equations to find the measure of each labeled angle.

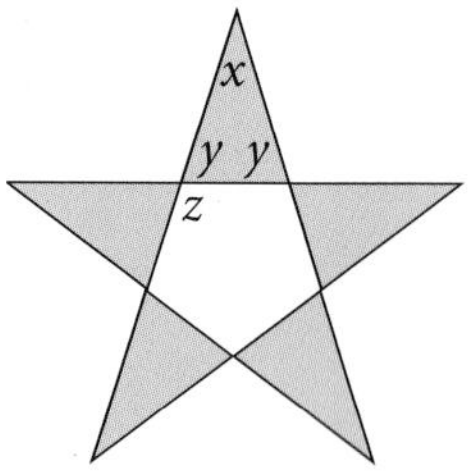

44. **Open-Ended** Write your own system having three variables. Begin by choosing the solution. Then write three equations that are true for your solution. Use elimination to solve the system.

45. Geometry In the regular polyhedron described below, all faces are congruent polygons. Use a system of three linear equations to find the numbers of vertices, edges, and faces.

Every face has five edges and every edge is shared by two faces. Every face has five vertices and every vertex is shared by three faces. The sum of the number of vertices and faces is two more than the number of edges.

Standardized Test Prep

Multiple Choice

46. What is the solution of the system? $\begin{cases} -3x + 2y - z = 6 \\ 3x + y + 2z = 5 \\ 2x - 2y - z = -5 \end{cases}$

A. (6, 5, −3) **B.** (1, 4, −1)
C. $\left(0, \frac{17}{5}, \frac{4}{5}\right)$ **D.** no solution

47. What is the solution of the system? $\begin{cases} x + 3y - 2z = -8 \\ 3x - y + z = 11 \\ 2x + 4y + 2z = 14 \end{cases}$

F. (2, 0, 5) **G.** (−8, 11, 14)
H. $\left(-2, \frac{4}{3}, 5\right)$ **I.** no solution

Take It to the NET
Online lesson quiz at **www.PHSchool.com**
Web Code: aga-0306

48. What is the solution of the system? $\begin{cases} y = -2x + 10 \\ -x + y - 2z = -2 \\ 3x - 2y + 4z = 7 \end{cases}$

A. $\left(3, -4, \frac{3}{2}\right)$ **B.** $\left(3, 16, \frac{15}{2}\right)$
C. $\left(-3, 16, \frac{15}{2}\right)$ **D.** $\left(3, 4, \frac{3}{2}\right)$

Short Response

49. Why is there no solution to the system? Explain your answer in terms of intersecting planes.

$\begin{cases} ① \; 2x - 3y + z = 5 \\ ② \; 2x - 3y + z = -2 \\ ③ \; -4x + 6y - 2z = 10 \end{cases}$

Mixed Review

Lesson 3-5

Graph each equation.

50. $x + y + 4z = 8$ **51.** $2x + 3y - z = 12$ **52.** $-3x + y + 5z = 15$

53. $-2x + 3y - z = 6$ **54.** $6x + 4y - 3z = -12$ **55.** $3x - 6y - 2z = 18$

Lesson 2-5

Graph each equation.

56. $y = |x + 4|$ **57.** $y = |3x - 2|$ **58.** $y = \left|\frac{1}{2}x + 3\right| - 2$

59. $y = |x - 2| + 1$ **60.** $y = |2x + 1|$ **61.** $y = |x + 3| - 2$

Lesson 1-4

Solve each inequality. Graph the solution on a number line.

62. $-4x + 3 \le 9$ **63.** $-(x + 4) - 3 \ge 11$ **64.** $2(3x - 1) < x - 7$

65. $6 - 2x > 2$ **66.** $3x + 2 < -x + 10$ **67.** $-2(x + 3) \ge x$

Test-Taking Strategies

Writing Extended Responses

Extended-response questions usually are worth 4 points and have multiple parts. If you can't answer one part, you may be able to get partial credit for the other parts.

EXAMPLE

You plan to put a fence around a rectangular lot. The length of the lot must be at least 52 feet. The cost of the fence along the length of the lot is \$2 per foot, and the cost of the fence along the width is \$3 per foot. The total cost cannot exceed \$360.

a. Use two variables to write a system of inequalities that models the problem.
b. Graph the system, and shade the feasible region.
c. What is the maximum width of the lot if the length is 60 feet?

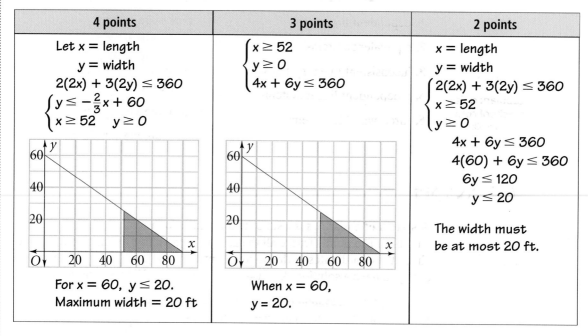

4 points	3 points	2 points
Let x = length y = width $2(2x) + 3(2y) \le 360$ $\begin{cases} y \le -\frac{2}{3}x + 60 \\ x \ge 52 \quad y \ge 0 \end{cases}$ 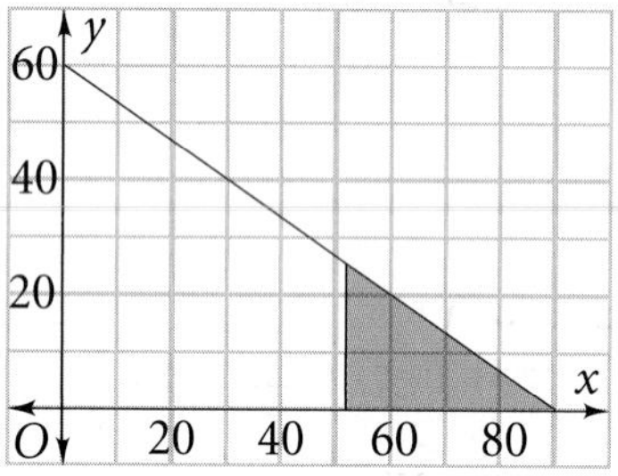 For $x = 60$, $y \le 20$. Maximum width = 20 ft	$\begin{cases} x \ge 52 \\ y \ge 0 \\ 4x + 6y \le 360 \end{cases}$ 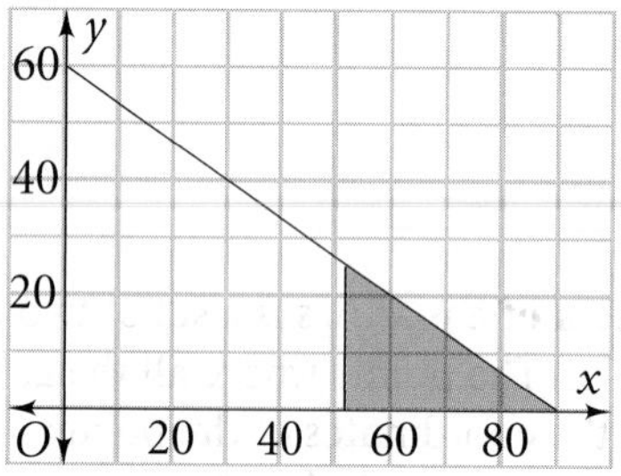 When $x = 60$, $y = 20$.	x = length y = width $\begin{cases} 2(2x) + 3(2y) \le 360 \\ x \ge 52 \\ y \ge 0 \end{cases}$ $4x + 6y \le 360$ $4(60) + 6y \le 360$ $6y \le 120$ $y \le 20$ The width must be at most 20 ft.

The 4-point response gives a complete and correct answer to each part. The 3-point response lost credit for not showing all the work. The 2-point response does not include an answer for part (b), but answers the other parts correctly.

EXERCISES

1. What did the 3-point response to the Example leave out?

2. **Open-Ended** Describe a response to the Example that would deserve only 1 point.

3. Suppose the minimum length of the lot in the Example is changed to 60 feet, the cost of the fence along the width is changed to \$2 per foot, and the cost of the fence along the length is changed to \$1.50 per foot. Find the new answers to parts (a), (b), and (c). Show your work.

Chapter 3

Chapter Review

Vocabulary

constraints (p. 135)
coordinate space (p. 142)
dependent system (p. 118)
equivalent systems (p. 125)
feasible region (p. 136)
inconsistent system (p. 118)
independent system (p. 118)
linear programming (p. 135)
linear system (p. 116)
objective function (p. 135)
ordered triples (p. 142)
system of equations (p. 116)
trace (p. 144)

Reading Math
Understanding Vocabulary

Match the vocabulary term in column 1 with the most appropriate phrase in column 2.

Column 1	Column 2
1. dependent linear systems	**A.** have many solutions
2. equivalent systems	**B.** have no solutions
3. inconsistent linear systems	**C.** have solutions that can be shown as the intersection of planes
4. independent linear systems	**D.** have the same solutions
5. three-variable systems	**E.** have unique solutions

Take It to the NET
Online vocabulary quiz at www.PHSchool.com
Web Code: agj-0351

Skills and Concepts

3-1 Objectives

▼ To solve a system by graphing (p. 116)

A **system of equations** is a set of two or more equations that use the same variables. The points where all the graphs intersect represent solutions. You must check the coordinates of the points of intersection in the original equations to be sure you have a solution. A **linear system** consists of linear equations.

An **independent system** has a unique solution while a **dependent system** does not have a unique solution. An **inconsistent system** has no solutions.

Solve each system by graphing.

6. $\begin{cases} y = 2x + 1 \\ y = 4x + 5 \end{cases}$

7. $\begin{cases} y = 3x - 2 \\ y = -2x + 8 \end{cases}$

8. $\begin{cases} y = 3x - 5 \\ 2y = 6x + 4 \end{cases}$

9. $\begin{cases} 3x + 2y = -6 \\ x - y = -2 \end{cases}$

10. $\begin{cases} 4x - y = 6 \\ -2x + 3y = 12 \end{cases}$

11. $\begin{cases} 12x + 3y = -9 \\ 4x + y = 7 \end{cases}$

Without graphing, classify each system as *independent*, *dependent*, or *inconsistent*.

12. $\begin{cases} 6x + 3y = 12 \\ y = -2x + 4 \end{cases}$

13. $\begin{cases} y = -x + 5 \\ x - y = -3 \end{cases}$

14. $\begin{cases} x + 2y = 2 \\ y = -0.5x - 2 \end{cases}$

15. Banking Suppose a bank charges a monthly rate of $10 for your checking account. You can switch to a different account that charges $6 plus $.20 per check. For what number of checks is the cost of the two accounts the same?

3-2 Objectives

- ▼ To solve a system by substitution (p. 123)
- ▼ To solve a system by elimination (p. 124)

If you can easily solve one equation in a system of two equations for one of the variables, you can substitute that expression in the other equation. Then you can find the value of the other variable.

Otherwise, you can multiply one or both equations by a nonzero quantity to create two terms that are additive inverses. This creates an **equivalent system** of equations. Adding the two equations then eliminates one variable. Again, you can solve for the other variable.

In either case, you substitute the value of this second variable into either of the original equations to find the value of the first variable. Recall that some systems have an infinite number of solutions and some have no solutions.

Solve using substitution.

16. $\begin{cases} 3x + 5y = 10 \\ y = -4 \end{cases}$

17. $\begin{cases} 4x + 3y = 12 \\ x = 5y - 20 \end{cases}$

18. $\begin{cases} 8x + y = 17 \\ x + 4y = 37 \end{cases}$

Solve using elimination.

19. $\begin{cases} 2x + y = 13 \\ x - y = -4 \end{cases}$

20. $\begin{cases} 2x + 3y = 4 \\ 4x + 6y = 9 \end{cases}$

21. $\begin{cases} a + b = \frac{1}{3} \\ a - b = \frac{1}{4} \end{cases}$

22. Nutrition Roast beef has 25 g of protein and 11 g of calcium per serving. A serving of mashed potatoes has 2 g of protein and 25 g of calcium. How many servings of each are needed to supply exactly 29 g of protein and 61 g of calcium?

3-3 Objectives

- ▼ To solve systems of linear inequalities (p. 130)

The solution of a system of inequalities is represented on a graph by the region of overlap of the inequalities. To solve a system by graphing, first graph the boundaries for each inequality. Then shade the regions of the plane containing the solutions for both inequalities.

Solve each system by graphing.

23. $\begin{cases} y < -x + 1 \\ y \geq \frac{3}{4}x - 6 \end{cases}$

24. $\begin{cases} x + y \leq 4 \\ y < 6 \end{cases}$

25. $\begin{cases} y > |x - 4| \\ y < \frac{1}{3}x \end{cases}$

26. For a community breakfast there should be at least three times as much regular coffee as decaffeinated coffee. A total of ten gallons is sufficient for the breakfast. Model this situation with a system of inequalities. Graph to solve the system.

3-4 Objectives

- ▼ To find maximum and minimum values (p. 135)
- ▼ To solve problems with linear programming (p. 137)

Linear programming is a technique used to find the maximum or minimum value of an **objective function**. Linear inequalities are **constraints** on the variables of the objective function. The solutions to the system of constraints are contained in the **feasible region**. The maximum or minimum value of the objective function occurs at a vertex of the feasible region.

Graph each system of constraints. Find all vertices. Then find the variable values that maximize or minimize the objective function.

27. $\begin{cases} x \leq 8 \\ y \leq 5 \\ x \geq 0, y \geq 0 \end{cases}$

Minimum for $C = x + 5y$

28. $\begin{cases} x \geq 2 \\ y \geq 0 \\ 3x + 2y \geq 12 \end{cases}$

Minimum for $C = 4x + y$

29. $\begin{cases} 3x + 2y \leq 12 \\ x + y \leq 5 \\ x \geq 0, y \geq 0 \end{cases}$

Maximum for $P = 3x + 5y$

30. Profit A lunch stand makes \$.75 profit on each chef's salad and \$1.20 profit on each Caesar salad. On a typical weekday, it sells between 40 and 60 chef's salads and between 35 and 50 Caesar salads. The total number sold has never exceeded 100 salads. How many of each type should be prepared in order to maximize profit?

3-5 Objectives

- To graph points in three dimensions (p. 142)
- To graph equations in three dimensions (p. 144)

You can plot **ordered triples** in **coordinate space.** To sketch a plane that is the graph of an equation in three variables, find the intercepts. To find the x-intercept, substitute 0 for y and z. Then find the other two intercepts. If the plane does not pass through the origin, connect the resulting intercepts on the three axes. These lines are called the **traces** of the plane.

Graph each point in coordinate space.

31. (0, 2, 0) **32.** (1, 0, 0) **33.** (0, 0, 3) **34.** (2, 3, 0) **35.** (1, 0, 4)

Find the coordinates of each point in the diagram at the right.

36. A

37. B

38. C

39. D

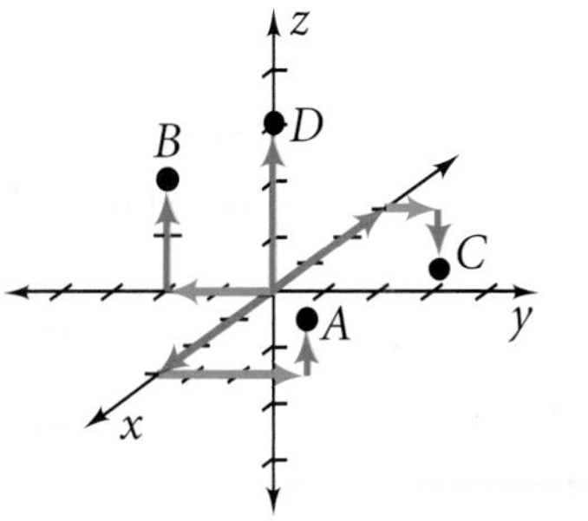

Sketch the graph of each equation.

40. $x - 2y + z = 4$ **41.** $10x - 4y - 5z = 20$ **42.** $2x + 6y + 3z = 18$

3-6 Objectives

- To solve systems in three variables by elimination (p. 148)
- To solve systems in three variables by substitution (p. 151)

You can solve systems of three equations in three variables using the technique of substitution you learned in Lesson 3-2.

Elimination with three equations in three variables involves pairing the equations. Use one equation twice. Then eliminate the same variable in both pairs. The result is a system of two equations in two variables. Proceed using the methods you learned in Lesson 3-2.

Solve each system.

43. $\begin{cases} x + y + z = 10 \\ 2x - y + z = 2 \\ -x + 2y - z = 5 \end{cases}$

44. $\begin{cases} x + 2y + z = 14 \\ y = z + 1 \\ x = -3z + 6 \end{cases}$

45. $\begin{cases} 3x + y - 2z = 22 \\ x + 5y + z = 4 \\ x = -3z \end{cases}$

Chapter 3

Chapter Test

Take It to the NET
Online chapter test at
www.PHSchool.com
Web Code: aga-0352

Classify each system without graphing. Then graph each system.

1. $\begin{cases} y = 5x - 2 \\ y = x + 4 \end{cases}$

2. $\begin{cases} 3x + 2y = 9 \\ 3x + 2y = 4 \end{cases}$

Solve using substitution.

3. $\begin{cases} 3x + 2y = 9 \\ x + y = 4 \end{cases}$

4. $\begin{cases} 0.3x - y = 0 \\ y = 2 + 0.25x \end{cases}$

Solve using elimination.

5. $\begin{cases} 3x - y = 1 \\ 2x + y = 14 \end{cases}$

6. $\begin{cases} 4x - 2y = 3 \\ 2y - 4x = \frac{3}{2} \end{cases}$

7. Writing Describe how to identify situations in which substitution may be the best method for solving a system of equations.

Graph each system.

8. $\begin{cases} 2x + y < 3 \\ x < y + 3 \end{cases}$

9. $\begin{cases} 3y + 9x < 3 \\ y \geq 2 \end{cases}$

10. $\begin{cases} |x + 3| > y \\ y > 2x - 1 \end{cases}$

11. $\begin{cases} y > -2x + 6 \\ y \leq \frac{1}{4}x - 3 \end{cases}$

Graph each system of constraints. Find all vertices. Evaluate the objective function at each vertex to find the maximum or minimum value.

12. $\begin{cases} x \leq 5 \\ y \leq 4 \\ x \geq 0, y \geq 0 \end{cases}$

Maximum for
$P = 2x + y$

13. $\begin{cases} x + y \leq 8 \\ x + 2y \geq 6 \\ x \geq 0, y \geq 0 \end{cases}$

Minimum for
$C = x + 3y$

14. Sales A pizza shop makes $1.50 on each small pizza and $2.15 on each large pizza. On a typical Friday, it sells between 70 and 90 small pizzas and between 100 and 140 large pizzas. The shop can make no more than 210 pizzas in a day. How many of each size of pizza must be sold in order to maximize profit?

15. Open-Ended Write a system of constraints whose graph is a parallelogram.

Graph each point in coordinate space.

16. $(0, 5, 0)$ **17.** $(-1, 0, 0)$ **18.** $(1, 0, 4)$

19. $(3, 0, -1)$ **20.** $(1, 4, -1)$ **21.** $(2, -2, 3)$

Graph each equation. Use intercepts and traces.

22. $x + y + z = 6$ **23.** $2x - 3y + z = 6$

24. $-2x + y - 5z = 10$ **25.** $x - y + 2z = 8$

26. You are planning a party. You have $24 to spend on decorations. Balloons cost $.06 each, party favors cost $.48 each, and streamers cost $.08 each. Write and graph an equation for the number of each you can buy.

Solve each system of equations.

27. $\begin{cases} x - y + z = 0 \\ 3x - 2y + 6z = 9 \\ -x + y - 2z = -2 \end{cases}$

28. $\begin{cases} 2x + y + z = 8 \\ x + 2y - z = -5 \\ z = 2x - y \end{cases}$

Write a system of equations to solve each problem.

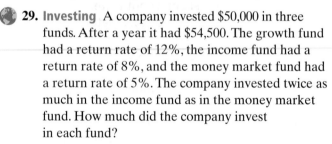

29. Investing A company invested $50,000 in three funds. After a year it had $54,500. The growth fund had a return rate of 12%, the income fund had a return rate of 8%, and the money market fund had a return rate of 5%. The company invested twice as much in the income fund as in the money market fund. How much did the company invest in each fund?

30. Earnings A student can make a weekly salary of $200 plus 15% commission on sales at the Radio Barn or a weekly salary of $300 plus 10% commission on sales at Woofer, Etc. For what amount of sales do these two jobs pay the same?

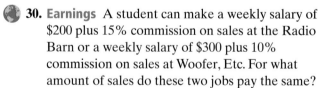

31. Purchasing To help passengers stranded by bad weather one winter, an airport made the purchases detailed below. Find the cost of a cot, a table, and a chair.

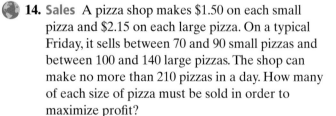

	Number of Cots	Number of Tables	Number of Chairs	Total Costs ($)
Nov	10	10	40	1950
Dec	20	0	20	1800
Jan	10	5	20	1350

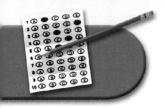

Standardized Test Prep

Reading Comprehension **Read the passage below. Then answer the questions on the basis of what is *stated* or *implied* in the passage.**

Hot and Cold Do you ever think about the math involved in filling a bathtub? Depending on the location and the season, the temperature of the cold water that enters a home may be 55°F. Some of the water goes to a water heater, where its temperature may be raised to 122°F.

Suppose you want a tub of 22 gallons of water at 78°F. You can write two equations, using x and y to represent the numbers of gallons of cold and hot water.

$x + y = 22$	**The full tub contains 22 gal.**
$55x + 122y = 22 \cdot 78$	***x* gal at 55° plus *y* gal at 122° is equivalent to 22 gal at 78°.**

If you solve the system of equations, you find that you need about 14.4 gallons of cold water.

1. In the given system of equations, what does x represent?
A. the number of gallons of hot water
B. the number of gallons of cold water
C. the capacity of the tub
D. the temperature of the hot water

2. In the given system of equations, what is the value of y?
F. about 1716 **G.** about 22
H. about 14.4 **I.** about 7.6

3. Which equation results from solving for x in the first equation of the system and then substituting that result into the second equation of the system?
A. $55x + 122(22 - x) = 1716$
B. $55(22 - y) + 122y = 1716$
C. $x = \frac{1716 - 122y}{55}$
D. $y = \frac{1716 - 55x}{122}$

4. Suppose a tub with 22 gallons of water contains a mixture of a gallons of cold water at 60°F and b gallons of hot water at 120°F. The desired bath temperature is 80°F. Which of the following systems models the problem?
F. $a + b = 80$
$60a + 120b = 22(80)$
G. $a + b = 120$
$120a + 60b = 12(80)$
H. $a + b = 22$
$60a + 120b = 22(80)$
I. $a + b = 22$
$120a + 60b = 22(80)$

5. How many gallons of hot water are needed for the bath described in Question 4?
A. $7\frac{1}{3}$
B. 11
C. $14\frac{2}{3}$
D. $16\frac{1}{2}$

6. Suppose a tub with 21 gallons of water contains a mixture of cold water at 65°F and hot water at 128°F. The desired bath temperature is 82°F. Write a system of equations to model the volume h of hot water and the volume c of cold water needed for the bath.

7. Consider the bath described in Question 6.
a. How many gallons of hot water are needed?
b. How many gallons of cold water are needed?

Where You've Been

- In Chapter 1, you learned to represent relationships using variables. You learned to evaluate and simplify variable expressions involving integers and fractions.
- In Chapter 2, you learned to represent two-variable equations in a variety of ways. You learned to graph linear equations and inequalities.
- In Chapter 3, you learned to graph systems of equations and inequalities, including systems of three equations in three variables.

Instant self-check online and on CD-ROM

Diagnosing Readiness

(For help, go to the Lesson in green.)

Evaluating Expressions (Lesson 1-2)

Evaluate $ad - bc$ for the given values of the variables.

1. $a = -1, b = -2, c = 5, d = 4$

2. $a = \frac{1}{2}, b = -1, c = -\frac{2}{3}, d = 2$

3. $a = 2, b = \frac{1}{2}, c = \frac{1}{4}, d = -\frac{1}{8}$

4. $a = -\frac{1}{3}, b = \frac{1}{2}, c = \frac{1}{4}, d = -\frac{2}{3}$

Solving Equations and Inequalities (Lessons 1-3 and 1-4)

Solve each equation or inequality. Check your answers.

5. $23 - x = 13 + 2x$

6. $\frac{x - 1}{5} = -2$

7. $a + 17 = -3a$

8. $2y - 3 \le 2y + 5$

9. $11 + 3t > -t$

10. $\frac{3s - 2}{2} < s$

Graphing Equations (Lesson 2-2)

Graph each equation on a coordinate plane.

11. $3x - 2y = 4$

12. $-3x = y$

13. $-7x - 3y = 14$

14. $y = \frac{2}{3}x - 3$

15. $y = 2x - 1$

16. $2x - 3y = -6$

17. $-2x = 3y + 12$

18. $-2y - 4x = 15$

Solving Systems of Equations (Lessons 3-2 and 3-6)

Solve each system.

19. $\begin{cases} -2x + y = -5 \\ 4x + y = -2 \end{cases}$

20. $\begin{cases} 4x - y = -2 \\ -\frac{1}{2}x - y = 1 \end{cases}$

21. $\begin{cases} 3x + y = 5 \\ -x + y = 2 \end{cases}$

22. $\begin{cases} x + y + z = 10 \\ 2x - y = 5 \\ y - z = 15 \end{cases}$

23. $\begin{cases} -x + y + 2z = 16 \\ 2x - 2y - 2z = -16 \\ x + y = 0 \end{cases}$

24. $\begin{cases} -2x + 3y + z = 1 \\ x - 3z = 7 \\ -y + z = -5 \end{cases}$

Matrices

Chapter 4

LESSONS

Key Vocabulary

- augmented matrix (p. 218)
- determinant (p. 196)
- dilation (p. 188)
- equal matrices (p. 173)
- image (p. 188)
- matrix (p. 164)
- matrix addition (p. 170)
- matrix element (p. 165)
- matrix equation (p. 172)
- matrix multiplication (p. 180)
- preimage (p. 188)
- row operations (p. 219)
- scalar product (p. 178)
- transformation (p. 188)
- variable matrix (p. 210)
- zero matrix (p. 171)

Where You're Going

- In Chapter 4, you will move from using matrices in organizing data to manipulating matrices through algebra.
- You will learn to represent real-world relationships by writing matrices and using operations such as addition and multiplication to develop new matrices.
- You will learn, by working with geometric figures, how matrices relate to graphic art.

Real World Snapshots Applying what you learn, on pages 230–231 you will do activities involving the profits and losses of a chocolate-making business.

4-1 Organizing Data Into Matrices

North Carolina Objectives — 1.04 Operate with matrices to model and solve problems.

Lesson Preview

What You'll Learn

OBJECTIVE 1 To identify matrices and their elements

OBJECTIVE 2 To organize data into matrices

. . . And Why

To organize gymnastics data, as in Example 4

✓ Check Skills You'll Need

(For help, go to Skills Handbook page 842.)

Use the table at the right.

1. How many cars were imported to the United States in 1980? How many were imported in 1995?
2. How many more cars were imported in 1990 than in 1980?
3. How many more cars were imported than exported in 1995?
4. Compare the percent increase of imports from 1980 to 1995 with the percent increase of exports from 1980 to 1995.

U.S. Passenger Car Imports and Exports (millions)

	1980	1990	1995
Imports	3.116	3.945	4.115
Exports	0.617	0.794	0.989

SOURCE: U.S. Department of Commerce. Go to **www.PHSchool.com** for a data update. Web Code: agg-2041

New Vocabulary

- matrix
- matrix element

Interactive lesson includes instant self-check, tutorials, and activities.

OBJECTIVE 1

Identifying Matrices

A **matrix** (plural: matrices) is a rectangular array of numbers written within brackets. You represent a matrix with a capital letter and classify it by its dimensions. The number of horizontal rows and the number of vertical columns determine the dimensions of a matrix.

Reading Math

For matrices, read × as "by." For example, read 2 × 3 as "two by three."

3 columns

$$A = \begin{bmatrix} 2 & 3 & 4 \\ 6 & 7 & 0 \end{bmatrix} \leftarrow \text{2 rows}$$

Matrix *A* is a 2 × 3 matrix.

1 EXAMPLE Writing the Dimensions of a Matrix

Write the dimensions of each matrix.

a. $\begin{bmatrix} 4 & 6 & 5 \\ 2 & -3 & -7 \\ 1 & 0 & 9 \end{bmatrix}$

3 rows × 3 columns

This is a 3 × 3 matrix.

b. $\begin{bmatrix} -4 & \frac{1}{3} & -3 \end{bmatrix}$

1 row × 3 columns

This is a 1 × 3 matrix.

c. $\begin{bmatrix} 1 \\ 2 \\ 0 \\ 0.5 \end{bmatrix}$

4 rows × 1 column

This is a 4 × 1 matrix.

✓ Check Understanding

1. Write the dimensions of each matrix.

a. $\begin{bmatrix} 4 & 5 & 0 \\ -2 & 0.5 & 17 \end{bmatrix}$ **b.** $[8 \quad -3 \quad 15]$ **c.** $\begin{bmatrix} 10 & 0 \\ 1 & -5 \\ -6.2 & 9 \end{bmatrix}$

Each number in a matrix is a **matrix element.** You can identify a matrix element by its position within the matrix. Use a lowercase letter with subscripts. The subscripts represent the element's row number and column number.

2 EXAMPLE Identifying a Matrix Element

Identify element a_{13} in matrix A below.

$$A = \begin{bmatrix} 17 & 24 & 3 \\ 10.4 & 12 & 15 \\ 9 & 30 & 15 \end{bmatrix}$$

a_{13} is the element in the first row and the third column.

Element a_{13} is 3.

Check Understanding 2 Identify each matrix element.

a. a_{33} **b.** a_{11} **c.** a_{21} **d.** a_{12}

OBJECTIVE 2

Organizing Statisical Data

Successful businesses must track great amounts of data in order to plan the best use of their resources. They use matrices to organize and compare statistical data.

3 EXAMPLE Real-World Connection

Real-World Connection

New appliances have labels that tell how much energy the appliance uses each year.

Energy Energy is often measured in British thermal units (Btus). Write a matrix to represent the data below. Estimate the values from the graph.

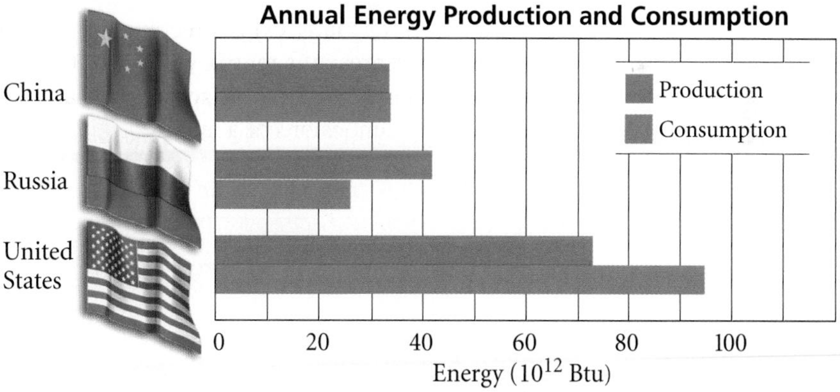

SOURCE: Energy Information Administration, International Energy Database. Go to **www.PHSchool.com** for a data update. Web Code: agg-2041

Let each row represent a country and each column represent production or consumption levels.

	Production	Consumption
China	33	34
Russia	41	26
United States	73	95

Check Understanding 3 **a.** Rewrite the matrix as a 2×3 matrix. Label the rows and columns.

b. How could you modify your matrix to include data from other countries?

c. **Critical Thinking** Explain the difference between a $c \times d$ matrix and a $d \times c$ matrix.

You can use matrices to show data from a table.

4 EXAMPLE Real-World Connection

Gymnastics The table below shows scores from the 2000 Olympics in Sydney, Australia.

Real-World Connection

Amy Chow was a member of the United States Gymnastics Team at the Olympic Games in 1996 and 2000.

U.S. Women's Olympic Gymnastics Team Qualification Scores

Gymnast	Floor Exercise	Vault	Balance Beam	Uneven Bars
Amy Chow	9.525	9.468	9.625	9.400
Dominique Dawes	9.087	9.393	8.600	9.675
Kristin Maloney	9.525	9.225	9.312	9.575
Elise Ray	9.225	9.468	9.687	9.687

SOURCE: NBC News

a. Write a matrix W to represent the information. Use a 4×4 matrix.

Each column represents a different event.

$$W = \begin{array}{r} \\ \text{A. Chow} \\ \text{D. Dawes} \\ \text{K. Maloney} \\ \text{E. Ray} \end{array} \begin{array}{c} \begin{array}{cccc} \text{Floor Exercise} & \text{Vault} & \text{Balance Beam} & \text{Uneven Bars} \end{array} \\ \begin{bmatrix} 9.525 & 9.468 & 9.625 & 9.400 \\ 9.087 & 9.393 & 8.600 & 9.675 \\ 9.525 & 9.225 & 9.312 & 9.575 \\ 9.225 & 9.468 & 9.687 & 9.687 \end{bmatrix} \end{array}$$

← Each row represents a different gymnast.

b. Which element represents Kristin Maloney's score on the vault?

Kristin Maloney's scores are in the third row. The vault scores are in the second column. Element w_{32} represents Kristin's score on the vault.

Check Understanding 4 **a.** Write a matrix M to represent the information from the table below.
b. Identify element m_{15}. What does this element represent?

U.S. Men's Olympic Gymnastics Team Qualification Scores

Gymnast	Floor Exercise	Pommel Horse	Still Rings	Vault	Parallel Bars	Horizontal Bars
Blaine Wilson	9.025	9.462	9.612	9.800	9.312	9.650
Stephen McCain	9.225	8.850	9.462	8.987	9.500	9.662
Paul Hamm	9.475	9.562	9.512	9.700	9.575	9.612

SOURCE: NBC News

EXERCISES

For more practice, see *Extra Practice*.

Practice and Problem Solving

A Practice by Example

Example 1 (page 164)

State the dimensions of each matrix.

1. $\begin{bmatrix} 4 & -2 & 2 \\ 1 & 4 & 1 \\ 0 & 5 & -7 \end{bmatrix}$ **2.** $\begin{bmatrix} 1 \\ -9 \\ 5 \end{bmatrix}$ **3.** $\begin{bmatrix} 2 & \sqrt{5} \end{bmatrix}$ **4.** $\begin{bmatrix} 3 & 2 & 1 \\ 2 & 0 & -3 \end{bmatrix}$ **5.** $\begin{bmatrix} 2.5 \\ -3 \\ -1.6 \\ 10.0 \end{bmatrix}$

Example 2 (page 165)

Refer to matrices A and B at the right. Identify each matrix element.

$$A = \begin{bmatrix} 0 & -1 \\ 1.5 & 3 \\ 7 & -2 \end{bmatrix} \quad B = \begin{bmatrix} 6 & -3 & \frac{1}{2} \end{bmatrix}$$

6. a_{21} **7.** b_{12} **8.** a_{31}

9. b_{13} **10.** a_{32} **11.** a_{12}

Example 3 (page 165)

Use the graph below for Exercises 12 and 13.

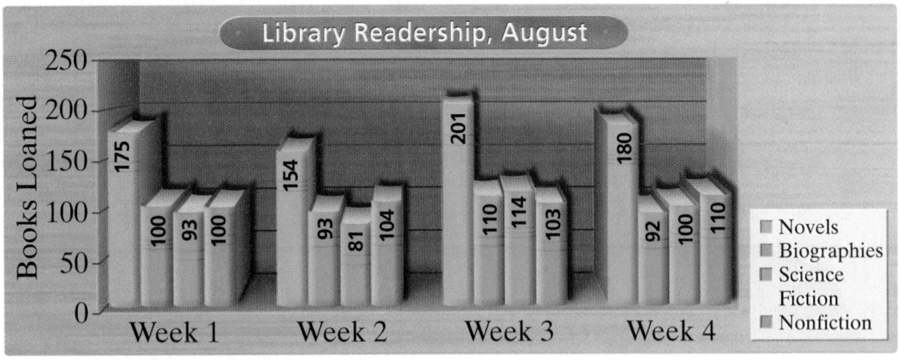

12. Write a matrix to represent the data. Label the rows and columns.

13. Write a different matrix to represent the data. Label the rows and columns.

Example 4 (page 166)

14. a. Write a matrix H to represent the data in the table below.
b. Find element h_{23}. What does this element represent?

Technology in Public Schools (millions)

Type of School	Videodisc Players	Modems	Networks	CD-ROMs
Elementary	25.9	35.1	26.4	37.9
Junior High	9.2	11.0	9.0	11.0
Senior High	10.7	14.5	12.9	14.0

SOURCE: Quality Education Data

B Apply Your Skills

Use the table below for Exercises 15–17.

15. Display the data in a matrix A with columns indicating years. Identify a_{23} and tell what it represents.

U.S. Households with Color TVs and VCRs (millions)

	1980	1985	1990	1992	1995	1997
Color TVs	63	78	90	91	94	97
VCRs	1	18	63	69	77	82

SOURCE: Nielsen Media Research

16. Display the data in a matrix A with rows indicating years. Identify a_{41} and tell what it represents.

17. State the dimensions of the matrices in Exercises 15 and 16.

18. Error Analysis A student identified element g_{32} from matrix G at the right as -3. What was the student's error?

$$G = \begin{bmatrix} 3 & 2.5 & 4.5 \\ 1.5 & 0 & -3 \\ -3 & 4.5 & 1.5 \end{bmatrix}$$

19. Writing Describe the information necessary to make a matrix containing numerical data meaningful.

State the dimensions of each matrix. Identify the indicated element.

20. $\begin{bmatrix} 4 & 6 & 5 \\ 2 & -3 & -7 \\ 1 & 0 & 9 \end{bmatrix}, a_{23}$

21. $\begin{bmatrix} -4 & 1 & -3 \\ 2 & 1 & 0 \end{bmatrix}, a_{12}$

22. $\begin{bmatrix} 1 & 1 & 1 \\ 1 & 0 & 0 \\ 1 & 0 & 0 \end{bmatrix}, a_{32}$

23. $\begin{bmatrix} -4 & 8 & 12 \end{bmatrix}, a_{13}$

24. $\begin{bmatrix} -5 \\ 4 \\ 3 \end{bmatrix}, a_{31}$

25. $\begin{bmatrix} -16 & 24 \\ 8 & -2 \end{bmatrix}, a_{21}$

26. Retail Sales The graph shows August sales figures at a music store.

Music Store Sales, August

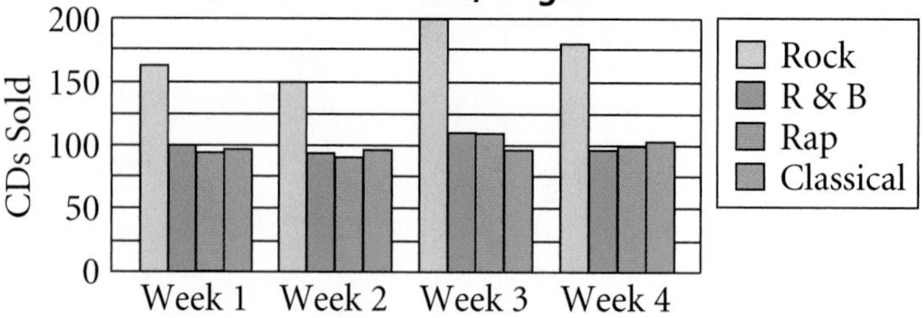

a. Estimation Record the data in a table.

b. Show the data in a matrix. What do the columns represent? What do the rows represent?

Challenge

27. Jobs The four tables display data from a study conducted by a school principal.

a. Use the information to create four 2×2 matrices.

b. How many boys in the school have part-time jobs?

c. How many girls in the school have part-time jobs?

d. What percent of the students with part-time jobs are girls?

Numbers of Students Who Work Part-time

9th Grade	Has Part-time Job	No Part-time Job
Boys	5	95
Girls	15	90

10th Grade	Has Part-time Job	No Part-time Job
Boys	35	65
Girls	30	55

11th Grade	Has Part-time Job	No Part-time Job
Boys	65	35
Girls	75	30

12th Grade	Has Part-time Job	No Part-time Job
Boys	70	25
Girls	65	45

28. Transportation Costs A computer accessory company makes computer carrying cases at four plants located in Atlanta, Boston, Chicago, and Denver. Represent the company's shipping costs in a matrix. Label the rows and columns.

Shipping Costs

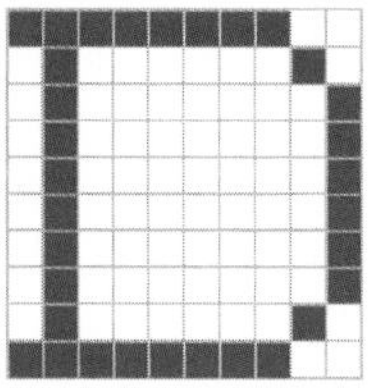

29. a. **Open-Ended** Using a 10×10 grid, create at least three different letters of the alphabet with a style similar to the one at the left.
    b. **Technology** The tiny lights that make up a computer screen are called pixels. To make a letter, the computer tells the screen which pixels to light up. Represent each letter from part (a) by writing a matrix. Use 1 for a lit pixel and 0 for an unlit pixel.

Standardized Test Prep

Multiple Choice

30. Which element in matrix $A = \begin{bmatrix} 5 & -2 & -\frac{1}{2} & 0 \end{bmatrix}$ is the number 0?

A. a_{40} B. a_4 C. a_{14} D. a_{41}

31. In which matrix is the value of a_{32} less than the value of a_{21}?

F. $\begin{bmatrix} -1 & 0 & 5 \\ 4 & 3 & -1 \\ -3 & 2 & 6 \end{bmatrix}$ G. $\begin{bmatrix} -1 & 5 & 0 \\ 3 & 4 & -1 \\ -3 & 6 & 2 \end{bmatrix}$ H. $\begin{bmatrix} 0 & 5 & -1 \\ -1 & 4 & 3 \\ 6 & 2 & -3 \end{bmatrix}$ I. $\begin{bmatrix} 0 & -1 & 5 \\ 0 & 3 & 4 \\ -3 & 1 & 6 \end{bmatrix}$

Quantitative Comparison

Use matrix X at the right. Compare the boxed quantity in Column A with the boxed quantity in Column B. Choose the best answer.

$$X = \begin{bmatrix} 3 & 2 & 4 \\ 5 & 0 & 1 \\ 5 & 1 & 0 \end{bmatrix}$$

A. The quantity in Column A is greater.
B. The quantity in Column B is greater.
C. The two quantities are equal.
D. The relationship cannot be determined from the information given.

	Column A	Column B
32.	the value of x_{12}	the value of x_{21}
33.	the value of x_{21}	the value of x_{31}

Take It to the NET
Online lesson quiz at **www.PHSchool.com**
Web Code: aga-0401

Mixed Review

Lesson 3-6 **Solve each system.**

34. $\begin{cases} 3x + 2y - 2z = -9 \\ 5x - 3z = -7 \\ x + 4y + 3z = 5 \end{cases}$

35. $\begin{cases} 2x + 3y + 4z = -1 \\ x - 2y + z = 9 \\ x + 4y - 2z = -12 \end{cases}$

Lesson 3-1 **Solve each system by graphing.**

36. $\begin{cases} 2x + y = 8 \\ x - 3y = -3 \end{cases}$

37. $\begin{cases} 2x + y = 7 \\ x + y = -5 \end{cases}$

38. $\begin{cases} x + 6y = 7 \\ 2x + 4y = -2 \end{cases}$

Lesson 2-3 **Find the constant of variation for a direct variation that includes the given values.**

39. $(2, 4)$ 40. $(-1, 7)$ 41. $(-4, -10)$ 42. $(3, 5)$ 43. $\left(\frac{1}{2}, 9\right)$

In each relation, y varies directly as x. Find y when $x = 9$.

44. $y = 6$ when $x = 4$

45. $y = 8$ when $x = 4$

4-2 Adding and Subtracting Matrices

North Carolina Objectives

1.04 Operate with matrices to model and solve problems.

Lesson Preview

What You'll Learn

OBJECTIVE 1 To add and subtract matrices

OBJECTIVE 2 To solve certain matrix equations

. . . And Why

To find SAT score totals, as in Example 1

✓ Check Skills You'll Need

(For help, go to Skills Handbook page 845.)

Simplify the elements of each matrix.

1. $\begin{bmatrix} 10+4 & 0+4 \\ -2+4 & -5+4 \end{bmatrix}$ **2.** $\begin{bmatrix} 5-2 & 3-2 \\ -1-2 & 0-2 \end{bmatrix}$ **3.** $\begin{bmatrix} -2+3 & 0-3 \\ 1-3 & -5+3 \end{bmatrix}$

4. $\begin{bmatrix} 3+1 & 4+9 \\ -2+0 & 5+7 \end{bmatrix}$ **5.** $\begin{bmatrix} 8-4 & -5-1 \\ 9-1 & 6-9 \end{bmatrix}$ **6.** $\begin{bmatrix} 2+4 & 6-8 \\ 4-3 & 5+2 \end{bmatrix}$

New Vocabulary • matrix addition • zero matrix • matrix equation • equal matrices

Interactive lesson includes instant self-check, tutorials, and activities.

OBJECTIVE 1

Adding and Subtracting Matrices

Sometimes you want to add or subtract matrices to get new information. You perform **matrix addition** on matrices with equal dimensions by adding the corresponding elements, which are elements in the same position in each matrix.

1 EXAMPLE Real-World Connection

Statistics Use the data in the table.

Mean SAT Scores				
	Verbal		Math	
Year	Male	Female	Male	Female
1995	505	502	525	490
1996	507	503	503	502
1997	507	503	530	494
1998	509	502	531	496

SOURCE: College Entrance Examination Board

a. Write two 2 × 4 matrices to represent the mean verbal and math SAT scores.

Verbal

$$\begin{array}{r} \\ \text{Male} \\ \text{Female} \end{array} \begin{array}{c} \begin{array}{cccc} 1995 & 1996 & 1997 & 1998 \end{array} \\ \begin{bmatrix} 505 & 507 & 507 & 509 \\ 502 & 503 & 503 & 502 \end{bmatrix} \end{array}$$

Math

$$\begin{array}{r} \\ \text{Male} \\ \text{Female} \end{array} \begin{array}{c} \begin{array}{cccc} 1995 & 1996 & 1997 & 1998 \end{array} \\ \begin{bmatrix} 525 & 503 & 530 & 531 \\ 490 & 502 & 494 & 496 \end{bmatrix} \end{array}$$

b. Find the combined mean SAT scores for each year in the table.

$$\begin{bmatrix} 505 & 507 & 507 & 509 \\ 502 & 503 & 503 & 502 \end{bmatrix} + \begin{bmatrix} 525 & 503 & 530 & 531 \\ 490 & 502 & 494 & 496 \end{bmatrix}$$

$$= \begin{bmatrix} 505+525 & 507+503 & 507+530 & 509+531 \\ 502+490 & 503+502 & 503+494 & 502+496 \end{bmatrix}$$

$$= \begin{array}{r} \\ \text{Male} \\ \text{Female} \end{array} \begin{array}{c} \begin{array}{cccc} 1995 & 1996 & 1997 & 1998 \end{array} \\ \begin{bmatrix} 1030 & 1010 & 1037 & 1040 \\ 992 & 1005 & 997 & 998 \end{bmatrix} \end{array}$$

Real-World Connection

Many schools have programs for students to help one another prepare for standardized tests.

Check Understanding **1** Find each sum.

a. $\begin{bmatrix} 1 & -2 & 0 \\ 3 & -5 & 7 \end{bmatrix} + \begin{bmatrix} 3 & 9 & -3 \\ -9 & 6 & 12 \end{bmatrix}$

b. $\begin{bmatrix} -12 & 24 \\ -3 & 5 \\ -1 & 10 \end{bmatrix} + \begin{bmatrix} -3 & 1 \\ 2 & -4 \\ -1 & 5 \end{bmatrix}$

Key Concepts

Definition **Matrix Addition**

To add matrices A and B with the same dimensions, add corresponding elements.

$A = \begin{bmatrix} a & b & c \\ d & e & f \end{bmatrix}$ $\quad B = \begin{bmatrix} r & s & t \\ u & v & w \end{bmatrix}$

$$A + B = \begin{bmatrix} a & b & c \\ d & e & f \end{bmatrix} + \begin{bmatrix} r & s & t \\ u & v & w \end{bmatrix} = \begin{bmatrix} a + r & b + s & c + t \\ d + u & e + v & f + w \end{bmatrix}$$

The additive identity matrix for the set of all $m \times n$ matrices is the **zero matrix** O, or $O_{m \times n}$, whose elements are all zeros. The opposite, or additive inverse, of an $m \times n$ matrix A is $-A$. $-A$ is the $m \times n$ matrix with elements that are the opposites of the corresponding elements of A.

2 EXAMPLE Using Identity and Inverse Matrices

Find each sum.

a. $\begin{bmatrix} 1 & 2 \\ 5 & -7 \end{bmatrix} + \begin{bmatrix} 0 & 0 \\ 0 & 0 \end{bmatrix}$

$= \begin{bmatrix} 1 + 0 & 2 + 0 \\ 5 + 0 & -7 + 0 \end{bmatrix}$

$= \begin{bmatrix} 1 & 2 \\ 5 & -7 \end{bmatrix}$

b. $\begin{bmatrix} 2 & 8 \\ -3 & 0 \end{bmatrix} + \begin{bmatrix} -2 & -8 \\ 3 & 0 \end{bmatrix}$

$= \begin{bmatrix} 2 + (-2) & 8 + (-8) \\ -3 + 3 & 0 + 0 \end{bmatrix}$

$= \begin{bmatrix} 0 & 0 \\ 0 & 0 \end{bmatrix}$

Check Understanding **2** Find each sum.

a. $\begin{bmatrix} 14 & 5 \\ 0 & -2 \end{bmatrix} + \begin{bmatrix} -14 & -5 \\ 0 & 2 \end{bmatrix}$

b. $\begin{bmatrix} 0 & 0 & 0 \\ 0 & 0 & 0 \end{bmatrix} + \begin{bmatrix} -1 & 10 & -5 \\ 0 & 2 & -3 \end{bmatrix}$

Some of the properties of real number addition also apply to matrix addition.

Key Concepts

Properties **Matrix Addition**

If A, B, and C are $m \times n$ matrices, then

$A + B$ is an $m \times n$ matrix.	Closure Property
$A + B = B + A$	Commutative Property of Addition
$(A + B) + C = A + (B + C)$	Associative Property of Addition
There exists a unique $m \times n$ matrix O such that $O + A = A + O = A$.	Additive Identity Property
For each A, there exists a unique opposite, $-A$. $A + (-A) = O$	Additive Inverse Property

You can define matrix subtraction by using the Additive Inverse Property.

Key Concepts

Property	**Matrix Subtraction**
If two matrices, A and B, have the same dimensions, then $A - B = A + (-B)$.	

3 EXAMPLE Subtracting Matrices

$A = \begin{bmatrix} 3 & 2 & 4 \\ -1 & 4 & 0 \end{bmatrix}$ and $B = \begin{bmatrix} 1 & 4 & 3 \\ -2 & 2 & 4 \end{bmatrix}$. Find $A - B$.

Method 1 Use additive inverses.

$$A - B = A + (-B) = \begin{bmatrix} 3 & 2 & 4 \\ -1 & 4 & 0 \end{bmatrix} + \begin{bmatrix} -1 & -4 & -3 \\ 2 & -2 & -4 \end{bmatrix}$$ **Write the elements of $-B$.**

$$= \begin{bmatrix} 3 + (-1) & 2 + (-4) & 4 + (-3) \\ -1 + 2 & 4 + (-2) & 0 + (-4) \end{bmatrix}$$ **Add corresponding elements.**

$$= \begin{bmatrix} 2 & -2 & 1 \\ 1 & 2 & -4 \end{bmatrix}$$ **Simplify.**

Method 2 Use subtraction.

$$A - B = \begin{bmatrix} 3 & 2 & 4 \\ -1 & 4 & 0 \end{bmatrix} - \begin{bmatrix} 1 & 4 & 3 \\ -2 & 2 & 4 \end{bmatrix}$$

$$= \begin{bmatrix} 3 - 1 & 2 - 4 & 4 - 3 \\ -1 - (-2) & 4 - 2 & 0 - 4 \end{bmatrix}$$ **Subtract corresponding elements.**

$$= \begin{bmatrix} 2 & -2 & 1 \\ 1 & 2 & -4 \end{bmatrix}$$ **Simplify.**

Check Understanding 3 Find each difference.

a. $\begin{bmatrix} 6 & -9 & 7 \\ -2 & 1 & 8 \end{bmatrix} - \begin{bmatrix} -4 & 3 & 0 \\ 6 & 5 & 10 \end{bmatrix}$ **b.** $\begin{bmatrix} -3 & 5 \\ -1 & 10 \end{bmatrix} - \begin{bmatrix} -3 & 1 \\ 2 & -4 \end{bmatrix}$

OBJECTIVE

2 Solving Matrix Equations

A **matrix equation** is an equation in which the variable is a matrix. You can use the addition and subtraction properties of equality to solve matrix equations.

4 EXAMPLE Solving a Matrix Equation

Solve $X - \begin{bmatrix} 1 & 1 \\ 3 & 2 \end{bmatrix} = \begin{bmatrix} 0 & 1 \\ 8 & 9 \end{bmatrix}$ for the matrix X.

$$X - \begin{bmatrix} 1 & 1 \\ 3 & 2 \end{bmatrix} = \begin{bmatrix} 0 & 1 \\ 8 & 9 \end{bmatrix}$$

$$X - \begin{bmatrix} 1 & 1 \\ 3 & 2 \end{bmatrix} + \begin{bmatrix} 1 & 1 \\ 3 & 2 \end{bmatrix} = \begin{bmatrix} 0 & 1 \\ 8 & 9 \end{bmatrix} + \begin{bmatrix} 1 & 1 \\ 3 & 2 \end{bmatrix}$$ **Add $\begin{bmatrix} 1 & 1 \\ 3 & 2 \end{bmatrix}$ to each side of the equation.**

$$X = \begin{bmatrix} 1 & 2 \\ 11 & 11 \end{bmatrix}$$ **Simplify.**

Check Understanding 4 Solve $X + \begin{bmatrix} -1 & 0 \\ 2 & 5 \end{bmatrix} = \begin{bmatrix} 10 & 7 \\ -4 & 4 \end{bmatrix}$.

Reading Math

In everyday language, the term *matrix* can be used to describe anything resembling a mathematical matrix, having a rectangular arrangement of elements in rows and columns.

Equal matrices are matrices with the same dimensions and equal corresponding elements.

5 EXAMPLE Determining Equal Matrices

Determine whether the two matrices in each pair are equal.

a. $A = \begin{bmatrix} -0.75 & \frac{1}{5} \\ \frac{1}{2} & -2 \end{bmatrix}, B = \begin{bmatrix} -\frac{3}{4} & 0.2 \\ 0.5 & -2 \end{bmatrix}$

$A = \begin{bmatrix} -0.75 & \frac{1}{5} \\ \frac{1}{2} & -2 \end{bmatrix}$ **Both A and B have two rows and two columns, and their corresponding elements are equal.** $B = \begin{bmatrix} -\frac{3}{4} & 0.2 \\ 0.5 & -2 \end{bmatrix}$

A and B are equal matrices.

b. $X = \begin{bmatrix} -1 & \frac{2}{3} & 2.5 \\ 0 & 1.5 & -\frac{5}{6} \end{bmatrix}, Y = \begin{bmatrix} 4-5 & 0.\overline{6} & \frac{5}{2} \\ 0 & 1 & -\frac{2}{3} \end{bmatrix}$

$X = \begin{bmatrix} -1 & \frac{2}{3} & 2.5 \\ 0 & 1.5 & -\frac{5}{6} \end{bmatrix}$ **Both X and Y have three rows and two columns, but $1.5 \neq 1$, and $-\frac{5}{6} \neq -\frac{2}{3}$.** $Y = \begin{bmatrix} 4-5 & 0.\overline{6} & \frac{5}{2} \\ 0 & 1 & -\frac{2}{3} \end{bmatrix}$

X and Y are *not* equal matrices.

Check Understanding 5 Determine whether the two matrices in each pair are equal.

a. $\begin{bmatrix} 4 \\ 6 \\ 8 \end{bmatrix}, \begin{bmatrix} \frac{8}{2} & \frac{18}{3} & \frac{16}{2} \end{bmatrix}$

b. $\begin{bmatrix} -2 & 3 \\ 5 & 0 \end{bmatrix}, \begin{bmatrix} -\frac{8}{4} & 6-3 \\ \frac{15}{3} & 4-4 \end{bmatrix}$

6 EXAMPLE Finding Unknown Matrix Elements

Solve the equation $\begin{bmatrix} 2x-5 & 4 \\ 3 & 3y+12 \end{bmatrix} = \begin{bmatrix} 25 & 4 \\ 3 & y+18 \end{bmatrix}$ for x and y.

$\begin{bmatrix} 2x-5 & 4 \\ 3 & 3y+12 \end{bmatrix} = \begin{bmatrix} 25 & 4 \\ 3 & y+18 \end{bmatrix}$

$2x - 5 = 25$ $\quad$ $3y + 12 = y + 18$ $\quad$ **Since the two matrices are equal, their corresponding elements are equal.**

$2x = 30$ $\quad$ $2y = 6$

$x = 15$ $\quad$ $y = 3$

The solutions are $x = 15$ and $y = 3$.

Check Understanding 6 Solve each equation for x and y.

a. $\begin{bmatrix} x+8 & -5 \\ 3 & -y \end{bmatrix} = \begin{bmatrix} 38 & -5 \\ 3 & 4y-10 \end{bmatrix}$

b. $\begin{bmatrix} 3x & 4 \end{bmatrix} = \begin{bmatrix} -9 & x+y \end{bmatrix}$

EXERCISES

For more practice, see *Extra Practice.*

Practice and Problem Solving

A **Practice by Example**

Example 1 (page 170)

1. **Sports** The modern pentathlon is a grueling all-day competition. Each member of a team competes in five events: target shooting, fencing, swimming, horseback riding, and cross-country running. Find the total scores of the U.S. women's team at the 2000 Olympic Games.

U.S. Women's Pentathlon Scores, 2000 Olympics

Event	Emily deRiel	Mary Beth Iagorashvili
Shoot	1156	964
Fence	800	960
Swim	1182	1205
Ride	1070	1040
Run	1102	960

SOURCE: U.S. Modern Pentathlon Association

a. Write two 5×1 matrices to represent the individual scores for each event.
b. Find the total score for the U.S. women's team for each event.

Examples 2 and 3 (pages 171 and 172)

Find each sum or difference.

2. $\begin{bmatrix} 2 & -3 & 4 \\ 5 & 6 & -7 \end{bmatrix} + \begin{bmatrix} 0 & 0 & 0 \\ 0 & 0 & 0 \end{bmatrix}$

3. $\begin{bmatrix} 1 & 3 \\ 4 & 0 \end{bmatrix} + \begin{bmatrix} 0 & 5 \\ -1 & 2 \end{bmatrix} + \begin{bmatrix} 0 & -5 \\ 1 & -2 \end{bmatrix}$

4. $\begin{bmatrix} 6.4 & -1.9 \\ -6.4 & 0.8 \end{bmatrix} + \begin{bmatrix} -2.5 & -0.4 \\ 5.8 & 8.3 \end{bmatrix}$

5. $\begin{bmatrix} 6 & -3 \\ -7 & 2 \end{bmatrix} + \begin{bmatrix} -6 & 3 \\ 7 & -2 \end{bmatrix}$

6. $\begin{bmatrix} 5 & 4 & 3 \\ 1 & -2 & 6 \end{bmatrix} - \begin{bmatrix} 1 & 1 & 1 \\ 1 & 1 & 1 \end{bmatrix}$

7. $\begin{bmatrix} 2 & 1 & 2 \\ 1 & 2 & 1 \end{bmatrix} - \begin{bmatrix} 2 & 3 & 2 \\ 3 & 2 & 3 \end{bmatrix}$

8. $\begin{bmatrix} 0.5 & 9.5 \\ -3.5 & 5.5 \end{bmatrix} - \begin{bmatrix} 0.5 & 9.5 \\ -3.5 & 5.5 \end{bmatrix}$

9. $\begin{bmatrix} 1.5 & -1.9 \\ 0 & 4.6 \end{bmatrix} - \begin{bmatrix} 8.3 & -3.2 \\ 2.1 & 5.6 \end{bmatrix}$

Example 4 (page 172)

Solve each matrix equation.

10. $\begin{bmatrix} 1 & 2 \\ 2 & 1 \\ -3 & 4 \end{bmatrix} + X = \begin{bmatrix} 5 & -6 \\ 1 & 0 \\ 8 & 5 \end{bmatrix}$

11. $\begin{bmatrix} 2 & 1 & -1 \\ 0 & 2 & 1 \end{bmatrix} - X = \begin{bmatrix} 11 & 3 & -13 \\ 15 & -9 & 8 \end{bmatrix}$

12. $X - \begin{bmatrix} 1 & 4 \\ -2 & 3 \end{bmatrix} = \begin{bmatrix} 5 & -2 \\ 1 & 0 \end{bmatrix}$

13. $X + \begin{bmatrix} 6 & 1 \\ -2 & 3 \end{bmatrix} = \begin{bmatrix} 2 & 0 \\ -3 & 1 \end{bmatrix}$

Example 5 (page 173)

Determine whether the two matrices in each pair are equal. Justify your reasoning.

14. $\begin{bmatrix} -2 & 3 \\ 5 & 0 \end{bmatrix}, \begin{bmatrix} 2(-1) & 2(1.5) \\ 2(2.5) & 2(0) \end{bmatrix}$

15. $\begin{bmatrix} 4 \\ -6 \\ -8 \end{bmatrix}, \begin{bmatrix} \sqrt{16} & -6 & \sqrt{64} \end{bmatrix}$

Example 6 (page 173)

Find the value of each variable.

16. $\begin{bmatrix} 2 & 2 \\ -1 & 6 \end{bmatrix} - \begin{bmatrix} 4 & -1 \\ 0 & 5 \end{bmatrix} = \begin{bmatrix} x & y \\ -1 & z \end{bmatrix}$

17. $\begin{bmatrix} 2 & 4 \\ 8 & 12 \end{bmatrix} = \begin{bmatrix} 4x - 6 & -10t + 5x \\ 4x & 15t + 1.5x \end{bmatrix}$

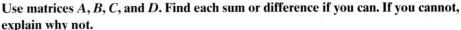

B Apply Your Skills

Use matrices A, B, C, and D. Find each sum or difference if you can. If you cannot, explain why not.

$$A = \begin{bmatrix} 3 & 4 \\ 6 & -2 \\ 1 & 0 \end{bmatrix} \quad B = \begin{bmatrix} -3 & 1 \\ 2 & -4 \\ -1 & 5 \end{bmatrix} \quad C = \begin{bmatrix} 1 & 2 \\ -3 & 1 \end{bmatrix} \quad D = \begin{bmatrix} 5 & 1 \\ 0 & 2 \end{bmatrix}$$

18. $A + B$ **19.** $B + D$ **20.** $C + D$ **21.** $B - A$ **22.** $C - D$

Real-World Connection

In the riding portion of the modern pentathlon, the athletes are given 20 min to get to know their horses before riding a 400-m course with 15 obstacles.

23. Riding Use the information in the table below.

U.S. Men's Pentathlon Scores, 2000 World Championship

Event	James Gregory	Velizar Iliev	Chad Senior
Shooting	1132	1072	1072
Fencing	760	910	610
Swimming	1173	1177	1285
Riding	1100	1100	1070
Running	1114	1118	1174

SOURCE: U.S. Modern Pentathlon Association

a. Put the information into three matrices. Label each matrix.
b. Find the total score for the U.S. men's pentathlon team for each event.
c. Open-Ended Find the differences between the scores of two of the athletes. In which event were the scores the most different? How different were they?

Solve each matrix equation for X.

24. $\begin{bmatrix} 1 & 2 & -3 \\ 2 & 1 & 3 \end{bmatrix} + X = \begin{bmatrix} 5 & 1 & 8 \\ -6 & 0 & 5 \end{bmatrix}$

25. $X - \begin{bmatrix} 4 & 12 \\ 75 & -1 \end{bmatrix} = \begin{bmatrix} 5 & 50 \\ 50 & -10 \end{bmatrix}$

26. Data Analysis Refer to the table.
a. Find the total number of people participating in each activity.
b. Find the difference between the numbers of males and females participating in each activity.
c. Reasoning In part (b), does the order of the matrices matter? Explain.

U.S. Participation in Selected Leisure Activities (millions)

Activity	Male	Female
Movies	62.2	65.9
Exercise Programs	70.7	78.1
Sports Events	46.2	34.5
Home Improvement	66.9	61.9

SOURCE: U.S. National Endowment for the Arts. Go to www.PHSchool.com for a data update.

27. Manufacturing The table below shows the number of beach balls produced during one shift at two manufacturing plants. Plant 1 has two shifts per day and Plant 2 has three shifts per day.

Beach Ball Production Per Shift

	1-color Plastic	1-color Rubber	3-color Plastic	3-color Rubber
Plant 1	500	700	1300	1900
Plant 2	400	1200	600	1600

a. Write matrices to represent one day's total output at the two plants.
b. Use your results from part (a). Find the difference between production totals at the plants. Which plant produces more three-color plastic balls? Which plant produces more one-color rubber balls?

28. **Writing** Suppose A and B are two matrices with the same dimensions.
   a. Explain how to find $A + B$ and $A - B$.
   b. Explain how to find a matrix C such that $A + C = O$.

Solve each equation for each variable.

29. $\begin{bmatrix} 4b + 2 & -3 & 4d \\ -4a & 2 & 3 \\ 2f - 1 & -14 & 1 \end{bmatrix} = \begin{bmatrix} 11 & 2c - 1 & 0 \\ -8 & 2 & 3 \\ 0 & 3g - 2 & 1 \end{bmatrix}$

30. $\begin{bmatrix} x^2 & 4 \\ -2 & y^2 \end{bmatrix} = \begin{bmatrix} 9 & 4 \\ -2 & 5y \end{bmatrix}$

31. $\begin{bmatrix} 4c & 2 - d & 5 \\ -3 & -1 & 2 \\ 0 & -10 & 15 \end{bmatrix} = \begin{bmatrix} 2c + 5 & 4d & g \\ -3 & h & f - g \\ 0 & -4c & 15 \end{bmatrix}$

C Challenge

32. Find the sum of $E = \begin{bmatrix} 3 \\ 4 \\ 7 \end{bmatrix}$ and the additive inverse of $G = \begin{bmatrix} -2 \\ 0 \\ 5 \end{bmatrix}$.

33. Prove that matrix addition is commutative for 2×2 matrices.

34. Prove that matrix addition is associative for 2×2 matrices.

Standardized Test Prep

Multiple Choice

Use matrices $A = \begin{bmatrix} 5 & 7 & 3 \\ -1 & 0 & -4 \end{bmatrix}$ and $C = \begin{bmatrix} -7 & 4 & 2 \\ 1 & -2 & -3 \end{bmatrix}$ for Exercises 35 and 36.

35. What is the sum $A + C$?
   A. The matrices cannot be added.
   B. $\begin{bmatrix} -2 & 11 & 5 \\ 0 & -2 & -7 \end{bmatrix}$
   C. $\begin{bmatrix} 12 & 3 & 1 \\ -2 & 2 & -1 \end{bmatrix}$
   D. $\begin{bmatrix} -35 & 28 & 6 \\ -1 & 0 & 12 \end{bmatrix}$

Take It to the NET
Online lesson quiz at
www.PHSchool.com
Web Code: aga-0402

36. What is matrix Y if $Y - A = \begin{bmatrix} 1 & 0 & 1 \\ 0 & 1 & 0 \end{bmatrix}$?
   F. $\begin{bmatrix} 4 & 7 & 2 \\ -1 & -1 & -5 \end{bmatrix}$
   G. $\begin{bmatrix} 6 & 7 & 4 \\ -1 & 1 & -4 \end{bmatrix}$
   H. $\begin{bmatrix} -6 & 4 & 3 \\ 1 & -1 & -3 \end{bmatrix}$
   I. $\begin{bmatrix} -4 & -7 & -2 \\ 1 & 1 & 5 \end{bmatrix}$

Short Response

Find the value of each variable.

37. $\begin{bmatrix} x & y - 2 \\ z & w + 4 \end{bmatrix} + \begin{bmatrix} 2 & 5 \\ -2 & 4 \end{bmatrix} = \begin{bmatrix} 6 & 1 \\ 4 & 8 \end{bmatrix}$

38. $\begin{bmatrix} x & 3 \\ x & -2 \end{bmatrix} + \begin{bmatrix} y & 6 \\ -y & 3 \end{bmatrix} = \begin{bmatrix} 6 & 9 \\ 4 & 1 \end{bmatrix}$

Mixed Review

Lesson 4-1

39. **Open-Ended** Write a real-world problem that you can represent with a matrix. Write a matrix for the problem. Label the rows and columns.

Lesson 3-2

40. **Business** Your friend's mother plans to open a restaurant. The initial investment is \$90,000. Weekly expenses will be about \$8200. If the weekly income is about \$8900, in how many weeks will she get back her investment?

Lesson 2-2

Find the slope and y-intercept of the graph of each function.

41. $y = 2x - 6$
42. $3y = 6 + 2x$
43. $-x - 2y = 12$
44. $y = 5x$

Technology — Working With Matrices

FOR USE WITH LESSON 4-2

You can use a graphing calculator to work with matrices. First you need to enter the matrix into the calculator.

Take It to the NET
Graphing Calculator procedures online at **www.PHSchool.com**
Web Code: age-2113

1 EXAMPLE

Enter matrix $A = \begin{bmatrix} -3 & 4 \\ 7 & -5 \\ 0 & -2 \end{bmatrix}$ into your graphing calculator. Select the EDIT option of the MATRX feature to edit matrix [A]. Specify a 3×2 matrix by pressing 3 ENTER 2 ENTER.

Enter the matrix elements one row at a time, pressing ENTER after each element. Then use the QUIT feature to return to the main screen.

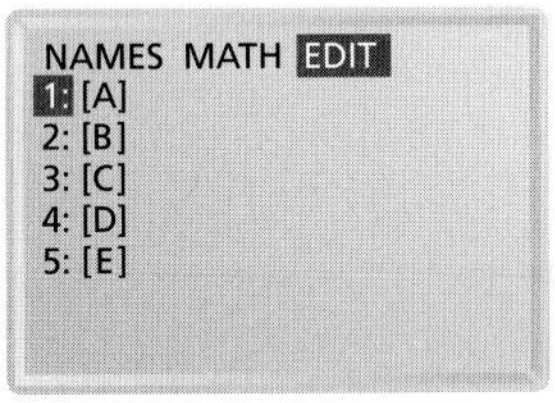

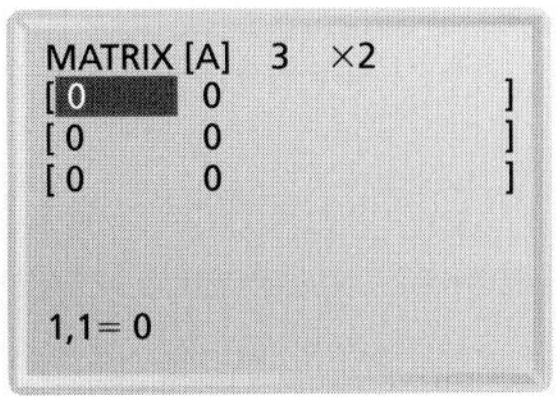

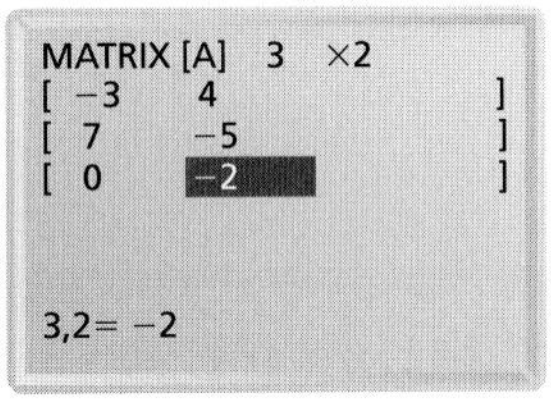

You can use a graphing calculator to perform matrix operations.

2 EXAMPLE

Perform each operation for matrix $A = \begin{bmatrix} -3 & 4 \\ 7 & -5 \\ 0 & -2 \end{bmatrix}$ and matrix $B = \begin{bmatrix} 10 & -7 \\ 4 & -3 \\ -12 & 11 \end{bmatrix}$.

a. $A + B$

Use the EDIT option to select the matrices you want to add. Press ENTER to see the sum.

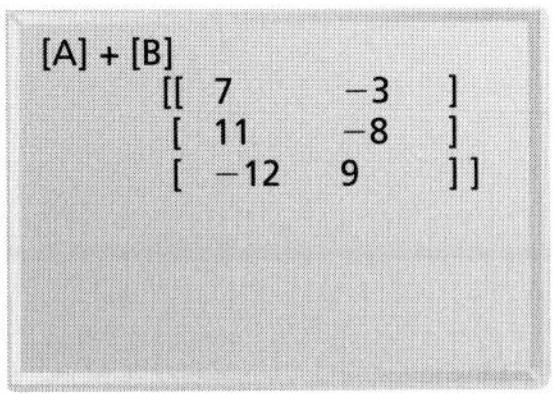

b. $A - B$

Use the EDIT option to select the matrices you want to subtract. Press ENTER to see the difference.

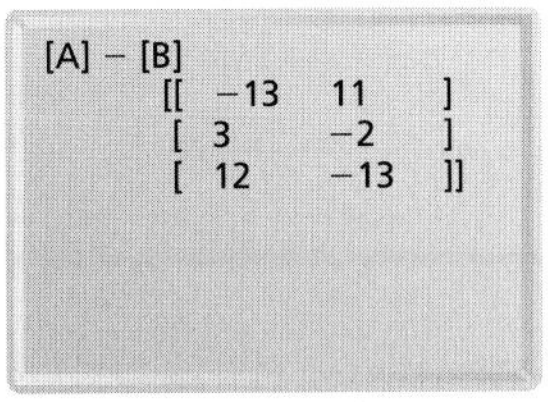

EXERCISES

Find each sum or difference.

1. $\begin{bmatrix} 0 & -3 \\ 5 & -7 \end{bmatrix} - \begin{bmatrix} -5 & 3 \\ 4 & 10 \end{bmatrix}$

2. $\begin{bmatrix} 3 & 5 & -7 \\ 0 & -2 & 0 \end{bmatrix} + \begin{bmatrix} -1 & 6 & 2 \\ -9 & 4 & 0 \end{bmatrix}$

3. $\begin{bmatrix} 3 \\ 5 \end{bmatrix} - \begin{bmatrix} -6 \\ 7 \end{bmatrix}$

4. $[3 \quad 5 \quad -8] + [-6 \quad 4 \quad 1]$

5. $\begin{bmatrix} 17 & 8 & 0 \\ 3 & -5 & 2 \end{bmatrix} - \begin{bmatrix} 4 & 6 & 5 \\ 2 & -2 & 9 \end{bmatrix}$

6. $[-9 \quad 6 \quad 4] + [-3 \quad 8 \quad 4]$

4-3 Matrix Multiplication

North Carolina Objectives 1.04 Operate with matrices to model and solve problems.

Lesson Preview

What You'll Learn

OBJECTIVE 1 To multiply a matrix by a scalar

OBJECTIVE 2 To multiply two matrices

. . . And Why

To calculate the gross income of a record store, as in Example 5

✓ Check Skills You'll Need

(For help, go to Lesson 4-2.)

Find each sum.

1. $\begin{bmatrix} 3 & 5 \\ 2 & 8 \end{bmatrix} + \begin{bmatrix} 3 & 5 \\ 2 & 8 \end{bmatrix} + \begin{bmatrix} 3 & 5 \\ 2 & 8 \end{bmatrix}$

2. $\begin{bmatrix} -4 \\ 7 \end{bmatrix} + \begin{bmatrix} -4 \\ 7 \end{bmatrix} + \begin{bmatrix} -4 \\ 7 \end{bmatrix} + \begin{bmatrix} -4 \\ 7 \end{bmatrix} + \begin{bmatrix} -4 \\ 7 \end{bmatrix}$

3. $\begin{bmatrix} -1 & 3 & 4 \\ 0 & -2 & -5 \end{bmatrix} + \begin{bmatrix} -1 & 3 & 4 \\ 0 & -2 & -5 \end{bmatrix} + \begin{bmatrix} -1 & 3 & 4 \\ 0 & -2 & -5 \end{bmatrix} + \begin{bmatrix} -1 & 3 & 4 \\ 0 & -2 & -5 \end{bmatrix}$

New Vocabulary • scalar • scalar product • matrix multiplication

Interactive lesson includes instant self-check, tutorials, and activities.

OBJECTIVE 1 Multiplying a Matrix by a Scalar

You can multiply a matrix by a real number.

$$3\begin{bmatrix} 3 & 5 \\ 2 & 8 \end{bmatrix} = \begin{bmatrix} 9 & 15 \\ 6 & 24 \end{bmatrix}$$

The real number factor (such as 3) is called a **scalar.**

Key Concepts

Definition **Scalar Multiplication**

Suppose c is a scalar (real number) and A is a matrix. You find the **scalar product** cA by multiplying each element of A by c.

SMALL LARGE
LOWFAT MILK $.35 $.67
ORANGE JUICE $.65 $.89
TOMATO JUICE $.58 $.75

1 EXAMPLE Real-World Connection

Prices Use the price list. The cafeteria plans to raise the cost of each beverage to one and a half times the current cost. How much will each beverage cost?

$$1.5\begin{bmatrix} 0.35 & 0.67 \\ 0.65 & 0.89 \\ 0.58 & 0.75 \end{bmatrix} = \begin{bmatrix} 1.5(0.35) & 1.5(0.67) \\ 1.5(0.65) & 1.5(0.89) \\ 1.5(0.58) & 1.5(0.75) \end{bmatrix}$$ **Multiply each element by 1.5.**

$$\approx \begin{bmatrix} 0.53 & 1.01 \\ 0.98 & 1.34 \\ 0.87 & 1.13 \end{bmatrix}$$ **Simplify.**

Milk will cost $.53 and $1.01. Orange juice will cost $.98 and $1.34. Tomato juice will cost $.87 and $1.13.

✓ Check Understanding

1 Find $-3\begin{bmatrix} 15 & -12 & 10 & 0 \\ 20 & -10 & 7 & 0 \end{bmatrix}$.

You can find sums and differences of scalar products.

2 EXAMPLE Using Scalar Products

Find the difference $5A - 3B$ for $A = \begin{bmatrix} 2 & 3 & -7 \\ 1 & 4 & 5 \end{bmatrix}$ and $B = \begin{bmatrix} 3 & 0 & 6 \\ -1 & 8 & 2 \end{bmatrix}$.

$$5A - 3B = 5\begin{bmatrix} 2 & 3 & -7 \\ 1 & 4 & 5 \end{bmatrix} - 3\begin{bmatrix} 3 & 0 & 6 \\ -1 & 8 & 2 \end{bmatrix}$$

$$= \begin{bmatrix} 10 & 15 & -35 \\ 5 & 20 & 25 \end{bmatrix} - \begin{bmatrix} 9 & 0 & 18 \\ -3 & 24 & 6 \end{bmatrix} = \begin{bmatrix} 1 & 15 & -53 \\ 8 & -4 & 19 \end{bmatrix}$$

Check Understanding **2** Use matrices A and B from Example 2. Find each sum or difference.

a. $5B - 4A$ **b.** $A + 6B$

Key Concepts

Properties **Scalar Multiplication**

If A, B, and O are $m \times n$ matrices and c and d are scalars, then

cA is an $m \times n$ matrix.	Closure Property
$(cd)A = c(dA)$	Associative Property of Multiplication
$c(A + B) = cA + cB$ $(c + d)A = cA + dA$	Distributive Property
$1 \cdot A = A$	Multiplicative Identity Property
$0 \cdot A = O$ and $cO = O$	Multiplicative Property of Zero

Need Help?

O is the $m \times n$ matrix with every element zero.

You can use the properties of scalar multiplication to solve matrix equations.

3 EXAMPLE Solving Matrix Equations with Scalars

Solve $4X + 2\begin{bmatrix} 3 & 4 \\ -2 & 1 \end{bmatrix} = \begin{bmatrix} 10 & 0 \\ 4 & 2 \end{bmatrix}$.

$$4X + 2\begin{bmatrix} 3 & 4 \\ -2 & 1 \end{bmatrix} = \begin{bmatrix} 10 & 0 \\ 4 & 2 \end{bmatrix}$$

$$4X + \begin{bmatrix} 6 & 8 \\ -4 & 2 \end{bmatrix} = \begin{bmatrix} 10 & 0 \\ 4 & 2 \end{bmatrix}$$ **Scalar multiplication**

$$4X = \begin{bmatrix} 10 & 0 \\ 4 & 2 \end{bmatrix} - \begin{bmatrix} 6 & 8 \\ -4 & 2 \end{bmatrix}$$ **Subtract $\begin{bmatrix} 6 & 8 \\ -4 & 2 \end{bmatrix}$ from each side.**

$$4X = \begin{bmatrix} 4 & -8 \\ 8 & 0 \end{bmatrix}$$ **Simplify.**

$$X = \frac{1}{4}\begin{bmatrix} 4 & -8 \\ 8 & 0 \end{bmatrix} = \begin{bmatrix} 1 & -2 \\ 2 & 0 \end{bmatrix}$$ **Multiply each side by $\frac{1}{4}$ and simplify.**

Check

$$4X + 2\begin{bmatrix} 3 & 4 \\ -2 & 1 \end{bmatrix} = \begin{bmatrix} 10 & 0 \\ 4 & 2 \end{bmatrix}$$

$$4\begin{bmatrix} 1 & -2 \\ 2 & 0 \end{bmatrix} + 2\begin{bmatrix} 3 & 4 \\ -2 & 1 \end{bmatrix} \stackrel{?}{=} \begin{bmatrix} 10 & 0 \\ 4 & 2 \end{bmatrix}$$ **Substitute.**

$$\begin{bmatrix} 4 & -8 \\ 8 & 0 \end{bmatrix} + \begin{bmatrix} 6 & 8 \\ -4 & 2 \end{bmatrix} \stackrel{?}{=} \begin{bmatrix} 10 & 0 \\ 4 & 2 \end{bmatrix}$$ **Multiply.**

$$\begin{bmatrix} 10 & 0 \\ 4 & 2 \end{bmatrix} = \begin{bmatrix} 10 & 0 \\ 4 & 2 \end{bmatrix}$$ ✓ **Simplify.**

Check Understanding 3 Solve each equation. Check your answer.

a. $2X = \begin{bmatrix} 4 & 12 \\ 1 & -4 \end{bmatrix} + \begin{bmatrix} -2 & 0 \\ 3 & 4 \end{bmatrix}$ b. $-3X + \begin{bmatrix} 7 & 0 & -1 \\ 2 & -3 & 4 \end{bmatrix} = \begin{bmatrix} 10 & 0 & 8 \\ -19 & -18 & 10 \end{bmatrix}$

OBJECTIVE 2

Multiplying Matrices

Investigation: Using Matrices

Use the data in the table.

	Lunch 1	Lunch 2	Lunch 3
Cost per Lunch	$2.50	$1.75	$2.00
Number Sold	50	100	75

1. How much money did the cafeteria collect selling lunch 1? Selling lunch 2? Selling lunch 3?
2. a. How much did the cafeteria collect selling all three lunches?
   b. Explain how you used the data in the table to find your answer.
3. a. Write a 1 × 3 matrix to represent the cost of the lunches.
   b. Write a 3 × 1 matrix to represent the number of lunches sold.
   c. **Writing** Describe a procedure for using your matrices to find how much money the cafeteria collected from selling all three lunches. Use the words *row*, *column*, and *element*.

Graphing Calculator Hint

You can use the MATRX feature of a graphing calculator to multiply matrices.

To perform **matrix multiplication,** multiply the elements of each *row* of the first matrix by the elements of each *column* of the second matrix. Add the products.

4 EXAMPLE Multiplying Matrices

Find the product of $\begin{bmatrix} -1 & 0 \\ 3 & -4 \end{bmatrix}$ and $\begin{bmatrix} -3 & 3 \\ 5 & 0 \end{bmatrix}$.

Multiply a_{11} and b_{11}. Then multiply a_{12} and b_{21}. Add the products.

$\begin{bmatrix} -1 & 0 \\ 3 & -4 \end{bmatrix}\begin{bmatrix} -3 & 3 \\ 5 & 0 \end{bmatrix} = \begin{bmatrix} ? & ■ \\ ■ & ■ \end{bmatrix}$ $(-1)(-3) + (0)(5) = 3$

The result is the element in the first row and first column.
Repeat with the rest of the rows and columns.

$\begin{bmatrix} -1 & 0 \\ 3 & -4 \end{bmatrix}\begin{bmatrix} -3 & 3 \\ 5 & 0 \end{bmatrix} = \begin{bmatrix} 3 & ? \\ ■ & ■ \end{bmatrix}$ $(-1)(3) + (0)(0) = -3$

$\begin{bmatrix} -1 & 0 \\ 3 & -4 \end{bmatrix}\begin{bmatrix} -3 & 3 \\ 5 & 0 \end{bmatrix} = \begin{bmatrix} 3 & -3 \\ ? & ■ \end{bmatrix}$ $(3)(-3) + (-4)(5) = -29$

$\begin{bmatrix} -1 & 0 \\ 3 & -4 \end{bmatrix}\begin{bmatrix} -3 & 3 \\ 5 & 0 \end{bmatrix} = \begin{bmatrix} 3 & -3 \\ -29 & ? \end{bmatrix}$ $(3)(3) + (-4)(0) = 9$

The product of $\begin{bmatrix} -1 & 0 \\ 3 & -4 \end{bmatrix}$ and $\begin{bmatrix} -3 & 3 \\ 5 & 0 \end{bmatrix}$ is $\begin{bmatrix} 3 & -3 \\ -29 & 9 \end{bmatrix}$.

✓ Check Understanding **4** **a.** Find the product of $\begin{bmatrix} -3 & 3 \\ 5 & 0 \end{bmatrix}$ and $\begin{bmatrix} -1 & 0 \\ 3 & -4 \end{bmatrix}$.

b. **Critical Thinking** Is matrix multiplication commutative? Explain.

Key Concepts

Definition **Matrix Multiplication**

To find element c_{ij} of the product matrix AB, multiply each element in the ith row of A by the corresponding element in the jth column of B, and then add.

You can use matrix multiplication to solve problems.

5 EXAMPLE Real-World Connection

Real-World Connection

The music on an LP record (a) plays continuously as the stylus travels along the groove. The music on a CD (b) plays in discrete intervals read by a laser.

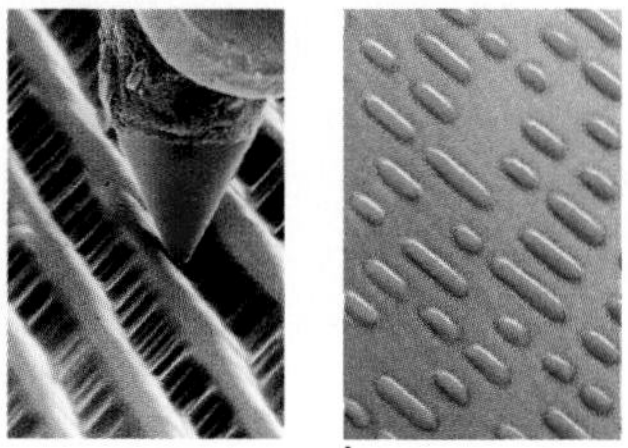

a b

Business A used-record store sells tapes, LP records, and compact discs. The matrices show today's information. Find the store's gross income for the day.

Prices

Tapes	LPs	CDs
[\$8	\$6	\$13]

Number of Items Sold

$$\begin{matrix} \text{Tapes} \\ \text{LPs} \\ \text{CDs} \end{matrix} \begin{bmatrix} 9 \\ 30 \\ 20 \end{bmatrix}$$

Multiply each price by the number of items sold and add the products.

$$\begin{bmatrix} 8 & 6 & 13 \end{bmatrix} \begin{bmatrix} 9 \\ 30 \\ 20 \end{bmatrix} = [8(9) + 6(30) + 13(20)] = [512]$$

The store's gross income for the day was \$512.

✓ Check Understanding **5** Find each product.

a. $\begin{bmatrix} 12 & 3 \end{bmatrix} \begin{bmatrix} 10 \\ -5 \end{bmatrix}$

b. $\begin{bmatrix} 10 \\ -5 \end{bmatrix} \begin{bmatrix} 12 & 3 \\ 0 & 0 \end{bmatrix}$

The product of two matrices A and B exists only if the number of *columns* of A is equal to the number of *rows* of B.

Key Concepts

Property **Dimensions of a Product Matrix**

If matrix A is an $m \times n$ matrix and matrix B is an $n \times p$ matrix, then the product matrix AB is an $m \times p$ matrix.

Example **matrix A** • **matrix B**

$$\underset{\text{3 rows, 2 columns}}{\begin{bmatrix} 1 & 2 \\ 3 & 4 \\ 5 & 6 \end{bmatrix}} \quad \underset{\text{2 rows, 4 columns}}{\begin{bmatrix} 7 & 8 & 9 & 10 \\ 11 & 12 & 13 & 14 \end{bmatrix}}$$

2 columns — equal — 2 rows

3 rows — dimensions of product matrix — 4 columns

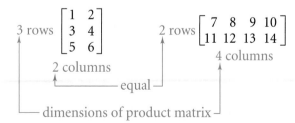

The dimenions of product matrix AB is 3×4.

6 EXAMPLE Determining Whether a Product Matrix Exists

Use matrices $G = \begin{bmatrix} 2 & 3 \\ -1 & 8 \\ 4 & 0 \end{bmatrix}$ and $H = \begin{bmatrix} 8 & 0 \\ 2 & -5 \end{bmatrix}$. Determine whether products GH and HG are *defined* (exist) or *undefined* (do not exist).

Find the dimensions of each product matrix.

GH	HG
$(3 \times 2)(2 \times 2) \rightarrow 3 \times 2$	$(2 \times 2)(3 \times 2)$
↑ ↑ equal; product matrix	↑ ↑ *not* equal

Product GH is defined and is a 3×2 matrix. Product HG is undefined, because the number of columns of H is not equal to the number of rows of G.

Check Understanding 6 Let $R = \begin{bmatrix} 4 & -2 \\ 5 & -4 \end{bmatrix}$ and $S = \begin{bmatrix} 8 & 0 & -1 & 0 \\ 2 & -5 & 1 & 8 \end{bmatrix}$.

a. Determine whether products RS and SR are *defined* or *undefined*.
b. Find each defined product.

Matrix multiplication has some of the properties of real number multiplication.

Key Concepts

Properties	**Matrix Multiplication**
If A, B, and C are $n \times n$ matrices, then	
AB is an $n \times n$ matrix.	Closure Property
$(AB)C = A(BC)$	Associative Property of Multiplication
$A(B + C) = AB + AC$ $(B + C)A = BA + CA$	Distributive Property
$OA = AO = O$, where O has the same dimensions as A.	Multiplicative Property of Zero

EXERCISES

For more practice, see *Extra Practice*.

Practice and Problem Solving

A Practice by Example

Examples 1 and 2 (pages 178 and 179)

Use matrices A, B, C, and D. Find each scalar product, sum, or difference.

$A = \begin{bmatrix} 3 & 4 \\ 6 & -2 \\ 1 & 0 \end{bmatrix}$ $B = \begin{bmatrix} -3 & 1 \\ 2 & -4 \\ -1 & 5 \end{bmatrix}$ $C = \begin{bmatrix} 1 & 2 \\ -3 & 1 \end{bmatrix}$ $D = \begin{bmatrix} 5 & 1 \\ 0 & 2 \end{bmatrix}$

1. $3A$ **2.** $4B$ **3.** $-3C$ **4.** $-D$

5. $A - 2B$ **6.** $3A + 2B$ **7.** $4C + 3D$ **8.** $2A - 5B$

Example 3 (page 179)

Solve each equation. Check your answers.

9. $3\begin{bmatrix} 2 & 0 \\ -1 & 5 \end{bmatrix} - 2X = \begin{bmatrix} -10 & 5 \\ 0 & 17 \end{bmatrix}$ **10.** $5X - \begin{bmatrix} 1.5 & -3.6 \\ -0.3 & 2.8 \end{bmatrix} = \begin{bmatrix} 0.2 & 1.3 \\ -5.6 & 1.7 \end{bmatrix}$

Example 4 (page 180)

Find each product.

11. $\begin{bmatrix} -3 & 4 \\ 5 & 2 \end{bmatrix}\begin{bmatrix} 1 & 0 \\ 2 & -3 \end{bmatrix}$
12. $\begin{bmatrix} 1 & 0 \\ 2 & -3 \end{bmatrix}\begin{bmatrix} -3 & 4 \\ 5 & 2 \end{bmatrix}$
13. $\begin{bmatrix} 0 & 2 \\ -4 & 0 \end{bmatrix}\begin{bmatrix} 0 & 2 \\ -4 & 0 \end{bmatrix}$

14. $\begin{bmatrix} -3 & 5 \end{bmatrix}\begin{bmatrix} -3 \\ 5 \end{bmatrix}$
15. $\begin{bmatrix} -3 & 5 \end{bmatrix}\begin{bmatrix} -3 & 0 \\ 5 & 0 \end{bmatrix}$
16. $\begin{bmatrix} -3 & 5 \end{bmatrix}\begin{bmatrix} 0 & -3 \\ 0 & 5 \end{bmatrix}$

17. $\begin{bmatrix} 0 & -3 \\ 0 & 5 \end{bmatrix}\begin{bmatrix} -3 & 0 \\ 5 & 0 \end{bmatrix}$
18. $\begin{bmatrix} 1 & 0 \\ -1 & -5 \\ 0 & 3 \end{bmatrix}\begin{bmatrix} -1 & 0 \\ 0 & -1 \end{bmatrix}$

Example 5 (page 181)

19. Business A florist creates three special floral arrangements. One uses three lilies. The second uses three lilies and four carnations. The third uses four daisies and three carnations. Lilies cost $2.15 each, carnations cost $.90 each, and daisies cost $1.30 each.

a. Write a matrix to represent the number of each type of flower in each arrangement.
b. Write a matrix to represent the cost of each type of flower.
c. Find the matrix representing the cost of each floral arrangement.

Example 6 (page 182)

Determine whether each product is defined or undefined.

$F = \begin{bmatrix} 2 & 3 \\ 6 & 9 \end{bmatrix}$ $G = \begin{bmatrix} -3 & 6 \\ 2 & -4 \end{bmatrix}$ $H = \begin{bmatrix} -5 \\ 6 \end{bmatrix}$ $J = \begin{bmatrix} 0 & 7 \end{bmatrix}$

20. FG **21.** GF **22.** FH **23.** HF **24.** GH
25. HG **26.** FJ **27.** JF **28.** HJ **29.** JH

B Apply Your Skills

Mental Math Find each product.

30. $2\begin{bmatrix} -1 & 4 \\ 2 & 5 \end{bmatrix}$
31. $-3\begin{bmatrix} 6 & -3 \\ -7 & 4 \end{bmatrix}$
32. $-1\begin{bmatrix} 9 & -7 & -4 \\ -8 & -2 & 3 \end{bmatrix}$

33. $\begin{bmatrix} -1 & 0 \\ 0 & -1 \end{bmatrix}\begin{bmatrix} -1 & 0 & 1 \\ 0 & -1 & 1 \end{bmatrix}$
34. $\begin{bmatrix} 1 & 0 \\ 0 & -1 \end{bmatrix}\begin{bmatrix} -1 & 0 \\ 0 & -1 \end{bmatrix}$

Find each product.

35. $-1\begin{bmatrix} 7.5 & 6.2 & 4.0 \\ 6.7 & 8.2 & 0 \end{bmatrix}$
36. $\frac{1}{4}\begin{bmatrix} 4 & 0 & -3 & 1 \\ 12 & 16 & 6 & -4 \\ 0 & -2 & 5 & 8 \end{bmatrix}$
37. $0.5\begin{bmatrix} 3 & 14 \\ 7 & -4 \end{bmatrix}$

Find the dimensions of each product matrix. Then find each product.

38. $\begin{bmatrix} 5 & 7 & 0 \\ -\frac{4}{5} & 3 & 6 \\ 0 & -\frac{2}{3} & 4 \end{bmatrix}\begin{bmatrix} 2 & -1 \\ 1 & 1 \\ 0 & -1 \end{bmatrix}$
39. $\begin{bmatrix} 0 & -1 & 3 \\ 0 & -5 & 2 \\ 0 & 0 & 2 \\ 1 & 0 & -3 \end{bmatrix}\begin{bmatrix} -1.5 & 4.3 & 0 \\ 1.6 & -2.2 & 1.8 \\ 1 & 0 & -1.2 \end{bmatrix}$

40. $\begin{bmatrix} w & x \\ y & z \end{bmatrix}\begin{bmatrix} 9 & -7 \\ 3 & 1 \end{bmatrix}$
41. $\begin{bmatrix} 1 & 0 & 0 \\ 1 & 0 & -2 \\ 0 & 0 & 2 \\ -1 & 0 & 1 \end{bmatrix}\begin{bmatrix} a & 0 & b & 0 \\ 0 & c & 0 & d \\ e & 0 & 0 & f \end{bmatrix}$

Geometry Review

Geometric Transformations

For Use With Lesson 4-4

Geometric patterns, such as those formed by geese flying south for the winter or tiles on a plane surface, can be described using geometric transformations. A transformation is a change made to a figure. There are four types.

A translation slides a figure a given distance and direction without changing its size or shape.

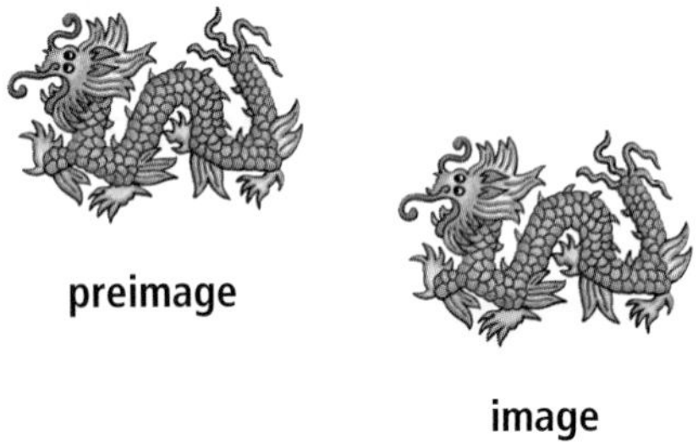

A rotation turns a figure through a given angle about a point called the center.

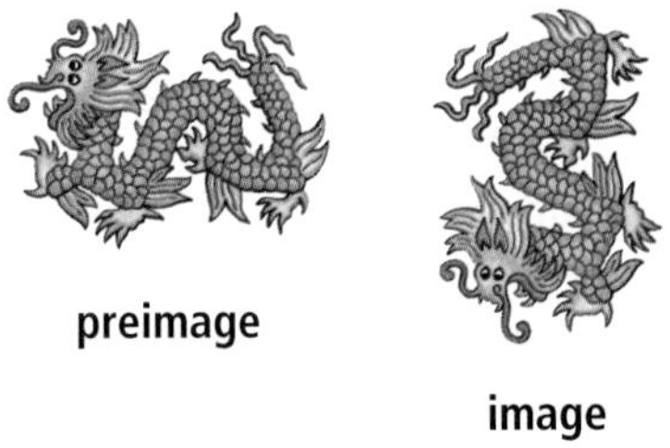

A reflection flips a figure over a given line called its axis of reflection.

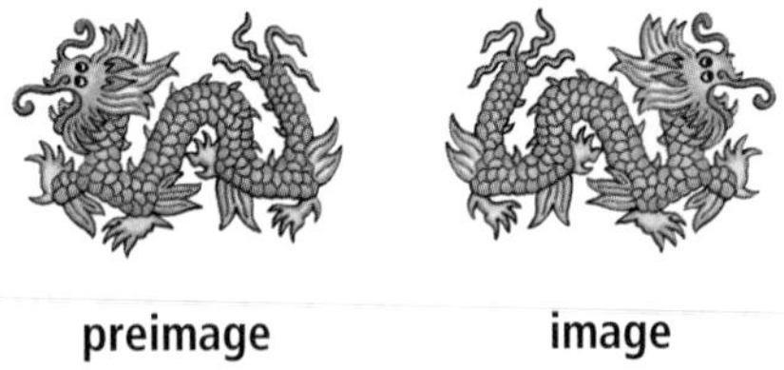

A dilation enlarges or reduces a figure by a given scale factor.

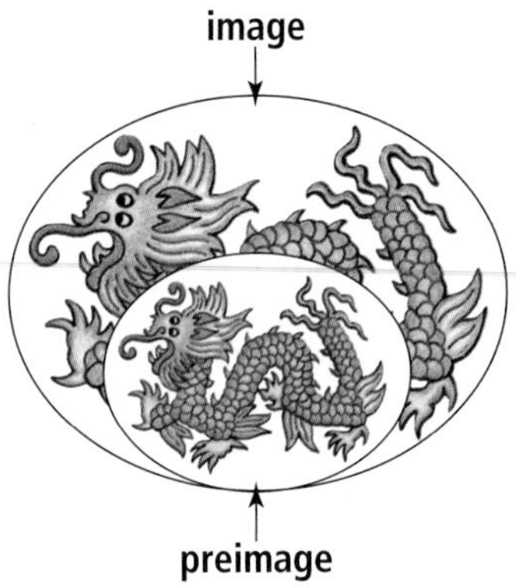

EXERCISES

Describe each transformation from the black figure to the blue figure as a *translation, rotation, reflection,* or *dilation.*

1. 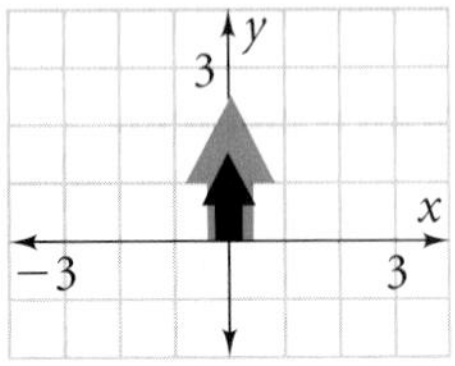

2. 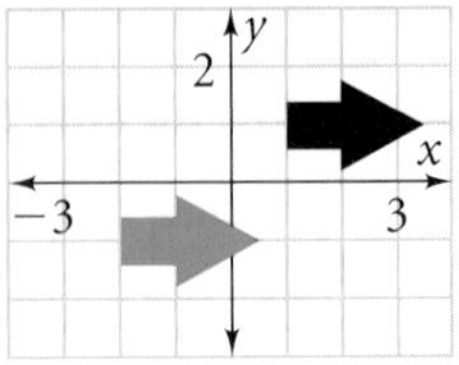

3. 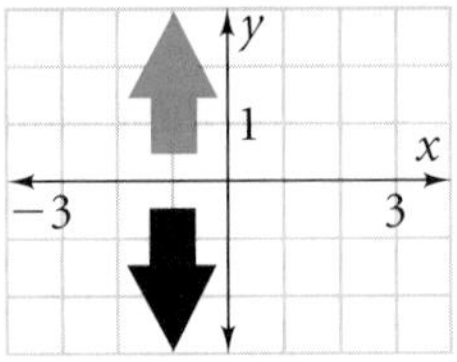

4. 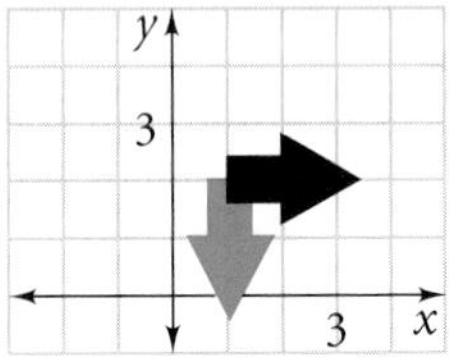

5. a. **Open-Ended** List the coordinates of the vertices of one black figure above. List the coordinates of the corresponding blue figure.
   b. **Make a Conjecture** How do the coordinates of the black figure relate to the coordinates of the corresponding blue figure? Use examples to verify your conjecture.

4-4 Geometric Transformations with Matrices

North Carolina Objectives

1.04 Operate with matrices to model and solve problems.

Lesson Preview

What You'll Learn

OBJECTIVE 1 To represent translations and dilations with matrices

OBJECTIVE 2 To represent reflections and rotations with matrices

. . . And Why

To transform a photo, as in Example 2

Check Skills You'll Need

(For help, go to Lesson 2-6.)

Without using graphing technology, graph each function and its translation. Write the new function.

1. $y = x + 2$; left 4 units
2. $f(x) = \frac{1}{2}x + 2$; up 5 units
3. $g(x) = |x|$; right 3 units
4. $y = x$; down 2 units
5. $y = |\frac{1}{3}x - 3|$; down 2 units
6. $f(x) = |-2x|$; right 2 units

New Vocabulary • transformation • image • preimage • translation • dilation • reflection • rotation • center of rotation

iTEXT Interactive lesson includes instant self-check, tutorials, and activities.

OBJECTIVE 1 Translations and Dilations with Matrices

Investigation: Translating a Geometric Figure

Geometry In Chapter 2 you used vertical and horizontal translations to graph functions. A translation shifts a graph without changing its size or shape.

1. Draw the figure on a coordinate grid as shown.
2. Translate the figure 4 units right and 6 units down. Label the new figure.
3. Identify the coordinates of the vertices of the original figure and the new figure.

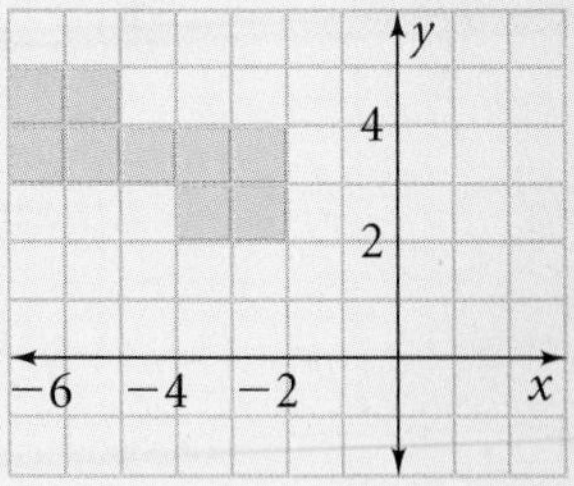

4. How does the translation *4 units right and 6 units down* relate the coordinates of the new figure to the coordinates of the original figure?
5. Without graphing, identify the coordinates that result from a translation of the original figure 10 units right and 3 units up.
6. Suppose the original figure is translated so that two vertices have coordinates (0, 0) and (2, 0). Find two possible translations. Write the coordinates for the vertices of each translated figure.
7. **Critical Thinking** What translations of the original figure will result in a tessellation?
8. **Open-Ended** Design another simple figure that will tessellate the plane. Describe the translations needed to fill the plane.

Need Help?

A tessellation is a repeating pattern of figures that covers a plane, without gaps or overlaps.

You can write the vertices of a figure as a matrix. For example, the matrix below represents the vertices of figure $ABCD$.

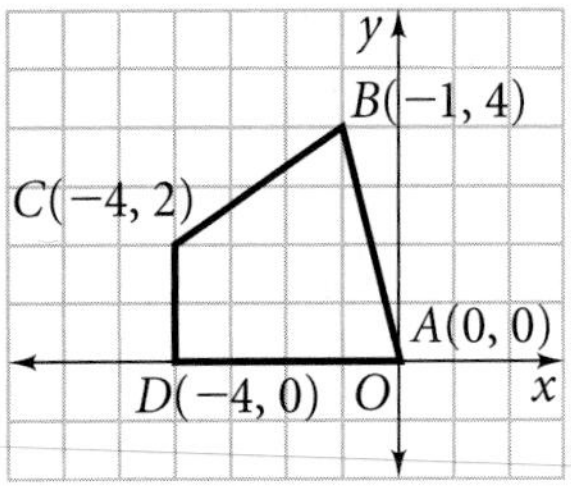

$$\begin{array}{l} \\ x\text{-coordinate} \\ y\text{-coordinate} \end{array} \begin{array}{c} \begin{matrix} A & B & C & D \end{matrix} \\ \begin{bmatrix} 0 & -1 & -4 & -4 \\ 0 & 4 & 2 & 0 \end{bmatrix} \end{array}$$

A **transformation** is a change made to a figure. The transformed figure is called the **image.** The original figure is called the **preimage.** A **translation** is a transformation that slides a figure without changing the size or shape of the figure. You can use matrix addition to translate all the vertices of a figure in one step.

Reading Math

Read the notation A' as "A prime," A'' as "A double prime," etc. The prime symbol tells you that something happened to point A to change it to point A'.

1 EXAMPLE Translating a Figure

Geometry Quadrilateral $ABCD$ above has vertices $A(0, 0)$, $B(-1, 4)$, $C(-4, 2)$, and $D(-4, 0)$. Use a matrix to find the coordinates of the vertices of the image translated 6 units right and 2 units down. Then graph $ABCD$ and its image $A'B'C'D'$.

Vertices of the Quadrilateral		Translation Matrix		Vertices of the Image

Add 6 to each x-coordinate.

$$\begin{array}{c} \begin{matrix} A & B & C & D \end{matrix} \\ \begin{bmatrix} 0 & -1 & -4 & -4 \\ 0 & 4 & 2 & 0 \end{bmatrix} \end{array} + \begin{bmatrix} 6 & 6 & 6 & 6 \\ -2 & -2 & -2 & -2 \end{bmatrix} = \begin{array}{c} \begin{matrix} A' & B' & C' & D' \end{matrix} \\ \begin{bmatrix} 6 & 5 & 2 & 2 \\ -2 & 2 & 0 & -2 \end{bmatrix} \end{array}$$

Subtract 2 from each y-coordinate.

The vertices of the image are $A'(6, -2)$, $B'(5, 2)$, $C'(2, 0)$, and $D'(2, -2)$.

Graph both quadrilaterals.

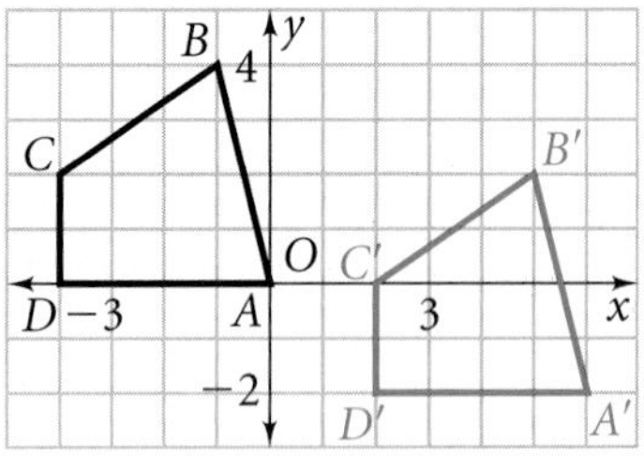

Check Understanding 1 a. **Critical Thinking** Explain how to translate quadrilateral $A'B'C'D'$ from Example 1 so that its image is quadrilateral $ABCD$.

b. What matrix would you use to translate the vertices of a pentagon 3 units left and 2 units up?

c. Use your answer to part (b) to translate the pentagon with vertices $(0, -5)$, $(-1, -1)$, $(-5, 0)$, $(1, 3)$, and $(4, 0)$. Find the coordinates of the vertices of the image. Graph the preimage and the image.

Graphing Calculator Hint

Enter the preimage and translation matrices as [A] and [B]. Use matrix addition to find the coordinates of the image.

A **dilation** is a transformation that changes the size of a figure. When the center of the dilation is the origin, you can use scalar multiplication to find the coordinates of the vertices of an image. All dilations in this book are centered at the origin.

2 EXAMPLE Real-World Connection

Graphic Arts An artist sends you a photo electronically. You increase the size of the photo by a factor of 1.2. Find the coordinates of the vertices of the enlargement.

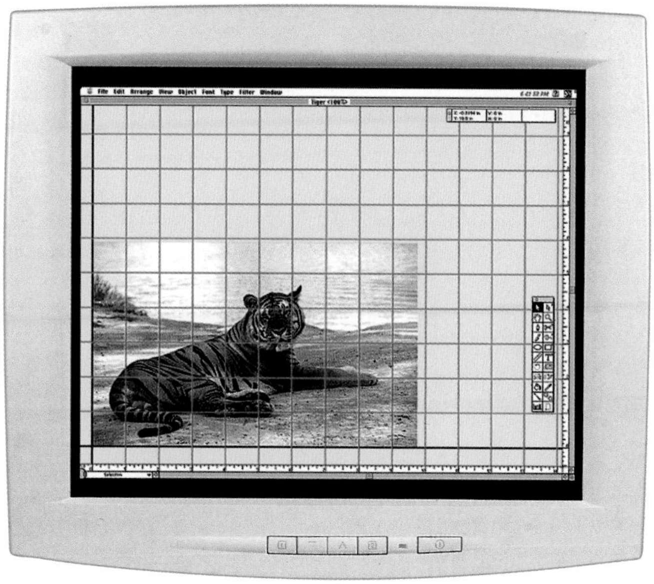

Write a matrix to represent the coordinates of the vertices, which are at (0, 0), (0, 5.875), (9.75, 5.875), and (9.75, 0). Then multiply by the factor 1.2.

$$1.2\begin{bmatrix} 0 & 0 & 9.75 & 9.75 \\ 0 & 5.875 & 5.875 & 0 \end{bmatrix} = \begin{bmatrix} 0 & 0 & 11.7 & 11.7 \\ 0 & 7.05 & 7.05 & 0 \end{bmatrix}$$

The new coordinates are (0, 0), (0, 7.05), (11.7, 7.05), and (11.7, 0).

Check Understanding 2 The coordinates of the vertices of figure ABC are $A(-5, 0)$, $B(8, -1)$, and $C(4, 5)$. Find the coordinates of each image under the following dilations. Then graph each image and its preimage on the same coordinate plane.

a. 4 **b.** $\frac{1}{5}$ **c.** -1.5

OBJECTIVE

2 Reflections and Rotations with Matrices

A **reflection,** or flip, is a transformation that creates symmetry on the coordinate plane. A reflection maps a point in the plane to its mirror image, using a specific line as the mirror. The lines used in this book are the x- and y-axes and the lines $y = x$ and $y = -x$.

You can use matrix multiplication to graph reflections in the coordinate plane.

Key Concepts

Properties **Matrices for Reflections in the Coordinate Plane**

Reflection in the y-axis	Reflection in the x-axis	Reflection in the line $y = x$	Reflection in the line $y = -x$
$\begin{bmatrix} -1 & 0 \\ 0 & 1 \end{bmatrix}$	$\begin{bmatrix} 1 & 0 \\ 0 & -1 \end{bmatrix}$	$\begin{bmatrix} 0 & 1 \\ 1 & 0 \end{bmatrix}$	$\begin{bmatrix} 0 & -1 \\ -1 & 0 \end{bmatrix}$

3 EXAMPLE Reflecting a Figure

Reflect the triangle with coordinates $A(0,0)$, $B(2,5)$, and $C(-2,3)$ in each line. Then graph each pair of triangles on the same coordinate plane.

a. y-axis

$$\begin{bmatrix} -1 & 0 \\ 0 & 1 \end{bmatrix}\begin{bmatrix} 0 & 2 & -2 \\ 0 & 5 & 3 \end{bmatrix} = \begin{bmatrix} 0 & -2 & 2 \\ 0 & 5 & 3 \end{bmatrix}$$

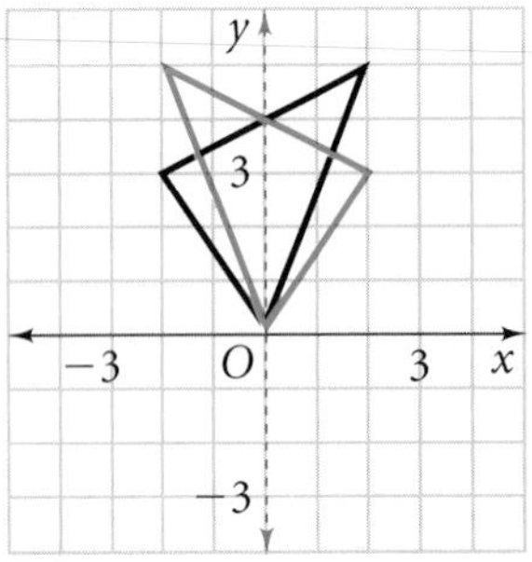

b. x-axis

$$\begin{bmatrix} 1 & 0 \\ 0 & -1 \end{bmatrix}\begin{bmatrix} 0 & 2 & -2 \\ 0 & 5 & 3 \end{bmatrix} = \begin{bmatrix} 0 & 2 & -2 \\ 0 & -5 & -3 \end{bmatrix}$$

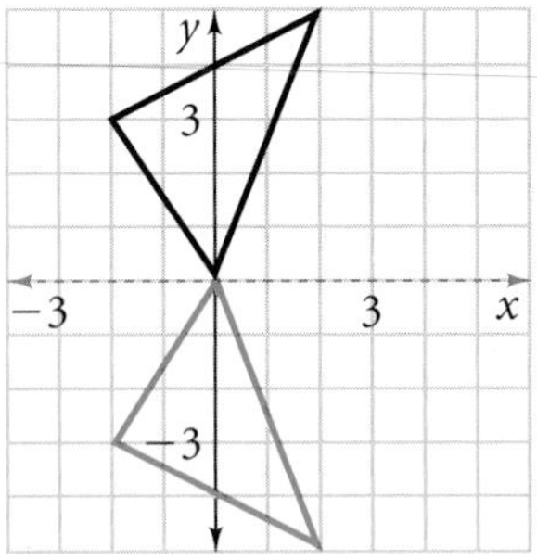

c. $y = x$

$$\begin{bmatrix} 0 & 1 \\ 1 & 0 \end{bmatrix}\begin{bmatrix} 0 & 2 & -2 \\ 0 & 5 & 3 \end{bmatrix} = \begin{bmatrix} 0 & 5 & 3 \\ 0 & 2 & -2 \end{bmatrix}$$

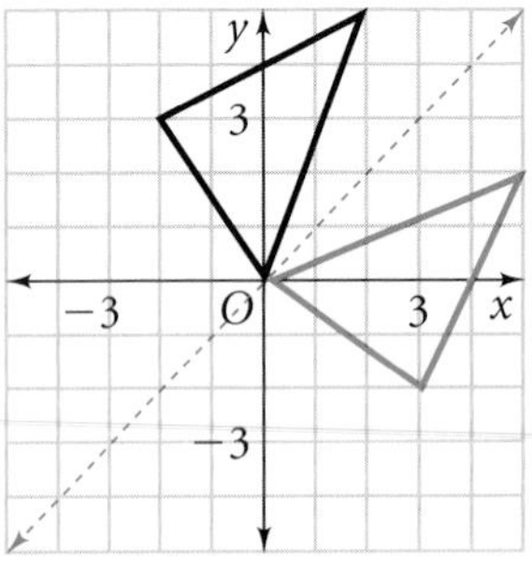

d. $y = -x$

$$\begin{bmatrix} 0 & -1 \\ -1 & 0 \end{bmatrix}\begin{bmatrix} 0 & 2 & -2 \\ 0 & 5 & 3 \end{bmatrix} = \begin{bmatrix} 0 & -5 & -3 \\ 0 & -2 & 2 \end{bmatrix}$$

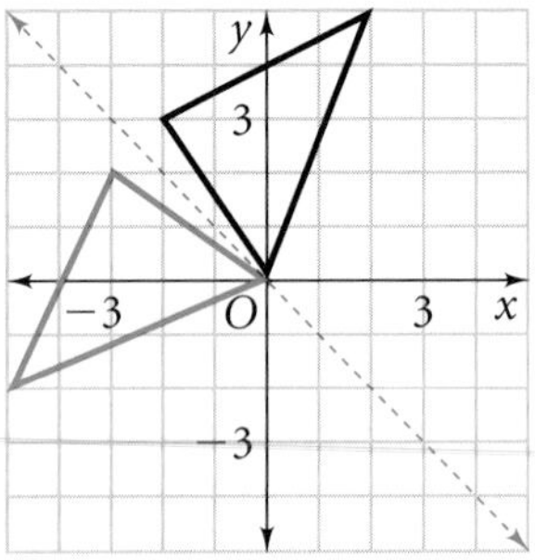

Check Understanding 3 Reflect the triangle with coordinates $D(-3,0)$, $E(-4,4)$, and $F(1,1)$ in each line. Then graph each pair of triangles on the same coordinate plane.

a. y-axis **b.** x-axis **c.** $y = x$ **d.** $y = -x$

Need Help?
There are 360 degrees in a circle.

A **rotation** is a transformation that turns a figure about a fixed point called the **center of rotation.** You can rotate a figure as much as 360 degrees. In this book, all rotations are counterclockwise about the origin.

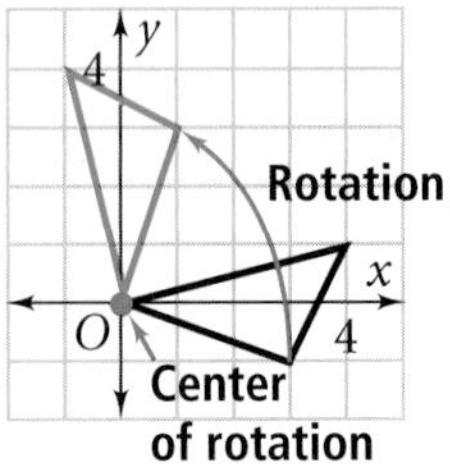

Key Concepts

Properties | **Matrices for Rotations in the Coordinate Plane**

Rotation of 90°	Rotation of 180°	Rotation of 270°	Rotation of 360°
$\begin{bmatrix} 0 & -1 \\ 1 & 0 \end{bmatrix}$	$\begin{bmatrix} -1 & 0 \\ 0 & -1 \end{bmatrix}$	$\begin{bmatrix} 0 & 1 \\ -1 & 0 \end{bmatrix}$	$\begin{bmatrix} 1 & 0 \\ 0 & 1 \end{bmatrix}$

4 EXAMPLE Rotating a Figure

Real-World Connection

The triangles in the windmill have 90° rotational symmetry.

Rotate the triangle with coordinates $A(0,0)$, $B(2,5)$, and $C(-2,3)$. Then graph each pair of triangles on the same coordinate plane.

a. 90°

$$\begin{bmatrix} 0 & -1 \\ 1 & 0 \end{bmatrix}\begin{bmatrix} 0 & 2 & -2 \\ 0 & 5 & 3 \end{bmatrix} = \begin{bmatrix} 0 & -5 & -3 \\ 0 & 2 & -2 \end{bmatrix}$$

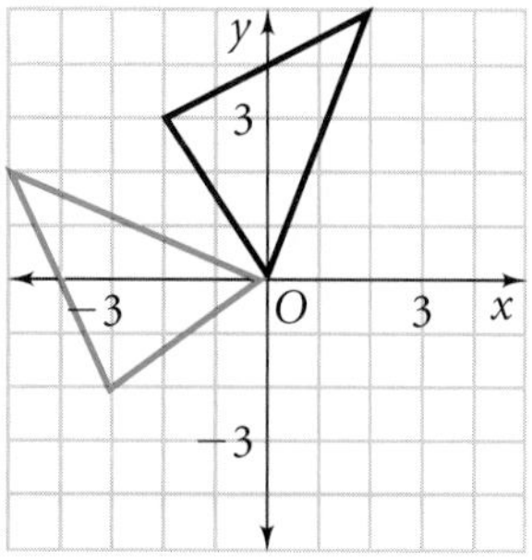

b. 180°

$$\begin{bmatrix} -1 & 0 \\ 0 & -1 \end{bmatrix}\begin{bmatrix} 0 & 2 & -2 \\ 0 & 5 & 3 \end{bmatrix} = \begin{bmatrix} 0 & -2 & 2 \\ 0 & -5 & -3 \end{bmatrix}$$

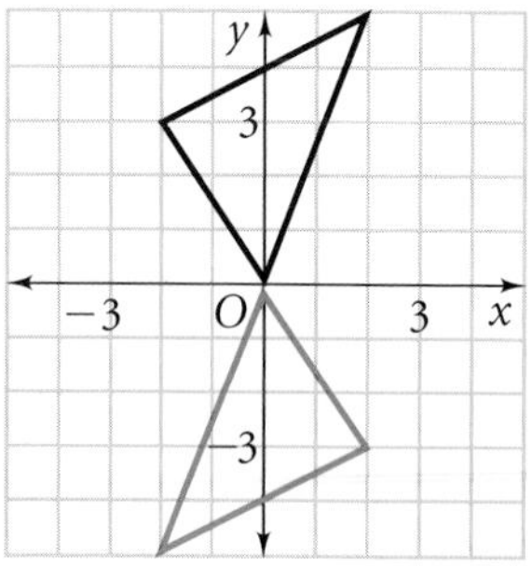

c. 270°

$$\begin{bmatrix} 0 & 1 \\ -1 & 0 \end{bmatrix}\begin{bmatrix} 0 & 2 & -2 \\ 0 & 5 & 3 \end{bmatrix} = \begin{bmatrix} 0 & 5 & 3 \\ 0 & -2 & 2 \end{bmatrix}$$

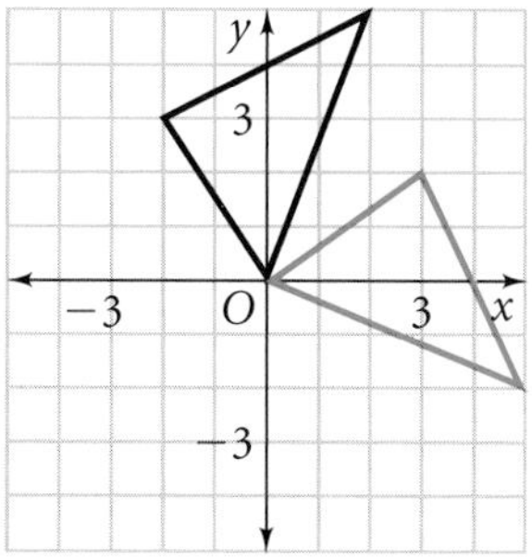

d. 360°

$$\begin{bmatrix} 1 & 0 \\ 0 & 1 \end{bmatrix}\begin{bmatrix} 0 & 2 & -2 \\ 0 & 5 & 3 \end{bmatrix} = \begin{bmatrix} 0 & 2 & -2 \\ 0 & 5 & 3 \end{bmatrix}$$

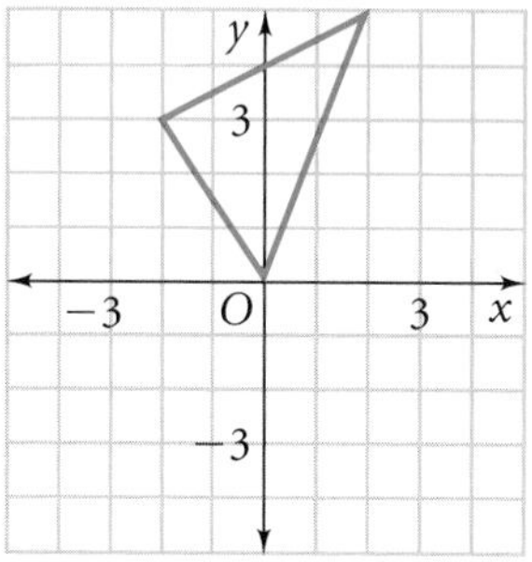

Check Understanding

4. Rotate the quadrilateral with coordinates $A(1,1)$, $B(3,1)$, $C(6,4)$, and $D(1,3)$. Then graph each pair of quadrilaterals on the same coordinate plane.

a. 90° **b.** 180° **c.** 270° **d.** 360°

EXERCISES

For more practice, see *Extra Practice*.

Practice and Problem Solving

A Practice by Example

Example 1 (page 188)

Use matrix addition to find the coordinates of each image after a translation of 3 units left and 5 units up. If possible, graph each pair of figures on the same coordinate plane.

1. $A(1,-3), B(1,1), C(5,1), D(5,-3)$

2. $G(0,0), H(4,4), I(4,-4), J(8,0)$

3. $J(-10,2), K(-16,a), L(12,-5)$

4. $R(9,3), S(3,6), T(3,3), U(6,-3)$

Example 2 (page 189)

Graph each figure and its image after the given dilation.

5. $\begin{bmatrix} 0 & 2 & 5 & 8 \\ 0 & 4 & 5 & 1 \end{bmatrix}, 2$

6. $\begin{bmatrix} -7 & -3 & 4 \\ -5 & 4 & 0 \end{bmatrix}, 0.5$

7. $\begin{bmatrix} 0 & -2 & -5 \\ 0 & 0 & 5 \end{bmatrix}, \frac{9}{10}$

8. $\begin{bmatrix} -10 & -5 & 0 & 5 & 10 \\ 8 & 16 & 20 & 16 & 8 \end{bmatrix}, \frac{1}{4}$

9. $\begin{bmatrix} -8 & 2 & 3 & 1 & -2 \\ 6 & 4 & 0 & -4 & 0 \end{bmatrix}, 1.5$

Example 3 (page 190)

Graph each figure and its image after reflection in the given line.

10. $\begin{bmatrix} 0 & -3 & 5 \\ 0 & 1 & 2 \end{bmatrix}$; $y = x$ **11.** $\begin{bmatrix} -1 & 0 & 5 \\ -1 & 5 & 0 \end{bmatrix}$; y-axis **12.** $\begin{bmatrix} -3 & -5 & -10 \\ 4 & 7 & 1 \end{bmatrix}$; x-axis

Find the coordinates of each image after reflection in the given line.

13. $\begin{bmatrix} 3 & 6 & 3 & 6 \\ -3 & 3 & 3 & -3 \end{bmatrix}$; $y = -x$ **14.** $\begin{bmatrix} 0 & 4 & 8 & 6 \\ 0 & 4 & 4 & 2 \end{bmatrix}$; x-axis

15. $\begin{bmatrix} 1 & 2 & 3 & 4 & 2.5 \\ 3 & 2 & 2 & 3 & 5 \end{bmatrix}$; $y = x$ **16.** $\begin{bmatrix} -1 & -2 & -4 & -6 & -2 \\ -4 & 0 & 0 & -3 & -4 \end{bmatrix}$; x-axis

Example 4 (page 191)

Graph each figure and its image after the given rotation.

17. $\begin{bmatrix} 0 & -3 & 5 \\ 0 & 1 & 2 \end{bmatrix}$; 90° **18.** $\begin{bmatrix} -1 & 0 & 5 \\ -1 & 5 & 0 \end{bmatrix}$; 180° **19.** $\begin{bmatrix} -5 & 6 & 0 \\ -1 & 2 & 4 \end{bmatrix}$; 90°

Find the coordinates of each image after the given rotation.

20. $\begin{bmatrix} 3 & 6 & 3 & 6 \\ -3 & 3 & 3 & -3 \end{bmatrix}$; 270° **21.** $\begin{bmatrix} 0 & 4 & 8 & 6 \\ 0 & 4 & 4 & 2 \end{bmatrix}$; 360°

22. $\begin{bmatrix} 1 & 2 & 3 & 4 & 2.5 \\ 3 & 2 & 2 & 3 & 5 \end{bmatrix}$; 180° **23.** $\begin{bmatrix} -1 & -2 & -4 & -6 & -2 \\ -4 & 0 & 0 & -3 & -4 \end{bmatrix}$; 270°

B Apply Your Skills

Geometry **Each matrix represents the vertices of a polygon. Translate each figure 5 units left and 1 unit up. Express your answer as a matrix.**

24. $\begin{bmatrix} -3 & -3 & 2 & 2 \\ -2 & -4 & -2 & -4 \end{bmatrix}$ **25.** $\begin{bmatrix} -3 & 0 & 3 & 0 \\ -9 & -6 & -9 & -12 \end{bmatrix}$ **26.** $\begin{bmatrix} 0 & 1 & -4 \\ 0 & 3 & 5 \end{bmatrix}$

For Exercises 27–34, use $\triangle ABC$. Write the coordinates of each image in matrix form.

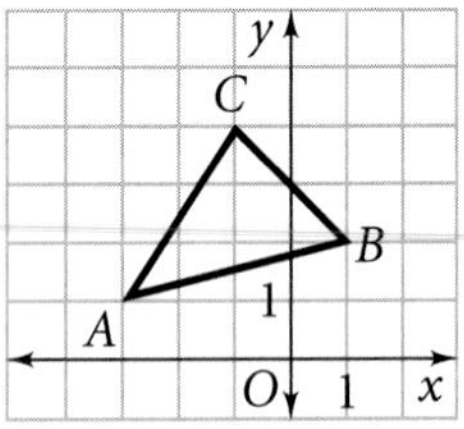

27. a dilation four times the original size

28. a translation 2 units left and 3 units down

29. a dilation half the original size

30. a translation 1 unit right and 7 units up

31. a rotation of 90°

32. a reflection in $y = x$

33. a rotation of 180°

34. a reflection in the x-axis

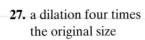

35. a. Graph $\begin{bmatrix} 9 & 10 & 6 \\ 1 & -3 & -2 \end{bmatrix}$ and $2\begin{bmatrix} 9 & 10 & 6 \\ 1 & -3 & -2 \end{bmatrix}$.

b. Writing Compare the graphs in part (a). Generalize how a dilation changes a graph.

Need Help?

A tessellation is a repeating pattern of figures that covers a plane, without gaps or overlap.

36. Geometry Create a tessellation based on the quadrilateral $\begin{bmatrix} 0 & -3 & -5 & 0 \\ 1 & 3 & -1 & -1 \end{bmatrix}$.

Translate the quadrilateral using $\begin{bmatrix} 5 & 5 & 5 & 5 \\ 2 & 2 & 2 & 2 \end{bmatrix}$ and $\begin{bmatrix} 3 & 3 & 3 & 3 \\ -4 & -4 & -4 & -4 \end{bmatrix}$.

37. Writing Explain why you might want to represent a transformation as a matrix.

38. Find $\begin{bmatrix} -3 & 0 \\ 0 & -3 \end{bmatrix}\begin{bmatrix} 1 & -2 & 4 \\ 1 & -1 & 2 \end{bmatrix}$ and $-3\begin{bmatrix} 1 & -2 & 4 \\ 1 & -1 & 2 \end{bmatrix}$. What do you notice?

Use matrices to represent the vertices of graph f and graph g. Name each transformation.

39.

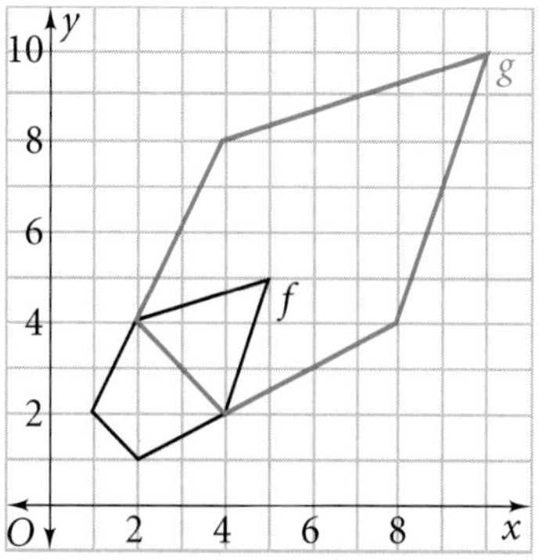

40.

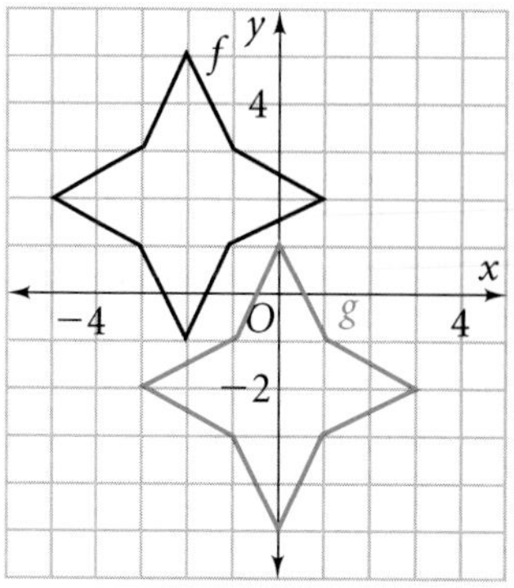

41.

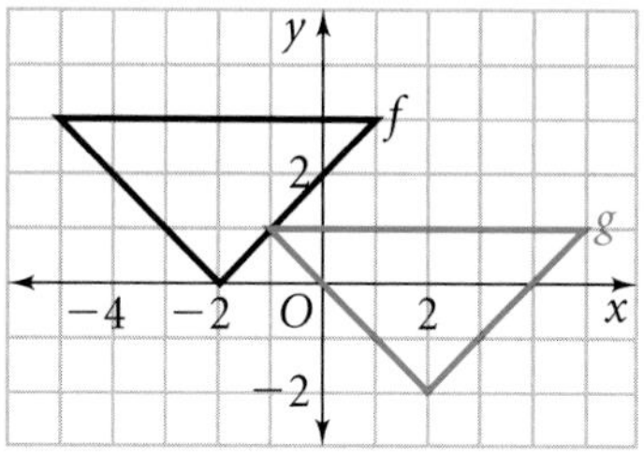

42.

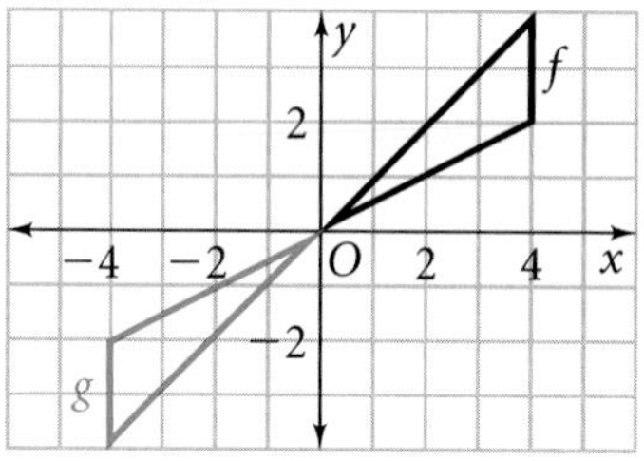

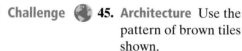

Graph each triangle and its translation on the same coordinate plane.

43. $\begin{bmatrix} 0 & 2 & 3 \\ 0 & 0 & 5 \end{bmatrix}$; 3 units right, 4 units down

44. $\begin{bmatrix} -5 & 3 & 4 \\ 5 & 1 & -4 \end{bmatrix}$; 2 units left, 5 units up

Challenge

45. Architecture Use the pattern of brown tiles shown.

a. Copy the graph. Mark scales on the axes so that the dimensions of the square tiles are 1 unit by 1 unit.

b. Write a matrix for the translation of tile $ABCD$ to tile $A'B'C'D'$. What are the coordinates of the vertices of the preimage and the image?

c. A brown tile is 6 units right and 6 units down from tile $ABCD$. Write a matrix to represent the coordinates of its vertices.

d. A tile has vertices at $(-6, 9)$, $(-6, 8)$, $(-7, 9)$, and $(-7, 8)$. What translation of tile $ABCD$ results in these coordinates?

Geometry Each matrix represents the vertices of a polygon. Write a matrix to represent the vertices of the image after each transformation.

46. $\begin{bmatrix} -3 & 0.5 & -5 \\ 0 & 3 & 3 \end{bmatrix}$; dilation of 2

47. $\begin{bmatrix} 4 & 7 & 10 \\ 0 & 2 & 0 \end{bmatrix}$; rotation of 270°

48. $\begin{bmatrix} 17 & 6 & 6 & 2 \\ 5 & 10 & 2 & 6 \end{bmatrix}$; reflection in $y = x$

49. $\begin{bmatrix} 3 & 4.5 & 5 & 3.5 \\ 3 & 1.5 & 2 & 4 \end{bmatrix}$; rotation of 90°

50. Let the matrix $\begin{bmatrix} x \\ y \end{bmatrix}$ represent points on the graph $y = |x|$.

a. Complete the table. Sketch the graph.

x	−3	−2	−1	0	1	2	3
y	■	■	■	■	■	■	■

b. **Critical Thinking** What does the matrix addition $\begin{bmatrix} x \\ y \end{bmatrix} + \begin{bmatrix} -1 \\ 2 \end{bmatrix}$ represent? Show your answer on your graph from part (a).

Standardized Test Prep

Multiple Choice

51. What are the coordinates of $X(5, 1)$, $Y(-5, -3)$, and $Z(-1, 3)$ reflected in the line $y = x$?

A. $X'(-5, -1)$, $Y'(5, 3)$, $Z'(1, -3)$ B. $X'(1, 5)$, $Y'(-3, -5)$, $Z'(3, -1)$
C. $X'(-1, -5)$, $Y'(3, 5)$, $Z'(-3, 1)$ D. $X'(5, 1)$, $Y'(-5, -3)$, $Z'(-1, 3)$

52. Reflection in which line takes the figure with vertices $A(0, 0)$, $B(-2, 4)$, $C(-4, 2)$, and $D(-3, 0)$ to $A'(0, 0)$, $B'(-2, -4)$, $C'(-4, -2)$, and $D'(-3, 0)$?

F. x-axis G. y-axis H. $y = x$ I. $y = -x$

Short Response

53. Each vertex of the triangle at the right is transformed by *right 3, up 2* and then by *left 5, up 4*. What is a matrix for the combined transformation? What are the coordinates of the vertices of the final triangle?

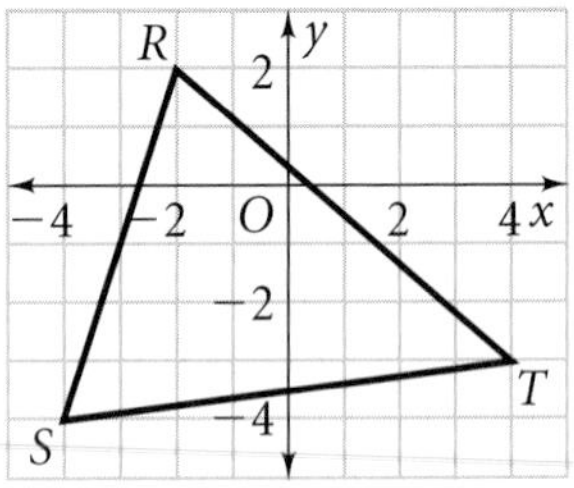

Extended Response

54. A quadrilateral has coordinates $\begin{bmatrix} 3 & 4 & -3 & -4 \\ 5 & 4 & -4 & -3 \end{bmatrix}$.

a. Graph the quadrilateral.

b. Find the product $\begin{bmatrix} 0 & -1 \\ 1 & 0 \end{bmatrix}\begin{bmatrix} 3 & 4 & -3 & -4 \\ 5 & 4 & -4 & -3 \end{bmatrix}$.

c. Graph the result as a new quadrilateral.

d. What is the relationship between the quadrilaterals in parts (a) and (c)?

Take It to the NET
Online lesson quiz at
www.PHSchool.com
Web Code: aga-0404

Mixed Review

Lesson 4-3

If possible, find the dimensions of each product matrix; then find each product. If the product is not defined, explain why not.

55. $\begin{bmatrix} 1 & 0 & -5 \\ 2 & -1 & 6 \end{bmatrix}\begin{bmatrix} 2 & 4 & -2 \\ 0 & 10 & 4 \\ 0 & 1 & -7 \end{bmatrix}$

56. $\begin{bmatrix} 0 & 7 & k & 5 \\ 0 & 6 & 0 & 5 \end{bmatrix}\begin{bmatrix} 9 & -1 & 3 & 0 \\ 7 & 0 & 7 & 0 \end{bmatrix}$

Lesson 3-5

Graph each equation.

57. $x + y - z = 5$

58. $2x - y + 3z = 12$

59. $-x + 4y - z = -6$

Lesson 2-1

Make a mapping diagram for each relation. Determine whether it is a function.

60. $(-2, 4), (-1, 1), (0, 0), (1, 1), (2, 4)$

61. $(27, -2), (3, -1), (0, 0), (3, 1), (27, 2)$

62. $(-2, 15), (-1, 1), (0, -3), (1, 3), (2, 15)$

63. $(-3, 8), (-2, 1), (1, -2), (0, -1), (1, 4)$

4-5 2×2 Matrices, Determinants, and Inverses

North Carolina Objectives

1.04 Operate with matrices to model and solve problems.

Lesson Preview

What You'll Learn

OBJECTIVE 1 To evaluate determinants of 2×2 matrices and find inverse matrices

OBJECTIVE 2 To use inverse matrices in solving matrix equations

. . . And Why

To predict cell phone ownership, as in Example 5

Check Skills You'll Need

(For help, go to Skills Handbook page 845.)

Simplify each group of expressions.

1. a. $3(4)$	**b.** $2(6)$	**c.** $3(4) - 2(6)$
2. a. $3(-4)$	**b.** $2(-6)$	**c.** $3(-4) - 2(-6)$
3. a. $-3(-4)$	**b.** $2(-6)$	**c.** $-3(-4) - 2(-6)$
4. a. $-3(4)$	**b.** $-2(-6)$	**c.** $-3(4) - (-2)(-6)$

New Vocabulary

- square matrix
- multiplicative identity matrix
- multiplicative inverse of a matrix
- determinant

Interactive lesson includes instant self-check, tutorials, and activities.

OBJECTIVE 1 Evaluating Determinants of 2×2 Matrices

A **square matrix** is a matrix with the same number of columns as rows.

For any real number a, the number 1 is the multiplicative identity of a, since $a \cdot 1 = 1 \cdot a = a$. Square matrices also have a multiplicative identity.

Key Concepts

Definition **Multiplicative Identity Matrix**

For an $n \times n$ square matrix, the **multiplicative identity matrix** is an $n \times n$ square matrix I, or $I_{n \times n}$, with 1's along the main diagonal and 0's elsewhere.

$$I_2 = \begin{bmatrix} 1 & 0 \\ 0 & 1 \end{bmatrix}, \qquad I_3 = \begin{bmatrix} 1 & 0 & 0 \\ 0 & 1 & 0 \\ 0 & 0 & 1 \end{bmatrix}, \qquad \text{and so forth}$$

If the product of the real numbers a and b is 1, then a and b are multiplicative inverses. Some, but not all, square matrices have multiplicative inverses.

Key Concepts

Definition **Multiplicative Inverse of a Matrix**

If A and X are $n \times n$ matrices, and $AX = XA = I$, then X is the multiplicative inverse of A, written A^{-1}.

$$AA^{-1} = A^{-1}A = I$$

If B is the multiplicative inverse of A, then A is the multiplicative inverse of B. To show that A and B are multiplicative inverses, show that $AB = I$ or that $BA = I$.

1 EXAMPLE Verifying Inverses

Need Help?
To review the multiplicative inverse of a number, go to Lesson 1-1.

Show that B is the multiplicative inverse of A.

$$A = \begin{bmatrix} 2 & 3 \\ 1 & 2 \end{bmatrix} \qquad B = \begin{bmatrix} 2 & -3 \\ -1 & 2 \end{bmatrix}$$

$$AB = \begin{bmatrix} 2 & 3 \\ 1 & 2 \end{bmatrix}\begin{bmatrix} 2 & -3 \\ -1 & 2 \end{bmatrix} = \begin{bmatrix} 2(2) + 3(-1) & 2(-3) + 3(2) \\ 1(2) + 2(-1) & 1(-3) + 2(2) \end{bmatrix} = \begin{bmatrix} 1 & 0 \\ 0 & 1 \end{bmatrix}$$

$AB = I$, so B is the multiplicative inverse of A. A is also the multiplicative inverse of B.

Check $$BA = \begin{bmatrix} 2 & -3 \\ -1 & 2 \end{bmatrix}\begin{bmatrix} 2 & 3 \\ 1 & 2 \end{bmatrix} = \begin{bmatrix} 2(2) + (-3)(1) & 2(3) + (-3)(2) \\ -1(2) + 2(1) & -1(3) + 2(2) \end{bmatrix} = \begin{bmatrix} 1 & 0 \\ 0 & 1 \end{bmatrix} \checkmark$$

Check Understanding **1** Show that the matrices are multiplicative inverses.

a. $\begin{bmatrix} 2 & 1 \\ 2.5 & 1 \end{bmatrix}$ and $\begin{bmatrix} -2 & 2 \\ 5 & -4 \end{bmatrix}$ **b.** $\begin{bmatrix} -2 & -5 \\ -3 & -8 \end{bmatrix}$ and $\begin{bmatrix} -8 & 5 \\ 3 & -2 \end{bmatrix}$

Every square matrix with real-number elements has a real-number determinant. Determinants can help you find inverses.

	Write	Read	Evaluate
$A = \begin{bmatrix} a & b \\ c & d \end{bmatrix}$	$\det A = \begin{vmatrix} a & b \\ c & d \end{vmatrix}$	the determinant of A	$\begin{vmatrix} a & b \\ c & d \end{vmatrix} = ad - bc$

Key Concepts

Definition **Determinant of a 2 × 2 Matrix**

The **determinant** of a 2 × 2 matrix $\begin{bmatrix} a & b \\ c & d \end{bmatrix}$ is $ad - bc$.

Symbols for the determinant of a matrix

$\det A$ $\qquad$ $\begin{vmatrix} a & b \\ c & d \end{vmatrix}$

2 EXAMPLE Evaluating the Determinant of a 2 × 2 Matrix

Evaluate each determinant.

a. $\det \begin{bmatrix} -3 & 4 \\ 2 & -5 \end{bmatrix} = \begin{vmatrix} -3 & 4 \\ 2 & -5 \end{vmatrix} = (-3)(-5) - (4)(2) = 15 - 8 = 7$

b. $\det \begin{bmatrix} 2 & -3 \\ 3 & -2 \end{bmatrix} = \begin{vmatrix} 2 & -3 \\ 3 & -2 \end{vmatrix} = (2)(-2) - (-3)(3) = -4 - (-9) = 5$

c. $\det \begin{bmatrix} a & 0 \\ 0 & a \end{bmatrix} = \begin{vmatrix} a & 0 \\ 0 & a \end{vmatrix} = a^2 - 0 = a^2$

Check Understanding **2** Evaluate the determinant of each matrix.

a. $\begin{bmatrix} 4 & 2 \\ 4 & 2 \end{bmatrix}$ **b.** $\begin{bmatrix} 8 & 7 \\ 2 & 3 \end{bmatrix}$ **c.** $\begin{bmatrix} k & 3 \\ 3 - k & -3 \end{bmatrix}$

The following test will help you determine whether a 2×2 matrix has an inverse. The test will also help you find the inverse, if it exists.

Key Concepts

Definition **Inverse of a 2×2 Matrix**

Let $A = \begin{bmatrix} a & b \\ c & d \end{bmatrix}$. If $\det A \neq 0$, then A has an inverse.

If $\det A \neq 0$, then $A^{-1} = \frac{1}{\det A}\begin{bmatrix} d & -b \\ -c & a \end{bmatrix} = \frac{1}{ad - bc}\begin{bmatrix} d & -b \\ -c & a \end{bmatrix}$.

3 EXAMPLE Finding an Inverse Matrix

Determine whether each matrix has an inverse. If an inverse matrix exists, find it.

a. $M = \begin{bmatrix} -2 & 2 \\ 5 & -4 \end{bmatrix}$

$ad - bc = (-2)(-4) - (2)(5)$ **Find det *M*.**

$= -2$ **Simplify.**

Since $\det M \neq 0$, the inverse of M exists.

$M^{-1} = \begin{bmatrix} -2 & 2 \\ 5 & -4 \end{bmatrix}^{-1}$ (**Change signs.** **Switch positions.**)

$= \frac{1}{\det M}\begin{bmatrix} -4 & -2 \\ -5 & -2 \end{bmatrix}$ **Use the determinant to write the inverse.**

$= \frac{1}{-2}\begin{bmatrix} -4 & -2 \\ -5 & -2 \end{bmatrix}$ **Substitute −2 for det *M*.**

$= \begin{bmatrix} 2 & 1 \\ 2.5 & 1 \end{bmatrix}$ **Multiply.**

b. $N = \begin{bmatrix} 3 & 9 \\ 2 & 6 \end{bmatrix}$

$ad - bc = (3)(6) - (9)(2)$ **Find det *N*.**

$= 0$ **Simplify.**

Since $\det N = 0$, the inverse of N does *not* exist.

Check Understanding **3** Determine whether each matrix has an inverse. If an inverse matrix exists, find it.

a. $\begin{bmatrix} 2 & 4 \\ 1 & 3 \end{bmatrix}$ **b.** $\begin{bmatrix} 0.5 & 2.3 \\ 3 & 7.2 \end{bmatrix}$

OBJECTIVE

2 Using Inverse Matrices to Solve Equations

If the inverse of matrix A exists, you can use it to solve matrix equations of the form $AX = B$. Multiply each side of the equation by A^{-1} to find X.

$AX = B$

$A^{-1}(AX) = A^{-1}B$ **Multiply each side by A^{-1}.**

$(A^{-1}A)X = A^{-1}B$ **Associative Property of Multiplication**

$IX = A^{-1}B$ **definition of multiplicative inverse**

$X = A^{-1}B$ **definition of multiplicative identity**

4 EXAMPLE Solving a Matrix Equation

Solve $\begin{bmatrix} -2 & -5 \\ 1 & 3 \end{bmatrix} X = \begin{bmatrix} -2 \\ 2 \end{bmatrix}$ for the matrix X.

The matrix equation has the form $AX = B$. First find A^{-1}.

$$A^{-1} = \frac{1}{ad - bc}\begin{bmatrix} d & -b \\ -c & a \end{bmatrix} = \frac{1}{-2(3) - (-5)1}\begin{bmatrix} 3 & 5 \\ -1 & -2 \end{bmatrix}$$ **Use the definition of inverse.**

$$= \begin{bmatrix} -3 & -5 \\ 1 & 2 \end{bmatrix}$$ **Simplify.**

Use the equation $X = A^{-1}B$. $$X = \begin{bmatrix} -3 & -5 \\ 1 & 2 \end{bmatrix}\begin{bmatrix} -2 \\ 2 \end{bmatrix}$$ **Substitute.**

$$= \begin{bmatrix} -3(-2) + -5(2) \\ 1(-2) + 2(2) \end{bmatrix} = \begin{bmatrix} -4 \\ 2 \end{bmatrix}$$ **Multiply and simplify.**

Check $$\begin{bmatrix} -2 & -5 \\ 1 & 3 \end{bmatrix} X = \begin{bmatrix} -2 \\ 2 \end{bmatrix}$$ **Use the original equation.**

$$\begin{bmatrix} -2 & -5 \\ 1 & 3 \end{bmatrix}\begin{bmatrix} -4 \\ 2 \end{bmatrix} \stackrel{?}{=} \begin{bmatrix} -2 \\ 2 \end{bmatrix}$$ **Substitute.**

$$\begin{bmatrix} -2(-4) + (-5)(2) \\ 1(-4) + 3(2) \end{bmatrix} \stackrel{?}{=} \begin{bmatrix} -2 \\ 2 \end{bmatrix}$$ **Multiply.**

$$\begin{bmatrix} -2 \\ 2 \end{bmatrix} = \begin{bmatrix} -2 \\ 2 \end{bmatrix} \checkmark$$ **Simplify.**

Check Understanding 4 Solve each matrix equation in the form $AX = B$. Use the equation $X = A^{-1}B$.

a. $\begin{bmatrix} 3 & -4 \\ 4 & -5 \end{bmatrix} X = \begin{bmatrix} 0 & -22 \\ 0 & -28 \end{bmatrix}$ **b.** $\begin{bmatrix} 7 & 5 \\ 3 & 2 \end{bmatrix} X = \begin{bmatrix} -9 \\ -4 \end{bmatrix}$

You can use matrices to make predictions about trends.

5 EXAMPLE Real-World Connection

Communications The diagram shows the trends in cell phone ownership over four consecutive years.

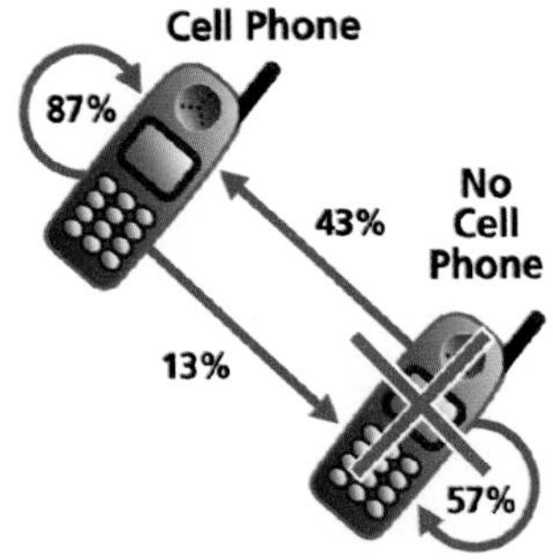

a. Write a matrix to represent the changes (or transitions) in cell phone use.

		From No cell	From Cell
To	No cell	0.57	0.13
	Cell	0.43	0.87

Write the percents as decimals.

b. In a stable population of 16,000 people, 9927 own cell phones, while 6073 do not. Assume the trends continue. Predict the number of people who will own cell phones next year.

$$\begin{matrix} \text{No cell} \\ \text{Cell} \end{matrix}\begin{bmatrix} 6073 \\ 9927 \end{bmatrix}$$ **Write the information in a matrix.**

$$\begin{bmatrix} 0.57 & 0.13 \\ 0.43 & 0.87 \end{bmatrix}\begin{bmatrix} 6073 \\ 9927 \end{bmatrix} \approx \begin{bmatrix} 4752 \\ 11{,}248 \end{bmatrix}$$ **Use the transition matrix from part (a). Multiply.**

Next year, about 11,248 people in the population will own cell phones.

Real-World Connection

Martin Cooper invented the portable cellular radio telephone in 1973.

c. Use the inverse of the matrix from part (a) to find the number of people who owned cell phones last year.

$$\begin{bmatrix} 0.57 & 0.13 \\ 0.43 & 0.87 \end{bmatrix}^{-1} \begin{bmatrix} 6073 \\ 9927 \end{bmatrix} = \begin{bmatrix} 9075 \\ 6925 \end{bmatrix}$$

Last year, 6925 people owned cell phones.

Check Understanding 5 **a. Critical Thinking** Find the percent of the population owning cell phones last year, this year, and next year. Estimate the percent two years from now.

b. Use the answer to Example 5, part (b), and the transition matrix to predict the number of people who will own cell phones two years from now.

c. Use the answer to Example 5, part (c), and the inverse of the transition matrix to estimate the number of people who owned cell phones two years ago.

EXERCISES

For more practice, see *Extra Practice.*

Practice and Problem Solving

A Practice by Example

Example 1 (page 196)

Show that the matrices are multiplicative inverses.

1. $\begin{bmatrix} 3 & 2 \\ 4 & 3 \end{bmatrix}, \begin{bmatrix} 3 & -2 \\ -4 & 3 \end{bmatrix}$

2. $\begin{bmatrix} -3 & 7 \\ -2 & 5 \end{bmatrix}, \begin{bmatrix} -5 & 7 \\ -2 & 3 \end{bmatrix}$

3. $\begin{bmatrix} \frac{1}{5} & -\frac{1}{10} \\ 0 & \frac{1}{4} \end{bmatrix}, \begin{bmatrix} 5 & 2 \\ 0 & 4 \end{bmatrix}$

Example 2 (page 196)

Evaluate the determinant of each matrix.

4. $\begin{bmatrix} 7 & 2 \\ 0 & -3 \end{bmatrix}$

5. $\begin{bmatrix} 6 & 2 \\ -6 & -2 \end{bmatrix}$

6. $\begin{bmatrix} 0 & 0.5 \\ 1.5 & 2 \end{bmatrix}$

7. $\begin{bmatrix} \frac{1}{2} & \frac{2}{3} \\ \frac{3}{5} & \frac{1}{4} \end{bmatrix}$

8. $\begin{bmatrix} -1 & 3 \\ 5 & 2 \end{bmatrix}$

9. $\begin{bmatrix} -2 & 0 \\ 2 & -1 \end{bmatrix}$

10. $\begin{bmatrix} 5 & 3 \\ -2 & 1 \end{bmatrix}$

11. $\begin{bmatrix} 5 & 2 \\ 1 & 3 \end{bmatrix}$

12. $\begin{bmatrix} 2 & -1 \\ 5 & -4 \end{bmatrix}$

13. $\begin{bmatrix} -4 & 3 \\ 2 & 0 \end{bmatrix}$

Example 3 (page 197)

Determine whether each matrix has an inverse. If an inverse matrix exists, find it.

14. $\begin{bmatrix} 2 & -1 \\ 1 & 0 \end{bmatrix}$

15. $\begin{bmatrix} 2 & 3 \\ 1 & 1 \end{bmatrix}$

16. $\begin{bmatrix} 2 & 3 \\ 2 & 4 \end{bmatrix}$

17. $\begin{bmatrix} 1 & 3 \\ 2 & 0 \end{bmatrix}$

18. $\begin{bmatrix} 6 & -8 \\ -3 & 4 \end{bmatrix}$

19. $\begin{bmatrix} 4 & 8 \\ -3 & -2 \end{bmatrix}$

20. $\begin{bmatrix} -1.5 & 3 \\ 2.5 & -0.5 \end{bmatrix}$

21. $\begin{bmatrix} 1 & -2 \\ 3 & 0 \end{bmatrix}$

Example 4 (page 198)

Solve each matrix equation. If an equation cannot be solved, explain why.

22. $\begin{bmatrix} 12 & 7 \\ 5 & 3 \end{bmatrix} X = \begin{bmatrix} 2 & -1 \\ 3 & 2 \end{bmatrix}$

23. $\begin{bmatrix} 0 & -4 \\ 0 & -1 \end{bmatrix} X = \begin{bmatrix} 0 \\ 4 \end{bmatrix}$

24. $\begin{bmatrix} 5 & -3 \\ 4 & -2 \end{bmatrix} X = \begin{bmatrix} 5 \\ 10 \end{bmatrix}$

Example 5 (pages 198–199)

25. Data Analysis Use the information in the diagram.

a. Write a transition matrix to represent the changes in cable television subscribers.

b. In a stable population of 30,000 people, 20,000 people subscribe to cable television, while 10,000 do not. Predict the number of people who will subscribe to cable television next year.

c. Use the inverse of the matrix from part (a) to find the number of people who subscribed to cable television last year.

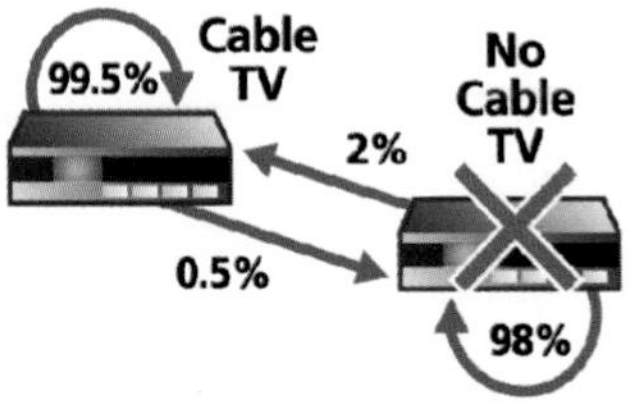

B Apply Your Skills

Evaluate each determinant.

26. $\begin{vmatrix} 4 & 5 \\ -4 & 4 \end{vmatrix}$ **27.** $\begin{vmatrix} -3 & 10 \\ 6 & 20 \end{vmatrix}$ **28.** $\begin{vmatrix} -\frac{1}{2} & 2 \\ -2 & 8 \end{vmatrix}$ **29.** $\begin{vmatrix} 2 & 0 \\ 0 & 1 \end{vmatrix}$ **30.** $\begin{vmatrix} 6 & 9 \\ 3 & 6 \end{vmatrix}$

Determine whether the matrices are multiplicative inverses. If they are not, explain why not.

31. $\begin{bmatrix} 2 & 0.5 \\ 5 & 1 \end{bmatrix}, \begin{bmatrix} -2 & 1 \\ 10 & -4 \end{bmatrix}$ **32.** $\begin{bmatrix} -3 & 4 \\ 6 & -8 \end{bmatrix}, \begin{bmatrix} -1 & 0 \\ 5 & 2 \end{bmatrix}$ **33.** $\begin{bmatrix} -2 & -5 \\ -2 & -4 \end{bmatrix}, \begin{bmatrix} -2.5 & 2 \\ 1 & -1 \end{bmatrix}$

Determine whether each matrix has an inverse. If an inverse matrix exists, find it. If it does not exist, explain why not.

34. $\begin{bmatrix} 1 & 4 \\ 1 & 3 \end{bmatrix}$ **35.** $\begin{bmatrix} 4 & 7 \\ 3 & 5 \end{bmatrix}$ **36.** $\begin{bmatrix} -3 & 11 \\ 2 & -7 \end{bmatrix}$ **37.** $\begin{bmatrix} 2 & 0 \\ 0 & 2 \end{bmatrix}$

38. $\begin{bmatrix} 0 & 3 \\ 3 & 0 \end{bmatrix}$ **39.** $\begin{bmatrix} -1 & 3 \\ 2 & 0 \end{bmatrix}$ **40.** $\begin{bmatrix} 1 & 2 \\ 2 & 1 \end{bmatrix}$ **41.** $\begin{bmatrix} 3 & 0 \\ 6 & 0 \end{bmatrix}$

Solve each matrix equation.

42. $\begin{bmatrix} 4 & 7 \\ 1 & 2 \end{bmatrix} X + \begin{bmatrix} 2 & 7 \\ -3 & 4 \end{bmatrix} = \begin{bmatrix} 6 & 2 \\ -2 & 3 \end{bmatrix}$ **43.** $\begin{bmatrix} 1 & 9 \\ 6 & -6 \end{bmatrix} = \begin{bmatrix} -7 & -9 \\ 4 & 5 \end{bmatrix} X + \begin{bmatrix} 3 & 4 \\ 4 & -3 \end{bmatrix}$

44. Writing Suppose $A = \begin{bmatrix} a & b \\ c & d \end{bmatrix}$ has an inverse. In your own words, describe how to switch or change the elements of A to write A^{-1}.

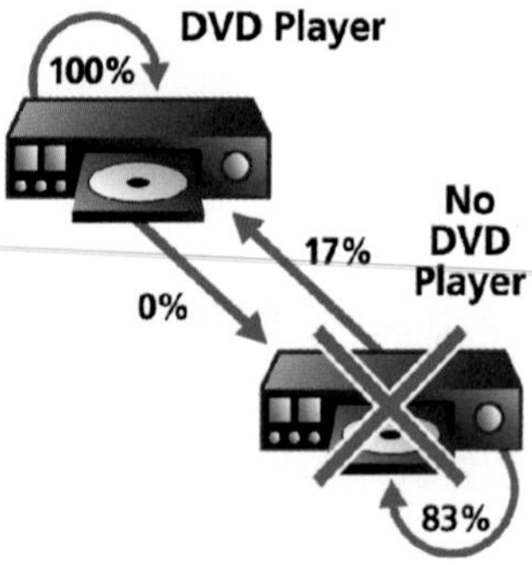

45. Entertainment Use the information in the diagram at the left.
a. Write a transition matrix to represent the changes in DVD-player ownership.
b. In a stable population of 30,000 people, 7000 people own DVD players, while 23,000 do not. Predict the number of people in the population who will own DVD players next year.
c. Use the inverse of the matrix from part (a) to estimate the number of people in the population who owned DVD players last year.
d. Error Analysis A student estimated that the number of people in the population who owned DVD players last year was 8434. What was the student's error?

C Challenge

46. Critical Thinking Suppose $A = \begin{bmatrix} a & b \\ c & d \end{bmatrix}$. For what values of a, b, c, and d will A be its own inverse? (*Hint:* There is more than one correct answer.)

Solve each matrix equation.

47. $-2\begin{bmatrix} -2 & 0 \\ 0 & -1 \end{bmatrix} + \begin{bmatrix} 0 & -3 \\ 5 & -4 \end{bmatrix} X + \begin{bmatrix} 0 & -3 \\ 5 & -4 \end{bmatrix} = \begin{bmatrix} 19 & -27 \\ 10 & -24 \end{bmatrix}$

48. $\begin{bmatrix} 0 & -6 \\ 1 & 2 \end{bmatrix} - \begin{bmatrix} 5 & 2 \\ 4 & 3 \end{bmatrix} X - \begin{bmatrix} 2 & -26 \\ 3 & -18 \end{bmatrix} = \begin{bmatrix} 3 & 25 \\ 2 & 24 \end{bmatrix}$

49. Critical Thinking Explain why $A_{2 \times 3}$ does not have a multiplicative inverse.

50. Let $M = \begin{bmatrix} a & b \\ c & d \end{bmatrix}$ and $N = \begin{bmatrix} e & f \\ g & h \end{bmatrix}$. Prove that the product of the determinants of M and N equals the determinant of the matrix product MN.

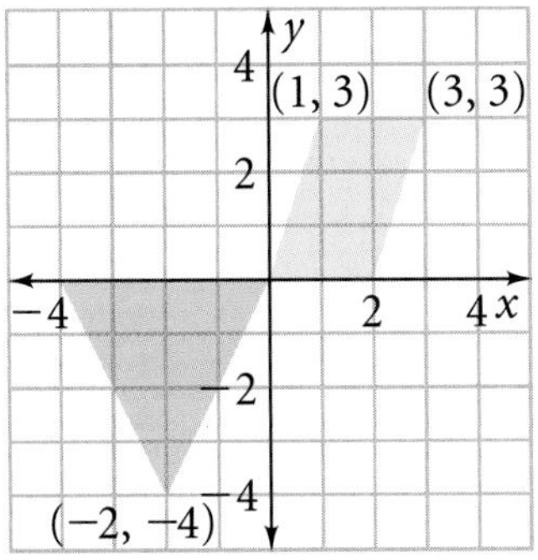

51. a. **Coordinate Geometry** Find the area of the parallelogram at the left.

b. Evaluate the determinant $\begin{vmatrix} 2 & 0 \\ 1 & 3 \end{vmatrix}$. Compare the value of the determinant to the area from part (a).

c. **Make a Conjecture** Consider the triangle at the left to be half a parallelogram. Make a conjecture about its area and the value of $\frac{1}{2}\begin{vmatrix} -4 & 0 \\ -2 & -4 \end{vmatrix}$.

d. **Open-Ended** Graph a different triangle with one vertex at the origin. Find the area of the triangle by writing and evaluating a determinant.

Standardized Test Prep

Gridded Response

52. What is the determinant of $\begin{bmatrix} -2 & -3 \\ 5 & 0 \end{bmatrix}$?

53. What is the determinant of $\begin{bmatrix} \frac{1}{10} & \frac{1}{5} \\ \frac{1}{8} & \frac{1}{3} \end{bmatrix}$? Enter your answer as a fraction.

54. If $A = \begin{bmatrix} 4 & 2 \\ -3 & -1 \end{bmatrix}$, and the inverse of A is $x\begin{bmatrix} -1 & -2 \\ 3 & 4 \end{bmatrix}$, what is the value of x? Enter your answer as a fraction.

55. If $B = \begin{bmatrix} 4 & -1 \\ 2 & 0 \end{bmatrix}$, what is det B^{-1}?

Take It to the NET
Online lesson quiz at
www.PHSchool.com
Web Code: aga-0405

Mixed Review

Lesson 4-4

Each matrix represents the vertices of a polygon. Write a matrix to represent the vertices of the image after each transformation.

56. $\begin{bmatrix} 0 & 0 & 5 \\ 0 & -4 & 0 \end{bmatrix}$; rotation of 90°

57. $\begin{bmatrix} -2 & -5 & 0 \\ 0 & 3 & 5 \end{bmatrix}$; reflection in $y = x$

58. $\begin{bmatrix} 5 & 3 & 2 \\ 7 & 1 & 3 \end{bmatrix}$; 2 units left, 1 unit down

59. $\begin{bmatrix} -3 & -2 & -1 \\ 4 & 1 & 5 \end{bmatrix}$; dilation of 2

Lesson 3-6

Solve each system by substitution.

60. $\begin{cases} x = 5 \\ x - y + z = 5 \\ x + y - z = -5 \end{cases}$

61. $\begin{cases} x - 3y = 2z \\ x + 2y - z = 0 \\ x + y + z = 10 \end{cases}$

62. $\begin{cases} 3x + 3y - z = 9 \\ 2y = x - z \\ x - y + 5z = 9 \end{cases}$

Lesson 2-4

63. a. **Exercise** Suppose you begin a training program by walking 2 miles every day. During the first week, the walk takes you 40 minutes per day. Each week after that, you reduce your time by one minute. Write a linear model for the number of minutes you take to walk 2 miles in week w.

b. **Critical Thinking** Can you continue to improve at the same rate? Explain.

4-6 3 × 3 Matrices, Determinants, and Inverses

North Carolina Objectives

1.04 Operate with matrices to model and solve problems.

Lesson Preview

What You'll Learn

OBJECTIVE 1 To evaluate determinants of 3 × 3 matrices

OBJECTIVE 2 To use inverse matrices in solving matrix equations

. . . And Why

To decode messages, as in Example 5

Check Skills You'll Need

(For help, go to Skills Handbook page 845.)

Find the product of the red elements in each matrix.

1. $\begin{bmatrix} 2 & 3 & 0 \\ -1 & 3 & -2 \\ 4 & -3 & -4 \end{bmatrix}$ **2.** $\begin{bmatrix} 2 & 3 & 0 \\ -1 & 3 & -2 \\ 4 & -3 & -4 \end{bmatrix}$ **3.** $\begin{bmatrix} 2 & 3 & 0 \\ -1 & 3 & -2 \\ 4 & -3 & -4 \end{bmatrix}$

4. $\begin{bmatrix} 2 & 3 & 0 \\ -1 & 3 & -2 \\ 4 & -3 & -4 \end{bmatrix}$ **5.** $\begin{bmatrix} 2 & 3 & 0 \\ -1 & 3 & -2 \\ 4 & -3 & -4 \end{bmatrix}$ **6.** $\begin{bmatrix} 2 & 3 & 0 \\ -1 & 3 & -2 \\ 4 & -3 & -4 \end{bmatrix}$

Interactive lesson includes instant self-check, tutorials, and activities.

OBJECTIVE 1 Evaluating Determinants of 3 × 3 Matrices

As you learned in Lesson 4-5, the determinant of a matrix helps you to find an inverse matrix and solve a matrix equation.

Key Concepts

Definition **The Determinant of a 3 × 3 Matrix**

The determinant of a 3 × 3 matrix $\begin{bmatrix} a_1 & b_1 & c_1 \\ a_2 & b_2 & c_2 \\ a_3 & b_3 & c_3 \end{bmatrix}$ is

$$\begin{vmatrix} a_1 & b_1 & c_1 \\ a_2 & b_2 & c_2 \\ a_3 & b_3 & c_3 \end{vmatrix} = (a_1b_2c_3 + a_2b_3c_1 + a_3b_1c_2) - (a_1b_3c_2 + a_2b_1c_3 + a_3b_2c_1)$$

Visualize the pattern this way:

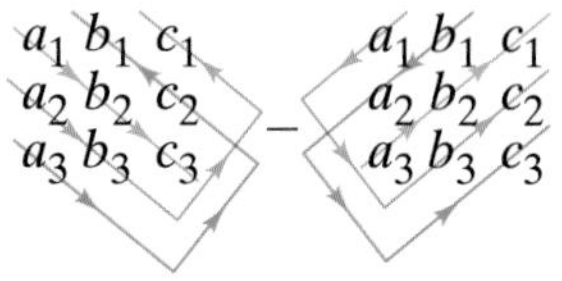

1 EXAMPLE Evaluating the Determinant of a 3 × 3 Matrix

Evaluate the determinant of $F = \begin{bmatrix} -1 & 3 & 5 \\ 2 & -4 & 6 \\ 0 & 1 & -1 \end{bmatrix}$.

$$\begin{vmatrix} -1 & 3 & 5 \\ 2 & -4 & 6 \\ 0 & 1 & -1 \end{vmatrix} = [-1(-4)(-1) + 2(1)(5) + 0(3)(6)] - [-1(1)(6) + 2(3)(-1) + 0(-4)(5)]$$ **Use the definition.**

$$= [-4 + 10 + 0] - [-6 + (-6) + 0]$$ **Multiply.**

$$= 6 - (-12) = 18$$ **Simplify.**

The determinant of F is 18.

Check Understanding **1** Evaluate each determinant.

a. $\begin{vmatrix} -3 & 4 & 0 \\ 2 & -5 & 1 \\ 0 & 2 & 3 \end{vmatrix}$ **b.** $\begin{vmatrix} 1 & -1 & 2 \\ 0 & 4 & 2 \\ 3 & -6 & 10 \end{vmatrix}$ **c.** $\begin{vmatrix} 2 & 0 & -1 \\ 0 & 0 & 0 \\ 1 & -5 & 3 \end{vmatrix}$

You can use a graphing calculator to evaluate the determinant of a 3×3 matrix.

2 EXAMPLE Using a Graphing Calculator

Enter matrix A into your graphing calculator. Use the matrix submenus to evaluate the determinant of A.

$$A = \begin{bmatrix} 1 & 7 & 2 \\ -1 & 1 & -2 \\ 1 & 1 & 1 \end{bmatrix}$$

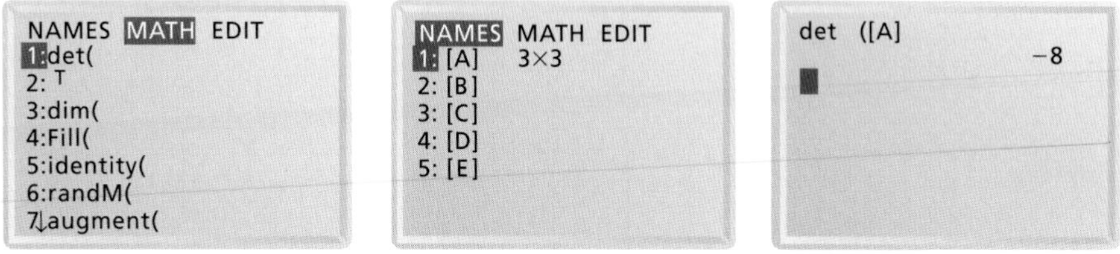

Check Understanding **2** Use a graphing calculator to evaluate the determinant of $\begin{bmatrix} 13 & 21 & 11 \\ -2 & 4 & -1 \\ 17 & -2 & 0 \end{bmatrix}$.

OBJECTIVE 2

Using Inverse 3 × 3 Matrices

Like 2×2 matrices, some 3×3 matrices do not have inverses.

3 EXAMPLE Verifying Inverses

Determine whether the matrices are multiplicative inverses.

Need Help?
If A and B are inverse matrices, then $AB = BA = I$.

a. $A = \begin{bmatrix} 1 & 5 & -1 \\ 1 & 0 & -1 \\ 1 & 0 & 0 \end{bmatrix}, B = \begin{bmatrix} 0 & 0 & 1 \\ 0.2 & -0.2 & 0 \\ 0 & -1 & 1 \end{bmatrix}$

$$\begin{bmatrix} 1 & 5 & -1 \\ 1 & 0 & -1 \\ 1 & 0 & 0 \end{bmatrix}\begin{bmatrix} 0 & 0 & 1 \\ 0.2 & -0.2 & 0 \\ 0 & -1 & 1 \end{bmatrix} = \begin{bmatrix} 1 & 0 & 0 \\ 0 & 1 & 0 \\ 0 & 0 & 1 \end{bmatrix}$$

Since $AB = I$, A and B are multiplicative inverses.

b. $C = \begin{bmatrix} 3 & 4 & 1 \\ -2 & 0 & 2 \\ 1 & 5 & 3 \end{bmatrix}, D = \begin{bmatrix} 0 & 1 & 0 \\ 1 & 0 & 1 \\ 0 & 1 & 0 \end{bmatrix}$

$$\begin{bmatrix} 3 & 4 & 1 \\ -2 & 0 & 2 \\ 1 & 5 & 3 \end{bmatrix}\begin{bmatrix} 0 & 1 & 0 \\ 1 & 0 & 1 \\ 0 & 1 & 0 \end{bmatrix} = \begin{bmatrix} 4 & 4 & 4 \\ 0 & 0 & 0 \\ 5 & 4 & 5 \end{bmatrix}$$

Since $CD \neq I$, C and D are not multiplicative inverses.

Check Understanding **3** **a.** Verify that A and B are inverses by showing that $BA = I$.
b. Verify that C and D are not inverses by showing that $DC \neq I$.

You can use 3 × 3 matrices to solve matrix equations.

4 EXAMPLE Solving a Matrix Equation

Solve the equation $\begin{bmatrix} 0 & 0 & 2 \\ 1 & 3 & -2 \\ 1 & -2 & 1 \end{bmatrix} X = \begin{bmatrix} 6 \\ -11 \\ 8 \end{bmatrix}$.

Let $A = \begin{bmatrix} 0 & 0 & 2 \\ 1 & 3 & -2 \\ 1 & -2 & 1 \end{bmatrix}$. Find A^{-1}.

```
[A]⁻¹
  [[ .1   .4   .6  ]
   [ .3   .2   -.2 ]
   [ .5   0    0   ]]
```

$$X = \begin{bmatrix} 0.1 & 0.4 & 0.6 \\ 0.3 & 0.2 & -0.2 \\ 0.5 & 0 & 0 \end{bmatrix} \begin{bmatrix} 6 \\ -11 \\ 8 \end{bmatrix}$$

← **Use the equation $X = A^{-1}C$.**

Multiply. →

```
[A]⁻¹[C]
     [[1 ]
      [-2]
      [3 ]]
```

$$X = \begin{bmatrix} 1 \\ -2 \\ 3 \end{bmatrix}$$

Check Understanding 4 **a.** Verify that A and A^{-1} are inverses.

b. Solve the equation $\begin{bmatrix} 0 & 0 & 2 \\ 1 & 3 & -2 \\ 1 & -2 & 1 \end{bmatrix} X = \begin{bmatrix} 0 \\ -6 \\ 19 \end{bmatrix}$.

You can use 3 × 3 matrices to encode and decode messages.

A	26	N	13
B	25	O	12
C	24	P	11
D	23	Q	10
E	22	R	9
F	21	S	8
G	20	T	7
H	19	U	6
I	18	V	5
J	17	W	4
K	16	X	3
L	15	Y	2
M	14	Z	1

$$E = \begin{bmatrix} 0.5 & 0.5 & 0.5 \\ 0.25 & 0.25 & -0.25 \\ 0.5 & 0 & -0.5 \end{bmatrix}$$

5 EXAMPLE Real-World Connection

Cryptography Use the alphabet table and the encoding matrix at the left.

a. Find the decoding matrix E^{-1}.

```
[E]⁻¹
  [[  1   -2    2   ]
   [  0   4    -2   ]
   [  1   -2    0   ]]
```

Use a graphing calculator.

b. Decode $\begin{bmatrix} 22.5 & 26 & 15.5 \\ 0.25 & 9 & 7.75 \\ -4 & 9 & 3.5 \end{bmatrix}$. Zero indicates a space holder.

$$\begin{bmatrix} 1 & -2 & 2 \\ 0 & 4 & -2 \\ 1 & -2 & 0 \end{bmatrix} \begin{bmatrix} 22.5 & 26 & 15.5 \\ 0.25 & 9 & 7.75 \\ -4 & 9 & 3.5 \end{bmatrix} = \begin{bmatrix} 14 & 26 & 7 \\ 9 & 18 & 24 \\ 22 & 8 & 0 \end{bmatrix}$$

Use the decoding matrix from part (a). Multiply.

The numbers 14 26 7 9 18 24 22 8 0 correspond to the letters MATRICES.

Check Understanding 5 **Literature** Use the information from Example 5. Decode the matrix at the right, which gives the title of a Pablo Neruda poem. Zero indicates a space between words.

$$\begin{bmatrix} 21 & 10.5 \\ 6 & 4.25 \\ 1 & 5 \end{bmatrix}$$

EXERCISES

For more practice, see *Extra Practice.*

Practice and Problem Solving

A Practice by Example

Example 1 (page 202)

Evaluate the determinant of each matrix.

1. $\begin{bmatrix} 1 & 2 & 5 \\ 3 & 1 & 0 \\ 1 & 2 & 1 \end{bmatrix}$ **2.** $\begin{bmatrix} 1 & 4 & 0 \\ 2 & 3 & 5 \\ 0 & 1 & 0 \end{bmatrix}$ **3.** $\begin{bmatrix} -2 & 4 & 1 \\ 3 & 0 & -1 \\ 1 & 2 & 1 \end{bmatrix}$ **4.** $\begin{bmatrix} 2 & 3 & 0 \\ 1 & 2 & 5 \\ 7 & 0 & 1 \end{bmatrix}$

Example 2 (page 203)

Use a graphing calculator to evaluate the determinant of each 3 × 3 matrix.

5. $\begin{bmatrix} 1 & 0 & 0 \\ 0 & 1 & 0 \\ 0 & 0 & 1 \end{bmatrix}$ **6.** $\begin{bmatrix} 0 & -2 & -3 \\ 1 & 2 & 4 \\ -2 & 0 & 1 \end{bmatrix}$ **7.** $\begin{bmatrix} 12.2 & 13.3 & 9 \\ 1 & -4 & -17 \\ 21.4 & -15 & 0 \end{bmatrix}$

Example 3 (page 203)

Determine whether the matrices are multiplicative inverses.

8. $\begin{bmatrix} 1 & 2 & -1 \\ -1.5 & -3 & 1.75 \\ 0 & -1 & 0.5 \end{bmatrix}, \begin{bmatrix} 1 & 0 & 2 \\ 3 & 2 & -1 \\ 6 & 4 & 0 \end{bmatrix}$ **9.** $\begin{bmatrix} 2 & 2 & 2 \\ -2 & 2 & -2 \\ -2 & -2 & -2 \end{bmatrix}, \begin{bmatrix} 2 & 2 & 2 \\ -2 & 2 & -2 \\ -2 & -2 & -2 \end{bmatrix}$

Example 4 (page 204)

Solve each equation.

10. $\begin{bmatrix} 5 & 1 & -4 \\ 2 & -3 & -5 \\ 7 & 2 & -6 \end{bmatrix} X = \begin{bmatrix} 5 \\ 2 \\ 5 \end{bmatrix}$ **11.** $\begin{bmatrix} 6 & 10 & -13 \\ 4 & -2 & 7 \\ 0 & 9 & -8 \end{bmatrix} X = \begin{bmatrix} 84 \\ 18 \\ 56 \end{bmatrix}$

Example 5 (page 204)

Literature **Use the information from Example 5. Decode each title.**

12. Emily Dickinson, $\begin{bmatrix} 23.5 & 12.5 \\ 4.75 & -0.25 \\ 6 & -3.5 \end{bmatrix}$ **13.** E. E. Cummings, $\begin{bmatrix} 18 & 14 & 17.5 \\ 0 & 3.5 & 8.75 \\ -3.5 & 2.5 & 4.5 \end{bmatrix}$

B Apply Your Skills

Verify that each matrix has no inverse.

14. $\begin{bmatrix} 1 & 0 & 1 \\ 0 & 1 & 0 \\ 1 & 0 & 1 \end{bmatrix}$ **15.** $\begin{bmatrix} 0 & 1 & 0 \\ 1 & 0 & 1 \\ 0 & 1 & 0 \end{bmatrix}$ **16.** $\begin{bmatrix} 0 & 1 & 0 \\ 0 & 1 & 0 \\ 1 & 1 & 1 \end{bmatrix}$

Real-World Connection

During World War II, these Navaho code talkers transmitted messages in an unbreakable code.

17. Cryptography Two members of the Hopewell High School math club share messages in code. They use the alphabet table from Example 5.

a. One of the students has lost her encoding matrix. Luckily, she remembers that the decoding matrix is

$E^{-1} = \begin{bmatrix} 1 & -1 & 0 \\ 0 & 1 & -1 \\ 0 & 0 & 1 \end{bmatrix}$. Compute E to find the encoding matrix.

b. Use your answer to part (a) to encode the message MATH IS COOL.

c. Open-Ended Use the encoding matrix from part (a) to encode a short sentence. Use the decoding matrix to check your work.

Evaluate the determinant of each matrix.

18. $\begin{bmatrix} 0 & 2 & -3 \\ 1 & 2 & 4 \\ -2 & 0 & 1 \end{bmatrix}$ **19.** $\begin{bmatrix} 5 & 1 & 0 \\ 0 & 2 & -1 \\ -2 & -3 & 1 \end{bmatrix}$ **20.** $\begin{bmatrix} 4 & 6 & -1 \\ 2 & 3 & 2 \\ 1 & -1 & 1 \end{bmatrix}$ **21.** $\begin{bmatrix} -3 & 2 & -1 \\ 2 & 5 & 2 \\ 1 & -2 & 0 \end{bmatrix}$

Find the inverse of each matrix, if it exists.

22. $\begin{bmatrix} -2 & 1 & -1 \\ 2 & 0 & 4 \\ 0 & 2 & 5 \end{bmatrix}$ **23.** $\begin{bmatrix} 2 & 0 & -1 \\ -1 & -1 & 1 \\ 3 & 2 & 0 \end{bmatrix}$ **24.** $\begin{bmatrix} 0 & 0 & 2 \\ 1 & 4 & -2 \\ 3 & -2 & 1 \end{bmatrix}$ **25.** $\begin{bmatrix} 1 & 2 & 6 \\ 1 & -1 & 0 \\ 1 & 0 & 2 \end{bmatrix}$

26. Writing Evaluate the determinant of each matrix. Describe any patterns.

a. $\begin{bmatrix} 1 & 2 & 3 \\ 1 & 2 & 3 \\ 1 & 2 & 3 \end{bmatrix}$ **b.** $\begin{bmatrix} -1 & -2 & -3 \\ -3 & -2 & -1 \\ -1 & -2 & -3 \end{bmatrix}$ **c.** $\begin{bmatrix} 1 & 2 & 3 \\ 2 & 3 & 1 \\ 1 & 2 & 3 \end{bmatrix}$ **d.** $\begin{bmatrix} -1 & 2 & -3 \\ 2 & -3 & -1 \\ -1 & 2 & -3 \end{bmatrix}$

C Challenge

Literature **Use the table and decoding matrix from Example 5. Decode each title.**

27. Maya Angelou, $\begin{bmatrix} 26.5 & 28 & 15.5 & 16.5 & 13.5 \\ 0.25 & 2 & -3.25 & 8.25 & 6.75 \\ -6 & -6 & -6.5 & 6.5 & 9 \end{bmatrix}$

28. Oliver Wendell Holmes, $\begin{bmatrix} 19 & 24 & 24.5 & 18.5 & 26.5 & 13.5 & 19.5 & 20 \\ 6.5 & 8.5 & 3.25 & 1.75 & 10.25 & 2.75 & 9.75 & 10 \\ 0.5 & 6 & 2 & -7.5 & 9 & 5.5 & 13 & 7 \end{bmatrix}$

Maya Angelou—poet, educator, historian, novelist, actress, and playwright

Solve each equation.

29. $\begin{bmatrix} 7 & -5 & 3 \\ 0 & 1 & 3 \\ 8 & 4 & -2 \end{bmatrix} X + \begin{bmatrix} 5 \\ -9 \\ 0 \end{bmatrix} = \begin{bmatrix} 54 \\ -12 \\ 96 \end{bmatrix}$

30. $\begin{bmatrix} -1 & 0 & 2 \\ -6 & -5 & 0 \\ 1 & 4 & 1 \end{bmatrix} - \begin{bmatrix} -4 & 0 & 2 \\ 0 & 3 & 6 \\ 0 & 5 & 0 \end{bmatrix} X = \begin{bmatrix} -21 & 10 & 26 \\ -54 & 1 & -15 \\ 1 & 4 & -24 \end{bmatrix}$

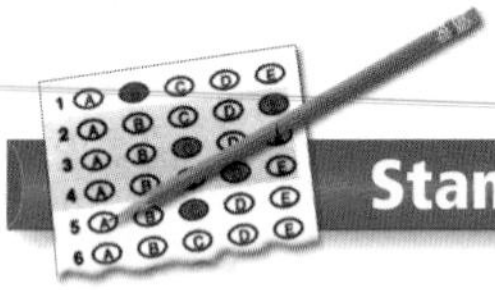

Standardized Test Prep

Multiple Choice

31. What is the determinant of $\begin{bmatrix} 5 & 0 & 0 \\ 0 & 5 & 0 \\ 0 & 0 & 5 \end{bmatrix}$?

A. 5 **B.** 25 **C.** 125 **D.** 555

Quantitative Comparison

Compare the boxed quantity in Column A with the boxed quantity in Column B. Choose the best answer.

A. The quantity in Column A is greater.
B. The quantity in Column B is greater.
C. The two quantities are equal.
D. The relationship cannot be determined from the information given.

	Column A	Column B
32.	$\begin{vmatrix} 1 & 0 & 5 \\ -5 & 0 & -1 \\ 0 & 5 & 0 \end{vmatrix}$	$\begin{vmatrix} -1 & 0 & -5 \\ -5 & 0 & -1 \\ 0 & -5 & 0 \end{vmatrix}$
33.	$\begin{vmatrix} 2 & 0 & 3 \\ 4 & 0 & 1 \\ 0 & 2 & 1 \end{vmatrix}$	$\begin{vmatrix} -2 & 0 & -3 \\ -4 & 0 & -1 \\ 0 & -2 & -1 \end{vmatrix}$

Take It to the NET
Online lesson quiz at **www.PHSchool.com**
Web Code: aga-0406

Mixed Review

Lesson 4-5 **Determine whether each matrix has an inverse. If an inverse matrix exists, find it.**

34. $\begin{bmatrix} -9 & 3 \\ 4 & 2.5 \end{bmatrix}$ **35.** $\begin{bmatrix} 2 & 3 \\ 8 & 12 \end{bmatrix}$ **36.** $\begin{bmatrix} -3 & 4 \\ 9 & 10 \end{bmatrix}$ **37.** $\begin{bmatrix} 0 & -1 \\ -1 & 0 \end{bmatrix}$

Lesson 3-1 **Solve each system of equations.**

38. $\begin{cases} 2x + 2y = 10 \\ 3x - y = 4 \end{cases}$ **39.** $\begin{cases} -x + y + z = 5 \\ 2x + y - z = 2 \\ 3x + 2y + 4z = 0 \end{cases}$

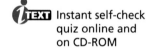

Checkpoint Quiz 2

Lessons 4-4 through 4-6

TEXT Instant self-check quiz online and on CD-ROM

Use $\triangle ABC$ at the right. Find the coordinates of the image under each transformation.

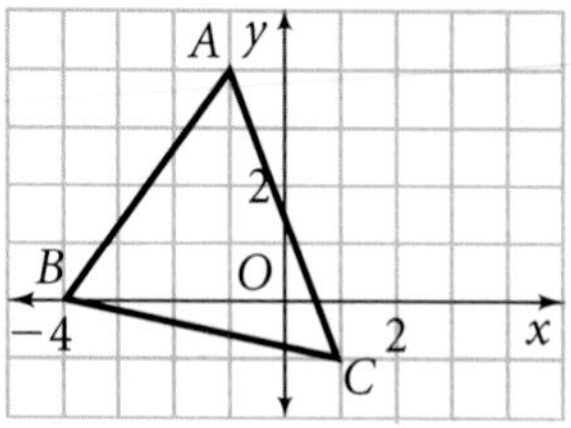

1. a dilation twice the original size

2. a translation 3 units left and 3 units up

3. a rotation of 270°

4. a reflection in $y = -x$

Solve each matrix equation.

5. $\begin{bmatrix} 0 & 3 \\ 5 & 0 \end{bmatrix} X = \begin{bmatrix} -12 & -15 \\ 10 & 15 \end{bmatrix}$ **6.** $\begin{bmatrix} -1 & 2 & 3 \\ 0 & 3 & 2 \\ 3 & -2 & 0 \end{bmatrix} X = \begin{bmatrix} 17 \\ 18 \\ 11 \end{bmatrix}$ **7.** $\begin{bmatrix} 4 & 5 \\ -1 & 5 \end{bmatrix} X = \begin{bmatrix} 32 \\ 42 \end{bmatrix}$

Evaluate the determinant of each matrix.

8. $\begin{bmatrix} -2 & 3 \\ 0 & 5 \end{bmatrix}$ **9.** $\begin{bmatrix} 0 & 5 & 4 \\ -1 & -1 & 3 \\ 2 & 5 & 0 \end{bmatrix}$ **10.** $\begin{bmatrix} -3 & 2 & 0 \\ 4 & 17 & 10 \\ 1 & -5 & -1 \end{bmatrix}$

A Point in Time

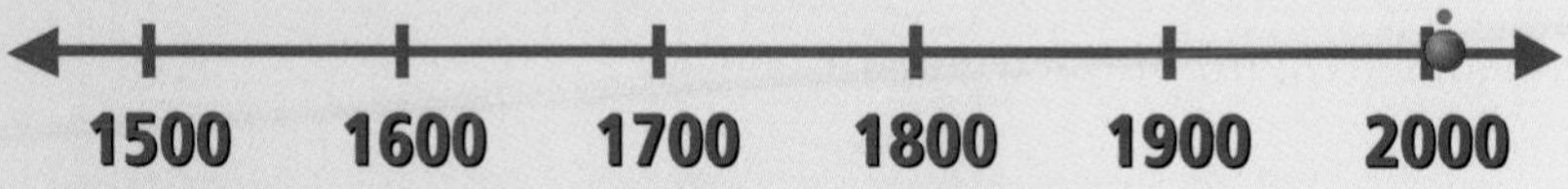

An artist who paints murals creates a sketch and then uses a dilation of the sketch for the actual mural. Judith Francisca Baca is a muralist who serves as the artistic director of the Great Wall of Los Angeles. The 13-ft-by-2400-ft mural, which depicts California's multicultural history, has involved over 400 youths, 100 scholars, and 50 assisting artists.

Take It to the NET For more information about murals, go to **www.PHSchool.com**
Web Code: age-2032

Extension Networks

For Use With Lesson 4-6

A finite graph is a set of points, called vertices, connected by curves, or paths.

You can use a matrix to describe a finite graph. A 1 indicates a path between two vertices or one vertex and itself. A 0 indicates that no path exists between two vertices or from one vertex to itself.

1 EXAMPLE

Write a matrix A to represent the finite graph. Explain the significance of element a_{41}.

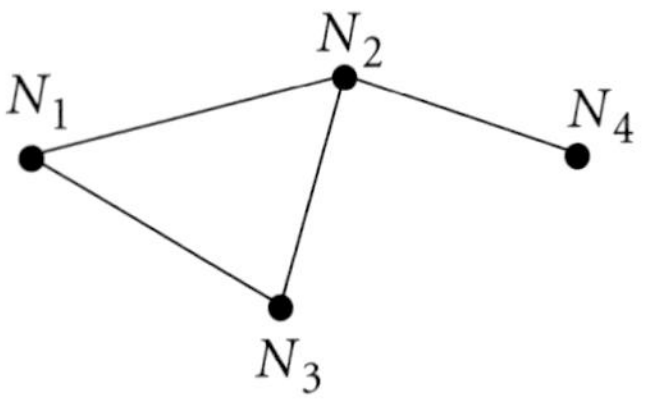

$$A = \begin{array}{c} \\ N_1 \\ N_2 \\ N_3 \\ N_4 \end{array} \begin{array}{c} \begin{array}{cccc} N_1 & N_2 & N_3 & N_4 \end{array} \\ \begin{bmatrix} 0 & 1 & 1 & 0 \\ 1 & 0 & 1 & 1 \\ 1 & 1 & 0 & 0 \\ 0 & 1 & 0 & 0 \end{bmatrix} \end{array}$$

← **There is a path from N_2 to N_4.**

Element a_{41} is 0. It indicates that there is no path between N_4 and N_1.

Directed graphs are finite graphs that indicate the direction of a path. The directed graph at the right below represents the information in the map.

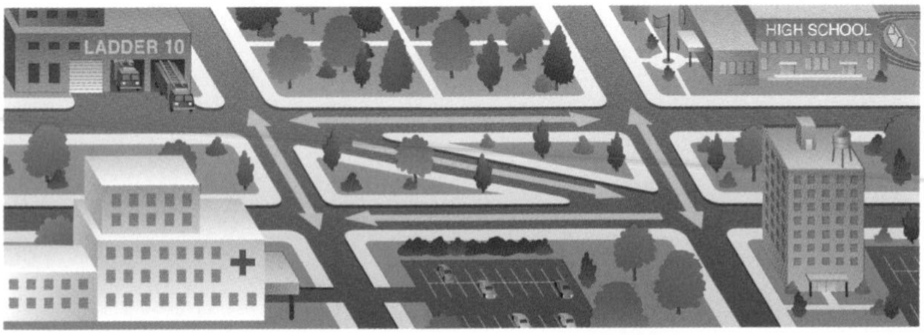

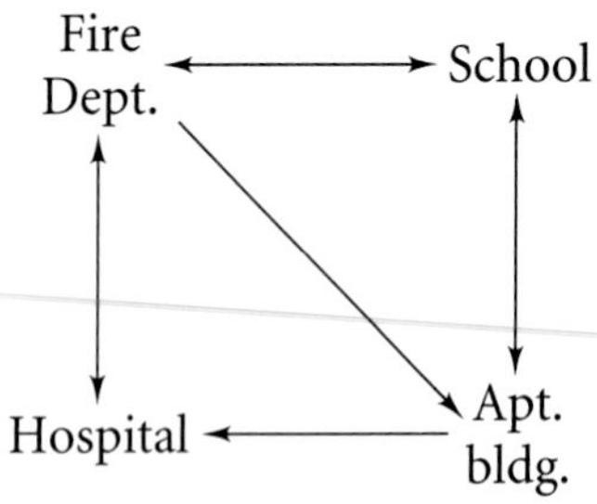

You can use a matrix to represent the information in a directed graph.

2 EXAMPLE

Write a matrix B to represent the information from the directed graph. Compare elements b_{12} and b_{21}.

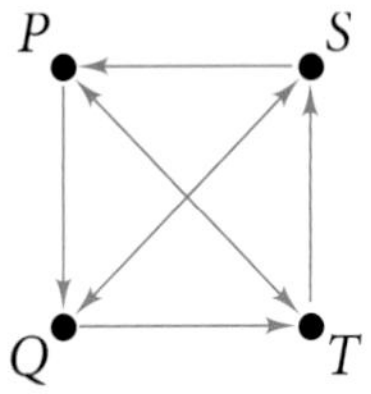

To → $P\ Q\ S\ T$

From →

$$B = \begin{array}{c} P \\ Q \\ S \\ T \end{array} \begin{bmatrix} 0 & 1 & 0 & 1 \\ 0 & 0 & 1 & 1 \\ 1 & 1 & 0 & 0 \\ 1 & 0 & 1 & 0 \end{bmatrix}$$

Element b_{12} is 1, and element b_{21} is 0. The path between P and Q is one way from P to Q.

You can use information in a matrix to draw a directed graph.

3 EXAMPLE

Draw a directed graph to represent the information in the matrix.

$$\begin{array}{r} \text{To}\rightarrow \\ A \\ \text{From}\rightarrow B \\ C \end{array}\begin{array}{c} \begin{array}{ccc} A & B & C \end{array} \\ \begin{bmatrix} 1 & 1 & 1 \\ 1 & 0 & 1 \\ 0 & 0 & 0 \end{bmatrix} \end{array}$$

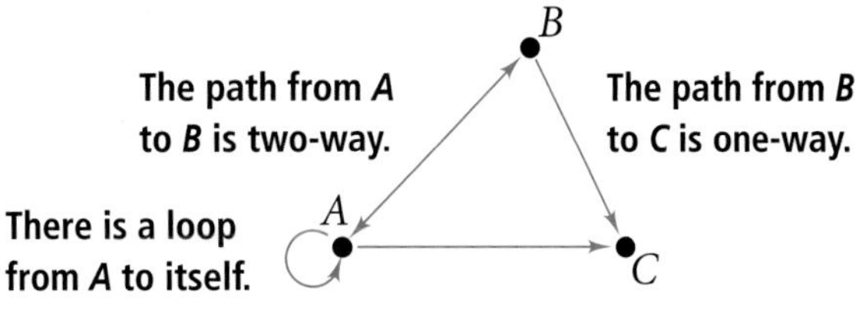

EXERCISES

Write a matrix to represent each finite or directed graph.

1. 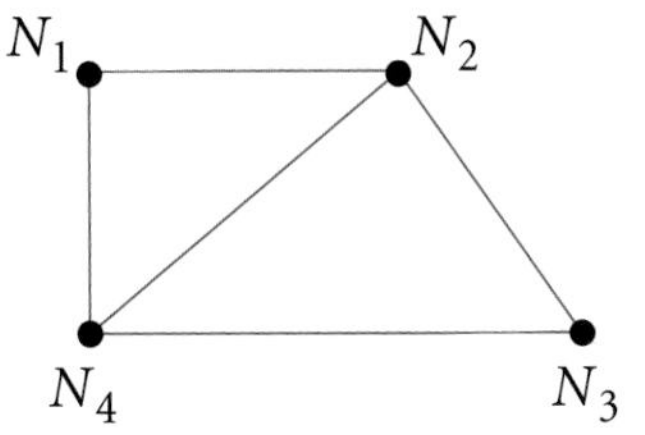

2. 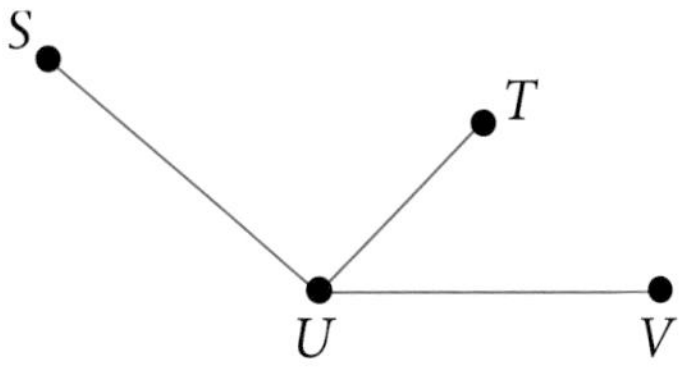

3. 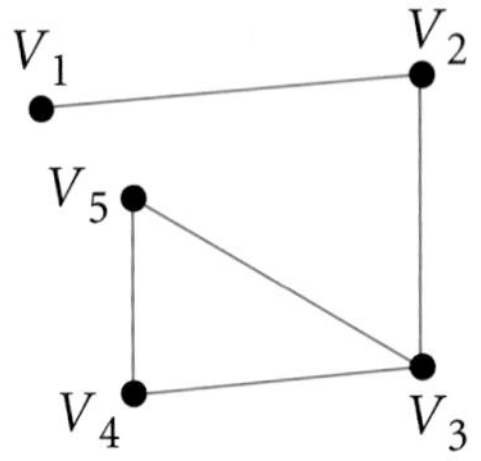

4. 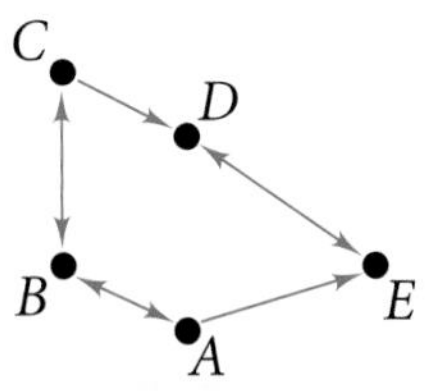

5. 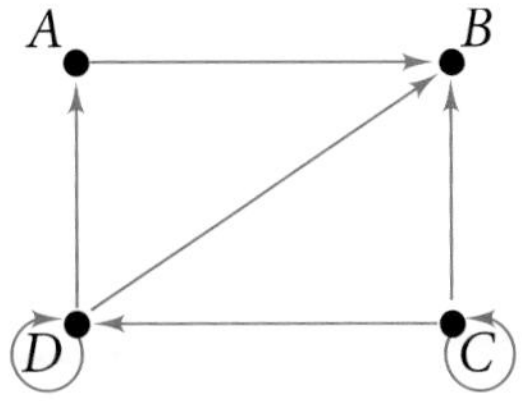

6. 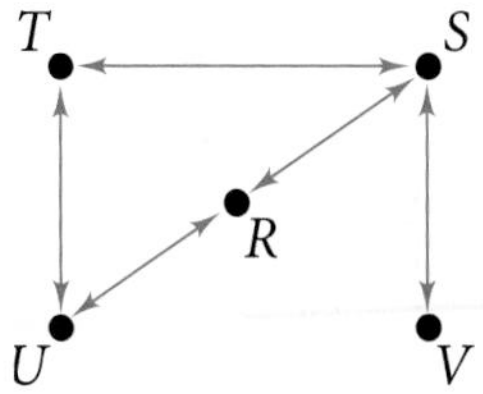

Draw a directed graph to represent the information in each matrix.

7. $\begin{array}{c} \\ J \\ K \\ L \\ M \end{array}\begin{array}{c} \begin{array}{cccc} J & K & L & M \end{array} \\ \begin{bmatrix} 0 & 0 & 0 & 1 \\ 0 & 0 & 1 & 1 \\ 0 & 1 & 0 & 1 \\ 1 & 1 & 1 & 0 \end{bmatrix} \end{array}$

8. $\begin{array}{c} \\ A \\ B \\ C \\ D \end{array}\begin{array}{c} \begin{array}{cccc} A & B & C & D \end{array} \\ \begin{bmatrix} 0 & 0 & 1 & 1 \\ 1 & 1 & 0 & 0 \\ 0 & 1 & 0 & 1 \\ 1 & 0 & 1 & 0 \end{bmatrix} \end{array}$

9. $\begin{array}{c} \\ N_1 \\ N_2 \\ N_3 \\ N_4 \end{array}\begin{array}{c} \begin{array}{cccc} N_1 & N_2 & N_3 & N_4 \end{array} \\ \begin{bmatrix} 1 & 1 & 1 & 1 \\ 0 & 0 & 1 & 1 \\ 1 & 0 & 0 & 0 \\ 0 & 0 & 1 & 0 \end{bmatrix} \end{array}$

10. Travel Alice and Becky live on Parkway East, at the intersections of Owens Bridge and Bay Bridge, respectively. Carl and David live on Parkway West, at the intersections of Bay Bridge and Owens Bridge, respectively. Parkway East is a one-way street running east. Parkway West is one way running west. Both bridges are two way.

a. Draw a directed graph indicating road travel between the houses.

b. Write a matrix T to represent the information in the directed graph.

c. Writing Calculate T^2. What does the new matrix model? Explain.

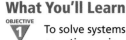

4-7 Inverse Matrices and Systems

North Carolina Objectives

1.04 Operate with matrices to model and solve problems.
2.10 Use systems of two or more equations to model and solve problems. Solve using matrix operations and algebraic properties.

Lesson Preview

What You'll Learn

OBJECTIVE 1 To solve systems of equations using inverse matrices

. . . And Why

To calculate business costs, as in Example 4

Check Skills You'll Need (For help, go to Lesson 3-6.)

Solve each system.

1. $\begin{cases} 5x + y = 14 \\ 4x + 3y = 20 \end{cases}$ **2.** $\begin{cases} x - y - z = -9 \\ 3x + y + 2z = 12 \\ x = y - 2z \end{cases}$ **3.** $\begin{cases} -x + 2y + z = 0 \\ y = -2x + 3 \\ z = 3x \end{cases}$

New Vocabulary • coefficient matrix • variable matrix • constant matrix

Interactive lesson includes instant self-check, tutorials, and activities.

OBJECTIVE 1

Solving Systems of Equations Using Inverse Matrices

You can represent a system of equations with a matrix equation.

System of equations	Matrix equation
$\begin{cases} x + 2y = 5 \\ 3x + 5y = 14 \end{cases}$	$\begin{bmatrix} 1 & 2 \\ 3 & 5 \end{bmatrix}\begin{bmatrix} x \\ y \end{bmatrix} = \begin{bmatrix} 5 \\ 14 \end{bmatrix}$

Each matrix in an equation of the form $AX = B$ has a name.

Coefficient matrix A	Variable matrix X	Constant matrix B
$\begin{bmatrix} 1 & 2 \\ 3 & 5 \end{bmatrix}$	$\begin{bmatrix} x \\ y \end{bmatrix}$	$\begin{bmatrix} 5 \\ 14 \end{bmatrix}$

Need Help?

To review the definitions of *coefficient* and *variable*, go to Lesson 1-2.

1 EXAMPLE Writing a System as a Matrix Equation

Write the system $\begin{cases} -b + 2c = 4 \\ a + b - c = 0 \\ 2a + 3c = 11 \end{cases}$ as a matrix equation. Then identify the coefficient matrix, the variable matrix, and the constant matrix.

Matrix equation: $\begin{bmatrix} 0 & -1 & 2 \\ 1 & 1 & -1 \\ 2 & 0 & 3 \end{bmatrix}\begin{bmatrix} a \\ b \\ c \end{bmatrix} = \begin{bmatrix} 4 \\ 0 \\ 11 \end{bmatrix}$

Coefficient matrix	Variable matrix	Constant matrix
$\begin{bmatrix} 0 & -1 & 2 \\ 1 & 1 & -1 \\ 2 & 0 & 3 \end{bmatrix}$	$\begin{bmatrix} a \\ b \\ c \end{bmatrix}$	$\begin{bmatrix} 4 \\ 0 \\ 11 \end{bmatrix}$

Check Understanding **1** Write each system as a matrix equation. Identify the coefficient matrix, the variable matrix, and the constant matrix.

a. $\begin{cases} 3x + 2y = 16 \\ y = 5 \end{cases}$ **b.** $\begin{cases} x - y + z = 0 \\ x - 2y - z = 5 \\ 2x - y + 2z = 8 \end{cases}$

Sometimes you can find the inverse of the coefficient matrix. Then you can use it to solve systems of equations quickly.

Need Help?

The inverse of $\begin{bmatrix} a & b \\ c & d \end{bmatrix}$ is $\frac{1}{ad - bc}\begin{bmatrix} d & -b \\ -c & a \end{bmatrix}$.

The matrix $\begin{bmatrix} a & b \\ c & d \end{bmatrix}$ has no inverse when $ad - bc = 0$.

2 EXAMPLE Solving a System of Two Equations

Solve the system $\begin{cases} 2x + 3y = 11 \\ x + 2y = 6 \end{cases}$.

$\begin{bmatrix} 2 & 3 \\ 1 & 2 \end{bmatrix}\begin{bmatrix} x \\ y \end{bmatrix} = \begin{bmatrix} 11 \\ 6 \end{bmatrix}$ **Write the system as a matrix equation.**

$A^{-1} = \begin{bmatrix} 2 & -3 \\ -1 & 2 \end{bmatrix}$ **Find A^{-1}.**

$\begin{bmatrix} x \\ y \end{bmatrix} = A^{-1}B = \begin{bmatrix} 2 & -3 \\ -1 & 2 \end{bmatrix}\begin{bmatrix} 11 \\ 6 \end{bmatrix} = \begin{bmatrix} 4 \\ 1 \end{bmatrix}$ **Solve for the variable matrix.**

The solution of the system is (4, 1).

Check			
	$2x + 3y = 11$	$x + 2y = 6$	**Use the original equations.**
	$2(4) + 3(1) \stackrel{?}{=} 11$	$4 + 2(1) \stackrel{?}{=} 6$	**Substitute.**
	$8 + 3 = 11$ ✓	$4 + 2 = 6$ ✓	**Simplify.**

Check Understanding **2** Solve each system. Check your answers.

a. $\begin{cases} 5a + 3b = 7 \\ 3a + 2b = 5 \end{cases}$ **b.** $\begin{cases} x + 3y = 22 \\ 3x + 2y = 10 \end{cases}$

You can use a graphing calculator to solve a system of three equations.

3 EXAMPLE Solving a System of Three Equations

Solve the system $\begin{cases} 2x + y + 3z = 1 \\ 5x + y - 2z = 8 \\ x - y - 9z = 5 \end{cases}$.

Step 1 Write the system as a matrix equation.

$$\begin{bmatrix} 2 & 1 & 3 \\ 5 & 1 & -2 \\ 1 & -1 & -9 \end{bmatrix}\begin{bmatrix} x \\ y \\ z \end{bmatrix} = \begin{bmatrix} 1 \\ 8 \\ 5 \end{bmatrix}$$

Step 2 Store the coefficient matrix as matrix A and the constant matrix as matrix B.

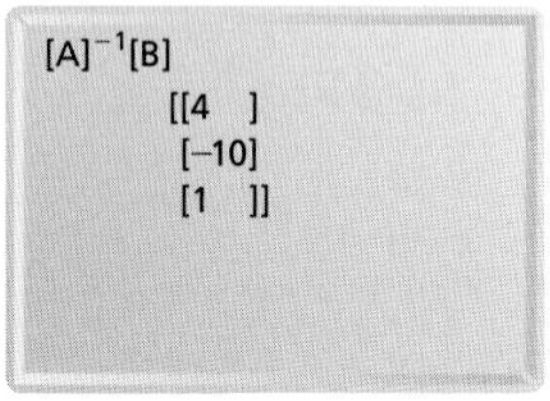

The solution is (4, −10, 1).

Check Understanding **3** **a.** Check the solution from Example 3 in each of the original equations.

b. Solve the system $\begin{cases} x + y + z = 2 \\ 2x + y = 5 \\ x + 3y - 3z = 14 \end{cases}$. Check your solution.

There are many business applications for matrices of systems of equations.

4 EXAMPLE Real-World Connection

Business A bead store has a sale on certain beads. Find the price of each size of bead.

Relate 2 large beads and 3 small beads cost \$3.25.
3 large beads and 4 small beads cost \$4.75.

Define Let $x =$ the price of one large bead.
Let $y =$ the price of one small bead.

Write $\begin{bmatrix} 2 & 3 \\ 3 & 4 \end{bmatrix}\begin{bmatrix} x \\ y \end{bmatrix} = \begin{bmatrix} 3.25 \\ 4.75 \end{bmatrix}$ **Write the system as a matrix equation.**

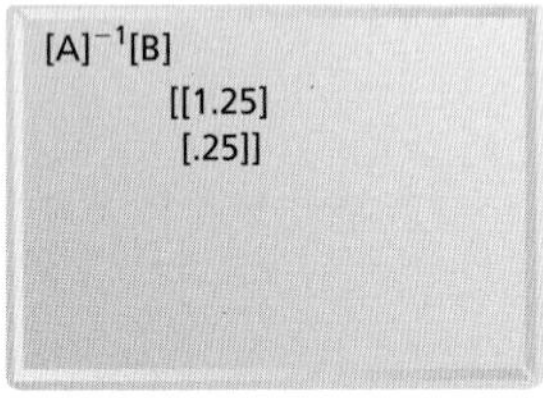

Use a graphing calculator. Store the coefficient matrix as matrix *A* and the constant matrix as matrix *B*.

The price of a large bead is \$1.25. The price of a small bead is \$.25.

Check Understanding 4 Suppose the sale is over, and the price of each package increases. The price of a package of two large beads and three small beads increases to \$5.55. The price of a package of three large beads and four small beads increases to \$8.05. Find the new price of each type of bead.

When the coefficient matrix of a system has an inverse, the system has a unique solution. Similarly, when the coefficient matrix does *not* have an inverse, the system does *not* have a unique solution. In that case, the system either has no solution or has an infinite number of solutions.

5 EXAMPLE Unique Solutions

Need Help?
$\det\begin{bmatrix} a & b \\ c & d \end{bmatrix} = ad - bc$

Write the coefficient matrix for each system. Use it to determine whether the system has a unique solution.

a. $\begin{cases} x + y = 3 \\ x - y = 7 \end{cases}$

$A = \begin{bmatrix} 1 & 1 \\ 1 & -1 \end{bmatrix}$; $\det A = \begin{vmatrix} 1 & 1 \\ 1 & -1 \end{vmatrix} = 1(-1) - 1(1) = -2$

Since $\det A \neq 0$, the matrix has an inverse, so the system has a unique solution.

b. $\begin{cases} x + 2y = 5 \\ 2x + 4y = 8 \end{cases}$

$A = \begin{bmatrix} 1 & 2 \\ 2 & 4 \end{bmatrix}$; $\det A = \begin{vmatrix} 1 & 2 \\ 2 & 4 \end{vmatrix} = 1(4) - 2(2) = 0$

Since $\det A = 0$, the matrix does not have an inverse and the system does *not* have a unique solution.

Check Understanding **5** **a.** Determine whether the system $\begin{cases} 3x + 5y = 1 \\ 2x - y = -8 \end{cases}$ has a unique solution.

b. You can use an inverse matrix to solve a system of equations. What happens when you try to do this with a graphing calculator and the system does not have a unique solution?

EXERCISES

For more practice, see *Extra Practice*.

Practice and Problem Solving

A Practice by Example

Example 1 (page 210)

Write each system as a matrix equation. Identify the coefficient matrix, the variable matrix, and the constant matrix.

1. $\begin{cases} x + y = 5 \\ x - 2y = -4 \end{cases}$ **2.** $\begin{cases} y = 3x - 7 \\ x = 2 \end{cases}$ **3.** $\begin{cases} 3a + 5b = 0 \\ a + b = 2 \end{cases}$

4. $\begin{cases} x + 3y - z = 2 \\ x + 2z = 8 \\ 2y - z = 1 \end{cases}$ **5.** $\begin{cases} r - s + t = 150 \\ 2r + t = 425 \\ s + 3t = 0 \end{cases}$ **6.** $\begin{cases} x + 2y = 11 \\ 2x + 3y = 18 \end{cases}$

Examples 2 and 3 (page 211)

Solve each system of equations. Check your answers.

7. $\begin{cases} x + 3y = 5 \\ x + 4y = 6 \end{cases}$ **8.** $\begin{cases} p - 3q = -1 \\ -5p + 16q = 5 \end{cases}$ **9.** $\begin{cases} 300x - y = 130 \\ 200x + y = 120 \end{cases}$

10. $\begin{cases} x + 5y = -4 \\ x + 6y = -5 \end{cases}$ **11.** $\begin{cases} 2x + 3y = 12 \\ x + 2y = 7 \end{cases}$ **12.** $\begin{cases} 2x + 3y = 5 \\ x + 2y = 6 \end{cases}$

13. $\begin{cases} x + y + z = 4 \\ 4x + 5y = 3 \\ y - 3z = -10 \end{cases}$ **14.** $\begin{cases} 9y + 2z = 18 \\ 3x + 2y + z = 5 \\ x - y = -1 \end{cases}$ **15.** $\begin{cases} 9y + 2z = 14 \\ 3x + 2y + z = 5 \\ x - y = -1 \end{cases}$

Example 4 (page 212)

16. Shopping Suppose you want to fill nine 1-lb tins with a holiday snack mix. You plan to buy almonds for \$2.45/lb, peanuts for \$1.85/lb, and raisins for \$.80/lb. You have \$15 and want the mix to contain twice as much of the nuts as of the raisins by weight. How much of each ingredient should you buy?

a. Writing Explain how each equation in the system at the right relates to the problem. What does each variable represent?

$$\begin{cases} x + y + z = 9 \\ 2.45x + 1.85y + 0.8z = 15 \\ x + y = 2z \end{cases}$$

b. Solve the system.

Example 5 (page 212)

Determine whether each system has a unique solution.

17. $\begin{cases} 20x + 5y = 240 \\ y = 20x \end{cases}$ **18.** $\begin{cases} 20x + 5y = 145 \\ 30x - 5y = 125 \end{cases}$ **19.** $\begin{cases} y = 2000 - 65x \\ y = 500 + 55x \end{cases}$

20. $\begin{cases} y = \frac{2}{3}x - 3 \\ y = -x + 7 \end{cases}$ **21.** $\begin{cases} 3x + 2y = 10 \\ 6x + 4y = 16 \end{cases}$ **22.** $\begin{cases} x + 2y + z = 4 \\ y = x - 3 \\ z = 2x \end{cases}$

B Apply Your Skills

Solve each matrix equation. If the coefficient matrix has no inverse, write *no unique solution.*

23. $\begin{bmatrix} 1 & 1 \\ 1 & 2 \end{bmatrix}\begin{bmatrix} x \\ y \end{bmatrix} = \begin{bmatrix} 8 \\ 10 \end{bmatrix}$ **24.** $\begin{bmatrix} 2 & -3 \\ -4 & 6 \end{bmatrix}\begin{bmatrix} a \\ b \end{bmatrix} = \begin{bmatrix} 1 \\ -2 \end{bmatrix}$ **25.** $\begin{bmatrix} 2 & 1 \\ 4 & 3 \end{bmatrix}\begin{bmatrix} x \\ y \end{bmatrix} = \begin{bmatrix} 10 \\ -2 \end{bmatrix}$

Solve each system.

26. $\begin{cases} -3x + 4y = 2 \\ x - y = -1 \end{cases}$

27. $\begin{cases} x + 2y = 10 \\ 3x + 5y = 26 \end{cases}$

28. $\begin{cases} x - 3y = -1 \\ -6x + 19y = 6 \end{cases}$

29. $\begin{cases} x = 5 - y \\ 3y = z \\ x + z = 7 \end{cases}$

30. $\begin{cases} -x = -4 - z \\ 2y = z - 1 \\ x = 6 - y - z \end{cases}$

31. $\begin{cases} -b + 2c = 4 \\ a + b - c = -10 \\ 2a + 3c = 1 \end{cases}$

32. $\begin{cases} x + y + z = 4 \\ 4x + 5y = 4 \\ y - 3z = -9 \end{cases}$

33. $\begin{cases} x + y + z = 4 \\ 4x + 5y = 3 \\ y - 3z = -10 \end{cases}$

34. $\begin{cases} -2w + x + y = 0 \\ -w + 2x - y + z = 1 \\ -2w + 3x + 3y + 2z = 6 \\ w + x + 2y + z = 5 \end{cases}$

35. $\begin{cases} -2w + x + y = -2 \\ -w + 2x - y + z = -4 \\ -2w + 3x + 3y + 2z = 2 \\ w + x + 2y + z = 6 \end{cases}$

Reading Math
For help with reading and solving Exercise 36, see p. 216.

36. Coordinate Geometry The coordinates (x, y) of a point in a plane are the solution of the system $\begin{cases} 2x + 3y = 13 \\ 5x + 7y = 31 \end{cases}$. Find the coordinates of the point.

37. Geometry A rectangle is twice as long as it is wide. The perimeter is 840 ft. Find the dimensions of the rectangle.

C Challenge

Open-Ended Complete each system for the given number of solutions.

38. infinitely many

$\begin{cases} x + y = 7 \\ 2x + 2y = \blacksquare \end{cases}$

39. one solution

$\begin{cases} x + y + z = 7 \\ y + z = \blacksquare \\ z = \blacksquare \end{cases}$

40. no solution

$\begin{cases} x + y + z = 7 \\ y + z = \blacksquare \\ y + z = \blacksquare \end{cases}$

41. Physics When you mix hot and cold liquids, you can find the temperature of the mixture by using the formula $T = \frac{ah + bc}{a + b}$, where T is the temperature of the mixture, h is the temperature of the hot liquid, c is the temperature of the cold liquid, and a and b represent the amounts of hot and cold liquids. Suppose you mix hot tea and cold milk in a ratio $a : b$ of 9 : 1, and find that the temperature of the mixture is 117°F. You then change the tea : milk ratio to 2 : 1, and the temperature drops to 96°F. Find the initial temperatures of the tea and the milk.

42. Nutrition A caterer combines ingredients to make a paella, a Spanish fiesta dish. The paella weighs 18 lb, costs $29.50, and supplies 850 g of protein.
a. Write a system of three equations to find the weight of each ingredient.
b. Solve the system. How many pounds of each ingredient did she use?

Paella Nutrition Chart

Food	Cost/lb	Protein/lb
Chicken	$1.50	100 g
Rice	$.40	20 g
Shellfish	$6.00	50 g

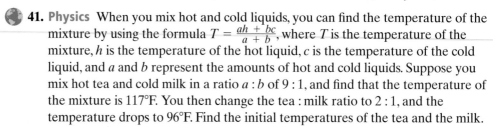

Standardized Test Prep

Multiple Choice

43. Which matrix equation represents the system $\begin{cases} 2x - 3y = -3 \\ -5x + y = 14 \end{cases}$?

A. $\begin{bmatrix} x \\ y \end{bmatrix}\begin{bmatrix} 2 & -3 \\ -5 & 1 \end{bmatrix} = \begin{bmatrix} -3 \\ 14 \end{bmatrix}$ **B.** $\begin{bmatrix} 2 & -3 \\ -5 & 1 \end{bmatrix}\begin{bmatrix} x \\ y \end{bmatrix} = \begin{bmatrix} -3 \\ 14 \end{bmatrix}$

C. $\begin{bmatrix} 2 & -3 \\ -5 & 1 \end{bmatrix}\begin{bmatrix} -3 \\ 14 \end{bmatrix} = \begin{bmatrix} x \\ y \end{bmatrix}$ **D.** $\begin{bmatrix} -3 \\ 14 \end{bmatrix}\begin{bmatrix} x & y \end{bmatrix} = \begin{bmatrix} 2 & -3 \\ -5 & 1 \end{bmatrix}$

44. What is the solution to the matrix equation $\begin{bmatrix} 3 & -1 \\ -1 & 2 \end{bmatrix}\begin{bmatrix} a \\ b \end{bmatrix} = \begin{bmatrix} 7 \\ -9 \end{bmatrix}$?

F. $a = 7, b = -9$ **G.** $a = 2, b = 1$ **H.** $a = \frac{7}{3}, b = -\frac{9}{2}$ **I.** $a = 1, b = -4$

Use the system $\begin{cases} 2x - 3y + z = 6 \\ x + 2y - 4z = 5 \\ -3x - 2y + 3z = -5 \end{cases}$ for Exercises 45–47.

45. Which matrix is the coefficient matrix for the system?

A. $\begin{bmatrix} 2 & 3 & 1 \\ 1 & 2 & 4 \\ 3 & 2 & 3 \end{bmatrix}$ **B.** $\begin{bmatrix} 2 & -3 & 1 & 6 \\ 1 & 2 & -4 & 5 \\ -3 & -2 & 3 & -5 \end{bmatrix}$ **C.** $\begin{bmatrix} 2 & -3 & 1 \\ 1 & 2 & -4 \\ -3 & -2 & 3 \end{bmatrix}$ **D.** $\begin{bmatrix} 6 \\ 5 \\ -5 \end{bmatrix}$

46. Which matrix is the constant matrix for the system?

F. $\begin{bmatrix} 2 & 3 & 1 \\ 1 & 2 & 4 \\ 3 & 2 & 3 \end{bmatrix}$ **G.** $\begin{bmatrix} 2 & -3 & 1 & 6 \\ 1 & 2 & -4 & 5 \\ -3 & -2 & 3 & -5 \end{bmatrix}$ **H.** $\begin{bmatrix} 2 & -3 & 1 \\ 1 & 2 & -4 \\ -3 & -2 & 3 \end{bmatrix}$ **I.** $\begin{bmatrix} 6 \\ 5 \\ -5 \end{bmatrix}$

Take It to the NET
Online lesson quiz at
www.PHSchool.com
Web Code: aga-0407

47. What is the determinant of the coefficient matrix?

A. -150 **B.** -27 **C.** 6 **D.** 29

Short Response

48. How can you write the three equations at the right as a matrix equation for a system? Explain your steps.

$2x - 3y + z + 10 = 0$
$x + 4y = 2z + 11$
$-2y + 3z + 7 = 3x$

Mixed Review

Lesson 4-6 **Evaluate the determinant of each matrix.**

49. $\begin{bmatrix} -1 & 3 & 7 \\ 5 & -4 & -2 \\ 0 & 2 & 10 \end{bmatrix}$ **50.** $\begin{bmatrix} 17 & 0 & 0 \\ 0 & 17 & 0 \\ 0 & 0 & 17 \end{bmatrix}$ **51.** $\begin{bmatrix} -3 & 0 & 5 \\ 5 & -3 & 2 \\ -3 & -5 & -2 \end{bmatrix}$

Lesson 4-2 **Add or subtract.**

52. $\begin{bmatrix} 5 & -3 \\ 4 & 11 \end{bmatrix} + \begin{bmatrix} 4 & 0 \\ -9 & 1 \end{bmatrix}$ **53.** $\begin{bmatrix} -1 & 2 & 0 \\ 10 & -5 & 15 \\ 17 & 3 & -4 \end{bmatrix} - \begin{bmatrix} 0 & 6 & -3 \\ 4 & -7 & 11 \\ -9 & 10 & -1 \end{bmatrix}$

Lesson 2-6 **Describe each translation of $f(x) = |x|$ as *vertical, horizontal,* or *diagonal.* Then graph the translation.**

54. $f(x) = |x + 4|$ **55.** $f(x) = |x| - 3$ **56.** $f(x) = |x - 5| + 3$

Reading Math

Reading for Problem Solving

For Use With Page 214, Exercise 36

Read the problem below. Then follow along with Jaime as he solves the problem. Check your understanding with the exercise at the bottom of the page.

Coordinate Geometry The coordinates (x, y) of a point in a plane are the solution of the system $\begin{cases} 2x + 3y = 13 \\ 5x + 7y = 31 \end{cases}$. Find the coordinates of the point.

What Jaime Thinks	What Jaime Writes
The problem tells me that the solution of this system is (x, y). I could graph the lines to see where they intersect, but that's not necessary when I can solve the system with matrices. I'll rewrite the system as a matrix equation.	$\begin{cases} 2x + 3y = 13 \\ 5x + 7y = 31 \end{cases}$ $\begin{bmatrix} 2 & 3 \\ 5 & 7 \end{bmatrix}\begin{bmatrix} x \\ y \end{bmatrix} = \begin{bmatrix} 13 \\ 31 \end{bmatrix}$
To solve for the variable matrix that includes x and y, I should multiply each side of the equation by the inverse of the coefficient matrix. I'll use the formula on page 197.	Inverse of $\begin{bmatrix} 2 & 3 \\ 5 & 7 \end{bmatrix} = \dfrac{1}{(2)(7) - (5)(3)}\begin{bmatrix} 7 & -3 \\ -5 & 2 \end{bmatrix}$ $= -1\begin{bmatrix} 7 & -3 \\ -5 & 2 \end{bmatrix} = \begin{bmatrix} -7 & 3 \\ 5 & -2 \end{bmatrix}$
Now that I have the inverse, I can multiply. Something is wrong. I can't multiply the matrices on the right side of this equation because the dimensions don't match.	$\begin{bmatrix} -7 & 3 \\ 5 & -2 \end{bmatrix}\begin{bmatrix} 2 & 3 \\ 5 & 7 \end{bmatrix}\begin{bmatrix} x \\ y \end{bmatrix} = \begin{bmatrix} 13 \\ 31 \end{bmatrix}\begin{bmatrix} -7 & 3 \\ 5 & -2 \end{bmatrix}$ 2×1 2×2 doesn't work!
Oh!!! I have to multiply the inverse matrix on the left, because matrix multiplication is not commutative!	$\begin{bmatrix} -7 & 3 \\ 5 & -2 \end{bmatrix}\begin{bmatrix} 2 & 3 \\ 5 & 7 \end{bmatrix}\begin{bmatrix} x \\ y \end{bmatrix} = \begin{bmatrix} -7 & 3 \\ 5 & -2 \end{bmatrix}\begin{bmatrix} 13 \\ 31 \end{bmatrix}$
I'll rewrite the equation correctly. The result will be a 2×1 matrix.	$\begin{bmatrix} x \\ y \end{bmatrix} = \begin{bmatrix} (-7)(13) + (3)(31) \\ (5)(13) + (-2)(31) \end{bmatrix} = \begin{bmatrix} 2 \\ 3 \end{bmatrix}$
This means the x-coordinate is 2 and the y-coordinate is 3. I'll write my answer in a sentence.	The coordinates of the point are (2, 3).

EXERCISE

Coordinate Geometry The coordinates (x, y) of a point in a plane are the solution of the system $\begin{cases} 12x + 13y = 14 \\ 5x + 7y = 9 \end{cases}$. Find the coordinates of the point.

4-8 Augmented Matrices and Systems

North Carolina Objectives

1.04 Operate with matrices to model and solve problems.
2.10 Use systems of two or more equations to model and solve problems. Solve using matrix operations and algebraic properties.

Lesson Preview

What You'll Learn

OBJECTIVE 1 To solve a system of equations using Cramer's Rule

OBJECTIVE 2 To solve a system of equations using augmented matrices

. . . And Why

To solve systems of three equations, as in Example 2

Check Skills You'll Need

(For help, go to Lessons 4-5 and 4-6.)

Evaluate the determinant of each matrix.

1. $\begin{bmatrix} -1 & 2 \\ 0 & 3 \end{bmatrix}$ **2.** $\begin{bmatrix} 0 & 1 \\ -1 & 3 \end{bmatrix}$ **3.** $\begin{bmatrix} 2 & 1 \\ -1 & 5 \end{bmatrix}$

4. $\begin{bmatrix} 0 & 1 & -3 \\ 4 & 5 & -1 \\ -1 & 0 & 1 \end{bmatrix}$ **5.** $\begin{bmatrix} 3 & 4 & 5 \\ -1 & 2 & 0 \\ 0 & -1 & 1 \end{bmatrix}$ **6.** $\begin{bmatrix} 0 & 2 & -1 \\ 3 & 4 & 0 \\ -2 & -1 & 5 \end{bmatrix}$

New Vocabulary • Cramer's Rule • augmented matrix • row operations

Interactive lesson includes instant self-check, tutorials, and activities.

OBJECTIVE 1 Solving Systems Using Cramer's Rule

You can solve a system of linear equations that has a unique solution by using determinants and a pattern called Cramer's Rule.

Key Concepts

Definition Cramer's Rule

System	Use the *x*- and *y*-coefficients. ↓	Replace the *x*-coefficients with the constants. ↓	Replace the *y*-coefficients with the constants. ↓
$\begin{cases} ax + by = m \\ cx + dy = n \end{cases}$	$D = \begin{vmatrix} a & b \\ c & d \end{vmatrix}$	$D_x = \begin{vmatrix} m & b \\ n & d \end{vmatrix}$	$D_y = \begin{vmatrix} a & m \\ c & n \end{vmatrix}$

The solution of the system is $x = \frac{D_x}{D}$ and $y = \frac{D_y}{D}$, or $\left(\frac{D_x}{D}, \frac{D_y}{D}\right)$.

Reading Math

Cramer's Rule was developed in 1750 by the Swiss mathematician Gabriel Cramer.

1 EXAMPLE Using Cramer's Rule

Use Cramer's Rule to solve the system $\begin{cases} 3x + 2y = 0 \\ x - y = -5 \end{cases}$.

Evaluate three determinants. Then find *x* and *y*.

$D = \begin{vmatrix} 3 & 2 \\ 1 & -1 \end{vmatrix} = -5$ $D_x = \begin{vmatrix} 0 & 2 \\ -5 & -1 \end{vmatrix} = 10$ $D_y = \begin{vmatrix} 3 & 0 \\ 1 & -5 \end{vmatrix} = -15$

$x = \frac{D_x}{D} = \frac{10}{-5} = -2$ $y = \frac{D_y}{D} = \frac{-15}{-5} = 3$

The solution of the system is $(-2, 3)$.

Check Understanding 1 Use Cramer's Rule to solve the system $\begin{cases} 3x + y = 5 \\ 2x + 3y = 8 \end{cases}$.

You can also use Cramer's Rule to solve a system of three equations.

2 EXAMPLE Using Cramer's Rule with Three Equations

Find the x-coordinate of the solution of the system $\begin{cases} y + 4z = 5 \\ x + y + z = 8. \\ 2x - 5y = 7 \end{cases}$

$D = \begin{vmatrix} 0 & 1 & 4 \\ 1 & 1 & 1 \\ 2 & -5 & 0 \end{vmatrix} = -26$ **Evaluate the determinant.**

$D_x = \begin{vmatrix} 5 & 1 & 4 \\ 8 & 1 & 1 \\ 7 & -5 & 0 \end{vmatrix} = -156$ **Replace the x-coefficients with the constants and evaluate again.**

$x = \frac{D_x}{D} = \frac{-156}{-26} = 6$ **Find x.**

The x-coordinate of the solution is 6.

Check Understanding 2 **a.** **Critical Thinking** How would you modify the determinant D to find D_z?
b. Solve the system for y and z.

OBJECTIVE 2

Solving Systems Using Augmented Matrices

Reading Math
Augmented means "enlarged."

You can solve some linear systems by using an augmented matrix. An **augmented matrix** contains the coefficients and the constants from a system of equations. Each row of the matrix represents an equation.

3 EXAMPLE Writing an Augmented Matrix

Write an augmented matrix to represent the system $\begin{cases} -6x + 2y = 10 \\ 4x = -20 \end{cases}$.

System of equations $\begin{cases} -6x + 2y = 10 \\ 4x \quad\quad = -20 \end{cases}$

x-coefficients ↕ ↕ y-coefficients ↕ constants

Augmented matrix $\left[\begin{array}{cc|c} -6 & 2 & 10 \\ 4 & 0 & -20 \end{array}\right]$

Draw a vertical bar to separate the coefficients from the constants.

An augmented matrix that represents the system is $\left[\begin{array}{cc|c} -6 & 2 & 10 \\ 4 & 0 & -20 \end{array}\right]$.

Check Understanding 3 Write an augmented matrix to represent each system.

a. $\begin{cases} x - 5y = 15 \\ 3x + 3y = 3 \end{cases}$

b. $\begin{cases} x + 2y + 3z = -4 \\ y - 2z = 8 \\ z = -3 \end{cases}$

An augmented matrix contains an entry of zero for any term missing from the system. You can write a system of equations from an augmented matrix.

4 EXAMPLE Writing a System from an Augmented Matrix

Write a system of equations for the augmented matrix $\left[\begin{array}{cc|c} 6 & 0 & 3 \\ 1 & 1 & -5 \end{array}\right]$.

Augmented matrix $\left[\begin{array}{cc|c} 6 & 0 & 3 \\ 1 & 1 & -5 \end{array}\right]$

x-coefficients ↕ ↕ y-coefficients ↕ constants

System of equations $\begin{cases} 6x = 3 \\ x + y = -5 \end{cases}$

Check Understanding 4 Write a system of equations for each augmented matrix.

a. $\left[\begin{array}{cc|c} 5 & 7 & -3 \\ 0 & -8 & 6 \end{array}\right]$

b. $\left[\begin{array}{ccc|c} -1 & 0 & 3 & -4 \\ 7 & 2 & -1 & 0 \\ 0 & 1 & 2 & -3 \end{array}\right]$

In Chapter 3 you learned how to solve systems of equations by using multiples of one or more of the equations to eliminate variables. You can do the same thing to an augmented matrix by using row operations.

Key Concepts

Definition **Row Operations**

To solve a system of equations using an augmented matrix, you can use one or more of the following **row operations.**

- Switch any two rows.
- Multiply a row by a constant.
- Add one row to another.
- Combine one or more of these steps.

5 EXAMPLE Using an Augmented Matrix

Use an augmented matrix to solve the system $\begin{cases} x + 2y = -1 \\ 2x + 5y = -4 \end{cases}$.

$\left[\begin{array}{cc|c} 1 & 2 & -1 \\ 2 & 5 & -4 \end{array}\right]$ **Write an augmented matrix.**

$$\begin{array}{rrr} -2(1 & 2 & -1) \\ 2 & 5 & -4 \\ \hline 0 & 1 & -2 \end{array}$$

Multiply Row 1 by −2 and add it to Row 2. Write the new augmented matrix.

$\left[\begin{array}{cc|c} 1 & 2 & -1 \\ 0 & 1 & -2 \end{array}\right]$

$$\begin{array}{rrr} 1 & 2 & -1 \\ -2(0 & 1 & -2) \\ \hline 1 & 0 & 3 \end{array}$$

Multiply new Row 2 by −2 and add it to Row 1. Write the final augmented matrix.

$\left[\begin{array}{cc|c} 1 & 0 & 3 \\ 0 & 1 & -2 \end{array}\right]$

The solution to the system is (3, −2).

Check		
$x + 2y = -1$	$2x + 5y = -4$	**Use the original equations.**
$3 + 2(-2) \stackrel{?}{=} -1$	$2(3) + 5(-2) \stackrel{?}{=} -4$	**Substitute.**
$3 + (-4) \stackrel{?}{=} -1$	$6 + (-10) \stackrel{?}{=} -4$	**Multiply.**
$-1 = -1$ ✓	$-4 = -4$ ✓	**Simplify.**

Check Understanding 5 Solve $\begin{cases} x + y = -10 \\ -x + y = 20 \end{cases}$. Check your solution.

You can use augmented matrices and row operations to solve systems of three equations. Graphing calculators have a feature that uses row operations to simplify matrices.

Graphing Calculator Hint

To find rref([A]), select B from the MATH option of the MATRX feature. (rref stands for "reduced row-echelon form.")

6 EXAMPLE Using a Graphing Calculator

Use a graphing calculator to solve the system $\begin{cases} 2x + 3y - z = 11 \\ 3x - 2y + 4z = 10. \\ x + 4y - 2z = 8 \end{cases}$

Step 1 Enter the augmented matrix as matrix A.

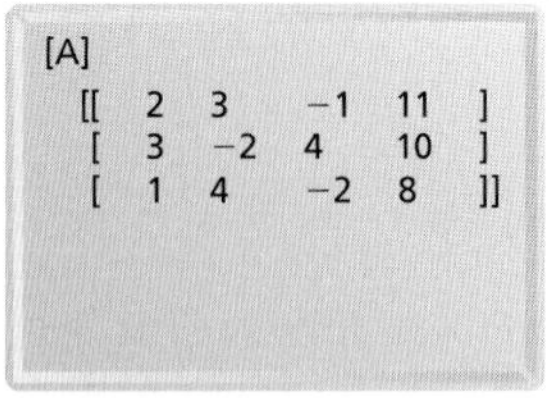

Step 2 Use the rref feature of your graphing calculator.

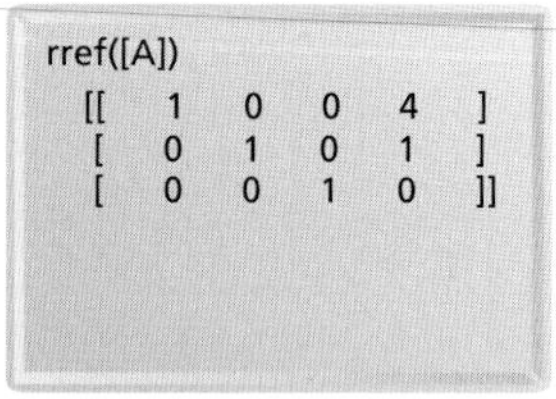

The simplified augmented matrix is equivalant to $\begin{cases} x = 4 \\ y = 1. \\ z = 0 \end{cases}$ The solution is $(4, 1, 0)$.

Partial Check $2x + 3y - z = 11$ **Use the first equation.**

$2(4) + 3(1) - (0) \stackrel{?}{=} 11$ **Substitute.**

$8 + 3 - 0 \stackrel{?}{=} 11$ **Multiply.**

$11 = 11$ ✓ **Simplify.**

Check Understanding 6 **a.** Check the solution to Example 6 in the remaining two equations.

b. Use a graphing calculator to solve the system $\begin{cases} x + 4y - z = 4 \\ x - 2y + z = -2. \\ 5x - 3y + 8z = 13 \end{cases}$ Check your answer.

EXERCISES

For more practice, see *Extra Practice.*

Practice and Problem Solving

A Practice by Example

Examples 1 and 2 (pages 217 and 218)

Use Cramer's Rule to solve each system.

1. $\begin{cases} 2x + y = 4 \\ 3x - y = 6 \end{cases}$ **2.** $\begin{cases} 2x + y = 7 \\ -2x + 5y = -1 \end{cases}$ **3.** $\begin{cases} 2x + 4y = 10 \\ 3x + 5y = 14 \end{cases}$

4. $\begin{cases} y + 4z = 5 \\ x + y + z = 8 \\ 2x - 5y = 7 \end{cases}$ **5.** $\begin{cases} 2x + 3y + z = 5 \\ x + y - 2z = -2 \\ -3x + z = -7 \end{cases}$

Example 3 (page 218)

Write an augmented matrix for each system.

6. $\begin{cases} 3x - 4y = 17 \\ 8x + y = -3 \end{cases}$ **7.** $\begin{cases} 3x - 7y + 3z = -3 \\ x + y + 2z = -3 \\ 2x - 3y + 5z = -8 \end{cases}$ **8.** $\begin{cases} -x + 5y = -1 \\ x - 2y = 1 \end{cases}$

Example 4 (page 219)

Write a system of equations for each augmented matrix.

9. $\left[\begin{array}{cc|c} 5 & 1 & -3 \\ -2 & 2 & 4 \end{array}\right]$

10. $\left[\begin{array}{cc|c} -1 & 2 & -6 \\ 1 & 1 & 7 \end{array}\right]$

11. $\left[\begin{array}{ccc|c} 2 & 1 & 1 & 1 \\ 1 & 1 & 1 & 2 \\ 1 & -1 & 1 & -2 \end{array}\right]$

Example 5 (page 219)

Use an augmented matrix to solve each system.

12. $\begin{cases} 2x - 2y = 15 \\ 4x + 4y = 10 \end{cases}$

13. $\begin{cases} 2x - 4y = 20 \\ 4x + 2y = -20 \end{cases}$

14. $\begin{cases} x + 2y = 3 \\ 4x + 2y = -6 \end{cases}$

15. $\begin{cases} x + 5y = -25 \\ 5x + y = 25 \end{cases}$

16. $\begin{cases} -x + 5y = 15 \\ 2x + 3y = 9 \end{cases}$

17. $\begin{cases} 3x + 6y = 2 \\ 2x - y = 3 \end{cases}$

Example 6 (page 220)

Solve each system.

18. $\begin{cases} x + y + z = 2 \\ 2y - 2z = 2 \\ x - 3z = 1 \end{cases}$

19. $\begin{cases} x - y + z = 3 \\ x + 3z = 6 \\ y - 2z = -1 \end{cases}$

20. $\begin{cases} x + y - z = -1 \\ 3x + 4y - z = 8 \\ 6x + 8y - 2z = 16 \end{cases}$

21. $\begin{cases} x + y - z = 1 \\ 3x + 3y + z = 3 \\ 2x + 2y - 2z = 2 \end{cases}$

22. $\begin{cases} x + y = 1 \\ y + z = 2 \\ x - z = -1 \end{cases}$

23. $\begin{cases} x + z = -4 \\ y - z = 1 \\ x + y = -3 \end{cases}$

B Apply Your Skills

Use Cramer's Rule to solve each system.

24. $\begin{cases} 0.5x + 1.5y = 7 \\ 2.5x - 3.5y = -9 \end{cases}$

25. $\begin{cases} -1.2x - 0.3y = 2.1 \\ -0.2x + 0.8y = 4.6 \end{cases}$

26. $\begin{cases} \frac{x}{5} - \frac{2y}{5} = 4 \\ \frac{2x}{5} - \frac{3y}{5} = 5 \end{cases}$

27. $\begin{cases} \frac{x}{2} + \frac{y}{4} = 4 \\ \frac{x}{4} - \frac{3y}{8} = -2 \end{cases}$

28. $\begin{cases} 2x + 3y + 5z = 12 \\ 4x + 2y + 4z = -2 \\ 5x + 4y + 7z = 7 \end{cases}$

Use an augmented matrix to solve each system.

29. $\begin{cases} x + y + z = 1 \\ y - 3z = 4 \\ x - z = 2 \end{cases}$

30. $\begin{cases} x + y + z = 0 \\ y + 4z = -6 \\ 2x - 2z = 4 \end{cases}$

31. $\begin{cases} 2x + y = 8 \\ x + z = 5 \\ y - z = -1 \end{cases}$

32. Business A manufacturer sells pencils and erasers in packages. The price of a package of five erasers and two pencils is \$.23. The price of a package of seven erasers and five pencils is \$.41. Find the price of one eraser and one pencil.

33. Investments Suppose you invested \$5000 in three different mutual funds for one year. The funds paid simple interest of 8%, 10%, and 7%, respectively. The total interest at the end of one year was \$405. You invested \$500 more at 10% than at 8%. How much did you invest in each mutual fund?

34. Open-Ended Write and solve a system of three equations in three unknowns using Cramer's Rule.

Solve each system.

35. $\begin{cases} 2x - 3y + 2z = 10 \\ x + 3y + 4z = 14 \\ 3x - y + z = 9 \end{cases}$

36. $\begin{cases} 4x - y + z = 3 \\ x + 2y + z = 0 \\ 3x + 7y - 3z = 6 \end{cases}$

37. $\begin{cases} x + 2y + z = 4 \\ 3x + 6y + 3z = 2 \\ x - y + z = 3 \end{cases}$

38. **Colors** A hardware store mixes paints in a ratio of two parts red to six parts yellow to make pumpkin orange. A ratio of five parts red to three parts yellow makes red-pepper red. A gallon of pumpkin orange sells for $25, and a gallon of red-pepper red sells for $28.

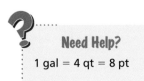

Need Help?
1 gal = 4 qt = 8 pt

a. Write a system of equations to model the situation.
b. Solve the system.
c. Find the cost of 1 qt of red paint and the cost of 1 qt of yellow paint.

39. **Sales** Refer to the signs below. Find the price per pound of each type of nut.

C Challenge

Solve using Cramer's Rule. (*Hint:* Start by substituting $m = \frac{1}{x}$ and $n = \frac{1}{y}$.)

40. $\begin{cases} \frac{4}{x} + \frac{1}{y} = 1 \\ \frac{8}{x} + \frac{4}{y} = 3 \end{cases}$

41. $\begin{cases} \frac{4}{x} - \frac{2}{y} = 1 \\ \frac{10}{x} + \frac{20}{y} = 0 \end{cases}$

Solve each system.

42. $\begin{cases} w + x + y + z = 3 \\ -w + x - 2y + z = -2 \\ 2x - y + z = 1 \\ w + y - z = 2 \end{cases}$

43. $\begin{cases} 2x + 2y + z = 4 \\ w + y - z = -2 \\ w + x + y + z = 3 \\ -4w + z = 2 \end{cases}$

44. **Nutrition** While stranded on an island, the crew of a sailboat has access to only three sources of food, as shown in the table below. One of the crew members designs a daily diet to supply each person with 120 g of fat, 220 g of carbohydrates, and 80 g of protein.

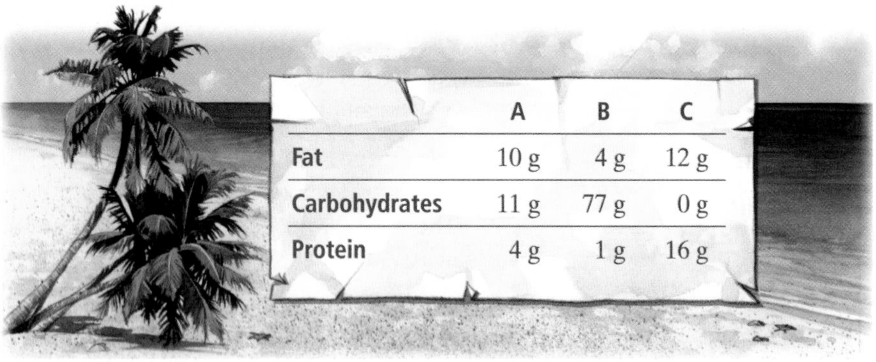

	A	B	C
Fat	10 g	4 g	12 g
Carbohydrates	11 g	77 g	0 g
Protein	4 g	1 g	16 g

a. Write a system of three equations in three variables to find the number of portions of each food each person must have to meet the daily diet.
b. Use an augmented matrix to solve the system of equations from part (a). Round each answer to the nearest tenth.
c. Writing Suppose food C runs out. How would this change the number of portions of food required each day?

45. **Geometry** The perimeter of the rectangle at the right is 28 cm. The perimeter of each of the triangles is 24 cm. The diagonal of the rectangle is 2 cm longer than the longer side of the rectangle.

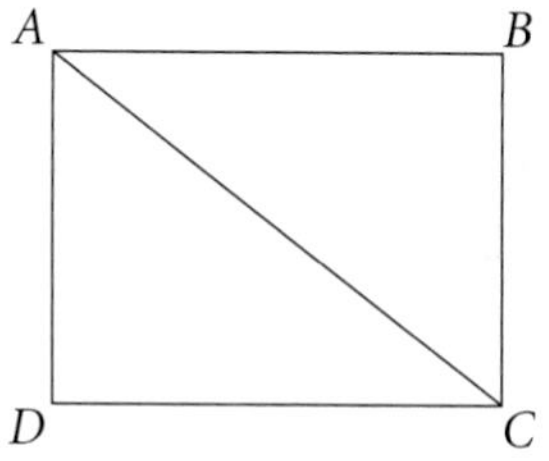

a. Write a system of three equations in three unknowns.
b. Simplify the system to a system of two equations in two unknowns.
c. Write an augmented matrix for the system in part (b).
d. Find the dimensions of the rectangle.
e. Find the length of the diagonal.

Standardized Test Prep

Multiple Choice

Use the system $\begin{cases} 5x - 4y = -13 \\ -3x + 6y = 6 \end{cases}$ for Exercises 46 and 47.

46. Which is the determinant D_x?

A. $\begin{vmatrix} 5 & -4 \\ -3 & 6 \end{vmatrix}$ B. $\begin{vmatrix} -13 & -4 \\ 6 & 6 \end{vmatrix}$ C. $\begin{vmatrix} 5 & -13 \\ -3 & 6 \end{vmatrix}$ D. $\begin{vmatrix} 5 & 4 & -13 \\ -3 & 6 & 6 \end{vmatrix}$

47. What is the solution of the system?

F. $(-13, 6)$ G. $\left(-\frac{13}{5}, 1\right)$ H. $\left(-3, -\frac{1}{2}\right)$ I. $2x + 2y = -7$

Use the system $\begin{cases} 2x + y - 3z = -2 \\ 4x - 3y + 6z = 9 \\ -2x - 2y + 9z = 7 \end{cases}$ for Exercises 48 and 49.

48. What is the value of the determinant D_y?

A. -36 B. -24 C. -18 D. 36

49. What is the value of the determinant D_z?

F. -36 G. -24 H. -18 I. 36

Take It to the NET
Online lesson quiz at **www.PHSchool.com**
Web Code: aga-0408

Mixed Review

Lesson 4-7 **Solve each system of equations by using the inverse of the coefficient matrix.**

50. $\begin{cases} x + 4y + 3z = 3 \\ 2x - 5y - z = 5 \\ 3x + 2y - 2z = -3 \end{cases}$

51. $\begin{cases} x + y + z = -1 \\ y + 3z = -5 \\ x + z = -2 \end{cases}$

Lesson 3-3 **Solve each system of inequalities by graphing.**

52. $\begin{cases} 2x + y < 3 \\ -x - y \geq 1 \end{cases}$

53. $\begin{cases} 2x \leq 0 \\ -x + y > -1 \end{cases}$

54. $\begin{cases} x < 3 \\ y \geq -4 \\ -x + y < 5 \end{cases}$

Lesson 2-2 **Write in point-slope form the equation of the line through each pair of points.**

55. $(0, 1)$ and $(2, -5)$ 56. $(-9, 3)$ and $(-4, -4)$ 57. $(1, 8)$ and $(7, 2)$

Test-Taking Strategies

Making Quantitative Comparisons

To answer Quantitative Comparison questions, you usually need to simplify, rewrite, or evaluate a given equation or the expressions in Columns A and B. Then choose the answer that correctly compares the values:

A. The quantity in Column A is greater.
B. The quantity in Column B is greater.
C. The two quantities are equal.
D. The relationship cannot be determined from the information given.

EXAMPLE

$$\begin{bmatrix} 0 & x \\ -1 & 0 \end{bmatrix}^2 = y\begin{bmatrix} 1 & 0 \\ 0 & 1 \end{bmatrix}$$

Column A	Column B
x^2	y^2

To find and compare x^2 and y^2, first simplify both sides of the given equation.

$$\begin{bmatrix} 0 & x \\ -1 & 0 \end{bmatrix}^2 = y\begin{bmatrix} 1 & 0 \\ 0 & 1 \end{bmatrix}$$

$$\begin{bmatrix} 0 & x \\ -1 & 0 \end{bmatrix}\begin{bmatrix} 0 & x \\ -1 & 0 \end{bmatrix} = \begin{bmatrix} y & 0 \\ 0 & y \end{bmatrix}$$

$$\begin{bmatrix} -x & 0 \\ 0 & -x \end{bmatrix} = \begin{bmatrix} y & 0 \\ 0 & y \end{bmatrix}$$

Since $-x = y, x^2 = y^2$. The quantities are equal. The answer is C.

EXERCISES

Compare the boxed quantity in Column A with the boxed quantity in Column B. Choose the best answer.

A. The quantity in Column A is greater.
B. The quantity in Column B is greater.
C. The two quantities are equal.
D. The relationship cannot be determined from the information given.

1. $x > 0$

$$\begin{bmatrix} 1 & x \\ 0 & 1 \end{bmatrix}^2 = \begin{bmatrix} 1 & y \\ 0 & 1 \end{bmatrix}$$

Column A	Column B
x	y

2. $$\begin{bmatrix} 1 & 1 & 1 \\ 0 & 1 & 1 \\ 0 & 0 & 1 \end{bmatrix} \cdot \begin{bmatrix} x \\ y \\ z \end{bmatrix} = \begin{bmatrix} 1 \\ 2 \\ 3 \end{bmatrix}$$

Column A	Column B
$x + y$	z

Chapter 4

Chapter Review

Vocabulary

augmented matrix (p. 218)
center of rotation (p. 190)
coefficient matrix (p. 210)
constant matrix (p. 210)
Cramer's Rule (p. 217)
determinant (p. 196)
dilation (p. 188)
equal matrices (p. 173)
image (p. 188)
matrix (p. 164)
matrix addition (p. 170)
matrix element (p. 165)
matrix equation (p. 172)
matrix multiplication (p. 180)
multiplicative identity matrix (p. 195)
multiplicative inverse matrix (p. 195)
preimage (p. 188)
reflection (p. 189)
rotation (p. 190)
row operations (p. 219)
scalar (p. 178)
scalar product (p. 178)
square matrix (p. 195)
transformation (p. 188)
translation (p. 188)
variable matrix (p. 210)
zero matrix (p. 171)

Reading Math
Understanding Vocabulary

Choose the correct vocabulary term to complete each sentence.

1. A _?_ is a rectangular array of numbers.

2. Translations, dilations, reflections and rotations are all _?_.

3. Cramer's Rule uses _?_ to solve a system of equations.

4. If corresponding elements of matrices are equal, the matrices are _?_.

5. The additive identity of a matrix is the _?_.

6. A _?_ consists of a coefficient matrix, a variable matrix, and a constant matrix.

7. An $n \times n$ matrix is called a _?_.

8. The image of a figure is a transformation of the _?_.

9. The product of a real number and a matrix is called a _?_.

10. A matrix is the inverse of another matrix if their product is the _?_.

Take It to the NET
Online vocabulary quiz at www.PHSchool.com
Web Code: agj-0451

Skills and Concepts

4-1 Objectives

- To identify and classify matrices and their elements (p. 164)
- To organize data into matrices (p. 165)

It is often useful to organize data into matrices. A **matrix** is a rectangular array of numbers classified by its dimensions. An $m \times n$ matrix has m rows and n columns. A **matrix element** a_{ij} is in the ith row and jth column of matrix A.

State the dimensions of each matrix A. Identify the indicated element.

11. $\begin{bmatrix} 5 & 8 & -7 \\ 1 & 11 & 3 \end{bmatrix}; a_{13}$ **12.** $\begin{bmatrix} 3 & 1 \\ -5 & 0 \\ 7 & 6 \end{bmatrix}; a_{21}$ **13.** $\begin{bmatrix} 5 & 1 & -2 \\ 4 & -7 & 12 \\ 0 & 78 & 3 \end{bmatrix}; a_{32}$

Use the matrix at the right for Exercises 14–16.

14. How many points has Tamika scored?

15. How many three-point shots has Tran made?

16. What percent of Johanna's points were from one-point shots?

	1-pt Shots	2-pt Shots	3-pt Shots
Tamika	22	30	48
Johanna	21	31	48
Tran	21	29	50

4-2 and 4-3 Objectives

- To add and subtract matrices (p. 170)
- To solve some matrix equations (p. 172)
- To multiply a matrix by a scalar (p. 178)
- To multiply two matrices (p. 180)

To perform **matrix addition** or subtraction, add or subtract the corresponding elements in the matrices. To obtain the **scalar product** of a matrix and a **scalar,** multiply each matrix element by the scalar. **Matrix multiplication** uses both multiplication and addition. The element in the ith row and jth column of the product of two matrices is the sum of the products of each element of the ith row of the first matrix and each element of the jth column of the second matrix. The first matrix must have the same number of columns as the second has rows.

Two matrices are **equal matrices** when corresponding elements are equal and they have the same dimensions. This principle is used to solve a **matrix equation.**

Solve each matrix equation for matrix X.

17. $\begin{bmatrix} 2 & -6 & 8 \end{bmatrix} + \begin{bmatrix} -1 & -2 & 4 \end{bmatrix} = X$

18. $\begin{bmatrix} t \\ 6 \end{bmatrix} - \begin{bmatrix} 1 \\ 3 \end{bmatrix} = X$

19. $\begin{bmatrix} 7 & -1 \\ 0 & 8 \end{bmatrix} + X = \begin{bmatrix} 4 & 9 \\ -3 & 11 \end{bmatrix}$

20. $X - \begin{bmatrix} -7 & 13 & 5 \\ 31 & 0 & -4 \end{bmatrix} = \begin{bmatrix} 9 & -5 & 8 \\ 2 & 0 & -3 \end{bmatrix}$

Solve for each variable.

21. $\begin{bmatrix} x-5 & 9 \\ 4 & t+2 \end{bmatrix} = \begin{bmatrix} -7 & w+1 \\ 8-r & 1 \end{bmatrix}$

22. $\begin{bmatrix} -4+t & 2y \\ r & w+4 \end{bmatrix} = \begin{bmatrix} 2t & 11 \\ -2r+12 & 9 \end{bmatrix}$

Use matrices A, B, C, and D. Find each scalar product, sum, or difference, if possible. If an operation is not defined, label it *undefined.*

$A = \begin{bmatrix} 6 & 1 & 0 & 8 \\ -4 & 3 & 7 & 11 \end{bmatrix}$ $\quad B = \begin{bmatrix} 1 & 3 \\ -2 & 4 \end{bmatrix}$ $\quad C = \begin{bmatrix} -2 & 1 \\ 4 & 0 \\ 2 & 2 \\ 1 & 1 \end{bmatrix}$ $\quad D = \begin{bmatrix} 5 & -2 \\ 3 & 6 \end{bmatrix}$

23. $3A$ **24.** $B - 2D$ **25.** AB **26.** BA **27.** $AC - BD$

4-4 Objectives

- To represent translations and dilations with matrices (p. 187)
- To represent reflections and rotations with matrices (p. 189)

A **transformation** is a change made to a figure. The original figure is the **preimage,** and the transformed figure is the **image.** A **translation** slides a figure without changing its size or shape. A **dilation** changes the size of a figure. You can use matrix addition to translate a figure and scalar multiplication to dilate a figure.

You can use multiplication by the appropriate matrix to perform transformations that are specific **reflections** or **rotations.** For example, to reflect a figure in the y-axis, multiply by $\begin{bmatrix} -1 & 0 \\ 0 & 1 \end{bmatrix}$. To rotate a figure 180°, multiply by $\begin{bmatrix} -1 & 0 \\ 0 & -1 \end{bmatrix}$.

For Exercises 28–35, use $\triangle ABC$ with vertices $A(3, 1)$, $B(-2, 0)$, and $C(1, 5)$. Write the coordinates of each image in matrix form.

28. a translation 1 unit right and 2 units down

29. a translation 3 units left and 4 units up

30. a reflection in the y-axis

31. a reflection in the line $y = x$

32. a rotation of 270°

33. a dilation half the original size

34. a dilation twice the original size

35. a rotation of 90°

4-5, 4-6 and 4-7 Objectives

- To evaluate determinants of 2 × 2 matrices and find inverse matrices (p. 195)
- To use inverse matrices in solving matrix equations (pp. 197 and 203)
- To evaluate determinants of 3 × 3 matrices (p. 202)
- To solve systems of equations using inverse matrices (p. 210)

A **square matrix** with 1's along its main diagonal and 0's elsewhere is the **multiplicative identity matrix,** I. If A and X are square matrices such that $AX = I$, then X is the **multiplicative inverse matrix** of A, A^{-1}.

You can use formulas to evaluate the determinants of 2 × 2 and 3 × 3 matrices.

$$\begin{vmatrix} a & b \\ c & d \end{vmatrix} = ad - bc \qquad \begin{vmatrix} a_1 & b_1 & c_1 \\ a_2 & b_2 & c_2 \\ a_3 & b_3 & c_3 \end{vmatrix} = a_1b_2c_3 + a_2b_3c_1 + a_3b_1c_2 - a_1b_3c_2 - a_2b_1c_3 - a_3b_2c_1$$

You can use a calculator to find the inverse of a matrix. The inverse of a 2 × 2 matrix can be found by using its determinant. $\begin{bmatrix} a & b \\ c & d \end{bmatrix}^{-1} = \dfrac{1}{ad - bc}\begin{bmatrix} d & -b \\ -c & a \end{bmatrix}$

You can use inverse matrices to solve some matrix equations.

You can also use inverse matrices to solve some systems of equations. When equations in a system are in standard form, the product of the **coefficient matrix** and the **variable matrix** equals the **constant matrix.** You solve the equation by multiplying both sides of the equation by the inverse of the coefficient matrix. If that inverse does not exist, the system does not have a unique solution.

Evaluate the determinant of each matrix, and find the inverse, if possible.

36. $\begin{bmatrix} 6 & 1 \\ 0 & 4 \end{bmatrix}$ **37.** $\begin{bmatrix} 5 & -2 \\ 10 & -4 \end{bmatrix}$ **38.** $\begin{bmatrix} 10 & 1 \\ 8 & 5 \end{bmatrix}$ **39.** $\begin{bmatrix} 1 & 0 & 2 \\ -1 & 0 & 1 \\ -1 & -2 & 0 \end{bmatrix}$

Use an inverse matrix to solve each equation or system.

40. $\begin{bmatrix} 3 & 5 \\ 6 & 2 \end{bmatrix}X = \begin{bmatrix} -2 & 6 \\ 4 & 12 \end{bmatrix}$ **41.** $\begin{cases} x - y = 3 \\ 2x - y = -1 \end{cases}$ **42.** $\begin{bmatrix} 4 & 1 \\ 2 & 1 \end{bmatrix}\begin{bmatrix} x \\ y \end{bmatrix} = \begin{bmatrix} 10 \\ 6 \end{bmatrix}$

43. $\begin{bmatrix} -6 & 0 \\ 7 & 1 \end{bmatrix}X = \begin{bmatrix} -12 & -6 \\ 17 & 9 \end{bmatrix}$ **44.** $\begin{cases} x + 2y = 15 \\ 2x + 4y = 30 \end{cases}$ **45.** $\begin{cases} a + 2b + c = 14 \\ b = c + 1 \\ a = -3c + 6 \end{cases}$

46. Physical Fitness A club of 17 students is going on a canoe trip. The group of people on the trip includes 5 chaperones, one for each canoe. Some canoes hold 5 people, while some hold 4 people. How many of each kind of canoe should the group rent?

4-8 Objectives

- To solve a system of equations using Cramer's Rule (p. 217)
- To solve a system of equations using augmented matrices (p. 218)

Cramer's Rule for solving systems of equations uses determinants to solve for each variable. D is the determinant of the coefficient matrix. D_y is the determinant formed by replacing the coefficients of y in D with the constant terms.

You can also use **row operations** on an augmented matrix to solve a system.

Solve each system using Cramer's Rule. Check your answers by solving each system using an augmented matrix.

47. $\begin{cases} 2x - y = 15 \\ x + 3y = -17 \end{cases}$ **48.** $\begin{cases} 3r + s - 2t = 22 \\ r + 5s + t = 4 \\ r = -3t \end{cases}$

Chapter 4

Chapter Test

Take It to the NET
Online chapter test at **www.PHSchool.com**
Web Code: aga-0452

History **Use the table below for Exercises 1–3.**

President	Years	Vetoes	Overrides
Kennedy	3	21	9
Johnson	5	30	0
Nixon	5.5	43	7
Ford	2.5	66	12
Carter	4	31	2
Reagan	8	78	9
G.H.W. Bush	4	46	1
Clinton	8	38	2

SOURCE: Congressional Research Service.
Go to **www.PHSchool.com** for a data update.
Web Code: agg-2041

1. Display the data in a matrix in which each row represents a president.
2. State the dimensions of the matrix.
3. Find and identify a_{32}.

Find each sum or difference.

4. $\begin{bmatrix} 4 & 7 \\ -2 & 1 \end{bmatrix} - \begin{bmatrix} -9 & 3 \\ 6 & 0 \end{bmatrix}$

5. $\begin{bmatrix} 4 & -5 & 1 \\ 10 & 7 & 4 \\ 21 & -9 & -6 \end{bmatrix} + \begin{bmatrix} -7 & -10 & 4 \\ 17 & 0 & 3 \\ -2 & -6 & 1 \end{bmatrix}$

Find each product.

6. $\begin{bmatrix} 2 & 6 \\ 1 & 0 \end{bmatrix}\begin{bmatrix} -1 & 5 \\ 3 & 1 \end{bmatrix}$

7. $2\begin{bmatrix} -8 & 5 & -1 \\ 0 & 9 & 7 \end{bmatrix}$

8. $\begin{bmatrix} 0 & 3 \\ -4 & 9 \end{bmatrix}\begin{bmatrix} -4 & 6 & 1 & 3 \\ 9 & -8 & 10 & 7 \end{bmatrix}$

Parallelogram $ABCD$ has coordinates $A(2, -1)$, $B(4, 3)$, $C(1, 5)$, and $D(-1, 1)$. Write a matrix for the vertices of its image after each transformation.

9. a dilation of size $\frac{2}{3}$
10. a translation right 2 units and down 4 units
11. a reflection in $y = x$
12. a rotation of 270°
13. Graph parallelogram $ABCD$ and its image from Question 11 on the same coordinate plane.

14. **Open-Ended** Write a matrix that has no inverse.
15. **Writing** Explain how to determine whether two matrices can be multiplied and what the dimensions of the product matrix will be.
16. Find the value of each variable.

$$\begin{bmatrix} x & 1 & y \\ 2 & 0 & 1 \end{bmatrix} = \begin{bmatrix} 1-x & z & 2 \\ 2+w & 4-t & 1 \end{bmatrix}$$

Find the determinant of each matrix.

17. $\begin{bmatrix} 1 & 0 & 0 \\ 0 & 1 & 0 \\ 0 & 0 & 1 \end{bmatrix}$

18. $\begin{bmatrix} 2 & 3 & 0 \\ -1 & 1 & 0 \\ 4 & 2 & 1 \end{bmatrix}$

19. $\begin{bmatrix} 8 & -3 \\ 2 & 9 \end{bmatrix}$

20. $\begin{bmatrix} 0 & 3 \\ x & t \end{bmatrix}$

21. $\begin{bmatrix} \frac{1}{2} & -1 \\ 3 & 0 \end{bmatrix}$

Find the inverse of each matrix, if it exists.

22. $\begin{bmatrix} 3 & 8 \\ -7 & 10 \end{bmatrix}$

23. $\begin{bmatrix} 0 & -5 \\ 9 & 6 \end{bmatrix}$

24. $\begin{bmatrix} \frac{1}{2} & -1 \\ 0 & 4 \end{bmatrix}$

25. $\begin{bmatrix} -8 & 4 & -11 \\ 5 & 2 & 9 \\ -5 & 6 & 2 \end{bmatrix}$

26. $\begin{bmatrix} 1 & 1 & 2 \\ 2 & 1 & 3 \\ 2 & 1 & 1 \end{bmatrix}$

Solve each matrix equation.

27. $\begin{bmatrix} 3 & -8 \\ 10 & 5 \end{bmatrix} - X = \begin{bmatrix} 2 & 8 \\ -1 & 12 \end{bmatrix}$

28. $\begin{bmatrix} 3 & 2 \\ -1 & 5 \end{bmatrix}X = \begin{bmatrix} -10 & -11 \\ 26 & -36 \end{bmatrix}$

29. $2X - \begin{bmatrix} -2 & 0 \\ 1 & 4 \end{bmatrix} = \begin{bmatrix} 5 & 10 \\ -15 & 9 \end{bmatrix}$

Solve each system using inverse matrices.

30. $\begin{cases} 2x - y = 5 \\ x + 4y = 7 \end{cases}$

31. $\begin{cases} x + 2y + z = -1 \\ 4x - y - z = -1 \\ 2z = -3y \end{cases}$

32. Solve $\begin{cases} -2x + 7y = 19 \\ x + 3y = 10 \end{cases}$ using Cramer's Rule.

33. Solve the system using an augmented matrix.

$$\begin{cases} x + y + z = 9 \\ 4x + 3y - z = -6 \\ -x - y + 2z = 21 \end{cases}$$

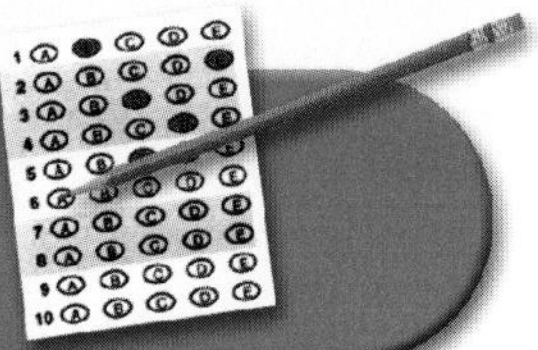

Standardized Test Prep

Multiple Choice

For Exercises 1–8, choose the correct letter.

1 Which number is irrational?
A. $8.\overline{12}$ **B.** $\sqrt{121}$ **C.** -5 **D.** $\sqrt{35}$

2. Which numbers are solutions of $\frac{5}{4}|2x - 9| = 5$?
F. $\frac{11}{8}, \frac{61}{8}$ **G.** $\frac{5}{2}, \frac{13}{2}$ **H.** $\frac{8}{5}, \frac{28}{5}$ **I.** 2, 7

3. Which equation represents the *xy*-trace of $20x - 70y - 50z = 100$?
A. $2x - 7y = 10$ **B.** $-7y - 5z = 10$
C. $2x - 5z = 10$ **D.** $5z = -10$

4. Which ordered pair is *not* a solution of the system $\begin{cases} x + y \leq 4 \\ 2x - y \geq -3 \end{cases}$?
F. (1, 1) **G.** (0, 3) **H.** (−5, −1) **I.** (3, 0)

5. What is the solution of $\begin{cases} 2x - y = 4 \\ y = 2 - x \end{cases}$?
A. (0, 2) **B.** (2, 0) **C.** (2, 4) **D.** (0, −4)

6. Which lines are perpendicular to $y = 3x - 8$?
I. $y = \frac{1}{3}x - 1$ **II.** $y = -\frac{1}{3}x + 1$
III. $y = 3x + 2$ **IV.** $y = 6x + 4$
F. I only **G.** III and IV **H.** I and II **I.** II only

7. What is the sum $\begin{bmatrix} 3 & 7 & -2 \\ 0 & 10 & 5 \end{bmatrix} + \begin{bmatrix} 6 & -8 & 1 \\ 9 & -4 & 11 \end{bmatrix}$?
A. $\begin{bmatrix} 9 & -1 & -1 \\ 9 & 6 & 16 \end{bmatrix}$ **B.** $\begin{bmatrix} 9 & 15 & -1 \\ 9 & 6 & 16 \end{bmatrix}$
C. $\begin{bmatrix} 9 & 15 & -3 \\ 9 & 6 & 16 \end{bmatrix}$ **D.** $\begin{bmatrix} -3 & 1 & -3 \\ -9 & 14 & -6 \end{bmatrix}$

8. Which equation has the solution $\begin{bmatrix} 1 & -2 & 0 \\ -5 & 4 & 7 \end{bmatrix}$?
F. $\begin{bmatrix} 7 & -2 & -3 \\ 0 & 1 & 8 \end{bmatrix} - X = \begin{bmatrix} 8 & -4 & -3 \\ -5 & 5 & 15 \end{bmatrix}$
G. $\begin{bmatrix} 10 & -8 & 12 \\ 4 & 0 & 5 \end{bmatrix} - \begin{bmatrix} -9 & -6 & 12 \\ -1 & -4 & -2 \end{bmatrix} = X$
H. $\begin{bmatrix} 0 & 6 & 5 \\ 2 & -1 & -9 \end{bmatrix} + X = \begin{bmatrix} 1 & 4 & 5 \\ -3 & 3 & -2 \end{bmatrix}$
I. $X - \begin{bmatrix} 3 & 7 & 4 \\ 8 & -6 & 1 \end{bmatrix} = \begin{bmatrix} 2 & -5 & 4 \\ -3 & 2 & 6 \end{bmatrix}$

Quantitative Comparison

Compare the boxed quantity in Column A with the boxed quantity in Column B. Choose the best answer.

A. The quantity in Column A is greater.
B. The quantity in Column B is greater.
C. The two quantities are equal.
D. The relationship cannot be determined from the information given.

	Column A	Column B
	$P = \begin{bmatrix} 4 & 1 & 9 \\ -5 & 3 & 2 \\ 7 & -4 & 1 \end{bmatrix}$	$Q = \begin{bmatrix} 4 & -5 & 7 \\ 1 & 3 & -4 \\ 9 & 2 & 1 \end{bmatrix}$
9.	p_{13}	p_{31}
10.	p_{13}	q_{31}
11.	det *P*	det *Q*

Gridded Response

12. What is the slope of the graph of $8x + 2y = 3$?

13. What is the value of $\begin{vmatrix} 7 & -1 \\ 3 & 2 \end{vmatrix}$?

Short Response

14. Write a matrix to translate $\begin{bmatrix} -1 & 4 & 5 \\ 0 & 7 & 2 \end{bmatrix}$ 7 units left and 2 units up. Use the matrix to find the coordinates of the image.

Extended Response

15. A dietitian wants to prepare a meal with 24 g of protein, 27 g of fat, and 20 g of carbohydrates, using the three foods shown in the table.

Food	Protein	Fat	Carbohydrates
A	2 g/oz	3 g/oz	4 g/oz
B	3 g/oz	3 g/oz	1 g/oz
C	3 g/oz	3 g/oz	2 g/oz

a. Set up a matrix equation for the data.
b. Solve the matrix equation.
c. How many ounces of each food are needed?

Real-World Snapshots

Building a Business

Applying Inequalities The efficiency of a factory depends on how you divide limited resources among the products produced. The bad news is that in any factory you have a limited number of machines and raw materials available. The good news is that these limitations lead to inequalities that you can use to decide how to maximize your profits.

1 The cacao tree grows in tropical jungles. It produces melonlike fruits, each containing 20–40 cocoa beans.

3 The inside of the cocoa bean is ground into a concentrated chocolate liquid.

2 After roasting, cocoa beans pass through a machine that separates the shell from the inside of the bean.

Activity

You are in charge of a small private chocolate factory that makes two popular and profitable chocolate bars, Cocoa Bar and Choco-Lot. Your goal is to figure out how many of each type of chocolate bar you should produce each day to maximize your company's profits.

Here are a few key pieces of information:

- The success of your chocolate recipes lies in your use of two secret ingredients, referred to as Flavor A and Flavor B to protect the company's interests. The table shows the production rate and requirements of the flavors.

	Flavor A	Flavor B
Production rate	126 kg/day	136 kg/day
Cocoa Bar requirements	1.8 g/bar	4.0 g/bar
Choco-Lot requirements	2.8 g/bar	1.7 g/bar

- One machine wraps both candy bars. It can wrap 50,000 chocolate bars per day.
- Your profit on each Cocoa Bar bar is 14¢, and your profit on each Choco-Lot bar is 12¢.

a. Write inequalities to describe each objective and constraint.

b. Graph the inequalities you wrote in part (a).

c. Find the quantity of each chocolate bar you should manufacture to maximize your daily profit. Calculate the profit you will earn.

Chocolate Fondue

To make chocolate fondue, melt chocolate gently over low heat. Dip pieces of fruit in the melted chocolate.

4 Milk and sugar are mixed together before being added to the cocoa bean liquid.

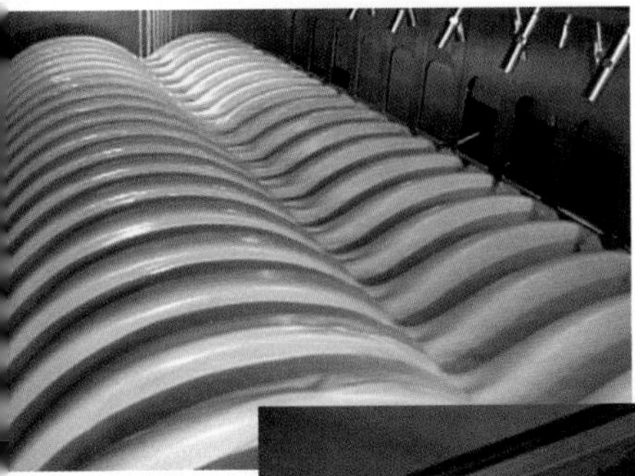

6 Any gritty particles are removed by machine.

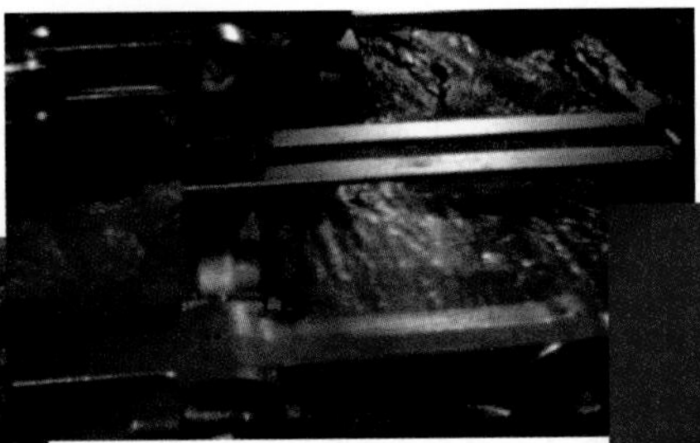

7 The chocolate paste is ready to be cooled and molded.

5 The cocoa, milk, and sugar mixture is dried to a powder and mixed with cocoa butter to make a chocolate paste.

8 The molded chocolate takes a bumpy ride along a conveyor belt to eliminate air bubbles as it cools. It's ready for wrapping!

White Chocolate

White chocolate is not a real chocolate, since it does not contain cocoa solids. A good white chocolate is made with cocoa butter as well as milk solids and sugar.

Take It to the NET For more information about manufacturing, go to **www.PHSchool.com**.
Web Code: age-0453

Where You've Been

- In Chapter 1, you learned to write and solve linear equations.
- In Chapter 2, you learned to graph linear functions.
- In Chapter 2, you learned to use linear functions to model real-world data.

Instant self-check online and on CD-ROM

Diagnosing Readiness

(For help, go to the Lesson in green.)

Simplifying Expressions (Lesson 1-2)

Simplify each expression.

1. $x^2 + 3x^2 - 5x$ **2.** $\frac{x^2}{2} - \frac{x^2}{3} + \frac{x^2}{5}$ **3.** $-6x(x + 2) - x(x + 1)$

Solving Linear Equations (Lesson 1-3)

Solve each equation. Check your answers.

4. $4 - 2x = x + 2$ **5.** $6x + 2.5 = 4x - 1.1$ **6.** $3(x - 1) = 8(2x - 2)$

Graphing Linear Functions (Lesson 2-2)

Graph each function.

7. $y = -5x - 1$ **8.** $y = 3x + 12$ **9.** $y = -6x + 6$

10. $2x - 3y = -4$ **11.** $-3x + 9y = -12$ **12.** $y - 1 = -4x$

Using Linear Models (Lesson 2-4)

Graph each set of values. Decide whether a linear model is reasonable. If so, draw a trend line and write its equation.

13. $\{(0, 12), (2, 17), (4, 25), (6, 29), (8, 36)\}$

14. $\{(5.5, 16), (6.8, 18.4), (7.5, 19.3), (8, 20), (8.5, 20.8)\}$

15. Each second, a car that begins with a speed of 40 ft/s increases its speed by 6 ft/s. Write and graph an equation to model the car's speed at s seconds.

Graphing Translations (Lesson 2-6)

16. Identify the parent function of $y = |x - 5|$. Graph $y = |x - 5|$ by translating its parent function.

Quadratic Equations and Functions

Chapter 5

LESSONS

Key Vocabulary

- axis of symmetry (p. 235)
- completing the square (p. 278)
- complex number (p. 271)
- complex number plane (p. 271)
- difference of two squares (p. 259)
- discriminant (p. 287)
- factoring (p. 255)
- *i* (p. 270)
- imaginary number (p. 270)
- parabola (p. 235)
- perfect square trinomial (p. 258)
- Quadratic Formula (p. 285)
- quadratic function (p. 234)
- standard form of a quadratic function (p. 234)
- vertex form of a quadratic function (p. 248)
- zero of a function (p. 264)
- Zero Product Property (p. 263)

Where You're Going

- In Chapter 5, you will learn to use quadratic functions to model real-world data.
- You will learn to graph and to solve quadratic equations.
- You will learn to graph complex numbers and to use them in solving quadratic equations.

Real-World Connection Applying what you learn, on page 265 you will solve a problem involving art.

5-1 Modeling Data With Quadratic Functions

North Carolina Objectives

2.02 Use quadratic functions and inequalities to model and solve problems; justify results. b) Interpret the constants and coefficients in the context of the problem.

Lesson Preview

What You'll Learn

OBJECTIVE 1 To identify quadratic functions and graphs

OBJECTIVE 2 To model data with quadratic functions

. . . And Why

To model the flow of water from a container, as in Example 4

Check Skills You'll Need

(For help, go to Lessons 1-2 and 2-2.)

Evaluate each function for $x = -3, -1, 0, 1,$ and 3.

1. $f(x) = x$
2. $f(x) = x^2$
3. $f(x) = -x$
4. $f(x) = -x^2$
5. $f(x) = \frac{1}{3}x^2$
6. $f(x) = -\frac{1}{3}x^2$

Write each equation in slope-intercept form.

7. $3x + 4y = 8$
8. $2x - y = -7$
9. $\frac{1}{2}x + 3y = 9$

New Vocabulary • quadratic function • standard form of a quadratic function • parabola • axis of symmetry • vertex of a parabola

Interactive lesson includes instant self-check, tutorials, and activities.

OBJECTIVE 1 Quadratic Functions and Their Graphs

A **quadratic function** is a function that can be written in the standard form $f(x) = ax^2 + bx + c$, where $a \neq 0$.

Key Concepts

Definition — **Standard Form of a Quadratic Function**

$$f(x) = \underbrace{ax^2}_{\text{quadratic term}} + \underbrace{bx}_{\text{linear term}} + \underbrace{c}_{\text{constant term}}$$

The condition $a \neq 0$ gives every quadratic function a quadratic term, but not necessarily a linear term or a constant term. If $a = 0$, then the function has no quadratic term, and it is not a quadratic function.

Need Help?

You can use the FOIL method to multiply.

First, Last, Inner, Outer: $y = (2x + 3)(x - 4)$

1 EXAMPLE Classifying Functions

Determine whether each function is linear or quadratic. Identify the quadratic, linear, and constant terms.

a. $y = (2x + 3)(x - 4)$

$= 2x^2 - 8x + 3x - 12$ **Multiply.**

$= 2x^2 - 5x - 12$ **Write in standard form.**

This is a quadratic function.
Quadratic term: $2x^2$
Linear term: $-5x$
Constant term: -12

b. $f(x) = 3(x^2 - 2x) - 3(x^2 - 2)$

$= 3x^2 - 6x - 3x^2 + 6$

$= -6x + 6$

This is a linear function.
Quadratic term: none
Linear term: $-6x$
Constant term: 6

Check Understanding **1** Determine whether each function is linear or quadratic. Identify the quadratic, linear, and constant terms.

a. $f(x) = (x^2 + 5x) - x^2$ **b.** $f(x) = (x - 5)(3x - 1)$ **c.** $f(x) = x(x + 3)$

Real-World Connection

Objects tossed into the air follow parabolic paths.

The graph of a quadratic function is a **parabola.** The **axis of symmetry** is the line that divides a parabola into two parts that are mirror images. The **vertex of a parabola** is the point at which the parabola intersects the axis of symmetry. The y-value of the vertex of a parabola represents the maximum or minimum value of the function.

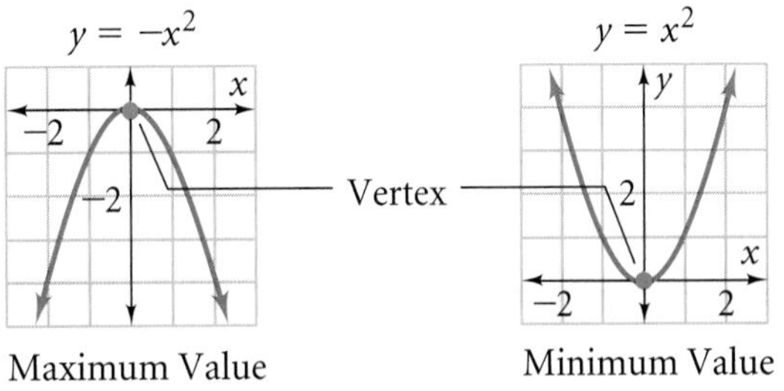

The axis of symmetry of the graph of a quadratic function is always a vertical line defined by the x-coordinate of the vertex. In each graph above, the axis of symmetry is the y-axis, $x = 0$.

Each point of the parabola has a corresponding point on its mirror image. Two corresponding points are the same distance from the axis of symmetry.

2 EXAMPLE Points on a Parabola

Below is the graph of $y = 2x^2 - 8x + 8$. Identify the vertex and the axis of symmetry. Identify points corresponding to P and Q.

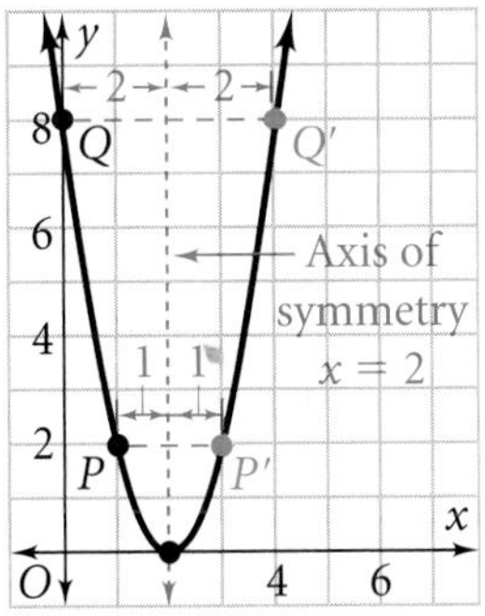

The vertex is (2, 0).

The axis of symmetry is $x = 2$, the vertical line passing through the vertex.

$P(1, 2)$ is one unit to the left of the axis of symmetry. Corresponding point $P'(3, 2)$ is one unit to the right of the axis of symmetry.

$Q(0, 8)$ is two units to the left of the axis of symmetry. Corresponding point $Q'(4, 8)$ is two units to the right of the axis of symmetry.

Check Understanding **2** Identify the vertex and the axis of symmetry of each parabola. Identify points corresponding to P and Q.

a.

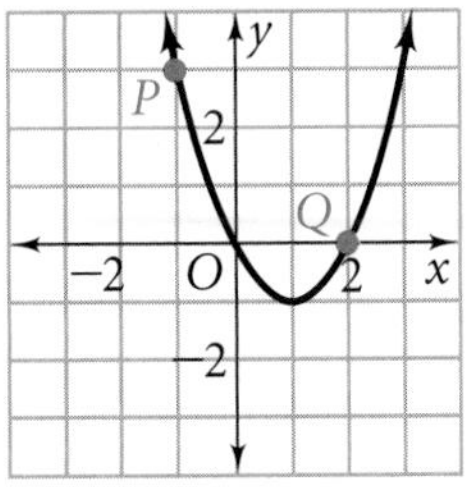

b.

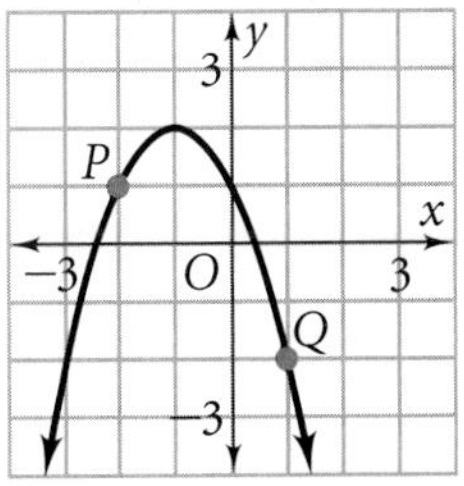

OBJECTIVE

2 Using Quadratic Models

You have already learned to use linear functions to model data. Some data can be modeled with a quadratic function.

3 EXAMPLE Finding a Quadratic Model

Find a quadratic function to model the values in the table.

x	y
2	3
3	13
4	29

Substitute the values of x and y into $y = ax^2 + bx + c$. The result is a system of three linear equations.

$y = ax^2 + bx + c$

$3 = a(2)^2 + b(2) + c = 4a + 2b + c$ **Use (2, 3).**

$13 = a(3)^2 + b(3) + c = 9a + 3b + c$ **Use (3, 13).**

$29 = a(4)^2 + b(4) + c = 16a + 4b + c$ **Use (4, 29).**

Using one of the methods of Chapter 3, solve the system. $\begin{cases} 4a + 2b + c = 3 \\ 9a + 3b + c = 13 \\ 16a + 4b + c = 29 \end{cases}$

The solution is $a = 3, b = -5, c = 1$. Substitute these values into standard form.

$y = (3)x^2 + (-5)x + (1)$

The quadratic function is $y = 3x^2 - 5x + 1$.

Check Understanding 3 Find a quadratic function with a graph that includes (1, 0), (2, −3), and (3, −10).

You can use the quadratic regression feature of a graphing calculator to find and graph a quadratic model.

4 EXAMPLE Real-World Connection

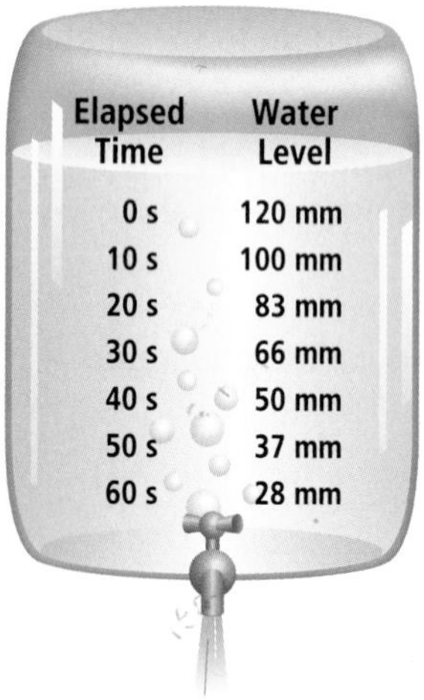

Elapsed Time	Water Level
0 s	120 mm
10 s	100 mm
20 s	83 mm
30 s	66 mm
40 s	50 mm
50 s	37 mm
60 s	28 mm

Hydraulics The table at the left shows the height of a column of water as it drains from its container. Model the data with a quadratic function. Graph the data and the function. Use the model to estimate the water level at 35 seconds.

Step 1 Enter the data. Use **QuadReg**.

Step 2 Graph the data and the function.

Step 3 Use the table feature to find $f(35)$.

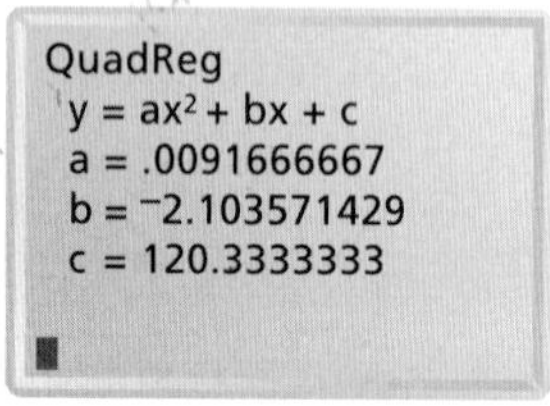
QuadReg
y = ax² + bx + c
a = .0091666667
b = ⁻2.103571429
c = 120.3333333

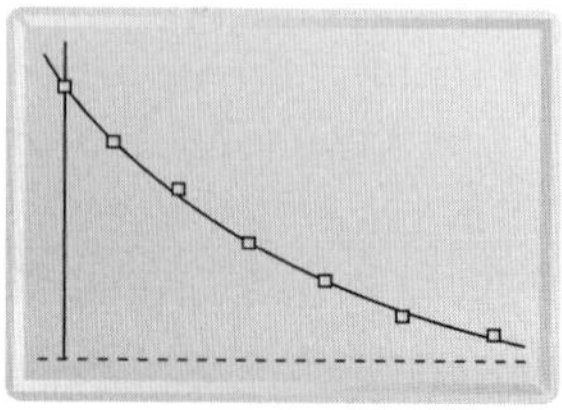

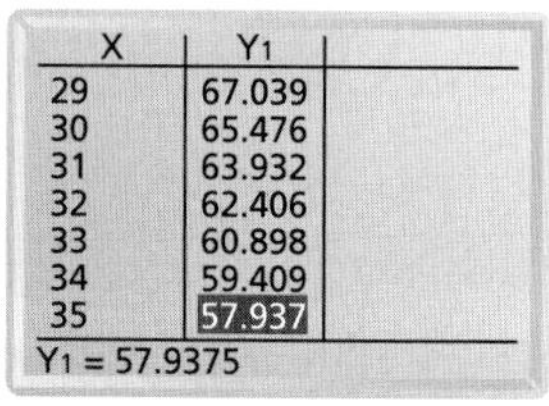
X Y1
29 67.039
30 65.476
31 63.932
32 62.406
33 60.898
34 59.409
35 57.937
Y1 = 57.9375

An approximate model of the quadratic function is $y = 0.009167x^2 - 2.10x + 120$. At 35 seconds the water level is approximately 58 mm.

Check Understanding 4 **a.** Use the quadratic model to estimate the water level at 25 seconds.
b. Use the quadratic model to predict the water level at 3 minutes.
c. **Critical Thinking** Is your prediction in part (b) reasonable? Explain.

EXERCISES

For more practice, see *Extra Practice.*

Practice and Problem Solving

A Practice by Example

Example 1 (page 234)

Determine whether each function is linear or quadratic. Identify the quadratic, linear, and constant terms.

1. $y = x + 4$ **2.** $y = 2x^2 - (3x - 5)$ **3.** $y = 3x(x - 2)$

4. $f(x) = x^2 - 7$ **5.** $y = (x - 2)(x + 5)$ **6.** $g(x) = -7(x - 4)$

7. $h(x) = (3x)(2x) + 6$ **8.** $y = x(1 - x) - (1 - x^2)$ **9.** $f(x) = -x(2x + 8)$

Example 2 (page 235)

Identify the vertex and the axis of symmetry of each parabola.

10.

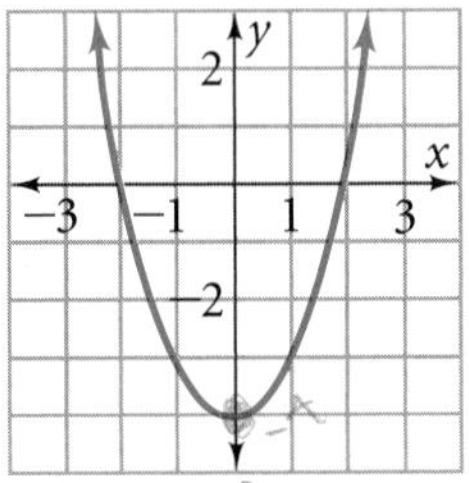

11.

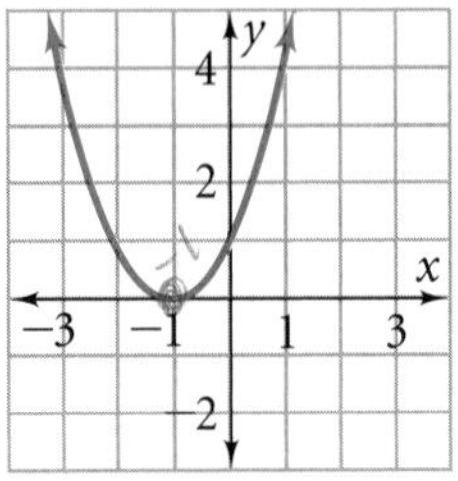

12.

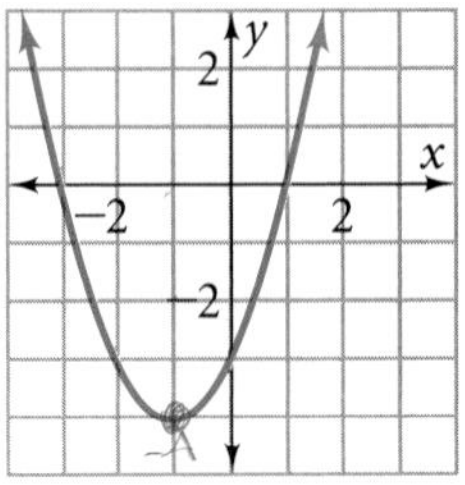

For each parabola, identify points corresponding to *P* and *Q*.

13.

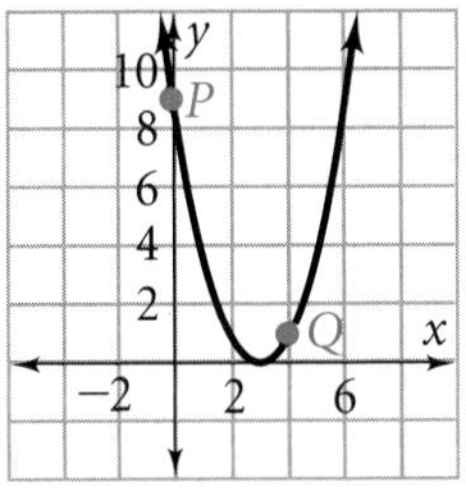

14.

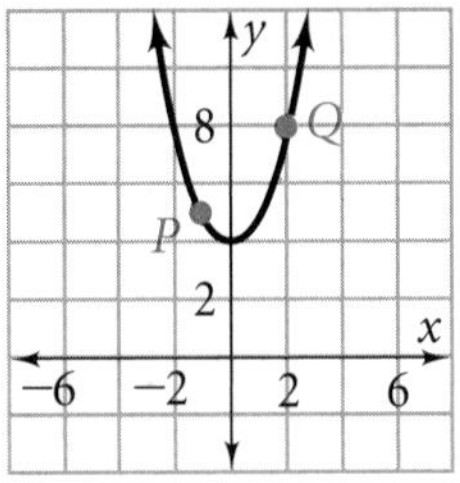

15.

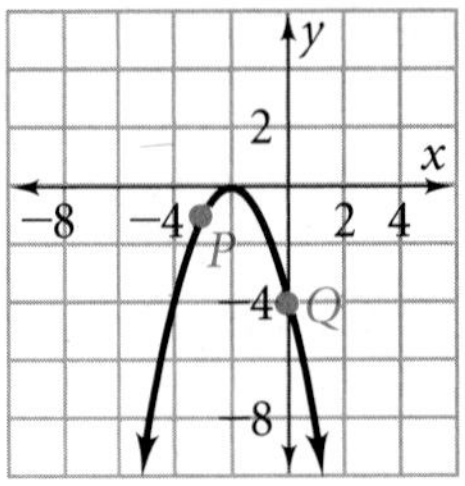

Example 3 (page 236)

Find a quadratic model for each set of values.

16. $(1, -2), (2, -2), (3, -4)$ **17.** $(1, -2), (2, -4), (3, -4)$ **18.** $(-1, 6), (1, 4), (2, 9)$

19.

x	−1	1	2
f(x)	−1	3	8

20.

x	−1	1	2
f(x)	17	17	8

Example 4 (page 236)

21. Physics A man throws a ball off the top of a building. The table shows the height of the ball at different times.

a. Find a quadratic model for the data.

b. Use the model to estimate the height of the ball at 2.5 seconds.

Height of a Ball

Time	Height
0 s	46 ft
1 s	63 ft
2 s	48 ft
3 s	1 ft

22. Communications The table shows the percent of U.S. houses with cable TV.

a. Find a quadratic model using 1960 as year 0, 1970 as year 10, and so on.

b. Use the model to estimate the percent of households with cable TV in 1995.

Television Cable Access

Year	1960	1970	1980	1990	2000
% of Households	0	7	20	56	68

SOURCE: *Time Almanac*

B Apply Your Skills

Determine whether a quadratic model exists for each set of values. If so, write the model.

23. $f(-2) = 16, f(0) = 0, f(1) = 4$

24. $f(0) = 5, f(2) = 3, f(-1) = 0$

25. $f(-1) = -4, f(1) = -2, f(2) = -1$

26. $f(-2) = 7, f(0) = 1, f(2) = 0$

Identify the vertex and the axis of symmetry for each function.

27.

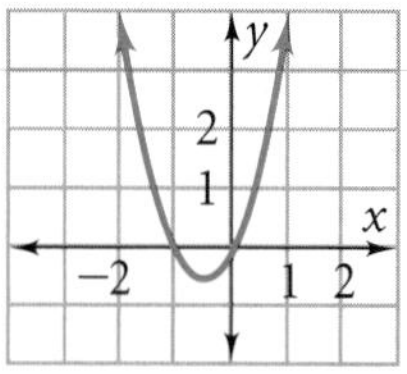

28.

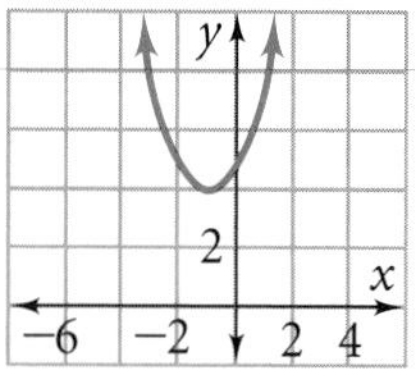

29.

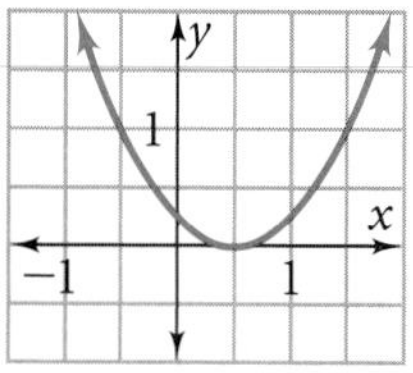

30. a. Geometry Copy and complete the table. It shows the total number of segments that can be drawn among x points, no three of which are collinear.

Number of points, x	2	3	■	■
Number of segments, y	1	3	■	■

b. Write a quadratic model for the data.

c. Predict the number of segments that can be drawn among ten points.

Real-World Connection

Aremy McCann won a stamp-design competition sponsored by the U.S. government.

31. a. Postal Rates Find a quadratic model for the data. Use 1974 as year 0.

Price of First-Class Stamp

Year	1974	1978	1981	1983	1988	1995	2001	2002
Price (cents)	10	15	18	20	25	32	34	37

b. Estimation Estimate when first-class postage was 29¢.

c. Predict when first-class postage will be 50¢. Explain why your prediction may not be valid.

The graph of each function contains the given point. Find the value of c.

32. $y = x^2 + c; (0, 3)$

33. $y = x^2 - c; (4, 8)$

34. $y = -5x^2 + c; (2, -14)$

35. $y = 2x^2 + c; \left(-\frac{3}{4}, -\frac{1}{4}\right)$

36. $y = -\frac{3}{4}x^2 + c; \left(3, -\frac{1}{2}\right)$

37. $y = (x + c)^2; (10, 0)$

38. Road Safety The table below gives the stopping distance for an automobile under certain road conditions.

Speed (mi/h)	20	30	40	50	55
Stopping Distance (ft)	17	38	67	105	127

a. Find a linear model for the data.

b. Find a quadratic model for the data.

c. Writing Compare the models. Which is better? Explain.

39. Open-Ended Write three different quadratic functions, each with a graph that includes (0, 0) and (5, −1).

Challenge

40. **Critical Thinking** What is the minimum number of data points you need to find a quadratic model for a data set? Explain.

41. How are the graphs of $y = x^2$ and $y = |x|$ similar? How are they different?

42. A parabola contains the points (0, −4), (2, 4), and (4, 4). Find the vertex.

43. A model for the height of an arrow shot into the air is $h(t) = -16t^2 + 72t + 5$, where t is time and h is height. Without graphing, consider the function's graph.
   a. What can you learn by finding the graph's intercept with the h-axis?
   b. What can you learn by finding the graph's intercept(s) with the t-axis?

Standardized Test Prep

Multiple Choice

44. For which quadratic function is −3 the constant term?
   A. $y = (3x + 1)(-x - 3)$ B. $y = x^2 - 3x + 3$
   C. $f(x) = (x - 3)(x - 3)$ D. $g(x) = -3x^2 + 3x + 9$

45. The vertex of a parabola is (3, 2). A second point on the parabola is (1, 7). Which point is also on the parabola?
   F. (−1, 7) G. (3, 7) H. (5, 7) I. (3, −2)

Take It to the NET
Online lesson quiz at **www.PHSchool.com**
Web Code: aga-0501

46. The graph of a quadratic function has vertex (−3, −2). What is the axis of symmetry?
   A. $x = -3$ B. $x = 3$ C. $y = -2$ D. $y = 2$

47. Which function is NOT a quadratic function?
   F. $y = (x - 1)(x - 2)$ G. $y = x^2 + 2x - 3$
   H. $y = 3x - x^2$ I. $y = -x^2 + x(x - 3)$

Extended Response

48. What is the quadratic function with a graph that includes (1, 6), (2, 11), and (3, 20)? Find the function by writing and solving a system of equations. Write the function in standard form. Show all your work.

Mixed Review

Lesson 4-8

Write the augmented matrix for each system. Then solve the system.

49. $\begin{cases} 3x - y = 7 \\ 2x + 2y = 10 \end{cases}$

50. $\begin{cases} 3x + y - 2z = -3 \\ x - 3y - z = -2 \\ 2x + 2y + 3z = 11 \end{cases}$

Lesson 4-3

Find each product.

51. $\begin{bmatrix} 2 & -3 \end{bmatrix} \begin{bmatrix} 3 & -2 & 4 & 1 \\ 2 & 0 & -3 & 2 \end{bmatrix}$

52. $\begin{bmatrix} 3 & 10 \\ 1 & 5 \end{bmatrix} \begin{bmatrix} -7 & 2 \\ 8 & 4 \end{bmatrix}$

Lesson 3-2

Solve each system by elimination.

53. $\begin{cases} x + y = 7 \\ 5x - y = 5 \end{cases}$

54. $\begin{cases} 2x - 3y = -14 \\ 3x - y = 7 \end{cases}$

55. $\begin{cases} x - 3y = 2 \\ x - 2y = 1 \end{cases}$

Lesson 2-3

For each direct variation, find the value of y when $x = 2$.

56. $y = 2$ when $x = 5$

57. $y = 1$ when $x = 4$

58. $y = -2$ when $x = 4$

Technology

Modeling Using Residuals

For Use With Lesson 5-1

You can use more than one model for a set of data. You can determine which is a better model by analyzing the differences between the *y*-values of the data and the *y*-values of each model. These differences are called residuals. The better model will have residuals that are closer to zero.

EXAMPLE

The calculator screen shows the graphs of a linear model and a quadratic model for the data below. Which model better fits the data?

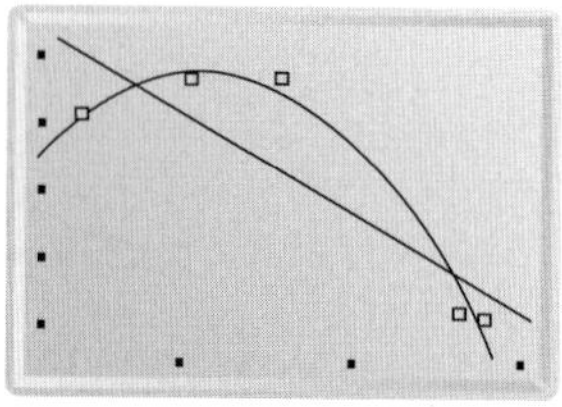

Participation in Baseball in the U.S.

Year (0 = 1900)	87	90	93	98	99
Millions of Participants	15.1	15.5	15.6	12.3	12.1

Step 1 Press STAT ENTER to enter the data in L_1 and L_2. Then use the LinReg and QuadReg features to find linear and quadratic models.

Step 2 Enter the linear model as Y_1 and the quadratic model as Y_2.

Step 3 To find the residuals of the linear model and store the differences in L_3, enter L_2 − VARS ▶ 1 1 (L_1) STO▶ L_3 ENTER.

Step 4 Find the residuals of the quadratic model. Store the differences in L_4.

Step 5 Compare the residuals in L_3 and L_4. The values in L_4 are closer to zero, so the quadratic model is the better fit.

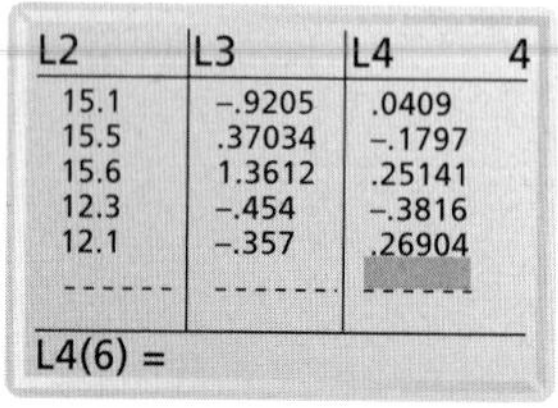

L2
L3
L4
4
15.1
15.5
15.6
12.3
12.1
-.9205
.37034
1.3612
-.454
-.357
.0409
-.1797
.25141
-.3816
.26904
L4(6) =

EXERCISES

For each set of data, find a linear model and a quadratic model. Which model is the better fit? Justify your reasoning.

1. **Money Spent in the U.S. on Personal Technology**

Year (0 = 1970)	0	10	20	22	24	26
Billions of Dollars	8.8	17.6	53.8	61.2	78.5	89.7

2. **Fishing Licenses Sold**

Year (0 = 1970)	0	5	10	15	20	25
Millions Sold	31.1	34.9	35.2	35.7	37.0	37.9

5-2 Properties of Parabolas

North Carolina Objectives

2.02 Use quadratic functions and inequalities to model and solve problems. a) Solve using graphs. b) Interpret the constants and coefficients in the context of the problem.

Lesson Preview

What You'll Learn

OBJECTIVE 1 To graph quadratic functions

OBJECTIVE 2 To find maximum and minimum values of quadratic functions

. . . And Why

To maximize a company's revenue

✓ Check Skills You'll Need

(For help, go to Lessons 2-2 and 2-5.)

Find the y-intercept of the graph of each function.

1. $y = 3x + 3$ **2.** $y = -2x - 1$ **3.** $4x - 3y = 12$

Find the vertex of the graph of each function.

4. $y = |-2x|$ **5.** $y = \left|-\frac{2}{3}x - 1\right|$ **6.** $y = |3x + 7|$

Graph each equation.

7. $y = -4x - 3$ **8.** $\frac{1}{2}x + y = -2$ **9.** $y = |5x - 5|$

Interactive lesson includes instant self-check, tutorials, and activities.

OBJECTIVE 1 Graphing Parabolas

The standard form of a quadratic function is $y = ax^2 + bx + c$. When $b = 0$, the function simplifies to $y = ax^2 + c$.

The graph of $y = ax^2 + c$ is a parabola with an axis of symmetry $x = 0$, the y-axis. The vertex of the graph is the y-intercept $(0, c)$.

Reading Math

The word *symmetry* comes from a prefix meaning "same" and a root meaning "measure."

1 EXAMPLE Graphing a Function of the Form $y = ax^2 + c$

Graph $y = -\frac{1}{2}x^2 + 2$.

Step 1 Graph the vertex, which is the y-intercept $(0, 2)$.

Step 2 Make a table of values to find some points on one side of the axis of symmetry $x = 0$. Graph the points.

x	1	2	3	4
y	$1\frac{1}{2}$	0	$-2\frac{1}{2}$	−6

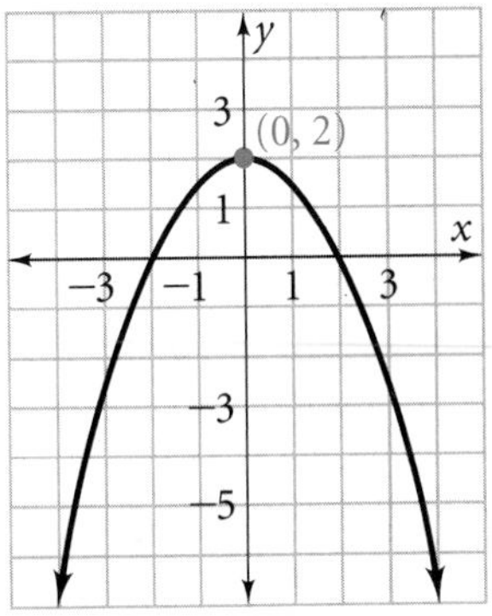

Step 4 Graph corresponding points on the other side of the axis of symmetry.

Step 5 Sketch the curve.

✓ Check Understanding

1 a. Graph $y = 2x^2 - 4$.

b. Graph $y = -5 + 3x^2$.

c. Reasoning What are the coordinates of the vertex of the graph of a function in the form $y = ax^2$?

When $b \neq 0$ in the standard form of a quadratic function, $y = ax^2 + bx + c$, the values of both a and b affect the position of the axis of symmetry.

You can use the values of a, b, and c to find characteristics of the graph of a quadratic function.

Key Concepts

Properties **Graph of a Quadratic Function in Standard Form**

The graph of $y = ax^2 + bx + c$ is a parabola when $a \neq 0$.

- When $a > 0$, the parabola opens up. When $a < 0$, the parabola opens down.
- The axis of symmetry is the line $x = -\frac{b}{2a}$.
- The x-coordinate of the vertex is $-\frac{b}{2a}$. The y-coordinate of the vertex is the value of y when $x = -\frac{b}{2a}$, or $y = f\left(-\frac{b}{2a}\right)$.
- The y-intercept is $(0, c)$.

Need Help?

The y-intercept is the point at which a line crosses the y-axis.

$y = ax^2 + bx + c,\ a > 0$

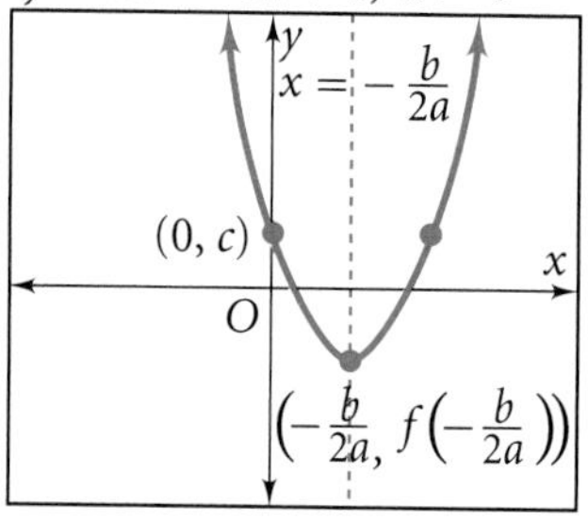

$y = ax^2 + bx + c,\ a < 0$

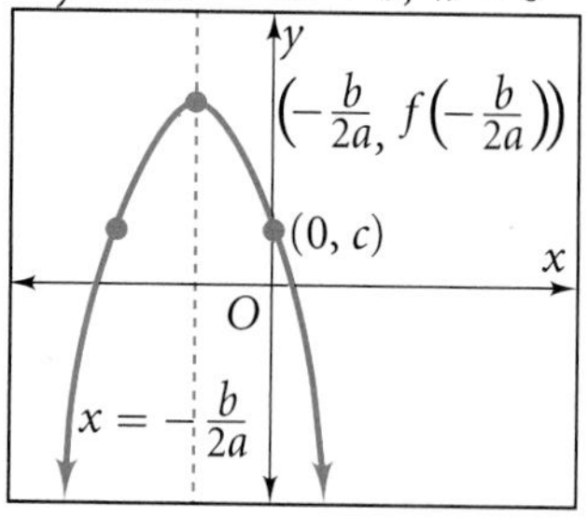

2 EXAMPLE Graphing a Function of the Form $y = ax^2 + bx + c$

Graph $y = x^2 - 2x - 3$. Label the vertex and the axis of symmetry.

Step 1 Find and graph the axis of symmetry.

$$x = -\frac{b}{2a} = -\frac{(-2)}{2(1)} = 1$$

Step 2 Find and graph the vertex. The x-coordinate of the vertex is $-\frac{b}{2a}$, or 1.

The y-coordinate is $y = (1)^2 - 2(1) - 3 = -4$. So the vertex is $(1, -4)$.

Step 3 Find and graph the y-intercept and its reflection. Since $c = -3$, the y-intercept is $(0, -3)$ and its reflection is $(2, -3)$.

Step 4 Evaluate the function for another value of x, such as $y = (3)^2 - 2(3) - 3 = 0$. Graph $(3, 0)$ and its reflection $(-1, 0)$.

Step 5 Sketch the curve.

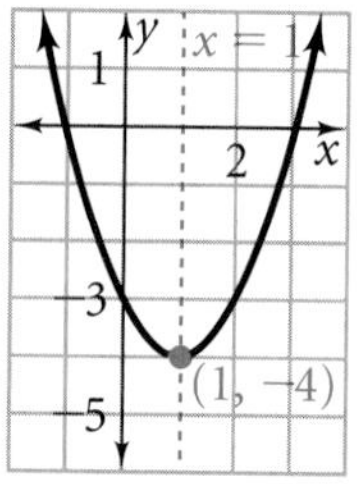

Since $a > 0$, the graph opens up.

Check Understanding 2 Graph each function. Label the vertex and the axis of symmetry.

a. $y = -x^2 + 4x + 2$

b. $y = -\frac{1}{3}x^2 - 2x - 3$

OBJECTIVE 2

Finding Maximum and Minimum Values

The y-coordinate of the vertex of a parabola represents the maximum or minimum value of a quadratic function.

3 EXAMPLE Finding a Minimum Value

Reading Math

Maximums and minimums are sometimes referred to as maxima and minima.

Graph $y = 3x^2 + 12x + 8$. What is the minimum value of the function?

Since $a > 0$, the graph of the function opens up, and the vertex represents the minimum value. Find the coordinates of the vertex.

$x = -\frac{b}{2a} = -\frac{12}{2(3)} = -2$ **Find the x-coordinate of the vertex.**

$y = 3(-2)^2 + 12(-2) + 8 = -4$ **Find the y-coordinate of the vertex.**

Graph the vertex and the axis of symmetry $x = -2$. Graph two points on one side of the axis of symmetry, such as $(0, 8)$ and $(-1, -1)$. Then graph corresponding points $(-4, 8)$ and $(-3, -1)$.

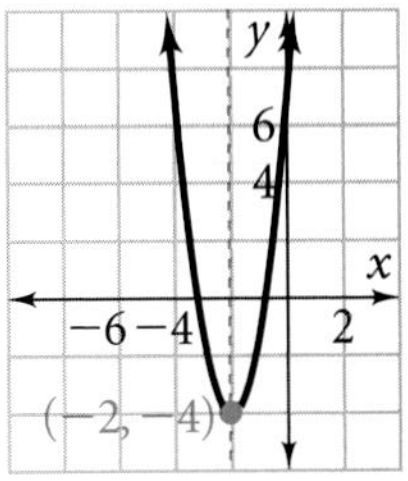

The minimum value of the function is -4.

Check Understanding 3 **a.** Graph $y = 2x^2 + 8x - 1$. Find the minimum value of the function.

b. Critical Thinking What is the maximum value of the function?

You can find a maximum or minimum value without graphing the function.

4 EXAMPLE Real-World Connection

Real-World Connection

The number of unicycles a company sells can be modeled by $-2.5p + 500$.

Economics The number of items a company sells frequently is a function of the item's price. The revenue from sales of the item is the product of the price and the number sold. Refer to the photo. What price will maximize the company's revenue from unicycle sales? What is the maximum revenue?

Relate revenue equals price times number of unicycles sold

Define Let R = revenue. Let p = price of a unicycle.

Let $-2.5p + 500$ = number of unicycles sold.

Write $R = p(-2.5p + 500)$

$= -2.5p^2 + 500p$ **Write in standard form.**

Find the maximum value of the function. Since $a < 0$, the graph of the function opens down, and the vertex represents a maximum value.

$p = -\frac{b}{2a} = -\frac{500}{2(-2.5)} = 100$ **Find p at the vertex.**

$R = -2.5(100)^2 + 500(100)$ **Evaluate R for $p = 100$.**

$= 25{,}000$ **Simplify.**

A price of \$100 will maximize revenue. The maximum revenue is \$25,000.

Check Understanding 4 The number of widgets the Woodget Company sells can be modeled by $-5p + 100$, where p is the price of a widget. What price will maximize revenue? What is the maximum revenue?

EXERCISES

For more practice, see *Extra Practice.*

Practice and Problem Solving

A Practice by Example

Example 1 (page 241)

Graph each function.

1. $y = -x^2 + 1$
2. $y = -x^2 - 1$
3. $y = 2x^2 + 4$
4. $y = 3x^2 - 6$
5. $y = -\frac{1}{3}x^2 - 1$
6. $y = -5x^2 + 12$
7. $y = \frac{1}{2}x^2 + 3$
8. $y = \frac{1}{4}x^2 - 3$
9. $y = -2x^2 + \frac{3}{4}$

Example 2 (page 242)

Graph each function. Label the vertex and the axis of symmetry.

10. $y = x^2 + 2x + 1$
11. $y = -x^2 + 2x + 1$
12. $y = x^2 + 4x + 1$
13. $y = x^2 + 6x + 9$
14. $y = -x^2 - 3x + 6$
15. $y = 2x^2 + 4x$
16. $y = 4x^2 - 12x + 9$
17. $y = -6x^2 - 12x - 1$
18. $y = -\frac{3}{4}x^2 + 6x + 6$
19. $y = 3x^2 - 12x + 10$
20. $y = \frac{1}{2}x^2 + 2x - 8$
21. $y = -4x^2 - 24x - 36$

Example 3 (page 243)

Graph each function. If $a > 0$ find the minimum value. If $a < 0$ find the maximum value.

22. $y = -x^2 + 2x + 5$
23. $y = 3x^2 - 4x - 2$
24. $y = -2x^2 - 3x + 4$
25. $y = \frac{1}{3}x^2 + 2x + 5$
26. $y = -x^2 - x + 6$
27. $y = 2x^2 + 5$

Example 4 (page 243)

28. Revenue A model for a company's revenue is $R = -15p^2 + 300p + 12{,}000$, where p is the price in dollars of the company's product. What price will maximize revenue? Find the maximum revenue.

29. Physics The equation for the motion of a projectile fired straight up at an initial velocity of 64 ft/s is $h = 64t - 16t^2$, where h is the height in feet and t is the time in seconds. Find the time the projectile needs to reach its highest point. How high it will go?

30. Manufacturing The equation for the cost in dollars of producing automobile tires is $C = 0.000015x^2 - 0.03x + 35$, where x is the number of tires produced. Find the number of tires that minimizes the cost. What is the cost for that number of tires?

B Apply Your Skills

Sketch each parabola using the given information.

31. vertex (3, 6), y-intercept 2
32. vertex (−1, −4), y-intercept 3
33. vertex (0, 5), point (1, −2)
34. vertex (2, 3), point (6, 9)

35. Find a pair of numbers with a sum of 26 and a product that is a maximum. Find the maximum product.

36. Find two numbers with a difference of 10 and a product that is a minimum. Find the minimum product.

Match each function with its graph.

37. $y = x^2 + 4x + 1$

38. $y = -x^2 - 4x + 1$

39. $y = -\frac{1}{2}x^2 - 2x + 1$

A.

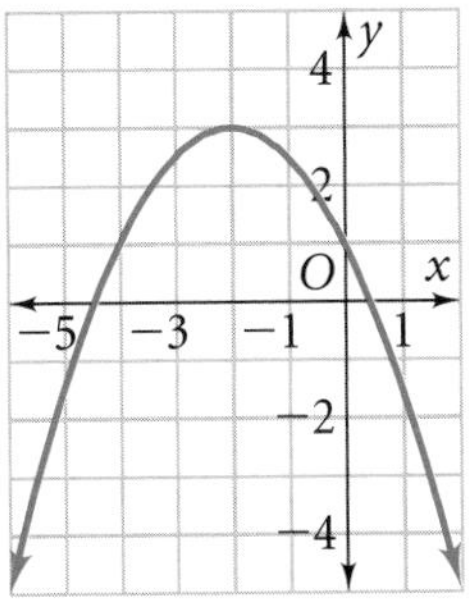

B.

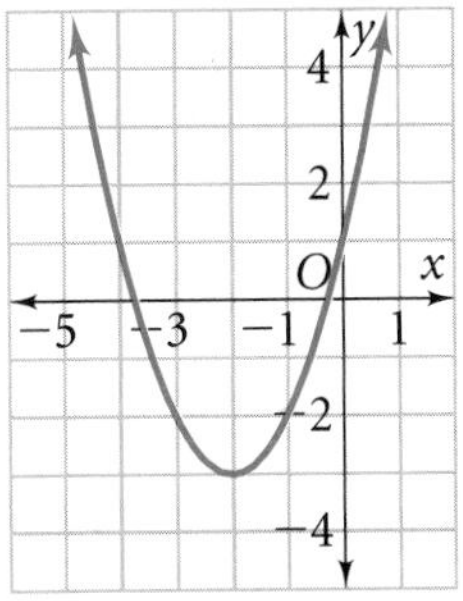

C.

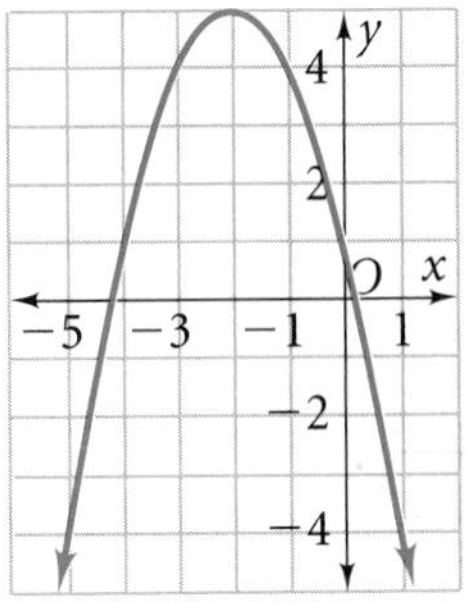

40. Open-Ended Write the equation of a parabola symmetric about $x = -10$.

41. Woodworking Suppose you want to frame a collage of pictures. You have a 9-ft strip of wood for the frame. What dimensions of the frame give you the maximum area for the collage? What is the maximum area?

Real-World Connection

Careers Picture framers choose the dimensions of frames that best suit works of art.

42. Physics Suppose you throw a ball over a 10-ft fence. Barely clearing the fence, the ball reaches its highest point directly above the fence and lands 10 ft from the fence. Using the fence as the axis of symmetry, write a quadratic function that models the ball's height.

43. Packaging The bottom of a box is to be a rectangle with a perimeter of 36 cm. The box must be 4 cm high. What dimensions give the maximum volume?

For each function, the vertex of the function's graph is given. Find *c*.

44. $y = x^2 - 6x + c; (3, -4)$

45. $y = -3x^2 + 6x + c; (1, 0)$

46. $y = x^2 + 10x + c; (-5, -27)$

47. $y = c - x^2 - 2x; (-1, 3)$

Find the quadratic function $y = ax^2 + c$ with a graph that has the given points.

48. $(0, 2), (3, 5)$

49. $(0, -3), (1, -7)$

50. $\left(2, \frac{5}{2}\right), \left(0, -\frac{1}{2}\right)$

51. $(-3, 89), (2, 39)$

52. $(-2, -10), (4, -40)$

53. $(-1, 14), (4, 104)$

54. A rock club's profit from booking local bands depends on the ticket price. Using past receipts, the owners find that the profit p can be modeled by the function $p = -15t^2 + 600t + 50$, where t represents the ticket price in dollars.

a. What price yields the maximum profit?

b. What is the maximum profit?

c. Open-Ended What price would you pay to see your favorite local band? How much profit would the club owner make using that ticket price?

55. Landscape Design A town is planning a child-care facility. It wants to fence in a rectangular playground using one of the walls of the building. What is the largest playground that can be fenced in using 100 ft of donated fencing?

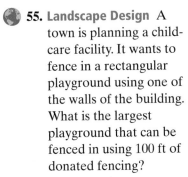

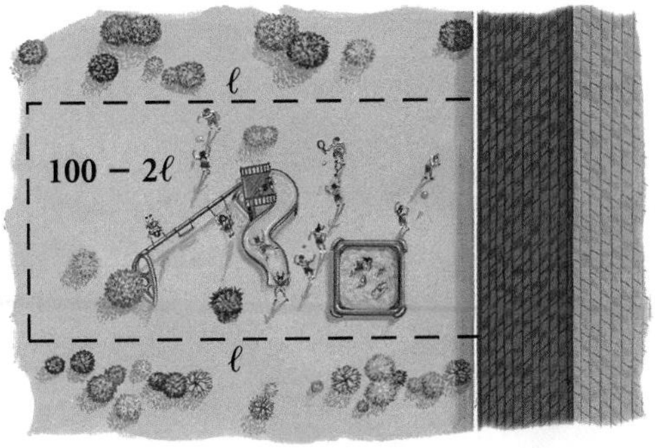

Real-World Connection

The archaeological remains of the Harappan city Mohenjo Daro show the thick walls that were built to keep out the hot sun.

56. History Around 2500 B.C. in the Indus Valley of South Asia, the Harappan people built one of the first cities. The Harappans built rectangular houses that had open central courtyards surrounded by solid brick walls.

a. Suppose you build a model of a Harappan house. For the outer walls you plan to use 2400 bricks. The walls of the model are 10 bricks high and 1 brick thick. Draw several possible floor plans.

b. Find the dimensions of the floor plan that give the model of maximum area.

Each point lies on a parabola that has its vertex at (0, 1). Write the equation of the parabola. Indicate whether the graph opens up or down.

57. $(-3, 10)$ **58.** $(-1, 6)$ **59.** $(2, -1)$ **60.** $(4, -7)$

61. $(3, 4)$ **62.** $(5, -4)$ **63.** $(8, -15)$ **64.** $(-6, -2)$

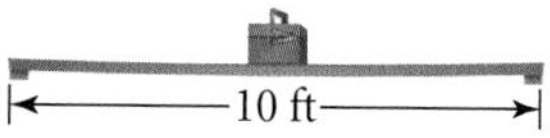

65. Construction A construction worker places his toolbox on a board that rests on two cement posts 10 ft apart. The toolbox is halfway between the posts. Under the weight of the toolbox, the board sags by one quarter inch. Model the shape of the board in three different ways by writing a function whose graph satisfies each condition below.

a. The origin of the graph corresponds to the position of the toolbox.

b. The origin of the graph corresponds to the position of the post on the left.

c. The origin of the graph corresponds to the position of the post on the right.

66. A student says that the graph of $y = ax^2 + bx + c$ gets wider as a increases.

a. Error Analysis Use examples to show that the student is wrong.

b. Writing Summarize the relationship between $|a|$ and the width of the graph of $y = ax^2 + bx + c$.

C Challenge

For each function, the vertex of the function's graph is given. Find a and b.

67. $y = ax^2 + bx - 27; (2, -3)$ **68.** $y = ax^2 + bx + 5; (-1, 4)$

69. $y = ax^2 + bx + 8; (2, -4)$ **70.** $y = ax^2 + bx; (-3, 2)$

The formula for the area enclosed by a parabola and the x-axis from x-intercepts x_1 to x_2 is $A = \frac{2}{3}h(x_2 - x_1)$, where h is the height. Find the enclosed area for each parabola.

71.

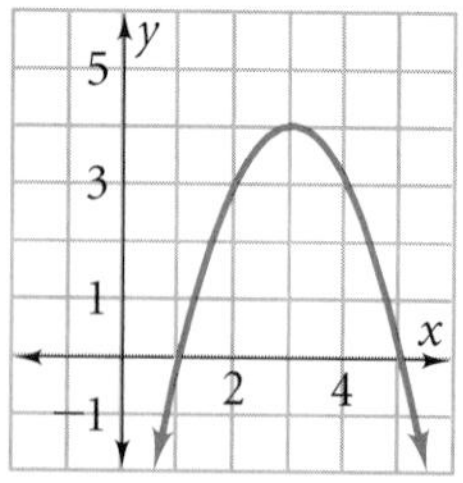

72.

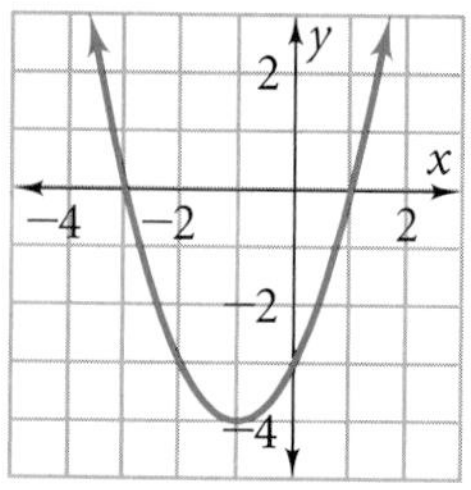

73.

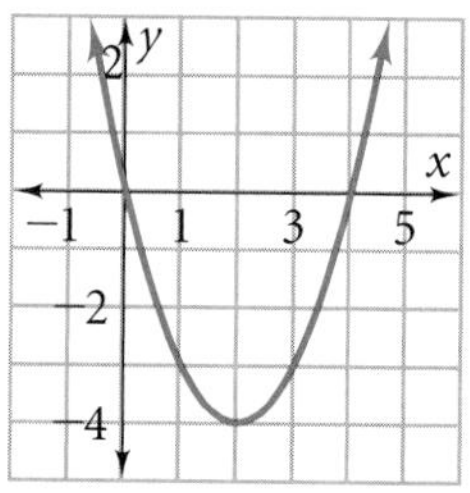

Standardized Test Prep

Multiple Choice

74. What is the vertex of $y = -2x^2 - 4x - 5$?
A. $(-2, -3)$ **B.** $(1, -3)$ **C.** $(1, -11)$ **D.** $(-1, -3)$

75. What is the y-intercept of $y = (x + 1)^2 - 2$?
F. $(0, -1)$ **G.** $(0, -3)$ **H.** $(0, 1)$ **I.** $(0, -2)$

76. What is the maximum area in square units of a rectangle with a perimeter of 128 units?
A. 4096 **B.** 1024 **C.** 256 **D.** 32

Take It to the NET
Online lesson quiz at **www.PHSchool.com**
Web Code: aga-0502

77. The vertex of the graph of $y = -x^2 - 16x - 62$ lies in which quadrant?
F. IV **G.** III **H.** II **I.** I

78. What percent of nonzero integers have squares that are odd numbers?
A. 25 **B.** 50 **C.** 75 **D.** 100

Short Response

79. Sketch the graph of $y = x^2 - 6x + 2$. Explain how to identify the vertex and two other points on the parabola.

Mixed Review

Lesson 5-1

80. Find a quadratic model for the values in the table.

x	0	5	10	15	20
y	17	39	54	61	61

Lesson 4-2

Solve each equation.

81. $X + \begin{bmatrix} 0 & 4 \\ -2 & 1 \end{bmatrix} = \begin{bmatrix} 3 & 0 \\ 1 & 1 \end{bmatrix}$

82. $X - \begin{bmatrix} 3 & 3 \\ -2 & -1 \end{bmatrix} = \begin{bmatrix} 1 & 0 \\ 0 & 1 \end{bmatrix}$

Lesson 3-3

83. **Manufacturing** A new factory will require at least 40,000 ft^2 of storage space. No more than 25,000 ft^2 of the space will be covered with a roof. Write a system of inequalities to represent the constraints. Solve the system by graphing.

Algebra at Work

Landscape Architect

Landscape architects create outdoor environments for parks, office buildings, and homes. They plan walls, staircases, pools, walkways, and plantings. Landscape architects blend ideas from art, science, nature, and math in their work. They need training in all three areas before they begin their careers. For example, when planning a decorative fountain, an architect needs to predict the parabolic path of the spray. The height and distance of the spray depend on the speed of the water and the angle at which it exits a pipe. Basic principles of physics often help architects. By making adjustments to a model, they can plan the effect they want.

Take It to the NET For more information about a career in landscape architecture, go to **www.PHSchool.com**.
Web Code: age-2032

5-3 Translating Parabolas

North Carolina Objectives

2.02 Use quadratic functions and inequalities to model and solve problems. a) Solve using graphs. b) Interpret the constants and coefficients in the context of the problem.

Lesson Preview

What You'll Learn

OBJECTIVE 1 To use the vertex form of a quadratic function

. . . And Why

To model a suspension bridge, as in Example 3

Check Skills You'll Need

(For help, go to Lesson 2-6.)

Identify the parent function of each function. Then graph the function by translating the parent function.

1. $y = -x + 2$ **2.** $y = |3x| + 2$ **3.** $y = -|x + 1| - 1$

Write an equation for each translation.

4. $y = 2x$, 2 units down **5.** $y = x$, 4 units up, 1 unit right

New Vocabulary • vertex form of a quadratic function

Interactive lesson includes instant self-check, tutorials, and activities.

OBJECTIVE 1

Using Vertex Form

Investigation: Vertex Form

1. Each function in the first column is written in standard form. In the second column, each function has been rewritten in vertex form. Use multiplication to verify that the functions in each row are equivalent.

Standard Form $y = ax^2 + bx + c$	$-\frac{b}{2a}$	Vertex Form $y = a(x - h)^2 + k$	h
$y = x^2 - 4x + 4$	■	$y = (x - 2)^2$	■
$y = x^2 + 6x + 8$	■	$y = (x + 3)^2 - 1$	■
$y = -3x^2 - 12x - 8$	■	$y = -3(x + 2)^2 + 4$	■
$y = 2x^2 + 12x + 19$	■	$y = 2(x + 3)^2 + 1$	■

2. a. **Patterns** Copy and complete the table.
   b. Compare the values of $-\frac{b}{2a}$ and h in each row. Write a formula to show the relationship between $-\frac{b}{2a}$ and h.

Need Help?

A translation shifts a graph horizontally, or vertically, or both.

In Chapter 2, you learned to graph linear functions and absolute value functions as translations of their parent functions. Similarly, you can graph a quadratic function as a translation of the parent function $y = ax^2$.

To translate the graph of a quadratic function, you can use the **vertex form of a quadratic function,** $y = a(x - h)^2 + k$.

Key Concepts

Properties **Graph of a Quadratic Function in Vertex Form**

The graph of $y = a(x - h)^2 + k$ is the graph of $y = ax^2$ translated h units horizontally and k units vertically.

- When h is positive the graph shifts right; when h is negative the graph shifts left.
- When k is positive the graph shifts up; when k is negative the graph shifts down.
- The vertex is (h, k), and the axis of symmetry is the line $x = h$.

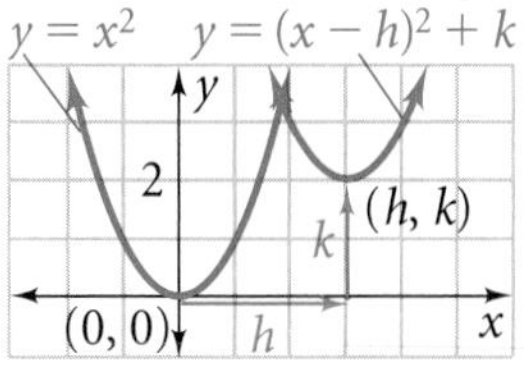

Reading Math

Vertex means "turning point."

A function in vertex form is easy to graph.

1 EXAMPLE Using Vertex Form to Graph a Parabola

Graph $y = -\frac{1}{2}(x - 2)^2 + 3$.

The graph of $y = -\frac{1}{2}(x - 2)^2 + 3$ is a translation of the graph of the parent function $y = -\frac{1}{2}x^2$. You can graph it by translating the parent function or by finding the vertex and the axis of symmetry.

Step 1 Graph the vertex $(2, 3)$. Draw the axis of symmetry $x = 2$.

Step 2 Find another point. When $x = 0$, $y = -\frac{1}{2}(0 - 2)^2 + 3 = 1$. Graph $(0, 1)$.

Step 3 Graph the point corresponding to $(0, 1)$. It is 2 units to the right of the axis of symmetry at $(4, 1)$.

Step 4 Sketch the curve.

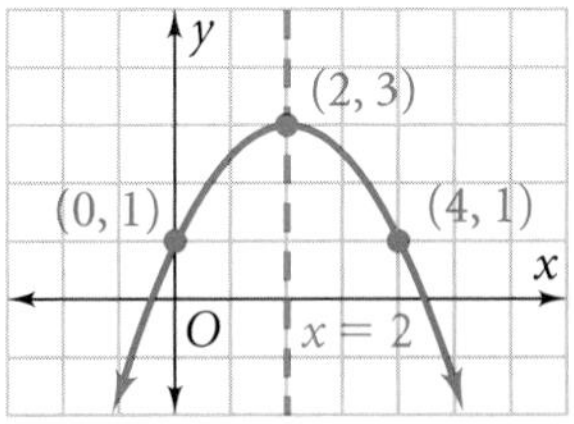

Check Understanding

1 **a.** Graph $y = 2(x + 1)^2 - 4$.

b. In graphing the function in part (a), which method did you use—translating the parent function, or graphing the vertex and axis of symmetry of the given function? Explain the reasons for your choice.

You can use the vertex form to write the equation of a parabola. Substitute values for h, k, and a point (x, y). Then solve for a.

2 EXAMPLE Writing the Equation of a Parabola

Write the equation of the parabola at the right.

$y = a(x - h)^2 + k$	**Use the vertex form.**
$y = a(x - 3)^2 + 4$	**Substitute $h = 3$ and $k = 4$.**
$-4 = a(5 - 3)^2 + 4$	**Substitute $(5, -4)$.**
$-8 = 4a$	**Simplify.**
$-2 = a$	**Solve for a.**

The equation of the parabola is $y = -2(x - 3)^2 + 4$.

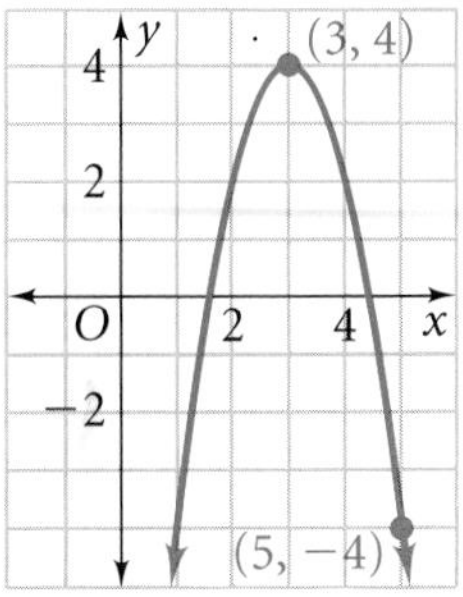

Check Understanding **2** Use vertex form to write the equation of the parabola below.

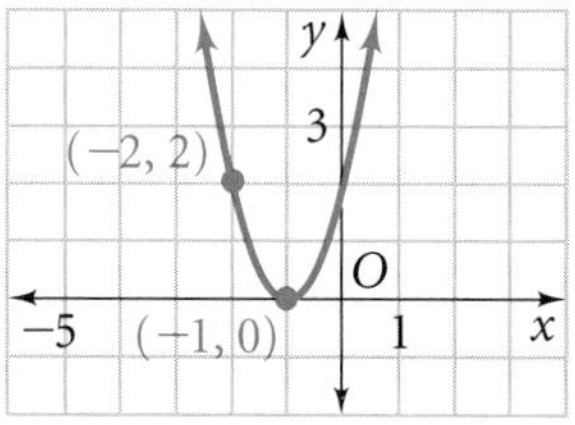

You can use vertex form to model real-world problems.

3 EXAMPLE Real-World Connection

Civil Engineering The photo shows the Verrazano–Narrows Bridge in New York, which has the longest span of any suspension bridge in the United States. A suspension cable of the bridge forms a curve that resembles a parabola. The curve can be modeled with the function $y = 0.0001432(x - 2130)^2$, where x and y are measured in feet.

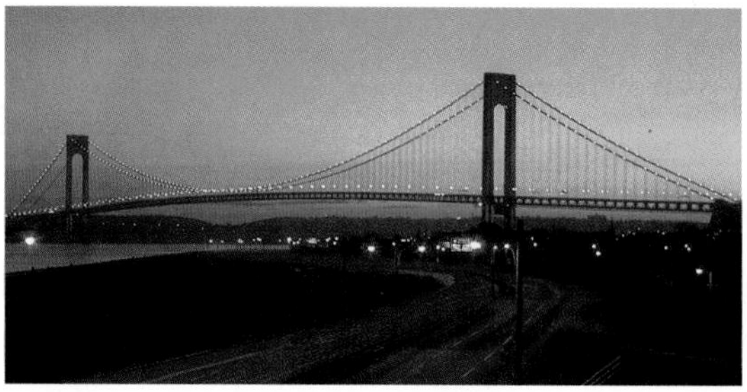

The origin of the function's graph is at the base of one of the two towers that support the cable. How far apart are the towers? How high are they?

Start by drawing a diagram.

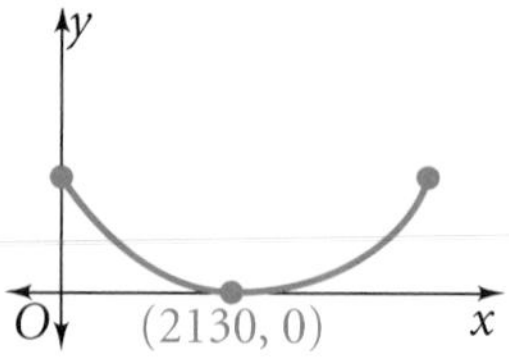

The function is in vertex form. Since $h = 2130$ and $k = 0$, the vertex is at (2130, 0). The vertex is halfway between the towers, so the distance between the towers is 2(2130 ft) = 4260 ft.

To find the tower's height, find y for $x = 0$.

$$y = 0.0001432(0 - 2130)^2$$
$$y = 0.0001432(-2130)^2$$
$$\approx 650$$

The towers are 4260 ft apart and about 650 ft high.

Check Understanding **3** Suppose the towers in Example 3 are 4000 ft apart and 600 ft high. Write a function that could model the curve of the suspension cable.

Both the vertex form and the standard form give useful information about a parabola. The standard form makes it easy to identify the y-intercept. The vertex form makes it easy to identify the vertex and to graph the parabola as a translation. The graph shows the relationship between the two forms.

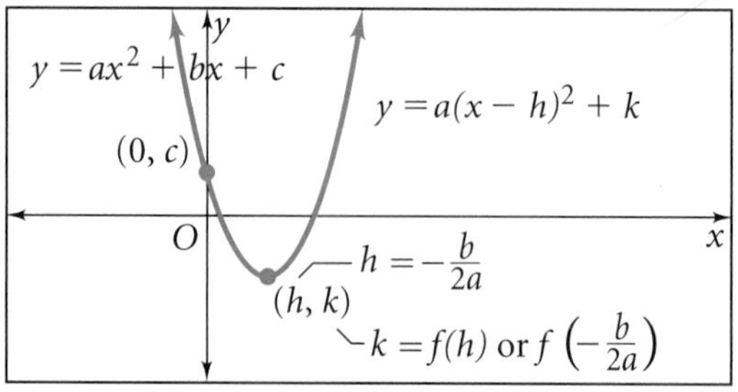

You can convert a function from standard form to vertex form.

4 EXAMPLE Converting to Vertex Form

Write $y = 2x^2 + 10x + 7$ in vertex form.

$x = -\frac{b}{2a}$ **Find the x-coordinate of the vertex.**

$= -\frac{10}{2(2)}$ **Substitute for a and b.**

$= -2.5$

$y = 2(-2.5)^2 + 10(-2.5) + 7$ **Find the y-coordinate of the vertex.**

$= -5.5$

The vertex is at $(-2.5, -5.5)$.

$y = a(x - h)^2 + k$ **Write the vertex form.**

$= 2(x - (-2.5))^2 - 5.5$ **Substitute for a, h, and k.**

$= 2(x + 2.5)^2 - 5.5$ **Simplify.**

The vertex form of the function is $y = 2(x + 2.5)^2 - 5.5$.

Check Understanding 4 Write $y = -3x^2 + 12x + 5$ in vertex form.

EXERCISES

For more practice, see *Extra Practice.*

Practice and Problem Solving

A Practice by Example

Example 1 (page 249)

Graph each function.

1. $y = (x - 1)^2 + 2$

2. $y = (x + 3)^2 - 4$

3. $y = 2(x - 2)^2 + 5$

4. $y = 2(x + 1)^2$

5. $y = -3(x + 7)^2 - 8$

6. $y = -\frac{1}{2}(x - 2)^2 + 1$

7. $y = (x - 5)^2 - 3$

8. $y = (x + 2)^2 - 3$

9. $y = -(x - 1)^2 + 4$

10. $y = 3(x + 5)^2 - 8$

11. $y = -(x - 7)^2 + 10$

12. $y = -4(x + 8)^2 - 6$

Example 2 (page 249)

Write the equation of each parabola in vertex form.

13.

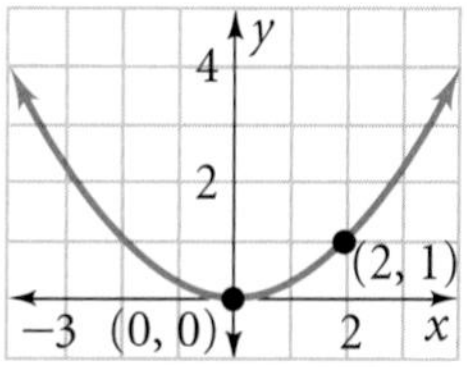

14.

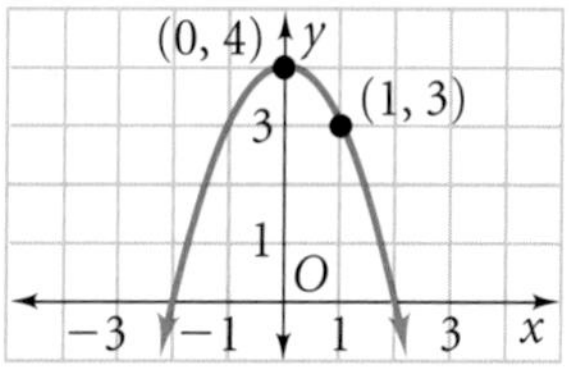

15.

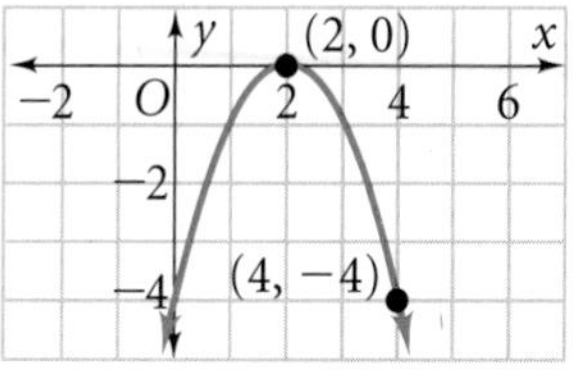

16.

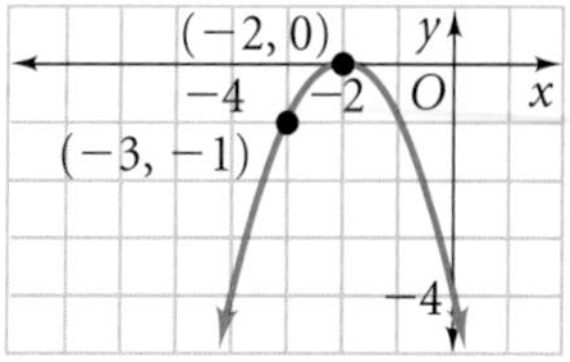

Write the equation of each parabola in vertex form.

17.

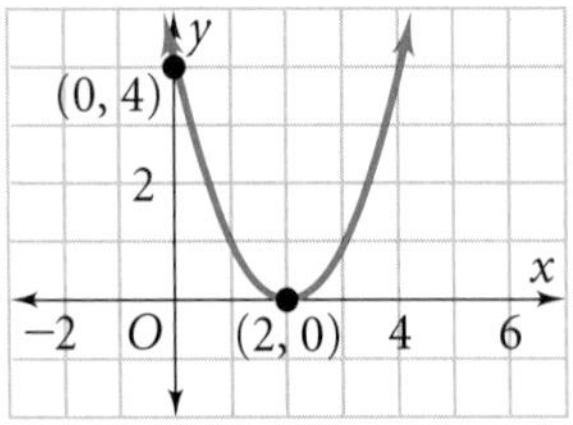

18.

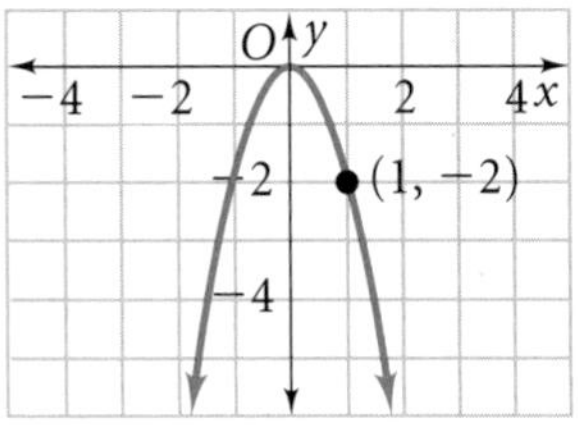

19.

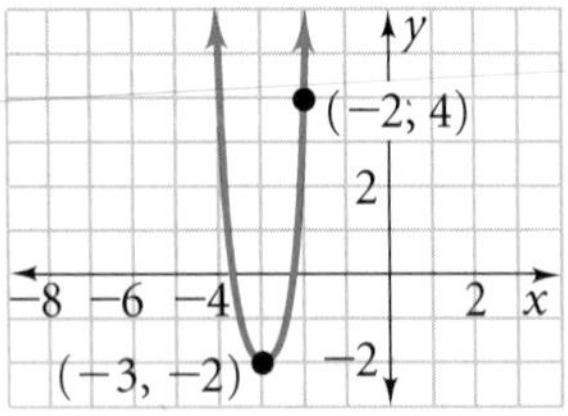

20.

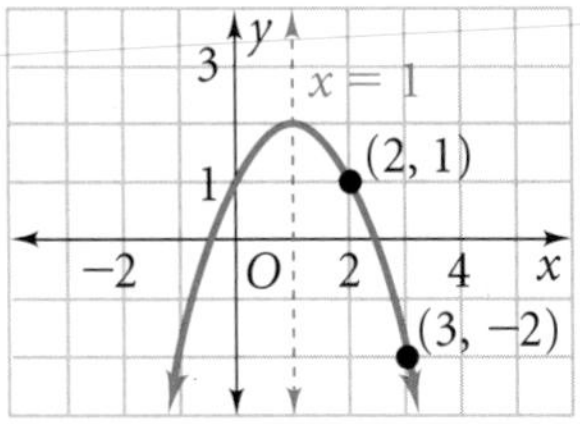

Example 3 (page 250)

Identify the vertex and the *y*-intercept of the graph of each function.

21. $y = -1.5(x + 20)^2$

22. $y = 0.1(x - 3.2)^2$

23. $y = 24(x + 5.5)^2$

24. $y = 0.0035(x + 1)^2 - 1$

25. $y = -(x - 4)^2 - 25$

26. $y = (x - 125)^2 + 125$

Example 4 (page 251)

Write each function in vertex form.

27. $y = x^2 - 4x + 6$

28. $y = x^2 + 2x + 5$

29. $y = 6x^2 - 10$

30. $y = -5x^2 + 12$

31. $y = 4x^2 + 7x$

32. $y = 2x^2 + x$

33. $y = 2x^2 - 5x + 12$

34. $y = -2x^2 + 8x + 3$

35. $y = \frac{9}{4}x^2 + 3x - 1$

B Apply Your Skills

Sketch each parabola.

36. $y = 2(x + 2)^2 - 3$

37. $y = -3(x - 2)^2$

38. $y = 5(x + 0.3)^2 - 10$

39. $y = -0.5(x - 2)^2 - 5$

40. $y = -2(x + 1)^2 + 1$

41. $y = 0.2(x - 12)^2 + 0.2$

Real-World Connection

Bagel sales in the United States total nearly $3 billion each year.

42. Business The Big Brick Bakery sells more bagels when it reduces its prices, but then its profit changes. The function $y = -1000(x - 0.55)^2 + 300$ models the bakery's daily profit in dollars, from selling bagels, where x is the price of a bagel in dollars. The bakery wants to maximize the profit.

a. What is the domain of the function? Can x be negative? Explain.

b. Find the daily profit for selling bagels for \$.40 each; for \$.85 each.

c. What price should the bakery charge to maximize its profit from bagels?

d. What is the maximum profit?

Write the equation of each parabola in vertex form.

43. vertex $(1, 2)$, point $(2, -5)$

44. vertex $(3, 6)$, y-intercept 2

45. vertex $(-3, 6)$, point $(1, -2)$

46. vertex $(-2, 6)$, y-intercept 12

47. vertex $(-1, -4)$, y-intercept 3

48. vertex $(0, 5)$, point $(1, -2)$

49. vertex $\left(\frac{1}{10}, -\frac{9}{10}\right)$, y-intercept -1

50. vertex $\left(\frac{1}{4}, -\frac{3}{2}\right)$, point $(1, 3)$

Write each function in standard form.

51. $y = (5x + 6)^2 - 9$

52. $y = -(3x - 4)^2 + 6$

53. $y = 2x(x + 7) + 8x$

54. $y = \frac{1}{2}(x - 5)^2 + 5$

55. $y = -0.1(10x + 20)^2$

56. $y = (1 - 4x)^2 + 1$

57. a. Technology Determine the axis of symmetry for each parabola defined by the spreadsheet values at the right.
b. How could you use the spreadsheet columns to verify that the axes of symmetry are correct?
c. Write functions in vertex form that model the data. Check that the axes of symmetry are correct.

	A	B
1	X1	Y1
2	1	−35
3	2	−15
4	3	−3
5	4	1
6	5	−3

	A	B
1	X2	Y2
2	1	10
3	2	2
4	3	2
5	4	10
6	5	26

58. Writing Describe the steps you would take to sketch the graph of $y = -2(x - 3)^2 + 4$.

Determine whether each function is written in vertex form. If a function is not in vertex form, rewrite the function.

59. $y = -2x^2 + 35$

60. $y = -8x^2$

61. $y = -3x^2 - 2x + 1$

62. $y = -2(x + 1)^2 - 1$

63. $y = x^2 + 2x + 8$

64. $y = \frac{3}{10}x^2 - 1$

65. $y = -4x^2 + 6x + 3$

66. $y = 0.5x^2 + 10$

67. $y = 100x^2 - 40x + 10$

Determine *a* and *k* so both points are on the graph of the function.

68. $(0, 1), (2, 1); y = a(x - 1)^2 + k$

69. $(-3, 2), (0, 11); y = a(x + 2)^2 + k$

70. $(1, 11), (2, -19); y = a(x + 1)^2 + k$

71. $(-2, 6), (3, 1); y = a(x - 3)^2 + k$

72. $(-2, 10), (1, -34); y = a(2x + 2)^2 + k$

73. $(4, 26), (5, -25); y = a(x - 30)^2 + k$

74. The equation of one of the parabolas in the graph at the right is $y = (x - 4)^2 + 2$. Write the equation of the other parabola in vertex form.

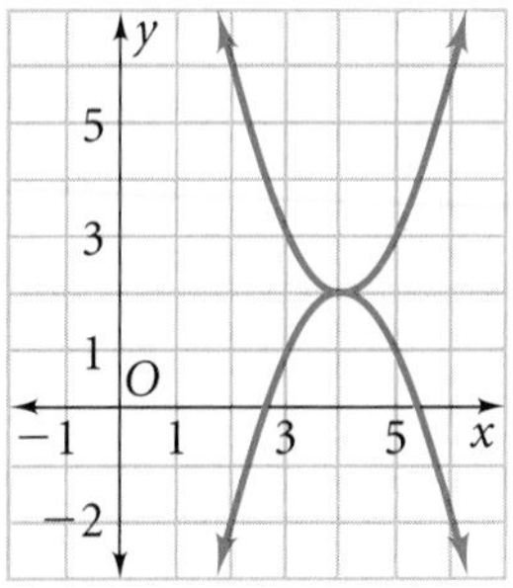

75. Open-Ended Write a quadratic function in vertex form for which the graph has a vertex at $(-2, 5)$. Rewrite the function in standard form.

76. Determine whether the function $f(x) = 0.25(2x - 15)^2 + 150$ has a maximum or a minimum value. Then find the value.

77. Critical Thinking Describe the differences between the graphs of $y = (x + 6)^2$ and $y = (x - 6)^2 + 7$.

C Challenge

78. a. In the function $y = ax^2 + bx + c$, c represents the y-intercept. Find the value of the y-intercept in the function $y = a(x - h)^2 + k$.
b. Under what conditions does k represent the y-intercept?

Find the quadratic function $y = a(x - h)^2$ for which the graph includes the given points.

79. $(-2, 1), (2, 1)$

80. $(-5, 2), (-1, 2)$

81. $(-1, -4), (7, -4)$

82. $(2, -1), (4, 0)$

83. $(-2, 18), (1, 0)$

84. $(1, -64), (-3, 0)$

Standardized Test Prep

Gridded Response

Use the following information about quadratic functions for Exercises 85–90.

vertex form: $y = a(x - h)^2 + k$ standard form: $y = ax^2 + bx + c$

85. When $y = -3x^2 - 18x - 23$ is written in vertex form, what is the value of k?

86. When $y = 2(x - 3)(x + 5)$ is written in standard form, what is the value of b?

87. When $y = -2(x + 3)^2 + 25$ is written in standard form, what is the value of c?

88. For $y = 3x^2 - 7x + 5$, what is the x-value of the vertex? Enter your answer as an improper fraction in simplest form.

89. What is the y-coordinate of the vertex of $y = -2(x + 1)^2 - 3$?

90. How many units down must you shift the graph of $y = 3(x + 3)^2$ to get the graph of $y = 3(x + 3)^2 - 2$?

Take It to the NET
Online lesson quiz at **www.PHSchool.com**
Web Code: aga-0503

Mixed Review

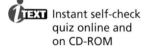

Lesson 5-2 **Graph each function.**

91. $y = x^2 - 5$ **92.** $y = x^2 - 4x + 8$ **93.** $y = 3x^2 + 6x + 5$

Lesson 4-5 **Solve each matrix equation.**

94. $\begin{bmatrix} 0 & 1 \\ -1 & 2 \end{bmatrix} X = \begin{bmatrix} 20 \\ 10 \end{bmatrix}$ **95.** $\begin{bmatrix} -1 & 3 \\ 1 & -2 \end{bmatrix} X = \begin{bmatrix} 4 \\ -4 \end{bmatrix}$

Lesson 3-4 **96.** Find the maximum and minimum values of the objective function $P = 2x + y$, under the constraints at the right.

$$\begin{cases} y \geq 2x - 2 & x \geq 0 \\ y \leq -x + 4 & y \geq 0 \end{cases}$$

Checkpoint Quiz 1 — Lessons 5-1 through 5-3

Instant self-check quiz online and on CD-ROM

Find a quadratic model in standard form for each set of values.

1. (0, 3), (1, 10), (2, 19) **2.** (−2, −15), (0, 1), (2, 1) **3.** (0, 0), (1, −5), (2, 0)

Graph each function.

4. $y = 4x^2 + 16x + 7$ **5.** $y = (x + 8)^2 - 3$ **6.** $y = -(x + 2)^2 - 7$

Determine whether each function has a maximum or minimum value. Then find the value.

7. $y = -x^2 + 6x + 5$ **8.** $y = \frac{1}{2}(x - 6)^2 + 7$

9. Rewrite the equation $y = -3x^2 - 6x - 8$ in vertex form. Identify the vertex and the axis of symmetry.

10. **Open-Ended** Write the equation of a parabola with a vertex at (3, 2). Write the axis of symmetry and the coordinates of two other points on the graph.

5-4 Factoring Quadratic Expressions

North Carolina Objectives

1.03 Operate with algebraic expressions (polynomial, rational, complex fractions) to solve problems.

Lesson Preview

What You'll Learn

OBJECTIVE 1 To find common and binomial factors of quadratic expressions

OBJECTIVE 2 To factor special quadratic expressions

. . . And Why

To model the cross section of a pipe, as in Example 8

Check Skills You'll Need

(For help, go to Lessons 1-2 and 5-1.)

Simplify each expression.

1. $x^2 + x + 4x - 1$ **2.** $6x^2 - 4(3)x + 2x - 3$ **3.** $4x^2 - 2(5 - x) - 3x$

Multiply.

4. $2x(5 - x)$ **5.** $(2x - 7)(2x - 7)$ **6.** $(4x + 3)(4x - 3)$

New Vocabulary
- factoring
- greatest common factor (GCF) of an expression
- perfect square trinomial
- difference of two squares

Interactive lesson includes instant self-check, tutorials, and activities.

OBJECTIVE 1 Finding Common and Binomial Factors

Investigation: Factoring

1. Since $6 \cdot 3 = 18$, 6 and 3 make up a factor pair for 18.
   a. Find the other factor pairs for 18, including negative integers.
   b. Find the sum of the integers in each factor pair for 18.
2. a. Does 12 have a factor pair with a sum of -8? A sum of -9?
   b. Using all the factor pairs of 12, how many sums are possible?
   c. How many sums are possible for the factor pairs of -12?

Need Help?
One number is a factor of another if the first divides into the second with no remainder.

Factoring is rewriting an expression as the product of its factors. The **greatest common factor (GCF) of an expression** is the common factor with the greatest coefficient and the greatest exponent. You can factor any expression with terms having a GCF greater than 1.

1 EXAMPLE Finding Common Factors

Factor each expression.

a. $4x^2 + 20x - 12$

$4x^2 + 20x - 12 = 4x^2 + 4(5x) - 4(3)$ **Factor out the GCF, 4.**

$= 4(x^2 + 5x - 3)$ **Rewrite using the Distributive Property.**

b. $9n^2 - 24n$

$9n^2 - 24n = 3n(3n) - 3n(8)$ **Factor out the GCF, 3*n*.**

$= 3n(3n - 8)$ **Rewrite using the Distributive Property.**

Check Understanding

1 Factor each expression.

a. $9x^2 + 3x - 18$ **b.** $7p^2 + 21$ **c.** $4w^2 + 2w$

Reading Math

A monomial is an expression with one term. A binomial has two terms, and a trinomial has three terms.

A quadratic trinomial is an expression in the form $ax^2 + bx + c$. You can factor many quadratic trinomials into two binomial factors. First find two factors with a product ac and a sum b. Then find common factors.

If ac and b are positive, then the factors of ac are both positive.

2 EXAMPLE Factoring When $ac > 0$ and $b > 0$

Factor $x^2 + 8x + 7$.

Step 1 Find factors with product ac and sum b.

Since $ac = 7$ and $b = 8$, find positive factors with product 7 and sum 8.

Factors of 7	1, 7
Sum of factors	8

These are the only positive factors of 7.

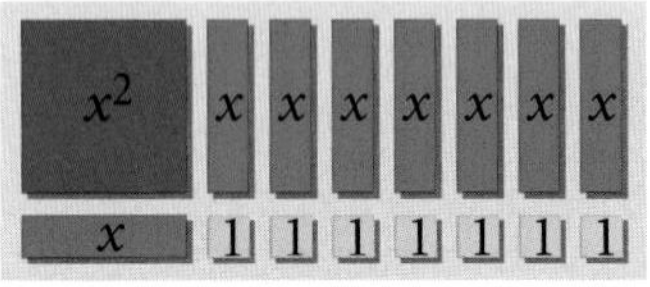

You can use algebra tiles to factor the expression in Example 2.

Step 2 Rewrite the term bx using the factors you found. Group the remaining terms and find the common factors for each group. After removing common factors from each group, you should find two identical binomials.

$x^2 + 8x + 7$

$\underbrace{x^2 + x} + \underbrace{7x + 7}$ **Rewrite bx: $8x = x + 7x$.**

$x(x + 1) + 7(x + 1)$ **Find common factors.**

Step 3 Rewrite the expression as the product of two binomials.

$x(x + 1) + 7(x + 1)$

$(x + 1)(x + 7)$ **Rewrite using the Distributive Property.**

Check $(x + 1)(x + 7) = x^2 + 7x + x + 7$

$= x^2 + 8x + 7$ ✓

Check Understanding 2 Factor each expression. Check your answers.

a. $x^2 + 6x + 8$ **b.** $x^2 + 12x + 32$ **c.** $x^2 + 14x + 40$

If ac is positive and b is negative, then the factors of ac are both negative.

3 EXAMPLE Factoring When $ac > 0$ and $b < 0$

Factor $x^2 - 17x + 72$.

Step 1 Find factors with product ac and sum b.

Since $ac = 72$ and $b = -17$, find negative factors with product 72 and sum -17.

Factors of 72	−1, −72	−2, −36	−3, −24	−4, −18	−6, −12	−8, −9
Sum of factors	−73	−38	−27	−22	−18	−17

Step 2 Rewrite the term bx using the factors you found. Then find common factors and rewrite the expression as the product of two binomials.

$x^2 - 17x + 72$

$\underbrace{x^2 - 8x} - \underbrace{9x + 72}$ **Rewrite bx.**

$x(x - 8) - 9(x - 8)$ **Find common factors.**

$(x - 9)(x - 8)$ **Rewrite using the Distributive Property.**

Check Understanding **3** Factor each expression.

a. $x^2 - 6x + 8$ **b.** $x^2 - 7x + 12$ **c.** $x^2 - 11x + 24$

Note in Example 3 that the factors of c, -9 and -8, appear in the binomials of the factored form, $(x - 9)(x - 8)$. That is also the case for the factors in Example 2, and it is the case whenever $a = 1$. So when $a = 1$, you can skip a few steps in factoring. See Example 4.

If ac is negative, then the factors of ac have different signs.

4 EXAMPLE Factoring When $ac < 0$

Factor $x^2 - x - 12$.

Step 1 Find factors with product ac and sum b.

Since $ac = -12$ and $b = -1$, find factors with product -12 and sum -1.

Factors of −12	1, −12	−1, 12	2, −6	−2, 6	3, −4	−3, 4
Sum of factors	−11	11	−4	4	−1	1

Step 2 Since $a = 1$, you can write binomials using the factors you found.

$x^2 - x - 12$

$(x - 4)(x + 3)$ **Use the factors you found.**

Check Understanding **4** Factor each expression.

a. $x^2 - 14x - 32$ **b.** $x^2 + 3x - 10$ **c.** $x^2 + 4x - 5$

If ac is positive, as in Examples 2 and 3, then the factors of ac have the same sign. This is true even when $a \neq 1$.

5 EXAMPLE Factoring When $a \neq 1$ and $ac > 0$

Factor $3x^2 - 16x + 5$.

Step 1 Find factors with product ac and sum b.

Since $ac = 15$ and $b = -16$, find negative factors with product 15 and sum -16.

Factors of 15	−1, −15	−3, −5
Sum of factors	−16	−8

Step 2 Rewrite the term bx using the factors you found. Then find common factors and rewrite the expression as the product of two binomials.

$3x^2 - 16x + 5$

$\underbrace{3x^2 - x} - \underbrace{15x + 5}$ **Rewrite *bx*.**

$x(3x - 1) - 5(3x - 1)$ **Find common factors.**

$(x - 5)(3x - 1)$ **Rewrite using the Distributive Property.**

Check Understanding **5** Factor each expression. Check your answers.

a. $2x^2 + 11x + 12$ **b.** $4x^2 + 7x + 3$ **c.** $2x^2 - 7x + 6$

Again, if ac is negative, then the factors of ac have different signs.

6 EXAMPLE Factoring When $a \neq 1$ and $ac < 0$

Factor $4x^2 - 4x - 15$.

Step 1 Find factors with product ac and sum b.

Since $ac = -60$ and $b = -4$, find factors with product -60 and sum -4.

Factors of −60	1, −60	−1, 60	2, −30	−2, 30	3, −20	−3, 20
Sum of factors	−59	59	−28	28	−17	17
Factors of −60	4, −15	−4, 15	5, −12	−5, 12	6, −10	−6, 10
Sum of factors	−11	11	−7	7	−4	4

Step 2 Rewrite the term bx using the factors you found. Then find common factors and rewrite the expression as the product of two binomials.

$4x^2 - 4x - 15$

$\underbrace{4x^2 + 6x} \underbrace{- 10x - 15}$ **Rewrite *bx*.**

$2x(2x + 3) - 5(2x + 3)$ **Find common factors.**

$(2x - 5)(2x + 3)$ **Rewrite using the Distributive Property.**

Check Understanding 6 Factor each expression.
a. $2x^2 + 7x - 9$ **b.** $3x^2 - 16x - 12$ **c.** $4x^2 + 5x - 6$

OBJECTIVE
2 Factoring Special Expressions

A **perfect square trinomial** is the product you obtain when you square a binomial. An example is $x^2 + 10x + 25$, which can be written as $(x + 5)^2$. The first term and the third term of the trinomial are always positive, as they represent the squares of the two terms of the binomial. The middle term of the trinomial is two times the product of the terms of the binomial.

Key Concepts

Property	Factoring Perfect Square Trinomials
$a^2 + 2ab + b^2 = (a + b)^2$	$a^2 - 2ab + b^2 = (a - b)^2$

7 EXAMPLE Factoring a Perfect Square Trinomial

Factor $9x^2 - 42x + 49$.

$9x^2 - 42x + 49 = (3x)^2 - 42x + 7^2$ **Rewrite the first and third terms as squares.**

$= (3x)^2 - 2(3x)(7) + 7^2$ **Rewrite the middle term to verify the perfect square trinomial pattern.**

$= (3x - 7)^2$ **$a^2 - 2ab + b^2 = (a - b)^2$**

Check Understanding 7 Factor each expression.
a. $4x^2 + 12x + 9$ **b.** $64x^2 - 16x + 1$ **c.** $25x^2 + 90x + 81$

An expression of the form $a^2 - b^2$ is defined as the **difference of two squares.** It also follows a pattern that makes it easy to factor.

Key Concepts

Property	Factoring a Difference of Two Squares
	$a^2 - b^2 = (a + b)(a - b)$

8 EXAMPLE **Real-World Connection**

Hydraulics The photo at the right shows the cross-section of a pipe. Express the pipe's cross-sectional area in completely factored form.

Need Help?
For a circle, $A = \pi r^2$.

Relate pipe's area equals the outer area minus the inner area

Define Let r = inner radius in feet.

Write area $=$ $\pi(3)^2$ $-$ πr^2

$$\begin{aligned} \text{area} &= \pi(3)^2 - \pi r^2 \\ &= \pi(3^2 - r^2) \\ &= \pi(3 + r)(3 - r) \end{aligned}$$

The cross-sectional area of the pipe in factored form is $\pi(3 + r)(3 - r)$ ft^2.

Check Understanding **8** Factor each expression.

a. $x^2 - 64$ **b.** $4a^2 - 49$

EXERCISES

For more practice, see *Extra Practice.*

Practice and Problem Solving

A Practice by Example

Find the GCF of each expression. Then factor the expression.

Example 1 (page 255)

1. $3a^2 + 9$ **2.** $25b^2 - 35$ **3.** $x^2 - 2x$

4. $5t^2 + 7t$ **5.** $14y^2 + 7y$ **6.** $27p^2 - 9p$

Factor each expression.

Example 2 (page 256)

7. $x^2 + 3x + 2$ **8.** $x^2 + 5x + 6$ **9.** $x^2 + 7x + 10$

10. $x^2 + 10x + 16$ **11.** $y^2 + 15y + 36$ **12.** $x^2 + 22x + 40$

Example 3 (page 256)

13. $x^2 - 3x + 2$ **14.** $x^2 - 13x + 12$ **15.** $r^2 - 11r + 18$

16. $x^2 - 10x + 24$ **17.** $d^2 - 12d + 27$ **18.** $x^2 - 13x + 36$

Example 4 (page 257)

19. $x^2 - 5x - 14$ **20.** $x^2 + x - 20$ **21.** $x^2 - 3x - 40$

22. $c^2 + 2c - 63$ **23.** $x^2 + 10x - 75$ **24.** $t^2 - 7t - 44$

Example 5 (page 257)

25. $3x^2 + 31x + 36$ **26.** $2x^2 - 19x + 24$ **27.** $5r^2 + 23r + 26$

28. $2m^2 - 11m + 15$ **29.** $5t^2 + 28t + 32$ **30.** $2x^2 - 27x + 36$

Example 6 (page 258)

Factor each expression.

31. $3x^2 + 7x - 20$ **32.** $5y^2 + 12y - 32$ **33.** $7x^2 - 8x - 12$

34. $2z^2 + z - 28$ **35.** $3x^2 + 8x - 16$ **36.** $28k^2 + 13k - 6$

Example 7 (page 258)

37. $x^2 + 2x + 1$ **38.** $t^2 - 14t + 49$ **39.** $x^2 - 18x + 81$

40. $4n^2 - 20n + 25$ **41.** $9x^2 + 48x + 64$ **42.** $81z^2 + 36z + 4$

43. $x^2 - 4$ **44.** $c^2 - 64$ **45.** $9x^2 - 1$

Example 8 (page 259)

46. **Manufacturing** Refer to the diagram at the right. A machine will cut a small square of plastic from a larger square. Write an expression for the remaining area. Factor the expression.

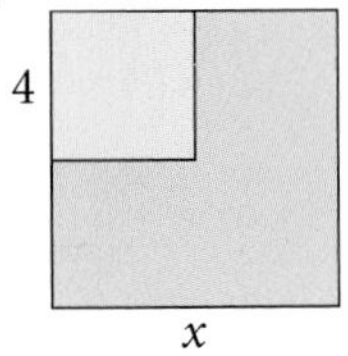

47. The area in square centimeters of a square mat is $25x^2 - 10x + 1$. Find the dimensions of the mat in terms of x.

B Apply Your Skills

48. The area of a rectangular cloth is $(6x^2 - 19x - 85)$ cm^2. The length is $(2x + 5)$ cm. Find the width.

49. Refer to the diagram at the right. Suppose you cut a small square from a square sheet of cardboard. Write an expression for the remaining area. Factor the expression.

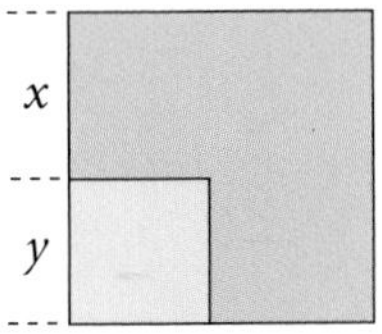

50. **Interior Design** Refer to the photo at the left. The area of the rug is $(x^2 - 11x + 28)$ ft^2. What is the width?

Factor each expression completely.

51. $9x^2 - 36$ **52.** $18z^2 - 8$ **53.** $12y^2 - 75$

54. $64t^2 - 16$ **55.** $12x^2 + 36x + 27$ **56.** $16x^2 - 80x + 100$

57. $2a^2 - 16a + 32$ **58.** $3x^2 - 24x - 27$ **59.** $18b^2 + 24b - 10$

60. $4n^2 - 20n + 24$ **61.** $3y^2 + 24y + 45$ **62.** $-x^2 + 5x - 4$

63. $4x^2 - 22x + 10$ **64.** $\frac{1}{2}x^2 - \frac{1}{2}$ **65.** $-6z^2 - 600$

66. **Geometry** Express the volume of the shaded pipe at the right in completely factored form.

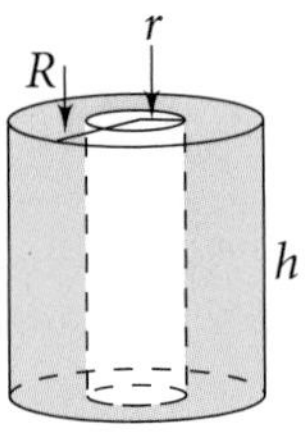

67. **Agriculture** The area in square feet of a rectangular field is $x^2 - 120x + 3500$. The width in feet is $x - 50$. Find the length.

68. **Writing** Explain how to factor $3x^2 + 6x - 72$ completely.

69. **Open-Ended** Write a quadratic trinomial that can be factored, where $a \neq 1$, $ac > 0$, and $b < 0$. Factor the expression.

70. **Error Analysis** Find the error below. Then factor the expression correctly.

$2x^2 - 7x + 5$

$2x^2 - 5x - 2x + 5$

$x(2x - 5) + (2x - 5)$

$(x + 1)(2x - 5)$

C Challenge

71. **Critical Thinking** Explain how to factor $4x^4 + 24x^3 + 32x^2$.

Factor each expression completely.

72. $0.25t^2 - 0.16$
73. $8100x^2 - 10{,}000$
74. $3600z^2 - 4900$
75. $(x + 3)^2 + 3(x + 3) - 54$
76. $(x - 2)^2 - 15(x - 2) + 56$
77. $6(x + 5)^2 - 5(x + 5) + 1$
78. $3(2a - 3)^2 + 17(2a - 3) + 10$

Standardized Test Prep

Multiple Choice

79. Which term is NOT a common factor of $4a^2c^2 + 2a^2c - 6ac^2$?
A. $4c$ B. $2a$ C. $2ac$ D. ac

80. How can you write $(m - 5)(m + 4) + 8$ as a product of two binomials?
F. $(m - 1)(m + 8)$ G. $(m - 4)(m + 3)$
H. $(m + 8)(m + 8)$ I. $(m - 5)(8m + 32)$

Take It to the NET
Online lesson quiz at **www.PHSchool.com**
Web Code: aga-0504

81. What is the factored form of $4x^2 + 15x - 4$?
A. $(2x + 2)(2x - 2)$ B. $(2x - 4)(2x + 1)$
C. $(4x + 1)(x - 4)$ D. $(4x - 1)(x + 4)$

82. Which is a factored form of $0.81p^2 - 0.09$?
F. $(0.9p + 0.045)(0.9p - 0.045)$ G. $(0.09p + 0.03)(0.09p - 0.03)$
H. $(0.9p + 0.3)(0.9p - 0.3)$ I. $(0.9p + 0.81)(0.9p - 0.81)$

Short Response

83. Explain how to rewrite the expression $a^2 - 2ab + b^2 - 25$ as the product of two trinomial factors.

Extended Response

84. Suppose you hit a baseball and its flight takes a parabolic path. The height of the ball at certain times appears in the table below.

Time (s)	0.5	0.75	1	1.25
Height (ft)	10	10.5	9	5.5

a. Find a quadratic model for the ball's height as a function of time.
b. Write the quadratic function in factored form.

Mixed Review

Lesson 5-3 **Write each function in vertex form.**

85. $y = x^2 - 2x + 1$
86. $y = -2x^2 + 2x + 5$
87. $y = 5x^2 - 1$

Lesson 4-6 **Evaluate each determinant.**

88. $\begin{vmatrix} 2 & -1 & 0 \\ 1 & 0 & 3 \\ 4 & -2 & 1 \end{vmatrix}$
89. $\begin{vmatrix} 1 & 5 & 0 \\ 3 & 3 & 5 \\ 0 & 1 & 2 \end{vmatrix}$
90. $\begin{vmatrix} 0 & 4 & 1 \\ 1 & 0 & 1 \\ 1 & 2 & 1 \end{vmatrix}$

Lesson 3-6

91. **Coins** The combined mass of a penny and a nickel and a dime is 9.8 g. Ten nickels and three pennies have the same mass as 25 dimes. Fifty dimes have the same mass as 18 nickels and 10 pennies. Write and solve a system of equations to find the mass of each type of coin.

Algebra 1 Review

Square Roots and Radicals

For Use With Lesson 5-5

A radical symbol $\sqrt{\ }$ indicates a square root. The expression $\sqrt{16}$ means the principal, or positive, square root of 16. The expression $-\sqrt{16}$ means the negative square root of 16.

Properties	Square Roots

Multiplication Property of Square Roots

For any numbers $a \geq 0$ and $b \geq 0$, $\sqrt{ab} = \sqrt{a} \cdot \sqrt{b}$.

Division Property of Square Roots

For any numbers $a \geq 0$ and $b > 0$, $\sqrt{\frac{a}{b}} = \frac{\sqrt{a}}{\sqrt{b}}$.

You can use the properties of square roots to simplify radical expressions.

1 EXAMPLE Radical Expressions Containing Perfect Squares

Simplify $\sqrt{48}$.

$\sqrt{48} = \sqrt{16} \cdot \sqrt{3}$ **Multiplication Property of Square Roots**

$= 4\sqrt{3}$ **Simplify.**

2 EXAMPLE Denominators Containing Radical Expressions

Simplify $-\sqrt{\frac{5}{7}}$.

$-\sqrt{\frac{5}{7}} = -\frac{\sqrt{5}}{\sqrt{7}}$ **Division Property of Square Roots**

$= -\frac{\sqrt{5}}{\sqrt{7}} \cdot \frac{\sqrt{7}}{\sqrt{7}}$ **Multiply both the numerator and the denominator by $\sqrt{7}$.**

$= -\frac{\sqrt{35}}{\sqrt{49}}$ **Multiplication Property of Square Roots**

$= -\frac{\sqrt{35}}{7}$ **Simplify.**

EXERCISES

Simplify each radical expression.

1. $\sqrt{18}$ **2.** $\sqrt{75}$ **3.** $-\sqrt{32}$ **4.** $\sqrt{\frac{3}{5}}$

5. $-\sqrt{\frac{7}{12}}$ **6.** $\sqrt{\frac{3}{8}}$ **7.** $-\sqrt{200}$ **8.** $5\sqrt{320}$

9. $(2\sqrt{27})^2$ **10.** $-\sqrt{10^4}$ **11.** $\sqrt{x^2y^2}$ **12.** $\sqrt{\frac{8}{x^2}}$

5-5 Quadratic Equations

North Carolina Objectives

2.02 Use quadratic functions and inequalities to model and solve problems; justify results. a) Solve using tables, graphs, and algebraic properties.

Lesson Preview

What You'll Learn

OBJECTIVE 1 To solve quadratic equations by factoring and by finding square roots

OBJECTIVE 2 To solve quadratic equations by graphing

. . . And Why

To solve equations involving art, as in Example 5

Check Skills You'll Need

(For help, go to Lessons 5-2 and 5-4.)

Factor each expression.

1. $x^2 + 5x - 14$ **2.** $4x^2 - 12x$ **3.** $9x^2 - 16$

Graph each function.

4. $y = x^2 - 2x - 5$ **5.** $y = x^2 - 4x + 4$ **6.** $y = x^2 - 4x$

New Vocabulary

- standard form of a quadratic equation
- Zero-Product Property
- zero of a function

Interactive lesson includes instant self-check, tutorials, and activities.

OBJECTIVE 1 Solving by Factoring and Finding Square Roots

The **standard form of a quadratic equation** is $ax^2 + bx + c = 0$, where $a \neq 0$. You can solve some quadratic equations in standard form by factoring the quadratic expression and then using the Zero-Product Property.

Key Concepts

Property	Zero-Product Property
If $ab = 0$, then $a = 0$ or $b = 0$.	
Example	If $(x + 3)(x - 7) = 0$, then $(x + 3) = 0$ or $(x - 7) = 0$.

1 EXAMPLE Solving by Factoring

Solve $2x^2 - 11x = -15$.

$2x^2 - 11x + 15 = 0$	**Write in standard form.**
$2x^2 - 5x - 6x + 15 = 0$	**Rewrite the *bx* term.**
$x(2x - 5) - 3(2x - 5) = 0$	**Find common factors.**
$(x - 3)(2x - 5) = 0$	**Rewrite using the Distributive Property.**
$x - 3 = 0$ or $2x - 5 = 0$	**Use the Zero-Product Property.**
$x = 3$ or $x = \frac{5}{2}$	**Solve for *x*.**

The solutions are 3 and $\frac{5}{2}$.

Check

$2x^2 - 11x = -15$

$2(3)^2 - 11(3) \stackrel{?}{=} -15$

$18 - 33 \stackrel{?}{=} -15$

$-15 = -15$ ✓

$2x^2 - 11x = -15$

$2\left(\frac{5}{2}\right)^2 - 11\left(\frac{5}{2}\right) \stackrel{?}{=} -15$

$\frac{25}{2} - \frac{55}{2} \stackrel{?}{=} -15$

$-15 = -15$ ✓

Check Understanding **1** Solve each equation by factoring. Check your answers.

a. $x^2 + 7x = 18$ **b.** $2x^2 + 4x = 6$ **c.** $16x^2 = 8x$

You can solve an equation in the form $ax^2 = c$ by finding square roots.

2 EXAMPLE Solving by Finding Square Roots

Solve $5x^2 - 180 = 0$.

$5x^2 - 180 = 0$

$5x^2 = 180$ **Rewrite in the form $ax^2 = c$.**

$\frac{5x^2}{5} = \frac{180}{5}$ **Isolate x^2.**

$x^2 = 36$ **Simplify.**

$x = \pm 6$ **Take the square root of each side.**

Check Understanding **2** Solve each equation by finding square roots.

a. $4x^2 - 25 = 0$ **b.** $3x^2 = 24$ **c.** $x^2 - \frac{1}{4} = 0$

Real-World Connection

Careers Smoke jumpers are firefighters who parachute into areas near forest fires.

3 EXAMPLE Real-World Connection

Firefighting Smoke jumpers are in free fall from the time they jump out of a plane until they open their parachutes. The function $y = -16t^2 + 1600$ models a jumper's height y in feet at t seconds for a jump from 1600 ft. How long is a jumper in free fall if the parachute opens at 1000 ft?

$y = -16t^2 + 1600$

$1000 = -16t^2 + 1600$ **Substitute 1000 for y.**

$-600 = -16t^2$ **Isolate t^2.**

$37.5 = t^2$

$\pm 6.1 \approx t$ **Take the square root of each side.**

The jumper is in free fall for about 6.1 seconds.

Check Is the answer reasonable? The negative number -6.1 is also a solution to the equation. However, since a negative value for time has no meaning in this case, only the positive solution is reasonable.

Check Understanding **3** **a.** A smoke jumper jumps from 1400 ft. The function describing the height is $y = -16t^2 + 1400$. Using square roots, find the time during which the jumper is in free fall if the parachute opens at 1000 ft.

b. Solve the equation in part (a) by factoring. Which method do you prefer—using square roots or factoring? Explain.

OBJECTIVE

2 Solving by Graphing

Not every quadratic equation can be solved by factoring or by taking the square root. You can solve a quadratic equation in standard form by graphing its related quadratic function $y = ax^2 + bx + c$. When the graph of the function intersects the x-axis, the value of the function is zero, and each x-value is a zero of the function. A **zero of a function** is a solution of the equation $ax^2 + bx + c = 0$.

4 EXAMPLE Solving by Graphing

Solve $x^2 - 5x + 2 = 0$.

Graph the related function $y = x^2 - 5x + 2$ with a graphing calculator. Use the **CALC** feature to find the two zeros of the function.

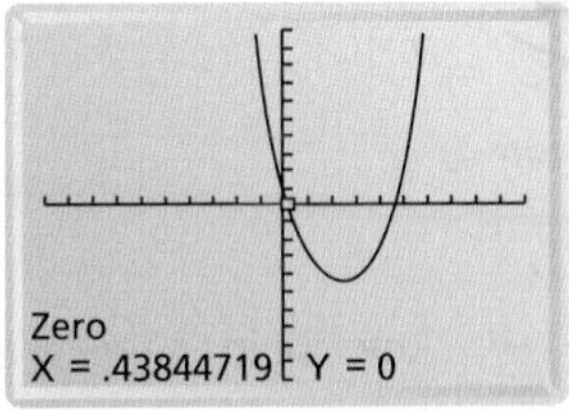

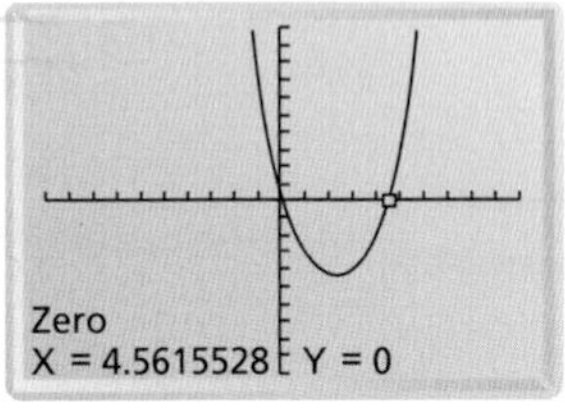

The solutions are $x \approx 0.44$ and $x \approx 4.56$.

Check Understanding **4** Use a graphing calculator to solve each equation. When necessary, round your answers to the nearest hundredth.

a. $x^2 + 6x + 4 = 0$ **b.** $3x^2 + 5x - 12 = 8$ **c.** $x^2 = -2x + 7$

5 EXAMPLE Real-World Connection

Need Help?

Two rectangles are similar if their corresponding sides are in proportion.

Art Artists often use a golden rectangle in their work because forms based on it are visually pleasing. You can divide a golden rectangle into a square of side length one and a smaller rectangle that is similar to the original one. The ratio of the longer side to the shorter side of a golden rectangle is the golden ratio. Use the figure at the right to find the golden ratio.

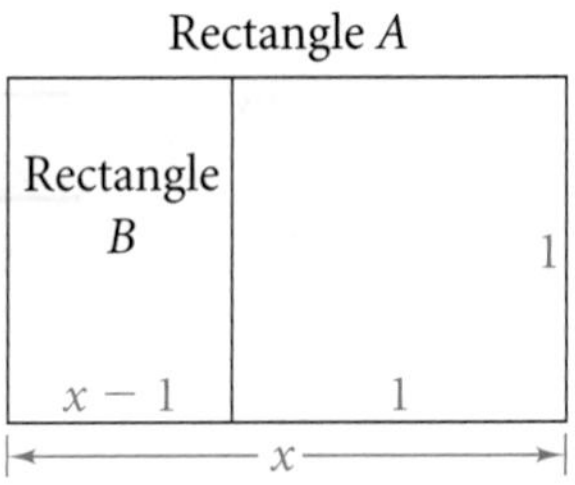

Relate $\dfrac{\text{longer side of } A}{\text{shorter side of } A} = \dfrac{\text{longer side of } B}{\text{shorter side of } B}$

Define Let x = longer side of rectangle A. Then $x - 1$ = shorter side of rectangle B.

Write $\dfrac{x}{1} = \dfrac{1}{x - 1}$

$x^2 - x = 1$ **Find cross-products.**

$x^2 - x - 1 = 0$ **Write in standard form.**

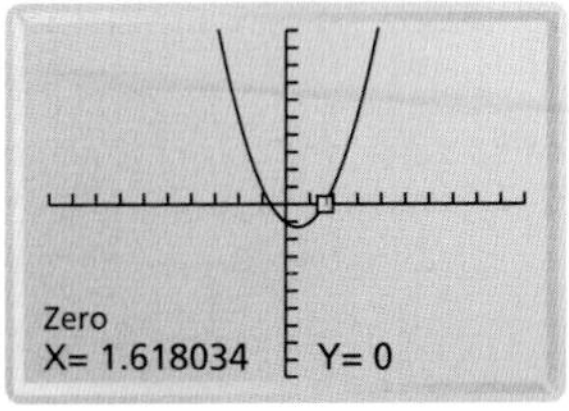

Graph the related function $y = x^2 - x - 1$. Use the CALC feature to find the positive solution.

The ratio is about 1.62 : 1.

Check Understanding **5** Solve each equation. When necessary, round to the nearest hundredth.

a. $x^2 - 2x = 4$ **b.** $x^2 + \frac{1}{2}x - \frac{1}{4} = 0$

Real-World Connection

Francisco José de Goya y Lucientes (1746–1828) was a Spanish painter. In *Portrait of a Man,* Goya placed the most significant elements of the painting within golden rectangles.

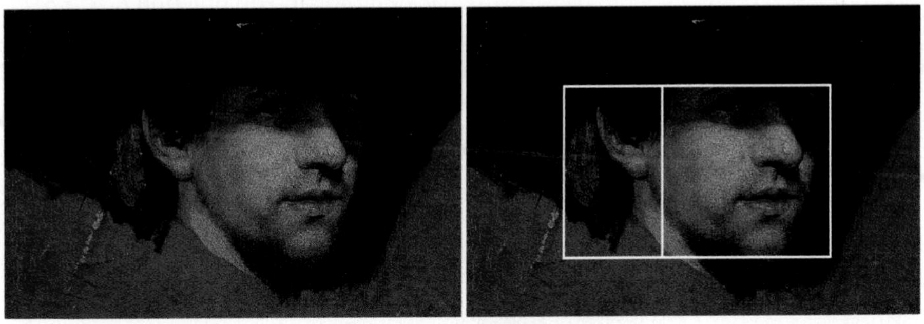

EXERCISES

For more practice, see *Extra Practice.*

Practice and Problem Solving

A Practice by Example

Example 1 (page 263)

Solve each equation by factoring. Check your answers.

1. $x^2 + 6x + 8 = 0$ **2.** $x^2 + 18 = 9x$ **3.** $2x^2 - x = 3$

4. $x^2 - 10x + 25 = 0$ **5.** $2x^2 + 6x = -4$ **6.** $3x^2 = 16x + 12$

Example 2 (page 264)

Solve each equation by finding square roots.

7. $5x^2 = 80$ **8.** $x^2 - 4 = 0$ **9.** $2x^2 = 32$

10. $9x^2 = 25$ **11.** $3x^2 - 15 = 0$ **12.** $5x^2 - 40 = 0$

Example 3 (page 264)

Solve each equation by factoring or by taking square roots.

13. $x^2 - 4x = 0$ **14.** $6x^2 + 4x = 0$ **15.** $12x^2 - 147 = 0$

16. $3x^2 = 48$ **17.** $2x^2 = x + 3$ **18.** $4x^2 - 80 = 0$

19. Firefighters A smoke jumper jumps from a plane that is 1700 ft above the ground. The function $y = -16t^2 + 1700$ gives the jumper's height y in feet at t seconds.
a. How long is the jumper in free fall if the parachute opens at 1000 ft?
b. How long is the jumper in free fall if the parachute opens at 940 ft?

Examples 4 and 5 (page 265)

Solve each equation by graphing. If necessary, round your answer to the nearest hundredth.

20. $x^2 + 5x + 3 = 0$ **21.** $x^2 - 7x = 11$ **22.** $2x^2 - x = 2$

23. $6x^2 = -19x - 15$ **24.** $3x^2 - 5x - 4 = 0$ **25.** $5x^2 - 7x - 3 = 8$

26. $6x^2 + 31x = 12$ **27.** $1 = 4x^2 + 3x$ **28.** $\frac{1}{2}x^2 - x = 8$

29. $x^2 = 4x + 8$ **30.** $x^2 + 4x = 6$ **31.** $2x^2 - 2x - 5 = 0$

B Apply Your Skills

32. a. Art Verify that the Chinese painting at the right is a golden rectangle.
b. What element in the painting divides it into a square and another golden rectangle?

33. Physics The period of a pendulum is the time the pendulum takes to swing back and forth. The function $\ell = 0.81t^2$ relates the length ℓ in feet of a pendulum to the time t in seconds that it takes to swing back and forth.
a. Find the period of a pendulum that is 2.5 ft long.
b. The convention center in Portland, Oregon, has the longest pendulum in the United States. The pendulum's length is 90 ft. Find the period.

34. Open-Ended Write an equation in standard form that you can solve by factoring and an equation that you cannot solve by factoring.

35. Gardening Suppose you want to expand the garden shown at the right by planting a border of flowers. The border will be of the same width around the entire garden. The flowers you bought will fill an area of 276 ft^2. How wide should the border be?

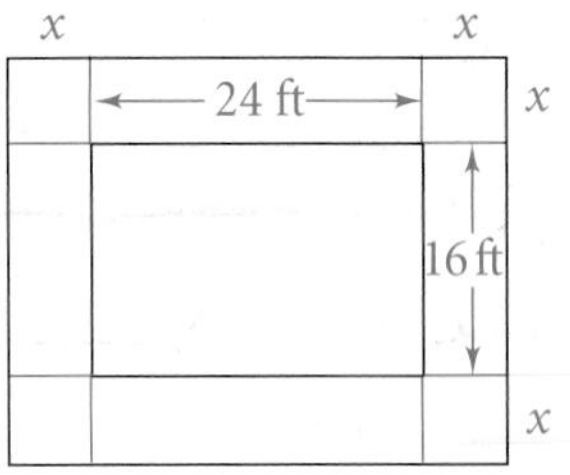

Solve each equation by factoring, by taking square roots, or by graphing. If necessary, round your answer to the nearest hundredth.

36. $x^2 + 6x + 5 = 45$ **37.** $x^2 - 11x + 24 = 0$ **38.** $3x^2 = 27$

39. $2x^2 - 5x - 3 = 0$ **40.** $x^2 + 2x = 6 - 6x$ **41.** $6x^2 + 13x + 6 = 0$

42. $2x^2 + 8x = 5x + 20$ **43.** $7x^2 - 243 = 0$ **44.** $3x^2 + 7x = 9$

45. $12x^2 - 154 = 0$ **46.** $x^2 + 4x = 0$ **47.** $x^2 = 8x - 7$

48. $x^2 + 2x = 15$ **49.** $x^2 + 11x + 10 = 0$ **50.** $4x^2 + 4x = 3$

51. $(x + 3)^2 = 9$ **52.** $2x^2 - 6x = 8$ **53.** $2x^2 + x - 28 = 0$

Critical Thinking **The graphs of each pair of functions intersect. Find their points of intersection without using a calculator. (*Hint:* Solve as a system using substitution.)**

54. $y = x^2$, $y = -\frac{1}{2}x^2 + \frac{3}{2}x + 3$

55. $y = x^2 - 2$, $y = 3x^2 - 4x - 2$

56. $y = -x^2 + x + 4$, $y = 2x^2 - 6$

57. Writing Explain how you found the intersections in Exercises 54–56.

Open-Ended **Write a quadratic equation with the given solutions.**

58. 3 and 5 **59.** -3 and 2 **60.** -1 and -6 **61.** $\frac{1}{2}$ and $\frac{2}{3}$

C Challenge

62. Matrices Find the possible values of x and y.

$$\begin{bmatrix} x & 2 \\ 3 & y \end{bmatrix}^2 = \begin{bmatrix} 22 & 10 \\ 15 & \blacksquare \end{bmatrix}$$

63. a. Write the equation of a parabola with vertex $(-3, 5)$ passing through $(-4, 6)$.
b. Find the values of x when $y = 8$.

64. The equation $x^2 - 10x + 24 = 0$ can be written in factored form as $(x - 4)(x - 6) = 0$. How can you use this fact to find the vertex of the graph of $y = x^2 - 10x + 24$?

65. Physics Suppose you throw a ball straight up from the ground with a velocity of 80 ft/s. As the ball moves upward, gravity slows it. Eventually the ball begins to fall back to the ground. The height h of the ball after t seconds in the air is given by the quadratic function $h(t) = -16t^2 + 80t$.
a. How high does the ball go?
b. For how many seconds is the ball in the air before it hits the ground?

66. a. Let $a > 0$. Use algebraic or arithmetic ideas to explain why the lowest point on the graph of $y = a(x - h)^2 + k$ must occur when $x = h$.
b. Suppose that the function in part (a) is $y = a(x - h)^3 + k$. Is your reasoning still valid? Explain.

Standardized Test Prep

Multiple Choice

67. What are the values of x that satisfy the equation $3 - 27x^2 = 0$?

A. $x = \pm 3$ **B.** $x = \pm\frac{1}{3}$

C. $x = \frac{1}{9}$ or $x = -\frac{1}{9}$ **D.** $x = 2\sqrt{6}$ or $x = -2\sqrt{6}$

68. What are the solutions of the equation $6x^2 + 9x - 15 = 0$?

F. $1, -15$ **G.** $1, -\frac{5}{2}$

H. $-1, -5$ **I.** $3, \frac{5}{2}$

69. For which equation is -3 NOT a solution?

A. $x^2 - 2x - 15 = 0$ **B.** $x^2 - 21 = 4x$

C. $2x^2 + 12x = -18$ **D.** $9 + x^2 = 0$

Quantitative Comparison

Compare the boxed quantity in Column A with the boxed quantity in Column B. Choose the best answer.

A. The quantity in Column A is greater.
B. The quantity in Column B is greater.
C. The two quantities are equal.
D. The relationship cannot be determined from the information given.

	Column A	Column B
70.	the solution of $x^2 - 6x + 9 = 0$	the solution of $x^2 - 10x + 25 = 0$
71.	the sum of the solutions of $x^2 - 8x + 15 = 0$	the product of the solutions of $x^2 - 8x - 9 = 0$
72.	the sum of the solutions of $x^2 + x - 6 = 0$	the product of the solutions of $x^2 + 6x + 9 = 0$

Take It to the NET
Online lesson quiz at
www.PHSchool.com
Web Code: aga-0505

Short Response

73. What are the solutions of the quadratic equation $6x^2 - 15x - 9 = 0$? Show the steps of your solution.

Mixed Review

Lesson 5-4 **Factor each expression.**

74. $3x^2 - 4x + 1$ **75.** $25z^2 - 9$ **76.** $6s^2 + 9s$

Lesson 4-1 **State the dimensions of each matrix. Identify the indicated element.**

77. $\begin{bmatrix} 4 & 6 & 5 \\ 1 & -3 & 0 \\ 1 & 1 & 9 \end{bmatrix}; a_{13}$ **78.** $\begin{bmatrix} 4 & -1 & 6 \\ 2 & 0 & 0 \end{bmatrix}; a_{21}$ **79.** $\begin{bmatrix} -9 & 1 & -1 \\ 0 & 6 & 0 \\ 1 & 0 & -2 \end{bmatrix}; a_{32}$

Lesson 1-1 **Name the property of real numbers illustrated by each equation.**

80. $3(2x + y) = 6x + 3y$ **81.** $3x^2 + 7y = 7y + 3x^2$

82. $4(3x) = (4 \cdot 3)x$ **83.** $3 + (-3) = 0$

Extension Quadratic Inequalities

FOR USE WITH LESSON 5-5

You can use a graphing calculator to graph quadratic inequalities and to solve systems of quadratic inequalities.

1 EXAMPLE

Graph $y \leq x^2 - 5x - 6$.

Enter the corresponding equation as shown. Place the cursor to the left of Y_1 and press ENTER three times to produce shading *below* the graph. The solution is represented by all the points in the shaded region. Solutions to $y = x^2 - 5x - 6$ are also part of the solution.

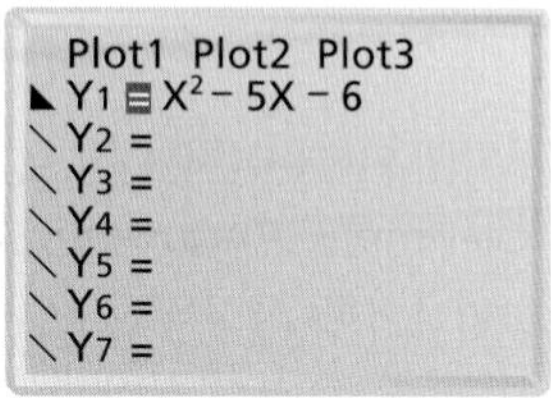

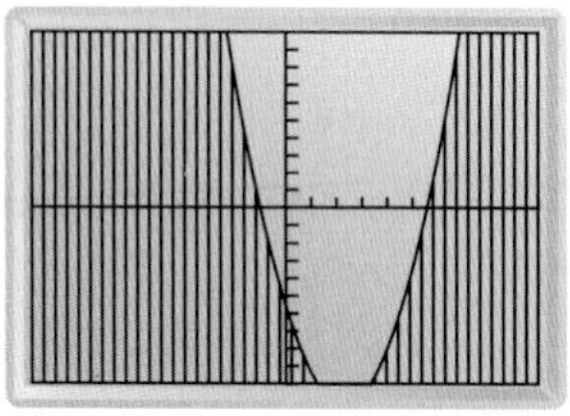

2 EXAMPLE

Solve $y \geq x^2 + 8x + 17$ and $y \leq -x^2 - 6x - 3$.

Enter the corresponding equations. For each equation, choose shading that corresponds to the inequality sign. The solution consists of all points within the double-shaded region.

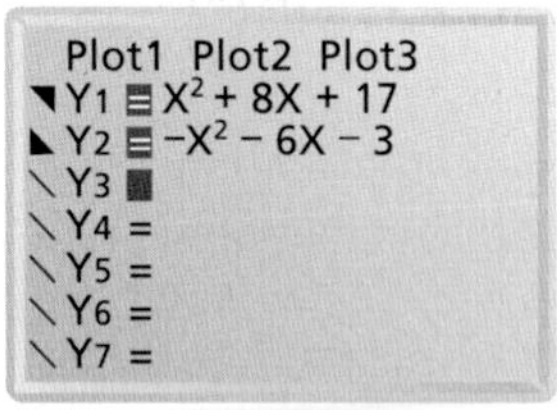

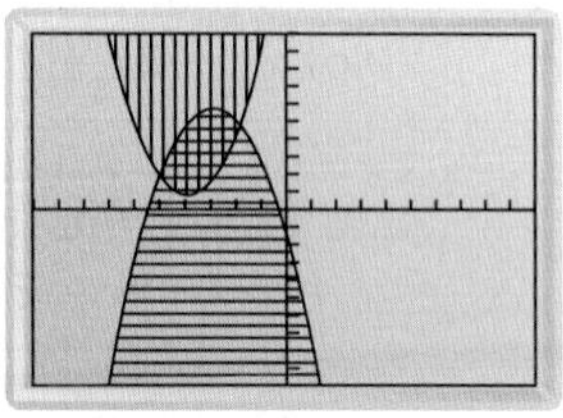

You can also use the **Shade** command from the **DRAW** menu. This command instructs the calculator to shade only the region of the intersection of the graphs.

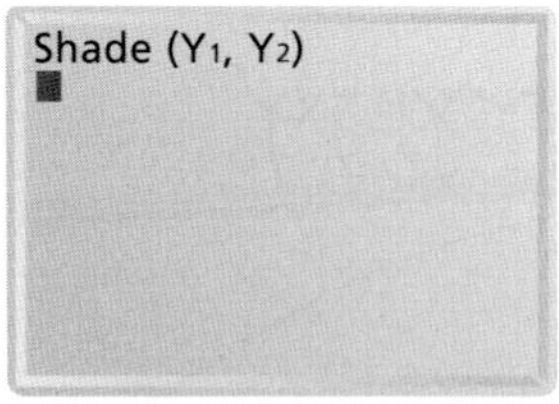

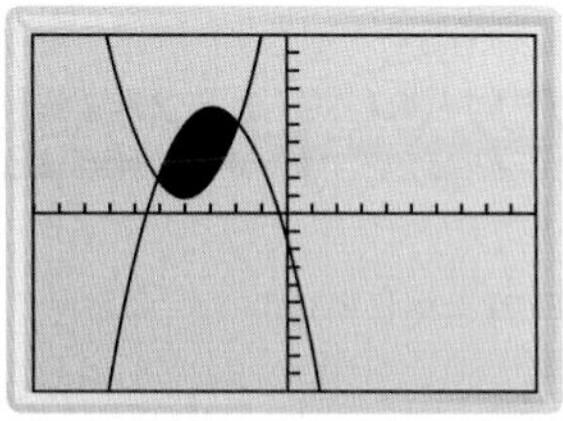

EXERCISES

Graph each quadratic inequality.

1. $y \geq 2x^2 + 7x - 4$

2. $y < -x^2 - 5x$

3. $y > -1.4x^2 + 2x + 7$

Solve each system of quadratic inequalities graphically.

4. $y \geq x^2 - 6x + 5$
$y \leq -x^2 + 6x$

5. $y \geq x^2 - x - 6$
$y \geq -x^2 - x + 6$

6. $y \geq x^2$
$y \geq (x - 3)^2$

5-6 Complex Numbers

North Carolina Objectives

1.02 Define and compute with complex numbers.

Lesson Preview

What You'll Learn

OBJECTIVE 1 To identify and graph complex numbers

OBJECTIVE 2 To add, subtract, and multiply complex numbers

. . . And Why

To explore fractals, as in Example 8

Check Skills You'll Need

(For help, go to Skills Handbook page 855.)

Simplify each expression.

1. $\sqrt{3^2 + 4^2}$ **2.** $\sqrt{(-2)^2 + 8^2}$ **3.** $\sqrt{5^2 + (-12)^2}$

4. $\sqrt{6^2 + 10^2}$ **5.** $\sqrt{x^2 + x^2}$ **6.** $\sqrt{(3x)^2 + (4x)^2}$

New Vocabulary

- i
- imaginary number
- complex numbers
- complex number plane
- absolute value of a complex number

Interactive lesson includes instant self-check, tutorials, and activities.

OBJECTIVE 1 Identifying Complex Numbers

When you learned to count, you used the natural numbers 1, 2, 3, and so on. Your number system has grown to include other types of numbers. You have used real numbers, which include both rational numbers such as $\frac{1}{2}$ and irrational numbers such as $\sqrt{2}$. Now your number system will expand to include numbers such as $\sqrt{-2}$.

The imaginary number ***i*** is defined as the number whose square is -1. So $i^2 = -1$ and $i = \sqrt{-1}$. An **imaginary number** is any number of the form $a + bi$, where $b \neq 0$.

Key Concepts

Property **Square Root of a Negative Real Number**

For any positive real number a, $\sqrt{-a} = i\sqrt{a}$.

Example $\sqrt{-4} = i\sqrt{4} = i \cdot 2 = 2i$

Note that $(\sqrt{-4})^2 = (i\sqrt{4})^2 = i^2\sqrt{4}^2 = -1 \cdot 4 = -4$ (not 4).

1 EXAMPLE Simplifying Numbers Using *i*

Simplify $\sqrt{-8}$ by using the imaginary number i.

$\sqrt{-8} = \sqrt{-1 \cdot 8}$	Factor -8 as $-1 \cdot 8$.
$= \sqrt{-1} \cdot \sqrt{8}$	Use the Multiplication Property of Square Roots.
$= i \cdot \sqrt{8}$	Substitute i for $\sqrt{-1}$.
$= i \cdot 2\sqrt{2}$	Simplify $\sqrt{8}$.
$= 2i\sqrt{2}$	Use the Commutative Property.

Check Understanding

1 Simplify each number by using the imaginary number i.

a. $\sqrt{-2}$ **b.** $\sqrt{-12}$ **c.** $\sqrt{-36}$

Imaginary numbers and real numbers together make up the set of **complex numbers.**

Key Concepts

Definition	Complex Numbers
A complex number can be written in the form $a + bi$, where a and b are real numbers, including 0.	$a + bi$ (a: Real part; bi: Imaginary part)

2 EXAMPLE Simplifying Imaginary Numbers

Write the complex number $\sqrt{-9} + 6$ in the form $a + bi$.

$\sqrt{-9} + 6 = 3i + 6$ **Simplify the radical expression.**

$= 6 + 3i$ **Write in the form $a + bi$.**

Check Understanding **2** Write the complex number $\sqrt{-18} + 7$ in the form $a + bi$.

The diagram below shows the sets of numbers that are part of the complex number system, and examples of each set.

Complex Numbers

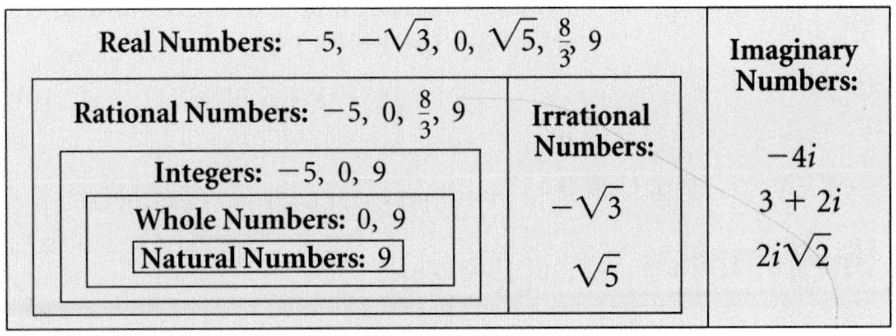

You can use the **complex number plane** to represent a complex number geometrically. Locate the real part of the number on the horizontal axis and the imaginary part on the vertical axis. You graph $3 - 4i$ in the same way you would graph $(3, -4)$ on the coordinate plane.

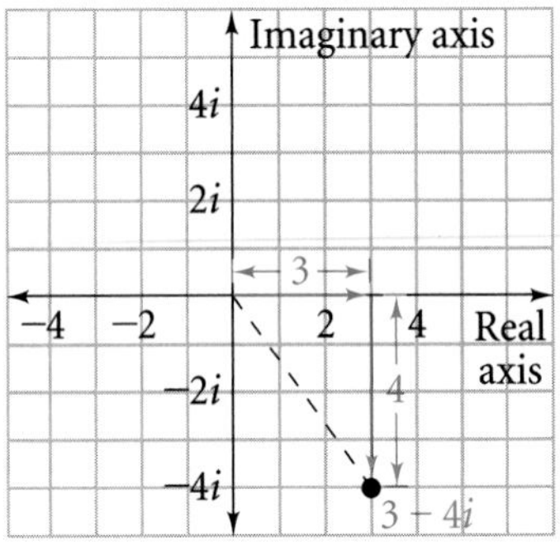

The **absolute value of a complex number** is its distance from the origin on the complex number plane. You can find the absolute value by using the Pythagorean Theorem. In general, $|a + bi| = \sqrt{a^2 + b^2}$.

Need Help?
The Pythagorean Theorem: $c^2 = a^2 + b^2$ and $c = \sqrt{a^2 + b^2}$

3 EXAMPLE Finding Absolute Value

a. Find $|5i|$.

$5i$ is 5 units from the origin on the imaginary axis. So $|5i| = 5$.

b. Find $|3 - 4i|$.

$|3 - 4i| = \sqrt{3^2 + (-4)^2}$

$= \sqrt{9 + 16} = 5$

Check Understanding **3** Find the absolute value of each complex number.

a. $|6 - 4i|$ **b.** $|-2 + 5i|$ **c.** $|4i|$

OBJECTIVE 2

Operations With Complex Numbers

You can apply the operations of real numbers to complex numbers.

If the sum of two complex numbers is 0, then each number is the opposite, or additive inverse, of the other.

4 EXAMPLE Additive Inverse of a Complex Number

Find the additive inverse of $-2 + 5i$.

$-2 + 5i$

$-(-2 + 5i)$ **Find the opposite.**

$2 - 5i$ **Simplify.**

Check Understanding 4 Find the additive inverse of each number.

a. $-5i$ **b.** $4 - 3i$ **c.** $a + bi$

To add or subtract complex numbers, combine the real parts and the imaginary parts separately.

5 EXAMPLE Adding Complex Numbers

Simplify the expression $(5 + 7i) + (-2 + 6i)$.

$(5 + 7i) + (-2 + 6i) = 5 + (-2) + 7i + 6i$ **Use commutative and associative properties.**

$= 3 + 13i$ **Simplify.**

Check Understanding 5 Simplify each expression.

a. $(8 + 3i) - (2 + 4i)$ **b.** $7 - (3 + 2i)$ **c.** $(4 - 6i) + 3i$

For two imaginary numbers bi and ci, $(bi)(ci) = bc(i)^2 = bc(-1) = -bc$.

You can multiply two complex numbers of the form $a + bi$ by using the procedure for multiplying binomials.

6 EXAMPLE Multiplying Complex Numbers

a. Find $(5i)(-4i)$.

$(5i)(-4i) = -20i^2$ **Multiply the real numbers.**

$= -20(-1)$ **Substitute −1 for i^2.**

$= 20$ **Multiply.**

b. Find $(2 + 3i)(-3 + 5i)$.

$(2 + 3i)(-3 + 5i) = -6 + 10i - 9i + 15i^2$ **Multiply the binomials.**

$= -6 + 10i - 9i + 15(-1)$ **Substitute −1 for i^2.**

$= -21 + i$ **Simplify.**

Check Understanding 6 Simplify each expression.

a. $(12i)(7i)$ **b.** $(6 - 5i)(4 - 3i)$ **c.** $(4 - 9i)(4 + 3i)$

Some quadratic equations have solutions that are complex numbers.

7 EXAMPLE Finding Complex Solutions

Solve $4x^2 + 100 = 0$.

$4x^2 + 100 = 0$

$4x^2 = -100$ **Isolate x^2.**

$x^2 = -25$

$x = \pm\sqrt{-25}$ **Find the square root of each side.**

$= \pm 5i$ **Simplify.**

Check $4x^2 + 100 = 0$

$4(5i)^2 + 100 \stackrel{?}{=} 0$

$4(25i^2) \stackrel{?}{=} -100$

$100(-1) \stackrel{?}{=} -100$

$-100 = -100$ ✓

$4x^2 + 100 = 0$

$4(-5i)^2 + 100 \stackrel{?}{=} 0$

$4(25i^2) \stackrel{?}{=} -100$

$100(-1) = -100$

$-100 = -100$ ✓

Check Understanding 7 Solve each equation. Check your answers.

a. $3x^2 + 48 = 0$ **b.** $-5x^2 - 150 = 0$ **c.** $8x^2 + 2 = 0$

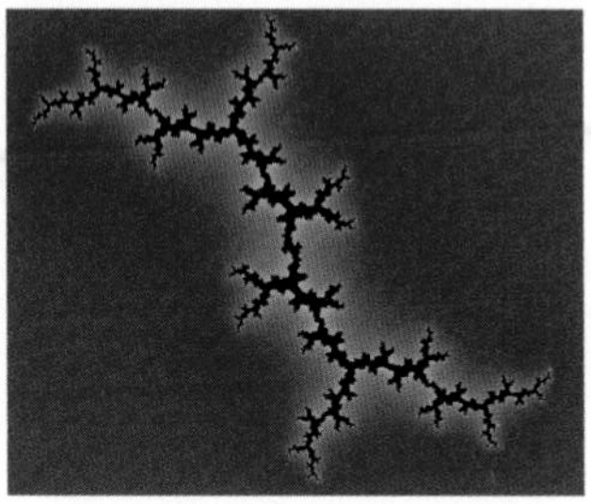

Functions of the form $f(z) = z^2 + c$ where c is a complex number generate fractal graphs on the complex plane like the one at the left. To test if z belongs to the graph, use z as the first input value and repeatedly use each output as the next input. If the output values do not become infinitely large, then z is on the graph.

8 EXAMPLE Real-World Connection

Fractals Find the first three output values for $f(z) = z^2 + i$.

$f(z) = z^2 + i$

$f(0) = 0^2 + i$ **Use $z = 0$ as the first input value.**

$= i$

$f(i) = i^2 + i$ **First output becomes second input. Evaluate for $z = i$.**

$= -1 + i$

$f(-1 + i) = (-1 + i)^2 + i$ **Second output becomes third input. Evaluate for $z = -1 + i$.**

$= [(-1)^2 + (-1)(i) + (-1)(i) + (i)^2] + i$

$= (1 - 2i - 1) + i$

$= -i$ **Third output would be next input.**

The first three output values are i, $-1 + i$, and $-i$.

Check Understanding 8 Find the first three output values for $f(z) = z^2 - 1 + i$.

EXERCISES

For more practice, see *Extra Practice.*

Practice and Problem Solving

A Practice by Example

Example 1 (page 270)

Simplify each number by using the imaginary number *i*.

1. $\sqrt{-4}$ **2.** $\sqrt{-7}$ **3.** $\sqrt{-15}$ **4.** $\sqrt{-81}$ **5.** $\sqrt{-50}$

6. $\sqrt{-16}$ **7.** $\sqrt{-32}$ **8.** $3\sqrt{-9}$ **9.** $-\sqrt{-100}$ **10.** $\sqrt{-72}$

Example 2 (page 271)

Write each number in the form $a + bi$.

11. $2 + \sqrt{-3}$ **12.** $\sqrt{-8} + 8$ **13.** $6 - \sqrt{-28}$ **14.** $\sqrt{-4} + 3$

15. $7 - \sqrt{-25}$ **16.** $\sqrt{-1} + 2$ **17.** $-\sqrt{-50} - 2$ **18.** $\sqrt{-72} + 4$

Example 3 (page 271)

Find the absolute value of each complex number.

19. $|2i|$ **20.** $|5 + 12i|$ **21.** $|2 - 2i|$ **22.** $|1 - 4i|$ **23.** $|3 - 6i|$

Example 4 (page 272)

Find the additive inverse of each number.

24. $4i$ **25.** $5 - 3i$ **26.** $9 + i$ **27.** $-3 - 2i$ **28.** $-4 + 7i$

Example 5 (page 272)

Simplify each expression.

29. $(2 + 4i) + (4 - i)$ **30.** $(-3 - 5i) + (4 - 2i)$ **31.** $(7 + 9i) + (-5i)$

32. $6 - (8 + 3i)$ **33.** $(12 + 5i) - (2 - i)$ **34.** $(-6 - 7i) - (1 + 3i)$

Example 6 (page 272)

35. $(-2i)(5i)$ **36.** $(4 - 3i)(5 + 2i)$ **37.** $(8 + i)(2 + 7i)$

38. $(-6 - 5i)(1 + 3i)$ **39.** $(-6i)^2$ **40.** $(9 + 4i)^2$

Example 7 (page 273)

Solve each equation. Check your answers.

41. $x^2 + 25 = 0$ **42.** $2x^2 + 1 = 0$ **43.** $3s^2 + 2 = -62$

44. $x^2 = -7$ **45.** $x^2 + 36 = 0$ **46.** $-5x^2 - 3 = 0$

Example 8 (page 273)

Find the first three output values of each fractal-generating function. Use $z = 0$ as the first input value.

47. $z^2 - i$ **48.** $f(z) = z^2 - 2i$ **49.** $f(z) = z^2 + 1 - i$

B Apply Your Skills

Solve each equation.

50. $x^2 + 16 = -49$ **51.** $x^2 - 30 = -79$ **52.** $3x^2 + 1 = x^2 - 1$

53. Writing In reality, is it possible for Mr. Milde's average to be an imaginary number? Explain.

ROBOTMAN by Jim Meddick

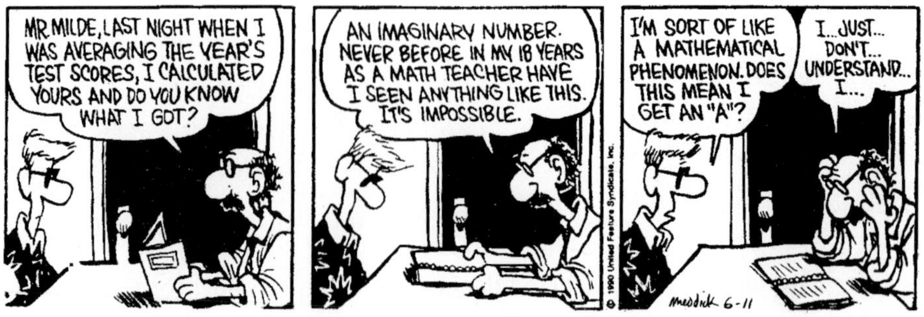

54. a. Name the complex number represented by each point on the graph at the right.
b. Find the additive inverse of each number.

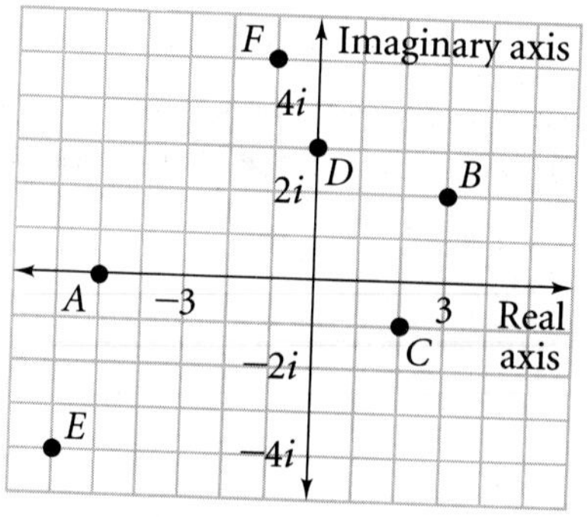

55. a. Open-Ended Name eight complex numbers that have absolute values of 10. Plot them in a complex number plane.
b. Geometry What is the geometric figure that contains *all* the points that have absolute values of 10?

56. Solve $(x + 3i)(x - 3i) = 34$.

Simplify each expression.

57. $(8i)(4i)(-9i)$

58. $(2 + \sqrt{-1}) + (-3 + \sqrt{-16})$

59. $(4 + \sqrt{-9}) + (6 - \sqrt{-49})$

60. $(10 + \sqrt{-9}) - (2 + \sqrt{-25})$

61. $(8 - \sqrt{-1}) - (-3 + \sqrt{-16})$

62. $2i(5 - 3i)$

63. $-5(1 + 2i) + 3i(3 - 4i)$

64. $(3 + \sqrt{-4})(4 + \sqrt{-1})$

65. $(-2 + \sqrt{-9})(6 + \sqrt{-25})$

66. $(1 - \sqrt{-4})(-3 - \sqrt{-25})$

67. a. Copy and complete the table.

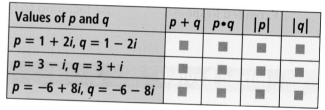

Values of p and q	$p + q$	$p \cdot q$	$\lvert p\rvert$	$\lvert q\rvert$
$p = 1 + 2i, q = 1 - 2i$	■	■	■	■
$p = 3 - i, q = 3 + i$	■	■	■	■
$p = -6 + 8i, q = -6 - 8i$	■	■	■	■

b. Number pairs such as p and q in the table are complex conjugates. Describe at least three patterns you see in complex conjugate pairs.
c. Plot each pair of conjugates. How are the points of each pair related?
d. True or false: The conjugate of an additive inverse is equal to the additive inverse of the conjugate. Explain your answer.

Two complex numbers $a + bi$ and $c + di$ are equal when $a = c$ and $b = d$. Solve each equation for x and y.

68. $2x + 3yi = -14 + 9i$ **69.** $3x + 19i = 16 - 8yi$ **70.** $-14 - 3i = 2x + yi$

C Challenge

71. Show that the product of a nonzero complex number $a + bi$ and its conjugate (as described in Exercise 67) is a real number.

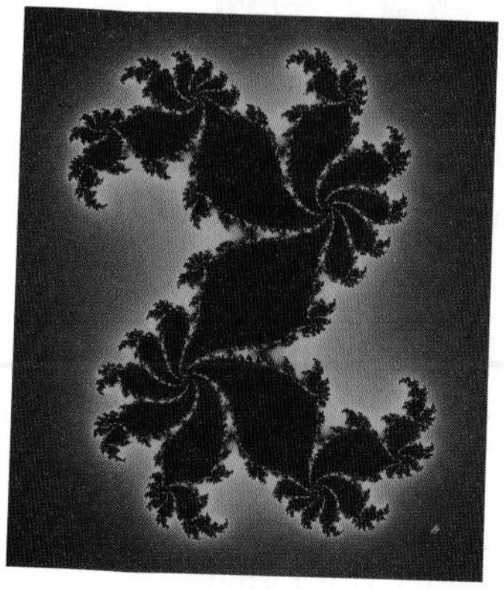

Exercise 72

72. Fractals The fractal at the left can be described by the function $f(z) = z^2 + c$. If $c = 0.383 + 0.11i$, find the first two output values of the function. Use $z = 0$ as the first input value.

73. For what real values of x and y is $(x + yi)^2$ an imaginary number?

74. Complex numbers can be used to generate interesting patterns. Here is a pattern generated by powers of $1 + 3i$.

$(1 + 3i)^1 = 1 + 3i$ and $1^2 + 3^2 = 10$
$(1 + 3i)^2 = -8 + 6i$ and $(-8)^2 + 6^2 = 10^2$
$(1 + 3i)^3 = -26 - 18i$ and $(-26)^2 + (-18)^2 = 10^3$
$(1 + 3i)^4 = 28 - 96i$ and $28^2 + (-96)^2 = 10^4$

Find the powers of $3 + 4i$ through $(3 + 4i)^5$. Generate and verify a similar pattern.

12. a. Sports Find a quadratic model for the attendance at college basketball games from 1995–1997 by solving three equations in *a*, *b*, and *c*.

b. Predict the year attendance will reach 12,000,000.

c. Use the quadratic regression feature of your calculator to find a model for all the data.

d. What does this regression model predict as the first year attendance will reach 12,000,000?

e. Find the maximum likely attendance.

Year	Attendance (thousands)
1995	4962
1996	5234
1997	6734
1998	7387
1999	8010
2000	8698

SOURCE: National Collegiate Athletic Association

5-2 and 5-3 Objectives

- To graph quadratic functions (p. 241)
- To find maximum and minimum values of quadratic functions (p. 243)
- To use the vertex form of a quadratic function (p. 248)

The constants *a*, *b*, and *c* characterize the graph of $y = ax^2 + bx + c$. The axis of symmetry is $x = -\frac{b}{2a}$, the vertex is at $\left(-\frac{b}{2a}, f\left(-\frac{b}{2a}\right)\right)$, and $f\left(-\frac{b}{2a}\right)$ is the maximum or minimum value. The **vertex form of a quadratic function** is $y = a(x - h)^2 + k$. The vertex is (h, k), the maximum or minimum value is k, and the axis of symmetry is the line $x = h$. If $a > 0$, the parabola opens up. If $a < 0$, it opens down.

Graph each function. Identify the vertex, *y*-intercept, and axis of symmetry.

13. $y = 2(x + 1)^2 - 4$

14. $y = (x - 5)^2$

15. $y = -(x - 2)^2 + 1$

16. $y = -x^2 + 7$

Write each function in vertex form. Find its maximum or minimum value.

17. $y = x^2 + x - 12$

18. $y = -x^2 + 2x + 2$

19. $y = 2x^2 + 8x - 3$

20. $y = -0.5x^2 + 5$

21.

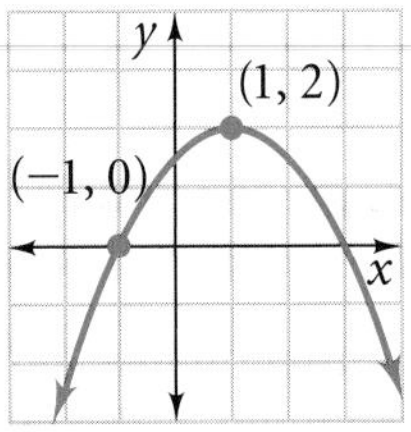

22.

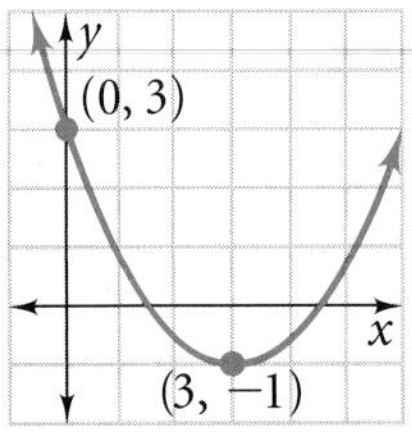

23.

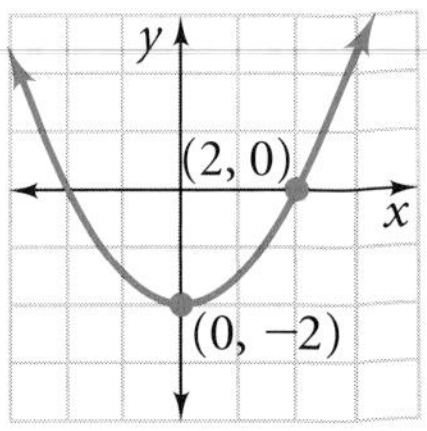

5-4 and 5-5 Objectives

- To find common and binomial factors of quadratic expressions (p. 255)
- To factor special quadratic expressions (p. 258)
- To solve quadratic equations by factoring and by finding square roots (p. 263)
- To solve quadratic equations by graphing (p. 264)

You can solve some quadratic equations by finding the square root of each side or by finding the zeros of the related function. You can solve some quadratic equations in the **standard form of a quadratic equation** $ax^2 + bx + c = 0$ by **factoring** if you can find two factors with product *ac* and sum *b*. Then use the **Zero Product Property**. For a **perfect square trinomial**, $ax^2 \pm 2abx + b^2 = (a \pm b)^2$. For the **difference of two squares,** $a^2 - b^2 = (a + b)(a - b)$. In all cases, first factor out the **greatest common factor (GCF) of the expression.**

Solve by factoring, taking square roots, or, if necessary, by graphing. Give exact radical answers. For answers found by graphing, round to the nearest hundredth.

24. $x^2 - 7x = 0$

25. $x^2 + 2x - 8 = 0$

26. $(x + 3)^2 = 9$

27. $4(x - 2)^2 = 32$

28. $2x^2 - 6x - 8 = 0$

29. $x^2 - 5x - 5 = 0$

30. $3x^2 - 14x + 8 = 0$

31. $x^2 - 3x - 4 = 0$

32. $x^2 + 8x + 16 = 0$

33. $x^2 - 6x + 9 = 0$

34. $4x^2 - 12x + 9 = 0$

35. $x^2 - 9 = 0$

36. $6x^2 - 13x - 5 = 0$

37. $4x^2 + 3 = -8x$

38. $3x^2 + 4x - 10 = 0$

5-6 Objectives

- To identify and graph complex numbers (p. 270)
- To add, subtract, and multiply complex numbers (p. 272)

An **imaginary number** has the form $a + bi$, where $b \neq 0$. The imaginary number $\boldsymbol{i}$ is defined as $i^2 = -1$. A **complex number** has the form $a + bi$, where a and b are any real numbers. The **absolute value of a complex number** is its distance from the origin in the **complex number plane**. You graph $a + bi$ in the complex plane just as you graphed (a, b) in the coordinate plane. Complex numbers follow rules of operation like those of real numbers. Some quadratic equations have imaginary numbers as roots. Functions of complex numbers may be used to generate fractals.

Simplify each expression.

39. $\sqrt{-25}$ **40.** $\sqrt{-2} - 1$ **41.** $-4 - \sqrt{-1}$ **42.** $\sqrt{-27}$

43. $2\sqrt{-32} + 4$ **44.** $|3 - i|$ **45.** $|-2 + 3i|$ **46.** $|4i|$

47. $(3 + 4i) - (7 - 2i)$ **48.** $(5 - i)(9 + 6i)$

49. $(3 + 8i) + (5 - 2i)$ **50.** $(4 + 6i)(2 + i)$

Find the additive inverse of each number. Graph the number and its inverse.

51. $2 - i$ **52.** $-4 + 3i$ **53.** $-7 - 4i$ **54.** $-2i$

Solve each equation.

55. $x^2 + 2 = 0$ **56.** $x^2 = -5$

57. $3x^2 + 12 = 0$ **58.** $6x^2 + 4 = 0$

Find the first three outputs of each fractal-generating function. Begin with $z = 0$.

59. $f(z) = z^2 - i$ **60.** $f(z) = i - z^2$

5-7 and 5-8 Objectives

- To solve equations by completing the square (p. 278)
- To rewrite functions in vertex form by completing the square (p. 280)
- To solve quadratic equations by using the Quadratic Formula (p. 285)
- To determine types of solutions by using the discriminant (p. 287)

Completing the square is based on the relationship $x^2 + bx + \left(\frac{b}{2}\right)^2 = \left(x + \frac{b}{2}\right)^2$. You can use it to write a quadratic function in vertex form. If the coefficient of the quadratic term is not 1, you must factor out the coefficient from the variable terms.

You can solve any quadratic equation by using the Quadratic Formula.

If $ax^2 + bx + c = 0$, then $x = \frac{-b \pm \sqrt{b^2 - 4ac}}{2a}$.

The discriminant $b^2 - 4ac$ determines the number and type of solutions of the equation. If $b^2 - 4ac > 0$, the equation has two real solutions. If $b^2 - 4ac = 0$, the equation has one real solution. If $b^2 - 4ac < 0$, the equation has no real solutions and two imaginary solutions.

Solve each equation by completing the square.

61. $9x^2 + 6x + 1 = 4$ **62.** $x^2 + 3x = -25$ **63.** $x^2 - 2x + 4 = 0$

64. $-x^2 + x - 7 = 0$ **65.** $2x^2 + 3x = 8$ **66.** $4x^2 - x - 3 = 0$

Rewrite the equation in vertex form by completing the square. Find the vertex.

67. $y = x^2 + 3x - 1$ **68.** $y = 2x^2 - x - 1$ **69.** $y = x^2 + x + 2$

Determine the number and type of solutions. Solve using the Quadratic Formula.

70. $x^2 - 6x + 2 = 0$ **71.** $-2x^2 + 7x = 10$ **72.** $x^2 + 4 = 6x$

Chapter 5

Chapter Test

Take It to the NET
Online chapter test at
www.PHSchool.com
Web Code: aga-0552

1. Write the equation of the parabola in standard form. Find the coordinates of the points corresponding to *P*, *Q*, and *R*.

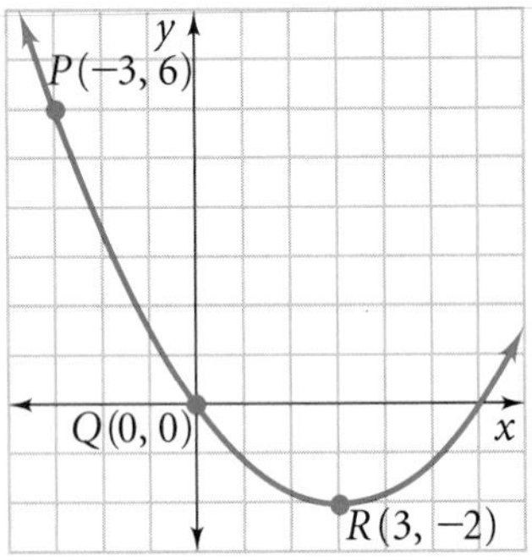

Sketch a graph of the parabola with the given vertex through the given point.

2. vertex $(0, 0)$, point $(-3, 3)$

3. vertex $(1, 5)$, point $(2, 11)$

Graph each quadratic function. Identify the axis of symmetry and the coordinates of the vertex.

4. $y = x^2 - 7$

5. $y = x^2 + 2x + 6$

6. $y = -x^2 + 5x - 3$

7. $y = -\frac{1}{2}x^2 - 8$

Simplify each expression.

8. $\sqrt{-16}$

9. $4\sqrt{-9} - 2$

10. $(4 - i) + (5 - 9i)$

11. $(2 + 3i)(8 - 5i)$

12. $(-3 + 2i) - (6 + i)$

13. $(7 - 4i)(10 - 2i)$

14. Physics For a model rocket, the altitude *h*, in meters, as a function of time *t*, in seconds, is given by $h = 68t - 8t^2$. Find the maximum height of the rocket. How long does it take to reach the maximum height?

Find the additive inverse of each number.

15. $3 - 7i$

16. $-2 + i$

Graph each number on the complex plane. Then find its absolute value.

17. $7 - 2i$

18. $8i$

19. $4 + 8i$

20. 5

21. $6 - 4i$

22. $-2 + 3i$

23. Writing Compare graphing a number on the complex plane to graphing a point on the coordinate plane. How are they similar? How are they different?

Solve each quadratic equation.

24. $x^2 - 25 = 0$

25. $x^2 + 5x - 24 = 0$

26. $x^2 + 8x - 9 = 0$

27. $3x^2 - 21x + 3 = 0$

28. $6x^2 = 9x$

29. $4x^2 + 4x + 4 = 0$

30. $5x^2 + x + 2 = 0$

31. $-3x^2 - 2x + 7 = 0$

32. $2x^2 + 6x + 12 = 0$

Write each function in vertex form. Sketch the graph of the function and label its vertex.

33. $y = x^2 - 6x + 5$

34. $y = -x^2 + 8x - 10$

35. $y = 2x^2 - 3x - 1$

36. $y = -\frac{1}{2}x^2 + 4x - 9$

Evaluate the discriminant of each equation. How many real and imaginary solutions does each have?

37. $x^2 + 6x - 7 = 0$

38. $3x^2 - x + 3 = 0$

39. $-2x^2 - 4x + 1 = 0$

40. $-x^2 + 6x - 9 = 0$

41. Open-Ended Sketch the graph of a parabola that has no real solutions.

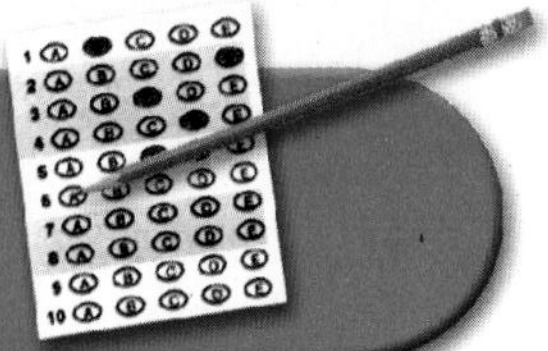

Standardized Test Prep

Reading Comprehension **Read the passage below. Then answer the questions on the basis of what is *stated* or *implied* in the passage.**

Dealing with Setbacks The boundary of a lot of land is called the property line. Many communities do not allow you to build up to the property line. Zoning laws may require a "setback" of several feet to ensure some distance between buildings and between a building and the property line.

Suppose the setback for a building is s feet on all four sides of a lot that has width 50 feet and length 60 feet. Then the maximum width of the building is $(50 - 2s)$ feet, and the maximum length of the building is $(60 - 2s)$ feet.

You can write and use functions in terms of s for the maximum area of the base of the building.

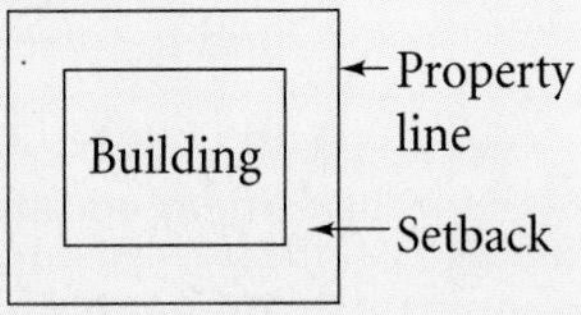

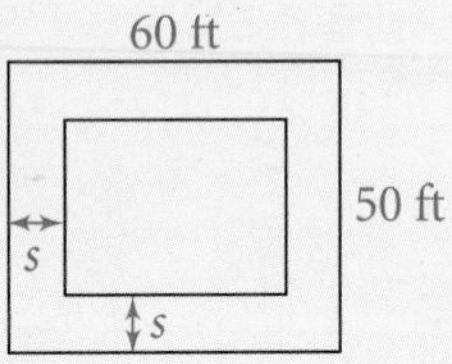

1. What is the area of the entire lot?
   A. 220 ft
   B. 2576 ft^2
   C. 3000 ft^2
   D. $(3000 - 4s^2)$ ft^2

2. Which function does NOT express the maximum area of the base of the building in terms of s?
   F. $A(s) = (50 - 2s)(60 - 2s)$
   G. $A(s) = 3000 - 220s + 4s^2$
   H. $A(s) = 4s^2 - 220s + 3000$
   I. $A(s) = 2[(50 - 2s) + (60 - 2s)]$

3. What is the maximum area of the base of the building when $s = 8$ ft?
   A. 64 ft^2
   B. 156 ft
   C. 1496 ft^2
   D. 2184 ft^2

4. What is the minimum area that is NOT occupied by the base of the building when $s = 6$ ft?
   F. 1176 ft^2
   G. 1824 ft^2
   H. 2376 ft^2
   I. 2856 ft^2

5. Suppose the building is set back five feet. Find the maximum area of the base of the building.

6. Suppose the maximum area of the base of the building is 2376 ft^2. What is the value of the setback?

7. Suppose the minimum area that is NOT occupied by the building is 1344 ft^2. What is the value of the setback?

8. Write a function for the perimeter of the base of the building in terms of s.

9. Suppose a lot is 30 feet by 90 feet. The setback is s feet. Write an expression for the maximum area of the base of the building.

10. Suppose a lot has length ℓ, width w, and setback s.
    a. Write an expression for the maximum area of the base of the building.
    b. Write an expression for the maximum perimeter of the base of the building.

11. A lot is 22 ft by 58 ft, and the setback on each side is s ft. Which formula expresses the maximum area of the base of the building in terms of s?
    A. $f(s) = 4s^2 - 160s + 1276$
    B. $f(s) = 1276 - 160s - 4s^2$
    C. $f(s) = (58 - s)(22 - s)$
    D. $f(s) = 1276 - s^2$

Where You've Been

- In Chapter 2, you learned to write and graph linear functions and to solve linear equations and inequalities.
- In Chapter 3, you learned to write, graph, and solve systems of linear equations and inequalities.
- In Chapter 5, you learned to write and graph quadratic functions and to solve quadratic equations.

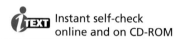

Instant self-check online and on CD-ROM

Diagnosing Readiness

(For help, go to the Lesson in green.)

Finding models (Lesson 5-1)

Find a quadratic model for each set of values.

1. $(-1, 3), (0, 1), (2, 9)$ **2.** $(0, -1), (2, -2), (4, -5)$ **3.** $(-4, 75), (0, 3), (11, 300)$

Graphing functions (Lessons 2-2 and 5-2)

Graph each function.

4. $6x - 4y = -10$ **5.** $y = 3x^2 - 10x + 2$ **6.** $y = \frac{3}{4}(x^2 + 12) + 1$

Solving systems by graphing (Lesson 5-5)

Solve each equation by graphing. Round to the nearest hundredth.

7. $1 = 4x^2 - 3x$ **8.** $\frac{1}{2}x^2 + x - 14 = 0$ **9.** $5x^2 + 30x = 12$

Solving equations algebraically (Lessons 5-5 and 5-8)

Solve each equation algebraically.

10. $x^2 - 5x - 36 = 0$ **11.** $2x^2 - 13x + 21 = 0$ **12.** $3x^2 - 4x = 3$

Finding the number and type of solutions (Lesson 5-8)

Evaluate the discriminant of each equation. Tell how many solutions each equation has and whether the solutions are real or imaginary.

13. $x^2 - 12x + 30 = 0$ **14.** $-4x^2 + 20x - 25 = 0$ **15.** $2x^2 = 8x - 8$

Finding probability (Lesson 1-6)

16. Suppose you select an integer from 100 to 200 at random. What is $P(\text{odd})$?

Polynomials and Polynomial Functions

Chapter 6

Where You're Going

- In Chapter 6, you will learn to write and graph polynomial functions and to solve polynomial equations.
- You will learn to use important theorems about the number of solutions to polynomial equations.
- You will learn to solve problems involving permutations, combinations, and binomial probability.

Real-World Snapshots Applying what you learn, on pages 358–359 you will do activities involving soccer.

Key Vocabulary

- Binomial Theorem (p. 348)
- combination (p. 340)
- conjugates (p. 331)
- Factor Theorem (p. 309)
- Fundamental Theorem of Algebra (p. 335)
- Imaginary Root Theorem (p. 332)
- Irrational Root Theorem (p. 331)
- multiplicity (p. 310)
- Pascal's Triangle (p. 347)
- polynomial function (p. 309)
- Rational Root Theorem (p. 329)
- Remainder Theorem (p. 317)
- standard form of a polynomial (p. 301)
- synthetic division (p. 315)

6-1

Polynomial Functions

North Carolina Objectives

2.04 Create and use best-fit models to solve problems.
2.06 Use cubic equations to model and solve problems. a) Solve using graphs. b) Interpret constants and coefficients.

Lesson Preview

What You'll Learn

OBJECTIVE 1 To classify polynomials

OBJECTIVE 2 To model data using polynomial functions

. . . And Why

To model the world's gold production, as in Example 3

Check Skills You'll Need

(For help, go to Lesson 1-2.)

Simplify each expression by combining like terms.

1. $3x + 5x - 7x$ **2.** $-8xy^2 - 2x^2y + 5x^2y$ **3.** $-4x + 7x^2 + x$

Find the number of terms in each expression.

4. $\frac{1}{2}bh$ **5.** $1 - x$ **6.** $4x^3 - x^2 - 9$

New Vocabulary • polynomial • polynomial function • degree • standard form of a polynomial • degree of a polynomial

Interactive lesson includes instant self-check, tutorials, and activities.

OBJECTIVE 1 Exploring Polynomial Functions

Investigation: Graphs of Polynomial Functions

- Use a graphing calculator to graph each equation listed at the right.
- Sketch each graph on a separate index card or sheet of paper. Label the graph with its equation.
- Sort the graphs into groups based on their shapes.

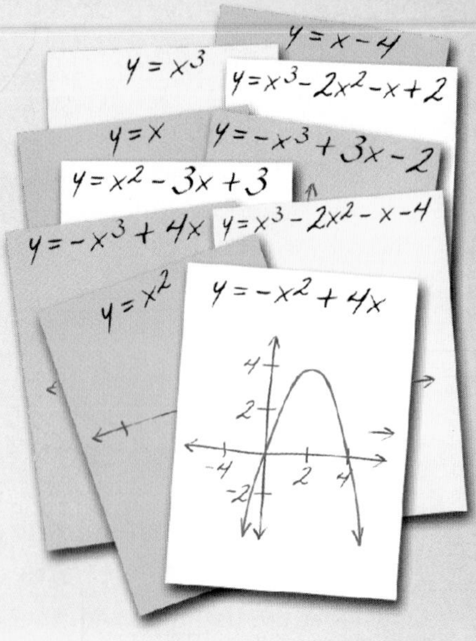

1. How are the graphs of the linear equations alike?
2. How are the graphs of the quadratic equations alike?
3. How are the graphs of the remaining equations alike? How are they different?
4. a. Estimate the *x*-intercept(s) of each graph. Write them on each card.

   b. **Make a Conjecture** Compare the number of *x*-intercepts of each graph and the greatest exponent found in its equation. What is the relationship?

A monomial is an expression that is either a real number, a variable, or a product of real numbers and variables with whole-number exponents. A **polynomial** is a monomial or the sum of monomials. For any polynomial, you can write the corresponding polynomial function, as shown below.

Key Concepts

Definition	**Polynomial Function**
$P(x) = a_n x^n + a_{n-1} x^{n-1} + \ldots + a_1 x + a_0$	where n is a nonnegative integer and the coefficients $a_n, \ldots, a_0$ are real numbers.

Reading Math

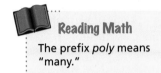

The prefix *poly* means "many."

The exponent of the variable in a term determines the **degree** of that term. The terms in the polynomial shown below are in *descending order* by degree. This order demonstrates the **standard form of a polynomial.** A one-variable polynomial in standard form has no two terms with the same degree, since all like terms have been combined.

$$P(x) = 2x^3 - 5x^2 - 2x + 5$$

← Polynomial

Leading coefficient: 2; Cubic term: $2x^3$; Quadratic term: $-5x^2$; Linear term: $-2x$; Constant term: $+5$

You can classify a polynomial by the number of terms it contains. A polynomial of more than three terms does not usually have a special name. You can also classify a polynomial by its degree. The **degree of a polynomial** is the largest degree of any term of the polynomial. The name assigned to each degree is listed below.

Degree	Name Using Degree	Polynomial Example	Number of Terms	Name Using Number of Terms
0	constant	6	1	monomial
1	linear	$x + 3$	2	binomial
2	quadratic	$3x^2$	1	monomial
3	cubic	$2x^3 - 5x^2 - 2x$	3	trinomial
4	quartic	$x^4 + 3x^2$	2	binomial
5	quintic	$-2x^5 + 3x^2 - x + 4$	4	polynomial of 4 terms

1 EXAMPLE Classifying Polynomials

Write each polynomial in standard form. Then classify it by degree and by number of terms.

a. $-7x + 5x^4$

$5x^4 - 7x$

The term with the largest degree is $5x^4$, so the polynomial is degree 4. It has two terms. The polynomial is a quartic binomial.

b. $x^2 - 4x + 3x^3 + 2x$

$3x^3 + x^2 - 2x$

The term with the largest degree is $3x^3$, so the polynomial is degree 3. It has three terms. The polynomial is a cubic trinomial.

Check Understanding

1 Write each polynomial in standard form. Then classify it by degree and by number of terms.

a. $4x - 6x + 5$ **b.** $3x^3 + x^2 - 4x + 2x^3$ **c.** $6 - 2x^5$

OBJECTIVE

2 Modeling Data With a Polynomial Function

You have already used lines and parabolas to model data. Sometimes you can fit data more closely by using a polynomial model of degree three or greater.

2 EXAMPLE Comparing Models

Using a graphing calculator, determine whether a linear model, a quadratic model, or a cubic model best fits the values in the table.

x	0	5	10	15	20
y	10.1	2.8	8.1	16.0	17.8

Enter the data. Use the LinReg, QuadReg, and CubicReg options of a graphing calculator to find the best-fitting model for each polynomial classification.

Graph each model and compare.

Linear model

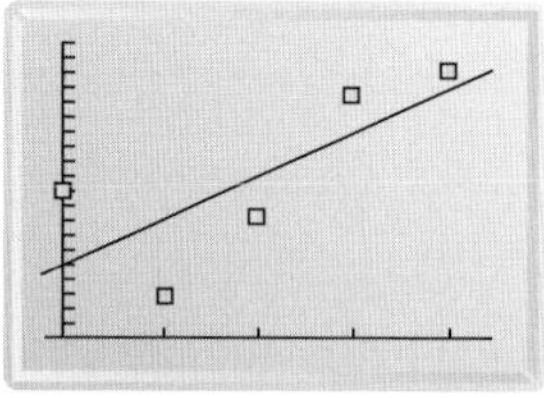

Quadratic model

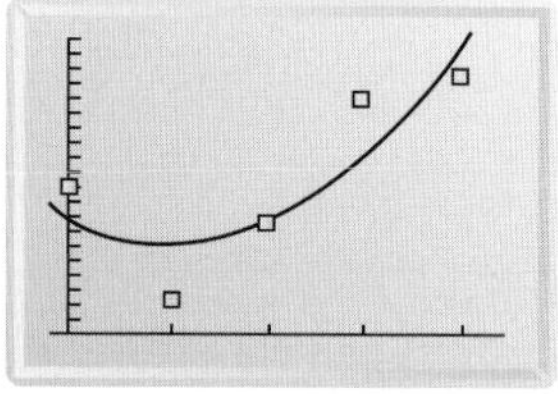

Cubic model

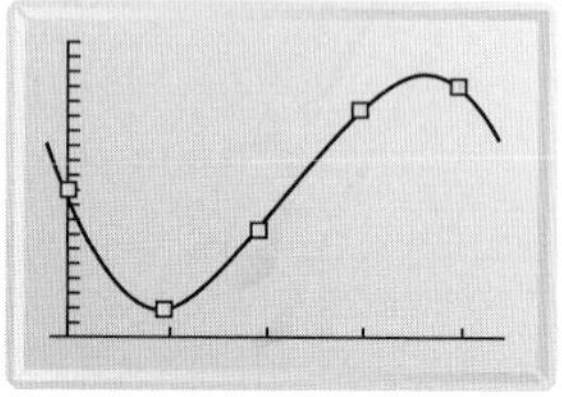

The cubic model appears to best fit the given values.

Check Understanding 2 Can you use the model in Example 2 to predict the value of y for $x = 25$? Explain.

Finding a close fit helps you estimate values between known data points.

3 EXAMPLE Real-World Connection

Gold The table below shows world gold production for several years. Find a quartic function to model the data. Use it to estimate production in 1988.

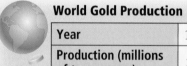

World Gold Production

Year	1975	1980	1985	1990	1995	2000
Production (millions of troy ounces)	38.5	39.2	49.3	70.2	71.8	82.6

SOURCES: *The World Almanac* and *World Gold*

Real-World Connection

The Federal Reserve stores gold in bars that weigh 400 troy ounces each.

Enter the data. Let 0 represent 1975. To find a quartic model, use the QuarticReg option of a graphing calculator. Graph the model.

```
QuarticReg
 y=ax⁴+bx³+...+e
 a=9.0333333E-4
 b=-.0519296296
 c=.9590277778
 d=-3.898862434
↓e=38.85753968
```

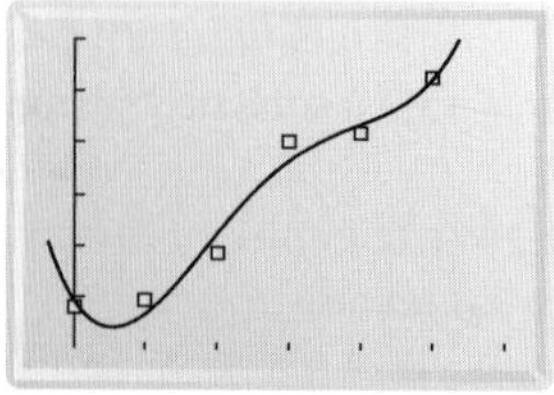

X	Y_1
7	42.915
8	46.157
9	49.519
10	52.875
11	56.12
12	59.168
13	61.959

X=13

The function $f(x) = 0.0009033x^4 - 0.05193x^3 + 0.959x^2 - 3.899x + 38.86$ is an approximate model for a quartic function.

To estimate gold production in 1988, you can use the Table option of a graphing calculator to find that $f(13) \approx 61.96$. According to the model, about 62 million troy ounces of gold were produced in 1988.

Check Understanding **3** Use the quartic model in Example 3 to estimate gold production in 1997.

EXERCISES

For more practice, see *Extra Practice*.

Practice and Problem Solving

A Practice by Example

Example 1 (page 301)

Write each polynomial in standard form. Then classify it by degree and by number of terms.

1. $7x + 3x + 5$

2. $5 - 3x$

3. $2m^2 - 3 + 7m$

4. $-x^3 + x^4 + x$

5. $-4p + 3p + 2p^2$

6. $5a^2 + 3a^3 + 1$

7. $-x^5$

8. $3 + 12x^4$

9. $6x^3 - x^3$

10. $7x^3 - 10x^3 + x^3$

11. $4x + 5x^2 + 8$

12. $x^2 - x^4 + 2x^2$

Example 2 (page 302)

Find a cubic model for each set of values.

13. $(-2, -7), (-1, 0), (0, 1), (1, 2), (2, 9)$

14. $(0, -12), (1, 10), (2, 4), (3, 42)$

15. $(-1, 2.5), (0, 1), (1, 1.5), (2, 13)$

16. $(-3, 91), (-2, 84), (-1, 93), (0, 100)$

17. Vital Statistics The data at the right indicate that the life expectancy for residents of the United States has been increasing. Recall that in Chapter 3 you found a linear model for this data set.
- **a.** Find a quadratic model for the data set.
- **b.** Find a cubic model for the data set.
- **c.** Graph each model. Compare the quadratic and cubic models to determine which one is a better fit.

Life Expectancy (years)

Year of Birth	Males	Females
1970	67.1	74.7
1980	70.0	77.4
1990	71.8	78.8
2000	73.2	80.2
2010	74.5	81.3

SOURCE: U.S. Bureau of the Census. Go to **www.PHSchool.com** for a data update.
Web Code: agg-2041

Example 3 (pages 302–303)

Find a cubic model for each function. Then use your model to estimate the value of y when $x = 17$.

18. $(-1, -3), (0, 0), (1, -1), (2, 0)$

19. $(10, 0), (11, 121), (12, 288), (13, 507)$

20. $(10, 500), (14, 588), (16, 512), (20, 0)$

21. $(1, 91), (10, 95), (20, 260), (30, 365)$

22.

x	0	3	5	6	9	11	12	14	16	18	20
y	42	31	26	21	17	15	19	22	28	30	29

23.

x	0	2	3	6	8	10	12	14	16	18	20
y	4.1	6	15.7	21.1	23.6	23.1	24.7	24.9	23.9	25.2	29.5

B Apply Your Skills

24. Open-Ended Write a third-degree polynomial function. Make a table of values and a graph. Find the x- and y-intercepts.

Write each polynomial in standard form. Then classify it by degree and by number of terms.

25. $8x - 4x + x^3$ **26.** $a^2 + a^3 - 4a^4$ **27.** 7

28. $2x(3x)$ **29.** $x^3(2 + x)$ **30.** $\frac{3x^5 + 4x}{6}$

31. Packaging Design The diagram at the right shows a cologne bottle that consists of a cylindrical base and a hemispherical top.

a. Write an expression for the cylinder's volume.

b. Write an expression for the volume of the hemispherical top.

c. Write a polynomial to represent the total volume.

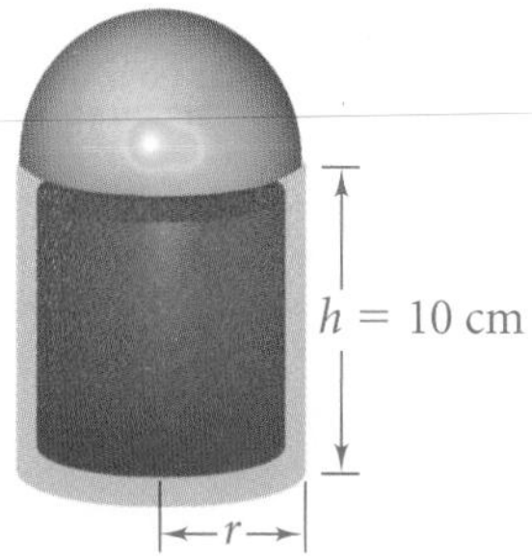

32. Writing Explain why cubic functions are useful for interpolating between known data points. Why are they often not reliable for extrapolating data?

Reading Math

To interpolate means to estimate a value inside the range of known values. To extrapolate means to estimate a value outside the range of known values.

Simplify. Classify each result by number of terms.

33. $(2c^2 + 9) - (3c^2 - 7)$ **34.** $(-8d^3 - 7) + (-d^3 - 6)$

35. $(7x^2 + 8x - 5) + (9x^2 - 9x)$ **36.** $(5x^3 - 6x + 8) - (3x^3 - 9)$

37. $(3a - 2b) + (6b - 2a)$ **38.** $(4x - 5y) - (4x + 7y)$

39. $(3x^2 - 6y - 1) + (5x^2 + 1)$ **40.** $(-a^2 - 3) - (3a - a^2 - 5)$

41. $(7x^3 + 9x^2 - 8x + 11) - (5x^3 - 13x - 16)$

42. $(-12x^3 + 5x - 23) - (4x^4 + 31 - 9x^3)$

43. $(30x^3 - 49x^2 + 7x) + (50x^3 - 75 - 60x^2)$

44. $(-3x^3 + 7x^2 - 8) - (-5x^3 + 9x^2 - 8x + 19)$

45. $(3a^2 - ab - 7) + (5a^2 + ab + 8) - (-2a^2 + 3ab - 9)$

Find each product. Classify the result by number of terms.

46. $x(2x)(4x + 1)$ **47.** $5x^2(6x - 2)$ **48.** $(2a - 5)(a^2 - 1)$

49. $b(b - 3)^2$ **50.** $(x - 2)^3$ **51.** $(x^2 + 1)^2$

52. $(2x + 5)^3 + 1$ **53.** $(a - b)^2 (a + b)$ **54.** $(a - 1)^4$

55. $(s + 3)(4s - 1)(3s + 7)$ **56.** $(x + 1)(x - 1)(x + 2)$

57. $(2c - 3)(2c + 4)(2c - 1)$ **58.** $(s + t)(s - t)(s + t)(s - t)$

59. The table shows U.S. energy production for a number of years.

a. Find a linear model, a cubic model, and a quartic model for the data set. Let 0 represent 1960.

b. Graph each model. Compare the three models to determine which fits best.

c. Use your answer to part (b) to estimate U.S. energy production in 1997.

U.S. Energy Production

Year	1960	1965	1970	1975	1980	1985	1990	1995	1999
Production ($\times 10^{15}$ Btu)	41.5	49.3	62.1	59.9	64.8	64.9	70.8	71.0	72.5

SOURCE: *The World Almanac*

C Challenge

60. **Geometry** Use the formula $V = \frac{\pi h}{3}(r^2 + rs + s^2)$ to find the volume of the truncated cone. Express your answer in scientific notation with the appropriate number of significant digits.

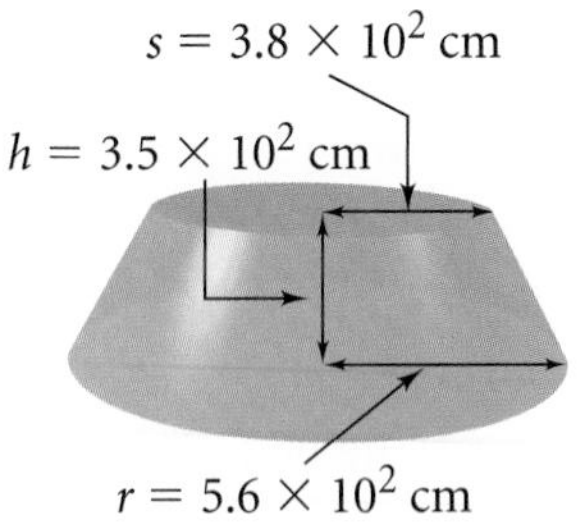

61. **Critical Thinking** Recall that each family of functions has a simplest function called the parent function.
   a. Compare the graphs of $y = x^3$ and $y = x^3 + 4$. Describe how the graph of $y = x^3 + 4$ relates to the graph of $y = x^3$.
   b. Compare the graphs of $y = x^3$ and $y = 4x^3$. Describe how the graph of $y = 4x^3$ relates to the graph of $y = x^3$.
   c. Identify the parent function among the functions in parts (a) and (b).

Standardized Test Prep

Quantitative Comparison

Compare the boxed quantity in Column A with the boxed quantity in Column B. Choose the best answer.

A. The quantity in Column A is greater.
B. The quantity in Column B is greater.
C. The two quantities are equal.
D. The relationship cannot be determined from the information given.

Take It to the NET
Online lesson quiz at
www.PHSchool.com
Web Code: agk-0601

	Column A	Column B
62.	the degree of the quadratic term of a polynomial	the degree of the cubic term of a polynomial
63.	the degree of $-5x^2 + 1 + 2x^2$, written in standard form	the degree of $x^2 - 2x^2 + x^2 + 4$, written in standard form
64.	the leading coefficient of $3x + 1$	the constant term of $x^3 + 5x^2 - 3$

Short Response

65. Why is finding the degree of a polynomial simplified when the polynomial is written in standard form?

Mixed Review

Lesson 5-8 **Use the discriminant to find the number of real solutions.**

66. $3x^2 + x - 6 = 0$ **67.** $5x^2 - 9 = 0$ **68.** $-x^2 + 2x - 8 = 0$

Lesson 5-3

69. Graph $f(x) = 3x^2 - 1$. Translate the graph right five units and down two units. What is the vertex of the new graph?

Lesson 4-4 **Each matrix represents the vertices of a polygon. Translate each figure 3 units left and 2 units down. Express your answer as a matrix.**

70. $\begin{bmatrix} 4 & 0 & 4 & 8 \\ -6 & -1 & 2 & -1 \end{bmatrix}$ **71.** $\begin{bmatrix} 5 & 0 & -3 \\ 7 & 0 & 2 \end{bmatrix}$ **72.** $\begin{bmatrix} 1 & 2 & 1 & 2 \\ -1 & -1 & -2 & -2 \end{bmatrix}$

Extension

End Behavior

FOR USE WITH LESSON 6-1

The end behavior of a graph describes the far left and the far right portions of the graph. The graphs of polynomial functions show four types of end behavior—*up and up, down and down, down and up,* and *up and down.*

Up and Up	Down and Down	Down and Up	Up and Down
(↖, ↗)	(↙, ↘)	(↙, ↗)	(↖, ↘)
Example	Example	Example	Example

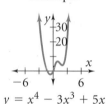

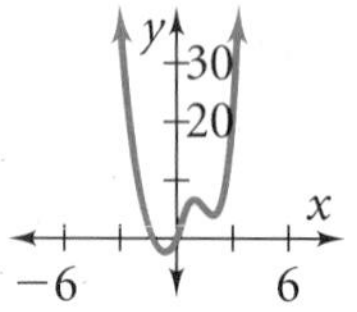

$y = x^4 - 3x^3 + 5x$

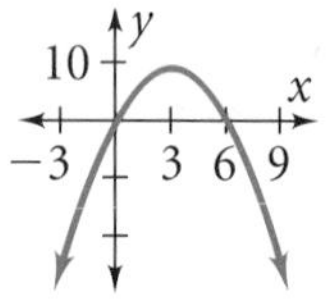

$y = -x^2 + 6x$

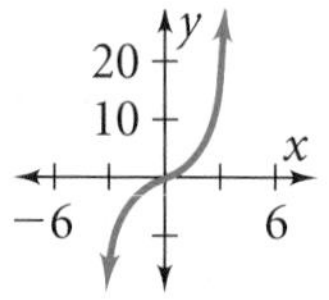

$y = x^3$

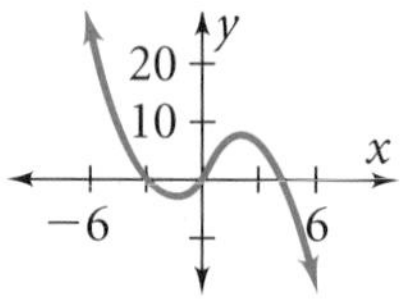

$y = -0.3x^3 + 4x + 2$

You can determine *by inspection* the end behavior of the graph of a polynomial function in standard form. Look at the coefficient and degree of the leading term.

Right If the leading coefficient is positive, then the graph rises to the right. If the leading coefficient is negative, then the graph falls to the right.

Left If the degree of the polynomial is even, then the left behavior is the same as the right behavior. If the degree of the polynomial is odd, then the left behavior is the opposite of the right behavior.

EXAMPLE **Describing End Behavior**

Determine by inspection the end behavior of the graph of each polynomial.

a. $y = 4x^3 - 3x$

The leading coefficient 4 is positive, so the graph rises to the right. The degree of the polynomial is 3, which is odd. The left behavior is opposite the right behavior, so the graph falls to the left. The end behavior is (↖, ↗).

b. $f(x) = -2x^4 + 8x^3 - 8x^2$

The leading coefficient –2 is negative, so the graph falls to the right. The degree of the polynomial is 4, which is even. The left behavior is the same as the right behavior, so the graph falls to the left. The end behavior is (↙, ↘).

EXERCISES

Determine by inspection the end behavior of the graph of each function.

1. $y = 3x + 2$
2. $y = 4x^3$
3. $g(t) = -t^2 + t$
4. $f(x) = 2x + x^5$
5. $g(x) = x^6$
6. $y = 3x^5 - 4x^4$
7. $y = -7x^8$
8. $f(x) = \frac{1}{2}x^4 - 2$
9. $y = -\frac{1}{2}x^3 + 4x^2 + x - 1$
10. $g(x) = x - x^3 + 5$

6-2 Polynomials and Linear Factors

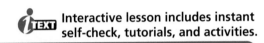

North Carolina Objectives

1.03 Operate with algebraic expressions (polynomial, rational, complex fractions) to solve problems.

Lesson Preview

What You'll Learn

Objective 1: To analyze the factored form of a polynomial

Objective 2: To write a polynomial function from its zeros

. . . And Why

To find the dimensions of carry-on luggage, as in Example 3

✔ Check Skills You'll Need

(For help, go to Lessons 5-1 and 5-4.)

Factor each quadratic expression.

1. $x^2 + 7x + 12$ **2.** $x^2 + 8x - 20$ **3.** $x^2 - 14x + 24$

Find each product.

4. $x(x + 4)$ **5.** $(x + 1)^2$ **6.** $(x - 3)^2(x + 2)$

New Vocabulary

- relative maximum
- relative minimum
- Factor Theorem
- multiple zero
- multiplicity

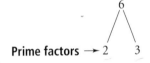

Interactive lesson includes instant self-check, tutorials, and activities.

Objective 1 The Factored Form of a Polynomial

Just as you can rewrite a whole number as a product of its prime factors, you can write a polynomial as a product of its linear factors. Compare the factor trees for the whole number 6 and the quadratic expression $x^2 + 4x - 12$.

6 → Prime factors → 2 3

$x^2 + 4x - 12$ → $(x + 6)(x - 2)$ ← Linear factors

In the factor tree for the whole number 6, each branch ends with a prime number. Likewise, in the factor tree for the polynomial $x^2 + 4x - 12$, each branch ends with a "prime" linear factor. A linear factor is similar to a prime number in that it cannot be factored any further. Once a polynomial has been factored completely to its linear factors, it is in factored form.

1 EXAMPLE Writing a Polynomial in Standard Form

Write the expression $(x + 1)(x + 2)(x + 3)$ as a polynomial in standard form.

$(x + 1)(x + 2)(x + 3)$	$= (x + 1)(x^2 + 3x + 2x + 6)$	Multiply $(x + 2)$ and $(x + 3)$.
	$= (x + 1)(x^2 + 5x + 6)$	Simplify.
	$= x(x^2 + 5x + 6) + 1(x^2 + 5x + 6)$	Distributive Property
	$= x^3 + 5x^2 + 6x + x^2 + 5x + 6$	Multiply.
	$= x^3 + 6x^2 + 11x + 6$	Simplify.

The expression $(x + 1)(x + 2)(x + 3)$ is the factored form of $x^3 + 6x^2 + 11x + 6$.

Need Help?

$a^n = a \cdot a \cdot a \cdot \ldots \cdot a$ (n factors of a)

$a^m \cdot a^n = a^{m+n}$

✔ Check Understanding **1** Write the expression $(x + 1)(x + 1)(x + 2)$ as a polynomial in standard form.

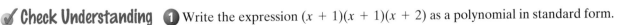

Need Help?

The GCF is the greatest common factor.

You can sometimes use the GCF of the terms to help you factor a polynomial.

2 EXAMPLE Writing a Polynomial in Factored Form

Write $2x^3 + 10x^2 + 12x$ in factored form.

$2x^3 + 10x^2 + 12x = 2x(x^2 + 5x + 6)$ **Factor out the GCF, 2*x*.**

$= 2x(x + 2)(x + 3)$ **Factor $x^2 + 5x + 6$.**

Check $2x(x + 2)(x + 3) = 2x(x^2 + 5x + 6)$ **Multiply $(x + 2)(x + 3)$.**

$= 2x^3 + 10x^2 + 12x$ ✓ **Distributive Property**

Check Understanding 2 Write $3x^3 - 3x^2 - 36x$ in factored form. Check by multiplication.

You can use polynomial functions to solve real-world problems. Consider the formula for volume: $V = \text{depth} \cdot \text{length} \cdot \text{width}$. Each dimension can represent a linear factor of a polynomial function.

3 EXAMPLE Real-World Connection

Real-World Connection

Airlines regulate the size of carry-on luggage because space is limited in a plane's overhead compartments.

Travel Several popular models of carry-on luggage have a length 10 in. greater than their depth. To comply with airline regulations, the sum of the length, width, and depth may not exceed 40 in.

a. Assume that the sum of the length, width, and depth is 40 in. Graph the function relating volume V to depth x. Find the x-intercepts. What do they represent?

Relate Volume = depth · length · width

Define Let x = depth. Then $x + 10$ = length, and

40 − (depth + length) = width.

Write $V(x) = x(x + 10)(40 - (x + x + 10))$

$= x(x + 10)(30 - 2x)$

Graph the function for volume. The x-intercepts of the function are $x = 0$, $x = -10$, and $x = 15$. These values of x produce a volume of zero.

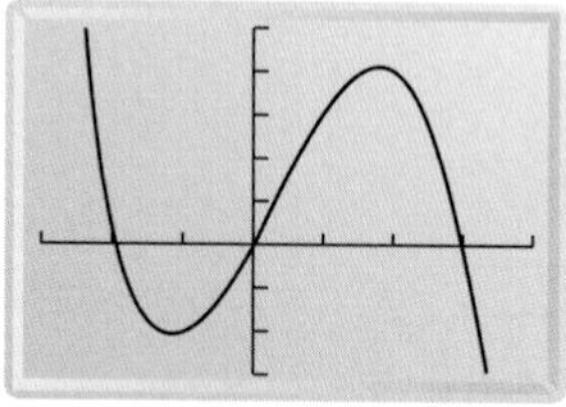

Xmin=–15
Xmax=20
Xscl=5
Ymin=–1500
Ymax=2500
Yscl=500

b. Describe a realistic domain.

The function has values over the set of all real numbers x. Since x represents the depth of the luggage, $x > 0$. Since the volume must be positive, $x < 15$. A realistic domain is $0 < x < 15$.

c. What is the maximum possible volume of a piece of luggage? What are the corresponding dimensions of the luggage?

Look for the greatest value of y that occurs within the domain $0 < x < 15$. Use the Maximum feature of a graphing calculator to find the maximum volume. A volume of approximately 2052 in.^{3} occurs for a depth of about 8.9 in. Then the length is about 18.9 in. and the width is about 12.2 in.

Check Understanding 3 Suppose an airline raises the allowable sum of the luggage dimensions to 45 in. Find the maximum possible volume and the corresponding dimensions.

The maximum value in Example 3 is the greatest value of the points in a region of the graph. It is called a **relative maximum.** Similarly, a **relative minimum** is the least y-value among nearby points on a graph.

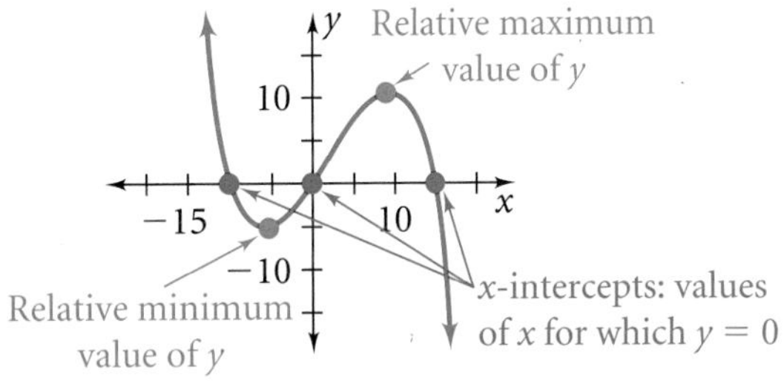

Recall that the x-intercepts of the graph of a function are called zeros because the value of the function is zero at each x-intercept.

OBJECTIVE 2

Factors and Zeros of a Polynomial Function

> **Need Help?**
> **Zero Product Property**
> If a product equals zero, then at least one of its factors must equal zero.

If a polynomial is in factored form, you can use the Zero Product Property to find values that will make the polynomial equal zero.

4 EXAMPLE Finding Zeros of a Polynomial Function

Find the zeros of $y = (x - 2)(x + 1)(x + 3)$. Then graph the function.

Using the Zero Product Property, find a zero for each linear factor.

$x - 2 = 0$ or $x + 1 = 0$ or $x + 3 = 0$

$x = 2$ $\quad x = -1$ $\quad x = -3$

The zeros of the function are 2, −1, and −3. Now graph the function.

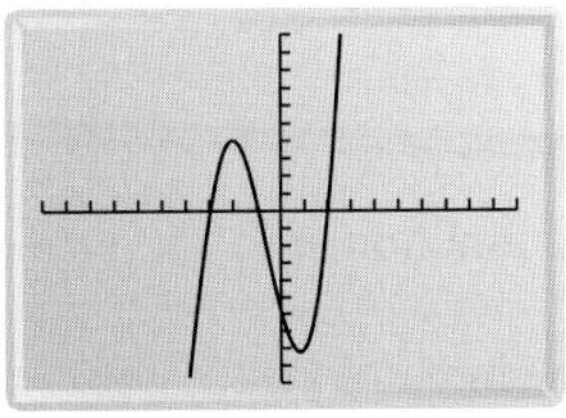

Zeros

X	Y1
−4	−18
−3	0
−2	4
−1	0
0	−6
1	−8
2	0

Y1=0

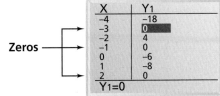

Check Understanding 4 **a.** Find the zeros of the function $y = (x - 7)(x - 5)(x - 3)$.
b. Graph the function and label the zeros.

You can reverse the process and write linear factors when you know the zeros. The relationship between the linear factors of a polynomial and the zeros of a polynomial is described by the Factor Theorem.

Key Concepts

Theorem **Factor Theorem**

The expression $x - a$ is a linear factor of a polynomial if and only if the value a is a zero of the related polynomial function.

5 EXAMPLE Writing a Polynomial Function From its Zeros

Write a polynomial function in standard form with zeros at −2, 3, and 3.

	$-2 \quad 3 \quad 3$	zeros
	$\downarrow \quad \downarrow \quad \downarrow$	
$f(x)$	$= (x + 2)(x - 3)(x - 3)$	**Write a linear factor for each zero.**
	$= (x + 2)(x^2 - 6x + 9)$	**Multiply $(x - 3)$ and $(x - 3)$.**
	$= x(x^2 - 6x + 9) + 2(x^2 - 6x + 9)$	**Distributive Property**
	$= x^3 - 6x^2 + 9x + 2x^2 - 12x + 18$	**Distributive Property**
	$= x^3 - 4x^2 - 3x + 18$	**Simplify.**

The function $f(x) = x^3 - 4x^2 - 3x + 18$ has zeros at −2, 3, and 3.

Check Understanding 5 **a.** Write a polynomial function in standard form with zeros at −4, −2, and 1.
b. Write a polynomial function in standard form with zeros at −4, −2, and 0.
c. **Critical Thinking.** Explain why the zero at 0 produces more than one possible answer to part (b).

Reading Math
Distinct means "separate and different."

While the polynomial function in Example 5 has three zeros, it has only two distinct zeros: −2 and 3. If a linear factor of a polynomial is repeated, then the zero is repeated. A repeated zero is called a **multiple zero.** A multiple zero has a **multiplicity** equal to the number of times the zero occurs. In Example 5, the zero 3 has a multiplicity of 2.

6 EXAMPLE Finding the Multiplicity of a Zero

Find any multiple zeros of $f(x) = x^4 + 6x^3 + 8x^2$ and state the multiplicity.

$f(x) = x^4 + 6x^3 + 8x^2$

$f(x) = x^2(x^2 + 6x + 8)$ **Factor out the GCF, x^2.**

$f(x) = x^2(x + 4)(x + 2)$ **Factor $x^2 + 6x + 8$.**

Since you can rewrite x^2 as $(x - 0)(x - 0)$, or $(x - 0)^2$, the number 0 is a multiple zero of the function, with multiplicity 2.

Check Understanding 6 For each function, find any multiple zeros and state the multiplicity.
a. $f(x) = (x - 2)(x + 1)(x + 1)^2$ **b.** $y = x^3 - 4x^2 + 4x$

The Factor Theorem helps relate four key facts about a polynomial. These facts are equivalent—that is, if you know one of them, you know them all.

Key Concepts

Summary **Equivalent Statements about Polynomials**

① −4 is a solution of $x^2 + 3x - 4 = 0$.
② −4 is an x-intercept of the graph of $y = x^2 + 3x - 4$.
③ −4 is a zero of $y = x^2 + 3x - 4$.
④ $x + 4$ is a factor of $x^2 + 3x - 4$.

EXERCISES

For more practice, see *Extra Practice.*

Practice and Problem Solving

A Practice by Example

Example 1 (page 307)

Write each expression as a polynomial in standard form.

1. $(x + 3)(x - 2)$ **2.** $(x + 3)(x + 4)(x + 5)$ **3.** $(x - 3)^2(x - 1)$

4. $x(x + 2)^2$ **5.** $x(x + 5)^2$ **6.** $x(x - 1)(x + 1)$

Example 2 (page 308)

Write each polynomial in factored form. Check by multiplication.

7. $x^3 - 36x$ **8.** $9x^3 + 6x^2 - 3x$ **9.** $10x^3 - 10x^2 + 15x$

10. $x^3 + 7x^2 + 10x$ **11.** $x^3 + 8x^2 + 16x$ **12.** $x^3 - 7x^2 - 18x$

Example 3 (pages 308–309)

Find the relative maximum, relative minimum, and zeros of each function.

13. $f(x) = x^3 + 4x^2 - 5x$ **14.** $f(x) = -x^3 + 16x^2 - 76x + 96$

15. Metalwork A metalworker wants to make an open box from a sheet of metal, by cutting equal squares from each corner as shown.

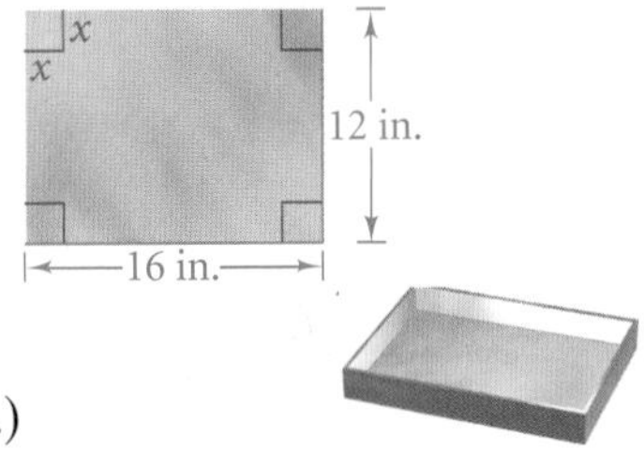

a. Write an expression for the length, width, and height of the open box.

b. Use your answer from part (a) to write a function for volume. (*Hint*: Use factored form.)

c. Graph the function. Find the maximum volume that can be contained by the box and the size of the square cut that produces this volume.

Example 4 (page 309)

Find the zeros of each function. Then graph the function.

16. $y = (x - 1)(x + 2)$ **17.** $y = (x - 2)(x + 9)$ **18.** $y = x(x + 5)(x - 8)$

19. $y = (x + 1)(x - 2)(x - 3)$ **20.** $y = (x + 1)(x - 1)(x - 2)$

Example 5 (page 310)

Write a polynomial function in standard form with the given zeros.

21. $x = 5, 6, 7$ **22.** $x = -2, 0, 1$ **23.** $x = -5, -5, 1$ **24.** $x = 3, 3, 3$

25. $x = 1, -1, -2$ **26.** $x = -1, -2, -3$ **27.** $x = 0, 0, 2$ **28.** $x = -\frac{1}{2}, 0, 4$

Example 6 (page 310)

Find the zeros of each function. State the multiplicity of multiple zeros.

29. $y = (x + 3)^3$ **30.** $y = x(x - 1)^3$ **31.** $y = 2x^3 + x^2 - x$

32. $y = 3x^3 - 3x$ **33.** $y = (x - 4)^2$ **34.** $y = (x - 2)^2(x - 1)$

35. $y = (2x + 3)(x - 1)^2$ **36.** $y = (x + 1)^2(x - 1)(x - 2)$

B Apply Your Skills

37. Geometry A box has length $2x + 1$ units, width $x + 4$ units, and height $x + 3$ units. To build the box using x^3, x^2, x, and unit (1) blocks, how many of each will you need?

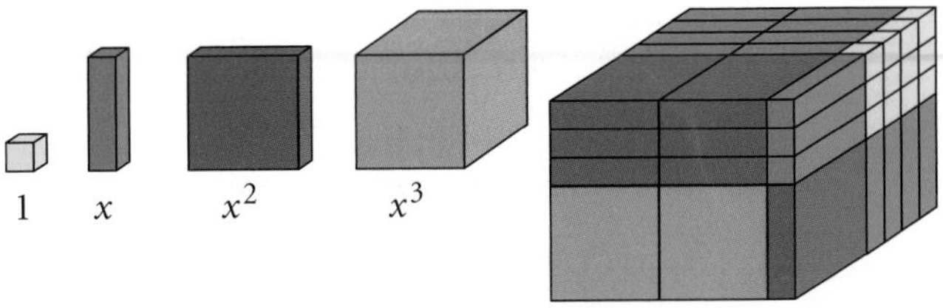

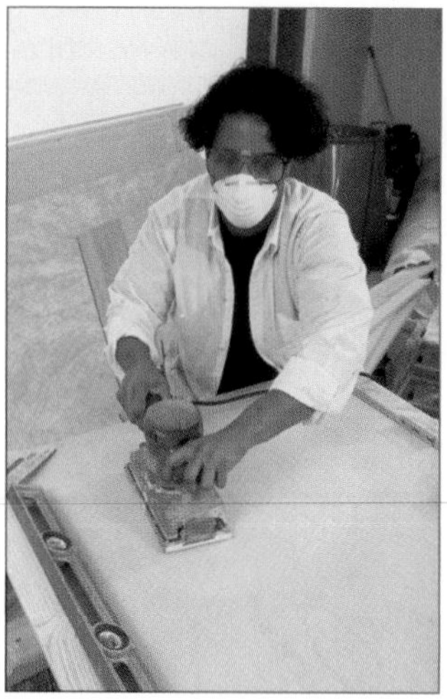

Real-World Connection

Careers Carpenters use math to design and measure components of buildings, furniture, and art.

38. **Carpentry** A carpenter hollowed out the interior of a block of wood as shown at the right.
   a. Express the volume of the original block and the volume of the wood removed as polynomials in standard form.
   b. Write a polynomial for the volume of the wood remaining.

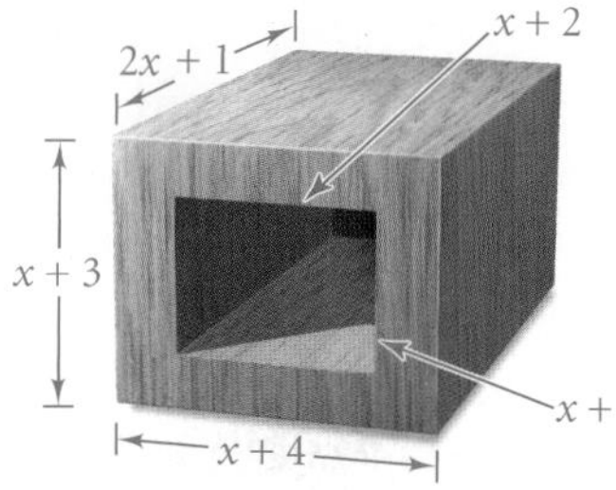

39. **Geometry** A rectangular box is $2x + 3$ units long, $2x - 3$ units wide, and $3x$ units high. Express its volume as a polynomial.

40. **Measurement** The volume in cubic feet of a CD holder can be expressed as $V(x) = -x^3 - x^2 + 6x$, or, when factored, as the product of its three dimensions. The depth is expressed as $2 - x$. Assume that the height is greater than the width.
   a. Factor the polynomial to find linear expressions for the height and the width.
   b. Graph the function. Find the x-intercepts. What do they represent?
   c. Describe a realistic domain for the function.
   d. Find the maximum volume of the CD holder.

Write each function in standard form.

41. $y = (x + 1)(x - 4)(3 - 2x)$
42. $y = (x + 7)(5x + 2)(x - 6)^2$

Write each function in factored form. Check by multiplication.

43. $y = 3x^3 - 27x^2 + 24x$
44. $y = -2x^3 - 2x^2 + 40x$
45. $y = x^4 + 3x^3 - 4x^2$
46. $y = \frac{1}{2}x^3 - \frac{1}{8}x$

Find the relative maximum, relative minimum, and zeros of each function.

47. $y = 2x^3 - 23x^2 + 78x - 72$
48. $y = x^4 + 3x^3 - x^2 - 3x$
49. $y = 8x^3 - 10x^2 - x - 3$
50. $y = (x + 1)^4 - 1$

Write a polynomial function in standard form with the given zeros.

51. $5, -2, 0$
52. 7 multiplicity 3
53. $-2, -1, 3, 4$

For each function, determine the zeros. State the multiplicity of any multiple zeros.

54. $y = (x + 4)(x - 5)^3$
55. $f(x) = x^4 + 2x^3 + x^2$
56. $f(x) = x^3 - 36x$

57. **Critical Thinking** How can you find where the graph of a polynomial function crosses the y-axis?

58. A storage company needs to design a new storage box that has twice the volume of its largest box. Its largest box is 5 ft long, 4 ft wide, and 3 ft high. The new box must be formed by increasing each dimension by the same amount. Find the increase in each dimension.

59. **Open-Ended** Write a polynomial function with the following features: it has three distinct zeros; one of the zeros is 1; another zero has a multiplicity of 2.

60. **Writing** Explain how the graph of a polynomial function can help you factor the polynomial.

61. **Critical Thinking** A polynomial function has a zero at $x = -2a$. Find one of its factors.

Challenge 62. **Coordinate Geometry** The diagram at the right shows a rectangular region with one corner on the graph of $y = -x^2 + 2x + 4$.

a. Write a polynomial in standard form for the area A of the rectangular region.

b. Find the area of the rectangular region for $x = 2\frac{1}{2}$.

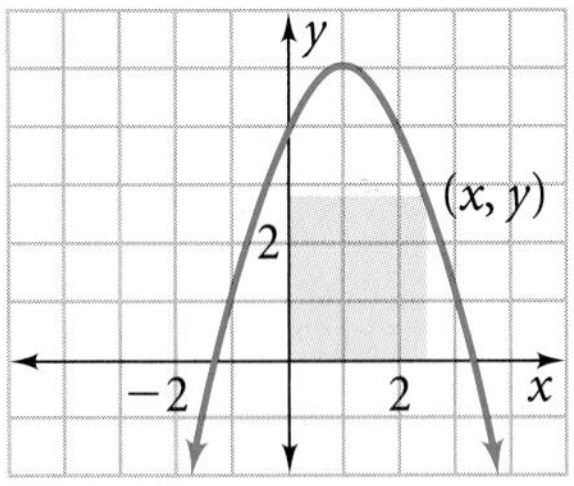

63. Find a fourth-degree polynomial function with zeros 1, −1, i, and $-i$. Write the function in both factored form and standard form.

64. a. Compare the graphs of $y = (x + 1)(x + 2)(x + 3)$ and $y = (x - 1)(x - 2)(x - 3)$. What transformation could you use to describe the change from one graph to the other?

b. Compare the graphs of $y = (x + 1)(x + 3)(x + 7)$ and $y = (x - 1)(x - 3)(x - 7)$. Does the transformation that you chose in part (a) still hold true? Explain.

c. **Make a Conjecture** What transformation could you use to describe the effect of changing the signs of the zeros of a polynomial function?

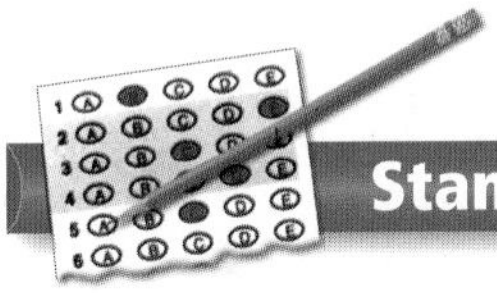

Standardized Test Prep

Multiple Choice

65. Which expression is the factored form of $x^3 + 2x^2 - 5x - 6$?

A. $(x + 1)(x + 1)(x - 6)$ B. $(x + 2)(2x - 5)(x - 6)$
C. $(x + 3)(x + 1)(x - 2)$ D. $(x - 3)(x - 1)(x + 2)$

Take It to the NET
Online lesson quiz at www.PHSchool.com
Web Code: agk-0602

66. What are the zeros of the polynomial function $y = (x - 3)(2x + 1)(x - 1)$?

F. $\frac{1}{2}$, 1, 3 G. −1, 1, 3 H. $-\frac{1}{2}$, 1, 3 I. −3, $\frac{1}{2}$, 1

67. Which polynomial function has zeros at −4, 3, and 5?

A. $f(x) = (x + 4)(x + 3)(x + 5)$ B. $g(x) = (x + 4)(x - 3)(x - 5)$
C. $h(x) = (x - 4)(x - 3)(x - 5)$ D. $k(x) = (x - 4)(x + 3)(x + 5)$

Short Response

68. What is the factored form of $f(x) = x^4 + 8x^3 - 9x^2$?

Extended Response

69. What is the polynomial function, in standard form, whose zeros are −2, 5, and 6, and whose leading coefficient is −2? Justify your reasoning.

Mixed Review

Lesson 6-1 **Write each polynomial in standard form. Then classify it by degree and by number of terms.**

70. $x^2 - 1 - 3x^5 + 2x^2$ 71. $-2x^3 - 7x^4 + x^3$ 72. $6x + x^3 - 6x - 2$

Lesson 5-4 **Factor each expression.**

73. $x^2 + 5x + 4$ 74. $x^2 - 2x - 15$ 75. $x^2 - 12x + 36$

Lesson 4-5 **Evaluate the determinant of each matrix.**

76. $A = \begin{bmatrix} 1 & -4 \\ 2 & 0 \end{bmatrix}$ 77. $B = \begin{bmatrix} 5 & 3 \\ 2 & -1 \end{bmatrix}$ 78. $C = \begin{bmatrix} 3 & -2 \\ 3 & -2 \end{bmatrix}$

6-3 Dividing Polynomials

North Carolina Objectives

1.03 Operate with algebraic expressions (polynomial, rational, complex fractions) to solve problems.

Lesson Preview

What You'll Learn

OBJECTIVE 1 To divide polynomials using long division

OBJECTIVE 2 To divide polynomials using synthetic division

. . . And Why

To find the dimensions of a sarcophagus, as in Example 4

Check Skills You'll Need

(For help, go to Lessons 5-1 and 6-1.)

Simplify each expression.

1. $(x + 3)(x - 4) + 2$

2. $(2x + 1)(x - 3)$

3. $(x + 2)(x + 1) - 11$

4. $-3(2 - x)(x + 5)$

Write each polynomial in standard form. Then list the coefficients.

5. $5x - 2x^2 + 9 + 4x^3$

6. $10 + 5x^3 - 9x^2$

7. $3x + x^2 - x + 7 - 2x^2$

8. $-4x^4 - 7x^2 + x^3 + x^4$

New Vocabulary • synthetic division • Remainder Theorem

Interactive lesson includes instant self-check, tutorials, and activities.

OBJECTIVE 1 Using Long Division

Need Help?

$$6\overline{)24}$$ with 4 ← Quotient, 24 ← Dividend, 6 ↑ Divisor

You can use polynomial division to help find all the zeros of a polynomial function. Division of polynomials is similar to numerical division.

Recall that when a numerical division has a remainder of zero, as shown below, the divisor and quotient are both factors of the dividend.

$$\begin{array}{r} 7 \\ 8\overline{)56} \\ \underline{56} \\ 0 \end{array}$$

7 and 8 are factors of 56.

If numerical division leaves a remainder, as shown below, then neither the divisor nor the quotient is a factor of the dividend.

$$\begin{array}{r} 8 \\ 5\overline{)42} \\ \underline{40} \\ 2 \end{array}$$

Neither 5 nor 8 is a factor of 42.

Division serves as a test of whether one number is a factor of another.

The same is true for polynomial division. If you divide a polynomial by one of its factors, then you get another factor. When a polynomial division leaves no remainder, as shown below with monomials, you have factored the polynomial.

$$\begin{array}{r} 2x \\ x\overline{)2x^2} \\ \underline{2x^2} \\ 0 \end{array}$$

x and $2x$ are factors of $2x^2$.

To divide polynomials other than monomials, follow the same procedure you use to divide whole numbers.

1 EXAMPLE Polynomial Long Division

Divide $x^2 + 3x - 12$ by $x - 3$.

$$\begin{array}{r} x \phantom{{}+3x-12} \\ x-3\overline{)x^2+3x-12} \\ \underline{x^2-3x} \phantom{{}-12} \\ 6x-12 \end{array}$$

Divide: $\frac{x^2}{x} = x$.

Multiply: $x(x - 3) = x^2 - 3x$.

Subtract: $x^2 + 3x - (x^2 - 3x) = 6x$. **Bring down** -12.

Repeat the process of dividing, multiplying, and subtracting.

$$\begin{array}{r} x+6 \phantom{{}-12} \\ x-3\overline{)x^2+3x-12} \\ \underline{x^2-3x} \phantom{{}-12} \\ 6x-12 \\ \underline{6x-18} \\ 6 \end{array}$$

Divide: $\frac{6x}{x} = 6$.

Multiply: $6(x - 3) = 6x - 18$.

Subtract: $6x - 12 - (6x - 18) = 6$.

The quotient is $x + 6$ with a remainder of 6, or simply $x + 6$, R 6.

Check Show that (divisor)(quotient) + remainder = dividend.

$(x - 3)(x + 6) + 6 = (x^2 + 6x - 3x - 18) + 6$ **Multiply $(x - 3)(x + 6)$.**

$= x^2 + 3x - 12$ **Simplify.**

Check Understanding 1 Divide $x^2 - 3x + 1$ by $x - 4$. Check your answer.

You can use polynomial long division to find the factors of a polynomial.

2 EXAMPLE Checking Factors

Determine whether $x + 4$ is a factor of each polynomial.

a. $x^2 + 6x + 8$

$$\begin{array}{r} x+2 \\ x+4\overline{)x^2+6x+8} \\ \underline{x^2+4x} \phantom{{}+8} \\ 2x+8 \\ \underline{2x+8} \\ 0 \end{array}$$

Since the remainder is zero, $x + 4$ is a factor of $x^2 + 6x + 8$.

b. $x^3 + 3x^2 - 6x - 7$

$$\begin{array}{r} x^2-x-2 \\ x+4\overline{)x^3+3x^2-6x-7} \\ \underline{x^3+4x^2} \phantom{{}-6x-7} \\ -x^2-6x \phantom{{}-7} \\ \underline{-x^2-4x} \phantom{{}-7} \\ -2x-7 \\ \underline{-2x-8} \\ 1 \end{array}$$

Since the remainder $\neq 0$, $x + 4$ is not a factor of $x^3 + 3x^2 - 6x - 7$.

Check Understanding 2 Determine whether each divisor is a factor of each dividend.

a. $(2x^2 - 19x + 24) \div (x - 8)$ **b.** $(x^3 - 4x^2 + 3x + 2) \div (x + 2)$

OBJECTIVE 2

Using Synthetic Division

To divide by a linear factor, you can use a simplified process that is known as **synthetic division.** In synthetic division, you omit all variables and exponents. By reversing the sign in the divisor, you can add throughout the process instead of subtracting.

3 EXAMPLE Using Synthetic Division

Reading Math

Synthetic division is sometimes called the method of detached coefficients.

Use synthetic division to divide $3x^3 - 4x^2 + 2x - 1$ by $x + 1$.

Step 1 Reverse the sign of the constant term in the divisor. Write the coefficients of the polynomial in standard form.

Write $x + 1\overline{)3x^3 - 4x^2 + 2x - 1}$

as $\underline{-1|}\ 3 \quad -4 \quad 2 \quad -1$

Step 2 Bring down the first coefficient.

$$\begin{array}{r|rrrr} -1 & 3 & -4 & 2 & -1 \\ & & \blacksquare & \blacksquare & \blacksquare \\ \hline & 3 & \blacksquare & \blacksquare & \blacksquare \end{array}$$

Bring down the 3. This begins the quotient.

Step 3 Multiply the first coefficient by the new divisor. Write the result under the next coefficient. Add.

$$\begin{array}{r|rrrr} -1 & 3 & -4 & 2 & -1 \\ & & -3 & \blacksquare & \blacksquare \\ \hline & 3 & -7 & \blacksquare & \blacksquare \end{array}$$

Multiply 3 by –1. Write the result under –4.

Add –4 and –3.

Step 4 Repeat the steps of multiplying and adding until the remainder is found.

$$\begin{array}{r|rrrr} -1 & 3 & -4 & 2 & -1 \\ & & -3 & 7 & -9 \\ \hline & 3 & -7 & 9 & -10 \end{array}$$

$3x^2 - 7x + 9$ Remainder

The quotient is $3x^2 - 7x + 9$, R -10.

Check Understanding 3 Use synthetic division to divide $x^3 + 4x^2 + x - 6$ by $x + 1$.

4 EXAMPLE Real-World Connection

Real-World Connection

For the ancient Greeks, Romans, and Egyptians, a sarcophagus was a work of art created to honor a loved one. They decorated the stone tomb with elaborate inscriptions and ornaments.

The volume in cubic feet of a sarcophagus (excluding the cover) can be expressed as the product of its three dimensions: $V(x) = x^3 - 13x + 12$. The length is $x + 4$.

a. Find linear expressions with integer coefficients for the other dimensions. Assume that the width is greater than the height.

$$\begin{array}{r|rrrr} -4 & 1 & 0 & -13 & 12 \\ & & -4 & 16 & -12 \\ \hline & 1 & -4 & 3 & 0 \end{array}$$

Divide. Use 0 as a place holder for any missing term.

$x^2 \quad -4x + 3$ Remainder

$x^2 - 4x + 3 = (x - 1)(x - 3)$ **Factor the quotient.**

The width and the height are $x - 1$ and $x - 3$, respectively.

b. If the length of the sarcophagus is 10 ft, what are the other two dimensions?

$x + 4 = 10$ **Substitute 10 into the expression for length. Find x.**

$x = 6$

Since the width equals $x - 1$ and the height equals $x - 3$, the width is 5 ft and the height is 3 ft.

Check Understanding **4** **a.** Use synthetic division to divide $x^3 - 2x^2 - 5x + 6$ by $x + 2$.
b. Use your answer from part (a) to completely factor $x^3 - 2x^2 - 5x + 6$.

In Example 1, you saw that $x - 3$ is not a factor of $x^2 + 3x - 12$ because their quotient has a remainder of 6. If $x - 3$ were a factor of $x^2 + 3x - 12$, then 3 would be a zero of $P(x) = x^2 + 3x - 12$, and $P(3)$ would equal zero. You know that $P(3)$ does not equal zero, but what *does* it equal?

You can find $P(3)$ by substituting 3 for x.

$$\begin{aligned} P(x) &= x^2 + 3x - 12 \\ P(3) &= (3)^2 + 3(3) - 12 \\ &= 6 \end{aligned}$$

$P(3)$ equals the remainder in Example 1, because

dividend = divisor × quotient + remainder.

$$\begin{aligned} P(x) &= (x - 3)(x + 6) + 6 \\ P(3) &= (3 - 3)(3 + 6) + 6 \\ &= 0(3 + 6) + 6 \\ &= 6 \end{aligned}$$

This relationship is defined by the **Remainder Theorem.**

Key Concepts

Theorem	**Remainder Theorem**
If a polynomial $P(x)$ of degree $n \geq 1$ is divided by $(x - a)$, where a is a constant, then the remainder is $P(a)$.	

You can use the Remainder Theorem to find values of $P(x)$.

5 EXAMPLE Evaluating a Polynomial by Synthetic Division

Use synthetic division to find $P(-4)$ for $P(x) = x^4 - 5x^2 + 4x + 12$.

By the Remainder Theorem, $P(-4)$ equals the remainder when $P(x)$ is divided by $x - (-4)$.

$$\begin{array}{r|rrrrr} -4 & 1 & 0 & -5 & 4 & 12 \\ & & -4 & 16 & -44 & 160 \\ \hline & 1 & -4 & 11 & -40 & 172 \end{array}$$

The remainder is 172, so $P(-4) = 172$.

Check Understanding **5** Use synthetic division to find $P(-1)$ for $P(x) = 2x^4 + 6x^3 - 5x^2 - 60$.

EXERCISES

For more practice, see *Extra Practice.*

Practice and Problem Solving

A Practice by Example

Example 1 (page 315)

Divide using long division. Check your answers.

1. $(x^2 - 3x - 40) \div (x + 5)$

2. $(3x^2 + 7x - 20) \div (x + 4)$

3. $(x^3 + 3x^2 - x + 2) \div (x - 1)$

4. $(2x^3 - 3x^2 - 18x - 8) \div (x - 4)$

5. $(9x^3 - 18x^2 - x + 2) \div (3x + 1)$

6. $(9x^2 - 21x - 20) \div (x - 1)$

7. $(x^2 - 7x + 10) \div (x + 3)$

8. $(x^3 - 13x - 12) \div (x - 4)$

Example 2 (page 315)

Determine whether each binomial is a factor of $x^3 + 4x^2 + x - 6$.

9. $x + 1$ **10.** $x + 2$ **11.** $x + 3$ **12.** $x - 3$

Example 3 (page 316)

Divide using synthetic division.

13. $(x^3 + 3x^2 - x - 3) \div (x - 1)$

14. $(x^3 - 4x^2 + 6x - 4) \div (x - 2)$

15. $(x^3 - 7x^2 - 7x + 20) \div (x + 4)$

16. $(x^3 - 3x^2 - 5x - 25) \div (x - 5)$

17. $(x^3 - 2x^2 - 5x + 6) \div (x - 1)$

18. $(-2x^3 + 5x^2 - x + 2) \div (x + 2)$

19. $(x^2 + 3) \div (x - 1)$

20. $(3x^3 + 17x^2 + 21x - 9) \div (x + 3)$

21. $(x^3 + 27) \div (x + 3)$

22. $(6x^2 - 8x - 2) \div (x - 1)$

Example 4 (pages 316–317)

Use synthetic division and the given factor to completely factor each polynomial function.

23. $y = x^3 + 2x^2 - 5x - 6; (x + 1)$

24. $y = x^3 - 4x^2 - 9x + 36; (x + 3)$

25. Geometry Refer to the diagram. The volume in cubic inches of the decorative box can be expressed as the product of the lengths of its sides as $V(x) = x^3 + x^2 - 6x$. Write linear expressions with integer coefficients for the locker's length and height.

Example 5 (page 317)

Use synthetic division and the Remainder Theorem to find $P(a)$.

26. $P(x) = x^3 + 4x^2 - 8x - 6; a = -2$

27. $P(x) = x^3 + 4x^2 + 4x; a = -2$

28. $P(x) = x^3 - 7x^2 + 15x - 9; a = 3$

29. $P(x) = x^3 + 7x^2 + 4x; a = -2$

30. $P(x) = 6x^3 - x^2 + 4x + 3; a = 3$

31. $P(x) = 2x^3 - x^2 + 10x + 5; a = \frac{1}{2}$

32. $P(x) = 2x^3 + 4x^2 - 10x - 9; a = 3$

33. $P(x) = 2x^4 + 6x^3 + 5x^2 - 45; a = -3$

B Apply Your Skills

34. Reasoning A polynomial $P(x)$ is divided by a binomial $x - a$. The remainder is zero. What conclusion can you draw? Explain.

35. Error Analysis A student represented the product of three linear factors as $x^3 - x^2 - 2x$. She used $x - 1$ as one of the factors. Use division to prove that the student made an error.

36. **Open-Ended** Write a polynomial division that has a quotient of $x + 3$ and a remainder of 2.

Divide.

37. $(2x^3 + 9x^2 + 14x + 5) \div (2x + 1)$
38. $(x^4 + 3x^2 + x + 4) \div (x + 3)$
39. $(x^5 + 1) \div (x + 1)$
40. $(x^4 + 4x^3 - x - 4) \div (x^3 - 1)$
41. $(3x^4 - 5x^3 + 2x^2 + 3x - 2) \div (3x - 2)$

Determine whether each binomial is a factor of $x^3 + x^2 - 16x - 16$.

42. $x + 2$
43. $x - 4$
44. $x + 1$
45. $x - 1$
46. $x - 2$
47. $x + 4$

Use synthetic division to determine whether each binomial is a factor of $3x^3 + 10x^2 - x - 12$.

48. $x + 3$
49. $x - 1$
50. $x + 2$
51. $x - 4$

Divide using synthetic division.

52. $(x^4 - 2x^3 + x^2 + x - 1) \div (x - 1)$
53. $(x^4 - 6x^2 - 27) \div (x + 2)$
54. $(x^4 - 5x^2 + 4x + 12) \div (x + 2)$
55. $\left(x^4 - \frac{9}{2}x^3 + 3x^2 - \frac{1}{2}x\right) \div \left(x - \frac{1}{2}\right)$

C Challenge

56. **Reasoning** Divide. Look for patterns in your answers.
 a. $(x^2 - 1) \div (x - 1)$ **b.** $(x^3 - 1) \div (x - 1)$ **c.** $(x^4 - 1) \div (x - 1)$
 d. Using the patterns, factor $x^5 - 1$.

57. Divide. Look for patterns in your answers.
 a. $(x^3 + 1) \div (x + 1)$ **b.** $(x^5 + 1) \div (x + 1)$ **c.** $(x^7 + 1) \div (x + 1)$
 d. Using the patterns, factor $x^9 + 1$.

58. **Critical Thinking** Explain why a polynomial of degree n, divided by a polynomial of degree 1, yields a quotient of degree $n - 1$ and a remainder that is a constant.

59. Use synthetic division to find $(x^2 + 4) \div (x - 2i)$.

60. **Writing** Suppose 3, −1, and 4 are zeros of a cubic polynomial function. Sketch a graph of the function. Could there be more than one graph? Explain.

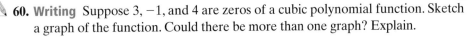

Standardized Test Prep

Multiple Choice

61. What is the remainder when $x^2 - 5x + 7$ is divided by $x + 1$?
 A. −13 B. −1 C. 1 D. 13

62. Which binomial is NOT a factor of $x^3 - x^2 - 17x - 15$?
 F. $x - 5$ G. $x + 1$ H. $x + 3$ I. $x + 5$

63. Which of the following, when multiplied by $x - 1$, results in a cubic polynomial whose standard form has three terms?
 A. $(x - 1)^2$ B. $x^2 - x$ C. $x^2 - 1$ D. $x - 1$

64. One factor of $x^3 - 7x^2 - x + 7$ is $x - 1$. What are all the zeros of the related polynomial function? Show your work.

Take It to the NET
Online lesson quiz at
www.PHSchool.com
Web Code: agk-0603

Mixed Review

Lesson 6-2 **Write a polynomial function in standard form with the given zeros.**

65. $3, -5$ **66.** $0, 1, 8$ **67.** $-1, 2, 5$ **68.** 1, multiplicity 4

Lesson 5-6 **Simplify each expression.**

69. $(-4i)(6i)$ **70.** $(2 + i)(2 - i)$ **71.** $(4 - 3i)(5 + i)$

Lesson 4-6 **Find the inverse of each matrix, if it exists.**

72. $\begin{bmatrix} 1 & 0 & 3 \\ 1 & 1 & 0 \\ -1 & 0 & -1 \end{bmatrix}$ **73.** $\begin{bmatrix} 1 & 2 & 0 \\ 0 & 2 & -2 \\ 1 & 0 & 2 \end{bmatrix}$ **74.** $\begin{bmatrix} 2 & 1 & 0 \\ -1 & 1 & -2 \\ 3 & -2 & 4 \end{bmatrix}$

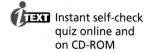

Checkpoint Quiz 1 — Lessons 6-1 through 6-3

TEXT Instant self-check quiz online and on CD-ROM

1. Write a polynomial function with at least three zeros that are negative, one of which has multiplicity 2.

Write each polynomial in standard form. Then classify it by degree and by number of terms.

2. $-2x^3 + 6 - x^3 + 5x$ **3.** $\frac{1}{2}x + x^4 - 3x^2 + 2x$ **4.** $3(x - 1)(x + 4)$

For each function, determine the zeros and their multiplicity.

5. $y = (x - 2)^2(x - 1)$ **6.** $y = (2x + 1)(x - 4)$ **7.** $y = x^3(x - 3)(x + 1)^2$

Divide.

8. $(x^3 + 3x^2 + 3x + 1) \div (x + 1)$ **9.** $(2x^3 - 7x^2 + 7x - 2) \div (x - 2)$

10. Use synthetic division to find $P(4)$ for $P(x) = 2x^4 - 3x^2 + 4x - 1$.

Algebra at Work

Quality Control Engineer

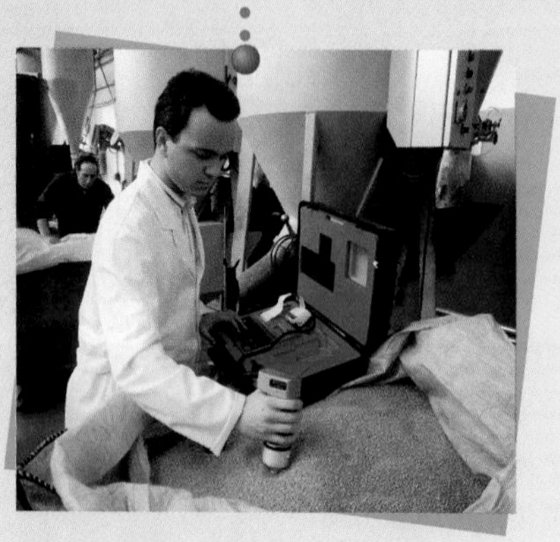

Quality control engineers establish procedures for assuring that products meet minimum standards of quality such as length or purity. Each product is sampled regularly. Data relating to each standard are collected and analyzed. All samples must fall within certain limiting parameters. Quality is further controlled by requiring that a significant portion of the samples fall within even stricter limiting parameters.

Take It to the NET For more information about quality control, go to **www.PHSchool.com**.
Web Code: agb-2031

6-4 Solving Polynomial Equations

North Carolina Objectives

1.03 Operate with algebraic expressions (polynomial, rational, complex fractions) to solve problems.

Lesson Preview

What You'll Learn

OBJECTIVE 1 To solve polynomial equations by graphing

OBJECTIVE 2 To solve polynomial equations by factoring

. . . And Why

To calculate the dimensions of a portable kennel, as in Example 2

✓ Check Skills You'll Need

(For help, go to Lessons 3-1 and 5-4.)

Graph each system. Find any points of intersection.

1. $\begin{cases} y = 3x + 1 \\ y = -2x + 6 \end{cases}$ **2.** $\begin{cases} -2x + 3y = 0 \\ x + 3y = 3 \end{cases}$ **3.** $\begin{cases} 2y = -x + 8 \\ x + 2y = -6 \end{cases}$

Factor each expression.

4. $x^2 - 2x - 15$ **5.** $x^2 - 9x + 14$ **6.** $x^2 + 6x + 5$

New Vocabulary

- sum of cubes
- difference of cubes

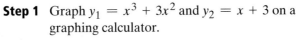

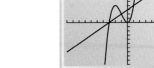

Interactive lesson includes instant self-check, tutorials, and activities.

OBJECTIVE 1

Solving Equations by Graphing

You can solve a polynomial equation by graphing each side of the equation separately and finding the x values at the point(s) of intersection.

1 EXAMPLE Solving by Graphing

Solve $x^3 + 3x^2 = x + 3$ by graphing.

Step 1 Graph $y_1 = x^3 + 3x^2$ and $y_2 = x + 3$ on a graphing calculator.

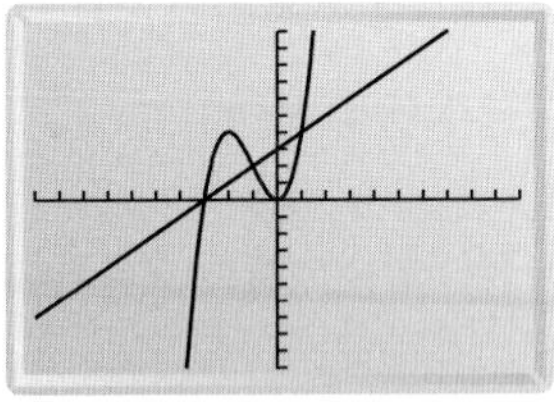

Step 2 Use the Intersect feature to find the x values at the points of intersection.

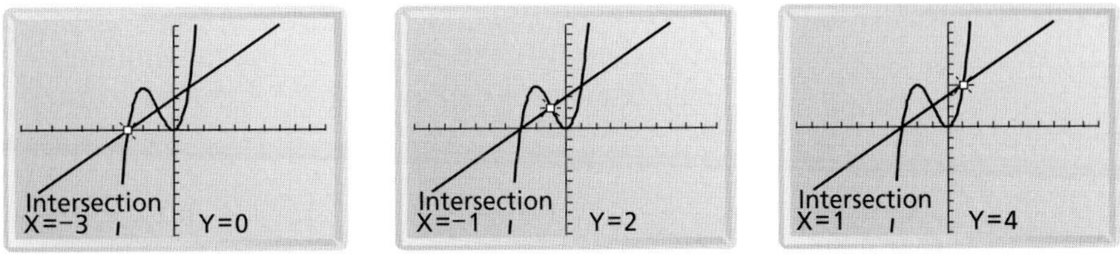

The solutions are -3, -1, and 1.

Check Show that each solution makes the original equation a true statement.

$x^3 + 3x^2 = x + 3$	$x^3 + 3x^2 = x + 3$	$x^3 + 3x^2 = x + 3$
$(-3)^3 + 3(-3)^2 \stackrel{?}{=} -3 + 3$	$(-1)^3 + 3(-1)^2 \stackrel{?}{=} -1 + 3$	$(1)^3 + 3(1)^2 \stackrel{?}{=} 1 + 3$
$-27 + 27 \stackrel{?}{=} -3 + 3$	$-1 + 3 \stackrel{?}{=} -1 + 3$	$1 + 3 \stackrel{?}{=} 1 + 3$
$0 = 0$ ✓	$2 = 2$ ✓	$4 = 4$ ✓

Graphing Calculator Hint

You can also solve the equation in Example 1 by graphing the related function $y = x^3 + 3x^2 - x - 3$ and finding its zeros.

✓ Check Understanding **1** Graph and solve $x^3 - 2x^2 = -3$. Check your answers.

You can write and solve a polynomial equation that models a real-world situation.

Real-World Connection

International regulations specify the allowable dimensions of pet transportation carriers.

2 EXAMPLE Real-World Connection

Pet Transportation The dimensions in inches of a portable kennel can be expressed as width x, length $x + 7$, and height $x - 1$. The volume is 5.9 ft^3. Find the portable kennel's dimensions.

$5.9\ ft^3 \cdot \frac{12^3\ in.^3}{ft^3} = 10{,}195.2\ in.^3$ **Convert the volume to cubic inches.**

$V = \ell \cdot w \cdot h$ **Write the formula for volume.**

$10{,}195.2 = (x + 7)x(x - 1)$ **Substitute.**

Graph $y_1 = 10{,}195.2$ and $y_2 = (x + 7)x(x - 1)$. Use the Intersect option of the calculator. When $y = 10{,}195.2, x \approx 20$. So $x + 7 \approx 27$ and $x - 1 \approx 19$.

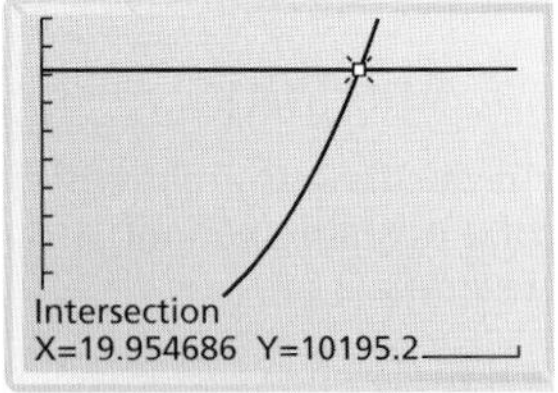

The dimensions of the portable kennel are about 27 in. by 20 in. by 19 in.

Check Understanding 2 Find the dimensions of a carrier with volume 7 ft^3, width x, length $x + 3$, and height $x - 2$.

OBJECTIVE

2 Solving Equations by Factoring

Sometimes you can solve polynomial equations by factoring the polynomial and using the Factor Theorem. Recall that a quadratic expression that is the *difference of squares* has a special factoring pattern. Similarly, a cubic expression may be the **sum of cubes** or the **difference of cubes.**

Key Concepts

Properties	Sum and Difference of Cubes
	$a^3 + b^3 = (a + b)(a^2 - ab + b^2)$ $a^3 - b^3 = (a - b)(a^2 + ab + b^2)$

You can verify the properties above by multiplying. Below are the steps for the sum of cubes. Note how opposite quadratic terms and linear terms drop out.

$$\begin{aligned}(a + b)(a^2 - ab + b^2) &= a(a^2 - ab + b^2) + b(a^2 - ab + b^2)\\ &= a^3 - a^2b + ab^2 + a^2b - ab^2 + b^3\\ &= a^3 + b^3\end{aligned}$$

3 EXAMPLE Factoring a Sum or Difference of Cubes

Factor $x^3 - 8$.

$x^3 - 8 = (x)^3 - (2)^3$ **Rewrite the expression as the difference of cubes.**

$= (x - 2)(x^2 + 2x + (2)^2)$ **Factor.**

$= (x - 2)(x^2 + 2x + 4)$ **Simplify.**

Check Understanding 3 Factor $8x^3 - 1$.

In Chapter 5, you found the complex roots of quadratic equations. You can do the same with polynomial equations of higher degree.

4 EXAMPLE Solving a Polynomial Equation

Solve $27x^3 + 1 = 0$. Find all complex roots.

$27x^3 + 1 = (3x)^3 + (1)^3$ **Rewrite the cubic expression as the sum of cubes.**

$= (3x + 1)((3x)^2 - 3x + 1)$ **Factor.**

$= (3x + 1)(9x^2 - 3x + 1)$ **Simplify.**

Since $3x + 1$ is a factor, $x = -\frac{1}{3}$ is a root.

The quadratic expression $9x^2 - 3x + 1$ cannot be factored, so use the Quadratic Formula to solve the related quadratic equation $9x^2 - 3x + 1 = 0$.

$x = \frac{-b \pm \sqrt{b^2 - 4ac}}{2a}$ **Quadratic Formula**

$= \frac{-(-3) \pm \sqrt{(-3)^2 - 4(9)(1)}}{2(9)}$ **Substitute 9 for *a*, −3 for *b*, and 1 for *c*.**

$= \frac{3 \pm \sqrt{-27}}{18}$ **Use the Order of Operations.**

$= \frac{3 \pm 3i\sqrt{3}}{18}$ **Simplify.**

$= \frac{1 \pm i\sqrt{3}}{6}$

The roots are $-\frac{1}{3}$ and $\frac{1 \pm i\sqrt{3}}{6}$.

Need Help?
$\sqrt{-1} = i$

Check Understanding 4 Solve each equation.

a. $x^3 + 8 = 0$

b. $27x^3 - 1 = 0$

You can sometimes factor a polynomial of higher degree by using the techniques you have used in solving polynomials of lower degree.

5 EXAMPLE Factoring by Using a Quadratic Form

Factor $x^4 - 2x^2 - 8$.

Step 1 Since $x^4 - 2x^2 - 8$ has the form of a quadratic expression, you can factor it like one. Make a temporary substitution of variables.

$x^4 - 2x^2 - 8 = (x^2)^2 - 2(x^2) - 8$ **Rewrite in the form of a quadratic expression.**

$= a^2 - 2a - 8$ **Substitute *a* for x^2.**

Step 2 Factor $a^2 - 2a - 8$.

$a^2 - 2a - 8 = (a - 4)(a + 2)$

Step 3 Substitute back to the original variable.

$(a - 4)(a + 2) = (x^2 - 4)(x^2 + 2)$ **Substitute x^2 for *a*.**

$= (x + 2)(x - 2)(x^2 + 2)$ **Factor completely.**

The factored form of $x^4 - 2x^2 - 8$ is $(x + 2)(x - 2)(x^2 + 2)$.

Check Understanding 5 Factor each expression.

a. $x^4 + 7x^2 + 6$

b. $x^4 - 3x^2 - 10$

6 EXAMPLE Solving a Higher-Degree Polynomial Equation

Solve $x^4 - x^2 = 12$.

$$x^4 - x^2 = 12$$

$$x^4 - x^2 - 12 = 0$$ **Rewrite so one side of the equation is equal to zero.**

$$(x^2)^2 - (x^2) - 12 = 0$$ **Write in the form of a quadratic expression. Think of the expression as $a^2 - a - 12$, which factors as $(a - 4)(a + 3)$.**

$$(x^2 - 4)(x^2 + 3) = 0$$

$$(x - 2)(x + 2)(x^2 + 3) = 0$$

$x = 2$ or $x = -2$ or $x^2 = -3$ **Use the Factor Theorem.**

$x = \pm 2$ or $x = \pm\sqrt{-3}$ **Solve for x.**

$x = \pm 2$ or $x = \pm i\sqrt{3}$ **Simplify.**

The solutions are 2, −2, $i\sqrt{3}$, and $-i\sqrt{3}$.

Check Understanding 6 Solve $x^4 + 11x^2 + 18 = 0$.

EXERCISES

For more practice, see *Extra Practice*.

Practice and Problem Solving

A Practice by Example

Examples 1 and 2 (pages 321 and 322)

Solve each equation by graphing. Check your answers.

1. $x^3 - 4x^2 - 7x = -10$ **2.** $3x^3 - 6x^2 - 9x = 0$ **3.** $4x^3 - 8x^2 + 4x = 0$

4. $6x^2 = 48x$ **5.** $x^3 + 3x^2 + 2x = 0$ **6.** $2x^3 + 5x^2 = 7x$

7. $4x^3 = 4x^2 + 3x$ **8.** $2x^4 - 5x^3 - 3x^2 = 0$ **9.** $x^2 - 8x + 7 = 0$

10. Savings The polynomial $1600x^3 + 1200x^2 + 800x$ represents your savings, with interest, from a summer job after three years. The annual interest rate equals $x - 1$. Find the interest rate needed so that you will have $4000 at the end of three years.

11. Geometry The volume V of a container is modeled by the function $V(x) = x^3 - 3x^2 - 4x$. Let x, $x + 1$, and $x - 4$ represent the width, the length, and the height respectively. The container has a volume of 70 ft^3. Find the container's dimensions.

Example 3 (page 322)

Factor each expression.

12. $x^3 + 64$ **13.** $x^3 - 1000$ **14.** $125x^3 - 27$

Example 4 (page 323)

Solve each equation.

15. $x^3 - 27 = 0$ **16.** $x^3 + 64 = 0$ **17.** $x^3 - 125 = 0$

18. $2x^3 + 2 = 0$ **19.** $8x^3 - 1 = 0$ **20.** $64x^3 + 8 = 0$

Example 5 (page 323)

Factor each expression.

21. $x^4 - 8x^2 + 7$ **22.** $x^4 + 8x^2 - 20$ **23.** $x^4 - 7x^2 + 12$

24. $x^4 - 5x^2 + 4$ **25.** $x^4 - 1$ **26.** $4x^4 - 6x^2 + 2$

Example 6 (page 324)

Solve each equation.

27. $x^4 - 10x^2 + 9 = 0$ **28.** $x^4 - 8x^2 + 16 = 0$ **29.** $x^4 - 12x^2 - 64 = 0$

30. $x^4 + 7x^2 - 18 = 0$ **31.** $x^4 + 4x^2 - 12 = 0$ **32.** $x^4 + 8x^2 + 15 = 0$

B Apply Your Skills

Solve each equation by graphing. Where necessary, round to the nearest hundredth.

33. $x^3 - x^2 - 6x - 4 = 0$ **34.** $2x^4 + 18x^3 = 0$

35. $x^4 + 2x^3 - 7x^2 - 8x = -12$ **36.** $x^4 + x^3 = 4x^2 + 4x - 5$

37. $x^3 + 13x = 10x^2$ **38.** $x^3 - 6x^2 + 6x = 0$ **39.** $12x^3 = 60x^2 + 75x$

40. The product of three consecutive integers $n - 1, n$, and $n + 1$ is 210. Write and solve an equation to find the numbers.

41. Design The chamber in each container below consists of a cylinder on top of a hemisphere. Each chamber holds 500 cm^3. Find the radius of each chamber.

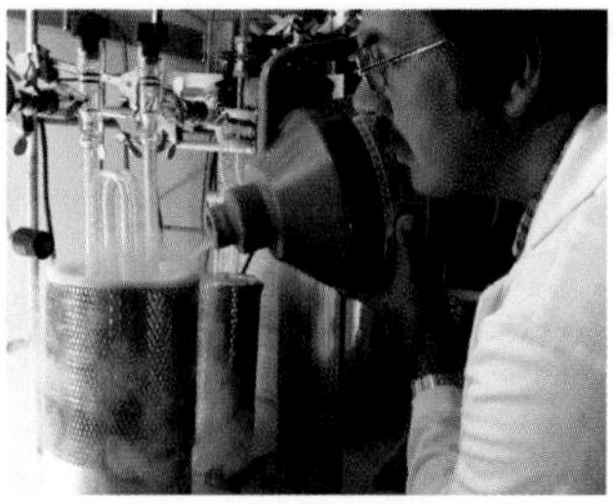

Real-World Connection

The vacuum bottle, or Dewar flask, was invented by the chemist James Dewar for storing liquefied gases.

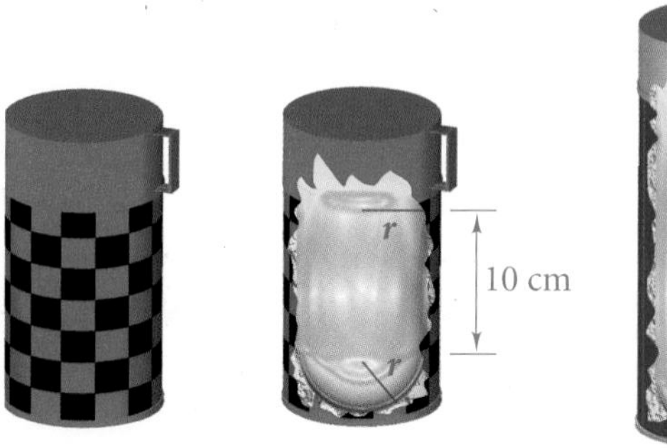

Solve each equation.

42. $125x^3 + 216 = 0$ **43.** $81x^3 - 192 = 0$ **44.** $x^4 - 64 = 0$

45. $-2x^4 + 46x^2 = -100$ **46.** $27 = -x^4 - 12x^2$ **47.** $x^5 - 5x^3 + 4x = 0$

48. $x^4 - 100 = 0$ **49.** $5x^3 = 5x^2 + 12x$ **50.** $64 - x^3 = 0$

51. $x^3 - 6x^2 + 6x = 0$ **52.** $2x^3 = 5x^2 + 12x$ **53.** $3x^4 + 12x^2 - 15 = 0$

54. $x^3 + 3x^2 - 4x - 12 = 0$ **55.** $x^3 - 5x^2 + 3x + 9 = 0$

56. $4x^3 - 16x^2 + 12x = 0$ **57.** $2x^4 - 14x^3 + 12x^2 = 0$

58. $4x^4 - 2x^2 - 4 = 2$ **59.** $9x^4 - 9x^2 + 2 = 20$

60. Open-Ended To solve a polynomial equation, you can use any combination of graphing, factoring, and the Quadratic Formula. Write and solve an equation to illustrate each method.

For Exercises 61 and 62, write a polynomial function to describe each volume. Then graph your function to solve each problem.

Reading Math

For help with reading and solving Exercise 61, see p. 327.

61. Geometry Suppose a 2-in. slice is cut from one face of the cheese block as shown. The remaining solid has a volume of 224 in.^{3}. Find the dimensions of the original block.

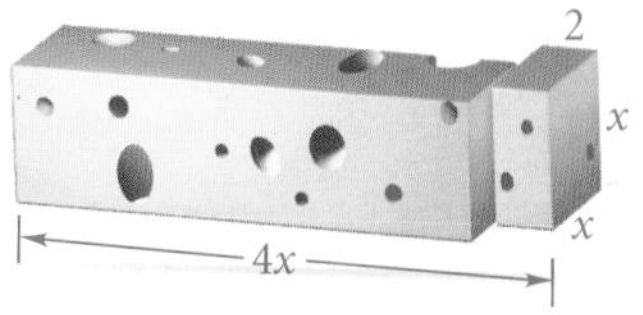

62. Geometry The width of a box is 2 m less than the length. The height is 1 m less than the length. The volume is 60 m^3. Find the length of the box.

Graph each function to find the zeros. Rewrite the function with the polynomial in factored form.

63. $y = 2x^2 + 3x - 5$ **64.** $y = x^4 - 10x^2 + 9$ **65.** $y = x^3 - 3x^2 + 4$

66. $y = x^3 - 2x^2 - 5x + 6$ **67.** $y = x^3 + 2x^2 - 11x - 12$

68. **Error Analysis** A student claims that 1, 2, 3, and 4 are the zeros of a cubic polynomial function. Explain why the student is mistaken.

C Challenge

69. a. **Open-Ended** Write and solve a fourth-degree polynomial equation that includes the difference of squares.

b. **Critical Thinking** Are all the roots real numbers? Justify your answer.

70. **Writing** From a large cube with edges a units long, you cut a smaller cube with edges three units long. Explain how the diagram at the right illustrates that $a^3 - 27 = (a - 3)(a^2 + 3a + 9)$.

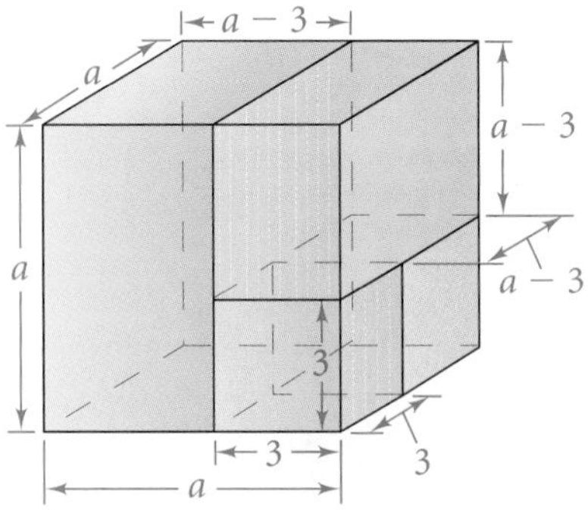

71. a. The sum of two positive numbers is 4 and the sum of their cubes is 28. What is the sum of their squares?

b. The product of two positive numbers is 96 and the sum of their squares is 208. What are the two numbers?

Standardized Test Prep

Multiple Choice

72. Which expression is a factor of $x^4 - 18x^2 + 81$?

A. $x^2 - 9$ **B.** $x^2 + 6x - 9$ **C.** $x^2 - 6x - 9$ **D.** $x^2 + 9$

Take It to the NET
Online lesson quiz at www.PHSchool.com
Web Code: agk-0604

73. Which value is NOT a solution of $x^4 - 3x^2 - 54 = 0$?

F. -3 **G.** 3 **H.** $-3i$ **I.** $-i\sqrt{6}$

Short Response

74. Show how you can rewrite $\frac{a^3}{b^6} + \frac{1}{8}$ as a sum of two cubes.

Extended Response

75. What are all the solutions to $8x^3 - 27 = 0$? Show your work.

Mixed Review

Lesson 6-3

Divide.

76. $(x^3 - 2x^2 - 13x - 10) \div (x + 1)$ **77.** $(2x^3 - 7x^2 - 7x + 14) \div (x - 4)$

Lesson 5-5

Solve each equation by factoring or by taking square roots.

78. $n^2 - 4n = 12$ **79.** $n^2 + 1 = 37$ **80.** $2n^2 - 5n - 3 = 0$

Lesson 4-7

Solve each matrix equation. If the coefficient matrix has no inverse, write *no unique solution.*

81. $\begin{bmatrix} 2 & -1 \\ -3 & 2 \end{bmatrix}\begin{bmatrix} x \\ y \end{bmatrix} = \begin{bmatrix} 5 \\ -10 \end{bmatrix}$ **82.** $\begin{bmatrix} 1 & 4 \\ -2 & -8 \end{bmatrix}\begin{bmatrix} x \\ y \end{bmatrix} = \begin{bmatrix} 2 \\ -4 \end{bmatrix}$

Reading Math

Reading for Problem Solving

For Use With Page 325, Exercise 61

Read the problem below. Then follow along with Ian as he solves the problem. Check your understanding with the exercise at the bottom of the page.

Write a polynomial function to describe the volume. Then graph your function to solve the problem.

Geometry Suppose a 2-in. slice is cut from one face of the cheese block as shown. The remaining solid has a volume of 224 in.^{3}. Find the dimensions of the original block.

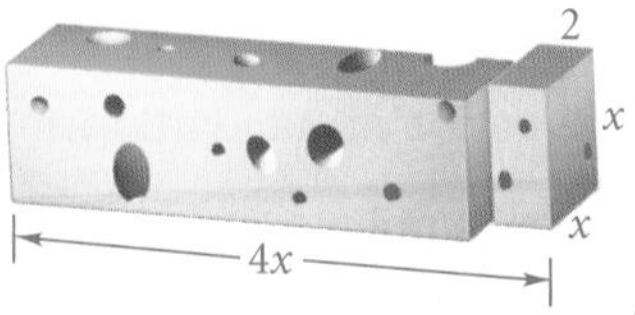

What Ian Thinks	What Ian Writes
From the diagram, it looks like the widths and heights of the two blocks are equal. I can subtract the amount cut off from the total length to find the length left.	length of leftover block = 4x − length of cut block = 4x − 2
The problem tells me that the volume of the leftover block is 224 in.^{3}. I can write a relationship, substitute, and simplify.	volume of leftover block = ℓwh = 224 $V = (4x - 2)(x)(x) = 224$ $(4x - 2)(x^2) = 224$ $4x^3 - 2x^2 = 224$
The polynomial equation is a cubic, and the problem asks me to solve by graphing. I'll graph two equations and find their intersection. I'll enter the equations as Y_1 and Y_2, and I'll change my window values to accommodate a y-value of 224.	$Y1 = 4x^3 - 2x^2$ $Y2 = 224$
Next, I'll use the INTERSECT feature. When $y = 224, x = 4$. OK! Now I know x.	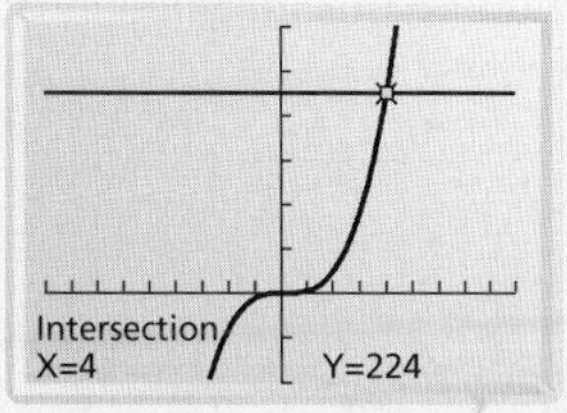 Xmin=–10 Xmax=10 Xscl=1 Ymin=–100 Ymax=100 Yscl=50
I can use x to find the dimensions of the original block.	Width = Height = x = 4 Length = 4x = 4(4) = 16 **The block of cheese measured 16 in. × 4 in. × 4 in.**

EXERCISE

Slices of wood $\frac{1}{4}$-in. thick are cut from opposite sides of a cube of wood. The remaining solid has a volume of 151.25 in.^{3}. Find the dimensions of the original block of wood.

Extension

Descartes's Rule of Signs

For Use With Lesson 6-4

René Descartes was a French mathematician, scientist, and philosopher. His many contributions to algebra include analytic geometry, which is the method of representing geometric figures with algebraic equations. He introduced the coordinate system we use, which is called the Cartesian system in his honor.

Descartes's Rule of Signs is a method for finding the number and sign of real roots of a polynomial equation in standard form.

The number of *positive* real roots of a polynomial equation $P(x) = 0$, with real coefficients, is equal to the number of sign changes (from positive to negative or vice versa) between the coefficients of the terms of $P(x)$, or is less than this number by a multiple of two.

The number of *negative* real roots of such a polynomial equation is equal to the number of sign changes between the coefficients of the terms of $P(-x)$, or is less than this number by a multiple of two.

EXAMPLE Using Descartes's Rule of Signs

Determine the possible number of positive and negative real roots of $x^4 - 4x^3 + 7x^2 - 6x - 18 = 0$.

Step 1 Count the number of sign changes of $P(x) = 0$.

$$\begin{array}{lccccccccc} P(x) = & x^4 & & -\,4x^3 & & +\,7x^2 & & -\,6x & & -\,18 \\ & \uparrow & & \uparrow & & \uparrow & & \uparrow & & \uparrow \\ & + & \text{to} & - & \text{to} & + & \text{to} & - & & - \end{array}$$

From + to − is one sign change. There are three sign changes.

The number of positive real roots of $P(x) = 0$ is three or one.

Step 2 Count the number of sign changes of $P(-x) = 0$.

$$\begin{aligned} P(-x) &= (-x)^4 - 4(-x)^3 + 7(-x)^2 - 6(-x) - 18 \\ &= x^4 + 4x^3 + 7x^2 + 6x - 18 \end{aligned}$$

$$\begin{array}{cccccc} x^4 & +\,4x^3 & +\,7x^2 & +\,6x & & -\,18 \\ \uparrow & \uparrow & \uparrow & \uparrow & & \uparrow \\ + & + & + & + & \text{to} & - \end{array}$$

There is one sign change.

The number of negative real roots of $P(x) = 0$ is one.

EXERCISES

Determine the possible number of positive and negative real roots of each polynomial equation.

1. $3x^3 + 10x^2 - x - 12 = 0$

2. $x^3 - 6x^2 + 11x - 6 = 0$

3. $x^3 - 12x - 16 = 0$

4. $3x^3 - 5x^2 - 4x + 4 = 0$

5. $x^4 + x^3 + x^2 - 9x - 10 = 0$

6. $-5x^4 + x^3 - 2x^2 + 4x + 7 = 0$

7. $x^4 - 3x^2 - 4 = 0$

8. $x^4 - 5x^2 + 4 = 0$

9. $x^5 - 3x^4 + 4x^3 - 8x^2 + 16 = 0$

10. $x^5 - 2x^4 - 3x^3 + 6x^2 - 4x + 8 = 0$

6-5 Theorems About Roots of Polynomial Equations

North Carolina Objectives
1.02 Define and compute with complex numbers.
1.03 Operate with algebraic expressions (polynomial, rational, complex fractions) to solve problems.

Lesson Preview

What You'll Learn

OBJECTIVE 1 To solve equations using the Rational Root Theorem

OBJECTIVE 2 To use the Irrational Root Theorem and the Imaginary Root Theorem

. . . And Why

To find all the roots of a polynomial equation, as in Example 2

Check Skills You'll Need

(For help, go to Lessons 1-1, 5-1, and 5-6.)

List all the integer factors of each number.

1. 12 **2.** 24 **3.** 36 **4.** 48

Multiply.

5. $(x - 5)(x^2 + 7)$ **6.** $(x + 2)(x + \sqrt{3})(x - \sqrt{3})$

Define each set of numbers.

7. rational **8.** irrational **9.** imaginary

New Vocabulary

- Rational Root Theorem
- Irrational Root Theorem
- Imaginary Root Theorem
- conjugates
- complex conjugates

Interactive lesson includes instant self-check, tutorials, and activities.

OBJECTIVE 1 The Rational Root Theorem

Reading Math
A polynomial equation has *roots*. A polynomial function has *zeros*.

You have learned several methods for finding the roots of a polynomial equation. Another method involves analyzing one or more integer coefficients of the polynomial in the equation.

Consider the equivalent equations $x^3 - 5x^2 - 2x + 24 = 0$ and $(x + 2)(x - 3)(x - 4) = 0$, which have -2, 3, and 4 as roots. The product of 2, 3, and 4 is 24. Notice that all the roots are factors of the constant term, 24. In general, if the coefficients (including the constant term) in a polynomial equation are integers, then any integer root of the equation is a factor of the constant term.

A similar pattern applies to rational roots. Consider the equivalent equations $24x^3 - 22x^2 - 5x + 6 = 0$ and $\left(x + \frac{1}{2}\right)\left(x - \frac{2}{3}\right)\left(x - \frac{3}{4}\right) = 0$, which have $-\frac{1}{2}, \frac{2}{3}$, and $\frac{3}{4}$ as roots. The numerators 1, 2, and 3 all are factors of the constant term, 6. The denominators 2, 3, and 4 are factors of the leading coefficient, 24.

Both the constant term and the leading coefficient of a polynomial can play a key role in identifying the rational roots of the related polynomial equation. This role is expressed in the Rational Root Theorem.

Key Concepts

Theorem **Rational Root Theorem**

If $\frac{p}{q}$ is in simplest form and is a rational root of the polynomial equation $a_nx^n + a_{n-1}x^{n-1} + \ldots + a_1x + a_0 = 0$ with integer coefficients, then p must be a factor of a_0 and q must be a factor of a_n.

You can use the Rational Root Theorem to find any rational roots of a polynomial equation with integer coefficients.

1 EXAMPLE Finding Rational Roots

Find the rational roots of $x^3 + x^2 - 3x - 3 = 0$.

Step 1 List the possible rational roots.

The leading coefficient is 1. The constant term is -3. By the Rational Root Theorem, the only possible rational roots of the equation have the form $\frac{\text{factor of } -3}{\text{factor of } 1}$.

The factors of -3 are ±1 and ±3. The factors of 1 are ±1. The only possible rational roots are ±1 and ±3.

Step 2 Test each possible rational root.

Test 1: $x^3 + x^2 - 3x - 3 = (1)^3 + (1)^2 - 3(1) - 3$

$= -4 \neq 0$

Test 3: $x^3 + x^2 - 3x - 3 = (3)^3 + (3)^2 - 3(3) - 3$

$= 24 \neq 0$

Test -1: $x^3 + x^2 - 3x - 3 = (-1)^3 + (-1)^2 - 3(-1) - 3$

$= 0$ **So -1 is a root.**

Test -3: $x^3 + x^2 - 3x - 3 = (-3)^3 + (-3)^2 - 3(-3) - 3$

$= -12 \neq 0$

The only rational root of $x^3 + x^2 - 3x - 3 = 0$ is -1.

Check Understanding 1 Find the rational roots of $x^3 - 4x^2 - 2x + 8 = 0$.

You can often use the Rational Root Theorem to find all the roots of a polynomial equation.

2 EXAMPLE Using the Rational Root Theorem

Find the roots of $2x^3 - x^2 + 2x - 1 = 0$.

Step 1 List the possible rational roots.

The leading coefficient is 2. The constant term is -1. By the Rational Root Theorem, the only possible rational roots of the equation have the form $\frac{\text{factor of } -1}{\text{factor of } 2}$.

The factors of -1 are ±1. The factors of 2 are ±1 and ±2. So the only possible rational roots are ±1 and $\pm\frac{1}{2}$.

Step 2 Test each possible rational root until you find a root.

Test 1: $2x^3 - x^2 + 2x - 1 = 2(1)^3 - (1)^2 + 2(1) - 1$

$= 2 \neq 0$

Test $\frac{1}{2}$: $2x^3 - x^2 + 2x - 1 = 2\left(\frac{1}{2}\right)^3 - \left(\frac{1}{2}\right)^2 + 2\left(\frac{1}{2}\right) - 1$

$= 0$ **So $\frac{1}{2}$ is a root.**

Step 3 Use synthetic division with the root you found in Step 2 to find the quotient.

$$\begin{array}{c|rrrr} \frac{1}{2} & 2 & -1 & 2 & -1 \\ & & 1 & 0 & 1 \\ \hline & 2 & 0 & 2 & 0 \\ & \downarrow & \downarrow & \downarrow & \downarrow \\ & 2x^2 & & +2 & \text{Remainder} \end{array}$$

Step 4 Find the roots of $2x^2 + 2 = 0$.

$$\begin{aligned} 2x^2 + 2 &= 0 \\ 2(x^2 + 1) &= 0 \quad \textbf{Factor out the GCF, 2.} \\ x^2 + 1 &= 0 \\ x^2 &= -1 \\ x &= \pm i \end{aligned}$$

The roots of $2x^3 - x^2 + 2x - 1 = 0$ are $\frac{1}{2}$, i, and $-i$.

Check Understanding **2** Find the roots of each equation.

a. $x^3 - 2x^2 - 5x + 10 = 0$

b. $3x^3 + x^2 - x + 1 = 0$

OBJECTIVE 2

Irrational Root Theorem and Imaginary Root Theorem

In Chapter 5 you learned to find irrational solutions to quadratic equations. For example, by the Quadratic Formula, the solutions of $x^2 - 4x - 1 = 0$ are $2 + \sqrt{5}$ and $2 - \sqrt{5}$. Number pairs of the form $a + \sqrt{b}$ and $a - \sqrt{b}$ are called **conjugates.**

You can often use conjugates to find the irrational roots of a polynomial equation.

Key Concepts

Theorem	**Irrational Root Theorem**
Let a and b be rational numbers and let $\sqrt{b}$ be an irrational number. If $a + \sqrt{b}$ is a root of a polynomial equation with rational coefficients, then the conjugate $a - \sqrt{b}$ also is a root.	

3 EXAMPLE Finding Irrational Roots

A polynomial equation with integer coefficients has the roots $1 + \sqrt{3}$ and $-\sqrt{11}$. Find two additional roots.

By the Irrational Root Theorem, if $1 + \sqrt{3}$ is a root, then its conjugate $1 - \sqrt{3}$ is also a root. If $-\sqrt{11}$ is a root, then its conjugate $\sqrt{11}$ also is a root.

The additional roots are $1 - \sqrt{3}$ and $\sqrt{11}$.

Check Understanding **3** **a.** A polynomial equation with rational coefficients has the roots $2 - \sqrt{7}$ and $\sqrt{5}$. Find two additional roots.

b. **Critical Thinking** One of the roots of a polynomial equation is $4 - \sqrt{2}$. Can you be certain that $4 + \sqrt{2}$ also is a root of the equation? Explain.

Number pairs of the form $a + bi$ and $a - bi$ are **complex conjugates.** You can use complex conjugates to find an equation's imaginary roots.

Key Concepts

Theorem	Imaginary Root Theorem
If the imaginary number $a + bi$ is a root of a polynomial equation with real coefficients, then the conjugate $a - bi$ also is a root.	

4 EXAMPLE Finding Imaginary Roots

A polynomial equation with integer coefficients has the roots $3 - i$ and $2i$. Find two additional roots.

By the Imaginary Root Theorem, if $3 - i$ is a root, then its complex conjugate $3 + i$ also is a root. If $2i$ is a root, then its complex conjugate $-2i$ also is a root.

The additional roots are $3 + i$ and $2i$.

Check Understanding 4 **a.** If a polynomial equation with real coefficients has $3i$ and $-2 + i$ among its roots, then what two other roots must it have?

b. **Critical Thinking** Describe the degree of the equation.

You can often use the Irrational Root Theorem and the Imaginary Root Theorem to write a polynomial equation if you know some of its roots.

5 EXAMPLE Writing a Polynomial Equation from Its Roots

Find a third-degree polynomial equation with rational coefficients that has roots 3 and $1 + i$.

Step 1 Find the other root using the Imaginary Root Theorem.

Since $1 + i$ is a root, then its complex conjugate $1 - i$ also is a root.

Step 2 Write the factored form of the polynomial using the Factor Theorem.

$(x - 3)(x - (1 + i))(x - (1 - i))$

Step 3 Multiply the factors.

$(x - 3)[x^2 - x(1 - i) - x(1 + i) + (1 + i)(1 - i)]$ **Multiply $(x - (1 + i))(x - (1 - i))$.**

$(x - 3)(x^2 - x + ix - x - ix + 1 - i^2)$ **Simplify.**

$(x - 3)(x^2 - x - x + 1 + 1)$

$(x - 3)(x^2 - 2x + 2)$ **Multiply.**

$x^3 - 5x^2 + 8x - 6$

A third-degree polynomial equation with rational coefficients and roots 3 and $1 + i$ is $x^3 - 5x^2 + 8x - 6 = 0$.

Check Understanding 5 **a.** Find a third-degree polynomial equation with rational coefficients that has roots -1 and $2 - i$.

b. Find a fourth-degree polynomial equation with rational coefficients that has roots i and $2i$.

EXERCISES

For more practice, see *Extra Practice.*

Practice and Problem Solving

A Practice by Example

Example 1 (page 330)

Use the Rational Root Theorem to list all possible rational roots for each polynomial equation. Then find any actual rational roots.

1. $x^3 - x^2 + 2x - 2 = 0$

2. $x^3 + 4x^2 + x - 6 = 0$

3. $x^3 + x^2 + 4x + 4 = 0$

4. $2x^3 - 9x^2 - 11x + 8 = 0$

5. $x^3 + 2x^2 - 8x - 16 = 0$

6. $x^4 + 2x^2 - 15 = 0$

Example 2 (pages 330–331)

Find the roots of each polynomial equation.

7. $x^3 - 2x^2 + 5x - 10 = 0$

8. $x^3 - 5x^2 + 7x - 35 = 0$

9. $2x^4 - 5x^3 - 17x^2 + 41x - 21 = 0$

10. $4x^3 + 16x^2 - 22x - 10 = 0$

11. $4x^4 - 37x^2 + 9 = 0$

12. $9x^4 + 3x^3 - 30x^2 + 6x + 12 = 0$

Examples 3 and 4 (pages 331 and 332)

A polynomial equation with rational coefficients has the given roots. Find two additional roots.

13. $\sqrt{5}$ and $-\sqrt{13}$

14. $4 - \sqrt{6}$ and $\sqrt{3}$

15. $1 - \sqrt{10}$ and $2 + \sqrt{2}$

16. $1 + i$ and $-5i$

17. $2 + 3i$ and $6i$

18. $4 - i$ and $3 + 7i$

Example 5 (page 332)

Find a third-degree polynomial equation with rational coefficients that has the given numbers as roots.

19. 1 and $3i$

20. -5 and $1 - i$

21. 2 and $-4i$

22. $3 + i$ and -3

23. $-2i$ and 6

24. -1 and $i + 1$

B Apply Your Skills

Use the Rational Root Theorem to list all possible rational roots for each polynomial equation. Then find any actual rational roots.

25. $12x^3 - 32x^2 + 25x - 6 = 0$

26. $10x^3 - 49x^2 + 68x - 20 = 0$

27. $6x^4 - 5x^3 - 65x^2 + 85x - 21 = 0$

28. $8x^3 - 28x^2 + 14x + 15 = 0$

Find a fourth-degree polynomial equation with integer coefficients that has the given numbers as roots.

29. $3 + i$ and $-2i$

30. $\sqrt{3}$ and $1 - i$

31. $3 + \sqrt{2}$ and $\sqrt{5}$

In each equation, *r*, *s*, and *t* represent integers. Indicate whether the statement is *sometimes*, *always*, or *never* true. Explain your answer.

32. A root of the equation $3x^3 + rx^2 + sx + 8 = 0$ is 5.

33. A root of the equation $3x^3 + rx^2 + sx + 8 = 0$ is -2.

34. If a is a root of $x^3 + rx^2 + sx + t = 0$, then a is a factor of t.

35. $\sqrt{5}$ and $-\sqrt{5}$ are roots of $x^3 + rx^2 + sx + t = 0$.

36. $2 + i$ and $-2 - i$ are roots of $x^3 + rx^2 + sx + t = 0$.

37. Error Analysis A student claims that $2i$ is the only imaginary root of a polynomial equation that has real coefficients. Explain the student's mistake.

38. Open-Ended Write a fourth-degree polynomial equation with integer coefficients that has two irrational roots and two imaginary roots.

39. **Critical Thinking** Explain why the Irrational Root Theorem requires that $\sqrt{b}$ of $a + \sqrt{b}$ be an irrational number.

Challenge

40. a. Using *real* and *imaginary* as types of roots, list all possible combinations of root type for a fourth-degree polynomial equation.
b. Repeat the process for a fifth-degree polynomial equation.
c. **Make a Conjecture** Make a conjecture about the number of real roots of an odd-degree polynomial equation.

41. **Writing** A student states that $2 + \sqrt{3}$ is a root of $x^2 - 2x - (3 + 2\sqrt{3}) = 0$. The student claims that $2 - \sqrt{3}$ is another root of the equation by the Irrational Root Theorem. Explain how you would respond to the student.

42. What polynomial equation with complex coefficients and no multiple roots has $-4i$ and $2 + 3i$ as its only roots?

43. a. Find a polynomial equation in which $1 + \sqrt{2}$ is the only root.
b. Find a polynomial equation with root $1 + \sqrt{2}$ of multiplicity 2.
c. Find c such that $1 + \sqrt{2}$ is a solution of $x^2 - 2x + c = 0$.

Standardized Test Prep

Multiple Choice

44. Three roots of a polynomial equation with rational coefficients are $5 + \sqrt{3}$, -17, and $2 - \sqrt{4}$. Which number also is a root of the equation?
A. 17 B. $2 + \sqrt{4}$ C. $4 - \sqrt{2}$ D. $5 - \sqrt{3}$

Take It to the NET
Online lesson quiz at www.PHSchool.com
Web Code: agk-0605

45. Two roots of a cubic polynomial equation with real coefficients are -3 and $-4i$. If the leading coefficient of the polynomial is 1, what is the equation?
F. $x^3 - 3x^2 + 16x - 48 = 0$ G. $x^3 - 3x^2 - 16x + 48 = 0$
H. $x^3 + 3x^2 + 16x + 48 = 0$ I. $x^3 + 3x^2 - 16x - 48 = 0$

Short Response

46. According to the Rational Root Theorem, what is the relationship between the polynomial equation $2x^4 - x^3 - 7x^2 + 3x + 3 = 0$ and rational roots of the form $\frac{p}{q}$, where $\frac{p}{q}$ is in simplest form?

Extended Response

47. A third-degree polynomial equation with rational coefficients has roots -4 and $-4i$. If the leading coefficient of the equation is $\frac{3}{2}$, what is the equation? Show your work.

Mixed Review

Lesson 6-4 **Solve each equation.**

48. $8x^3 + 27 = 0$ 49. $x^4 - x^2 - 20 = 0$ 50. $2x^4 - 50 = 0$

Lesson 5-7 **Solve each equation by completing the square.**

51. $x^2 - 6x - 7 = 0$ 52. $p^2 + 4p = -8$ 53. $4x^2 - 11 = 12x$

Lesson 4-8 **Use Cramer's Rule to solve each system.**

54. $\begin{cases} -3x + y = -7 \\ 5x + 2y = -3 \end{cases}$ 55. $\begin{cases} x - 3y = -12 \\ 2x + 7y = 2 \end{cases}$ 56. $\begin{cases} 2x - 8y = 10 \\ -3x + y = -15 \end{cases}$

6-6 The Fundamental Theorem of Algebra

North Carolina Objectives

1.02 Define and compute with complex numbers.
1.03 Operate with algebraic expressions (polynomial, rational, complex fractions) to solve problems.

Lesson Preview

What You'll Learn

OBJECTIVE 1 To use the Fundamental Theorem of Algebra in solving polynomial equations with complex roots

. . . And Why

To find all the zeros of a polynomial function, as in Example 2

✓ Check Skills You'll Need

(For help, go to Lessons 5-8 and 6-1.)

Find the degree of each polynomial.

1. $3x^2 - x + 5$ **2.** $-x + 3 - x^3$ **3.** $-4x^5 + 1$

Solve each equation using the quadratic formula.

4. $x^2 + 16 = 0$ **5.** $x^2 - 2x + 3 = 0$ **6.** $2x^2 + 5x + 4 = 0$

New Vocabulary • Fundamental Theorem of Algebra

Interactive lesson includes instant self-check, tutorials, and activities.

OBJECTIVE

1 The Fundamental Theorem of Algebra

Investigation: Counting Zeros

In this activity you will find the solutions to polynomial equations, identify the types of solutions, and then count the number of solutions.

1. a. Find the solutions of $x^4 - 5x^2 + 4 = 0$.
b. Identify each solution as *real* or *imaginary*.
c. How many solutions are there?

2. a. Find the solutions of $x^4 + 7x^2 + 12 = 0$.
b. Identify each solution as *real* or *imaginary*.
c. How many solutions are there?

3. Make a conjecture about the number of zeros of a fourth-degree polynomial function, regardless of the types of zeros.

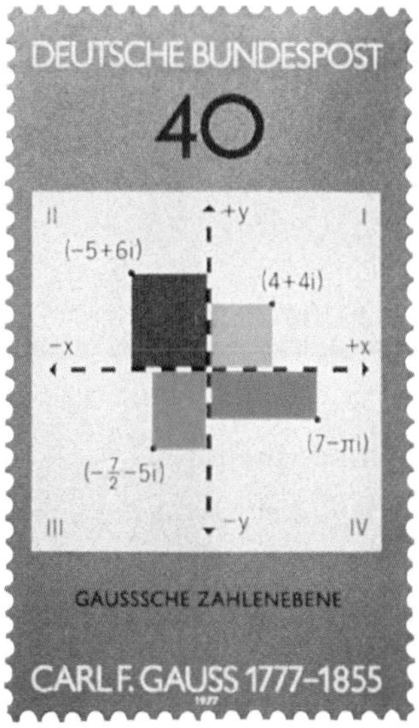

Real-World Connection

Germany issued this stamp in honor of the bicentennial of the birth of Gauss.

You have solved polynomial equations and found that their roots are included in the set of complex numbers. That is, the roots have been integers, rational numbers, irrational numbers, and imaginary numbers. But can all polynomial equations be solved using complex numbers?

In 1799, the German mathematician Carl Friedrich Gauss (1777–1855) proved that the answer to this question is yes. The roots of every polynomial equation, even those with imaginary coefficients, are complex numbers. The answer is so important that his theorem is called the **Fundamental Theorem of Algebra.**

A corollary to the Fundamental Theorem of Algebra describes the relationship between the degree of a polynomial and the number of zeros of the related polynomial function.

Key Concepts

Theorem — **Fundamental Theorem of Algebra**

If $P(x)$ is a polynomial of degree $n \geq 1$ with complex coefficients, then $P(x) = 0$ has at least one complex root.

Corollary

Including imaginary roots and multiple roots, an nth degree polynomial equation has exactly n roots; the related polynomial function has exactly n zeros.

Reading Math

A corollary is a deduction.

In other words, the corollary says that you can factor a polynomial of degree n into n linear factors. The number n includes multiple roots. For example, the equation $x^3 = 0$ should have three roots by the corollary to the Fundamental Theorem of Algebra. Since $x^3 = 0$ can be rewritten as $x \cdot x \cdot x = 0$ or $(x - 0)(x - 0)(x - 0) = 0$, the equation has three linear factors and three roots, all of which are zero.

1 EXAMPLE Using the Fundamental Theorem of Algebra

For the equation $x^3 + 2x^2 - 4x - 6 = 0$, find the number of complex roots, the possible number of real roots, and the possible rational roots.

By the corollary to the Fundamental Theorem of Algebra, $x^3 + 2x^2 - 4x - 6 = 0$ has three complex roots.

By the Imaginary Root Theorem, the equation has either no imaginary roots or two imaginary roots (one conjugate pair). So the equation has either three real roots or one real root.

By the Rational Root Theorem, the possible rational roots of the equation are $\pm1, \pm2, \pm3$, and ±6.

Check Understanding 1 For the equation $x^4 - 3x^3 + x^2 - x + 3 = 0$, find the number of complex roots, the possible number of real roots, and the possible rational roots.

You can often find all the zeros of a polynomial function by using some combination of graphing, the Factor Theorem, polynomial division, the Remainder Theorem, and the Quadratic Formula.

2 EXAMPLE Finding All Zeros of a Polynomial Function

Find the number of complex zeros of $f(x) = x^3 + x^2 - x + 2$. Find all the zeros.

By the corollary to the Fundamental Theorem of Algebra, there are three complex zeros. You can use synthetic division to find a rational zero.

Step 1 Find a rational root from the possible roots of ±1 and ±2. Use synthetic division to test each possible root until you get a remainder of zero.

$$\begin{array}{r|rrrr} -2 & 1 & 1 & -1 & 2 \\ & & -2 & 2 & -2 \\ \hline & 1 & -1 & 1 & 0 \end{array}$$

$$\downarrow \quad \downarrow \quad \downarrow$$

$$1x^2 - 1x + 1$$

So -2 is one of the roots.

Step 2 Since the expression $x^2 - x + 1$ cannot be factored, use the Quadratic Formula to solve the related quadratic equation $x^2 - x + 1 = 0$.

$$x = \frac{-b \pm \sqrt{b^2 - 4ac}}{2a}$$

$$x = \frac{-(-1) \pm \sqrt{(-1)^2 - 4(1)(1)}}{2(1)}$$

$$x = \frac{1 \pm \sqrt{-3}}{2}$$

$$x = \frac{1 \pm i\sqrt{3}}{2}$$

The polynomial function $f(x) = x^3 + x^2 - x + 2$ has one real zero of $x = -2$, and two complex zeros of $x = \frac{1 + i\sqrt{3}}{2}$ and $x = \frac{1 - i\sqrt{3}}{2}$.

Check Understanding **2** **a.** Find all zeros of $y = x^3 - 2x^2 + 4x - 8$.
b. Explain how you could use a graphing calculator to verify the zeros.

EXERCISES

For more practice, see *Extra Practice*.

Practice and Problem Solving

A Practice by Example

Example 1 (page 336)

For each equation, state the number of complex roots, the possible number of real roots, and the possible rational roots.

1. $x^3 + 4x^2 + 5x - 1 = 0$

2. $3x^2 - 7 = 0$

3. $-x^4 = 0$

4. $2x^5 - 4x^4 - 4x^2 + 5 = 0$

5. $x^7 - x^3 - 2x - 3 = 0$

6. $4x + 8 = 0$

7. $-2x^6 - x^2 + x - 7 = 0$

8. $x^{10} + x^8 - x^4 + 3x^2 - x + 1 = 0$

Example 2 (pages 336–337)

Find all the zeros of each function.

9. $y = 2x^3 + x^2 + 1$

10. $f(x) = x^3 - 3x^2 + x - 3$

11. $g(x) = x^3 - 5x^2 + 5x - 4$

12. $y = x^3 - 2x^2 - 3x + 6$

13. $y = x^4 - 6x^2 + 8$

14. $f(x) = x^4 - 3x^2 - 4$

15. $y = x^3 - 3x^2 - 9x$

16. $y = x^3 + 6x^2 + x + 6$

B Apply Your Skills

For each equation, state the number of complex roots, the possible number of real roots, and the possible rational roots.

17. $2x^4 - x^3 + 2x^2 + 5x - 26 = 0$

18. $x^5 - x^3 - 11x^2 + 9x + 18 = 0$

19. $-12 + x + 10x^2 + 3x^3 = 0$

20. $4x^6 - x^5 - 24 = 0$

Find all the zeros of each function.

21. $y = x^3 - 4x^2 + 9x - 36$

22. $f(x) = x^3 + 2x^2 - 5x - 10$

23. $y = 2x^3 + 14x^2 + 13x + 6$

24. $y = 4x^3 + 9x^2 + 22x + 5$

25. $g(x) = x^3 - \frac{1}{2}x^2 + 20x - 10$

26. $y = 15x^3 - x^2 + 3x - 2$

27. **Open-Ended** Write a polynomial function that has four possible rational zeros but no actual rational zeros.

Challenge

Graph each function. Approximate the real zeros to the nearest hundredth.

28. $f(x) = x^4 + 3x^2 - 2$

29. $f(x) = x^4 + 2x^3 - 2x^2 + 4x - 8$

30. Writing Using the Rational Root Theorem, explain why the following statement is false: If a polynomial has no constant term, then the corresponding polynomial equation has only the number 0 as a possible rational root.

31. Critical Thinking Consider a polynomial with integer coefficients in which the leading coefficient is not equal to 1. Can the related polynomial equation have a rational root that is an integer? Explain.

Standardized Test Prep

Multiple Choice

32. Which number is a root of $f(x) = x^3 + 6x^2 + 9x$ that has multiplicity 1?

A. 3 **B.** 1 **C.** 0 **D.** -3

33. Three roots of a polynomial equation with real coefficients are 3, $5 - 3i$, and $-3i$. Which number(s) MUST also be roots of the equation?

I. -3 **II.** $5 + 3i$ **III.** $3i$

A. II only **B.** I and II only **C.** II and III only **D.** I, II, and III

Quantitative Comparison

Compare the boxed quantity in Column A with the boxed quantity in Column B. Choose the best answer.

A. The quantity in Column A is greater.
B. The quantity in Column B is greater.
C. The two quantities are equal.
D. The relationship cannot be determined from the information given.

Take It to the NET
Online lesson quiz at **www.PHSchool.com**
Web Code: agk-0606

	Column A	Column B
34.	the number of zeros of a degree four polynomial function	the number of zeros of the function $y = (2x - 5)(2x + 5)$
35.	the degree of the polynomial $P(x) = (2x + 3)(x - 5)$	the degree of the quotient of $f(x) = 4x^5 + 3x^4 + x^2 - x + 1$ and $g(x) = 3x^3 - 2x^2 + x + 1$

Mixed Review

Lesson 6-5

36. Find a fourth-degree polynomial equation with integer coefficients that has $2i$ and $-3 + i$ as roots.

Lesson 5-8

Solve each equation using the Quadratic Formula.

37. $x^2 - 6x + 9 = 0$

38. $2x^2 + 5x = -9$

39. $2(x^2 + 2) = 3x$

Lesson 5-1

Find a quadratic model for each function.

40. $f(-1) = 0, f(2) = 3, f(1) = 4$

41. $f(-4) = 11, f(-5) = 5, f(-6) = 3$

6-7 Permutations and Combinations

Lesson Preview

What You'll Learn

OBJECTIVE 1 To count permutations

OBJECTIVE 2 To count combinations

. . . And Why

To find the number of ways you can vote for candidates, as in Example 5

Check Skills You'll Need

(For help, go to Lesson 1-2.)

Simplify each expression.

1. $10 \cdot 9 \cdot 8 \cdot 7 \cdot 6$ **2.** $\frac{4 \cdot 3 \cdot 2}{6 \cdot 5}$ **3.** $\frac{7 \cdot 6 \cdot 5 \cdot 4 \cdot 3 \cdot 2 \cdot 1}{4 \cdot 3 \cdot 2 \cdot 1}$

Let $a * b = 2a(a + b)$. Evaluate each expression.

4. $3 * 4$ **5.** $2 * 7$ **6.** $5 * 1$ **7.** $6 * 10$

New Vocabulary • permutation • *n* factorial • combination

Interactive lesson includes instant self-check, tutorials, and activities.

OBJECTIVE 1 Permutations

A **permutation** is an arrangement of items in a particular order. You can often find the number of permutations of some set of items by using the Multiplication Counting Principle or factorial notation.

You can use the Multiplication Counting Principle or factorial notation when you plan to choose all of the items of a particular set. Suppose you want to find the number of permutations for three items. There are three ways to choose the first item, two ways to choose the second item, and only one way to choose the third item. By the Multiplication Counting Principle, there are $3 \cdot 2 \cdot 1$ permutations. Using factorial notation, you can write $3 \cdot 2 \cdot 1$ as 3!, read "three factorial."

Key Concepts

Definition ***n* Factorial**

For any positive integer n, $n! = n(n - 1) \cdot \ldots \cdot 3 \cdot 2 \cdot 1$.
For $n = 0$, $n! = 1$.

1 EXAMPLE Finding Permutations

In how many different orders can ten dogs line up to be groomed?

Since all ten dogs are being groomed, you are using all the items from the original set. You can use the Multiplication Counting Principle or factorial notation.

There are ten ways to select the first dog in line, nine ways to select the next dog, and so on. The total number of permutations is $10 \cdot 9 \cdot \ldots \cdot 2 \cdot 1 = 10!$.

$10! = 3{,}628{,}800$

The ten dogs can line up in 3,628,800 different orders.

Graphing Calculator Hint

To calculate factorials, press MATH and then choose the PRB menu and the ! option.

Check Understanding

1 In how many ways can you arrange six trophies on a shelf?

Some permutations do not use all the items available in a set. You can still use the Multiplication Counting Principle or factorial notation. The relationship between permutations and factorials can be summarized with a formula.

Key Concepts

Definition **Number of Permutations**

The number of permutations of n items of a set arranged r items at a time is ${}_n\mathrm{P}_r$.

$${}_n\mathrm{P}_r = \frac{n!}{(n - r)!} \text{ for } 0 \le r \le n$$

Example ${}_{10}\mathrm{P}_4 = \frac{10!}{(10 - 4)!} = \frac{10!}{6!} = 5040$

Real-World Connection

In how many ways can these boats finish first, second, and third?

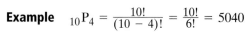

2 EXAMPLE Real-World Connection

Boating Seven yachts enter a race. First, second, and third places will be given to the three fastest yachts. How many arrangements of first, second, and third places are possible with seven yachts?

Method 1 Use the Multiplication Counting Principle.
$7 \cdot 6 \cdot 5 = 210$

Method 2 Use the permutation formula. Since there are seven yachts arranged three at a time, $n = 7$ and $r = 3$.

$${}_7\mathrm{P}_3 = \frac{7!}{(7 - 3)!} = \frac{7!}{4!} = 210$$

There are 210 possible arrangements of first, second, and third places.

Check Understanding 2 How many arrangements of first, second, and third places are possible with ten yachts?

OBJECTIVE

2 Combinations

In Example 2, you found the number of ways in which three of seven yachts can finish first, second, and third in a race. Each yacht would have a unique place. Consider a situation in which the three fastest yachts win the race with equal status, that is, without first, second, and third places. In that case, the *order* in which the three winning yachts cross the finish line does not matter. A selection in which order does not matter is a **combination.**

As with permutations, you can calculate the number of combinations of n items chosen r at a time by using a formula.

Key Concepts

Definition **Number of Combinations**

The number of combinations of n items of a set chosen r items at a time is ${}_n\mathrm{C}_r$.

$${}_n\mathrm{C}_r = \frac{n!}{r!(n - r)!} \text{ for } 0 \le r \le n$$

Example ${}_5\mathrm{C}_3 = \frac{5!}{3!(5 - 3)!} = \frac{5!}{3! \cdot 2!} = \frac{120}{6 \cdot 2} = 10$

3 EXAMPLE Finding Combinations

Evaluate ${}_{12}C_3$.

$$
\begin{aligned}
{}_{12}C_3 &= \frac{12!}{3!(12-3)!} && \text{Use the formula } {}_nC_r = \frac{n!}{r!(n-r)!}. \\
&= \frac{12!}{3!\cdot 9!} && \text{Simplify.} \\
&= \frac{12\cdot 11\cdot 10\cdot \cancel{9}\cdot \cancel{8}\cdot \cancel{7}\cdot \cancel{6}\cdot \cancel{5}\cdot \cancel{4}\cdot \cancel{3}\cdot \cancel{2}\cdot \cancel{1}}{3\cdot 2\cdot 1\cdot \cancel{9}\cdot \cancel{8}\cdot \cancel{7}\cdot \cancel{6}\cdot \cancel{5}\cdot \cancel{4}\cdot \cancel{3}\cdot \cancel{2}\cdot \cancel{1}} && \text{Simplify each factorial.} \\
&= \frac{12\cdot 11\cdot 10}{3\cdot 2\cdot 1} \\
&= 220
\end{aligned}
$$

Check Understanding 3 Evaluate each expression.

a. ${}_{10}C_5$ b. ${}_8C_2$ c. ${}_{25}C_7$

You can use a graphing calculator to find combinations.

4 EXAMPLE Real-World Connection

Graphing Calculator Hint

To find permutations and combinations, press MATH, and then choose the PRB menu.

Literature A reading list for a course in world literature has 20 books on it. In how many ways can you choose four books to read?

Relate 20 books chosen 4 books at a time

Define Let n = total number of books.

Let r = number of books chosen at a time.

Write ${}_nC_r = {}_{20}C_4$

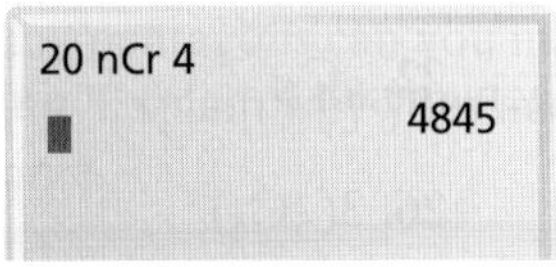

Use the ${}_nC_r$ feature of your calculator.

You can choose four books in 4845 different ways.

Check Understanding 4 Of the 20 books, in how many ways can you choose seven books? Twelve books?

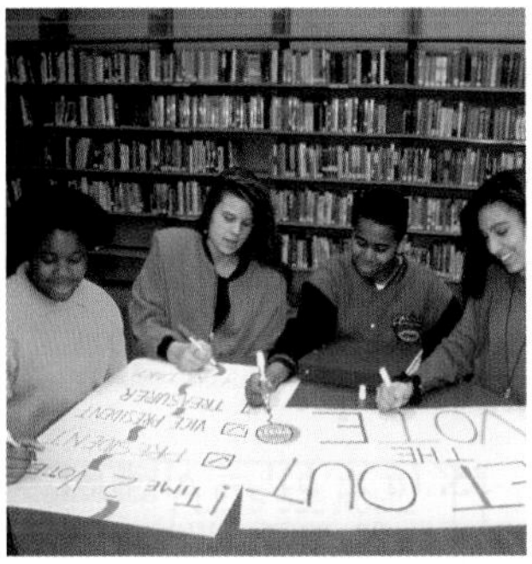

The National Association of Student Councils has more than 18,000 member schools.

5 EXAMPLE Real-World Connection

Government Ten candidates are running for three seats in the student government. You may vote for as many as three candidates. In how many ways can you vote for three or fewer candidates?

You may vote for	3 people,	2 people,	1 person,	or none.
	↓	↓	↓	↓
	${}_{10}C_3$	${}_{10}C_2$	${}_{10}C_1$	${}_{10}C_0$
	120	45	10	1

The total number of ways to vote is 120 + 45 + 10 + 1 = 176.

There are 176 ways to cast your ballot.

Check Understanding 5 In how many ways can you vote for five or fewer people?

Challenge

69. **a.** The graph at the right shows the function $y = {}_xC_2$. Use it to graph the function $y = {}_xC_{x-2}$.
   b. **Critical Thinking** Explain why the graph consists of discrete points rather than a continuous curve.

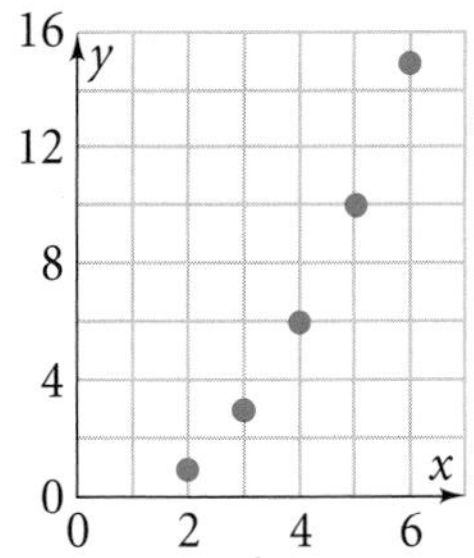

70. **a.** In how many ways can you choose three flags from a collection of seven different flags?
   b. Once you choose three flags, in how many different orders can you arrange them?
   c. **Writing** You want to arrange three flags from a group of seven. Explain how you can use ${}_7C_3 \cdot 3!$ to create the permutation formula.

71. In the sequence $1!, 2!, 3!, 4!, 5!, 6!, \ldots$, the first term that ends with a zero is $5!$.
   a. Explain why $5!$ and all the terms following $5!$ end with a zero.
   b. Find the number of zeros with which $100!$ ends.

72. Find a number n for which entering $n!$ in your calculator causes overflow error.

73. **Data Analysis** The bar graph at the right shows the results of 40 responses to a survey.
   a. How many people said they squeeze the toothpaste from the middle of the tube?
   b. Use your answer to part (a). Find the number of possible combinations of five people who squeeze toothpaste from the middle of the tube.
   c. Suppose five people are chosen at random from all the people who responded to the survey. How many combinations of five people are possible?
   d. **Probability** What is the probability that the five people selected at random all squeeze toothpaste from the middle of the tube?

Toothpaste Survey Results

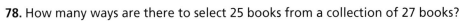

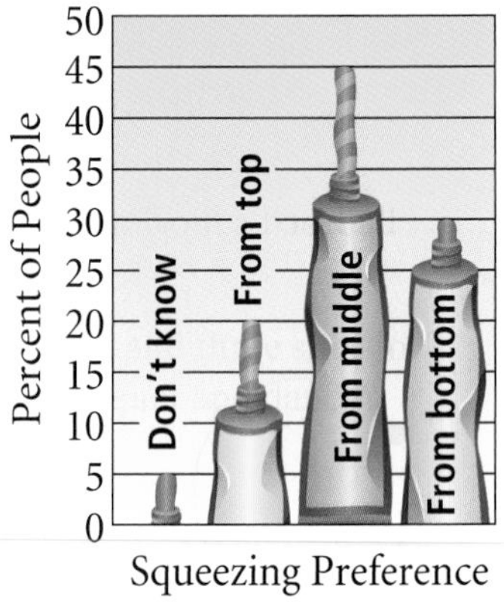

Standardized Test Prep

Gridded Response

74. Find the value of 7!.

75. What is the value of $\frac{5!}{8!}$? Write your answer as a fraction in simplest terms.

76. What is the value of ${}_7C_2$?

77. Find the value of $(3 + 2)! - (4 - 2)!$.

78. How many ways are there to select 25 books from a collection of 27 books?

79. What is the value of the sum $\frac{2!}{3!} + \frac{3!}{4!} + \frac{4!}{5!}$? Express your answer as a fraction in simplest terms.

80. A box has 10 items, and you select 3 of them. What is the value of $P - C$, if P represents the number of permutations possible when selecting 3 of the items, and C is the number of combinations possible when selecting 3 of the items?

Take It to the NET
Online lesson quiz at **www.PHSchool.com**
Web Code: agk-0607

Mixed Review

Lesson 6-6

81. For the equation $12x^3 - 17x^2 + 3x + 2 = 0$, find the number of complex roots, the possible number of real roots, and the possible rational roots.

82. Find all the zeros of the function $f(x) = x^3 - 2x^2 + 6x - 12$.

Lesson 6-1

Write each polynomial in standard form. Then classify it by degree and by number of terms.

83. $-3x^2 + 6 - x^3$ **84.** $2(x - 1)^2 + 6$ **85.** $t^2 - 3t + 4t^2$

86. $-100 + x^4$ **87.** $x(x + 2)(x - 2)$ **88.** $(t^2 - t)^2$

Lesson 5-4

Factor each expression completely.

89. $4x^2 - 8x + 4$ **90.** $-x^2 - 6x - 9$ **91.** $3x^2 - 75$

Lesson 5-2

Determine whether the function has a maximum or minimum value. Then find the value.

92. $y = x^2 + 4x - 8$ **93.** $y = -2x^2 + 5x + 1$ **94.** $y = 4x^2 - 7$

Checkpoint Quiz 2 — Lessons 6-4 through 6-7

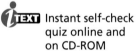

TEXT Instant self-check quiz online and on CD-ROM

Solve each equation.

1. $x^3 - 2x^2 = 5x - 6$ **2.** $27x^3 - 1 = 0$ **3.** $x^4 - 4x^2 - 45 = 0$

Use the Rational Root Theorem to find all the roots of each equation.

4. $2x^3 + x^2 + x - 1 = 0$ **5.** $3x^3 + 4x^2 - 12x - 16 = 0$

6. Two roots of a polynomial equation with real coefficients are $3 - 5i$ and $\sqrt{2}$.
a. Find two additional roots.
b. Describe the degree of the polynomial.

7. How many roots does a fifth-degree polynomial equation have? Explain.

8. Evaluate each expression.
a. ${}_4P_3 + {}_6P_5$ **b.** ${}_4C_3 + {}_6C_5$

9. Food Preparation The students at a culinary arts school are learning to prepare seven different items. In how many ways can you choose each number of items?
a. two items **b.** three items **c.** four items **d.** five items

10. Advertising Use the ad and the telephone keypad shown below. Find the last seven digits of this phone number. How many seven-number arrangements can be made with these digits?

Investigation

Pascal's Triangle

For Use With Lesson 6-8

Suppose you are standing at the corner of the grid shown below (point A1). You are allowed to travel down or to the right only.

The only way you can get to point A2 is by traveling down one unit. You can get to point B1 by traveling to the right one unit. The numbers of ways you can get to points A2, B1, and B2 are written next to these points.

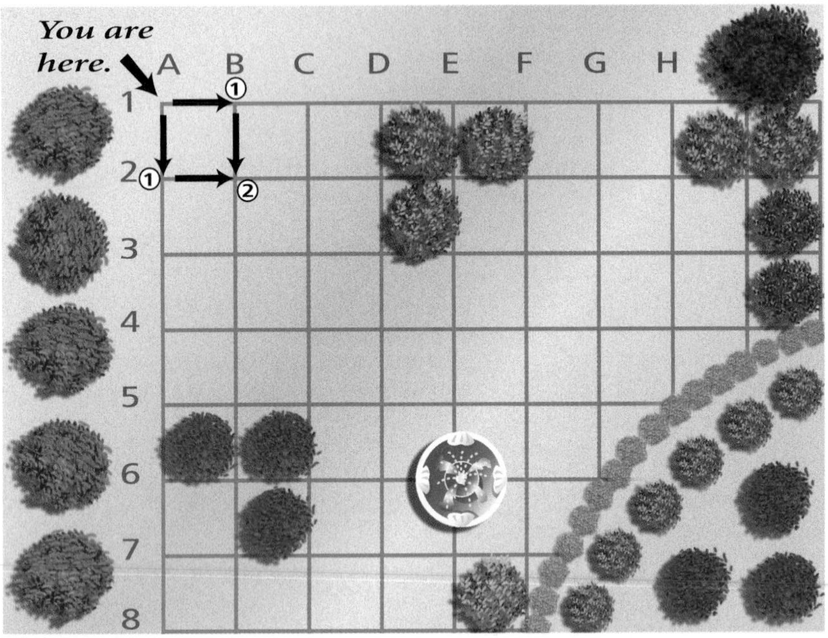

1. The number 2 is written next to point B2. What are the two different ways you can get from point A1 to point B2?
2. Copy the grid. Travel only down or to the right. In how many ways can you get from point A1 to point A3?
3. Use your copy of the grid from Exercise 2. In how many ways can you get from point A1 to point C2?
4. In how many ways can you get to the fountain at point E6 from your starting point at A1?
5. Mark the number of ways you can get to each point from point A1.
6. **Reasoning** Describe any patterns you see in the numbers on the grid.
7. **a.** Make a copy of your completed grid. Color the numbers that are multiples of 2. (You may need to extend the grid to see a pattern.)
   b. The pattern you see in part (a) is called the Sierpinski triangle. Find another way to describe how to obtain this pattern.
8. **Writing** The completed grid is called Pascal's Triangle. Turn your copy of the grid so that point A1 is at the top. Explain why the grid is called a triangle.

6-8 The Binomial Theorem

North Carolina Objectives

1.03 Operate with algebraic expressions (polynomial, rational, complex fractions) to solve problems.

Lesson Preview

What You'll Learn

OBJECTIVE 1 To use Pascal's Triangle

OBJECTIVE 2 To use the Binomial Theorem

. . . And Why

To find probabilities associated with basketball, as in Example 4

Check Skills You'll Need

(For help, go to Lessons 5-1 and 6-7.)

Multiply.

1. $(x + 2)^2$ **2.** $(2x + 3)^2$ **3.** $(x - 3)^3$ **4.** $(a + b)^4$

Evaluate.

5. ${}_5C_0$ **6.** ${}_5C_1$ **7.** ${}_5C_2$ **8.** ${}_5C_3$ **9.** ${}_5C_4$

New Vocabulary • expand • Pascal's Triangle • Binomial Theorem

Interactive lesson includes instant self-check, tutorials, and activities.

OBJECTIVE 1 Binomial Expansion and Pascal's Triangle

You have learned to multiply binomials using the FOIL method and the Distributive Property. If you are raising a *single* binomial to a power, you have another option for finding the product.

Consider the expansion of several binomials. To **expand** a binomial being raised to a power, first multiply; then write the result as a polynomial in standard form.

$$(a + b)^2 = (a + b)(a + b) = a^2 + 2ab + b^2$$

$$(a + b)^3 = (a + b)(a + b)(a + b) = a^3 + 3a^2b + 3ab^2 + b^3$$

In the first case, the coefficients of the product are 1, 2, 1. In the second case, they are 1, 3, 3, 1. Notice that each set of coefficients matches a row of **Pascal's Triangle** below. Pascal's Triangle is a triangular array of numbers formed by first lining the border with 1's, and then placing the sum of two adjacent numbers within a row between and underneath the two original numbers.

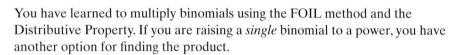

Coefficients of an Expansion (Pascal's Triangle)

$(a + b)^0$ → 1

$(a + b)^1$ → 1 1

$(a + b)^2$ → 1 2 1

$(a + b)^3$ → 1 3 3 1

$(a + b)^4$ → 1 4 6 4 1

$(a + b)^5$ → 1 5 10 10 5 1

The earliest known version of Pascal's Triangle was developed between 300 and 200 B.C. by the Indian mathematician Halayudha. Although other cultures were aware of the triangle, it has been named for Blaise Pascal (1623–1662), a French mathematician.

Each row of Pascal's Triangle contains coefficients for the expansion of $(a + b)^n$. For example, when $n = 6$, you can find the coefficients for the expansion of $(a + b)^6$ in the row that begins 1, 6, 15, . . .

Real-World Connection

In addition to his famous triangle, Pascal made many contributions to math, physics, and philosophy. In 1642 he built the first mechanical digital calculating machine.

1 EXAMPLE Using Pascal's Triangle

Pascal's Triangle

								1								
							1		1							
						1		2		1						
					1		3		3		1					
				1		4		6		4		1				
			1		5		10		10		5		1			
		1		6		15		20		15		6		1		
	1		7		21		35		35		21		7		1	
1		8		28		56		70		56		28		8		1

Use Pascal's Triangle to expand $(a + b)^6$.

Use the row that has 6 as its second number.

The exponents for a begin with 6 and decrease.

$$1a^6b^0 + 6a^5b^1 + 15a^4b^2 + 20a^3b^3 + 15a^2b^4 + 6a^1b^5 + 1a^0b^6$$

The exponents for b begin with 0 and increase.

In simplest form, the expansion is $a^6 + 6a^5b + 15a^4b^2 + 20a^3b^3 + 15a^2b^4 + 6ab^5 + b^6$.

Check Understanding 1 Use Pascal's Triangle to expand $(a + b)^8$.

Sometimes the terms of the binomial have coefficients other than 1. You can still base the expansion to standard form on the pattern for $(a + b)^n$.

2 EXAMPLE Expanding a Binomial

Use Pascal's Triangle to expand $(x - 2)^3$.

First write the pattern for raising a binomial to the third power.

coefficients from Pascal's Triangle 1, 3, 3, 1

$$(a + b)^3 = a^3 + 3a^2b + 3ab^2 + b^3$$

Since $(x - 2)^3 = (x + (-2))^3$, substitute x for a and -2 for b.

$$(x + (-2))^3 = x^3 + 3x^2(-2) + 3x(-2)^2 + (-2)^3$$
$$= x^3 - 6x^2 + 12x - 8$$

The expansion of $(x - 2)^3$ is $x^3 - 6x^2 + 12x - 8$.

Check Understanding 2 Use Pascal's Triangle to expand $(x - 2)^4$.

OBJECTIVE 2

The Binomial Theorem

You can also use combinations to help find the terms of a binomial expansion. For example, if you evaluate the combinations ${}_4C_0, {}_4C_1, {}_4C_2, {}_4C_3$, and ${}_4C_4$, you can see a pattern. The results, 1, 4, 6, 4, and 1 match the row of Pascal's Triangle that you would use to expand $(a + b)^4$. You can use the **Binomial Theorem** as a general formula for expanding a binomial.

Key Concepts

Theorem **Binomial Theorem**

For every positive integer n, $(a + b)^n =$
${}_nC_0a^n + {}_nC_1a^{n-1}b + {}_nC_2a^{n-2}b^2 + \dots + {}_nC_{n-1}ab^{n-1} + {}_nC_nb^n$

Notice that the sequence of exponents decreases for a while it increases for b.

3 EXAMPLE Using the Binomial Theorem

Graphing Calculator Hint

To evaluate a combination, use the MATH feature, the PRB menu, and the ${}_nC_r$ option.

Use the Binomial Theorem to expand $(g + h)^4$.

Write the pattern for raising a binomial to the fourth power.

$$(a + b)^4 = {}_4C_0a^4 + {}_4C_1a^3b + {}_4C_2a^2b^2 + {}_4C_3ab^3 + {}_4C_4b^4$$

Substitute g for a and h for b. Evaluate each combination.

$$(g + h)^4 = {}_4C_0g^4 + {}_4C_1g^3h + {}_4C_2g^2h^2 + {}_4C_3gh^3 + {}_4C_4h^4$$
$$= g^4 + 4g^3h + 6g^2h^2 + 4gh^3 + h^4$$

The expansion of $(g + h)^4$ is $g^4 + 4g^3h + 6g^2h^2 + 4gh^3 + h^4$.

Check Understanding 3 Use the Binomial Theorem to expand each binomial.

a. $(v + w)^9$ **b.** $(c - 2)^5$

You can use the Binomial Theorem to solve probability problems. Suppose an event has a probability of success p and a probability of failure q. Each term in the expansion of $(p + q)^n$ represents a probability. For example, ${}_{10}C_2p^8q^2$ represents the probability of eight successes in ten trials.

Real-World Connection

WNBA star Dawn Staley makes about 90% of the free throws she attempts.

4 EXAMPLE Real-World Connection

Sports Refer to the photo. Assume that Dawn's probability of success on any single shot is the same as her cumulative record to date. Find the probability that she will make exactly 6 out of 10 consecutive free throws.

Since you want 6 successes (and 4 failures), use the term containing p^6q^4. This term has the coefficient ${}_{10}C_4$.

Probability (6 out of 10) $= {}_{10}C_4p^6q^4$

$= \frac{10!}{4! \cdot 6!} \cdot (0.9)^6(0.1)^4$ **The probability p of success = 90%, or 0.9.**

$= 0.011160261$ **Simplify.**

Dawn Staley has about a 1% chance of making exactly 6 out of 10 consecutive free throws.

Check Understanding 4 **a.** Find the probability that Dawn Staley will make exactly 9 out of 10 consecutive free throw attempts.

b. Find the probability that she will make exactly 10 out of 10 attempts.

EXERCISES

For more practice, see *Extra Practice*.

Practice and Problem Solving

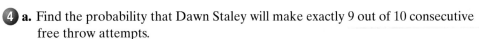

A Practice by Example

Examples 1 and 2 (page 348)

Use Pascal's Triangle to expand each binomial.

1. $(a + b)^3$ **2.** $(x - y)^2$ **3.** $(a + b)^4$

4. $(x - y)^5$ **5.** $(a - b)^6$ **6.** $(x - y)^7$

7. $(x + y)^8$ **8.** $(d + e)^9$ **9.** $(x - 3)^3$

10. $(a + 3b)^4$ **11.** $(x - 2)^6$ **12.** $(x - 4)^8$

Example 3 (page 349)

Use the Binomial Theorem to expand each binomial.

13. $(x + y)^4$ **14.** $(w + 1)^5$ **15.** $(s - t)^2$ **16.** $(x - 1)^6$

17. $(x - y)^4$ **18.** $(p + q)^7$ **19.** $(x - 3)^5$ **20.** $(4 - x)^3$

Example 4 (page 349)

21. Probability A coin is tossed ten times. The probability of heads on each toss is 0.5. Evaluate each probability.

a. exactly 5 heads **b.** exactly 6 heads **c.** exactly 7 heads

22. A calculator contains four batteries. With normal use, each battery has a 90% chance of lasting for one year. Find the probability that all four batteries will last a year.

B Apply Your Skills

Expand each binomial.

23. $(x + y)^7$ **24.** $(x - 5y)^8$ **25.** $(3x - y)^4$ **26.** $(x - 4y)^5$

27. $(7 - 2x)^6$ **28.** $(2x + 3y)^3$ **29.** $(x^2 + y^2)^2$ **30.** $(x^2 - 2y)^3$

31. $(x + 1)^6$ **32.** $(x - 1)^6$ **33.** $(x + 2)^5$ **34.** $(x - 2)^5$

35. $(2x + 3y)^4$ **36.** $(3x + 5y)^3$ **37.** $(2x + 2y)^6$ **38.** $(3x + 2y)^4$

39. $(2x + y)^5$ **40.** $(3x + y)^7$ **41.** $(x + 3y)^6$ **42.** $(x + 5y)^3$

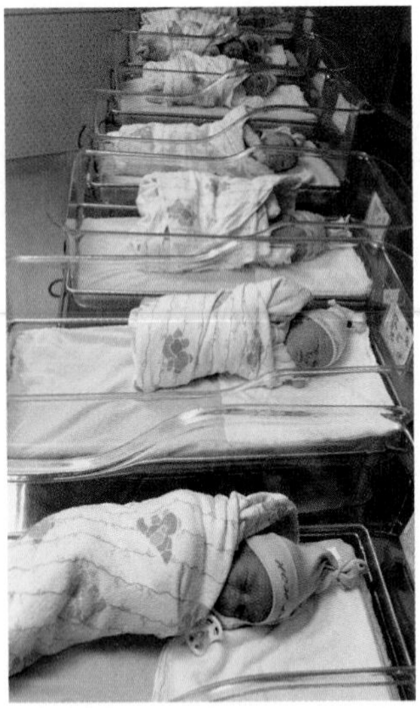

Real-World Connection

Worldwide, about 51.4% of babies born are male.

43. Genetics A family has five children. Assume that the probability of having a boy is 0.5. Write the term in the expansion of $(b + g)^5$ for each outcome described. Then evaluate each probability.

a. exactly 3 boys **b.** exactly 4 boys **c.** exactly 4 girls

44. In the expansion of $(m + n)^9$, one of the terms contains m^3.

a. What is the exponent of n in this term?

b. What is the coefficient of this term?

45. Suppose ${}_8C_3x^5y^3$ is a term of a binomial expansion. Write the next term.

46. The term $126c^4d^5$ appears in the expansion of $(c + d)^n$. Find n.

47. The coefficient of the second term in the expansion of $(r + s)^n$ is 7. Find the value of n, and write the complete term.

Find the specified term of each binomial expansion.

48. Third term of $(x + 3)^{12}$ **49.** Fourth term of $(x + 2)^5$

50. Second term of $(x + 3)^9$ **51.** Third term of $(x - 2)^{12}$

52. Twelfth term of $(2 + x)^{11}$ **53.** Seventh term of $(x - 2y)^6$

54. Eighth term of $(x - 2y)^{15}$ **55.** Third term of $(3x - 2)^9$

56. Seventh term of $(x^2 - 2y)^{11}$ **57.** Eighth term of $(x^2 + y^2)^{13}$

58. Writing Explain why the terms of $(a - 4)^6$ have alternating positive and negative signs.

59. Geometry A cube has sides of length s. Suppose each of the dimensions of the cube is increased by 0.5.

a. Write a binomial expression for the volume of the new cube.

b. Expand the binomial.

60. Error Analysis A student claims that ${}_7C_5p^2q^4$ is a term in a binomial expansion. Explain the student's error.

State the number of terms in each expansion and give the first two terms.

61. $(d + e)^{12}$ **62.** $(x - y)^{15}$ **63.** $(2a + b)^5$ **64.** $(x - 3y)^7$

Challenge

65. a. Expand $(1 + i)^4$.

b. Verify that $1 - i$ is a fourth root of -4 by repeating the process in part (a) for $(1 - i)^4$.

66. Verify that $-1 + \sqrt{3}i$ is a cube root of 8 by expanding $(-1 + \sqrt{3}i)^3$.

67. Open-Ended Write a probability problem for which ${}_5C_3(0.5)^2(0.5)^3$ is the solution.

68. a. Show that $(k + 1)! = (k + 1) \cdot k!$.

b. Show that ${}_nC_k + {}_nC_{k+1} = {}_{n+1}C_{k+1}$.

c. Suppose $n = 4$ and $k = 2$. What entries in Pascal's Triangle are represented by ${}_nC_k$, ${}_nC_{k+1}$, and ${}_{n+1}C_{k+1}$? Verify that the equation in part (b) is true for these entries.

Standardized Test Prep

Multiple Choice

69. What is the expanded form of $(a - b)^3$?
A. $a^3 + a^2b + ab^2 + b^3$
B. $a^3 + 3a^2b + 3ab^2 + b^3$
C. $a^3 - a^2b + ab^2 - b^3$
D. $a^3 - 3a^2b + 3ab^2 - b^3$

70. What is the third term in the expansion of $(a - b)^7$?
F. $-21a^5b^2$
G. $-7a^6b$
H. $7a^6b$
I. $21a^5b^2$

71. What is the coefficient of the third term in the expansion of $(2a - b)^5$?
A. -80
B. 32
C. 40
D. 80

Take It to the NET
Online lesson quiz at
www.PHSchool.com
Web Code: agk-0608

72. Which term in the expansion of $(2a - 3b)^6$ has coefficient 2160?
F. second term
G. third term
H. fourth term
I. fifth term

Short Response

73. One term of a binomial expansion is ${}_7C_2x^5y^2$. What is the term just before that term?

Extended Response

74. Explain how you can use the Binomial Theorem to find the sixth term in the expansion of $(2x - 3y)^7$.

Mixed Review

Lesson 6-7 **Simplify each expression.**

75. ${}_5P_2$ **76.** $4!$ **77.** ${}_7C_3$

78. $11!$ **79.** $\frac{7!}{3!(7-3)!}$ **80.** ${}_5C_2 + {}_5C_3$

Lesson 6-2 **Find the relative maximum, relative minimum, and zeros of each function.**

81. $f(x) = x^3 - 2x^2 - 11x + 12$ **82.** $f(x) = -x^3 - x^2 + 25x + 25$

Lesson 5-3 **Write each function in vertex form.**

83. $y = x^2 - 6x + 2$ **84.** $y = x^2 + 7x - 1$ **85.** $y = -4x^2 + 9$

Test-Taking Strategies

Drawing a Diagram

A picture or a graph can help you solve a problem. If a test problem does not already have a diagram, you can draw one.

1 EXAMPLE

How many real and how many imaginary solutions does the equation $x^5 = x + 5$ have?

The question asks for the number of solutions, not the solutions themselves. Graph $y_1 = x^5$ and $y_2 = x + 5$. There is just one point of intersection. So the equation has just one real solution. Since the related function $y = x^5 - x - 5$ is a fifth-degree function with five zeros, the other four solutions must be imaginary.

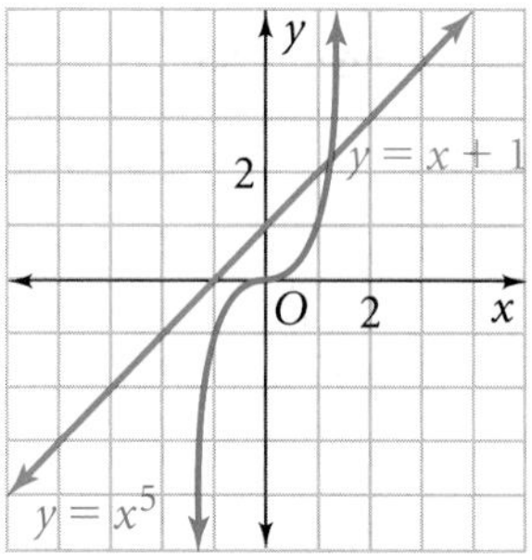

The equation $x^5 = x + 5$ has one real and four imaginary solutions.

2 EXAMPLE

In how many ways can the titles president, vice-president, and treasurer be assigned to 5 people?

Method 1 Assign titles to people. Draw 5 spaces to represent the 5 people. Assign president (P) to the first person. Then you can assign vice-president (V) to any of the remaining 4, and treasurer (T) to any of the remaining 3. There are $4 \cdot 3$, or 12, ways to assign the titles V and T, if the first person is president. Since P can be assigned to 5 people, there are $5 \cdot 12$ ways to assign the titles.

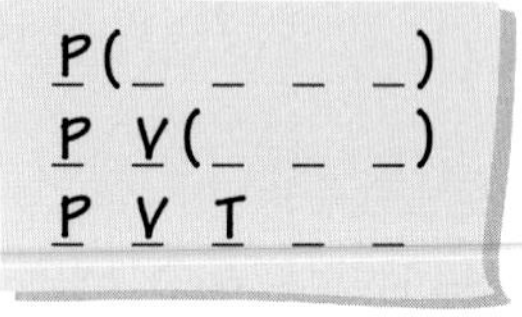

The answer is 60 ways.

Method 2 Assign people to titles. Draw 3 spaces to represent the 3 titles. Five people can be assigned to the first title, 4 to the second title, and 3 to the third title. There are $5 \cdot 4 \cdot 3$ ways to assign people to titles.

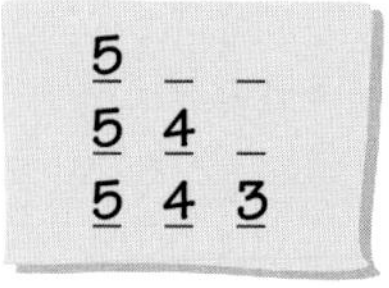

Again, the answer is 60 ways.

EXERCISES

Find the number of real solutions.

1. $x + 3 = (x - 5)^2$

2. $x^4 = x - 10$

3. $x^3 = 5 - x$

4. In how many ways can two cars be assigned to six people, if no car can be assigned to more than one person, and no person can be assigned to more than one car?

5. Is it easier to draw a diagram that assigns 3 jobs to 100 people, or to draw a diagram that assigns 100 people to 3 jobs? Explain.

Chapter 6 Chapter Review

Vocabulary

Binomial Theorem (p. 348)
combination (p. 340)
complex conjugates (p. 332)
conjugates (p. 331)
degree (p. 301)
degree of a polynomial (p. 301)
difference of cubes (p. 322)
expand (p. 347)
Factor Theorem (p. 309)
Fundamental Theorem of Algebra (p. 335)
Imaginary Root Theorem (p. 332)
Irrational Root Theorem (p. 331)
multiple zero (p. 310)
multiplicity (p. 310)
n factorial (p. 339)
Pascal's Triangle (p. 347)
permutation (p. 339)
polynomial (p. 301)
polynomial function (p. 301)
Rational Root Theorem (p. 329)
relative maximum (p. 309)
relative minimum (p. 309)
Remainder Theorem (p. 317)
standard form of a polynomial (p. 301)
sum of cubes (p. 322)
synthetic division (p. 315)

Reading Math
Understanding Vocabulary

Take It to the NET
Online vocabulary quiz at **www.PHSchool.com**
Web Code: agj-0651

Choose the correct vocabulary word or phrase to complete each sentence.

1. The exponent of the variable in a term determines its _?_.
2. The _?_ has terms written in descending order by degree.
3. The number of appearances of a zero of a polynomial function describes the _?_ of that zero.
4. The numbers $a + bi$ and $a - bi$ are called _?_.
5. Order is not important when counting _?_.

Skills and Concepts

6-1 Objectives

- To classify polynomials (p. 300)
- To model data using polynomial functions (p. 302)

A **polynomial** is a monomial or a sum of monomials with whole-number exponents. The exponent of the variable in a term is the **degree** of that term. The **degree of a polynomial** is the largest degree of any term of the polynomial. When the terms of a polynomial are in descending order by degree, the polynomial is in standard form. You can classify a polynomial by the number of terms it contains or by its degree. A **polynomial function** in one variable can be written in the form $P(x) = a_nx^n + a_{n-1}x^{n-1} + \ldots + a_1x + a_0$, where $n \geq 0$ and the coefficients $a_n, \ldots, a_0$ are complex numbers.

You can use a calculator to find cubic or quartic polynomial functions to model data, just as you have done with linear and quadratic polynomial functions.

Write each polynomial in standard form. Then classify it by degree and by number of terms.

6. $p^3 - 2p + 2p^3$ **7.** $3 - 5x^9$ **8.** $x - x^3 - x^5$

9. $3x + 2x^2 - x + 4x^3$ **10.** $5 + x + x^4 - x^2 + x^7$ **11.** s

12. Find both a cubic and a quartic model for the set of values. Graph each model. Compare the two models to determine which is a better fit.

x	1.2	1.4	1.6	1.8	2.0	2.2
y	3.1	–4.2	4.1	7.5	–8.9	10

6-2 and 6-3 Objectives

- To analyze the factored form of a polynomial (p. 307)
- To write a polynomial function from its zeros (p. 309)
- To divide polynomials using long division (p. 314)
- To divide polynomials using synthetic division (p. 315)

A polynomial can be factored into linear factors. The **Factor Theorem** states that the expression $x - a$ is a linear factor of a polynomial if and only if a is a zero of the related polynomial function. Then a is an x-intercept of the polynomial function and is a solution of the related polynomial equation.

If the zeros of a polynomial function are known, a polynomial function can be determined by finding the product of the corresponding linear factors. If $x - a$ is repeated as a factor k times, then a is a **multiple zero** of the polynomial—a zero of **multiplicity** k.

When you consider only neighboring points on a graph, the greatest y-value occurs at a **relative maximum** and the least y-value occurs at a **relative minimum.**

You can divide a polynomial by one of its factors to find another factor. When you divide by a linear factor, you can simplify this division by writing only the coefficients of each term. This process is called **synthetic division**. The **Remainder Theorem** guarantees that $P(a)$ is the remainder when $P(x)$ is divided by $x - a$.

Write each polynomial function in factored form. List the zeros of the function, and their multiplicity. Find any relative maximum or relative minimum values. Round to the nearest hundredth if necessary.

13. $f(x) = x^3 - x^2 - 12x$ **14.** $g(x) = 4 - x^2$ **15.** $y = x^3(x + 2)^4$

Write a polynomial function in standard form with the given zeros.

16. $-3, -2, 0, 2$ **17.** $1, 1, 2$ **18.** $-3, 0, 0, 1$ **19.** $-2, -2, -2$

Divide. Use both long division and synthetic division. Show your work.

20. $(x^3 + 3x^2 - 2x - 4) \div (x - 2)$ **21.** $(x^4 - x + 2) \div (x + 1)$

Use synthetic division and the given factor to completely factor each polynomial.

22. $x^3 - 3x^2 - x + 3; x + 1$ **23.** $x^3 - 4x^2 - 3x + 18; x - 3$

Use synthetic division and the Remainder Theorem to find $P(a)$.

24. $P(x) = x^4 + x^3 - x^2 - 2x; a = 3$ **25.** $P(x) = 4 - x - x^5; a = 2$

26. $P(x) = 5x^4 - x^2 + 1; a = -2$ **27.** $P(x) = x^3 - 8x^2 + 5x - 7; a = 1$

6-4 Objectives

- To solve polynomial equations by graphing (p. 321)
- To solve polynomial equations by factoring (p. 322)

You can solve polynomial equations by graphing or by factoring. The **sum of cubes** and the **difference of cubes** have factor formulas. Sometimes you can use the Quadratic Formula to factor polynomial expressions of higher degree.

Solve each equation by graphing. If necessary, round to the nearest hundredth.

28. $x^3 - 4x^2 + 5 = 0$ **29.** $x - 3 = 4 - x^2 + x^3$ **30.** $x^3 + x = 3x^2 - 3x^3$

31. $x^3 + x + 5 = 0$ **32.** $-5 = 2 - x^2 + x^3$ **33.** $x^3 + 4 = x^3 - 3x^2$

Factor the expression on the left side of each equation. Then solve each equation.

34. $x^3 - 8 = 0$ **35.** $4t^6 - t^4 = 0$ **36.** $8x^3 + 1 = 0$

37. $x^3 - 5x^2 + 4x = 0$ **38.** $x^3 - 2x^2 - 5x = 0$ **39.** $x^6 + 16x^3 + 64 = 0$

6-5 and 6-6 Objectives

- To solve equations using the Rational Root Theorem (p. 329)
- To use the Irrational Root Theorem and the Imaginary Root Theorem (p. 331)
- To use the Fundamental Theorem of Algebra (p. 335)
- To solve polynomial equations with complex zeros (p. 336)

The **Rational Root Theorem** identifies all possible rational roots of a polynomial equation with integer coefficients. A rational root of a polynomial equation is the quotient of a factor of the constant term and a factor of the leading coefficient.

Number pairs of the form $a + \sqrt{b}$ and $a - \sqrt{b}$ are called **conjugates,** while those of the form $a + bi$ and $a - bi$ are called **complex conjugates.** The **Irrational Root Theorem** states that irrational roots of a polynomial equation with rational coefficients occur in conjugate pairs. Similarly, the **Imaginary Root Theorem** states that imaginary roots of a polynomial equation with real coefficients occur in complex conjugate pairs.

The **Fundamental Theorem of Algebra** and its corollary assert that an nth degree polynomial equation, where $n \geq 1$, has exactly n complex roots.

For each equation, state the number of complex roots, the possible number of real roots, and the possible rational roots. Then find all the roots.

40. $x^3 - 6x^2 + 11x - 6 = 0$

41. $10x^4 - 13x^3 - 21x^2 + 10x + 8 = 0$

42. $x^4 - 6x^2 + 7 = 0$

43. $x^4 + 6x^3 + 13x^2 + 12x + 4 = 0$

44. $x^3 - 3x^2 + x + 5 = 0$

45. $x^4 - 2x^3 - 7x^2 + 18x - 18 = 0$

Write a polynomial equation of least possible degree, with integer coefficients, that has the given numbers as roots.

46. $2, i, -i$

47. $4 + \sqrt{2}, 4 - \sqrt{3}$

48. $3 + i, 2 - i$

49. $0, -2i, 3 + \sqrt{2}$

50. $1 + 2i, 3 - \sqrt{3}$

51. $\sqrt{5}, -\sqrt{7}$

6-7 and 6-8 Objectives

- To count permutations (p. 339)
- To count combinations (p. 340)
- To use Pascal's Triangle (p. 347)
- To use the Binomial Theorem (p. 348)

The notation $n!$, read **"n factorial,"** means $n(n - 1)(n - 2) \cdot \ldots \cdot 3 \cdot 2 \cdot 1$, and $0! = 1$.

A **permutation** is an arrangement of items in a particular order. You can count permutations using the Multiplication Counting Principle or factorial notation. To compute the number of permutations of n objects chosen r at a time, you can also use the formula ${}_nP_r = \frac{n!}{(n - r)!}$, for $0 \leq r \leq n$.

A selection in which order does not matter is a **combination.** The number of combinations of n objects chosen r at a time is ${}_nC_r = \frac{n!}{r!(n - r)!}$, for $0 \leq r \leq n$.

Use the **Binomial Theorem** to **expand** a binomial raised to a power. For $n \geq 0$, $(a + b)^n = {}_nC_0a^n + {}_nC_1a^{n-1}b + {}_nC_2a^{n-2}b^2 + \ldots + {}_nC_{n-1}ab^{n-1} + {}_nC_nb^n$. The coefficients in the expansion of $(a + b)^n$ are found in **Pascal's Triangle.** You can also use the Binomial Theorem to find probabilities when an event has only two possible outcomes.

Evaluate each expression.

52. $3(4!)$

53. ${}_4P_3$

54. ${}_7C_4$

55. ${}_5P_2 + {}_5C_3$

56. $\frac{{}_6C_3}{{}_5C_3}$

57. In how many ways can you arrange 5 different canisters in a row on a shelf?

58. Find the fourth term in the binomial expansion of $(2x + 3y)^6$.

59. A coin is tossed seven times. Find the probability of getting exactly four heads.

Chapter 6

Chapter Test

Take It to the NET
Online chapter test at
www.PHSchool.com
Web Code: aga-0652

Write each polynomial in standard form. Then classify it by degree and by number of terms.

1. $3x^2 - 7x^4 + 9 - x^4$

2. $11x^2 + \frac{3}{8}x - 3x^2$

3. $2x(x - 3)(x + 2)$

4. $(t - 2)(t + 1)(t + 1)$

Graph each function. Approximate the real zeros to the nearest hundredth.

5. $P(x) = -x^3 - x^2 + x$

6. $P(x) = (x + 1)(x + 2)(x^2 + 4x - 5)$

7. $f(x) = x^4 + 3x^3 - 1$

8. $g(x) = -x^6 - x^3 + 2$

9. $f(x) = x^3 - 3x^2 + 2$

Write a polynomial function with rational coefficients in standard form with the given zeros.

10. $x = 1, 2, \frac{3}{5}$

11. $x = -2, 0, \sqrt{3}$

12. $x = -4, -4, -4$

13. $x = -1, 1, 1$

14. $x = \sqrt{2}, -i$

15. $x = 3 + i, 1 - \sqrt{5}$

16. Open-Ended Write a polynomial function with real coefficients that has an imaginary zero and an irrational zero.

Solve each equation.

17. $(2x - 3)(3x + 2)(x + 2)(x + 2)\left(x - \frac{7}{8}\right) = 0$

18. $(x^2 - 3)(x^2 + 3x - 4) = 0$

19. $\left(x + \frac{2}{3}\right)(x^2 + 5x + 1) = 0$

20. $x^3 - 2x^2 + x = 0$

21. $x^3 + 3x^2 - 5x - 4 = 0$

Divide using long division.

22. $(x^2 + 3x - 4) \div (x - 1)$

23. $(x^3 + 7x^2 - 5x - 6) \div (x + 2)$

Divide using synthetic division.

24. $(3x^2 - 3x + 4) \div (x + 1)$

25. $(x^3 + x^2 + x - 14) \div (x + 2)$

Use synthetic division and the Remainder Theorem to find $P(a)$.

26. $P(x) = 6x^4 + 19x^3 - 2x^2 - 44x - 24; a = \frac{-2}{3}$

27. $P(x) = -x^3 - x^2 + x; a = 0$

28. $P(x) = 2x^3 - 2x^2 - 12x; a = 3$

29. $P(x) = x^4 + 3x^3 - 7x^2 - 9x + 12; a = 3$

30. $P(x) = x^3 + 3x^2 - 5x - 4; a = -1$

Evaluate each expression.

31. $6!$

32. $\frac{6!}{4!2!}$

33. ${}_7C_3$

34. ${}_5P_2$

35. ${}_{11}P_9$

36. ${}_9C_8$

37. $2({}_5C_4) - {}_3C_2$

Indicate whether each situation involves a combination or a permutation. Then solve.

38. How many ways are there to select five actors from a troupe of nine to improvise a scene?

39. How many different three-student study groups can be formed from a class of 15?

40. You are looking for a new apartment. There are five apartments available. In how many ways can you inspect the apartments?

Use the Binomial Theorem to expand each binomial.

41. $(x + z)^5$

42. $(1 - 2t)^2$

43. A weighted coin has $P(\text{heads}) = \frac{2}{5}$. The coin is tossed seven times. Find the probability of getting exactly six heads.

44. Writing Describe how to use combinations to produce row n of Pascal's Triangle.

45. Geometry The volume V of a prism is modeled by $V = 2\ell^3 - 2\ell$, where ℓ is the length of the prism. The width of the prism equals $\ell - 1$. Find the height of the prism.

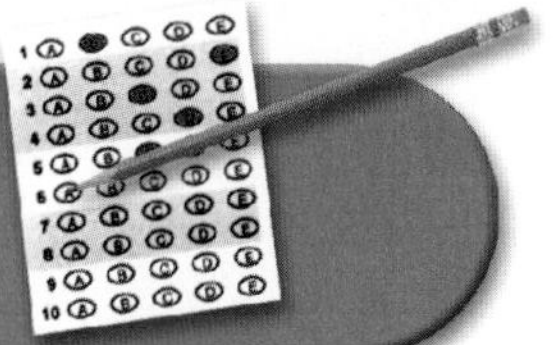

Standardized Test Prep

Multiple Choice

For Exercises 1–10, choose the correct letter.

1. For which function is 5 a zero?
A. $y = (x - 5)^2$ **B.** $y = (x + 5)^2$
C. $y = (x - 1)^2 + 5$ **D.** $y = (x + 1)^2 - 5$

2. The graph of which line is perpendicular to the graph of $y = 2x + 1$?
F. $y = \frac{1}{2}x + 7$ **G.** $x + 2y = 4$
H. $y = -2x - 5$ **I.** $x - 2y = 10$

3. What is the equation of the function $y = x^2$ translated 3 units up and 4 units left?
A. $y = (x - 3)^2 - 4$ **B.** $y = (x + 4)^2 + 3$
C. $y = (x - 4)^2 + 3$ **D.** $y = (x + 3)^2 - 4$

4. What is the axis of symmetry of the graph of a quadratic function with vertex at $(5, -1)$?
F. $x = 5$ **G.** $x = -5$
H. $y = -1$ **I.** $y = 1$

5. What is the solution of the matrix equation?

$$\begin{bmatrix} 1 & 0 & 2 \\ 3 & 1 & 1 \\ -5 & 4 & 0 \end{bmatrix} X = \begin{bmatrix} 0 & -1 & 20 \\ -2 & 2 & 27 \\ 22 & -5 & -22 \end{bmatrix}$$

A. $\begin{bmatrix} 1 & 3 & -2 \\ -1 & 0 & 1 \\ 7 & 2 & 6 \end{bmatrix}$ **B.** $\begin{bmatrix} -2 & 1 & 6 \\ 3 & 0 & 2 \\ 1 & -1 & 7 \end{bmatrix}$

C. $\begin{bmatrix} -2 & 3 & 1 \\ 1 & 0 & 1 \\ 6 & 2 & 7 \end{bmatrix}$ **D.** $\begin{bmatrix} -2 & 0 & 7 \\ 3 & 1 & -1 \\ 1 & 2 & 6 \end{bmatrix}$

6. Which relation is NOT a function?
F. $y = 3\sqrt{x} - 1$ **G.** $y = |x - 7|$
H. $y = \pm 3x$ **I.** $y = 1 - x^3$

7. Which is a factor of $x^4 + 2x^3 - 3x^2 - 4x + 4$?
I. $x + 2$ **II.** $x - 1$ **III.** $x + 1$
A. I only **B.** II only
C. I and II **D.** II and III

8. Which ordered pair is a solution of this system?

$$\begin{cases} y \leq 2x + 3 \\ y > |x + 1| \\ y < -x + 4 \end{cases}$$

I. $(0, 2)$ **II.** $(1, -3)$ **III.** $(-1, 4)$
F. II and III **G.** II only
H. I and II **I.** I only

9. At which point is the cost function $C = 3x + y$ minimized for the restrictions $x + y \geq 1$, $x \geq 0$, and $y \geq 0$?
A. $(3, 1)$ **B.** $(1, 0)$ **C.** $(0, 1)$ **D.** $(0, 0)$

10. What are the solutions of $x^3 + 4x^2 + x - 6 = 0$?
F. $-1, -2, 3$ **G.** $-1, 2, -3$
H. $1, -2, -3$ **I.** $-1, 2, 3$

Quantitative Comparison

Compare the boxed quantity in Column A with the boxed quantity in Column B. Choose the best answer.

A. The quantity in Column A is greater.
B. The quantity in Column B is greater.
C. The two quantities are equal.
D. The relationship cannot be determined from the information given.

	Column A	Column B
11.	${}_8C_2$	${}_8P_2$
12.	$[3 - (2 - x)]$	$1 + x$
13.	sum of the roots of $x^2 + 4x + 3 = 0$	degree of $2x^4 - 3x^2$

Gridded Response

14. Find 7!.

15. Find ${}_3P_2 - {}_3C_2$.

16. What is the coefficient of a^2b^3 in the expansion of $(a + b)^5$?

Short Response

17. An employer is selecting 4 out of 30 workers as employees of the month.
a. Does this situation involve a combination or a permutation? Explain.
b. How many different selections are possible?

Extended Response

18. **Open-Ended** Graph a polygon. Use matrices to find the image of the polygon after a reflection in the x-axis followed by a rotation of 90° counterclockwise. Show your work.

Real-World Snapshots

As the Ball Flies

Applying Quadratic Functions Have you ever wondered how far a soccer player can kick a ball? Ignoring wind and air resistance, you can use a linear function and a quadratic function to describe the path of a soccer ball. These functions depend on two factors that are within the soccer player's control: velocity of the kick (v_k) and angle of the kick (θ). A good high-school soccer player can kick the ball at speeds ranging from 50 to 60 mi/h. A strong professional player can kick the ball at nearly 80 mi/h.

Activity 1

a. Use the information in the diagram on the facing page to calculate the horizontal and vertical velocities of a ball kicked at a 35° angle with an initial velocity of 60 mi/h. Convert the velocities to ft/s.

b. The equations $x(t) = v_x t$ and $y(t) = v_y t + 0.5gt^2$ describe the x- and y-coordinates of a soccer ball as a function of time. (The gravitational constant g is described on the facing page.) Use the second equation to calculate the time the ball will take to complete its path.

c. Use the first equation to calculate how far the ball will travel horizontally from its original position.

The Soccer Ball

The easily recognized form of a soccer ball is due to its unique combination of pentagons and hexagons.

Men's Soccer

Jurgen Klinsmann is one of Germany's most successful strikers. He led his team to the 1996 European Championship.

In practice, air resistance and wind play a role in determining the ball's path, but these factors make the equations more complex.

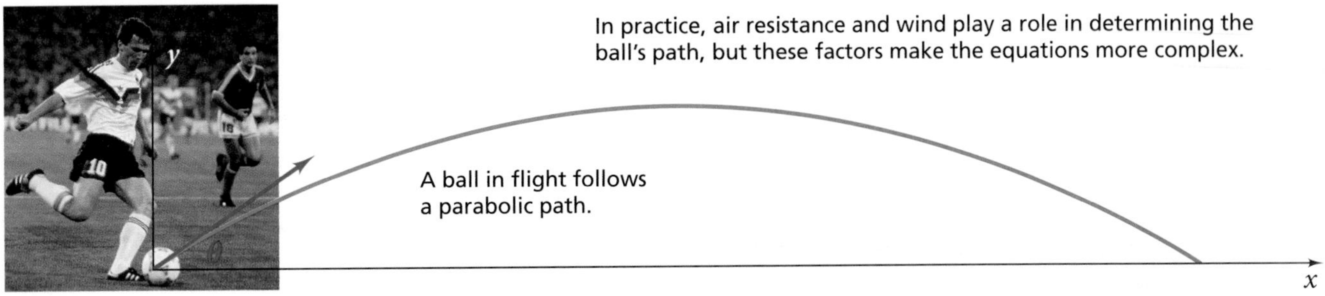

A ball in flight follows a parabolic path.

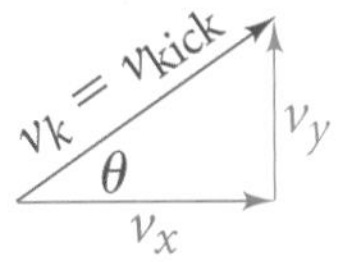

Vectors

The vectors at the left describe the initial velocity of the soccer ball as the combination of a vertical and a horizontal velocity.

$v_x = v_k \cos \theta$
$v_y = v_k \sin \theta$

Gravity

The constant g represents the acceleration of any object as a result of Earth's gravity. The value of g near the surface of Earth is about -32 ft/s^2.

Activity 2

a. Use the technique developed in Activity 1 to calculate the horizontal distance of the kick for angles in 5° increments from 5° to 90°. (You may find a spreadsheet helpful for making these calculations.)

b. Graph the horizontal distance of the kick as a function of the angle of the kick. Which angle gives the greatest distance?

Activity 3

Suppose you played soccer on the moon, where the gravitational acceleration is about one sixth of its value on Earth. What are the maximum height and maximum horizontal distance you could kick the ball by giving it an initial velocity of 48 mi/h?

The Women's World Cup

Cindy Parlow of the U.S. women's soccer team avoids a tackle in the 1999 final against China.

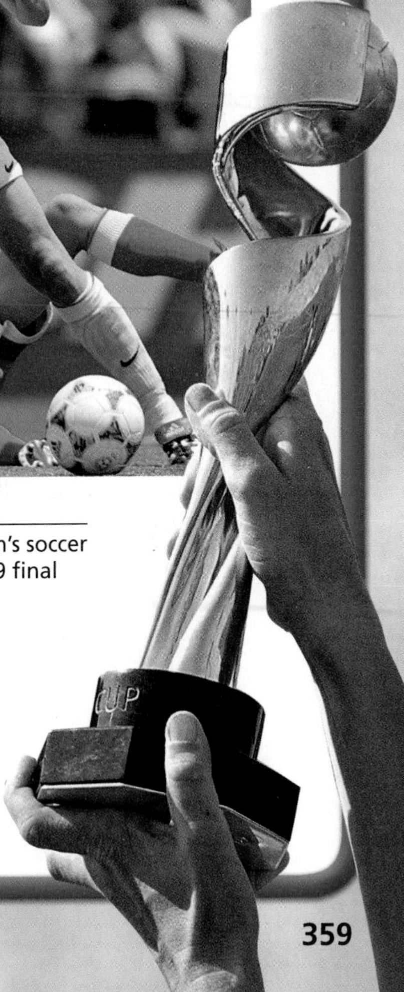

Take It to the NET For more information about soccer, go to **www.PHSchool.com**.
Web Code: age-0653

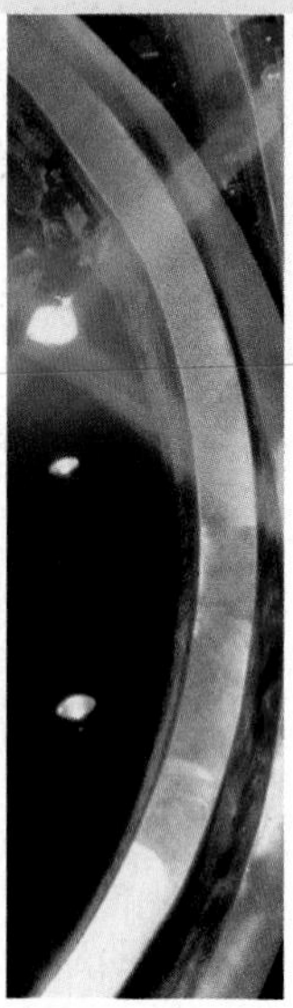

Where You've Been

- In Chapter 2, you learned about relations and functions and their domains and ranges. You also learned to draw graphs of relations and functions on the coordinate plane.
- In Chapter 5, you reviewed square roots and the multiplication and division of square roots. Then you used these skills in graphing and solving quadratic equations.
- In Chapter 6, you learned to graph polynomial functions and solve polynomial equations.

Instant self-check online and on CD-ROM

Diagnosing Readiness

(For help, go to the Lesson in green.)

Multiplying Binomials (Lesson 6-2)

Multiply.

1. $(3y - 2)(y - 4)$ **2.** $(7a + 10)(7a - 10)$ **3.** $(x - 3)(x + 6)(x + 1)$

Simplifying Exponential Expressions (Skills Handbook p. 852)

Simplify each expression. Use only positive integers.

4. $(3x^3)^2$ **5.** $(2b^{-2})(4b^5)$ **6.** $(xy^{-3})^2$ **7.** $\frac{18a^2}{3a^{-4}}$ **8.** $\frac{4ab^{-3}}{6a^2b^3}$

Solving by Factoring (Lessons 5-5 and 6-4)

Solve each equation by factoring.

9. $x^2 - 5x - 14 = 0$ **10.** $2x^2 - 11x + 15 = 0$ **11.** $3x^2 + 10x - 8 = 0$

12. $12x^2 - 12x + 3 = 0$ **13.** $8x^2 - 98 = 0$ **14.** $x^4 - 14x^2 + 49 = 0$

Finding the Domain and Range of Functions (Lesson 2-1)

Find the domain and range of each function.

15. $\{(1, 2), (2, 3), (3, 4), (4, 5)\}$ **16.** $\{(1, 2), (2, 2), (3, 2), (4, 2)\}$

17. $f(x) = -x - 1$ **18.** $f(x) = 2x^2 + 3$

Graphing Quadratic Functions (Lesson 5-3)

Graph each function.

19. $y = 2x^2 - 4$ **20.** $y = -3(x^2 + 1)$ **21.** $y = \frac{1}{2}(x - 3)^2 + 1$

22. $y = -(x + 4)^2 - 5$ **23.** $y = \frac{1}{4}(x + 2)^2 - 1$ **24.** $y = 7 - (5 - x)^2$

Radical Functions and Rational Exponents

Chapter 7

Where You're Going

- In Chapter 7, you will extend your knowledge of roots to include cube roots, fourth roots, fifth roots, and so on.
- You will learn to add, subtract, multiply, and divide radical expressions, including binomial radical expressions.
- You will solve radical equations, and graph translations of radical functions and their inverses.

Real-World Connection Applying what you learn, on page 380 you will solve a problem involving space travel.

LESSONS

Key Vocabulary

Algebra 1 Review

Properties of Exponents

For Use With Lesson 7-1

Exponents are used to indicate powers. Their properties are listed below. Assume throughout your work that no denominator is equal to zero and that m and n are positive integers.

- $a^0 = 1, a \neq 0$
- $a^{-n} = \frac{1}{a^n}$
- $a^m \cdot a^n = a^{m+n}$
- $\frac{a^m}{a^n} = a^{m-n}$
- $(ab)^n = a^n b^n$
- $\left(\frac{a}{b}\right)^n = \frac{a^n}{b^n}$
- $(a^m)^n = a^{mn}$

EXAMPLE

Simplify and rewrite each expression using only positive exponents.

a. $(7a^2)(-2a^{-5})$

$$(7a^2)(-2a^{-5}) = 7(-2)a^{2+(-5)} = -14a^{-3} = \frac{-14}{a^3}, \text{ or } -\frac{14}{a^3}$$

b. $(-2x^{-1}y^2)^3$

$$(-2x^{-1}y^2)^3 = (-2)^3(x^{-1})^3(y^2)^3 = -8x^{-3}y^6 = \frac{-8y^6}{x^3}, \text{ or } -\frac{8y^6}{x^3}$$

c. $\frac{2ab^5c^2}{a^3bc^2}$

$$\frac{2ab^5c^2}{a^3bc^2} = 2a^{1-3}b^{5-1}c^{2-2} = 2a^{-2}b^4c^0 = \frac{2b^4}{a^2}$$

EXERCISES

Simplify each expression. Use only positive exponents.

1. $(3a^2)(4a^6)$
2. $(-4x^2)(-2x^{-2})$
3. $(4x^3y^5)^2$
4. $(2x^{-5}y^4)^3$
5. $\frac{8a^5}{2a^2}$
6. $\frac{6x^7y^5}{3x^{-1}}$
7. $\frac{(4x^2)^0}{2xy^5}$
8. $\left(\frac{3x^2}{2}\right)^2$
9. $(-6m^2n^2)(3mn)$
10. $(3x^4y^5)^{-3}$
11. $\frac{(2r^{-1}s^2t^0)^{-2}}{2rs}$
12. $x^5(2x)^3$
13. $\frac{x^4x^{-2}}{x^{-5}}$
14. $\frac{(12x^2y^6)^2}{8x^4y^7}$
15. $(4p^2q)(p^2q^3)$
16. $\frac{4x^3}{2x}$
17. $(p^2)^{-2}$
18. $\frac{-15x^4}{3x}$
19. $\frac{r^2s^3t^4}{r^2s^4t^{-4}}$
20. $\frac{xy^2}{2} \cdot \frac{6x}{y^2}$
21. $(s^2t)^3(st)$
22. $(3x^{-3}y^{-2})^{-2}$
23. $(h^4k^5)^0$
24. $\frac{s^2t^3}{r} \cdot \frac{sr^3}{t}$

25. Writing Write a numerical example for each property of exponents shown above. Which properties could be called distributive properties for exponents? Explain.

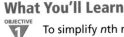

7-1 Roots and Radical Expressions

North Carolina Objectives

1.01 Simplify and perform operations with rational exponents and logarithms (common and natural) to solve problems.

Lesson Preview

What You'll Learn

OBJECTIVE 1 To simplify *n*th roots

. . . And Why

To solve a packaging problem, as in Example 4

Check Skills You'll Need

(For help, go to Lesson 5-4.)

Write each number as a square of a number.

1. 25 **2.** 0.09 **3.** $\frac{4}{49}$

Write each expression as a square of an expression.

4. x^{10} **5.** x^4y^2 **6.** $169x^6y^{12}$

New Vocabulary • *n*th root • radicand • index • principal root

Interactive lesson includes instant self-check, tutorials, and activities.

OBJECTIVE 1

Roots and Radical Expressions

Since $5^2 = 25$, 5 is a square root of 25.

Since $5^3 = 125$, 5 is a cube root of 125.

Since $5^4 = 625$, 5 is a fourth root of 625.

Since $5^5 = 3125$, 5 is a fifth root of 3125.

This pattern leads to the definition of *n*th root.

Key Concepts

Definition ***n*th Root**

For any real numbers a and b, and any positive integer n, if $a^n = b$, then a is an ***n*th root** of b.

Reading Math

The term *root* is used in two ways in mathematics:
- root of an equation
- root of a number.

The roots of the equation $y^4 = 16$ are the fourth roots of 16.

Since $2^4 = 16$ and $(-2)^4 = 16$, both 2 and -2 are fourth roots of 16.

Since there is no real number x such that $x^4 = -16$, -16 has no real fourth root.

Since -5 is the only real number whose cube is -125, -5 is the only real cube root of -125.

Some roots, such as the square roots of 10, are irrational numbers. Nevertheless, there is a positive square root and a negative square root of 10.

Here is a summary of the number of possible real roots of a real number.

Type of Number	Number of Real *n*th Roots When *n* Is Even	Number of Real *n*th Roots When *n* Is Odd
positive	2	1
0	1	1
negative	none	1

1 EXAMPLE Finding All Real Roots

Find all the real roots.

a. the cube roots of 0.008, -1000, and $\frac{1}{27}$

Since $(0.2)^3 = 0.008$, 0.2 is the cube root of 0.008.
Since $(-10)^3 = -1000$, -10 is the cube root of -1000.
Since $\left(\frac{1}{3}\right)^3 = \frac{1}{27}$, $\frac{1}{3}$ is the cube root of $\frac{1}{27}$.

b. the fourth roots of 1, -0.0001, and $\frac{16}{81}$

Since $1^4 = 1$ and $(-1)^4 = 1$, 1 and -1 are fourth roots of 1.
There is no real number with a fourth power of -0.0001.
Since $\left(\frac{2}{3}\right)^4 = \frac{16}{81}$ and $\left(-\frac{2}{3}\right)^4 = \frac{16}{81}$, $\frac{2}{3}$ and $-\frac{2}{3}$ are fourth roots of $\frac{16}{81}$.

Check Understanding 1 **a.** Find all the real fifth roots of 0, -1, and 32.
b. Find all the real square roots of 0.0001, -1, and $\frac{36}{121}$.

Reading Math

Like the word *radish*, *radical* comes from the Latin word for root.

A radical sign is used to indicate a root. The number under the radical sign is the **radicand.** The **index** gives the degree of the root.

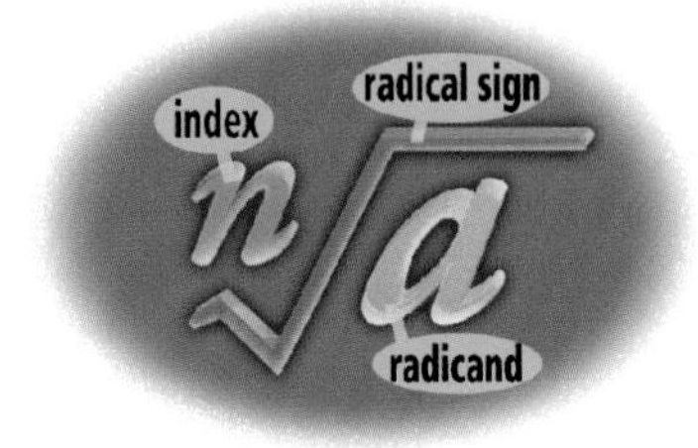

When a number has two real roots, the positive root is called the **principal root** and the radical sign indicates the principal root. The principal fourth root of 16 is written as $\sqrt[4]{16}$.

The principal fourth root of 16 is 2 because $\sqrt[4]{16}$ equals $\sqrt[4]{2^4}$. The other fourth root of 16 is written as $-\sqrt[4]{16}$, which equals -2.

2 EXAMPLE Finding Roots

Find each real-number root.

a. $\sqrt[3]{-8}$

$\sqrt[3]{-8} = \sqrt[3]{(-2)^3}$ **Rewrite −8 as the third power of a number.**

$= -2$ **Simplify.**

b. $\sqrt{-100}$

There is no real number whose square is -100.

Check Understanding 2 Find each real-number root.

a. $\sqrt[3]{-27}$ **b.** $\sqrt[4]{81}$ **c.** $\sqrt{49}$

Notice that when $x = 5$, $\sqrt{x^2} = \sqrt{5^2} = \sqrt{25} = 5 = x$,
and when $x = -5$, $\sqrt{x^2} = \sqrt{(-5)^2} = \sqrt{25} = 5 \neq x$.

Key Concepts

Property	*n*th Root of a^n, $a < 0$
For any negative real number a, $\sqrt[n]{a^n} = \lvert a \rvert$ when n is even.	

3 EXAMPLE Simplifying Radical Expressions

Need Help?

$(a^m)^n = a^{mn}$

Simplify each radical expression.

a. $\sqrt{4x^6}$

$\sqrt{4x^6} = \sqrt{2^2(x^3)^2} = \sqrt{(2x^3)^2} = 2|x^3|$

Absolute value symbols ensure that the root is positive when x is negative.

b. $\sqrt[3]{a^3b^6}$

$\sqrt[3]{a^3b^6} = \sqrt[3]{a^3(b^2)^3} = \sqrt[3]{(ab^2)^3} = ab^2$

Absolute value symbols must not be used here. If a is negative, then the radicand is negative and the root must also be negative.

c. $\sqrt[4]{x^4y^8}$

$\sqrt[4]{x^4y^8} = \sqrt[4]{x^4(y^2)^4} = \sqrt[4]{(xy^2)^4} = |x|y^2$

Absolute value symbols ensure that the root is positive when x is negative. They are not needed for y because y^2 is never negative.

Check Understanding 3 Simplify each radical expression. Use absolute value symbols when needed.

a. $\sqrt{4x^2y^4}$ **b.** $\sqrt[3]{-27c^6}$ **c.** $\sqrt[4]{x^8y^{12}}$

4 EXAMPLE Real-World Connection

Packaging A citrus grower wants to ship a select grade of oranges that weigh from 8 to 9 ounces in gift cartons. Each carton will hold three dozen oranges, in 3 layers of 3 oranges by 4 oranges.

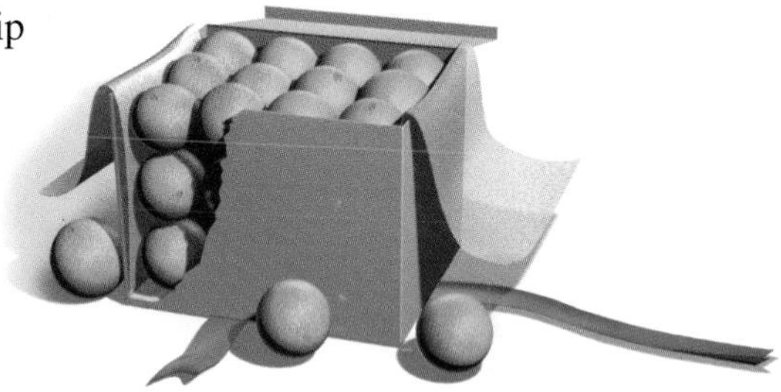

The weight of an orange is related to its diameter by the formula $w = \frac{d^3}{4}$, where d is the diameter in inches and w is the weight in ounces. Cartons can be ordered in whole-inch dimensions. What size cartons should the grower order?

Graphing Calculator Hint

Use the $\sqrt[3]{\ }$ feature in the MATH menu to find cube roots. For other roots, type the index first and then select the $\sqrt[x]{\ }$ feature.

Find the diameters of the oranges.

$8 \le w \le 9$	**Write an inequality.**
$8 \le \frac{d^3}{4} \le 9$	**Substitute for w in terms of d.**
$32 \le d^3 \le 36$	**Multiply by 4.**
$\sqrt[3]{32} \le \sqrt[3]{d^3} \le \sqrt[3]{36}$	**Take cube roots.**
$3.17 \le d \le 3.30$	**The diameters range from 3.17 in. to 3.30 in.**

The length of a row of 4 of the largest oranges is 4(3.30 in.) = 13.2 in. The length of a row of 3 of the largest oranges is 3(3.30 in.) = 9.90 in. The grower should order cartons that are 14 in. long by 10 in. wide by 10 in. high to accommodate three dozen of the largest oranges.

Check Understanding 4 Use the formula in Example 4 to find the diameter of each orange.

a. 3 oz **b.** 5.5 oz **c.** 6.25 oz

EXERCISES

For more practice, see *Extra Practice.*

Practice and Problem Solving

A Practice by Example

Example 1 (page 364)

Find all the real square roots of each number.

1. 225 **2.** 0.0049 **3.** $-\frac{1}{121}$ **4.** $\frac{64}{169}$

Find all the real cube roots of each number.

5. -64 **6.** 0.125 **7.** $-\frac{27}{216}$ **8.** 0.000343

Find all the real fourth roots of each number.

9. 16 **10.** -16 **11.** 0.0081 **12.** $\frac{10,000}{81}$

Example 2 (page 364)

Find each real-number root.

13. $\sqrt{36}$ **14.** $-\sqrt{36}$ **15.** $\sqrt{-36}$ **16.** $\sqrt{0.36}$

17. $-\sqrt[3]{64}$ **18.** $\sqrt[3]{-64}$ **19.** $-\sqrt[4]{81}$ **20.** $\sqrt[4]{-81}$

Example 3 (page 365)

Simplify each radical expression. Use absolute value symbols when needed.

21. $\sqrt{16x^2}$ **22.** $\sqrt{0.25x^6}$ **23.** $\sqrt{x^8y^{18}}$ **24.** $\sqrt{64b^{48}}$

25. $\sqrt[3]{-64a^3}$ **26.** $\sqrt[3]{27y^6}$ **27.** $\sqrt[4]{x^8y^{12}}$ **28.** $\sqrt[5]{32y^{10}}$

Example 4 (page 365)

Geometry The formula for the volume of a sphere is $V = \frac{4}{3}\pi r^3$. Find the radius to the nearest hundredth of a sphere with each volume.

29. 10 in.^{3} **30.** 20 ft^3 **31.** 0.45 cm^3 **32.** 0.002 mm^3

B Apply Your Skills

Find the two real-number solutions of each equation.

33. $x^2 = 100$ **34.** $x^4 = 1$ **35.** $x^2 = 0.25$ **36.** $x^4 = \frac{16}{81}$

37. Arrange the numbers $\sqrt[3]{-64}$, $-\sqrt[3]{-64}$, $\sqrt{64}$, and $\sqrt[6]{64}$ in order from least to greatest.

Real-World Connection

The waterline of a boat is the intersection of the boat with the surface of the water when the boat is at rest.

38. Boat Building Boat builders share an old rule of thumb for sailboats. The maximum speed K in knots is 1.35 times the square root of the length L in feet of the boat's waterline.

a. A customer is planning to order a sailboat with a maximum speed of 8 knots. How long should the waterline be?

b. How much longer would the waterline have to be to achieve a maximum speed of 10 knots?

Simplify each radical expression. Use absolute value symbols when needed.

39. $\sqrt[3]{0.125}$ **40.** $\sqrt[3]{\frac{8}{216}}$ **41.** $\sqrt[4]{0.0016}$ **42.** $\sqrt[4]{\frac{1}{256}}$

43. $\sqrt[4]{16c^4}$ **44.** $\sqrt[3]{81x^3y^6}$ **45.** $\sqrt{144x^3y^4z^5}$ **46.** $\sqrt[5]{y^{20}}$

47. $\sqrt[5]{-y^{20}}$ **48.** $\sqrt[5]{k^{15}}$ **49.** $\sqrt[5]{-k^{15}}$ **50.** $\sqrt{(x+3)^2}$

51. $\sqrt{(x+1)^4}$ **52.** $\sqrt[2n]{x^{2n}}$ **53.** $\sqrt[2n]{x^{4n}}$ **54.** $\sqrt[2n]{x^{6n}}$

55. Open-Ended Find three radical expressions that simplify to $-2x^2$.

56. **Critical Thinking** For what positive integers n is each of the statements true?
a. If $x^n = b$, then x is an nth root of b. **b.** If $x^n = b$, then $x = \sqrt[n]{b}$.

57. **Writing** Is 10 a first root of 10? Explain.

Tell whether each equation is true for *all, some,* or *no values* of the variable. Explain your answers.

58. $\sqrt{x^4} = x^2$ **59.** $\sqrt{x^6} = x^3$ **60.** $\sqrt[3]{x^8} = x^2$ **61.** $\sqrt[3]{x^3} = |x|$

C Challenge

Simplify each rational expression. *n* is an even number.

62. $\sqrt[n]{m^n}$ **63.** $\sqrt[n]{m^{2n}}$ **64.** $\sqrt[n]{m^{3n}}$ **65.** $\sqrt[n]{m^{4n}}$

Simplify each rational expression. *n* is an odd number.

66. $\sqrt[n]{m^n}$ **67.** $\sqrt[n]{m^{2n}}$ **68.** $\sqrt[n]{m^{3n}}$ **69.** $\sqrt[n]{m^{4n}}$

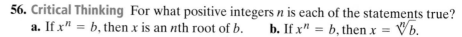

Standardized Test Prep

Multiple Choice

70. Which equation has more than one real-number solution?
A. $x^2 = 0$ B. $x^2 = 1$ C. $x^2 = -1$ D. $x^3 = -1$

71. Which number is greatest?
F. $\sqrt{0.5}$ G. $\sqrt[3]{0.5}$ H. $\sqrt[4]{0.5}$ I. $\sqrt[5]{0.5}$

72. Which statement is NOT true?
A. $-3 = -\sqrt{9}$ B. $-3 = -\sqrt{-9}$
C. $-3 = \sqrt[3]{-27}$ D. $-3 = -\sqrt[4]{81}$

Take It to the NET
Online lesson quiz at
www.PHSchool.com
Web Code: aga-0701

73. Absolute value symbols are needed when you simplify some of these expressions. Which ones are they?
I. $\sqrt[3]{-x^3y^6}$ II. $\sqrt{x^2y^4}$ III. $\sqrt[4]{x^8y^{12}}$ IV. $\sqrt{x^4y^6}$
F. II and III only G. II and IV only
H. II, III and IV only I. I, II, III and IV

Short Response

74. For what values of x and y does $\sqrt{x^2y^4}$ equal $\sqrt[3]{x^3y^6}$? Explain your answer.

Mixed Review

Lesson 6-8 **Expand each binomial.**

75. $(x + y)^5$ **76.** $(2 - 3y)^4$ **77.** $(3x - 5)^6$ **78.** $(2a - b)^7$

Lesson 6-2 **Write each function in factored form. Check by multiplying.**

79. $y = 4x^3 - 49x$ **80.** $y = 81x^2 + 36x + 4$

81. $y = 4x^3 + 8x^2 + 4x$ **82.** $y = 12x^3 + 14x^2 + 2x$

Lesson 5-3 **Rewrite each equation in vertex form.**

83. $y = 3x^2 - 7$ **84.** $y = -2x^2 + x - 10$ **85.** $y = \frac{x^2}{4} + 2x - 1$

7-2 Multiplying and Dividing Radical Expressions

North Carolina Objectives

1.01 Simplify and perform operations with rational exponents and logarithms (common and natural) to solve problems.

Lesson Preview

What You'll Learn

OBJECTIVE 1 To multiply radical expressions

OBJECTIVE 2 To divide radical expressions

. . . Any Why

To transform a famous formula, as in Example 6

Check Skills You'll Need

(For help, go to page 362.)

Find each missing factor.

1. $150 = 5^2(\blacksquare)$

2. $54 = (\blacksquare)^3(2)$

3. $48 = 4^2(\blacksquare)$

4. $x^5 = (\blacksquare)^2(x)$

5. $3a^3b^4 = (\blacksquare)^3(3b)$

6. $75a^7b^8 = (\blacksquare)^2(3a)$

New Vocabulary • rationalize the denominator

Interactive lesson includes instant self-check, tutorials, and activities.

OBJECTIVE 1 Multiplying Radical Expressions

To multiply radicals consider the following.

$\sqrt{16} \cdot \sqrt{9} = 4 \cdot 3 = 12$ and $\sqrt{16 \cdot 9} = \sqrt{144} = 12$.

So $\sqrt{16} \cdot \sqrt{9} = \sqrt{16 \cdot 9}$.

$\sqrt[3]{-8} \cdot \sqrt[3]{27} = -2 \cdot 3 = -6$ and $\sqrt[3]{-8 \cdot 27} = \sqrt[3]{-216} = -6$.

So $\sqrt[3]{-8} \cdot \sqrt[3]{27} = \sqrt[3]{-8 \cdot 27}$.

In general, the product of the principal nth roots of two numbers equals the principal nth root of their product.

Key Concepts

Property **Multiplying Radical Expressions**

If $\sqrt[n]{a}$ and $\sqrt[n]{b}$ are real numbers, then $\sqrt[n]{a} \cdot \sqrt[n]{b} = \sqrt[n]{ab}$.

1 EXAMPLE Multiplying Radicals

Multiply. Simplify if possible.

a. $\sqrt{2} \cdot \sqrt{8}$

$\sqrt{2} \cdot \sqrt{8} = \sqrt{2 \cdot 8} = \sqrt{16} = 4$

b. $\sqrt[3]{-5} \cdot \sqrt[3]{25}$

$\sqrt[3]{-5} \cdot \sqrt[3]{25} = \sqrt[3]{-125} = \sqrt[3]{(-5)^3} = -5$

c. $\sqrt{-2} \cdot \sqrt{8}$

The property for multiplying radicals does *not* apply. $\sqrt{-2}$ is not a real number.

Check Understanding

1 Multiply. Simplify if possible.

a. $\sqrt{3} \cdot \sqrt{12}$ **b.** $\sqrt[3]{3} \cdot \sqrt[3]{-9}$ **c.** $\sqrt[4]{4} \cdot \sqrt[4]{-4}$

$2\sqrt[3]{3}$ is considered to be a simplified form of $\sqrt[3]{24}$. You can use the property for multiplying radical expressions to simplify some radical expressions.

Reading Math

The phrase *all variables are positive* is a short way of saying that the domain of the variables is the set of positive numbers.

2 EXAMPLE Simplifying Radical Expressions

Simplify each expression. Assume that all variables are positive. Then absolute value symbols are never needed in the simplified expression.

a. $\sqrt{72x^3}$

$\sqrt{72x^3}$	$= \sqrt{6^2 \cdot 2 \cdot x^2 \cdot x}$	**Factor into perfect squares.**
	$= \sqrt{6^2x^2} \cdot \sqrt{2x}$	$\sqrt[n]{a} \cdot \sqrt[n]{b} = \sqrt[n]{ab}$
	$= 6x\sqrt{2x}$	**Simplify.**

b. $\sqrt[3]{80n^5}$

$\sqrt[3]{80n^5}$	$= \sqrt[3]{2^3 \cdot 10 \cdot n^3 \cdot n^2}$	**Factor into perfect cubes.**
	$= \sqrt[3]{2^3n^3} \cdot \sqrt[3]{10n^2}$	$\sqrt[n]{a} \cdot \sqrt[n]{b} = \sqrt[n]{ab}$
	$= 2n\sqrt[3]{10n^2}$	**Simplify.**

Check Understanding 2 Simplify $\sqrt{50x^4}$ and $\sqrt[3]{18x^4}$. Assume that x is positive.

Simplify the products of radicals as much as possible.

3 EXAMPLE Multiplying Radical Expressions

Multiply and simplify $\sqrt[3]{54x^2y^3} \cdot \sqrt[3]{5x^3y^4}$. Assume that all variables are positive.

$\sqrt[3]{54x^2y^3} \cdot \sqrt[3]{5x^3y^4}$	$= \sqrt[3]{54x^2y^3 \cdot 5x^3y^4}$	$\sqrt[n]{a} \cdot \sqrt[n]{b} = \sqrt[n]{ab}$
	$= \sqrt[3]{3^3x^3(y^2)^3 \cdot 10x^2y}$	**Factor into perfect cubes.**
	$= \sqrt[3]{3^3x^3(y^2)^3} \cdot \sqrt[3]{10x^2y}$	$\sqrt[n]{a} \cdot \sqrt[n]{b} = \sqrt[n]{ab}$
	$= 3xy^2\sqrt[3]{10x^2y}$	**Simplify.**

Check Understanding 3 Multiply and simplify $3\sqrt{7x^3} \cdot 2\sqrt{21x^3y^2}$. Assume that all variables are positive.

OBJECTIVE

2 Dividing Radical Expressions

To divide radicals, consider the following.

$\frac{\sqrt{36}}{\sqrt{25}} = \frac{6}{5}$ and $\sqrt{\frac{36}{25}} = \sqrt{\left(\frac{6}{5}\right)^2} = \frac{6}{5}$. So $\frac{\sqrt{36}}{\sqrt{25}} = \sqrt{\frac{36}{25}}$.

In general, the quotient of the principal nth roots of two numbers equals the principal nth root of their quotient.

Key Concepts

Property	Dividing Radical Expressions
If $\sqrt[n]{a}$ and $\sqrt[n]{b}$ are real numbers and $b \neq 0$, then $\frac{\sqrt[n]{a}}{\sqrt[n]{b}} = \sqrt[n]{\frac{a}{b}}$.	

4 EXAMPLE Dividing Radicals

Divide and simplify. Assume that all variables are positive.

a. $\dfrac{\sqrt[3]{32}}{\sqrt[3]{-4}}$

$$\frac{\sqrt[3]{32}}{\sqrt[3]{-4}} = \sqrt[3]{\frac{32}{-4}} = \sqrt[3]{-8} = -2$$

b. $\dfrac{\sqrt[3]{162x^5}}{\sqrt[3]{3x^2}}$

$$\frac{\sqrt[3]{162x^5}}{\sqrt[3]{3x^2}} = \sqrt[3]{\frac{162x^5}{3x^2}} = \sqrt[3]{54x^3} = \sqrt[3]{3^3x^3 \cdot 2} = \sqrt[3]{3^3x^3} \cdot \sqrt[3]{2} = 3x\sqrt[3]{2}$$

Check Understanding **4** Divide and simplify. Assume that all variables are positive.

a. $\dfrac{\sqrt{243}}{\sqrt{27}}$ **b.** $\dfrac{\sqrt{12x^4}}{\sqrt{3x}}$ **c.** $\dfrac{\sqrt[4]{1024x^{15}}}{\sqrt[4]{4x}}$

To **rationalize the denominator** of an expression, rewrite it so there are no radicals in any denominator and no denominators in any radical.

Rationalizing the denominator of a numerical expression makes it easier to calculate its decimal approximation. For example, $\frac{1}{\sqrt{2}} = \frac{\sqrt{2}}{2}$ and it is easier to divide by 2 than by $\sqrt{2}$.

5 EXAMPLE Rationalizing the Denominator

Rationalize the denominator of each expression. Assume that all variables are positive.

a. $\dfrac{\sqrt{2}}{\sqrt{3}}$

Method 1

$$\frac{\sqrt{2}}{\sqrt{3}} = \sqrt{\frac{2}{3}} = \sqrt{\frac{2 \cdot 3}{3 \cdot 3}} = \sqrt{\frac{6}{3^2}} = \frac{\sqrt{6}}{\sqrt{3^2}} = \frac{\sqrt{6}}{3}$$

Rewrite as a square root of a fraction. Then make the denominator a perfect square.

Method 2

$$\frac{\sqrt{2}}{\sqrt{3}} = \frac{\sqrt{2} \cdot \sqrt{3}}{\sqrt{3} \cdot \sqrt{3}} = \frac{\sqrt{6}}{3}$$

Multiply the numerator and denominator by $\sqrt{3}$ so the denominator becomes a whole number.

b. $\dfrac{\sqrt{x^3}}{\sqrt{5xy}}$

$$\frac{\sqrt{x^3}}{\sqrt{5xy}} = \frac{\sqrt{x^3} \cdot \sqrt{5xy}}{\sqrt{5xy} \cdot \sqrt{5xy}} = \frac{\sqrt{5x^4y}}{5xy} = \frac{x^2\sqrt{5y}}{5xy} = \frac{x\sqrt{5y}}{5y}$$

c. $\sqrt[3]{\dfrac{2}{3x}}$

$$\sqrt[3]{\frac{2}{3x}} = \sqrt[3]{\frac{2 \cdot 3^2x^2}{3x \cdot 3^2x^2}} = \sqrt[3]{\frac{18x^2}{3^3x^3}} = \frac{\sqrt[3]{18x^2}}{3x}$$

Rewrite the fraction so the denominator is a perfect cube.

Check Understanding **5** Rationalize the denominator of each expression. Assume that the variables are positive.

a. $\sqrt{\dfrac{7}{5}}$ **b.** $\dfrac{\sqrt{2x^3}}{\sqrt{10xy}}$ **c.** $\dfrac{\sqrt[3]{4}}{\sqrt[3]{6x}}$

6 EXAMPLE Real-World Connection

Einstein's famous formula $E = mc^2$ relates energy E, mass m, and the speed of light c. Express c in terms of E and m and rationalize the denominator.

$E = mc^2$

$c^2 = \frac{E}{m}$

$c = \sqrt{\frac{E}{m}} = \sqrt{\frac{Em}{m^2}} = \frac{\sqrt{Em}}{\sqrt{m^2}} = \frac{\sqrt{Em}}{m}$

Check Understanding **6** The formula $a = \frac{d}{t^2}$ relates the acceleration a of a moving object to the distance d it moves in the time t. Solve the formula for t and rationalize the denominator.

EXERCISES

For more practice, see *Extra Practice*.

Practice and Problem Solving

A Practice by Example

Example 1 (page 368)

Multiply, if possible. Then simplify.

1. $\sqrt{8} \cdot \sqrt{32}$ **2.** $\sqrt[3]{4} \cdot \sqrt[3]{16}$ **3.** $\sqrt[3]{9} \cdot \sqrt[3]{-81}$ **4.** $\sqrt[4]{8} \cdot \sqrt[4]{32}$

5. $\sqrt{-5} \cdot \sqrt{5}$ **6.** $\sqrt[3]{-5} \cdot \sqrt[3]{-25}$ **7.** $\sqrt[3]{9} \cdot \sqrt[3]{-24}$ **8.** $\sqrt[3]{-12} \cdot \sqrt[3]{-18}$

Example 2 (page 369)

Simplify. Assume that all variables are positive.

9. $\sqrt{20x^3}$ **10.** $\sqrt[3]{81x^2}$ **11.** $\sqrt{50x^5}$ **12.** $\sqrt[3]{32a^5}$

13. $\sqrt[3]{54y^{10}}$ **14.** $\sqrt{200a^6b^7}$ **15.** $\sqrt[3]{-250x^6y^5}$ **16.** $\sqrt[4]{64x^3y^6}$

Example 3 (page 369)

Multiply and simplify. Assume that all variables are positive.

17. $\sqrt[3]{6} \cdot \sqrt[3]{16}$ **18.** $\sqrt{8y^5} \cdot \sqrt{40y^2}$

19. $\sqrt{7x^5} \cdot \sqrt{42xy^9}$ **20.** $4\sqrt{2x} \cdot 5\sqrt{6xy^2}$

21. $3\sqrt[3]{5y^3} \cdot 2\sqrt[3]{50y^4}$ **22.** $-\sqrt[3]{2x^2y^2} \cdot 2\sqrt[3]{15x^5y}$

Example 4 (page 370)

Divide and simplify. Assume that all variables are positive.

23. $\frac{\sqrt{500}}{\sqrt{5}}$ **24.** $\frac{\sqrt{48x^3}}{\sqrt{3xy^2}}$ **25.** $\frac{\sqrt{56x^5y^5}}{\sqrt{7xy}}$ **26.** $\frac{\sqrt[3]{250x^7y^3}}{\sqrt[3]{2x^2y}}$

Example 5 (page 370)

Rationalize the denominator of each expression. Assume that all variables are positive.

27. $\frac{\sqrt{x}}{\sqrt{2}}$ **28.** $\frac{\sqrt{5}}{\sqrt{8x}}$ **29.** $\frac{\sqrt[3]{x}}{\sqrt[3]{2}}$ **30.** $\sqrt[3]{\frac{5}{3x}}$

31. $\frac{\sqrt[4]{2}}{\sqrt[4]{5}}$ **32.** $\frac{15\sqrt{60x^5}}{3\sqrt{12x}}$ **33.** $\frac{\sqrt{3xy^2}}{\sqrt{5xy^3}}$ **34.** $\frac{\sqrt{5x^4y}}{\sqrt{2x^2y^3}}$

Example 6 (page 371)

35. Physics The formula $F = \frac{Gm_1m_2}{r^2}$ relates the gravitational force F between an object of mass m_1 and an object of mass m_2 separated by distance r. G is a constant known as the constant of gravitation. Solve the formula for r. Rationalize the denominator.

B Apply Your Skills

36. a. Simplify $\frac{\sqrt{2} + \sqrt{3}}{\sqrt{75}}$ by multiplying the numerator and denominator by $\sqrt{75}$.
    b. Simplify the expression in (a) by multiplying by $\sqrt{3}$ instead of $\sqrt{75}$.
    c. Explain how you would simplify $\frac{\sqrt{2} + \sqrt{3}}{\sqrt{98}}$.

Simplify each expression. Rationalize all denominators. Assume that all variables are positive.

37. $\sqrt{5} \cdot \sqrt{40}$

38. $\sqrt[3]{4} \cdot \sqrt[3]{80}$

39. $\sqrt{x^5y^5} \cdot 3\sqrt{2x^7y^6}$

40. $5\sqrt{2xy^6} \cdot 2\sqrt{2x^3y}$

41. $\sqrt{2}(\sqrt{50} + 7)$

42. $3(5 + \sqrt{21})$

43. $\sqrt{5}(\sqrt{5} + \sqrt{15})$

44. $\sqrt[3]{2x} \cdot \sqrt[3]{4} \cdot \sqrt[3]{2x^2}$

45. $\sqrt[3]{3x^2} \cdot \sqrt[3]{x^2} \cdot \sqrt[3]{9x^3}$

46. $\frac{\sqrt{5x^4}}{\sqrt{2x^2y^3}}$

47. $\frac{5\sqrt{2}}{3\sqrt{7x}}$

48. $\frac{1}{\sqrt[3]{9x}}$

49. $\frac{10}{\sqrt[3]{5x^2}}$

50. $\frac{\sqrt[3]{14}}{\sqrt[3]{7x^2y}}$

51. $\frac{3\sqrt{11x^3y}}{-2\sqrt{12x^4y}}$

52. $-2\left(\sqrt[3]{32} + \sqrt[3]{54}\right)$

53. $\frac{3 + \sqrt{5}}{\sqrt{5}}$

54. $\frac{\sqrt{3} - \sqrt{2}}{\sqrt{8}}$

Real-World Connection

A satellite being launched from the cargo bay of the space shuttle

55. **Satellites** The circular velocity *v*, in miles per hour, of a satellite orbiting Earth is given by the formula $v = \sqrt{\frac{1.24 \times 10^{12}}{r}}$, where *r* is the distance in miles from the satellite to the center of Earth. How much greater is the velocity of a satellite orbiting at an altitude of 100 mi than one orbiting at an altitude of 200 mi? (The radius of Earth is 3950 mi.)

56. **Geometry** A rectangular shelf is $\sqrt{440}$ cm by $\sqrt{20}$ cm. Find its area.

57. **Error Analysis** Explain the error in this simplification of radical expressions.
    $\sqrt{-2} \cdot \sqrt{-8} = \sqrt{-2(-8)} = \sqrt{16} = 4$

58. **Physics** A freely falling object hit the ground in $\sqrt{18a^5}$ seconds. It fell *h* feet. Use the formula $h = 16t^2$ to find *h* in terms of *a*.

59. **Writing** Does $\sqrt{x^3} = \sqrt[3]{x^2}$ for all, some, or no values of *x*? Explain.

60. **Open-Ended** Of the equivalent expressions $\sqrt{\frac{2}{3}}$, $\frac{\sqrt{2}}{\sqrt{3}}$, and $\frac{\sqrt{6}}{3}$, which do you prefer to use for finding a decimal approximation with a calculator? Justify your reasoning.

C Challenge

Simplify each expression. Rationalize all denominators. Assume that all variables are positive.

61. $\sqrt{\sqrt{16x^4y^4}}$

62. $\sqrt[3]{\sqrt{64x^6y^{12}}}$

63. $\sqrt{\sqrt[3]{8000}}$

64. $\sqrt[3]{x^{-1}y^{-2}}$

65. $\sqrt[5]{x^{-4}y}$

66. $\sqrt[6]{\frac{y^{-3}}{x^{-4}}}$

67. **Critical Thinking** When $\sqrt{x^ay^b}$ is simplified, the result is $\frac{1}{x^cy^{3d}}$, where *c* and *d* are positive integers. Express *a* in terms of *c*, and *b* in terms of *d*.

68. **Critical Thinking** In Example 3 you saw that $\sqrt[3]{54x^2y^3} \cdot \sqrt[3]{5x^3y^4}$ simplifies to $3xy^2\sqrt[3]{10x^2y}$, if you assume that all the variables are positive. Now assume that the variables represent any real numbers. What changes must be made in the answer? Explain.

Standardized Test Prep

Multiple Choice

69. Which expression does NOT simplify to -10?

A. $-\sqrt[3]{1000}$ B. $\sqrt{25} \cdot \sqrt[3]{-8}$

C. $-\sqrt{25} \cdot \sqrt[5]{-32}$ D. $\sqrt[3]{-125} \cdot \sqrt[4]{16}$

70. How can you write $\sqrt[3]{\frac{5}{2xy}}$ with a rationalized denominator?

F. $\frac{\sqrt[3]{5}}{2xy}$ G. $\frac{\sqrt[3]{20}}{2xy}$ H. $\frac{\sqrt[3]{20x^2y^2}}{2xy}$ I. $\frac{\sqrt[3]{4x^2y^2}}{2xy}$

Take It to the NET
Online lesson quiz at **www.PHSchool.com**
Web Code: aga-0702

71. What is the simplified form of $\frac{3 - \sqrt{5}}{\sqrt{5}}$?

A. $\frac{3\sqrt{5} - 5}{5}$ B. $\frac{5\sqrt{3} - 5}{5}$

C. $\frac{3\sqrt{3} - \sqrt{15}}{5}$ D. $\frac{14 - 6\sqrt{5}}{5}$

72. To rationalize the denominator of $\sqrt[3]{\frac{2}{9}}$, by what number would you multiply the numerator and denominator of the fraction?

F. 2 G. 3 H. 6 I. 9

73. Which of the following expressions is in simplest form?

A. $\sqrt{20x^3}$ B. $\sqrt[3]{81x}$ C. $\sqrt{\frac{6}{2}}$ D. $\frac{\sqrt{2}}{5}$

Short Response

74. For what values of x is $\sqrt{x} \cdot \sqrt{-x}$ a real number? Explain.

Extended Response

75. Rationalize the denominator of $\sqrt[3]{\frac{3}{2x}}$. Explain your steps.

Mixed Review

Lesson 7-1

Simplify each radical expression. Use absolute value symbols as needed.

76. $\sqrt{121a^{90}}$

77. $-\sqrt{81c^{48}d^{64}}$

78. $\sqrt[3]{-64a^{81}}$

79. $\sqrt[5]{32y^{25}}$

80. $\sqrt{0.25x^6}$

81. $\sqrt[7]{x^{14}y^{35}}$

82. $\sqrt[4]{16x^{36}y^{96}}$

83. $\sqrt{0.0064x^{40}}$

Lesson 6-3

Divide. Tell whether each divisor is a factor of the dividend.

84. $(y^3 - 64) \div (y + 4)$

85. $(x^3 + 27) \div (x + 3)$

86. $(6a^3 + a^2 - a + 4) \div (2a + 1)$

87. $(2x^4 - 3x^3 - 4x + 10) \div (x - 2)$

Lesson 5-7

Complete the square.

88. $x^2 + 10x + ■$

89. $x^2 - 10x + ■$

90. $x^2 + 11x + ■$

91. $x^2 - 11x + ■$

92. $x^2 - \frac{x}{3} + ■$

93. $x^2 + 0.3x + ■$

94. $x^2 - \frac{3}{4}x + ■$

95. $x^2 + \frac{3}{5}x + ■$

7-3 Binomial Radical Expressions

North Carolina Objectives

1.01 Simplify and perform operations with rational exponents and logarithms (common and natural) to solve problems.

Lesson Preview

What You'll Learn

OBJECTIVE 1 To add and subtract radical expressions

OBJECTIVE 2 To multiply and divide binomial radical expressions

. . . And Why

To find the dimensions of a window design, as in Example 2

Check Skills You'll Need

(For help, go to Lesson 5-1 or Skills Handbook page 853.)

Multiply.

1. $(5x + 4)(3x - 2)$

2. $(-8x + 5)(3x - 7)$

3. $(x + 4)(x - 4)$

4. $(4x + 5)(4x - 5)$

5. $(x + 5)^2$

6. $(2x - 9)^2$

New Vocabulary • like radicals

Interactive lesson includes instant self-check, tutorials, and activities.

OBJECTIVE 1

Adding and Subtracting Radical Expressions

Like radicals are radical expressions that have the same index and the same radicand. To add or subtract like radicals, use the Distributive Property.

1 EXAMPLE Adding and Subtracting Radical Expressions

Add or subtract if possible.

a. $5\sqrt[3]{x} - 3\sqrt[3]{x}$

$5\sqrt[3]{x} - 3\sqrt[3]{x} = (5 - 3)\sqrt[3]{x}$ **Distributive Property**

$= 2\sqrt[3]{x}$ **Subtract.**

b. $4\sqrt{2} + 5\sqrt{3}$

The radicals are not like radicals. They cannot be combined.

Check Understanding 1 Add or subtract if possible.

a. $2\sqrt{7} + 3\sqrt{7}$ **b.** $7\sqrt[4]{5} - 2\sqrt[3]{5}$ **c.** $4\sqrt{xy} + 5\sqrt{xy}$

2 EXAMPLE Real-World Connection

Art This is a design for a stained glass window. Each small square is 5 in. on a side. Express the dimensions of the window and its perimeter in simplest radical form.

The diagonal of a square with side length s is $s\sqrt{2}$. So the window's height is $2(5\sqrt{2})$ in., or $10\sqrt{2}$ in. The length is $4(5\sqrt{2})$ in., or $20\sqrt{2}$ in. The perimeter is $2(10\sqrt{2} + 20\sqrt{2})$in., or $60\sqrt{2}$ in.

Check Understanding 2 Find the perimeter of the window if each small square is 6 in. on a side.

Simplify radicals before adding or subtracting so you can find all the like radicals.

3 EXAMPLE Simplifying Before Adding or Subtracting

Simplify $6\sqrt{18} + 4\sqrt{8} - 3\sqrt{72}$.

$$
\begin{aligned}
6\sqrt{18} + 4\sqrt{8} - 3\sqrt{72} &= 6\sqrt{3^2 \cdot 2} + 4\sqrt{2^2 \cdot 2} - 3\sqrt{6^2 \cdot 2} && \textbf{Factor each radicand.}\\
&= 6 \cdot 3\sqrt{2} + 4 \cdot 2\sqrt{2} - 3 \cdot 6\sqrt{2} && \textbf{Simplify each radical.}\\
&= 18\sqrt{2} + 8\sqrt{2} - 18\sqrt{2} && \textbf{Multiply.}\\
&= (18 + 8 - 18)\sqrt{2} && \textbf{Distributive Property}\\
&= 8\sqrt{2}
\end{aligned}
$$

Check Understanding 3 Simplify $\sqrt{50} + 3\sqrt{32} - 5\sqrt{18}$.

OBJECTIVE

2 Multiplying and Dividing Binomial Radical Expressions

Multiply radical expressions that are in the form of binomials by using FOIL.

4 EXAMPLE Multiplying Binomial Radical Expressions

Multiply $(3 + 2\sqrt{5})(2 + 4\sqrt{5})$.

$$
\begin{aligned}
(3 + 2\sqrt{5})(2 + 4\sqrt{5}) &= 3 \cdot 2 + 3 \cdot 4\sqrt{5} + 2 \cdot 2\sqrt{5} + 2\sqrt{5} \cdot 4\sqrt{5} && \textbf{Use FOIL.}\\
&= 6 + 12\sqrt{5} + 4\sqrt{5} + 40 && \textbf{Multiply.}\\
&= 6 + (12 + 4)\sqrt{5} + 40 && \textbf{Combine like radicals.}\\
&= 46 + 16\sqrt{5}
\end{aligned}
$$

Check Understanding 4 Multiply $(\sqrt{2} - \sqrt{3})^2$.

Need Help?
To review conjugates, go to Lesson 6-5.

Conjugates are expressions, such as $\sqrt{a} + \sqrt{b}$ and $\sqrt{a} - \sqrt{b}$, that differ only in the sign of the second terms. If a and b are rational numbers, then the product of these conjugates is a rational number.

Let a and b represent rational numbers.

$$
\begin{aligned}
(\sqrt{a} + \sqrt{b})(\sqrt{a} - \sqrt{b}) &= (\sqrt{a})^2 - (\sqrt{b})^2 && \textbf{The product is the difference of squares.}\\
&= a - b && \textbf{Simplify.}
\end{aligned}
$$

The difference of the rational numbers a and b is a rational number. So the product of the conjugates is a rational number.

5 EXAMPLE Multiplying Conjugates

Multiply $(2 + \sqrt{3})(2 - \sqrt{3})$.

$$
\begin{aligned}
(2 + \sqrt{3})(2 - \sqrt{3}) &= 2^2 - (\sqrt{3})^2 && (\boldsymbol{a} + \boldsymbol{b})(\boldsymbol{a} - \boldsymbol{b}) = \boldsymbol{a}^2 - \boldsymbol{b}^2\\
&= 4 - 3\\
&= 1
\end{aligned}
$$

Check Understanding 5 Multiply $(\sqrt{5} + \sqrt{2})(\sqrt{5} - \sqrt{2})$.

Sometimes you need to rationalize the denominator of a fraction when the denominator is a binomial radical expression. Multiply the numerator and denominator of the fraction by the conjugate of the denominator.

6 EXAMPLE Rationalizing Binomial Radical Denominators

Rationalize the denominator of $\frac{3 + \sqrt{5}}{1 - \sqrt{5}}$.

$$\frac{3 + \sqrt{5}}{1 - \sqrt{5}} = \frac{3 + \sqrt{5}}{1 - \sqrt{5}} \cdot \frac{1 + \sqrt{5}}{1 + \sqrt{5}}$$ **$1 + \sqrt{5}$ is the conjugate of $1 - \sqrt{5}$.**

$$= \frac{(3 + \sqrt{5})(1 + \sqrt{5})}{(1 - \sqrt{5})(1 + \sqrt{5})}$$ **Multiply.**

$$= \frac{3 + 3\sqrt{5} + \sqrt{5} + (\sqrt{5})^2}{1^2 - (\sqrt{5})^2}$$ **Simplify.**

$$= \frac{8 + 4\sqrt{5}}{-4}$$

$$= \frac{8}{-4} + \frac{4\sqrt{5}}{-4}$$

$$= -2 - \sqrt{5}$$

Check Understanding 6 Rationalize the denominator of $\frac{6 + \sqrt{15}}{4 - \sqrt{15}}$.

EXERCISES

For more practice, see *Extra Practice*.

Practice and Problem Solving

A Practice by Example

Examples 1 and 2 (page 374)

Add or subtract if possible.

1. $5\sqrt{6} + \sqrt{6}$ **2.** $6\sqrt[3]{3} - 2\sqrt[3]{3}$ **3.** $4\sqrt{3} + 4\sqrt[3]{3}$

4. $3\sqrt{x} - 5\sqrt{x}$ **5.** $14\sqrt{x} + 3\sqrt{y}$ **6.** $7\sqrt[3]{x^2} - 2\sqrt[3]{x^2}$

Example 3 (page 375)

Simplify.

7. $6\sqrt{18} + 3\sqrt{50}$ **8.** $14\sqrt{20} - 3\sqrt{125}$ **9.** $\sqrt{18} + \sqrt{32}$

10. $\sqrt[3]{54} + \sqrt[3]{16}$ **11.** $3\sqrt[3]{81} - 2\sqrt[3]{54}$ **12.** $\sqrt[4]{32} + \sqrt[4]{48}$

Example 4 (page 375)

Multiply.

13. $(3 + \sqrt{5})(1 + \sqrt{5})$ **14.** $(2 + \sqrt{7})(1 + 3\sqrt{7})$

15. $(3 - 4\sqrt{2})(5 - 6\sqrt{2})$ **16.** $(\sqrt{3} + \sqrt{5})^2$

17. $(\sqrt{13} + 6)^2$ **18.** $(2\sqrt{5} + 3\sqrt{2})^2$

Example 5 (page 375)

Multiply each pair of conjugates.

19. $(5 - \sqrt{11})(5 + \sqrt{11})$ **20.** $(4 - 2\sqrt{3})(4 + 2\sqrt{3})$

21. $(2\sqrt{6} + 8)(2\sqrt{6} - 8)$ **22.** $(\sqrt{3} + \sqrt{5})(\sqrt{3} - \sqrt{5})$

Example 6 (page 376)

Rationalize each denominator. Simplify the answer.

23. $\frac{4}{1 + \sqrt{3}}$ **24.** $\frac{4}{3\sqrt{3} - 2}$ **25.** $\frac{5 + \sqrt{3}}{2 - \sqrt{3}}$ **26.** $\frac{3 + \sqrt{8}}{2 - 2\sqrt{8}}$

B Apply Your Skills

Simplify. Rationalize all denominators. Assume that all the variables are positive.

27. $\sqrt{72} + \sqrt{32} + \sqrt{18}$

28. $\sqrt{75} + 2\sqrt{48} - 5\sqrt{3}$

29. $5\sqrt{32x} + 4\sqrt{98x}$

30. $\sqrt{75} - 4\sqrt{18} + 2\sqrt{32}$

31. $4\sqrt{216y^2} + 3\sqrt{54y^2}$

32. $3\sqrt[3]{16} - 4\sqrt[3]{54} + \sqrt[3]{128}$

33. $(\sqrt{3} - \sqrt{7})(\sqrt{3} + 2\sqrt{7})$

34. $(2\sqrt{5} + 3\sqrt{2})(5\sqrt{5} - 7\sqrt{2})$

35. $(1 + \sqrt{72})(5 + \sqrt{2})$

36. $(2 - \sqrt{98})(3 + \sqrt{18})$

37. $(\sqrt{x} + \sqrt{3})(\sqrt{x} + 2\sqrt{3})$

38. $(2\sqrt{y} - 3\sqrt{2})(4\sqrt{y} - 5\sqrt{2})$

39. $\dfrac{4 + \sqrt{27}}{2 - 3\sqrt{27}}$

40. $\dfrac{4 + \sqrt{6}}{\sqrt{2} + \sqrt{3}}$

41. $\dfrac{5 - \sqrt{21}}{\sqrt{3} - \sqrt{7}}$

42. $\dfrac{3 + \sqrt[3]{2}}{\sqrt[3]{2}}$

43. $\dfrac{5 + \sqrt[4]{x}}{\sqrt[4]{x}}$

44. $\dfrac{4 - 2\sqrt[3]{6}}{\sqrt[3]{4}}$

Real-World Connection

The Golden Ratio is found in the growth patterns of many plants. $\frac{AC}{CD} = \frac{BC}{BD} = \frac{1 + \sqrt{5}}{2}$

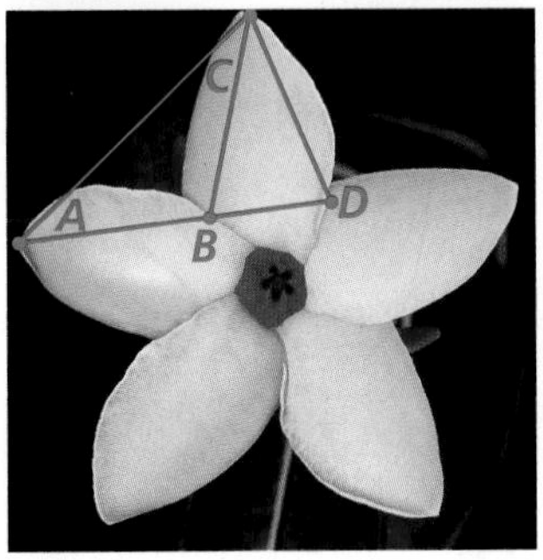

45. The Golden Ratio is $\frac{1 + \sqrt{5}}{2}$. Find the reciprocal of the Golden Ratio and compare it with the number that is 1 less than the Golden Ratio.

46. **Critical Thinking** Describe the possible values of a such that $\sqrt{72} + \sqrt{a}$ can be simplified to a single term.

47. **Geometry** A rectangular walk is $\sqrt{7}$ m wide and $6\sqrt{7}$ m long. What is the perimeter of the walk?

48. **Writing** Discuss the advantages and disadvantages of first simplifying $\sqrt{72} + \sqrt{32} + \sqrt{18}$ in order to estimate its decimal value.

49. **Open-Ended** Find two pairs of conjugates with a product of 3.

50. **Physics** An object is moving at a speed of $(3 + \sqrt{2})$ ft/s. How long will it take the object to travel 20 ft?

C Challenge

Add or subtract.

51. $\dfrac{1}{1 - \sqrt{5}} + \dfrac{1}{1 + \sqrt{5}}$

52. $\dfrac{4}{\sqrt{5} - \sqrt{3}} - \dfrac{4}{\sqrt{5} + \sqrt{3}}$

53. For what values of a and b does $\sqrt{a} + \sqrt{b} = \sqrt{a + b}$?

54. **Error Analysis** A student used the steps shown below to simplify an expression. Find the student's error and explain why the step is incorrect.

$$\begin{aligned} \frac{1}{(1 - \sqrt{2})^2} &= (1 - \sqrt{2})^{-2} \\ &= 1^{-2} - (\sqrt{2})^{-2} \\ &= \frac{1}{1^2} - \frac{1}{(\sqrt{2^2})} \\ &= \frac{1}{1} - \frac{1}{2} \\ &= \frac{1}{2} \end{aligned}$$

55. In the expression $\sqrt[n]{x^m}$, m and n are positive integers and x is a real number. The expression can be simplified.

a. If $x > 0$, what are the possible values for m and n?

b. If $x < 0$, what are the possible values for m and n?

c. If $x < 0$ and an absolute value symbol is needed in the simplified expression, what are the possible values of m and n?

Standardized Test Prep

Multiple Choice

56. Which expression does NOT simplify to one term?
 A. $-4\sqrt{8} + \sqrt{18}$ B. $\sqrt{27} - \sqrt{8}$
 C. $\sqrt{32} + 3\sqrt{8}$ D. $\sqrt{12} - \sqrt{75}$

57. What is an expression for $\sqrt{20} - \sqrt{80} + \sqrt{125}$?
 F. $\sqrt{65}$ G. $13\sqrt{5}$ H. $11\sqrt{5}$ I. $3\sqrt{5}$

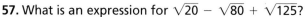

Take It to the NET
Online lesson quiz at www.PHSchool.com
Web Code: aga-0703

58. Which expression is NOT equal to 13?
 A. $(4 + \sqrt{3})(4 - \sqrt{3})$ B. $(5 - 2\sqrt{3})(5 + 2\sqrt{3})$
 C. $(6 + \sqrt{23})(6 - \sqrt{23})$ D. $(7 - \sqrt{6})(7 + \sqrt{6})$

59. How can you write $\frac{1 + \sqrt{3}}{5 - \sqrt{3}}$ with a rationalized denominator?
 F. -1 G. $-2 - 3\sqrt{3}$ H. $4 + 3\sqrt{3}$ I. $\frac{4 + 3\sqrt{3}}{11}$

60. Which of the following is equivalent to $(2 + 3\sqrt{5})(3 + 3\sqrt{5})$?
 A. 51 B. $6 + 9\sqrt{5}$ C. $6 + 24\sqrt{5}$ D. $51 + 15\sqrt{5}$

Short Response

61. Is the product $(1 - \sqrt[3]{8})(1 + \sqrt[3]{8})$ a rational number? Explain.

Extended Response

62. What is the value of $\frac{2}{5 + 2\sqrt{2}} - \frac{3}{5 - 2\sqrt{2}}$? Show your work.

Mixed Review

Lesson 7-2

Simplify each expression. Rationalize all denominators. Assume that all variables are positive.

63. $\sqrt[3]{3} \cdot \sqrt[3]{18}$
64. $\sqrt{3x} \cdot \sqrt{5x}$
65. $\frac{\sqrt{32}}{\sqrt{2}}$
66. $\frac{\sqrt{62}}{\sqrt{6}}$
67. $\sqrt[3]{2x^2} \cdot \sqrt[3]{4x}$
68. $\sqrt{7x} \cdot \sqrt{14x^3}$
69. $\frac{\sqrt{6m}}{\sqrt{2mn}}$
70. $\sqrt[3]{\frac{4}{5x}}$

Lesson 6-4

Solve each equation.

71. $2x^3 - 16 = 0$
72. $x^3 + 1000 = 0$
73. $125x^3 - 1 = 0$
74. $x^4 - 14x^2 + 49 = 0$
75. $25x^4 - 40x^2 + 16 = 0$
76. $81x^4 - 1 = 0$

Checkpoint Quiz 1 — Lessons 7-1 through 7-3

iTEXT Instant self-check quiz online and on CD-ROM

Simplify each radical expression. Use absolute value symbols when needed.

1. $\sqrt[4]{b^4c^8}$
2. $\sqrt[5]{x^5y^{10}}$
3. $\sqrt[3]{-a^3}$
4. $\sqrt[5]{-y^{10}}$

Simplify each expression. Rationalize all denominators. Assume that all variables are positive.

5. $\sqrt{8}(\sqrt{24} + 3\sqrt{8})$
6. $2\sqrt{5x^3} \cdot 3\sqrt{28x^3y^2}$
7. $4\sqrt[3]{81} - 3\sqrt[3]{54}$
8. $\frac{4\sqrt{2xy}}{9\sqrt{5x^2y}}$
9. $(\sqrt{5} + 2\sqrt{3})(\sqrt{5} - 2\sqrt{3})$
10. $\frac{5}{4\sqrt{7} + 5}$

7-4 Rational Exponents

North Carolina Objectives

1.01 Simplify and perform operations with rational exponents and logarithms (common and natural) to solve problems.

Lesson Preview

What You'll Learn

OBJECTIVE 1 To simplify expressions with rational exponents

. . . And Why

To model simulated gravity in a spacecraft, as in Example 3

Check Skills You'll Need

(For help, go to page 362.)

Simplify.

1. 2^{-4}

2. $(3x)^{-2}$

3. $(5x^2y)^{-3}$

4. $2^{-2} + 4^{-1}$

5. $(2a^{-2}b^3)^4$

6. $(4a^3b^{-1})^{-2}$

New Vocabulary • rational exponent

Interactive lesson includes instant self-check, tutorials, and activities.

OBJECTIVE 1 Simplifying Expressions With Rational Exponents

Another way to write a radical expression is to use a **rational exponent.** See the examples at the right.

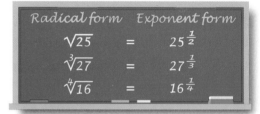

Radical form		Exponent form
$\sqrt{25}$	=	$25^{\frac{1}{2}}$
$\sqrt[3]{27}$	=	$27^{\frac{1}{3}}$
$\sqrt[4]{16}$	=	$16^{\frac{1}{4}}$

Like the radical form, the exponent form always indicates the principal root.

Reading Math

Exponent comes from the Latin word meaning "place outside."

1 EXAMPLE Simplifying Expressions With Rational Exponents

Simplify each expression.

a. $125^{\frac{1}{3}}$

$125^{\frac{1}{3}} = \sqrt[3]{125}$ **Rewrite as a radical.**

$= \sqrt[3]{5^3}$ **Rewrite 125 as a cube.**

$= 5$ **Simplify.**

b. $5^{\frac{1}{2}} \cdot 5^{\frac{1}{2}}$

$5^{\frac{1}{2}} \cdot 5^{\frac{1}{2}} = \sqrt{5} \cdot \sqrt{5}$ **Rewrite as radicals.**

$= 5$ **By definition, $\sqrt{5}$ is the number whose square is 5.**

c. $10^{\frac{1}{3}} \cdot 100^{\frac{1}{3}}$

$10^{\frac{1}{3}} \cdot 100^{\frac{1}{3}} = \sqrt[3]{10} \cdot \sqrt[3]{100}$ **Rewrite as radicals.**

$= \sqrt[3]{10 \cdot 100}$ **Property for multiplying radical expressions**

$= \sqrt[3]{10^3}$ **Rewrite the radicand as a cube.**

$= 10$ **Simplify.**

Check Understanding

1 Simplify each expression.

a. $16^{\frac{1}{4}}$ **b.** $2^{\frac{1}{2}} \cdot 2^{\frac{1}{2}}$ **c.** $2^{\frac{1}{2}} \cdot 8^{\frac{1}{2}}$

A rational exponent may have a numerator other than 1. The property $(a^m)^n = a^{mn}$ shows how to rewrite an expression with an exponent that is an improper fraction.

$$25^{\frac{3}{2}} = 25^{(3 \cdot \frac{1}{2})} = (25^3)^{\frac{1}{2}} = \sqrt{25^3} \quad \text{or} \quad 25^{\frac{3}{2}} = 25^{(\frac{1}{2} \cdot 3)} = (25^{\frac{1}{2}})^3 = (\sqrt{25})^3$$

Key Concepts

Definition	Rational Exponents
If the nth root of a is a real number and m is an integer, then $a^{\frac{1}{n}} = \sqrt[n]{a}$ and $a^{\frac{m}{n}} = \sqrt[n]{a^m} = (\sqrt[n]{a})^m$. If m is negative, $a \neq 0$.	

2 EXAMPLE Converting to and From Radical Form

a. Write the exponential expressions $x^{\frac{3}{5}}$ and $y^{-2.5}$ in radical form.

$x^{\frac{3}{5}} = \sqrt[5]{x^3}$ or $(\sqrt[5]{x})^3$

$y^{-2.5} = y^{-\frac{5}{2}} = \frac{1}{\sqrt{y^5}}$ or $\frac{1}{(\sqrt{y})^5}$

b. Write the radical expressions $\sqrt{a^3}$ and $(\sqrt[5]{b})^2$ in exponential form.

$\sqrt{a^3} = a^{\frac{3}{2}}$

$(\sqrt[5]{b})^2 = b^{\frac{2}{5}}$

Check Understanding **2** **a.** Write the expressions $y^{-\frac{3}{8}}$ and $z^{0.4}$ in radical form.

b. Write the expressions $\sqrt[3]{x^2}$ and $(\sqrt{y})^3$ in exponential form.

c. Critical Thinking Refer to the definition of rational exponents. Explain the need for the following restriction: If m is negative, $a \neq 0$.

3 EXAMPLE Real-World Connection

Graphing Calculator Hint

Use the ^ key to enter an exponent. If the exponent is a fraction, enclose it in parentheses. For example, $729^{\frac{2}{3}}$ is entered as 729 ^ (2 ÷ 3).

Space Travel Bone loss for astronauts on lengthy space voyages may be prevented with a bedlike apparatus that rotates to simulate the effect of gravity. In the formula $N = \frac{a^{0.5}}{2\pi r^{0.5}}$, N is the rate of rotation in revolutions per second, a is the simulated acceleration in m/s^2, and r is the radius of the apparatus in meters. How fast would an apparatus with a radius of 1.7 m have to rotate to simulate the acceleration of 9.8 m/s^2 that is due to Earth's gravity?

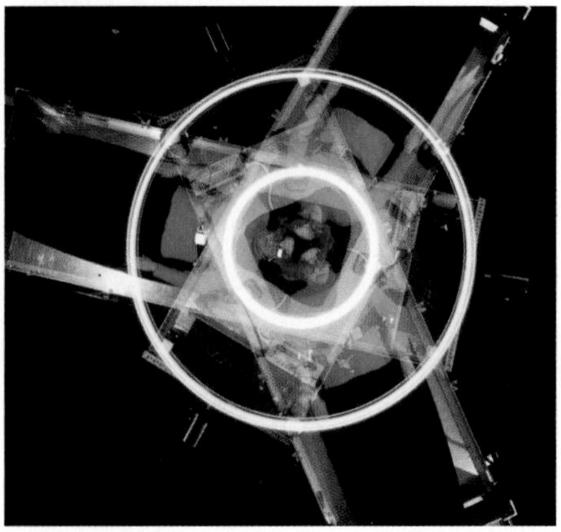

$N = \frac{a^{0.5}}{2\pi r^{0.5}}$ **Write the formula.**

$= \frac{9.8^{0.5}}{2\pi(1.7)^{0.5}}$ **Substitute for *a* and *r*.**

≈ 0.382 **Use a calculator.**

The apparatus would have to rotate about 0.382 revolutions per second, or about 23 revolutions per minute.

Check Understanding **3** Calculate the rate of rotation needed for the apparatus in Example 3 to simulate a gravitational acceleration half as strong as Earth's.

All of the properties of integer exponents also apply to rational exponents. Here is a summary.

Key Concepts

Need Help?
Refer to the properties of integer exponents on p. 362.

Summary **Properties of Rational Exponents**

Let m and n represent rational numbers. Assume that no denominator equals 0.

Property	Example
$a^m \cdot a^n = a^{m+n}$	$8^{\frac{1}{3}} \cdot 8^{\frac{2}{3}} = 8^{\frac{1}{3}+\frac{2}{3}} = 8^1 = 8$
$(a^m)^n = a^{mn}$	$\left(5^{\frac{1}{2}}\right)^4 = 5^{\frac{1}{2}\cdot 4} = 5^2 = 25$
$(ab)^m = a^m b^m$	$(4 \cdot 5)^{\frac{1}{2}} = 4^{\frac{1}{2}} \cdot 5^{\frac{1}{2}} = 2 \cdot 5^{\frac{1}{2}}$
$a^{-m} = \frac{1}{a^m}$	$9^{-\frac{1}{2}} = \frac{1}{9^{\frac{1}{2}}} = \frac{1}{3}$
$\frac{a^m}{a^n} = a^{m-n}$	$\frac{\pi^{\frac{3}{2}}}{\pi^{\frac{1}{2}}} = \pi^{\frac{3}{2}-\frac{1}{2}} = \pi^1 = \pi$
$\left(\frac{a}{b}\right)^m = \frac{a^m}{b^m}$	$\left(\frac{5}{27}\right)^{\frac{1}{3}} = \frac{5^{\frac{1}{3}}}{27^{\frac{1}{3}}} = \frac{5^{\frac{1}{3}}}{3}$

You can simplify a number with a rational exponent by using the properties of exponents or by converting the expression to a radical expression.

4 EXAMPLE Simplifying Numbers With Rational Exponents

Simplify each number.

a. $(-32)^{\frac{3}{5}}$

Method 1

$$(-32)^{\frac{3}{5}} = ((-2)^5)^{\frac{3}{5}}$$
$$= (-2)^{5 \cdot \frac{3}{5}}$$
$$= (-2)^3$$
$$= -8$$

Method 2

$$(-32)^{\frac{3}{5}} = \left(\sqrt[5]{-32}\right)^3$$
$$= \left(\sqrt[5]{(-2)^5}\right)^3$$
$$= (-2)^3$$
$$= -8$$

b. $4^{-3.5}$

Method 1

$$4^{-3.5} = 4^{-\frac{7}{2}}$$
$$= (2^2)^{-\frac{7}{2}}$$
$$= 2^{2 \cdot -\frac{7}{2}}$$
$$= 2^{-7}$$
$$= \frac{1}{2^7}$$
$$= \frac{1}{128}$$

Method 2

$$4^{-3.5} = 4^{-\frac{7}{2}}$$
$$= \frac{1}{4^{\frac{7}{2}}}$$
$$= \frac{1}{(\sqrt{4})^7}$$
$$= \frac{1}{2^7}$$
$$= \frac{1}{128}$$

Check Understanding **4** Simplify each number.

a. $25^{-\frac{3}{2}}$ **b.** $32^{\frac{3}{5}}$ **c.** $(-32)^{\frac{4}{5}}$

To write an expression with rational exponents in simplest form, write every exponent as a positive number.

5 EXAMPLE Writing Expressions in Simplest Form

Write $\left(16y^{-8}\right)^{-\frac{3}{4}}$ in simplest form.

$$\begin{aligned}\left(16y^{-8}\right)^{-\frac{3}{4}} &= \left(2^4y^{-8}\right)^{-\frac{3}{4}}\\ &= 2^{4\cdot\left(-\frac{3}{4}\right)}\cdot y^{-8\cdot\left(-\frac{3}{4}\right)}\\ &= 2^{-3}y^6\\ &= \frac{y^6}{2^3}\\ &= \frac{y^6}{8}\end{aligned}$$

Check Understanding 5 Write $(8x^{15})^{-\frac{1}{3}}$ in simplest form.

EXERCISES

For more practice, see *Extra Practice.*

Practice and Problem Solving

A Practice by Example

Example 1 (page 379)

Simplify each expression.

1. $36^{\frac{1}{2}}$
2. $27^{\frac{1}{3}}$
3. $49^{\frac{1}{2}}$
4. $10^{\frac{1}{2}}\cdot 10^{\frac{1}{2}}$
5. $(-3)^{\frac{1}{3}}\cdot(-3)^{\frac{1}{3}}\cdot(-3)^{\frac{1}{3}}$
6. $3^{\frac{1}{2}}\cdot 12^{\frac{1}{2}}$
7. $2^{\frac{1}{2}}\cdot 32^{\frac{1}{2}}$
8. $3^{\frac{1}{3}}\cdot 9^{\frac{1}{3}}$
9. $3^{\frac{1}{4}}\cdot 27^{\frac{1}{4}}$

Example 2 (page 380)

Write each expression in radical form.

10. $x^{\frac{1}{6}}$
11. $x^{\frac{1}{5}}$
12. $x^{\frac{2}{7}}$
13. $y^{\frac{2}{5}}$
14. $y^{-\frac{9}{8}}$
15. $t^{-\frac{3}{4}}$
16. $x^{1.5}$
17. $y^{1.2}$

Write each expression in exponential form.

18. $\sqrt{-10}$
19. $\sqrt{7x^3}$
20. $\sqrt{(7x)^3}$
21. $\left(\sqrt{7x}\right)^3$
22. $\sqrt[3]{a^2}$
23. $\left(\sqrt[3]{a}\right)^2$
24. $\sqrt[4]{c^2}$
25. $\sqrt[3]{(5xy)^6}$

Example 3 (page 380)

The optimal height *h* of the letters of a message printed on pavement is given by the formula $h = \frac{0.00252d^{2.27}}{e}$. Here *d* is the distance of the driver from the letters and *e* is the height of the driver's eye above the pavement. All of the distances are in meters. Find *h* for the given values of *d* and *e*.

26. $d = 100$ m, $e = 1.2$ m
27. $d = 50$ m, $e = 1.2$ m
28. $d = 50$ m, $e = 2.3$ m
29. $d = 25$ m, $e = 2.3$ m

Example 4 (page 381)

Simplify each number.

30. $8^{\frac{2}{3}}$
31. $64^{\frac{2}{3}}$
32. $(-8)^{\frac{2}{3}}$
33. $(-32)^{\frac{6}{5}}$
34. $(32)^{-\frac{4}{5}}$
35. $4^{1.5}$
36. $16^{1.5}$
37. $10{,}000^{0.75}$

Example 5 (page 382)

Write each expression in simplest form. Assume that all variables are positive.

38. $\left(x^{\frac{2}{3}}\right)^{-3}$ **39.** $\left(x^{-\frac{4}{7}}\right)^{7}$ **40.** $\left(3x^{\frac{2}{3}}\right)^{-1}$ **41.** $5\left(x^{\frac{2}{3}}\right)^{-1}$

42. $\left(-27x^{-9}\right)^{\frac{1}{3}}$ **43.** $\left(-32y^{15}\right)^{\frac{1}{5}}$ **44.** $\left(\frac{x^{3}}{x^{-1}}\right)^{-\frac{1}{4}}$ **45.** $\left(\frac{x^{2}}{x^{-11}}\right)^{\frac{1}{3}}$

46. $\left(x^{\frac{1}{2}}y^{-\frac{2}{3}}\right)^{-6}$ **47.** $\left(x^{\frac{2}{3}}y^{-\frac{1}{6}}\right)^{-12}$ **48.** $\left(\frac{x^{\frac{1}{4}}}{y^{-\frac{3}{4}}}\right)^{12}$ **49.** $\left(\frac{x^{-\frac{2}{3}}}{y^{-\frac{1}{3}}}\right)^{15}$

B Apply Your Skills

Simplify each number.

50. $(-343)^{\frac{1}{3}}$ **51.** $(-243)^{\frac{1}{5}}$ **52.** $32^{1.2}$ **53.** $243^{1.2}$

54. $64^{3.5}$ **55.** $100^{4.5}$ **56.** $32^{-0.4}$ **57.** $64^{-0.5}$

58. $(-216)^{-\frac{2}{3}}$ **59.** $2(16)^{\frac{3}{4}}$ **60.** $-(-27)^{-\frac{4}{3}}$ **61.** $\frac{1000^{\frac{4}{3}}}{100^{\frac{3}{2}}}$

Real-World Connection

Archaeologists estimate the ages of artifacts and fossils by using exponential functions.

62. Archaeology The ratio R of radioactive carbon to nonradioactive carbon left in a sample of an organism that died T years ago can be approximated by the formula $R = A(2.7)^{-\frac{T}{8033}}$. Here A is the ratio of radioactive carbon to nonradioactive carbon in the living organism. What percent of A is left after 2000 years? After 4000 years? After 8000 years?

63. Biology The expression $0.036m^{\frac{3}{4}}$ is used in the study of fluids. Evaluate the expression for $m = 46 \times 10^{4}$.

64. Physics In the expression $PV^{\frac{7}{5}}$, P represents the pressure and V represents the volume of a sample of a gas. Evaluate the expression for $P = 6$ and $V = 32$.

Simplify each expression. Assume that all variables are positive.

65. $x^{\frac{2}{7}} \cdot x^{\frac{3}{14}}$ **66.** $y^{\frac{1}{2}} \cdot y^{\frac{3}{10}}$ **67.** $x^{\frac{3}{5}} \div x^{\frac{1}{10}}$ **68.** $y^{\frac{5}{7}} \div y^{\frac{3}{14}}$

69. $\frac{x^{\frac{2}{3}}y^{-\frac{1}{4}}}{x^{\frac{1}{2}}y^{-\frac{1}{2}}}$ **70.** $\frac{x^{\frac{1}{2}}y^{-\frac{1}{3}}}{x^{\frac{3}{4}}y^{\frac{1}{2}}}$ **71.** $\left(\frac{16x^{14}}{81y^{18}}\right)^{\frac{1}{2}}$ **72.** $\left(\frac{81y^{16}}{16x^{12}}\right)^{\frac{1}{2}}$

73. $\left(x^{\frac{1}{2}} \cdot x^{\frac{5}{12}}\right)^{\frac{1}{3}} \div x^{\frac{2}{3}}$ **74.** $\left(x^{\frac{3}{4}} \div x^{\frac{7}{8}}\right) \cdot x^{-\frac{1}{6}}$ **75.** $\left[\left(x^{-\frac{1}{2}}\right)^{2}\right]^{\frac{1}{3}}$ **76.** $\left[\left(\sqrt{x^{3}y^{3}}\right)^{\frac{1}{3}}\right]^{-1}$

77. Writing Explain why $(-64)^{\frac{1}{3}} = -64^{\frac{1}{3}}$ and $(-64)^{\frac{1}{2}} \neq -64^{\frac{1}{2}}$.

78. Error Analysis Explain why the following simplification is incorrect.

$5\left(4 - 5^{\frac{1}{2}}\right) = 5(4) - 5\left(5^{\frac{1}{2}}\right) = 20 - 25^{\frac{1}{2}} = 15$

79. a. Open-Ended Find three numbers a such that $a\left(4 + 5^{\frac{1}{2}}\right)$ is a rational number.

b. Critical Thinking Are there any rational numbers a such that $a\left(4 + 5^{\frac{1}{2}}\right)$ is a rational number?

80. a. Reasoning Show that $\sqrt[4]{x^{2}} = \sqrt{x}$ by using the definition of fourth root.

b. Reasoning Show that $\sqrt[4]{x^{2}} = \sqrt{x}$ by rewriting $\sqrt[4]{x^{2}}$ in exponential form.

C Challenge

Exponents that are irrational numbers can be defined so that all the properties of rational exponents are also true for irrational exponents. Use those properties to simplify each expression.

81. $\left(7^{\sqrt{2}}\right)^{\sqrt{2}}$ **82.** $\frac{3^{3+\sqrt{5}}}{3^{1+\sqrt{5}}}$ **83.** $\frac{x^{4\pi}}{x^{2\pi}}$

84. $5^{2\sqrt{3}} \cdot 25^{-\sqrt{3}}$ **85.** $9^{\frac{1}{\sqrt{2}}}$ **86.** $\left(3^{2+\sqrt{2}}\right)^{2-\sqrt{2}}$

87. Weather Using data for the effect of temperature and wind on an exposed face, the National Weather Service uses the following formula.

$$\text{Wind Chill Index} = 35.74 + 0.6215T - 35.75V^{0.16} + 0.4275TV^{0.16}$$

T is the temperature in degrees Fahrenheit and V is the velocity of the wind in miles per hour. Frostbite occurs in about 15 minutes when the wind chill index is about -20. Find the wind speed that produces a wind chill index of -20 when the temperature is 5°F.

Standardized Test Prep

Multiple Choice

88. Which expression is NOT equivalent to $\sqrt[4]{4n^2}$?

A. $(4n^2)^{\frac{1}{4}}$ **B.** $2n^{\frac{1}{2}}$ **C.** $(2n)^{\frac{1}{2}}$ **D.** $\sqrt{2n}$

89. Which expression is NOT equivalent to $\sqrt[6]{81x^4y^8}$?

F. $(3xy^2)^{\frac{2}{3}}$ **G.** $(3x)^{\frac{2}{3}}y^{\frac{4}{3}}$ **H.** $(3x^2y^4)^{\frac{1}{3}}$ **I.** $\sqrt[3]{9x^2y^4}$

Short Response

90. What is the value of x if $32^{0.8}x = 1$? Simplify the answer.

Quantitative Comparison

Compare the boxed quantity in Column A with the boxed quantity in Column B. Choose the best answer.

A. The quantity in Column A is greater.
B. The quantity in Column B is greater.
C. The two quantities are equal.
D. The relationship cannot be determined from the information given.

	Column A	Column B
91.	$14^{\frac{2}{3}}$	$14^{\frac{3}{2}}$
92.	$5^{-\frac{3}{4}}$	$5^{-\frac{4}{3}}$
93.	$16^{-\frac{3}{4}}$	$32^{-\frac{3}{5}}$
94.	$(-17)^{100}$	$(-17)^{101}$

Take It to the NET
Online lesson quiz at **www.PHSchool.com**
Web Code: aga-0704

Mixed Review

Lesson 7-3

Simplify. Rationalize all denominators.

95. $6\sqrt[3]{3} - 2\sqrt[3]{3}$ **96.** $3\sqrt{18} + 2\sqrt{72}$ **97.** $(\sqrt{5} - 1)(\sqrt{5} + 4)$

98. $(\sqrt{8} - \sqrt{7})^2$ **99.** $\frac{2 + \sqrt{10}}{2 - 3\sqrt{5}}$ **100.** $\frac{-2 + \sqrt{8}}{-3 - \sqrt{2}}$

Lesson 5-4

Factor each expression.

101. $4x^3 - 8x^2 + 16x$ **102.** $x^2 + 4x + 4$ **103.** $x^2 - 18x + 81$

104. $16a^2 - 9b^2$ **105.** $25x^2 - 40xy + 16y^2$ **106.** $9x^2 + 48x + 64$

7-5

Solving Radical Equations

North Carolina Objectives

2.07 Use equations with radical expressions to model and solve problems; justify results. a) Solve using tables, graphs, and algebraic properties.

Lesson Preview

What You'll Learn

OBJECTIVE 1 To solve radical equations

. . . And Why

To find the radius of a circular solar cell, as in Example 3

✓ Check Skills You'll Need

(For help, go to Lesson 5-4.)

Solve by factoring.

1. $x^2 = -x + 6$

2. $x^2 = 5x + 14$

3. $2x^2 + x = 3$

4. $3x^2 - 2 = 5x$

5. $4x^2 = -8x + 5$

6. $6x^2 = 5x + 6$

New Vocabulary

- radical equation

Interactive lesson includes instant self-check, tutorials, and activities.

OBJECTIVE

1 Solving Radical Equations

A **radical equation** is an equation that has a variable in a radicand or has a variable with a rational exponent.

$3 + \sqrt{x} = 10$ **radical equation**

$(x - 2)^{\frac{2}{3}} = 25$ **radical equation**

$\sqrt{3} + x = 10$ **not a radical equation**

To solve a radical equation, isolate the radical on one side of the equation and then raise both sides of the equation to the same power.

If $\sqrt[n]{x} = k$, then $\left(\sqrt[n]{x}\right)^n = k^n$ and $x = k^n$.

1 EXAMPLE Solving Radical Equations With Index 2

Solve $2 + \sqrt{3x - 2} = 6$.

$2 + \sqrt{3x - 2} = 6$

$\sqrt{3x - 2} = 4$ **Isolate the radical.**

$\left(\sqrt{3x - 2}\right)^2 = 4^2$ **Square each side.**

$3x - 2 = 16$

$3x = 18$

$x = 6$

Check $2 + \sqrt{3x - 2} = 6$

$2 + \sqrt{3(6) - 2} \stackrel{?}{=} 6$

$2 + \sqrt{16} \stackrel{?}{=} 6$

$2 + 4 \stackrel{?}{=} 6$

$6 = 6$ ✓

✓ Check Understanding **1** Solve $\sqrt{5x + 1} - 6 = 0$.

You can solve equations of the form $x^{\frac{n}{m}} = k$ by raising each side of the equation to the power $\frac{n}{m}$, the reciprocal of $\frac{m}{n}$. If n is even, then $(x^{\frac{m}{n}})^{\frac{n}{m}} = |x|$. If n is odd, then $(x^{\frac{m}{n}})^{\frac{n}{m}} = x$.

2 EXAMPLE Solving Radical Equations With Rational Exponents

Solve $2(x - 2)^{\frac{2}{3}} = 50$.

$2(x - 2)^{\frac{2}{3}} = 50$

$(x - 2)^{\frac{2}{3}} = 25$ **Divide each side by 2.**

$\left((x - 2)^{\frac{2}{3}}\right)^{\frac{3}{2}} = 25^{\frac{3}{2}}$ **Raise each side to the $\frac{3}{2}$ power.**

$|x - 2|^1 = 25^{\frac{3}{2}}$ **Multiply exponents. Use absolute value when taking an even root.**

$x - 2 = \pm 125$ **Simplify.**

$x = 127$ or $x = -123$

Check

$2(x - 2)^{\frac{2}{3}} = 50$	$2(x - 2)^{\frac{2}{3}} = 50$
$2(127 - 2)^{\frac{2}{3}} \stackrel{?}{=} 50$	$2(-123 - 2)^{\frac{2}{3}} \stackrel{?}{=} 50$
$2(5^3)^{\frac{2}{3}} \stackrel{?}{=} 50$	$2(-125)^{\frac{2}{3}} \stackrel{?}{=} 50$
$2(5)^2 \stackrel{?}{=} 50$	$2(-5)^2 \stackrel{?}{=} 50$
$50 = 50$ ✓	$50 = 50$ ✓

Check Understanding 2 Solve $2(x + 3)^{\frac{3}{2}} = 54$

3 EXAMPLE Real-World Connection

Solar Energy A company manufactures solar cells that produce 0.02 watts of power per square centimeter of surface area. A circular solar cell needs to produce at least 10 watts. What is its minimum radius?

Relate	area of cell	·	power per square centimeter	≥	total power
Define	Let r = the radius in centimeters.				
Write	πr^2	·	0.02	≥	10

$\pi r^2 \cdot 0.02 \geq 10$

$r^2 \geq \frac{10}{0.02\pi}$

$r^2 \geq \frac{1000}{2\pi}$

$r^2 \geq \frac{500}{\pi}$

$(r^2)^{\frac{1}{2}} \geq \left(\frac{500}{\pi}\right)^{\frac{1}{2}}$

$r \geq 12.62$ **Use a calculator.**

The minimum radius is about 12.62 cm.

Real-World Connection

Solar cells convert sunlight directly into electricity. They power calculators, emergency road signs, satellites, and experimental vehicles.

Check Understanding 3 Find the minimum radius of a circular solar cell that will produce 20 watts of power.

Extraneous solutions can be introduced when you raise both sides of an equation to a power. So check all possible solutions in the original equation.

4 EXAMPLE Checking for Extraneous Solutions

Need Help?
To review extraneous solutions, go to Lesson 1-5.

Solve $\sqrt{x-3}+5=x$. Check for extraneous solutions.

$\sqrt{x-3}+5=x$

$\sqrt{x-3}=x-5$ **Isolate the radical.**

$(\sqrt{x-3})^2=(x-5)^2$ **Square each side.**

$x-3=x^2-10x+25$ **Simplify.**

$0=x^2-11x+28$ **Combine like terms.**

$0=(x-4)(x-7)$ **Factor.**

$x-4=0$ or $x-7=0$ **Factor Theorem**

$x=4$ or $x=7$

Check $\sqrt{x-3}+5=x$ $\qquad$ $\sqrt{x-3}+5=x$

$\sqrt{4-3}+5\stackrel{?}{=}4$ $\qquad$ $\sqrt{7-3}+5\stackrel{?}{=}7$

$\sqrt{1}+5\stackrel{?}{=}4$ $\qquad$ $\sqrt{4}+5\stackrel{?}{=}7$

$6\neq 4$ $\qquad$ $7=7$

The only solution is 7.

Check Understanding 4 Solve $\sqrt{5x-1}+3=x$. Check for extraneous solutions.

If an equation contains two radical expressions (or two terms with rational exponents), isolate one of the radicals (or one of the terms).

5 EXAMPLE Solving Equations With Two Rational Exponents

Solve $(2x+1)^{0.5}-(3x+4)^{0.25}=0$. Check for extraneous solutions.

$(2x+1)^{0.5}-(3x+4)^{0.25}=0$

$(2x+1)^{0.5}=(3x+4)^{0.25}$

$((2x+1)^{0.5})^4=((3x+4)^{0.25})^4$ **Raise each side to the 4th power.**

$(2x+1)^2=3x+4$ **Simplify exponents.**

$4x^2+4x+1=3x+4$ **Simplify.**

$4x^2+x-3=0$ **Combine like terms.**

$(4x-3)(x+1)=0$ **Factor.**

$x=\frac{3}{4}$ or $x=-1$ **Factor Theorem**

Check $(2x+1)^{0.5}-(3x+4)^{0.25}=0$ $\qquad$ $(2x+1)^{0.5}-(3x+4)^{0.25}=0$

$\left(2\cdot\frac{3}{4}+1\right)^{0.5}-\left(3\cdot\frac{3}{4}+4\right)^{0.25}\stackrel{?}{=}0$ $\qquad$ $(2(-1)+1)^{0.5}-(3(-1)+4)^{0.25}\stackrel{?}{=}0$

$\left(\frac{5}{2}\right)^{0.5}-\left(\frac{25}{4}\right)^{0.25}\stackrel{?}{=}0$ $\qquad$ $(-1)^{0.5}-(1)^{0.25}\stackrel{?}{=}0$

$\left(\frac{5}{2}\right)^{0.5}-\left(\left(\frac{5}{2}\right)^2\right)^{0.25}\stackrel{?}{=}0$ $\qquad$ $(-1)^{0.5}$ is not a real number.

$\left(\frac{5}{2}\right)^{0.5}-\left(\frac{5}{2}\right)^{0.5}=0$

The only solution is $\frac{3}{4}$.

Check Understanding 5 Solve $\sqrt{3x+2}-\sqrt{2x+7}=0$. Check for extraneous solutions.

Investigation: Checking for Extraneous Solutions

You can use a graphing calculator to check for extraneous solutions.

1. a. Solve $x = \sqrt{x + 7} + 5$. How many apparent solutions do you get?
   b. Any or all of the apparent solutions may be extraneous. One way to find out is to let y_1 equal the left side of the equation and let y_2 equal the right side. Graph the two equations. In how many points do they intersect?
   c. The x-values of the points of intersection are solutions of the original equation. Are any of the apparent solutions extraneous?
   d. Substitute the apparent solutions in the original equation. Does this algebraic check agree with the calculator check?
2. Use a graphing calculator to determine the number of solutions of each equation.
   a. $\sqrt{x} = x - 2$ b. $\sqrt{x^2 + 3} = 2x - 1$ c. $x + 8 = 4\sqrt{x + 5}$

EXERCISES

For more practice, see *Extra Practice*.

Practice and Problem Solving

A Practice by Example

Example 1 (page 385)

Solve.

1. $3\sqrt{x} + 3 = 15$

2. $4\sqrt{x} - 1 = 3$

3. $\sqrt{x + 3} = 5$

4. $\sqrt{3x + 4} = 4$

5. $\sqrt{2x + 3} - 7 = 0$

6. $\sqrt{6 - 3x} - 2 = 0$

Example 2 (page 386)

Solve.

7. $(x + 5)^{\frac{2}{3}} = 4$

8. $(x - 2)^{\frac{2}{3}} = 9$

9. $3(x - 2)^{\frac{3}{4}} = 24$

10. $3(x + 3)^{\frac{3}{4}} = 81$

11. $(x + 1)^{\frac{3}{2}} - 2 = 25$

12. $3 + (4 - x)^{\frac{3}{2}} = 11$

Example 3 (page 386)

13. Volume. A spherical water tank holds 15,000 ft^3 of water. Find the diameter of the tank. (*Hint:* $V = \frac{\pi}{6}d^3$)

14. Hydraulics The maximum flow of water in a pipe is modeled by the formula $Q = Av$, where A is the cross-sectional area of the pipe and v is the velocity of the water. Find the diameter of a pipe that allows a maximum flow of 50 ft^3/min of water flowing at a velocity of 600 ft/min. Round your answer to the nearest inch.

Example 4 (page 387)

Solve. Check for extraneous solutions.

15. $\sqrt{11x + 3} - 2x = 0$

16. $(5x + 4)^{\frac{1}{2}} - 3x = 0$

17. $\sqrt{3x + 13} - 5 = x$

18. $\sqrt{x + 7} + 5 = x$

19. $(x + 3)^{\frac{1}{2}} - 1 = x$

20. $(5 - x)^{\frac{1}{2}} = x + 1$

Example 5 (page 387)

Solve. Check for extraneous solutions.

21. $\sqrt{3x} = \sqrt{x + 6}$

22. $(x + 5)^{\frac{1}{2}} - (5 - 2x)^{\frac{1}{4}} = 0$

23. $(7x + 6)^{\frac{1}{2}} = (9 + 4x)^{\frac{1}{2}}$

24. $\sqrt{3x + 7} = x - 1$

25. $\sqrt{x + 7} - x = 1$

26. $\sqrt{-3x - 5} = x + 3$

27. $(3x + 2)^{\frac{1}{2}} - (2x + 7)^{\frac{1}{2}} = 0$

28. $x + 8 = (x^2 + 16)^{\frac{1}{2}}$

29. $(2x)^{\frac{1}{2}} = (x + 5)^{\frac{1}{2}}$

30. $1 = (3 + x)^{\frac{1}{2}}$

B Apply Your Skills

31. Geometry The formula for the area A of a square whose side is s units long is $A = s^2$. Solve the formula for s. Find the length of the side of a square that has an area of 32 m^2.

32. a. Package Design The formula for the area A of a hexagon with a side s units long is $A = \frac{3s^2\sqrt{3}}{2}$. See the figure below. Solve the formula for s and rationalize the denominator.

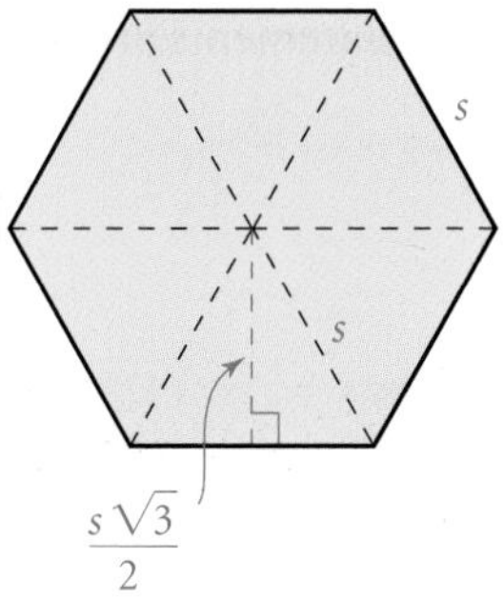

b. A package designer wants the hexagonal base of a hat box to have an area of about 200 in.^{2}. About how long is each side?

c. What is the distance between opposite sides of the hat box?

33. a. Form a pair of simultaneous equations by letting y_1 equal the left side and y_2 equal the right side of $\sqrt{5} - x = 1$. Graph the equations.

b. Repeat part (a) with the equivalent equation $\sqrt{5} = x + 1$.

c. Repeat part (a) with the equivalent equation $\sqrt{5} - x - 1 = 0$.

d. Writing Describe the similarities and differences among the graphs of the three sets of simultaneous equations.

Solve. Check for extraneous solutions.

34. $3\sqrt{2x} - 3 = 9$

35. $2(2x)^{\frac{1}{3}} + 1 = 5$

36. $\sqrt{2x - 1} - 3 = 0$

37. $(2x + 3)^{\frac{1}{2}} - 7 = 0$

38. $\sqrt{x^2 + 3} = x + 1$

39. $\sqrt{x - 5} - \sqrt{x} = -2$

40. $(2x + 3)^{\frac{3}{4}} - 3 = 5$

41. $2(x - 1)^{\frac{4}{3}} + 4 = 36$

42. $x^{\frac{1}{2}} - (x - 5)^{\frac{1}{2}} = 2$

43. $\sqrt{x} = \sqrt{x - 8} + 2$

44. $\sqrt{5x + 1} - \sqrt{4x + 3} = 0$

45. $\sqrt{x + 10} + \sqrt{3 - x} = 5$

46. $(3x + 2)^{\frac{1}{2}} = 8(3x + 2)^{-\frac{1}{2}}$

47. $\sqrt{4x - 10} = 3\sqrt{x - 5}$

48. $(x - 9)^{\frac{1}{2}} + 1 = x^{\frac{1}{2}}$

49. $\sqrt{10x} - 2\sqrt{5x - 25} = 0$

50. $(2x + 1)^{\frac{1}{3}} = (2 + 3x)^{\frac{1}{3}}$

51. $(2x - 1)^{\frac{1}{3}} = (x + 1)^{\frac{1}{6}}$

52. **Physics** The velocity v of an object dropped from a tall building is given by the formula $v = \sqrt{64d}$, where d is the distance the object has dropped. Solve the formula for d.

53. **Open-Ended** Write an equation that has two radical expressions and no real roots.

C Challenge

Solve. Check for extraneous solutions.

54. $\sqrt{x + 1} + \sqrt{2x} = \sqrt{5x + 3}$

55. $\sqrt{x + \sqrt{2x}} = 2$

56. $\sqrt{\sqrt{x + 25}} = \sqrt{x + 5}$

57. **Critical Thinking** Devise a plan to find the value of x.

$x = \sqrt{2 + \sqrt{2 + \sqrt{2 + \ldots}}}$

58. **Critical Thinking** You have solved equations containing square roots by squaring both sides. You were using the property that if $a = b$ then $a^2 = b^2$. Show that the following statements are *not* true for all real numbers.

a. If $a^2 = b^2$ then $a = b$.

b. If $a < b$ then $a^2 < b^2$.

Standardized Test Prep

Gridded Response

59. Solve $\sqrt{4x - 23} - 3 = 2$.

60. Solve $(x + 2)^{\frac{3}{4}} = 27$.

61. Solve $\sqrt{2x + 1} - \sqrt[4]{x + 11} = 0$.

62. Solve $5\sqrt{x} + 7 = 8$.

63. Solve $-\sqrt[3]{x} + 3 = 0$.

64. Solve $\sqrt{x + 2} = x$.

Take It to the NET
Online lesson quiz at
www.PHSchool.com
Web Code: aga-0705

Mixed Review

Lesson 7-4 **Simplify each expression.**

65. $64^{\frac{2}{3}}$ 66. $25^{1.5}$ 67. $6^{\frac{1}{2}} \cdot 12^{\frac{1}{2}}$ 68. $8^{\frac{1}{2}} \cdot 40^{\frac{1}{2}}$ 69. $3^{\frac{1}{3}} \cdot 18^{\frac{1}{3}}$

70. $81^{-0.25}$ 71. $4^{3.5}$ 72. $125 \cdot 125^{-\frac{1}{3}}$ 73. $32 \cdot 256^{-\frac{1}{2}}$ 74. $100^{-\frac{3}{2}} \cdot 0.01^{\frac{3}{2}}$

Lesson 6-7 **Evaluate each expression.**

75. ${}_7P_1$ 76. ${}_7P_3$ 77. ${}_5P_3$ 78. ${}_8P_4$ 79. ${}_4P_4$

80. ${}_5C_2$ 81. ${}_7C_5$ 82. ${}_5C_5$ 83. ${}_6C_5$ 84. ${}_7C_1$

Lesson 5-5 **Solve each equation by factoring.**

85. $x^2 - 7x + 12 = 0$ 86. $x^2 - 8x + 15 = 0$ 87. $x^2 + 9x + 20 = 0$

88. $3x^2 + 8x + 4 = 0$ 89. $9x^2 + 15x + 4 = 0$ 90. $4x^2 + 11x + 6 = 0$

Geometry Review

Radical Expressions in Formulas

FOR USE WITH LESSON 7-5

You frequently need to use radical expressions in geometry formulas.

EXAMPLE

The cube at the right fits in (is inscribed in) the sphere. How much more than the cube does the sphere hold?

A. 25% more **B.** 50% more **C.** 100% more **D.** 150% more

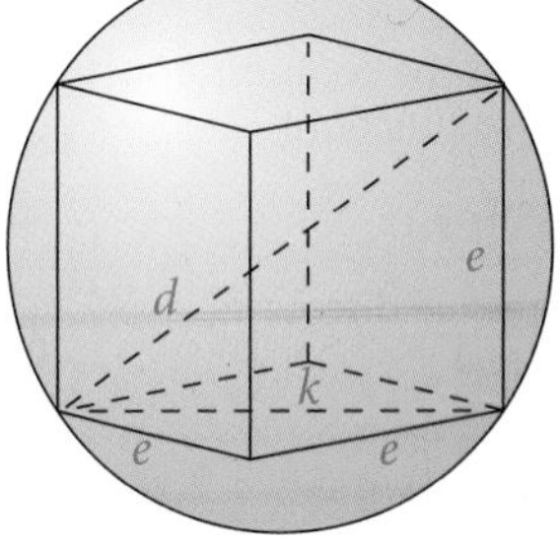

Step 1 Find k.

k is the diagonal of the square that is the base of the cube. Use the Pythagorean Theorem.

$$k^2 = e^2 + e^2$$
$$= 2e^2$$
$$k = e\sqrt{2}$$

Step 2 Find the radius of the sphere.

The diameter d of the sphere is also the diagonal of the cube and the hypotenuse of a right triangle with legs k and e.

$$d^2 = k^2 + e^2$$
$$= (e\sqrt{2})^2 + e^2$$
$$= 2e^2 + e^2$$
$$= 3e^2$$
$$d = e\sqrt{3}.$$

So the radius of the sphere is $\frac{d}{2}$ or $\frac{e\sqrt{3}}{2}$.

Step 3 Find the ratio of the volume of the sphere to the volume of the cube.

The volume of a sphere is $V = \frac{4}{3}\pi r^3$.

The volume of the cube is e^3.

$$\frac{\text{volume of sphere}}{\text{volume of cube}} = \frac{\frac{4}{3}\pi\left(\frac{e\sqrt{3}}{2}\right)^3}{e^3}$$
$$= \frac{4\pi \cdot 3e^3\sqrt{3}}{3 \cdot 8 \cdot e^3}$$
$$= \frac{\pi\sqrt{3}}{2} \approx 2.7$$

The sphere holds about 2.7 times as much as the cube, so it holds 1.7 times more, or 170% more than the cube. If you chose answer D, you are a very good estimator!

EXERCISES

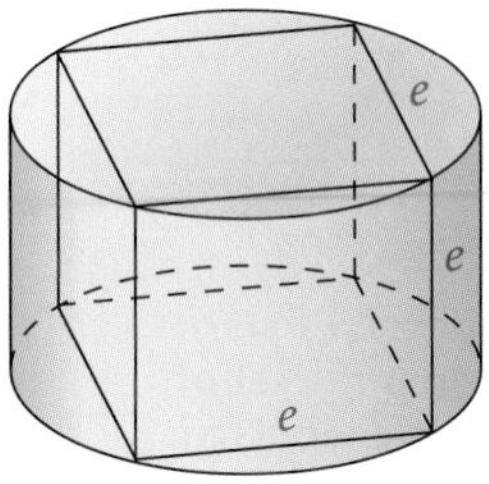

1. **a.** The cube at the right is inscribed in a cylinder. Estimate the percent by which the volume of the cylinder exceeds the volume of the cube. Then compute the percent. (The formula for the volume of a cylinder is $V = \pi r^2 h$.)

   b. Estimate the percent by which the surface area of the cylinder exceeds the surface area of the cube. Then compute the percent. (The formula for the surface area of a cylinder is S.A. $= 2\pi r^2 + 2\pi rh$.)

2. Estimate the percent by which the surface area of a sphere exceeds the surface area of its inscribed cube. Then compute the percent. (The formula for the surface area of a sphere is S.A. $= 4\pi r^2$.)

3. Estimate the percent by which the area and circumference of a circle exceed the area and perimeter of its inscribed square. Then compute the percents.

7-6 Function Operations

North Carolina Objectives

2.01 Use the composition and inverse of functions to model and solve problems; justify results.

Lesson Preview

What You'll Learn

OBJECTIVE 1 To add, subtract, multiply, and divide functions

OBJECTIVE 2 To find the composite of two functions

. . . And Why

To find successive discounts, as in Example 4

Check Skills You'll Need

(For help, go to Lesson 2-1.)

Find the domain and range of each function.

1. $\{(0, -5), (2, -3), (4, -1)\}$
2. $\{(-1, 0), (0, 0), (1, 0)\}$
3. $f(x) = 2x - 12$
4. $g(x) = x^2$

Evaluate each function for the given value of x.

5. Let $f(x) = 3x + 4$. Find $f(2)$.
6. Let $g(x) = 2x^2 - 3x + 1$. Find $g(-3)$.

New Vocabulary
- composite function

Interactive lesson includes instant self-check, tutorials, and activities.

OBJECTIVE 1 Operations With Functions

If an airplane has an airspeed of 415 mi/h, then $f(x) = 415x$ represents the distance traveled by the plane in still air in x hours. If the wind speed is 30 mi/h, then $g(x) = 30x$ represents the motion of the wind, and $f(x) + g(x) = 415x + 30x$ represents the distance traveled by the airplane flying with the wind.

You can add, subtract, multiply, and divide functions.

Key Concepts

Definition Function Operations

Addition	$(f + g)(x) = f(x) + g(x)$
Multiplication	$(f \cdot g)(x) = f(x) \cdot g(x)$
Subtraction	$(f - g)(x) = f(x) - g(x)$
Division	$\left(\frac{f}{g}\right)(x) = \frac{f(x)}{g(x)}, g(x) \neq 0$

Need Help?

The domain of a function is the set of all possible inputs of the function.

The range of a function is the set of all possible outputs of the function.

The domains of the sum, difference, product, and quotient functions consist of the x-values that are in the domains of both f and g. However, the domain of a quotient function does not contain any x-value for which $g(x) = 0$.

1 EXAMPLE Adding and Subtracting Functions

Let $f(x) = 3x + 8$ and $g(x) = 2x - 12$. Find $f + g$ and $f - g$ and their domains.

$(f + g)(x) = f(x) + g(x) = (3x + 8) + (2x - 12) = 5x - 4$

$(f - g)(x) = f(x) - g(x) = (3x + 8) - (2x - 12) = x + 20$

The domains of $f + g$ and $f - g$ are the set of real numbers.

Check Understanding 1 Let $f(x) = 5x^2 - 4x$ and $g(x) = 5x + 1$. Find $f + g$ and $f - g$ and their domains.

2 EXAMPLE Multiplying and Dividing Functions

Let $f(x) = x^2 - 1$ and $g(x) = x + 1$. Find $f \cdot g$ and $\frac{f}{g}$ and their domains.

$$(f \cdot g)(x) = f(x) \cdot g(x) = (x^2 - 1)(x + 1) = x^3 + x^2 - x - 1$$

$$\left(\frac{f}{g}\right)(x) = \frac{f(x)}{g(x)} = \frac{x^2 - 1}{x + 1} = \frac{(x + 1)(x - 1)}{x + 1} = x - 1, x \neq -1$$

The domains of f and g are the set of real numbers, so the domain of $f \cdot g$ is also. The domain of $\frac{f}{g}$ does not include -1 because $g(-1) = 0$.

Check Understanding 2 Let $f(x) = 6x^2 + 7x - 5$ and $g(x) = 2x - 1$. Find $f \cdot g$ and $\frac{f}{g}$ and their domains.

OBJECTIVE

2 Composition of Functions

The diagram below shows what happens when you apply one function $g(x)$ after another function $f(x)$.

Reading Math

Composite means "put together."

The output from the first function becomes the input for the second function. When you combine two functions as in the diagram above, you form a **composite function.**

Key Concepts

Definition **Composition of Functions**

The composition of function g with function f is written as $g \circ f$ and is defined as $(g \circ f)(x) = g(f(x))$, where the domain of $g \circ f$ consists of the values a in the domain of f such that $f(a)$ is in the domain of g.

$$(g \circ f)(x) = g(f(x))$$

① **Evaluate the inner function $f(x)$ first.**

② **Then use your answer as the input of the outer function $g(x)$.**

3 EXAMPLE Composition of Functions

Let $f(x) = x - 2$ and $g(x) = x^2$. Find $(g \circ f)(-5)$.

Method 1

$(g \circ f)(x) = g(f(x)) = g(x - 2) = (x - 2)^2$

$(g \circ f)(-5) = (-5 - 2)^2$

$= (-7)^2$

$= 49$

Method 2

$(g \circ f)(x) = g(f(x))$

$g(f(-5)) = g(-5 - 2)$

$= g(-7)$

$= (-7)^2 = 49$

Check Understanding 3 **a.** Find $(f \circ g)(x)$ and evaluate $(f \circ g)(-5)$ for the functions f and g defined in Example 3.

b. **Critical Thinking** Is a composition of functions commutative? Explain.

4 EXAMPLE Real-World Connection

Consumer Issues Suppose you are shopping in the store in the photo. You have a coupon worth \$5 off any item.

a. Use functions to model discounting an item by 20% and to model applying the coupon.

Let x = the original price.

Cost with 20% discount:

$f(x) = x - 0.2x = 0.8x$

Cost with a coupon for \$5:

$g(x) = x - 5$

b. Use a composition of your two functions to model how much you would pay for an item if the clerk applies the discount first and then the coupon.

$$\begin{aligned}(g \circ f)(x) &= g(f(x)) && \textbf{applying the discount first}\\ &= g(0.8x)\\ &= 0.8x - 5\end{aligned}$$

c. Use a composition of your two functions to model how much you would pay for an item if the clerk applies the coupon first and then the discount.

$$\begin{aligned}(f \circ g)(x) &= f(g(x)) && \textbf{applying the coupon first}\\ &= f(x - 5)\\ &= 0.8(x - 5)\\ &= 0.8x - 4\end{aligned}$$

d. How much more is any item if the clerk applies the coupon first?

$$\begin{aligned}(f \circ g)(x) - (g \circ f)(x) &= (0.8x - 4) - (0.8x - 5) && \textbf{Subtract the functions.}\\ &= 1\end{aligned}$$

Any item will cost \$1 more.

Check Understanding **4** A store is offering a 10% discount on all items. In addition, employees get a 25% discount.

a. Write a composite function to model taking the 10% discount first.

b. Write a composite function to model taking the 25% discount first.

c. Suppose you are an employee. Which discount would you prefer to take first?

EXERCISES

For more practice, see *Extra Practice*.

Practice and Problem Solving

A Practice by Example

Examples 1 and 2 (pages 392 and 393)

Let $f(x) = 3x + 5$ and $g(x) = x^2$. Perform each function operation.

1. $f(x) + g(x)$	**2.** $g(x) - f(x)$	**3.** $f(x) - g(x)$
4. $f(x) \cdot g(x)$	**5.** $\frac{f(x)}{g(x)}$	**6.** $\frac{g(x)}{f(x)}$
7. $(f + g)(x)$	**8.** $(f - g)(x)$	**9.** $(g - f)(x)$
10. $(f \cdot g)(x)$	**11.** $\left(\frac{f}{g}\right)(x)$	**12.** $\left(\frac{g}{f}\right)(x)$

Let $f(x) = 2x^2 + x - 3$ and $g(x) = x - 1$. Perform each function operation and then find the domain.

13. $f(x) + g(x)$ 14. $g(x) - f(x)$ 15. $f(x) - g(x)$

16. $f(x) \cdot g(x)$ 17. $\frac{f(x)}{g(x)}$ 18. $\frac{g(x)}{f(x)}$

19. Let $f(x) = 9x$ and $g(x) = 3x$. Find $(f \cdot g)(x)$ and $\left(\frac{f}{g}\right)(x)$ and their domains.

Example 3 (page 393)

Use each diagram to find $(g \circ f)(x)$. Then evaluate $(g \circ f)(3)$ and $(g \circ f)(-2)$.

20.

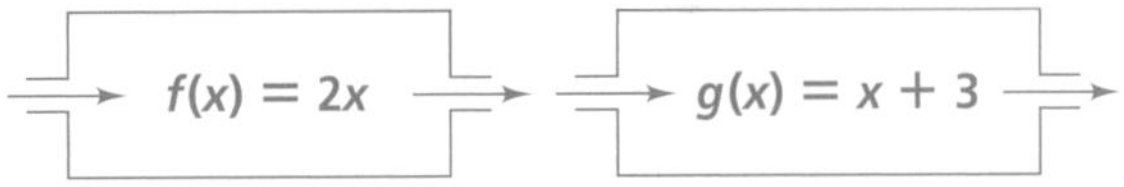

21.

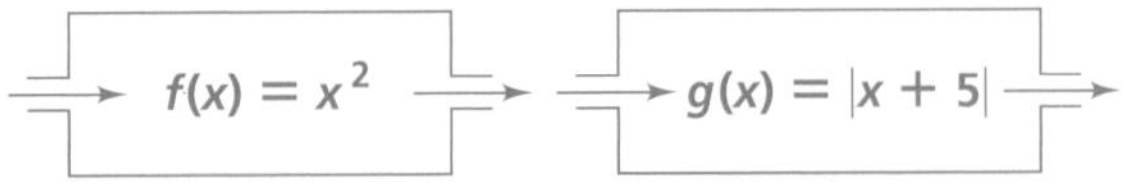

Let $g(x) = 2x$ and $h(x) = x^2 + 4$. Evaluate each expression.

22. $(h \circ g)(1)$ 23. $(h \circ g)(-5)$ 24. $(h \circ g)(-2)$

25. $(g \circ h)(-2)$ 26. $(g \circ h)(0)$ 27. $(g \circ h)(-1)$

28. $(g \circ g)(3)$ 29. $(h \circ h)(2)$ 30. $(h \circ h)(-4)$

Let $f(x) = x^2$ and $g(x) = x - 3$. Find each value or expression.

31. $(g \circ f)(-2)$ 32. $(f \circ g)(-2)$ 33. $(g \circ f)(0)$

34. $(f \circ g)(0)$ 35. $(g \circ f)(3.5)$ 36. $(f \circ g)(3.5)$

37. $(f \circ g)\left(\frac{1}{2}\right)$ 38. $(g \circ f)\left(\frac{1}{2}\right)$ 39. $(f \circ g)(c)$

40. $(g \circ f)(c)$ 41. $(f \circ g)(-a)$ 42. $(g \circ f)(-a)$

Example 4 (page 394)

43. **Sales** A car dealer offers a 10% discount off the list price x for any car on the lot. At the same time, the manufacturer offers a \$2000 rebate for each purchase of a car.
   a. Write a function $f(x)$ to represent the price after the discount.
   b. Write a function $g(x)$ to represent the price after the \$2000 rebate.
   c. Suppose the list price of a car is \$18,000. Use a composite function to find the price of the car if the discount is applied before the rebate.
   d. Suppose the list price of a car is \$18,000. Use a composite function to find the price of the car if the rebate is applied before the discount.

Real-World Connection

International companies must often compute their costs in many currencies.

44. **Economics** Suppose the function $f(x) = 0.12x$ represents the number of U.S. dollars equivalent to x Chinese yuan and the function $g(x) = 9.14x$ represents the number of Mexican pesos equivalent to x U.S. dollars.
   a. Write a composite function that represents the number of Mexican pesos equivalent to x Chinese yuan.
   b. Find the value in Mexican pesos of an item that costs 15 Chinese yuan.

B **Apply Your Skills**

Let $f(x) = 2x + 5$ and $g(x) = x^2 - 3x + 2$. Perform each function operation.

45. $f(x) + g(x)$ **46.** $3f(x) - 2$ **47.** $g(x) - f(x)$

48. $-2g(x) + f(x)$ **49.** $f(x) - g(x) + 10$ **50.** $4f(x) + 2g(x)$

Let $f(x) = 3x^2 + 2x - 8$ and $g(x) = x + 2$. Perform each function operation and then find the domain.

51. $-f(x) + 4g(x)$ **52.** $f(x) - 2g(x)$ **53.** $f(x) \cdot g(x)$

54. $-3f(x) \cdot g(x)$ **55.** $\frac{f(x)}{g(x)}$ **56.** $\frac{5f(x)}{g(x)}$

57. Writing Evaluate $(g \circ f)(3)$, when $f(x) = 2x$ and $g(x) = x + 1$. Explain what you do first and why.

Let $g(x) = 3x + 2$ and $f(x) = \frac{x-2}{3}$. Find each value.

58. $f(g(1))$ **59.** $g(f(-4))$ **60.** $f(g(0))$ **61.** $g(f(2))$

Reading Math

For help with reading and solving Exercise 62a, see p. 399.

62. Geometry You toss a pebble into a pool of water and watch the circular ripples radiate outward. You find that the function $r(x) = 12.5x$ describes the radius r in inches of a circle x seconds after it was formed. The function $A(x) = \pi x^2$ describes the area A of a circle with radius x.

a. Find $(A \circ r)(x)$ when $x = 2$. Interpret your answer.

b. Find the area of a circle 4 seconds after it was formed.

For each pair of functions, find $f(g(x))$ and $g(f(x))$.

63. $f(x) = 3x, g(x) = x^2$ **64.** $f(x) = x + 3, g(x) = x - 5$

65. $f(x) = 3x^2 + 2, g(x) = 2x$ **66.** $f(x) = \frac{x-3}{2}, g(x) = 2x - 3$

67. $f(x) = -x - 7, g(x) = 4x$ **68.** $f(x) = \frac{x+5}{2}, g(x) = x^2$

69. Open-Ended Write a function rule that approximates each value.

a. The amount you save is a percent of what you earn. (You choose the percent.)

b. The amount you earn depends on how many hours you work. (You choose the hourly wage.)

c. Write and simplify a composite function that expresses your savings as a function of the number of hours you work. Interpret your results.

70. a. Technology Suppose $f(x) = 3x$ and $g(x) = x^2 + 3$. In the spreadsheet, values for x are in Column A. What do the formulas in B and C represent?

	A	B	C	D	E
1		=3*A1	=A1^2+3	■	■
2	0	■	■	■	■
3	5	■	■	■	■
4	10	■	■	■	■

b. If the formulas in columns B and C are copied down the columns, what numbers will appear?

c. Find $(f \circ g)(x)$.

d. Complete column D for $(f \circ g)(x)$.

e. Find $(g \circ f)(x)$.

f. Complete column E for $(g \circ f)(x)$.

Real-World Connection

Careers A craftsman and business owner uses math to find profit.

71. **Profit** A craftsman makes and sells violins. The function $C(x) = 1000 + 700x$ represents his cost in dollars to produce x violins. The function $I(x) = 5995x$ represents the income in dollars from selling x violins.
   a. Write and simplify a function $P(x) = I(x) - C(x)$.
   b. Find $P(30)$, the profit earned when he makes and sells 30 violins.

72. **Writing** A salesperson earns a 3% bonus on weekly sales over \$5000.

$$g(x) = 0.03x$$
$$h(x) = x - 5000$$

   a. Explain what each function above represents.
   b. Which composition, $(h \circ g)(x)$ or $(g \circ h)(x)$, represents the weekly bonus? Explain.

Let $f(x) = 3x - 2$ and $g(x) = x^2 + 1$. Perform each function operation and use the properties of real numbers to justify each step in simplifying your answer.

73. $(f + g)(x)$ 74. $(f - g)(x)$ 75. $(f \circ g)(x)$

76. **Grades** Suppose your teacher offers to give the whole class a bonus if everyone passes the next math test. The teacher says she will (1) give everyone a 10-point bonus and (2) increase everyone's grade by 9% of their score.
   a. Let x represent the original test scores. Write statements (1) and (2) as the functions $f(x)$ and $g(x)$, respectively.
   b. Explain the meaning of $f(g(x))$. Evaluate $f(g(75))$.
   c. Explain the meaning of $g(f(x))$. Evaluate $g(f(75))$.
   d. Does $g(f(x)) = f(g(x))$?

C Challenge

Let $f(x) = x^4 + 2x^3 - 5x^2 - 10x$ and $g(x) = x^3 - 3x^2 - 5x + 15$. Perform each function operation and simplify, and then find the domain.

77. $f(x) \cdot g(x)$ 78. $\frac{f(x)}{g(x)}$ 79. $\frac{g(x)}{f(x)}$

Find each composition of functions. Simplify your answer.

80. Let $f(x) = \frac{1}{x}$. Find $f(f(x))$.

81. Let $f(x) = \frac{1}{x}$. Find $f(f(f(x)))$.

82. Let $f(x) = 1 - \frac{x}{2}$. Find $f(f(f(x)))$.

83. Let $f(x) = 2x - 3$. Find $\frac{f(1 + h) - f(1)}{h}$, $h \neq 0$.

84. Let $f(x) = 4x - 1$. Find $\frac{f(a + h) - f(a)}{h}$, $h \neq 0$.

Standardized Test Prep

Multiple Choice

85. Let $f(x) = -4x + 1$ and $g(x) = 2x - 6$. Find $(g - f)(x)$.
   A. $6x - 5$ B. $6x - 7$ C. $-6x + 5$ D. $-6x + 7$

86. If $f(x) = 2x^2$ and $g(x) = 3x$, what is $(g \circ f)(x)$?
   F. $6x^2$ G. $9x^2$ H. $18x^2$ I. $8x^4$

Short Response

87. If $f(x) = 3x - 4$ and $g(x) = x + 3$, what does $(f \cdot g)(x)$ mean? What is the value of $(f \cdot g)(x)$? Simplify the answer.

Quantitative Comparison

For problems 88–91, use $f(x) = 2x^2$, $g(x) = 3x - 5$, and $h(x) = \frac{1}{x}$. Compare the boxed quantity in Column A with the boxed quantity in Column B. Choose the best answer.

A. The quantity in Column A is greater.
B. The quantity in Column B is greater.
C. The two quantities are equal.
D. The relationship cannot be determined from the information given.

	Column A	Column B
88.	$(f \circ g)(5)$	$(g \circ f)(5)$
89.	$(h \cdot f)(x)$	$(f \cdot h)(x)$
90.	$(h \circ f)(1)$	$(f \circ h)(1)$
91.	$(g \cdot h)(x)$	$(h \cdot g)(x)$

Take It to the NET
Online lesson quiz at
www.PHSchool.com
Web Code: aga-0706

Mixed Review

Lesson 7-5 **Solve. Check for extraneous solutions.**

92. $\sqrt{x^2 + 3} = x + 1$ **93.** $x + 8 = (x^2 + 16)^{\frac{1}{2}}$ **94.** $\sqrt{x^2 + 9} = x + 1$

95. $(x^2 - 9)^{\frac{1}{2}} - x = -3$ **96.** $\sqrt{x^2 + 12} - 2 = x$ **97.** $(3x)^{\frac{1}{2}} = (x + 6)^{\frac{1}{2}}$

Lesson 6-8 **Expand each binomial.**

98. $(x + 4)^8$ **99.** $(x + y)^6$ **100.** $(2x - y)^4$ **101.** $(2x - 3y)^7$

102. $(9 - 2x)^5$ **103.** $(4x - y)^5$ **104.** $(x^2 + x)^4$ **105.** $(x^2 + 2y^3)^6$

Lesson 5-6 **Simplify each expression.**

106. $(2 - 3\sqrt{-4}) + (4 + 2\sqrt{-16})$ **107.** $3\sqrt{-50} - (2 - \sqrt{-32})$

108. $(6 + \sqrt{-20}) - (-7 - \sqrt{-45})$ **109.** $(5 - \sqrt{-9})(2 - \sqrt{-36})$

Checkpoint Quiz 2 — Lessons 7-4 through 7-6

TEXT Instant self-check quiz online and on CD-ROM

Simplify each expression.

1. $(-27x^3)^{\frac{4}{3}}$ **2.** $(32y^5)^{-0.4}$

Solve each equation.

3. $\sqrt{3x + 1} - 4 = 0$ **4.** $(5x + 2)^{\frac{2}{3}} = 9$

Solve each equation. Check for extraneous solutions.

5. $\sqrt{3x + 3} - 3 = 3x$ **6.** $(2 - x)^{0.5} - x = 4$

Let $f(x) = 2x + 3$ and $g(x) = x^2 - x$. Find each value.

7. $(f + g)\left(\frac{1}{2}\right)$ **8.** $(f \cdot g)(1)$ **9.** $\left(\frac{f}{g}\right)(2)$ **10.** $(f \circ g)(5)$

Reading Math

Reading Mathematical Symbols

FOR USE WITH PAGE 396, EXERCISE 62A

Read the problem below. Then read how function notation is used. Check your understanding with the exercise at the bottom of the page.

Geometry You toss a pebble into a pool of water and watch the circular ripples radiate outward. You find that the function $r(x) = 12.5x$ describes the radius r in inches of a circle x seconds after it was formed. The function $A(x) = \pi x^2$ describes the area A of a circle with radius x.

a. Find $(A \circ r)(x)$ when $x = 2$. Interpret your answer.

The problem uses function notation. Here is the way to read function notation.

Write	$f(x)$	$f(g(x))$	$(f \circ g)(x) = f(g(x))$
Read	f of x	f of g of x	The composition of f with g equals f of g of x.

Examples For $f(x) = x^2$, find $f(3)$.

$f(3) = 3^2 = 9$ **Substitute the value 3 for x and simplify.**

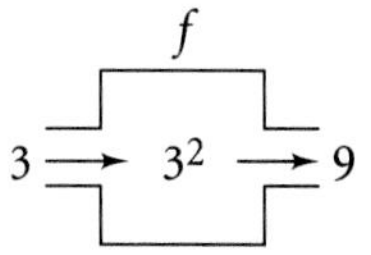

For $f(x) = x^2$ and $g(x) = 2x$, find $(f \circ g)(5)$.

$(f \circ g)(5) = f(g(5))$

$g(x) = 2 \cdot 5 = 10$ **Find g(5) first.**

$f(10) = 10^2 = 100$ **Use the output g(5) = 10 as the input for f(x).**

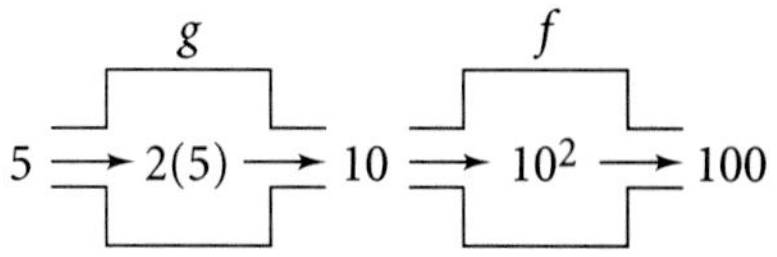

Now find $(A \circ r)(x)$ when $x = 2$. Recall that $r(x) = 12.5x$ and $A(x) = \pi x^2$.

$(A \circ r)(2) = A(r(2))$

$r(2) = 12.5(2) = 25$ **Find r(2) first.**

$A(25) = \pi(25)^2$ **Use the output r(2) = 25 as the input for A(x).**

$= 625\pi \approx 1963$

To interpret your answer is to explain what your answer means in terms of the problem. The problem tells you that $A(x)$ is the area of a circle with radius x and that $r(x)$ is the radius of a circle x seconds after it was formed.

So $(A \circ r)(2)$ is the area of a circle after 2 seconds. The area is about 1963 in.^{2}.

EXERCISE

You toss a pebble into a pool of water and watch the circular ripples radiate outward. You find that the function $r(x) = 12.5x$ describes the radius of the first circle r in inches after x seconds. The function $C(x) = 2\pi x$ describes the circumference C of a circle with radius x. Find $(C \circ r)(x)$ when $x = 3$. Interpret your answer.

7-7 Inverse Relations and Functions

North Carolina Objectives

2.01 Use the composition and inverse of functions to model and solve problems; justify results.

Lesson Preview

What You'll Learn

OBJECTIVE 1 To find the inverse of a relation or function

. . . And Why

To estimate the speed of a car, as in Example 5

✓ Check Skills You'll Need

(For help, go to Lesson 3-1)

Graph each pair of functions on a single coordinate plane.

1. $y = x - 6$
$y = x + 6$

2. $y = \frac{x - 7}{2}$
$y = 2x + 7$

3. $y = 3x - 1$
$y = \frac{x + 1}{3}$

4. $y = 0.5x + 1$
$y = 2x - 2$

5. $y = -x + 4$
$y = \frac{-x + 4}{-1}$

6. $y = \frac{x + 4}{5}$
$y = 5x - 4$

New Vocabulary • inverse relation • inverse functions

Interactive lesson includes instant self-check, tutorials, and activities.

OBJECTIVE 1

The Inverse of a Function

Investigation: Inverses

- Function f doubles the input and then subtracts 8. $f(x) = 2x - 8$
- Function g adds 8 to the input and then divides by 2. $g(x) = \frac{x + 8}{2}$

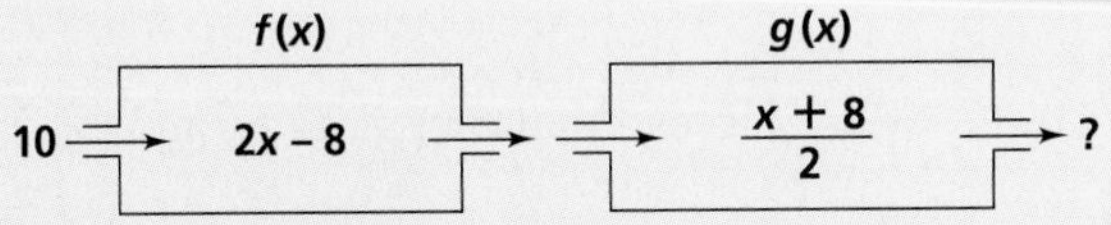

1. a. Find $f(10)$ and $g(f(10))$.
b. Find $f(0)$ and $g(f(0))$.
c. Find $f(-7)$ and $g(f(-7))$.
d. Without computing, use the pattern in parts (a)–(c) to find $g(f(-1496))$.

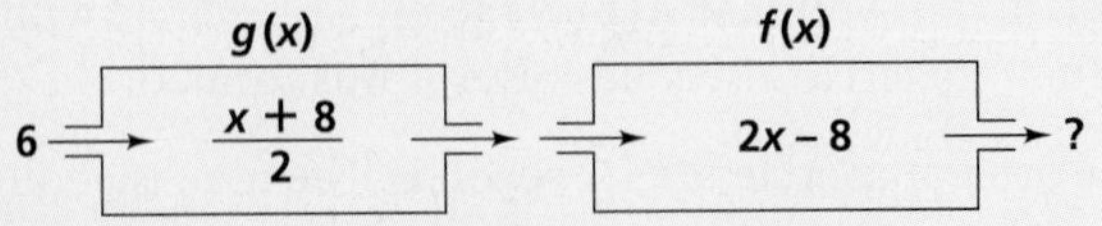

2. a. Find $g(6)$ and $f(g(6))$.
b. Find $g(0)$ and $f(g(0))$.
c. Find $g(-32)$ and $f(g(-32))$.
d. Without computing, use the pattern in parts (a)–(c) to find $f(g(\pi))$.

3. a. Interchange the x and y variables in $y = 2x - 8$ and solve for y.
b. Graph your two equations in part (a) on the same coordinate axes. Fold your graph paper so the two lines coincide. How are the two graphs related?

Need Help?

Both relations and functions are sets of ordered pairs.

When each element of the domain is associated with only one element of the range, the relation is a function.

If a relation maps element a of its domain to element b of its range, the **inverse relation** "undoes" the relation and maps b back to a. So, if (a, b) is an ordered pair of a relation, then (b, a) is an ordered pair of its inverse.

This diagram shows a relation r and its inverse.

The range of the relation is the domain of the inverse, and the domain of the relation is the range of the inverse.

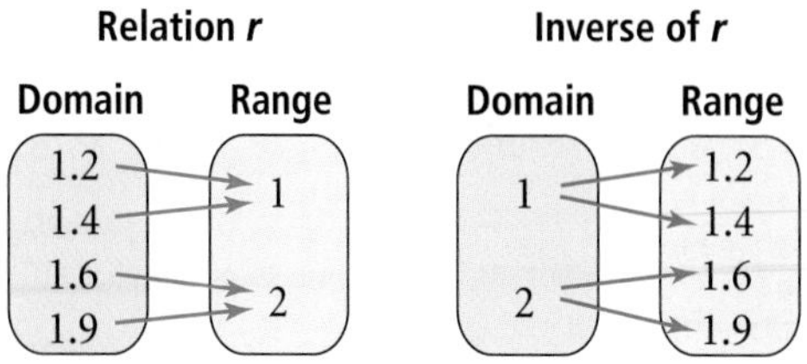

1 EXAMPLE Finding the Inverse of a Relation

a. Find the inverse of relation s.

Relation s

x	1	2	3	4
y	–1	0	1	1

Interchange the x and y values to get the inverse.

Inverse of Relation s

x	–1	0	1	1
y	1	2	3	4

b. Graph s and its inverse.

Relation s

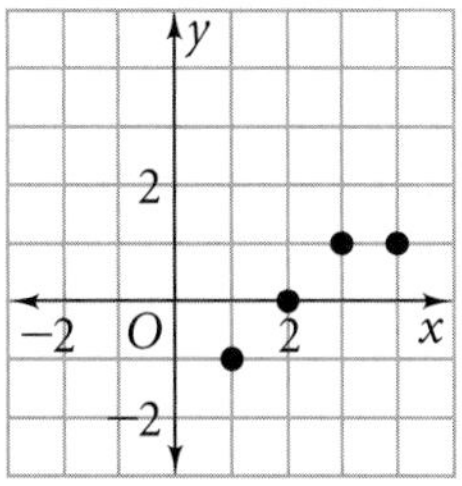

Reversing the Ordered Pairs

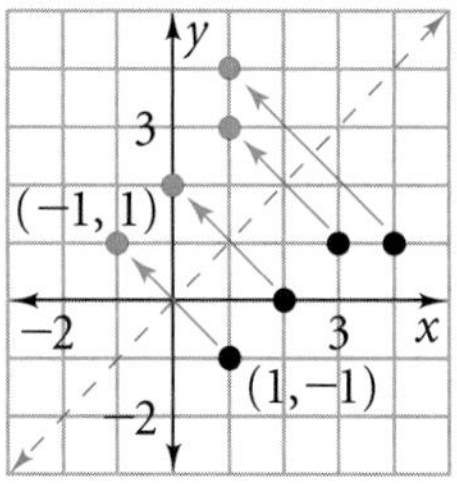

Inverse of s

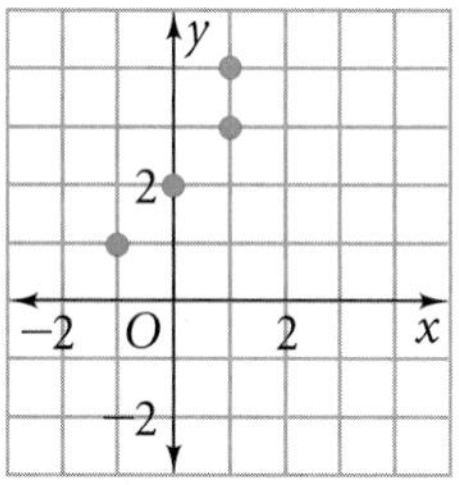

Check Understanding **1** **a.** Describe how the line $y = x$ is related to the graphs of s and its inverse.
b. In Example 1, is relation s a function? Is the inverse of s a function?

As shown in Example 1, the graph of the inverse of a relation is the reflection in the line $y = x$ of the graph of the relation. If a relation or function is described by an equation in x and y, you can interchange x and y to get the inverse.

2 EXAMPLE Interchanging *x* and *y*

Find the inverse of $y = x^2 + 3$.

$y = x^2 + 3$

$x = y^2 + 3$ **Interchange x and y.**

$x - 3 = y^2$ **Solve for y.**

$\pm\sqrt{x - 3} = y$ **Find the square root of each side.**

Check Understanding **2** **a.** Does $y = x^2 + 3$ define a function? Is its inverse a function? Explain.
b. Find the inverse of $y = 3x - 10$. Is the inverse a function? Explain.

3 EXAMPLE Graphing a Relation and Its Inverse

Graph $y = x^2 + 3$ and its inverse, $y = \pm\sqrt{x - 3}$.

The graph of $y = x^2 + 3$ is a parabola that opens upward with vertex (0, 3). The reflection of the parabola in the line $y = x$ is the graph of the inverse.

You can also find points on the graph of the inverse by reversing the coordinates of points on $y = x^2 + 3$.

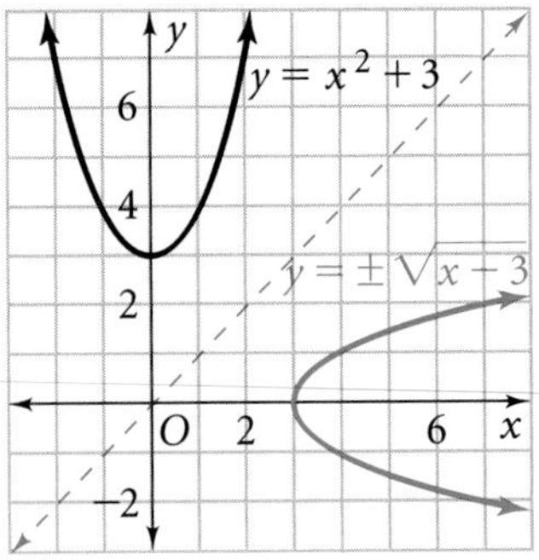

Check Understanding 3 Graph $y = 3x - 10$ and its inverse.

> **Reading Math**
>
> For a number x, x^{-1} is the multiplicative inverse of x, or $\frac{1}{x}$.
>
> For a function f, f^{-1} is the relation that is the inverse of f.

The inverse of function f is denoted by f^{-1}. Read f^{-1} as "the inverse of f" or as "f inverse." The notation $f(x)$ is used for functions, but $f^{-1}(x)$ may be a relation that is *not* a function.

4 EXAMPLE Finding an Inverse Function

Consider the function $f(x) = \sqrt{x + 1}$.

a. Find the domain and range of f.

Since the radicand cannot be negative, the domain is the set of numbers greater than or equal to -1. Since the principal square root is nonnegative, the range is the set of nonnegative numbers.

b. Find f^{-1}.

$f(x) = \sqrt{x + 1}$

$y = \sqrt{x + 1}$ **Rewrite the equation using y.**

$x = \sqrt{y + 1}$ **Interchange x and y. Since x equals a principal square root, x ≥ 0.**

$x^2 = y + 1$ **Square both sides.**

$y = x^2 - 1$ **Solve for y.**

So, $f^{-1}(x) = x^2 - 1,\ x \geq 0$.

c. Find the domain and range of f^{-1}.

The domain of f^{-1} equals the range of f, which is the set of nonnegative numbers. Since $x^2 \geq 0$, $x^2 - 1 \geq -1$. Thus the range of f^{-1} is the set of numbers greater than or equal to -1. Note that the range of f^{-1} is the same as the domain of f.

d. Is f^{-1} a function? Explain.

For each x in the domain of f^{-1}, there is only one value of $f^{-1}(x)$. So f^{-1} is a function.

Check Understanding 4 Let $f(x) = 10 - 3x$. Find each of the following.

a. the domain and range of f
b. f^{-1}
c. the domain and range of f^{-1}
d. $f^{-1}(f(3))$
e. $f(f^{-1}(2))$

Functions that model real-life situations are frequently expressed as formulas with letters that remind you of the variables they represent. When finding the inverse of a formula, it would be very confusing to interchange the letters. Keep the letters the same and just solve the formula for the other variable.

Real-World Connection

Many safe driving programs include experience with braking distance.

5 EXAMPLE Real-World Connection

Physics The function $d = \frac{r^2}{24}$ is a model for the distance d in feet that a car with locked brakes skids in coming to a complete stop from a speed of r mi/h. Find the inverse of the function. Use the inverse to estimate the speed of a car that made skid marks 114 feet long.

$d = \frac{r^2}{24}$

$r^2 = 24d$ **Solve for *r*. Do not interchange the variables.**

$r = \sqrt{24d}$ **Rate of speed must be positive.**

$= \sqrt{24 \cdot 114}$ **Substitute 114 for *d*.**

≈ 52 **Use a calculator.**

The car was traveling about 52 mi/h.

Check Understanding 5 The function $d = \frac{v^2}{64}$ is a model relating the distance a stone has fallen in feet to its velocity in feet per second (ft/s). Find the inverse of the function and use it to find the velocity of a stone that has fallen 30 ft.

If f and f^{-1} are both functions, and if f pairs a with b, then f^{-1} must pair b with a.

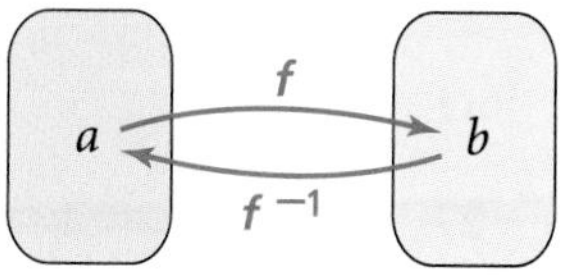

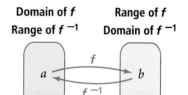

If f and f^{-1} are functions, they are called **inverse functions.** For inverse functions, $f^{-1}(f(x)) = x$ and $f(f^{-1}(x)) = x$.

Key Concepts

Property	Composition of Inverse Functions
If f and f^{-1} are inverse functions, then $(f^{-1} \circ f)(x) = x$ and $(f \circ f^{-1})(x) = x$.	

6 EXAMPLE Composition of Inverse Functions

For the function $f(x) = \frac{x - 7}{6}$, find $(f^{-1} \circ f)(374)$ and $(f \circ f^{-1})(-99\pi)$.

Since f is a linear function, so is f^{-1}. Therefore f^{-1} is a function.

So $(f^{-1} \circ f)(374) = 374$ and $(f \circ f^{-1})(-99\pi) = -99\pi$.

Check Understanding 6 For $f(x) = 5x + 11$, find $(f^{-1} \circ f)(777)$ and $(f \circ f^{-1})(-5802)$.

EXERCISES

For more practice, see *Extra Practice.*

Practice and Problem Solving

A Practice by Example

Example 1 (page 401)

Find the inverse of each relation. Graph the given relation and its inverse.

1.

x	1	2	3	4
y	0	1	0	2

2.

x	1	2	3	4
y	0	1	2	3

3.

x	0	1	2	3
y	0	1	4	9

4.

x	−3	−2	−1	0
y	2	2	2	2

Example 2 (page 401)

Find the inverse of each function. Is the inverse a function?

5. $y = 3x + 1$ **6.** $y = 2x - 1$ **7.** $y = 4 - 3x$

8. $y = 5 - 2x^2$ **9.** $y = x^2 + 4$ **10.** $y = 3x^2 - 5$

11. $y = (x + 1)^2$ **12.** $y = (3x - 4)^2$ **13.** $y = (1 - 2x)^2 + 5$

Example 3 (page 402)

Graph each relation and its inverse.

14. $y = 2x - 3$ **15.** $y = 3 - 7x$ **16.** $y = -x$

17. $y = 3x^2$ **18.** $y = -x^2$ **19.** $y = 4x^2 - 2$

20. $y = (x - 1)^2$ **21.** $y = (2 - x)^2$ **22.** $y = (3 - 2x)^2 - 1$

Example 4 (page 402)

For each function f, find f^{-1} and the domain and range of f and f^{-1}. Determine whether f^{-1} is a function.

23. $f(x) = 3x + 4$ **24.** $f(x) = \sqrt{x - 5}$

25. $f(x) = \sqrt{x + 7}$ **26.** $f(x) = \sqrt{-2x + 3}$

27. $f(x) = 2x^2 + 2$ **28.** $f(x) = -x^2 + 1$

Example 5 (page 403)

29. The formula for converting from Celsius to Fahrenheit temperatures is $C = \frac{9}{5}F + 32$.

a. Find the inverse of the formula. Is the inverse a function?
b. Use the inverse to find the Fahrenheit temperature that corresponds to 25°C.

30. Geometry The formula for the volume of a sphere is $V = \frac{4}{3}\pi r^3$.

a. Find the inverse of the formula. Is the inverse a function?
b. Use the inverse to find the radius of a sphere that has a volume of 35,000 ft ^{3}.

Example 6 (page 403)

For Exercises 31–34, $f(x) = 10x - 10$. Find each value.

31. $(f^{-1} \circ f)(10)$ **32.** $(f \circ f^{-1})(-10)$

33. $(f^{-1} \circ f)(0.2)$ **34.** $(f \circ f^{-1})(d)$

B Apply Your Skills

Find the inverse of each function. Is the inverse a function?

35. $f(x) = 1.5x^2 - 4$ **36.** $f(x) = \frac{3x^2}{4}$ **37.** $f(x) = \sqrt{2x - 1} + 3$

38. $f(x) = (x + 1)^2$ **39.** $f(x) = (2x - 1)^2$ **40.** $f(x) = (x + 1)^2 - 1$

41. $f(x) = x^3$ **42.** $f(x) = x^4$ **43.** $f(x) = \frac{2x^2}{5} + 1$

Real-World Connection

Water towers are tall because each foot of height provides 0.43 lb/in.^{2} of pressure. A typical tower holds about a one-day supply for users.

44. Water Supply The velocity of the water that flows from an opening at the base of a tank depends on the height of water above the opening. The function $v(x) = \sqrt{2gx}$ models the velocity v in feet per second where g, the acceleration due to gravity, is about 32 ft/s^2 and x is the height in feet of the water. Find the inverse function and use it to find the depth of water when the flow is 40 ft/s, and when the flow is 20 ft/s.

45. Writing Explain how you can find the range of the inverse of $f(x) = \sqrt{x - 1}$ without finding the inverse itself.

46. A function consists of the pairs (2, 3), $(x, 4)$ and (5, 6). What values, if any, may x not assume?

For each function f, find f^{-1}, the domain and range of f and f^{-1}, and determine whether f^{-1} is a function.

47. $f(x) = -\sqrt{x}$	**48.** $f(x) = \sqrt{x} + 3$	**49.** $f(x) = \sqrt{-x + 3}$
50. $f(x) = \sqrt{x + 2}$	**51.** $f(x) = \frac{x^2}{2}$	**52.** $f(x) = \frac{1}{x^2}$
53. $f(x) = (x - 4)^2$	**54.** $f(x) = (7 - x)^2$	**55.** $f(x) = \frac{1}{(x + 1)^2}$
56. $f(x) = 4 - 2\sqrt{x}$	**57.** $f(x) = \frac{3}{\sqrt{x}}$	**58.** $f(x) = \frac{1}{\sqrt{-2x}}$

59. a. Copy the mapping diagram at the right. Complete it by writing members of the domain and range and connecting them with arrows so that r is a function and r^{-1} is not a function.

b. Repeat part (a) so that r is not a function and r^{-1} is a function.

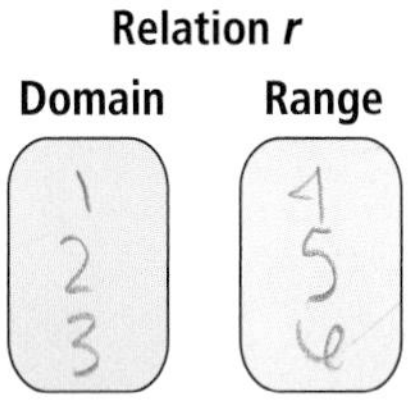

60. Critical Thinking Relation r has one element in its domain and two elements in its range. Is r a function? Is the inverse of r a function? Explain.

61. Geometry Write a function that gives the length of the hypotenuse of an isosceles right triangle with side length s. Evaluate the inverse of the function to find the side length of an isosceles right triangle with a hypotenuse of 6 in.

62. Open-Ended Write a function f such that the graph of f^{-1} lies in Quadrants III and IV.

C Challenge

Find the inverse of each function. Is the inverse a function?

63. $f(x) = \frac{1}{5}x^3$	**64.** $f(x) = \sqrt[3]{x - 5}$	**65.** $f(x) = \frac{\sqrt[3]{x}}{3}$
66. $f(x) = (x - 2)^3$	**67.** $f(x) = \sqrt[4]{x}$	**68.** $f(x) = 1.2x^4$

Standardized Test Prep

Multiple Choice

69. What is the inverse of $y = 5x - 1$?

A. $y = 5x + 1$ **B.** $y = \frac{x + 1}{5}$ **C.** $y = \frac{x}{5} + 1$ **D.** $y = \frac{x}{5} - 1$

70. If $f(x) = 4x - 3$, what is $(f^{-1} \circ f)(10)$?

F. $\frac{13}{4}$ **G.** 10 **H.** 37 **I.** $\frac{481}{4}$

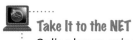

Take It to the NET
Online lesson quiz at www.PHSchool.com
Web Code: aga-0707

71. What is the inverse of $y = x^2 - 3$?

A. $y = \pm\sqrt{x} + 3$
B. $y = \pm\sqrt{x} - 3$
C. $y = \pm\sqrt{x + 3}$
D. $y = \pm\sqrt{x - 3}$

Short Response

72. What is the inverse of $y = 4x^2 + 5$? For what values of x is the inverse a real number?

Extended Response

73. What is the inverse of $y = x^2 - 2x + 1$? Is the inverse a function? Explain.

Mixed Review

Lesson 7-6

Let $f(x) = 4x$, $g(x) = \frac{1}{2}x + 7$, and $h(x) = |-2x + 4|$. Simplify each function.

74. $(f \circ g)(x)$
75. $(g \circ f)(x)$
76. $(h \circ g)(x)$
77. $g(x) + g(x)$
78. $(h \circ (g \circ f))(x)$
79. $(f \circ g)(x) + h(x)$

Lesson 7-1

Find each indicated root if it is a real number.

80. $\sqrt[4]{16}$
81. $-\sqrt[4]{16}$
82. $\sqrt[4]{-16}$
83. $\sqrt[5]{243}$
84. $-\sqrt[5]{243}$
85. $\sqrt[5]{-243}$
86. $\sqrt[3]{0.064}$
87. $\sqrt[4]{810{,}000}$

Lesson 6-5

List all possible rational roots for each equation. Then use the Rational Root Theorem to find each root.

88. $2x^3 + 3x^2 - 8x - 12 = 0$
89. $3x^3 - 5x^2 - 4x + 4 = 0$
90. $3x^3 + 10x^2 - x - 12 = 0$
91. $2x^3 - 11x^2 - x + 30 = 0$
92. $x^3 - 6x^2 + 11x - 6 = 0$
93. $x^3 + 3x^2 - 4x - 12 = 0$

Algebra at Work

Demographer

Demographers study human populations. They collect, analyze, and present data relating to the basic life cycle: birth, marriage, divorce, family formation, employment, aging, migration, and death. Demographers draw on the related disciplines of sociology, economics, political science, anthropology, psychology, public health, and ecology.

Demography is also concerned with the broader nature of social and economic change and its impact on the natural environment. It includes studying family structure, the role of women, and the value of children, as well as the social, cultural, and institutional context of demographic change. Demography is an essential component of many activities, such as planning government policies and market research.

Take It to the NET For more information about demography, go to **www.PHSchool.com.**
Web Code: agb-2031

Technology

Graphing Inverses

FOR USE WITH LESSON 7-7

You can graph inverses of functions on a graphing calculator by using the DrawInv feature or by using parametric equations. It takes more keystrokes to set up parametric equations, but once you do you can easily change from one function to another and quickly see graphs of a function and its inverse.

EXAMPLE

Graph $y = 0.3x^2 + 1$ and its inverse.

Method 1 Use the DrawInv feature.

Step 1 Press Y= and enter the equation. Press ZOOM 5 to see a graph of the function with equal x- and y-intervals.

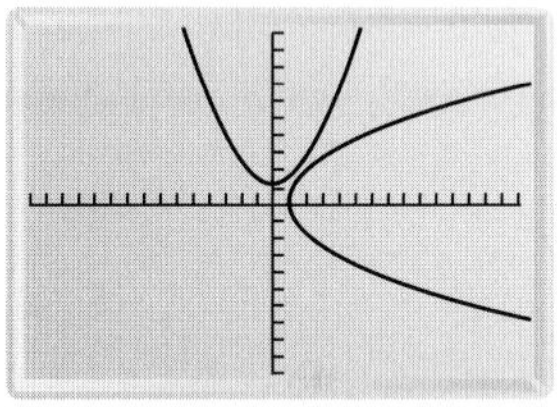

Step 2 Press **DRAW** 8. You will see **DrawInv** followed by a flashing cursor. Select equation Y_1 by pressing VARS ▶ 1 1. Press ENTER to see the graph of the function and its inverse.

Method 2 Use parametric equations.

Step 1 Set to parametric mode. Press MODE, select **Par**, and press **QUIT**.

Step 2 Enter the given equation in parametric form. Press Y= and enter the equations $X_{1T} = T$ and $Y_{1T} = .3T^2 + 1$.

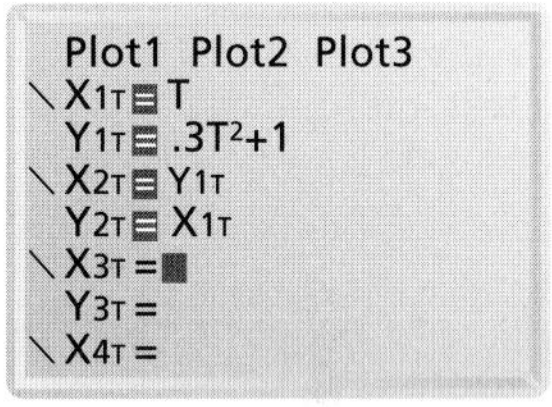

Step 3 Now use $X_{2T} = Y_{1T}$ and $Y_{2T} = X_{1T}$ to interchange the x- and y-values of the first parametric equation. Press Y= and move the cursor to follow X_{2T} =. Select Y_{1T} by pressing VARS ▶ 2 2. Enter the equation $Y_{2T} = X_{1T}$ in a similar fashion.

Step 4 Press ZOOM 5. Adjust the Window so that Tmin and Tmax approximately agree with Xmin and Xmax. Press GRAPH to see the graph of the function and its inverse.

EXERCISES

Graph each function and its inverse with a graphing calculator. Then sketch the graphs.

1. $y = x^2 - 5$

2. $y = (x - 3)^2$

3. $y = 0.01x^4$

4. $y = 0.5x^3 - 3$

5. Critical Thinking In Method 2, suppose you added a third pair of parametric equations that interchanged the x- and y-values of the second pair ($X_{3T} = Y_{2T}$ and $Y_{3T} = X_{2T}$). What would be the effect on the graphs? Explain.

6. Writing Change the parametric equation $X_{2T} = Y_{1T}$ in Method 2, Step 3 to $X_{2T} = -Y_{1T}$. Describe the graph that results.

7-8 Graphing Radical Functions

North Carolina Objectives

2.07 Use equations with radical expressions to model and solve problems. a) Solve using graphs. b) Interpret the degree, constants, and coefficients in the context of the problem.

Lesson Preview

What You'll Learn

OBJECTIVE 1 To graph radical functions

. . . And Why

To estimate the mass of a giraffe, as in Example 5

Check Skills You'll Need

(For help, go to Lesson 5-3.)

Graph each equation.

1. $y = (x + 2)^2$ **2.** $y = (x - 3)^2$ **3.** $y = -(x + 4)^2$

4. $y = -x^2 - 1$ **5.** $y = -(x + 1)^2 + 1$ **6.** $y = 3x^2 + 3$

New Vocabulary • radical function

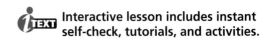

Interactive lesson includes instant self-check, tutorials, and activities.

OBJECTIVE 1

Radical Functions

A horizontal line can intersect the graph of $f(x) = x^2$ in two points. For example, $f(-2) = f(2)$. Therefore, a vertical line can intersect the graph of the inverse of $f(x) = x^2$ in two points, and f^{-1} is *not* a function.

Need Help?

To review the vertical line test, go to Lesson 2-1.

$f(x) = x^2$

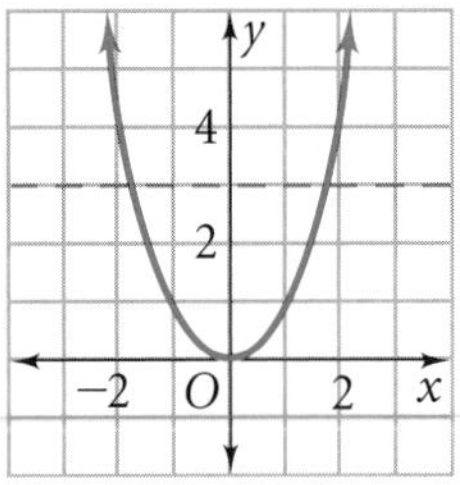

$f^{-1}(x) = \pm\sqrt{x}$

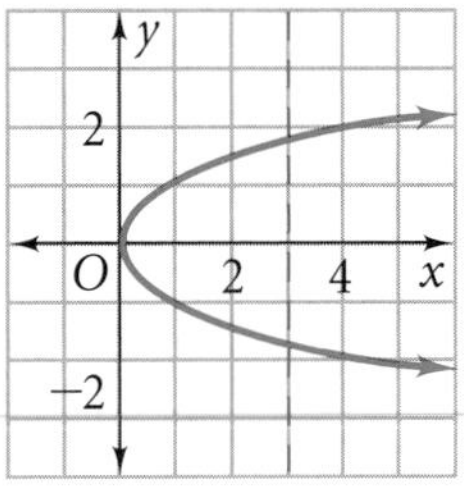

You can restrict the domain of f so that its inverse is a function.

$f(x) = x^2, x \geq 0$

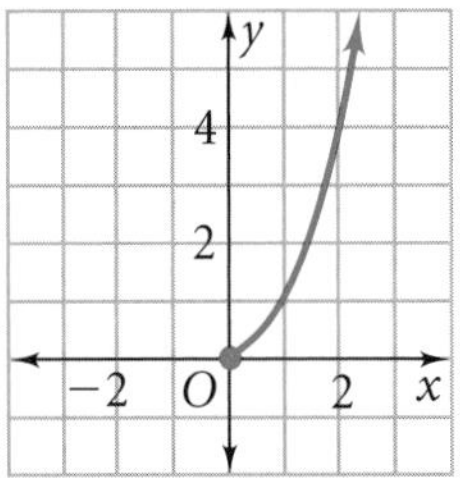

$f^{-1}(x) = \sqrt{x}$

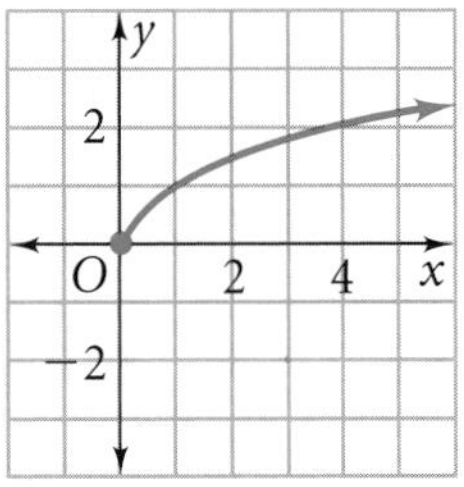

The inverse of $g(x) = x^3$ is a function.

$g(x) = x^3$

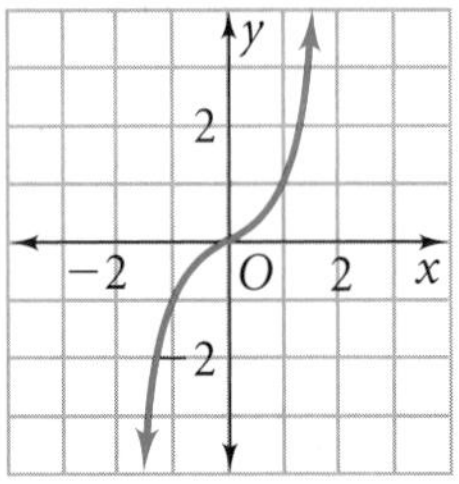

$g^{-1}(x) = \sqrt[3]{x}$

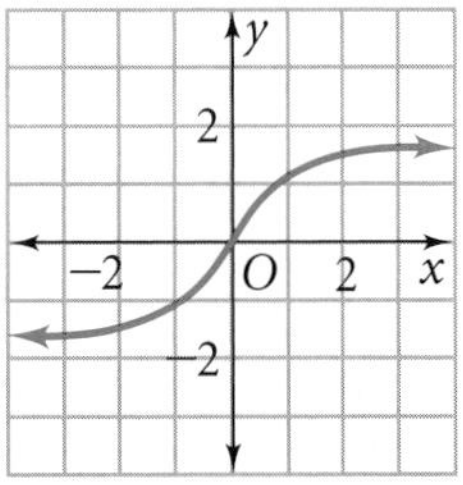

A radical equation defines a **radical function.** The graph of the radical function $y = \sqrt{x} + k$ is a translation of the graph of $y = \sqrt{x}$. If k is positive, the graph is translated k units up. If k is negative, the graph is translated $|k|$ units down.

1 EXAMPLE Translating Square Root Functions Vertically

Graph $y = \sqrt{x} + 2$ and $y = \sqrt{x} - 1$.

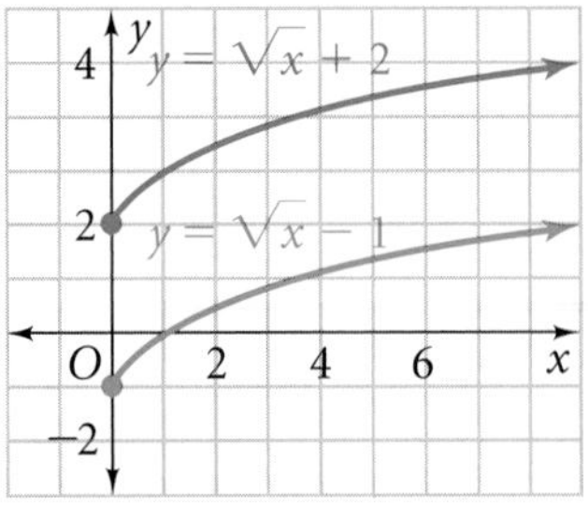

The graph of $y = \sqrt{x} + 2$ is the graph of $y = \sqrt{x}$ shifted up 2 units. The graph of $y = \sqrt{x} - 1$ is the graph of $y = \sqrt{x}$ shifted down 1 unit.

The domains of both functions are the set of nonnegative numbers, but their ranges differ.

Check Understanding 1 Graph $y = \sqrt{x} - 3$ and $y = \sqrt{x} + 3$.

The graph of $y = \sqrt{x - h}$ is a translation of $y = \sqrt{x}$. If h is positive, the graph is translated h units right. If h is negative, the graph is translated $|h|$ units left.

2 EXAMPLE Translating Square Root Functions Horizontally

Graph $y = \sqrt{x + 3}$ and $y = \sqrt{x - 2}$.

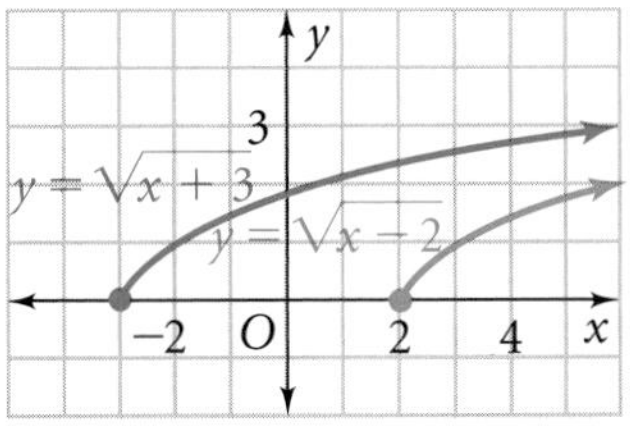

The graph of $y = \sqrt{x + 3}$ is the graph of $y = \sqrt{x}$ shifted left 3 units. The graph of $y = \sqrt{x - 2}$ is the graph of $y = \sqrt{x}$ shifted right 2 units.

The ranges of both functions are the set of nonnegative numbers, but their domains differ.

Check Understanding 2 Graph $y = \sqrt{x - 1}$ and $y = \sqrt{x + 4}$.

The graph of $y = a\sqrt{x}$ is a vertical stretch or compression of the graph of $y = \sqrt{x}$ by a factor of $|a|$. If $a < 0$, the graph is a reflection across the x-axis.

3 EXAMPLE Graphing Square Root Functions

Graph $y = \sqrt{x}$, $y = 0.5\sqrt{x}$, and $y = 2\sqrt{x}$.

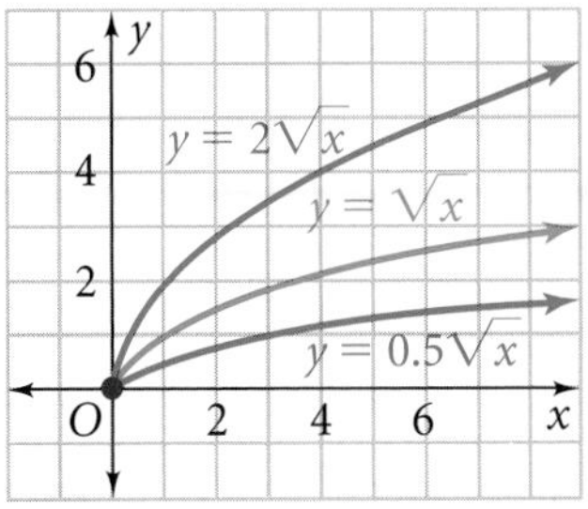

Each y-value of $y = 2\sqrt{x}$ is four times the corresponding y-value of $y = 0.5\sqrt{x}$.

The domains and ranges of all three functions are the set of nonnegative numbers.

Check Understanding 3 Graph $y = -\sqrt{x}$ and $y = -2\sqrt{x}$.

In general, the graph of $y = a\sqrt{x-h} + k$ is a translation h units horizontally and k units vertically of $y = a\sqrt{x}$. The vertical stretch or compression is determined by a.

4 EXAMPLE Graphing Square Root Functions

Graph $y = -2\sqrt{x+1} - 3$.

$y = -2\sqrt{x-(-1)} + (-3)$, so translate the graph of $y = -2\sqrt{x}$ left 1 unit and down 3 units.

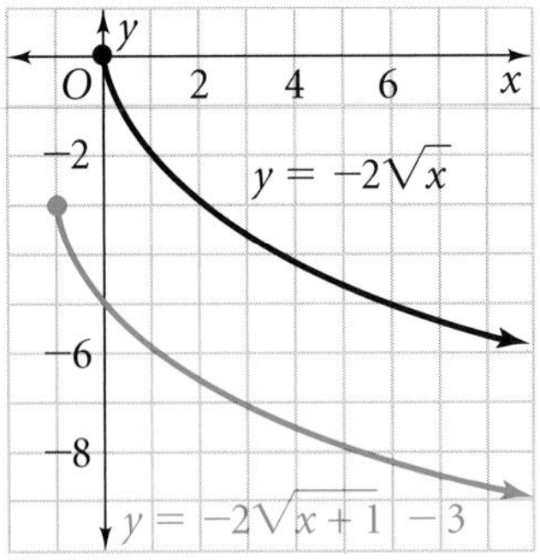

Check Understanding 4 Graph $y = \frac{1}{4}\sqrt{x-2} - 4$.

5 EXAMPLE Real-World Connection

Zoology The function $h(x) = 0.4\sqrt[3]{x}$ models the height h in meters of a female giraffe that has a mass of x kilograms. Graph the model with a graphing calculator. Use the graph to estimate the mass of the young giraffe in the photograph.

The height of the young giraffe is 2.5 m. Graph $y = 0.4\sqrt[3]{x}$ and $y = 2.5$. Adjust the window so the graphs intersect. Use the Intersect feature to find that $x \approx 244$ when $y = 2.5$.

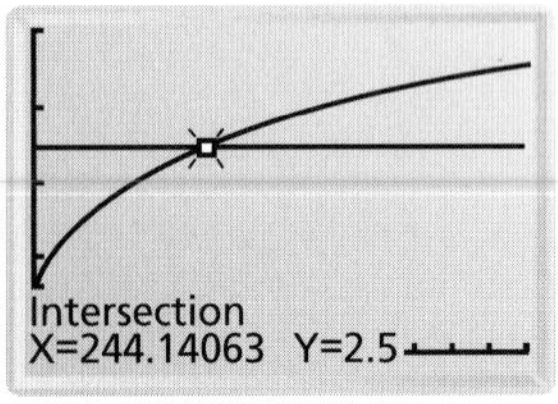

The giraffe has a mass of about 244 kilograms.

Check Understanding 5 Use a graphing calculator to estimate the mass of a 3.2-meter female giraffe.

The pattern for graphing square root functions applies to other radical functions. For example, the graph of $y = a\sqrt[3]{x-h} + k$ is a translation h units horizontally and k units vertically of $y = a\sqrt[3]{x}$.

6 EXAMPLE Graphing Cube Root Functions

Graph $y = 2\sqrt[3]{x+3} - 1$.

The graph of $y = 2\sqrt[3]{x+3} - 1$ is the graph of $y = 2\sqrt[3]{x}$ translated 3 units left and 1 unit down.

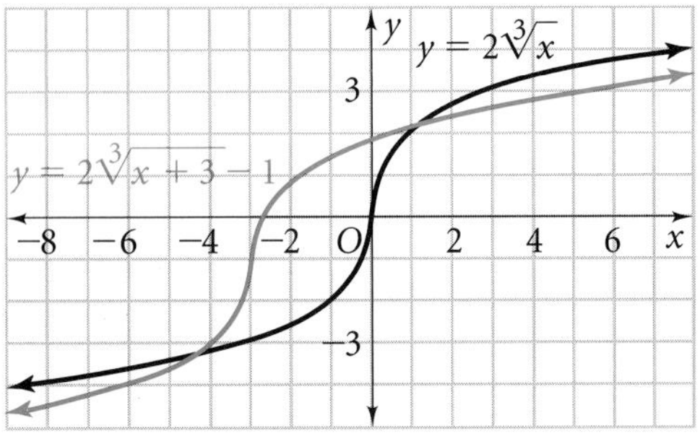

Check Understanding 6 Graph $y = 3 - \sqrt[3]{x+1}$.

Sometimes you have to rewrite a radical equation so you can graph it using a translation.

7 EXAMPLE Transforming Radical Equations.

Rewrite $y = \sqrt{4x - 12}$ to make it easy to graph using a translation. Describe the graph.

$y = \sqrt{4x - 12} = \sqrt{4(x - 3)} = 2\sqrt{x - (3)}$

The graph of $y = \sqrt{4x - 12}$ is the graph of $y = 2\sqrt{x}$ translated 3 units right.

Check Understanding 7 Rewrite $y = \sqrt[3]{8x - 24} + 3$ to make it easy to graph using a translation. Describe the graph.

EXERCISES

For more practice, see *Extra Practice*.

Practice and Problem Solving

A Practice by Example

Examples 1 and 2 (page 409)

Graph each function.

1. $y = \sqrt{x} + 1$
2. $y = \sqrt{x} - 2$
3. $y = \sqrt{x} - 4$
4. $y = \sqrt{x} + 5$
5. $y = \sqrt{x - 3}$
6. $y = \sqrt{x + 1}$
7. $y = \sqrt{x + 6}$
8. $y = \sqrt{x - 4}$

Example 3 (page 409)

Graph each function.

9. $y = 3\sqrt{x}$
10. $y = -0.25\sqrt{x}$
11. $y = \frac{1}{3}\sqrt{x}$
12. $y = -4\sqrt{x}$
13. $y = \frac{2}{5}\sqrt{x}$
14. $y = -5\sqrt{x}$
15. $y = -0.75\sqrt{x}$
16. $y = -0.5\sqrt{x}$

Examples 4 and 5 (page 410)

Graph each function.

17. $y = -\sqrt{x - 1}$
18. $y = 3\sqrt{x + 1} + 4$
19. $y = -2\sqrt{x + 4} - 5$
20. $y = -\sqrt{x - 3} + 2$
21. $y = \frac{1}{4}\sqrt{x + 2} - 1$
22. $y = -0.4\sqrt{x - 6} + 7$

23. **Agriculture** A center-pivot irrigation system can water from 1 to 130 acres of crop land. The length ℓ in feet of rotating pipe needed to irrigate A acres is given by the function $\ell = 117.75\sqrt{A}$.
    a. Graph the equation on your calculator. Make a sketch of the graph.
    b. Find the lengths of pipe needed to irrigate 40, 80, and 130 acres.

Example 6 (page 410)

Graph each function.

24. $y = \sqrt[3]{x + 5}$
25. $y = \sqrt[3]{x - 4}$
26. $y = \sqrt[3]{x + 2} - 7$
27. $y = -\sqrt[3]{x + 3} - 1$
28. $y = 2\sqrt[3]{x - 6} - 9$
29. $y = \frac{1}{2}\sqrt[3]{x - 1} + 3$

Example 7 (page 411)

Rewrite each function to make it easy to graph using a translation. Describe the graph.

30. $y = \sqrt{9x - 9}$
31. $y = -\sqrt{16x + 32}$
32. $y = -2\sqrt{49x + 49}$
33. $y = \sqrt[3]{64x + 128}$
34. $y = \sqrt{64x - 128} - 3$
35. $y = \sqrt[3]{27x - 54} + 1$

B Apply Your Skills

Graph. Find the domain and the range of each function.

36. $y = \sqrt{x} + 7$ **37.** $y = \sqrt{x} - 6$ **38.** $y = \sqrt{x - 6}$

39. $y = -3\sqrt{x} + 2$ **40.** $y = -\frac{4}{5}\sqrt{x}$ **41.** $y = 7 - \sqrt{2x - 1}$

42. $y = 4\sqrt[3]{x - 2} + 1$ **43.** $y = \frac{1}{2}\sqrt{x - 1} + 3$ **44.** $y = -3\sqrt[3]{x - 4} - 3$

45. $y = -\sqrt{x + \frac{1}{2}}$ **46.** $y = -\sqrt[3]{8x} + 5$ **47.** $y = -2\sqrt[3]{x - 4}$

48. $y = -1 - \sqrt{4x + 20}$ **49.** $y = 4 - \sqrt[3]{x + 2.5}$ **50.** $y = -3\sqrt{x - \frac{3}{4}} + 7$

Real-World Connection

The length of the pendulum formed by an aerialist on a trapeze depends on how far he hangs below the bar.

51. **Circus** The time t in seconds for a trapeze to complete one full cycle is given by the function $t = 1.11\sqrt{\ell}$, where ℓ is the length of the trapeze in feet.
   a. Graph the equation on your calculator. Make a sketch of the graph.
   b. How long is a full cycle if the trapeze is 15 ft. long? 30 ft. long?

52. a. Graph $y = \sqrt{x - 2} - 2$.
   b. Find the domain and the range.
   c. At what coordinate point does the graph start?
   d. **Critical Thinking** What is the relationship of the point at which the graph starts to the domain and the range?

53. a. The graph of $y = \sqrt{x}$ is translated five units to the right and two units down. Write an equation of the translated function.
   b. The translated graph from part (a) is again translated, this time four units left and three units down. Write an equation of the translated function.

54. a. Graph $y = \sqrt{x - 2} + 1$ and $y = -\sqrt{x - 2} + 1$.
   b. Find the domain and the range of each function.

Rewrite each function to make it easy to graph using a translation. Describe the graph.

55. $y = \sqrt{25x - 100} - 1$ **56.** $y = \sqrt{36x + 108} + 4$ **57.** $y = -\sqrt[3]{8x - 2}$

58. $y = \sqrt{\frac{x - 1}{4}} - 2$ **59.** $y = 10 - \sqrt[3]{\frac{x + 3}{27}}$ **60.** $y = \sqrt{\frac{x}{9} + 1} + 5$

61. **Open-Ended** Write a cube root function in which the vertical translation of $y = \sqrt[3]{x}$ is twice the horizontal translation.

62. **Electronics** The size of a television screen is the length of the screen's diagonal d in inches. The equation $d = \sqrt{2A}$ models the length of a diagonal of a television screen with area A.
   a. Graph the equation on your calculator.
   b. Suppose you want to buy a new television that has twice the area of your old television. Your old television has an area of 100 in.^{2}. What size screen should you buy?

63. **Writing** Explain the effect that a has on the graph of $y = a\sqrt{x}$.

C Challenge

Rewrite each function to make it easy to graph using a translation. Describe the graph. Find the domain and the range of each function.

64. $y = -\sqrt{2x + 8}$ **65.** $y = -\sqrt{2(4x - 3)}$

66. $y = \sqrt{3x - 5} + 6$ **67.** $y = -3 - \sqrt{12x + 18}$

68. a. Graph $y = \sqrt{-x}$, $y = \sqrt{1 - x}$, and $y = \sqrt{2 - x}$.

b. Make a Conjecture How does the graph of $y = \sqrt{h - x}$ differ from the graph of $y = \sqrt{x - h}$?

69. For what positive integers n are the domain and range of $y = \sqrt[n]{x}$ the set of real numbers? Assume that x is a real number.

Standardized Test Prep

Multiple Choice

70. How is the graph of $y = \sqrt{x + 7}$ translated from the graph of $y = \sqrt{x}$?

A. shifted 7 units left **B.** shifted 7 units right
C. shifted 7 units up **D.** shifted 7 units down

71. How is the graph of $y = \sqrt{x} - 5$ translated from the graph of $y = \sqrt{x}$?

F. shifted 5 units left **G.** shifted 5 units right
H. shifted 5 units up **I.** shifted 5 units down

Take It to the NET
Online lesson quiz at **www.PHSchool.com**
Web Code: aga-0708

72. The graph of $y = -\sqrt{x}$ is shifted 4 units up and 3 units right. Which equation represents the new graph?

A. $y = -\sqrt{x - 4} + 3$ **B.** $y = -\sqrt{x - 3} + 4$
C. $y = -\sqrt{x + 3} + 4$ **D.** $y = -\sqrt{x + 4} + 3$

73. Which equation shows $y + 3 = \sqrt{\frac{x}{16} + 2}$ rewritten in the form $y = a\sqrt{x - h} + k$?

F. $y = \frac{3}{4}\sqrt{x - (-2)}$ **G.** $y = \frac{1}{4}\sqrt{x - (-2)} + (-3)$
H. $y = \frac{1}{4}\sqrt{x - (-32)} + (-3)$ **I.** $y = \frac{1}{8}\sqrt{x + 32} + (-3)$

Short Response

74. At the right is the graph of $y = \sqrt{x}$. How are the graphs of $f(x) = \sqrt{x - 1}$ and $g(x) = \sqrt{x} - 1$ like that graph, and how are they different?

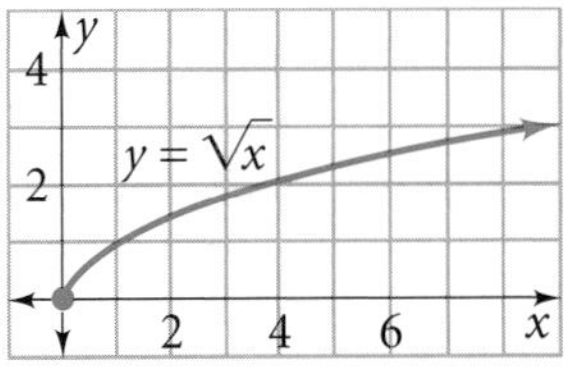

Extended Response

75. What are the differences in the domains and ranges of functions $f(x)$ and $g(x)$ from Exercise 74?

Mixed Review

Lesson 7-7 **Find the inverse of each function. Is the inverse a function?**

76. $f(x) = 4x - 1$ **77.** $f(x) = \frac{2}{3}x - 3$ **78.** $f(x) = 2.4x^2 + 1$

79. $f(x) = \sqrt{x + 3} - 4$ **80.** $f(x) = (2x + 1)^2$ **81.** $f(x) = 2x^3$

Lesson 7-2 **Rationalize the denominator of each expression. Assume that all variables are positive.**

82. $\frac{\sqrt{36x^3}}{\sqrt{12x}}$ **83.** $\sqrt[3]{\frac{3x}{2y}}$ **84.** $\frac{\sqrt[3]{x}}{\sqrt[3]{3y}}$ **85.** $\sqrt[5]{\frac{3x^3}{2y}}$

Lesson 5-8 **Solve using the Quadratic Formula.**

86. $5x^2 + x = 3$ **87.** $3x^2 + 9x = 27$ **88.** $x^2 - 9x + 15 = 0$

89. $x^2 + 10x + 11 = 0$ **90.** $x^2 - 12x + 25 = 0$ **91.** $8x^2 + 2x - 15 = 0$

Test-Taking Strategies

Finding Multiple Correct Answers

In some multiple-choice questions, there may be several correct answers.

1 EXAMPLE

Which of the following are true for all values of x?

I. $\sqrt[3]{2^x} = \left(\sqrt[3]{2}\right)^x$ **II.** $\sqrt{x^2} = \sqrt[3]{x^3}$ **III.** $\sqrt{x^2 + 1} = |x| + 1$

A. I only **B.** I and II only **C.** I and III only **D.** II and III only

Determine whether each statement is true for all values of x.

Equation I $\sqrt[3]{2^x} = (2^x)^{\frac{1}{3}} = \left(2^{\frac{1}{3}}\right)^x = \left(\sqrt[3]{2}\right)^x$ *True*

Equation II $\sqrt{x^2} = |x| \neq x = \sqrt[3]{x^3}$ *False*

Equation III Square each side to get
$x^2 + 1 = x^2 + 2|x| + 1$,
or $0 = 2|x|$, which is true only for $x = 0$. *False*

Only statement I is true for all values of x. The answer is A.

2 EXAMPLE

Which of the following are equal to x for all nonzero values of x?

I. $\sqrt{x^2}$ **II.** $\sqrt[3]{x^3}$ **III.** $\dfrac{\sqrt[3]{x^4}}{\sqrt[3]{x}}$

A. I only **B.** II only **C.** II and III only **D.** I, II and III

Rewrite each statement.

Expression I $\sqrt{x^2} = x$ only when x is positive.

Expression II $\sqrt[3]{x^3} = x$ for all values of x.

Expression III $\dfrac{\sqrt[3]{x^4}}{\sqrt[3]{x}} = \dfrac{x^{\frac{4}{3}}}{x^{\frac{1}{3}}} = x^{\frac{4}{3} - \frac{1}{3}} = x$ when $x \neq 0$.

Expressions II and III are correct choices. The answer is C.

EXERCISES

1. Test each equation in Example 1 with $x = 2$ and $x = -2$. What do your results show about each of the three equations?

2. **Critical Thinking** Test each equation in Example 1 with $x = 0$ and $x = 1$. Explain why these values do not help you choose the true equations.

3. Which of the following equations are true?

   I. $\left(\sqrt[4]{\sqrt{3}}\right)^8 = 3$ **II.** $\left(\sqrt[4]{\sqrt{3}}\right)^6 = 3$ **III.** $\dfrac{1}{\left(\frac{3}{5}\right)^{-1}} = \dfrac{5}{3}$

   A. I only **B.** I and II only **C.** I and III only **D.** II and III only

Chapter 7

Chapter Review

Vocabulary

composite function (p. 393)
index (p. 364)
inverse functions (p. 403)
inverse relation (p. 401)
like radicals (p. 374)
***n*th root** (p. 363)
principal root (p. 364)
radical equation (p. 385)
radical function (p. 409)
radicand (p. 364)
rational exponent (p. 379)
rationalize the denominator (p. 370)

Reading Math
Understanding Vocabulary

Choose the correct vocabulary term to complete each sentence.

1. In the expression $\sqrt[3]{8}$, 8 is called the *(principal root, radicand)*.
2. In the expression $\sqrt[3]{8}$, 3 is called the *(principal root, index)*.
3. When you rewrite an expression so there are no radicals in any denominator and no denominators in any radical, you *(rationalize the denominator, compose two functions)*.
4. The expressions $\sqrt{x}$ and $\sqrt[5]{x}$ *(are, are not)* examples of like radicals.
5. The definition of *(rational exponents, inverse functions)* allows us to write $7^{\frac{2}{3}} = \sqrt[3]{7^2}$.
6. If $g(x) = x - 4$ and $h(x) = x^2$, $(g \circ h)(x) = x^2 - 4$ is a *(radical function, composite function)*.
7. To multiply expressions you sometimes add *(radicands, rational exponents)*.
8. If f and f^{-1} are *(composite functions, inverse functions)*, then $(f \circ f^{-1})(x) = x$ and $(f^{-1} \circ f)(x) = x$.
9. $(x - 7)^{\frac{1}{2}} + 2 = x$ is an example of *(a radical equation, an inverse relation)*.
10. The positive even root of a number is called the *(principal root, rational exponent)*.

Take It to the NET
Online vocabulary quiz at **www.PHSchool.com**
Web Code: agj-0751

Skills and Concepts

7-1 and 7-2 Objectives

- To simplify *n*th roots (p. 363)
- To multiply radical expressions (p. 368)
- To divide radical expressions (p. 369)

For any real numbers a and b, and any positive integer n, if $a^n = b$, then a is an nth root of b. The **principal root** of a number with two real roots is the positive root. The principal nth root of b is written as $\sqrt[n]{b}$. b is the **radicand** and n is the **index** of the radical.

For any negative real number a, $\sqrt[n]{a^n} = |a|$ when n is even.

If $\sqrt[n]{a}$ and $\sqrt[n]{b}$ are real numbers, then $\sqrt[n]{a} \cdot \sqrt[n]{b} = \sqrt[n]{ab}$, and, if $b \neq 0$, then $\frac{\sqrt[n]{a}}{\sqrt[n]{b}} = \sqrt[n]{\frac{a}{b}}$.

To **rationalize the denominator** of an expression, rewrite it so there are no radicals in any denominator and no denominators in any radical.

Find each indicated root if it is a real number.

11. $\sqrt{144}$ **12.** $\sqrt[3]{-0.064}$ **13.** $\sqrt[4]{7^4}$ **14.** $\sqrt{0.25}$ **15.** $-\sqrt[3]{27}$

Simplify each radical expression. Use absolute value symbols as needed.

16. $\sqrt{49x^2y^{10}}$ **17.** $\sqrt[3]{-64y^9}$ **18.** $\sqrt{(a-1)^4}$

19. $\sqrt[5]{243x^{15}}$ **20.** $\sqrt[3]{(y+3)^6}$ **21.** $\sqrt{32x^9y^5}$

Simplify each expression. Assume that all variables are positive.

22. $\sqrt{10}\cdot\sqrt{40}$ **23.** $\sqrt[3]{12}\cdot\sqrt[3]{36}$ **24.** $2\sqrt[3]{2x^2y}\cdot 5\sqrt[3]{6x^4y^4}$

25. $\sqrt{7x^3}\cdot\sqrt{14x}$ **26.** $\sqrt{5x^4y^3}\cdot\sqrt{45x^3y}$ **27.** $3\sqrt[4]{4x^3}\cdot\sqrt[4]{8xy^5}$

28. $\frac{\sqrt{128}}{\sqrt{8}}$ **29.** $\frac{\sqrt[3]{56y^5}}{\sqrt[3]{7y}}$ **30.** $\frac{\sqrt{75x^3}}{\sqrt{3x}}$ **31.** $\frac{\sqrt{216x^3y^2}}{\sqrt{2}}$ **32.** $\frac{\sqrt[3]{81a^8b^5}}{\sqrt[3]{3a^2b}}$

Simplify each expression. Rationalize all denominators. Assume that all variables are positive.

33. $\frac{\sqrt{8}}{\sqrt{6}}$ **34.** $\frac{\sqrt{3x^5}}{\sqrt{8x^2}}$ **35.** $\frac{\sqrt[3]{5}}{\sqrt[3]{x^4}}$ **36.** $\frac{\sqrt{2a^7b^2}}{\sqrt{32b^3}}$ **37.** $\frac{\sqrt[3]{6x^2y^4}}{2\sqrt[3]{5x^7y}}$

7-3 and 7-4 Objectives

- To add and subtract radical expressions (p. 374)
- To multiply and divide binomial radical expressions (p. 375)
- To simplify expressions with rational exponents (p. 379)

Like radicals have the same index and the same radicand. Use the distributive property to add or subtract them. Simplify radicals to find all the like radicals.

Use FOIL to multiply binomial radical expressions.

Binomials such as $a + b$ and $a - b$ are called conjugate expressions.

If the denominator of a fraction is a binomial radical expression, multiply both the numerator and denominator of the fraction by the conjugate of the denominator to rationalize the denominator.

The definition of **rational exponents** states that if the nth root of a is a real number and m is an integer, then $a^{\frac{1}{n}} = \sqrt[n]{a}$ and $a^{\frac{m}{n}} = \sqrt[n]{a^m} = \left(\sqrt[n]{a}\right)^m$. If m is negative, $a \neq 0$. The usual properties of exponents hold for rational exponents.

Simplify each expression.

38. $\sqrt{27}+\sqrt{75}-\sqrt{12}$ **39.** $(5+\sqrt{3})(2-\sqrt{3})$ **40.** $(7-\sqrt{6})(7+\sqrt{6})$

Simplify each expression. Rationalize all denominators. Assume that all variables are positive.

41. $\sqrt{2x}-\sqrt{8x}+\sqrt{18x}$ **42.** $\frac{6}{7+2\sqrt{3}}$ **43.** $\frac{\sqrt{2}}{1-\sqrt{5}}$

Write each expression in radical form.

44. $3^{\frac{1}{5}}$ **45.** $x^{\frac{2}{3}}$ **46.** $2^{-\frac{3}{4}}$ **47.** $3^{0.2}$ **48.** $p^{-2.25}$

Simplify each expression. Assume that all variables are positive.

49. $(243)^{\frac{4}{5}}$ **50.** $36^{\frac{3}{2}}$ **51.** $\left(x^{\frac{3}{4}}\right)^{\frac{4}{3}}$ **52.** $x^{\frac{1}{6}}\cdot x^{\frac{2}{3}}$ **53.** $\left(x^{-\frac{3}{8}}y^{\frac{1}{4}}\right)^{16}$

7-5 Objective

▼ To solve radical equations (p. 385)

To solve a **radical equation,** isolate a radical or a term with a rational exponent on one side of the equation. Then raise both sides of the equation to the same power. Check all possible solutions in the original equation to eliminate extraneous solutions.

Solve each equation. Check for extraneous solutions.

54. $\sqrt[3]{3x + 1} = -5$ **55.** $\sqrt{x + 7} = x + 1$ **56.** $x^{\frac{1}{2}} - 3 = 8$

7-6 and 7-7 Objectives

▼ To add, subtract, multiply, and divide functions (p. 392)

▼ To find the composite of two functions (p. 393)

▼ To find the inverse of a relation or function (p. 400)

The following are definitions of function operations.

Addition $(f + g)(x) = f(x) + g(x)$ Subtraction $(f - g)(x) = f(x) - g(x)$

Multiplication $(f \cdot g)(x) = f(x) \cdot g(x)$ Division $\left(\frac{f}{g}\right)(x) = \frac{f(x)}{g(x)}, g(x) \neq 0$

The composition of function g with function f is written as $g \circ f$ and is defined as $(g \circ f)(x) = g(f(x))$. The domain of the **composite function** $g \circ f$ consists of the values a in the domain of f such that $f(a)$ is in the domain of g.

If (a, b) is an ordered pair of a relation, then (b, a) is an ordered pair of its **inverse relation.** If a relation or function is described by an equation in x and y, you can interchange x and y to get the inverse. The inverse of a function is denoted by f^{-1}.

If f and f^{-1} are both functions, they are called **inverse functions,** and $(f^{-1} \circ f)(x) = x$ and $(f \circ f^{-1})(x) = x$.

Let $f(x) = 2x + 5$ and $g(x) = x^2 - 3x + 2$. Perform each function operation.

57. $(f + g)(x)$ **58.** $f(x) - g(x)$ **59.** $g(x) \cdot f(x)$ **60.** $(g - f)(x)$ **61.** $\frac{g(x)}{f(x)}$

Let $f(x) = x^2$ and $g(x) = x - 3$. Evaluate each expression.

62. $(g \circ f)(-2)$ **63.** $(f \circ g)(-2)$ **64.** $(f \circ g)(0)$ **65.** $(g \circ g)(7)$ **66.** $(f \circ g)(c)$

Find the inverse of each function. Is the inverse a function?

67. $y = 6x + 2$ **68.** $y = 2x^3 + 1$ **69.** $y = (x - 2)^4$ **70.** $y = \sqrt{x + 2}$

Let $f(x) = 3x + 1$. Find each value.

71. $(f^{-1} \circ f)(5)$ **72.** $(f^{-1} \circ f)(-5)$ **73.** $(f^{-1} \circ f)(6)$ **74.** $(f^{-1} \circ f)(t)$

7-8 Objective

▼ To graph radical functions (p. 408)

A **radical function** such as $y = \sqrt{x}$ has a restricted domain. For $y = \sqrt{x}$, the domain is the set of nonnegative real numbers.

The graph of $y = a\sqrt{x - h} + k$ is a translation h units horizontally and k units vertically of $y = a\sqrt{x}$.

Graph each function.

75. $y = \sqrt{x} + 3$ **76.** $y = \sqrt{x - 1}$

77. $y = -3\sqrt{x} + 6$ **78.** $y = \sqrt{x + 7} - 2$

Chapter 7

Chapter Test

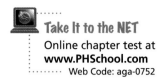

Take It to the NET
Online chapter test at www.PHSchool.com
Web Code: aga-0752

Simplify each radical expression. Use absolute value symbols when they are needed.

1. $\sqrt[3]{-0.027}$
2. $\sqrt{54x^3y^5}$
3. $\sqrt[5]{-64x^{14}y^{20}}$
4. $\sqrt{(x-2)^4}$

Simplify each expression. Rationalize all denominators. Assume that all variables are positive.

5. $\sqrt{7x^3} \cdot \sqrt{14x}$
6. $\sqrt{3y^3} \cdot \sqrt{4xy^4} \cdot \sqrt{6x^5y^2}$
7. $\dfrac{\sqrt{7x^4y}}{\sqrt{63xy^2}}$
8. $\dfrac{1-\sqrt{3x}}{\sqrt{6x}}$
9. $\sqrt{48} + 2\sqrt{75} + 5\sqrt{12}$
10. $\sqrt{98} + \sqrt{50} - \sqrt{5}$
11. $(3 + 2\sqrt{5})(1 - \sqrt{20})$
12. $(7 + \sqrt{3})(3 + 5\sqrt{3})$
13. $\dfrac{5}{3 - 2\sqrt{6}}$
14. $\dfrac{1+\sqrt{3}}{\sqrt{3}-\sqrt{2}}$

Simplify each expression. Assume that all variables are positive.

15. $(125)^{-\frac{2}{3}}$
16. $x^{\frac{1}{6}} \cdot x^{\frac{1}{3}}$
17. $\left(\dfrac{8x^9y^3}{27x^2y^{12}}\right)^{\frac{2}{3}}$

Solve each equation. Check for extraneous solutions.

18. $\sqrt{x-3} = x - 5$
19. $\sqrt{x+4} = \sqrt{3x}$
20. $(3x+4)^{\frac{1}{3}} = -5$
21. $x - 6 = (x-4)^{\frac{1}{2}}$

Let $f(x) = x - 2$ and $g(x) = x^2 - 3x + 2$. Perform each function operation and then find the domain.

22. $g(x) - f(x)$
23. $-2g(x) + f(x)$
24. $\dfrac{g(x)}{f(x)}$
25. $-f(x) \cdot g(x)$

For each pair of functions, find $f(g(x))$ and $g(f(x))$.

26. $f(x) = x^2 - 2, g(x) = 4x + 1$
27. $f(x) = 2x^2 + x - 7, g(x) = -3x - 1$

28. **Writing** Explain why -108 has no real 6th roots.

29. **Discounts** While purchasing a pair of shoes on sale for 50% off, you noticed that the price on the cash register was only 25% off. The cashier then took another 25% off that price.
   a. Write a function $f(x)$ to represent the 50%-off price of the shoes.
   b. Write a function $g(x)$ to represent the price the cash register rang up the first time.
   c. Write a composite function to represent the price of the shoes after the cashier's solution to the problem.
   d. Compare the result of the cashier's solution to the correct price of the shoes.

Rewrite each function to make it easy to graph using a translation. Describe the graph.

30. $y = \sqrt{16x + 80} - 1$
31. $y = \sqrt{9x + 3}$

Graph. Find the domain and range of each function.

32. $y = 2\sqrt{x} + 3$
33. $y = \sqrt{2x + 3}$
34. $y = -\frac{1}{2}\sqrt{x - 4}$
35. $y = \sqrt{x+3} - 4$

Let $f(x) = x^3 + 1$ and $g(x) = 7x - 4$. Find each value.

36. $f(g(-2))$
37. $g(f(3))$
38. $f(g(0))$

Find the inverse of each function. Is the inverse a function?

39. $f(x) = 3x^3 - 2$
40. $g(x) = \sqrt{x+3} - 1$
41. $g(x) = \sqrt{2x+1}$
42. $f(x) = \frac{1}{4}x^4$

43. a. **Geometry** For a sphere, $V = \frac{4}{3}\pi r^3$. Find the volume of a sphere with radius 4 in.
   b. Solve the formula in part (a) for r.
   c. Find to the nearest hundredth the radius of a sphere of volume 100 in.^{3}.

44. **Open-Ended** Write a relation rule that is not a function, but whose inverse is a function.

45. **Measurement** The time t in seconds for a swinging pendulum to complete one full cycle is given by the function $t = 0.2\sqrt{\ell}$, where ℓ is the length of the pendulum in cm. How long is a full cycle if the pendulum is 10 cm long? 20 cm long?

Standardized Test Prep

Reading Comprehension **Read the passage below. Then answer the questions on the basis of what is *stated* or *implied* in the passage.**

Boxing Match You can make an open box from a piece of flat cardboard. First, cut congruent squares from the four corners of the cardboard. Then, fold and tape the sides.

Let x equal the side of each congruent square. As x increases, so does the depth of the box. The usable area of cardboard decreases as x increases, and so do the length and width of the box.

What happens to the volume of the box? Does it increase or decrease as x increases? Would the answer *both* surprise you?

What size squares should you cut from the corners to maximize the volume of your box?

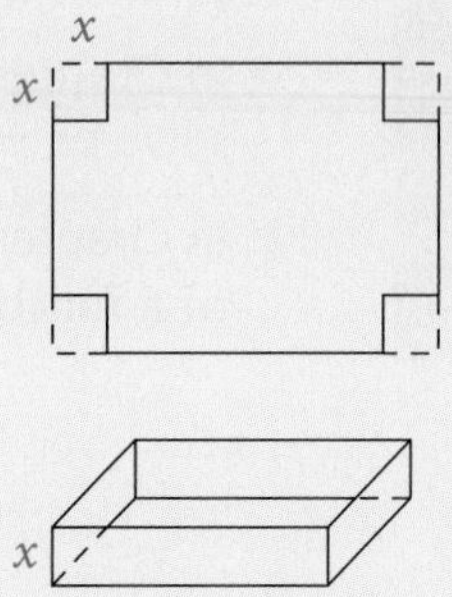

For Questions 1–6, consider a box made from a piece of cardboard that is 80 centimeters by 54 centimeters.

1. What are the dimensions of the box in centimeters?
   A. $80 - x$, $54 - x$, x
   B. $80 - 2x$, $54 - 2x$, $2x$
   C. $80 - 2x$, $54 - 2x$, x
   D. $x - 80$, $x - 54$, x

2. Which function models the area of the cardboard after the corners are cut away?
   F. $A(x) = (80 - 2x)(54 - 2x)$
   G. $A(x) = (80 - 2x)(54 - 2x) + 4x^2$
   H. $A(x) = 4320 - 4x^2$
   I. $A(x) = 4320 - 4(2x)^2$

3. By how much does the area of the cardboard decrease when x changes from 8 cm to 9 cm?
   A. 145 cm^2 **B.** 68 cm^2
   C. 26 cm^2 **D.** 17 cm^2

4. Which function models the volume of the box?
   F. $V(x) = (80 - x)(54 - x)x$
   G. $V(x) = (80 - x)(54 - x) + x$
   H. $V(x) = (80 - 2x)(54 - 2x)x$
   I. $V(x) = (80 - 2x) + (54 - 2x) + x$

5. What is a reasonable domain for x?
   A. $0 \leq x \leq 27$
   B. $0 \leq x \leq 40$
   C. $0 \leq x \leq 54$
   D. all real numbers

6. Which is the best value for the maximum volume of the box?
   F. about 20,440 cm^2
   G. about 20,444 cm^2
   H. about 20,450 cm^2
   I. about 20,452 cm^2

For Questions 7–9, consider a box made from a piece of cardboard that is 18 inches square.

7. Write a function that models the volume of the box.

8. What is a reasonable domain for x?

9. Find the maximum volume. Is this the maximum of the volume function? Explain.

10. **Open-Ended** Find the dimensions of three different rectangular pieces of cardboard you could use to make a box with volume 432 $unit^3$.

Where You've Been

- In Chapters 1 and 2, you learned to model linear functions and to solve linear equations.
- In Chapter 5, you learned to model quadratic functions and to solve quadratic equations.
- In Chapter 6, you learned to model polynomial functions and to solve polynomial equations.
- In Chapter 7, you learned to find and graph the inverse of a function.

Instant self-check online and on CD-ROM

Diagnosing Readiness

(For help, go to the Lesson in green.)

Evaluating Expressions (Lesson 1-2)

Evaluate each expression for $x = -2, -1, 0, 1,$ and 2.

1. 10^{x+1} **2.** $\left(\frac{3}{2}\right)^x$ **3.** $x^4 - x^2$

Using Linear Models (Lesson 2-4)

4. Each day, a squirrel buries three acorns.
  a. Write and graph a function to model the number n of acorns the squirrel buries in d days.
  b. Use your function to find the number of acorns buried in four weeks.
  c. Suppose the squirrel had started out with nine acorns already buried. Explain how this would change your function and its graph.

Using Quadratic Models (Lesson 5-1)

Find a quadratic function to model each set of values. Then graph the function.

5. $\{(0, 0), (2, -4), (3, -3)\}$ **6.** $\{(0, 7), (2, 15), (5, 72)\}$

Graphing Translations (Lesson 5-3)

Identify the parent function of each equation. Graph each equation as a translation of its parent function.

7. $y = -(x - 1)^2 + 4$ **8.** $y = 3(x + 2)^2 - 1$

Graphing Inverse Functions (Lesson 7-7)

Graph each function and its inverse on a coordinate plane.

9. $y = -5x$ **10.** $y = \sqrt{5x + 12}$ **11.** $y = 2x^3$

Exponential and Logarithmic Functions

Chapter 8

LESSONS

Key Vocabulary

- asymptote (p. 425)
- Change of Base Formula (p. 453)
- common logarithm (p. 439)
- continuously compounded interest formula (p. 433)
- decay factor (p. 425)
- exponential equation (p. 453)
- exponential function (p. 422)
- growth factor (p. 422)
- logarithm (p. 439)
- logarithmic equation (p. 455)
- logarithmic function (p. 440)
- natural logarithmic function (p. 462)

Where You're Going

- In Chapter 8, you will learn to use exponential functions to model real-world data.
- You will learn to graph exponential functions and their inverses, logarithmic functions.
- You will learn to solve exponential and logarithmic equations.

Real-World Snapshots Applying what you learn, on pages 474–475 you will do activities involving world population.

8-1 Exploring Exponential Models

North Carolina Objectives
2.03 Use exponential functions to model and solve problems.
2.04 Create and use best-fit mathematical models of exponential functions to solve problems involving sets of data.

Lesson Preview

What You'll Learn

OBJECTIVE 1 To model exponential growth

OBJECTIVE 2 To model exponential decay

. . . And Why

To model a car's depreciation, as in Example 6

Check Skills You'll Need

(For help, go to Lesson 1-2.)

Evaluate each expression for the given value of x.

1. 2^x for $x = 3$ **2.** 4^{x+1} for $x = 1$ **3.** 2^{3x+4} for $x = -1$

4. $3^x 3^{x-2}$ for $x = 2$ **5.** $\left(\frac{1}{2}\right)^x$ for $x = 0$ **6.** 2^x for $x = -2$

New Vocabulary • exponential function • growth factor • decay factor • asymptote

Interactive lesson includes instant self-check, tutorials, and activities.

OBJECTIVE 1 Exponential Growth

Need Help?
If the value of a function depends on the value of x, then x is the independent variable.

For some data, the best model is a function that uses the independent variable as an exponent. An **exponential function** is a function with the general form $y = ab^x$, where x is a real number, $a \neq 0, b > 0$, and $b \neq 1$.

You can use an exponential function to model growth when $b > 1$. When $b > 1$, b is the **growth factor.**

Exponential Growth

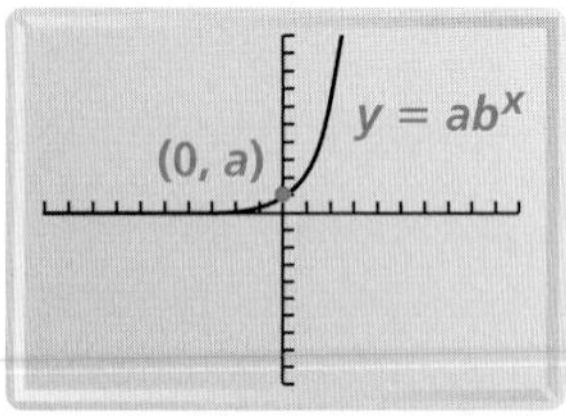

Growth factor $b > 1$

1 EXAMPLE Graphing Exponential Growth

Graph $y = 2^x$.

Step 1 Make a table of values.

x	2^x	y
−3	2^{-3}	$\frac{1}{8} = 0.125$
−2	2^{-2}	$\frac{1}{4} = 0.25$
−1	2^{-1}	$\frac{1}{2} = 0.5$
0	2^0	1
1	2^1	2
2	2^2	4
3	2^3	8

Step 2 Graph the coordinates. Connect the points with a smooth curve.

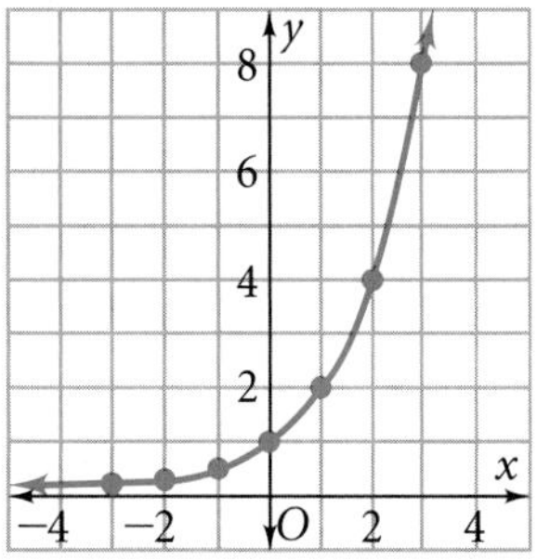

Check Understanding

1 Graph each function.

a. $y = 4(2)^x$ **b.** $y = 3^x$

You can use an exponential function to model population growth. If you know the rate of increase r, you can find the growth factor by using the equation $b = 1 + r$.

2 EXAMPLE Real-World Connection

Real-World Connection

The United States counts its population every 10 years.

Population Refer to the graph. In 2000, the annual rate of increase in the U.S. population was about 1.24%.

a. Find the growth factor for the U.S. population.

b. Suppose the rate of increase continues to be 1.24%. Write a function to model U.S. population growth.

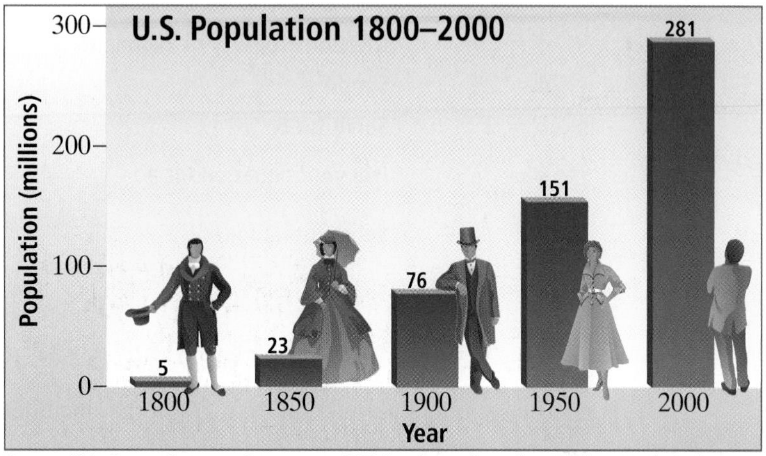

SOURCE: U.S. Census Bureau. Go to **www.PHSchool.com** for a data update. Web Code: agg-2041

a. Find the growth factor.

$b = 1 + r$

$= 1 + 0.0124$ **Substitute 1.24%, or 0.0124, for *r*.**

$= 1.0124$ **Simplify.**

b. Write a function.

Relate The population increases exponentially, so use the general form of an exponential function, $y = ab^x$.

Define Let x = number of years after 2000.

Let y = the population in millions.

Write $y = a(1.0124)^x$

$281 = a(1.0124)^0$ **To find *a*, substitute the 2000 values: $y = 281, x = 0$.**

$281 = a \cdot 1$ **Any number to the zero power equals 1.**

$281 = a$ **Simplify.**

$y = 281(1.0124)^x$ **Substitute *a* and *b* into $y = ab^x$.**

The function $y = 281(1.0124)^x$ models U.S. population growth.

Check Understanding

2 **a.** Predict U.S. population in 2015 to the nearest million.

b. Critical Thinking Explain why the model and your prediction may not be valid for 2015.

c. Suppose the rate of population increase changes to 1.4%. Write a function to model population growth and use it to predict the 2015 population to the nearest million.

You can write an exponential function from two points on the function's graph.

3 EXAMPLE Writing an Exponential Function

Write an exponential function $y = ab^x$ for a graph that includes (2, 2) and (3, 4).

$y = ab^x$	Use the general form.
$2 = a \cdot b^2$	Substitute for x and y using (2, 2).
$\frac{2}{b^2} = a$	Solve for a.
$y = ab^x$	Use the general form.
$4 = \frac{2}{b^2}b^3$	Substitute for x and y using (3, 4) and for a using $\frac{2}{b^2}$.
$4 = 2b^{3-2}$	Division Property of Exponents
$4 = 2b$	Simplify.
$b = 2$	Solve for b.
$a = \frac{2}{b^2}$	Use your equation for a.
$a = \frac{2}{2^2}$	Substitute 2 for b.
$a = \frac{1}{2}$	Simplify.
$y = \frac{1}{2} \cdot 2^x$	Substitute $\frac{1}{2}$ for a and 2 for b in $y = ab^x$.

The exponential function for a graph that includes (2, 2) and (3, 4) is $y = \frac{1}{2} \cdot 2^x$.

Check Understanding 3 Write an exponential function $y = ab^x$ for a graph that includes (2, 4) and (3, 16).

OBJECTIVE

2 Exponential Decay

Real-World Connection

On a day in March, the NCAA announces the selection of 64 teams for its annual tournament.

Investigation: Tournament Play

The National Collegiate Athletic Association (NCAA) holds an annual basketball tournament. The top 64 teams in Division I are invited to play each spring. When a team loses, it is out of the tournament.

1. How many teams are left in the tournament after the first round of basketball games?
2. a. Copy, complete, and extend the table until only one team is left.

   b. Graph the points from your table on graph paper.

After Round x	Number of Teams Left in Tournament (y)
0	64
1	■
2	■

3. How many rounds are played in the tournament?
4. Does the graph represent a linear function? Explain.
5. How does the number of teams left in each round compare to the number of teams in the previous round?

An exponential function can be used to model decay when $0 < b < 1$. When $b < 1$, b is a **decay factor.**

Exponential Decay

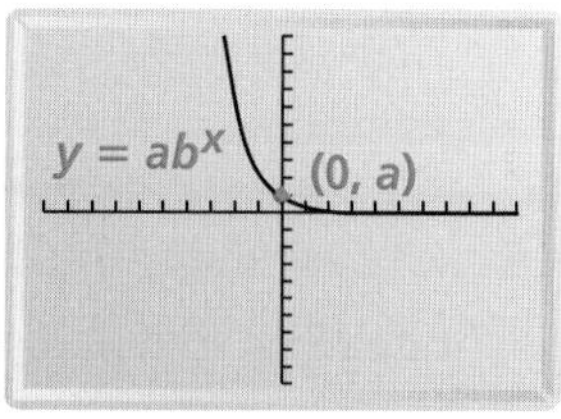

Decay factor $b < 1$

4 EXAMPLE Analyzing a Function

Without graphing, determine whether the function $y = 14(0.95)^x$ represents exponential growth or exponential decay.

In $y = 14(0.95)^x$, $b = 0.95$. Since $b < 1$, the function represents exponential decay.

Check Understanding 4 Without graphing, determine whether each function represents exponential growth or exponential decay.

a. $y = 100(0.12)^x$ **b.** $y = 0.2(5)^x$ **c.** $y = 16\left(\frac{1}{2}\right)^x$

Reading Math

In the word asymptote, *asym* means "not together."

An **asymptote** is a line that a graph approaches as x or y increases in absolute value.

5 EXAMPLE Graphing Exponential Decay

Graph $y = 24\left(\frac{1}{2}\right)^x$. Identify the horizontal asymptote.

Step 1 Make a table of values.

x	−3	−2	−1	0	1	2	3
y	192	96	48	24	12	6	3

Step 2 Graph the coordinates. Connect the points with a smooth curve.

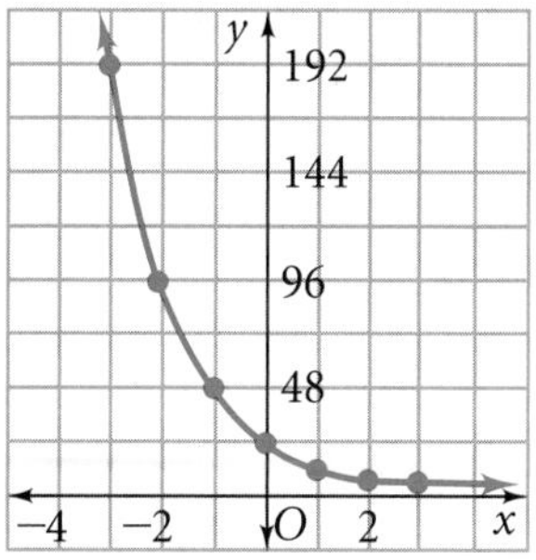

As x increases, y approaches 0.

The asymptote is the x-axis, $y = 0$.

Check Understanding 5 Graph each decay function. Identify the horizontal asymptote.

a. $y = 24\left(\frac{1}{3}\right)^x$ **b.** $y = 100(0.1)^x$

Reading Math

Depreciate comes from a prefix meaning "lower" and a root meaning "price."

Depreciation is the decline in an item's value resulting from age or wear. When an item loses about the same percent of its value each year, you can use an exponential function to model the depreciation.

6 EXAMPLE Real-World Connection

Depreciation The exponential decay graph shows the expected depreciation for a car over four years. Estimate the value of the car after six years.

Expected Decrease in Value

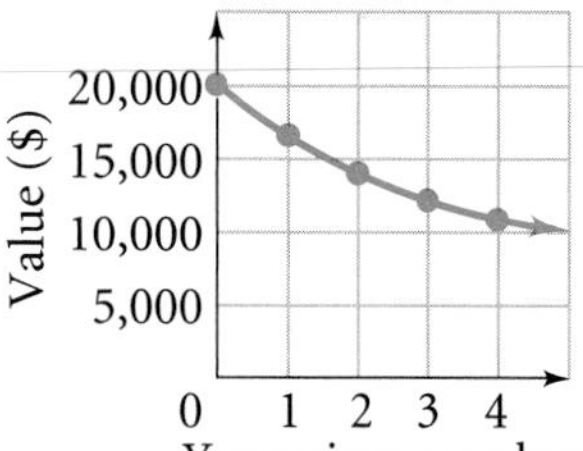

The decay factor b equals $1 + r$, where r is the annual rate of decrease. The initial value of the car is \$20,000. After one year the value of the car is about \$17,000.

$r = \frac{\text{final value} - \text{initial value}}{\text{initial value}}$ **Write an equation for r.**

$= \frac{17{,}000 - 20{,}000}{20{,}000}$ **Substitute.**

$= -0.15$ **Simplify.**

$b = 1 + r$ **Use r to find b.**

$= 1 + (-0.15) = 0.85$ **Simplify.**

Write a function, and then evaluate it for $x = 6$.

Relate The value of the car decreases exponentially; $b = 0.85$.

Define Let x = number of years. Let y = value of the car.

Write $y = ab^x$

$20{,}000 = a(0.85)^0$ **Substitute using (0, 20,000).**

$20{,}000 = a$ **Solve for a.**

$y = 20{,}000(0.85)^x$ **Substitute a and b into $y = ab^x$.**

$y = 20{,}000(0.85)^6$ **Evaluate for $x = 6$.**

≈ 7542.99 **Simplify.**

The car's value after six years will be about \$7540.

Check Understanding 6 Estimate the value of the car after 10 years.

EXERCISES

For more practice, see *Extra Practice*.

Practice and Problem Solving

A Practice by Example

Example 1 (page 422)

Graph each function.

1. $y = 6^x$
2. $y = 3(10)^x$
3. $y = 1000(2)^x$
4. $y = 9(3)^x$
5. $f(x) = 2(3)^x$
6. $s(t) = 1.5^t$
7. $y = 8(5)^x$
8. $y = 2^{2x}$

Example 2 (page 423)

9. **Population** The world population in 2000 was approximately 6.08 billion. The annual rate of increase was about 1.26%.
   a. Find the growth factor for the world population.
   b. Suppose the rate of increase continues to be 1.26%. Write a function to model world population growth.

Example 3 (page 424)

Write an exponential function $y = ab^x$ for a graph that includes the given points.

10. $(4, 8), (6, 32)$ **11.** $(2, 122.5), (3, 857.5)$ **12.** $(2, 18), (5, 60.75)$

13. $\left(-1, 8\frac{1}{3}\right), (2, 1.8)$ **14.** $(-3, 24), (-2, 12)$ **15.** $(0, 24), \left(3, \frac{8}{9}\right)$

Example 4 (page 425)

Without graphing, determine whether each function represents exponential growth or exponential decay.

16. $y = 129(1.63)^x$ **17.** $f(x) = 2(0.65)^x$ **18.** $y = 12\left(\frac{17}{10}\right)^x$ **19.** $y = 0.8\left(\frac{1}{8}\right)^x$

20. $f(x) = 4\left(\frac{5}{6}\right)^x$ **21.** $y = 0.45 \cdot 3^x$ **22.** $y = \frac{1}{100}\left(\frac{4}{3}\right)^x$ **23.** $f(x) = 2^{-x}$

Example 5 (page 425)

Graph each function. Identify the horizontal asymptote.

24. $y = (0.75)^x$ **25.** $y = 2(0.5)^x$ **26.** $y = (0.25)^x$ **27.** $g(x) = 5(0.2)^x$

28. $f(x) = \left(\frac{1}{5}\right)^x$ **29.** $y = 81\left(\frac{1}{3}\right)^x$ **30.** $s(t) = \left(\frac{1}{10}\right)^t$ **31.** $y = \frac{1}{2}\left(\frac{1}{2}\right)^x$

Example 6 (page 426)

Write an exponential function for each graph. Evaluate the function for $x = 6$.

32.

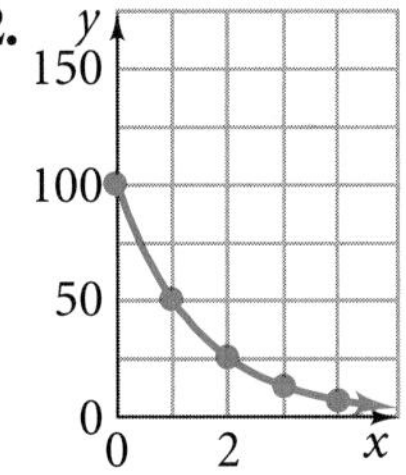

33.

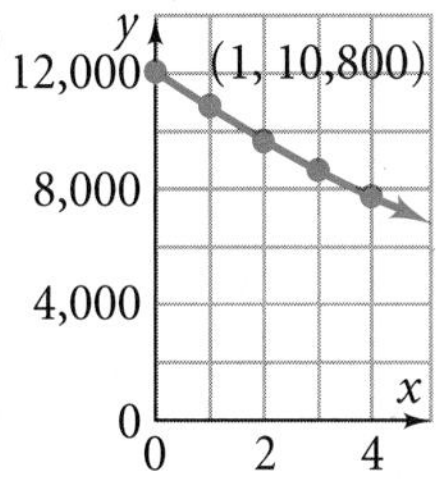

34.

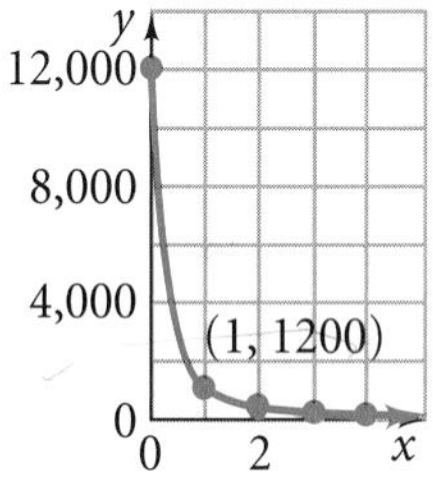

35. Business A computer valued at \$6500 depreciates at the rate of 14.3% per year.

a. Write a function that models the value of the computer.

b. Find the value of the computer after three years.

B Apply Your Skills

36. Social Studies The table below shows information about the population of the four largest cities in the world in 2000.

World's Largest Cities

Rank in 2000	City	2000 Population	Projected Average Annual Growth
1	Tokyo, Japan	26,444,000	0.00%
2	Mexico City, Mexico	18,131,000	0.39%
3	Bombay, India	18,066,000	2.51%
4	São Paulo, Brazil	17,755,000	0.94%

SOURCE: *The World Almanac*

a. Using the appropriate projected growth rate, project the population of each city for the year 2010.

b. According to your prediction, does the order of the cities' ranks change by 2010? If so, rank the cities in order.

For each function, find the annual percent increase or decrease that the function models.

37. $y = 1298(1.63)^x$ **38.** $y = 0.65(1.3)^x$ **39.** $f(x) = 2(0.65)^x$

40. $y = 12\left(\frac{17}{10}\right)^x$ **41.** $y = 0.8\left(\frac{1}{8}\right)^x$ **42.** $y = 16\left(\frac{1}{4}\right)^x$

Real-World Connection

Careers Oceanographers model conditions on the ocean floor, interactions between plant and animal life, and the impact of pollution on seawater.

43. Oceanography The function $y = 20 \cdot 0.975^x$ models the intensity of sunlight beneath the surface of the ocean. The output y represents the percent of surface sunlight intensity that reaches a depth of x feet. The model is accurate from about 20 feet to about 600 feet beneath the surface.

a. Find the percent of sunlight 50 feet beneath the surface of the ocean.

b. Find the percent of sunlight at a depth of 370 ft.

44. a. Depreciation Each graph below shows the expected decrease in a car's value over the next five years. Write a function to model each car's depreciation. Determine which car will be worth more after 10 years.

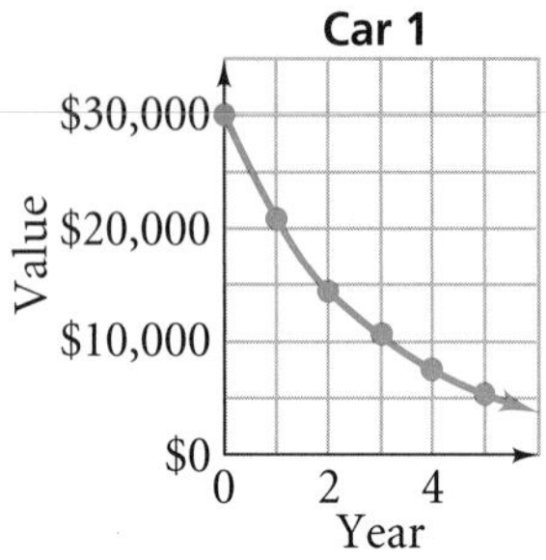

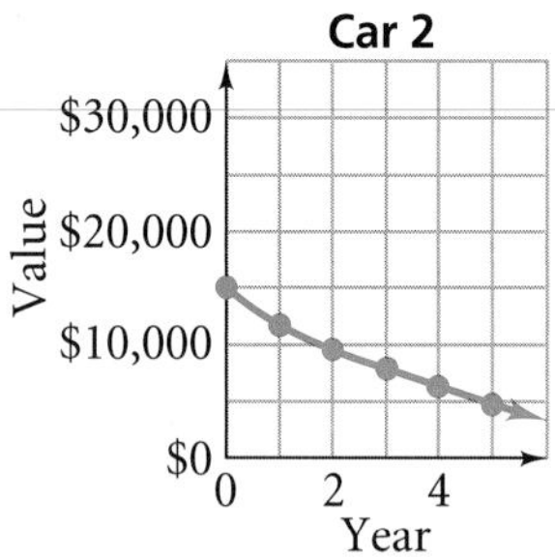

b. Data Collection Find the initial value and the expected decrease in value of your favorite type of car. Write an exponential function to model the car's depreciation.

45. The population of a certain animal species decreases at a rate of 3.5% per year. You have counted 80 of the animals in the habitat you are studying.

a. Write a function that models the change in the animal population.

b. Graph the function. Estimate the number of years until the population first drops below 15 animals.

For each annual rate of change, find the corresponding growth or decay factor.

46. +70% **47.** +500% **48.** −75% **49.** −55%

50. +12.5% **51.** −0.1% **52.** +0.1% **53.** +100%

54. Communications Cellular phone usage grew about 26% each year from 1995 (about 34 million) to 1999. Write a function to model U.S. cellular phone usage over that time period.

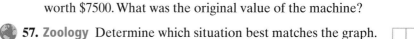

U.S. Cellular Phone Usage, 1995–1999

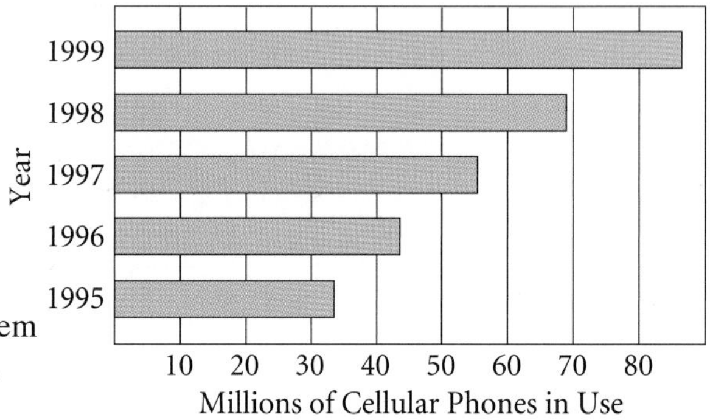

SOURCE: The CTIA Semi-Annual Wireless Survey

55. Open-Ended Write a problem that could be modeled with $y = 20(1.1)^x$.

C Challenge

56. The value of an industrial machine has a decay factor of 0.75 per year. After six years, the machine is worth \$7500. What was the original value of the machine?

57. Zoology Determine which situation best matches the graph.

A. A population of 120 cougars decreases 98.75% yearly.

B. A population of 125 cougars increases 1.25% yearly.

C. A population of 115 cougars decreases 1.25% yearly.

D. A population of 200 cougars decreases 50% yearly.

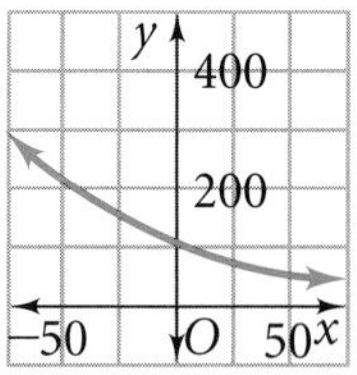

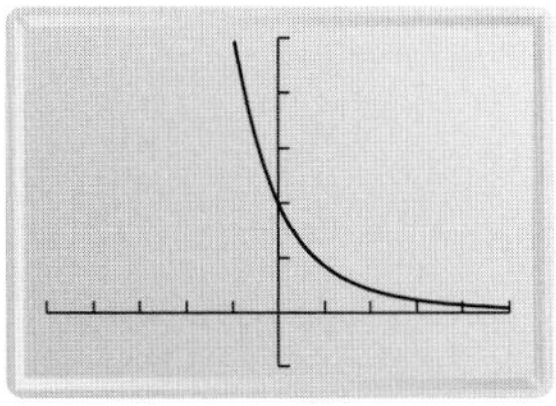

58. **Critical Thinking** Analyze the graph at the left to determine which function the graph represents. Explain your reasoning.

A. $y = \left(\frac{1}{3}\right)2^x$ **B.** $y = 2\left(\frac{1}{3}\right)^x$ **C.** $y = -2\left(\frac{1}{3}\right)^x$

59. **Economics** The table gives the 1998 gross domestic product and the real growth rate for several countries.

a. Writing Explain how a negative growth rate affects the equation for an exponential model.

b. Write a function for each country to model the GDP.

c. Suppose the given real growth rates continue. Predict the gross domestic product for each country in 2005.

Domestic Product Growth Rates

Country	1998 Gross Domestic Product (billions)	1998 Real Growth Rate
Armenia	\$9.2	6%
Canada	\$688.3	3%
Oman	\$18.6	−8.5%
Paraguay	\$19.8	−0.5%

SOURCE: *Time Almanac*

Standardized Test Prep

Multiple Choice

60. Which function represents exponential growth?

A. $y = 35x^{1.35}$ **B.** $y = 35 \cdot (0.35)^x$
C. $y = 35 \cdot (1.35)^x$ **D.** $y = 35 \div (1.35)^x$

Take It to the NET
Online lesson quiz at **www.PHSchool.com**
Web Code: aga-0801

61. Which function represents the value after x years of a delivery van that was purchased new for \$17,500 and depreciates 11% each year?

F. $y = -11(17{,}500)^x$ **G.** $y = 17{,}500(0.11)^x$
H. $y = 17{,}500(0.89)^x$ **I.** $y = 17{,}500(1.11)^x$

62. What is the equation of the asymptote of $y = 15 \cdot \left(\frac{1}{3}\right)^x$?

A. $y = 1$ **B.** $y = 0$ **C.** $y = x$ **D.** $y = \frac{1}{3}$

Short Response

63. Sketch the graph of the function $y = 2 \cdot \left(\frac{1}{4}\right)^x$.

Extended Response

64. Write an exponential equation in the form $y = ab^x$ for a graph that includes (2, 54) and $\left(\frac{1}{2}, 2\right)$. Show your work.

Mixed Review

Lesson 7-8 **Graph each function.**

65. $y = \sqrt{x + 2}$ 66. $y = -2\sqrt[3]{x} + 4$ 67. $y = \sqrt{9x - 153} - 5$

Lesson 7-2 **Simplify each expression.**

68. $\sqrt{180n^5}$ 69. $3\sqrt[3]{72r^5} \cdot 2\sqrt[3]{343r^3}$ 70. $\frac{\sqrt{64x^4}}{\sqrt{144x^5}}$

Lesson 6-2 **Construct a polynomial function with the given zeros.**

71. $x = 0, 1, 4$ 72. $x = -2, -1, 3$ 73. $x = 5, 0, 2$

Lesson 5-2 **Each point lies on a parabola with vertex (0, 2). Write the equation of the parabola.**

74. $(1, 3)$ 75. $(1, -3)$ 76. $(-1, 4)$ 77. $(2, 42)$

78. $(-2, 8)$ 79. $(-1, 5)$ 80. $(2, 0)$ 81. $(2, -2)$

Technology

Fitting Exponential Curves to Data

For Use With Lesson 8-1

You can use your graphing calculator to fit an exponential curve to data and find the exponential function.

Take It to the NET
Graphing Calculator procedures online at **www.PHSchool.com**
Web Code: age-2123

EXAMPLE

The table at the right shows the number of degrees above room temperature for a cup of coffee after x minutes of cooling. Graph the data. Find the best-fitting exponential function.

Step 1 Press STAT ENTER to enter the data in lists.

Step 2 Use the **STAT PLOT** feature to plot the points.

Step 3 Find the equation for the best-fitting exponential function. Press STAT ▶ 0 ENTER to use the **ExpReg** feature. The line of best fit can be approximated by $f(x) = 133.458\,(0.942)^x$.

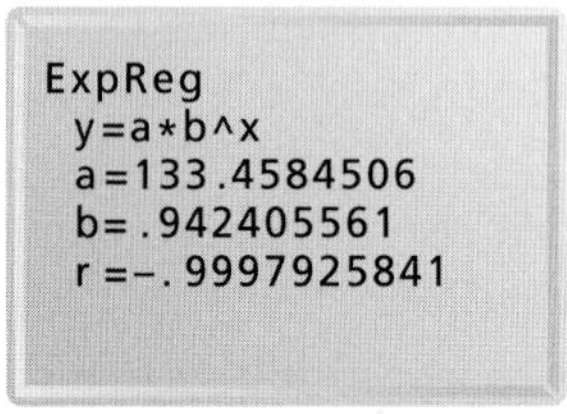

Step 4 Graph the function. Press Y= CLEAR VARS 5 ▶ ▶ ENTER to enter the **ExpReg** results. Press GRAPH to display the data and the function together. Press ZOOM 9 to automatically adjust the window.

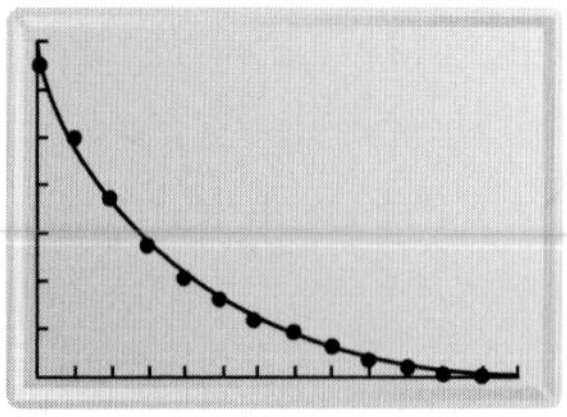

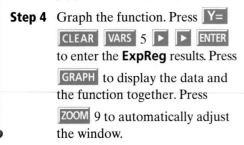

Cooling Coffee

Time (min)	°F Above Room Temperature
0	135
5	100
10	74
15	55
20	41
25	30
30	22
35	17
40	12
45	9
50	7
55	5
60	4

EXERCISES

Use a graphing calculator to find the exponential function that best fits each set of data. Graph each function. Sketch your graph.

1.

x	−3	−2	−1	0	1	2
y	50	25	12.5	6.25	3.13	1.56

2.

x	0	1	2	3	4	5
y	2	2.4	2.88	3.46	4.15	5

3.

x	1	2	3	4	5	6
y	1.2	4.8	19.2	76.8	307.2	1228.8

4.

x	−10	−9	−8	−7	−6	−5
y	0.03	0.07	0.14	0.27	0.55	1.09

5. **Writing** In the example above, the function appears to level off. Explain why this happens.

6. Explain how you could decide whether an exponential model is a better fit than a linear model.

8-2 Properties of Exponential Functions

North Carolina Objectives

2.03 Use exponential functions to model and solve problems. a) Solve using tables, graphs, and algebraic properties. b) Interpret the constants, coefficients, and bases in the context of the problem.

Lesson Preview

What You'll Learn

OBJECTIVE 1 To identify the role of constants in $y = ab^{cx}$

OBJECTIVE 2 To use e as a base

. . . And Why

To model the half-life of a radioactive substance, as in Example 3

Check Skills You'll Need

(For help, go to Lessons 2-6, 5-3, and 7-4.)

Write an equation for each translation.

1. $y = |x|$, 1 unit up, 2 units left
2. $y = -|x|$, 2 units down
3. $y = x^2$, 2 units down, 1 unit right
4. $y = -x^2$, 3 units up, 1 unit left

Write each equation in simplest form. Assume that all variables are positive.

5. $y = \left(x^{-\frac{5}{4}}\right)^4$
6. $y = \left(x^{-\frac{1}{7}}\right)^{-7}$
7. $y = \left(x^{\frac{5}{6}}\right)^6$

8. Use the formula for simple interest $I = Prt$. Find the interest for a principal of \$550 at a rate of 3% for 2 years.

New Vocabulary • continuously compounded interest formula

Interactive lesson includes instant self-check, tutorials, and activities.

OBJECTIVE 1 Comparing Graphs

Need Help?
A reflection is a transformation that creates symmetry on the coordinate plane.

So far you have graphed functions of the form $y = ab^x$ for values of a greater than zero. When $a < 0$, the graph of $y = ab^x$ is a reflection of $y = |a|b^x$ over the x-axis.

1 EXAMPLE Graphing $y = ab^x$ When $a < 0$

Graph $y = \frac{1}{2} \cdot 2^x$ and $y = -\frac{1}{2} \cdot 2^x$. Label the asymptote of each graph.

Step 1 Make a table of values.

x	$y = \frac{1}{2} \cdot 2^x$	$y = -\frac{1}{2} \cdot 2^x$
−2	$\frac{1}{8}$	$-\frac{1}{8}$
−1	$\frac{1}{4}$	$-\frac{1}{4}$
0	$\frac{1}{2}$	$-\frac{1}{2}$
1	1	−1
2	2	−2
3	4	−4

Step 2 Graph the functions.

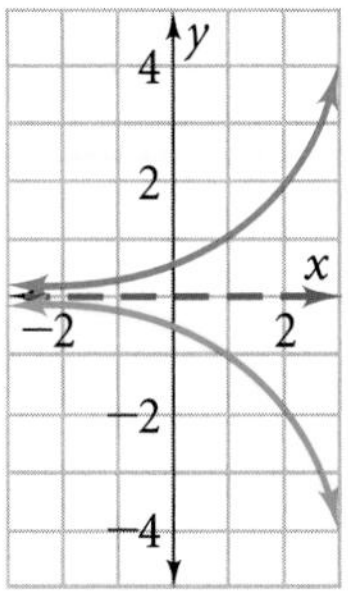

The y-intercept is a, or $\frac{1}{2}$.

The asymptote is $y = 0$ for both graphs.

The y-intercept is a, or $-\frac{1}{2}$.

Check Understanding

1 Graph each function.

a. $y = -4(2)^x$

b. $y = -3^x$

You can graph many exponential functions as translations of the parent function $y = ab^x$. The graph of $y = ab^{x-h} + k$ is the graph of $y = ab^x$ translated h units horizontally and k units vertically.

2 EXAMPLE Translating $y = ab^x$

Graph $y = 8\left(\frac{1}{2}\right)^x$ and $y = 8\left(\frac{1}{2}\right)^{x+2} + 3$.

Step 1 Graph $y = 8\left(\frac{1}{2}\right)^x$. The horizontal asymptote is $y = 0$.

Step 2 For $y = 8\left(\frac{1}{2}\right)^{x+2} + 3$, $h = -2$ and $k = 3$. So shift the graph of the parent function 2 units left and 3 units up. The horizontal asymptote is $y = 3$.

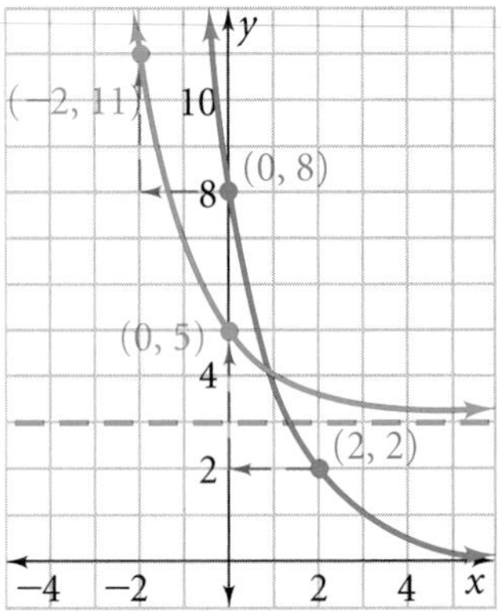

Check Understanding 2 Graph each function as a translation of $y = 9(3)^x$.

a. $y = 9(3)^{x+1}$

b. $y = 9(3)^x - 4$

c. $y = 9(3)^{x-3} - 1$

Some exponential functions are of the form $y = ab^{cx}$, where c is a nonzero constant.

3 EXAMPLE Real-World Connection

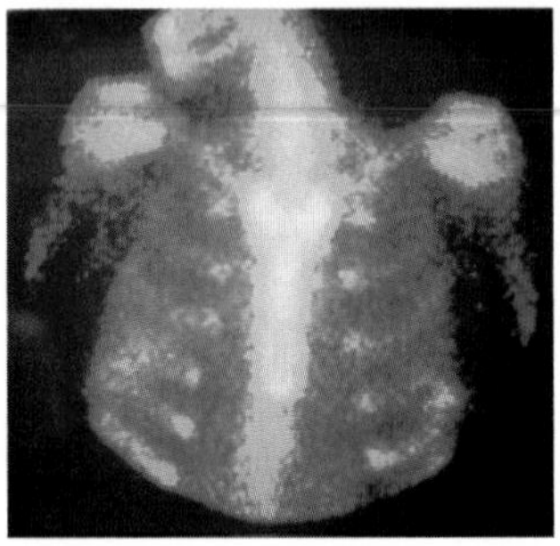

Real-World Connection

As technetium-99*m* decays, it emits low-energy gamma rays. The rays are detected by a gamma camera to produce images like the one above.

Medicine The half-life of a radioactive substance is the time it takes for half of the material to decay. A hospital prepares a 100-mg supply of technetium-99*m*, which has a half-life of 6 hours. Make a table showing the amount of technetium-99*m* that remains at the end of each 6-hour interval for 36 hours. Then write an exponential function to find the amount of technetium-99*m* that remains after 75 hours.

The amount of technetium-99*m* is reduced by one half each 6 hours.

Number of 6-h Intervals	0	1	2	3	4	5	6
Number of Hours Elapsed	0	6	12	18	24	30	36
Technetium-99*m* (mg)	100	50	25	12.5	6.25	3.13	1.56

Relate The amount of technetium-99*m* is an exponential function of the number of half-lives. The initial amount is 100 mg. The decay factor is $\frac{1}{2}$. One half-life equals 6 h.

Define Let y = the amount of technetium-99*m*.

Let x = the number of hours elapsed. Then $\frac{1}{6}x$ = the number of half-lives.

Write $y = 100\left(\frac{1}{2}\right)^{\frac{1}{6}x}$

$y = 100\left(\frac{1}{2}\right)^{\frac{1}{6} \cdot 75}$ **Substitute 75 for x.**

$= 100\left(\frac{1}{2}\right)^{12.5}$ **Simplify.**

≈ 0.017 **Use a calculator.**

After 75 hours, about 0.017 mg of technetium-99*m* remains.

Check Understanding **3** Arsenic-74 is used to locate brain tumors. It has a half-life of 17.5 days. Write an exponential decay function for a 90-mg sample. Use the function to find the amount remaining after 6 days.

OBJECTIVE

2 The Number e

At the right is part of the graph of the function $y = \left(1 + \frac{1}{x}\right)^x$. One of the graph's asymptotes is $y = e$, where e is an irrational number approximately equal to 2.71828.

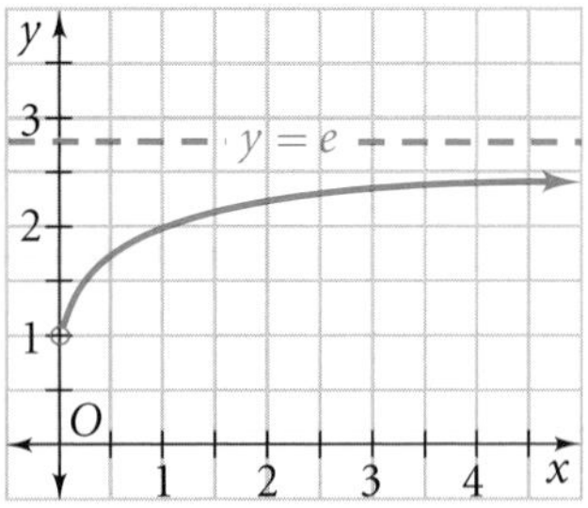

Exponential functions with a base of e are useful for describing continuous growth or decay. Your graphing calculator has a key for e^x.

4 EXAMPLE Evaluating e^x

Graph $y = e^x$. Evaluate e^2 to four decimal places.

Graphing Calculator Hint
After graphing e^x, press TRACE 2 ENTER to find y for $x = 2$.

Step 1 Graph $y = e^x$.

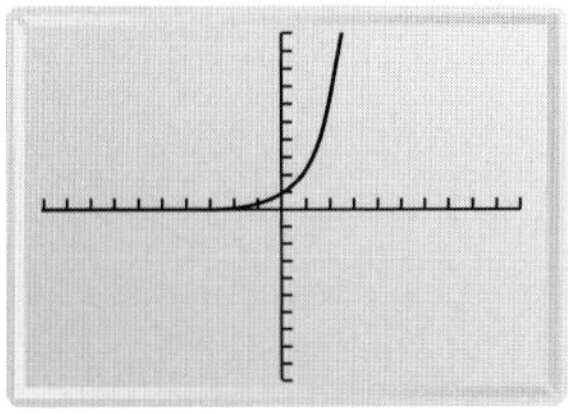

Step 2 Find y when $x = 2$.

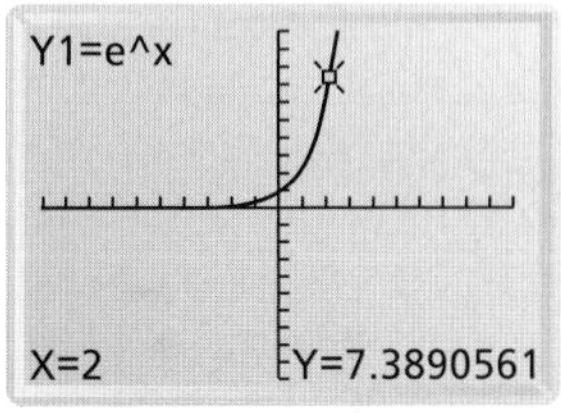

The value of e^2 is about 7.3891.

Check Understanding **4** Use the graph of $y = e^x$ to evaluate each expression to four decimal places.

a. e^4 **b.** e^{-3} **c.** $e^{\frac{1}{2}}$

In previous courses, you have studied simple interest and compound interest. The more frequently interest is compounded, the more quickly the amount in an account increases. The formula for *continuously* compounded interest uses the number e.

Key Concepts

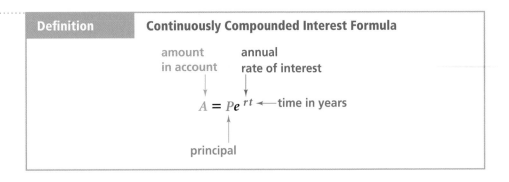

Definition	Continuously Compounded Interest Formula

$$A = Pe^{rt}$$

A: amount in account; P: principal; r: annual rate of interest; t: time in years

5 EXAMPLE Real-World Connection

Investments Suppose you invest \$1050 at an annual interest rate of 5.5% compounded continuously. How much will you have in the account after five years?

$A = Pe^{rt}$

$= 1050 \cdot e^{0.055(5)}$ **Substitute 1050 for *P*, 0.055 for *r*, and 5 for *t*.**

$= 1050 \cdot e^{0.275}$ **Simplify.**

$\approx 1050(1.316531)$ **Evaluate $e^{0.275}$.**

≈ 1382.36 **Simplify.**

You will have about \$1382 in the account after five years.

Check Understanding 5 Suppose you invest \$1300 at an annual interest rate of 4.3% compounded continuously. Find the amount you will have in the account after three years.

EXERCISES

For more practice, see *Extra Practice.*

Practice and Problem Solving

A Practice by Example

Example 1 (page 431)

Graph each function. Label the asymptote of each graph.

1. $y = -5^x$ **2.** $y = -\left(\frac{1}{2}\right)^x$ **3.** $y = -2(4)^x$ **4.** $y = -9(3)^x$

5. $y = -3(2)^x$ **6.** $y = -24\left(\frac{1}{2}\right)^x$ **7.** $y = -4^x$ **8.** $y = -\left(\frac{1}{3}\right)^x$

Example 2 (page 432)

Graph each function as a translation of its parent function.

9. $y = 8^x + 5$ **10.** $y = 15\left(\frac{4}{3}\right)^x - 8$ **11.** $y = -(0.3)^{x-2}$

12. $y = -2(5)^{x+3}$ **13.** $y = 52\left(\frac{2}{13}\right)^{x-1} + 26$ **14.** $y = 9\left(\frac{1}{3}\right)^{x+7} - 3$

Example 3 (page 432)

15. **Botany** Phosphorus-32 is used to study a plant's use of fertilizer. It has a half-life of 14.3 days. Write the exponential decay function for a 50-mg sample. Find the amount of phosporus-32 remaining after 84 days.

16. **Public Works** Iodine-131 is used to find leaks in water pipes. It has a half-life of 8.14 days. Write the exponential decay function for a 200-mg sample. Find the amount of iodine-131 remaining after 72 days.

17. **Archaeology** Carbon-14 is used to determine the age of artifacts in carbon dating. It has a half-life of 5730 years. Write the exponential decay function for a 24-mg sample. Find the amount of carbon-14 remaining after 30 millennia (1 millennium = 1000 years).

Example 4 (page 433)

Use the graph of $y = e^x$ to evaluate each expression to four decimal places.

18. e^3 **19.** e^6 **20.** e^{-2} **21.** e^0 **22.** $e^{\frac{5}{2}}$ **23.** e^e

Example 5 (page 434)

Find the amount in a continuously compounded account for the given conditions.

24. principal: \$2000
annual interest 5.1%
time: 3 yr

25. principal: \$400
annual interest 7.6%
time: 1.5 yr

26. principal: \$950
annual interest 6.5%
time: 10 yr

B Apply Your Skills

27. Find the value of a for which the graph of $y = ab^x$ is a horizontal line.

28. Find the value of b for which the graph of $y = ab^x$ is a horizontal line.

29. Assume that a and b are positive. Describe the effects of $c < 0, c = 0,$ and $c > 0$ on the graph of the function $y = ab^{cx}$.

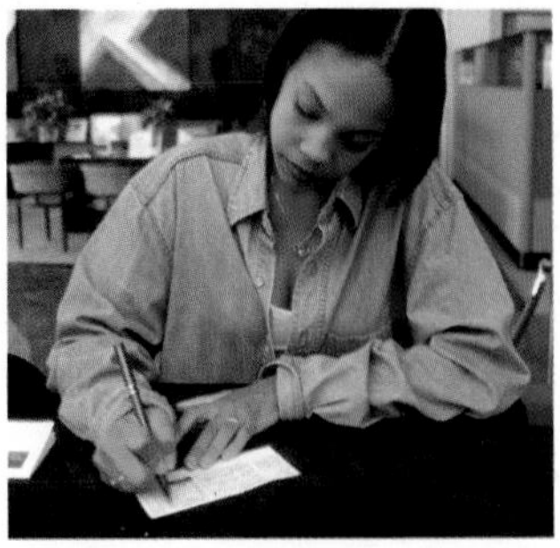

Real-World Connection

A savings plan can be an important part of preparing for college.

30. **Savings** A student wants to save \$8000 for college in five years. How much should be put into an account that earns 5.2% annual interest compounded continuously?

31. When $a < 0$ and $b > 1$, $y = ab^x$ models negative exponential growth.
   a. **Open-Ended** Write an exponential function that models negative growth.
   b. Give an example of a situation that could be modeled by your function.
   c. **Critical Thinking** Explain one difference between negative exponential growth and exponential decay.

The parent function for each graph below is of the form $y = ab^x$. Write the parent function. Then write a function for the translation indicated.

32.
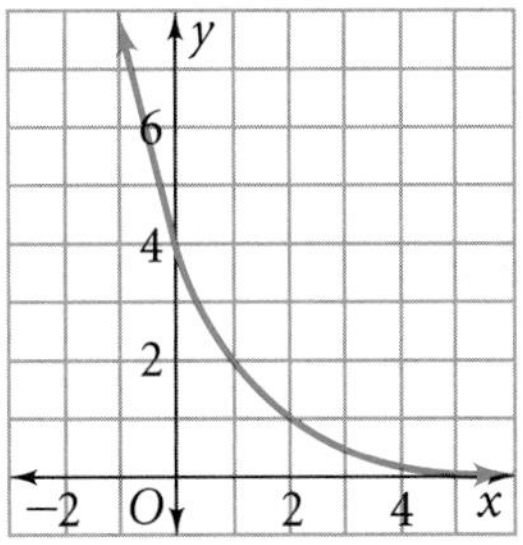

translation: left 4 units, up 3 units

33.
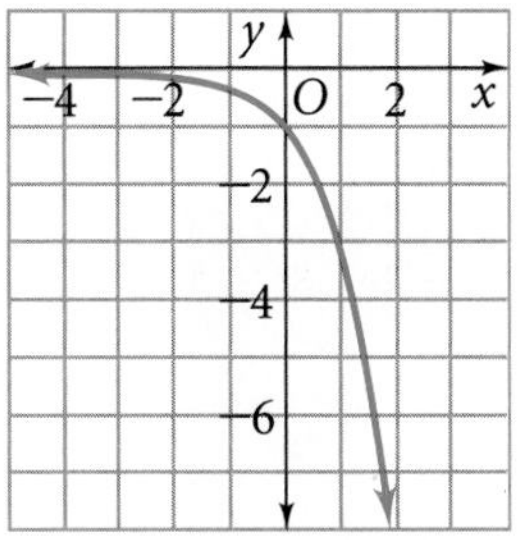

translation: right 8 units, up 2 units

34.
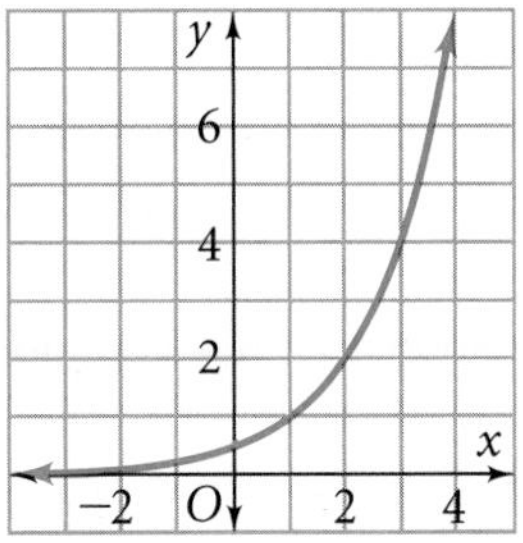

translation: right 6 units, down 7 units

35.
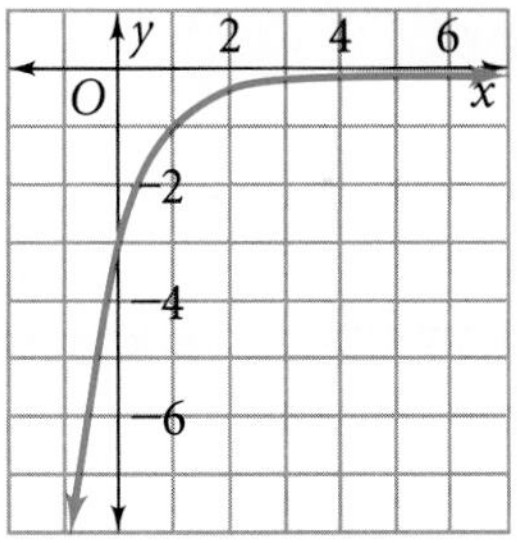

translation: left 5 units, down 1 unit

Reading Math

The pascal is the metric unit of pressure.

36. **Physics** At a constant temperature, the atmospheric pressure p in pascals is given by the formula $p = 101.3e^{-0.001h}$, where h is the altitude in meters. Find p at an altitude of 300 m.

37. **Investment** How long would it take to double your principal at an annual interest rate of 8% compounded continuously?

38. **Writing** Like a debt, a deficit is a negative amount of money. Explain how you would model a deficit that is growing exponentially. In $y = ab^{cx}$, would the values of a and c be positive or negative? Would the value of b be greater than 1 or less than 1?

39. **Economics** The gross domestic product, or GDP, of the United States was about 8.511 trillion in 1998.
   a. Assume that GDP grows 3.8% each year. Write an exponential function to describe such growth.
   b. Describe the GDP growth that occurs over 18 years.
   c. Describe the growth in half that time.

Need Help?

The compound interest formula is $A = P\left(1 + \frac{r}{n}\right)^{nt}$, where n is the number of times per year the interest is compounded.

40. Suppose you invest \$2000 at an annual interest rate of 4.5%, compounded quarterly.
a. How much will you have in the account after five years?
b. Determine how much more you would have if the interest were compounded continuously.

41. An investor withdraws all \$525 from an account that was neglected for 8 years. It earned 3.4% annual interest, compounded continuously. How much was the initial deposit?

Without graphing, determine whether each equation represents exponential growth or exponential decay.

42. $s(t) = 5e^t$ **43.** $y = \frac{1}{6}e^x$ **44.** $y = \left(\frac{1}{e}\right)^x$

45. $y = \frac{7}{5}\left(\frac{e}{2}\right)^x$ **46.** $f(x) = \left(\frac{e}{3.7}\right)^x$ **47.** $y = -70e^t$

C Challenge

48. Biology A new flu virus is introduced when a stranger visits an isolated village of 8000 people. Every infected person infects two more each day.
a. Write an exponential function to model the number of *uninfected* people.
b. Determine how many people remain uninfected after one week.
c. After how many days will the entire population be infected?

Real-World Connection

Careers Psychologists use models to evaluate and predict learning rates.

49. Psychology Psychologists use an exponential model of the learning process, $f(t) = c(1 - e^{-kt})$, where c is the total number of tasks to be learned, k is the rate of learning, t is time, and $f(t)$ is the number of tasks learned.
a. Suppose you move to a new school, and you want to learn the names of 30 classmates in your homeroom. If your learning rate for new tasks is 20% per day, how many complete names will you know after 2 days? After 8 days?
b. Graph the function on your graphing calculator. How many days will it take to learn everyone's name? Explain.
c. Open-Ended Does this function seem to describe your own learning rate? If not, how could you adapt it to reflect your learning rate?

50. Work begins on digging a moat on the perimeter of a property. After the first weekend, the first worker recruits a friend to help. After every succeeding weekend, each moat-digger recruits another friend. One person can dig 15 m^3 of dirt per weekend. The moat should be 4 m wide and 3 m deep, and it must lie entirely within the 60 m-by-70 m property.
a. Geometry Determine the volume of dirt that must be removed for the moat.
b. Write an exponential function to model the volume of dirt remaining to be shoveled after x weekends.
c. On which weekend will the moat be completed?

Standardized Test Prep

Multiple Choice

51. How is the graph of $y = 4 \cdot \left(\frac{1}{2}\right)^{x-3}$ translated from the graph of $y = 4 \cdot \left(\frac{1}{2}\right)^x$?
A. 3 units right **B.** 3 units left **C.** 3 units down **D.** 3 units up

52. How is the graph of $y = 4 \cdot \left(\frac{1}{2}\right)^x + 3$ translated from the graph of $y = 4 \cdot \left(\frac{1}{2}\right)^x$?
F. 3 units right **G.** 3 units left **H.** 3 units down **I.** 3 units up

Take It to the NET

Online lesson quiz at www.PHSchool.com

Web Code: aga-0802

53. A savings account earns 4.62% annual interest, compounded continuously. After approximately how many years will a principal of $500 double?
A. 2 years B. 10 years C. 15 years D. 44 years

54. Sodium-24 has a half-life of 15 hours. How much sodium-24 will you have after 60 hours if your original sample is 64 mg?
F. 4 mg G. 16 mg H. 32 mg I. 64 mg

Short Response

55. How much should you invest in a continuously compounded account at an annual interest rate of 6% if you want exactly $8000 after four years? Show how you got your answer.

Mixed Review

Lesson 8-1

Write an exponential equation $y = ab^x$ for a graph that includes the given points.

56. $(0, 1), (1, 3)$ **57.** $(1, -8), (2, -32)$ **58.** $(0, -5), (2, -20)$

59. $(-1, 16), (3, 1)$ **60.** $(-3, 0.07), (-1, 7)$ **61.** $(2, 6400), (4, 4096)$

Lesson 7-3

Simplify each expression.

62. $5\sqrt{5} + \sqrt{5}$ **63.** $\sqrt[3]{4} - 2\sqrt[3]{4}$ **64.** $\sqrt{75} + \sqrt{125}$ **65.** $\sqrt[4]{32} + \sqrt[4]{128}$

66. $5\sqrt{3} - 2\sqrt{12}$ **67.** $3\sqrt{63} + \sqrt{28}$ **68.** $(3 - \sqrt{6})^2$ **69.** $\frac{-2 - 2\sqrt{5}}{1 - \sqrt{5}}$

Lesson 6-3

Divide using either long division or synthetic division.

70. $(x^2 - 3x - 1) \div x$ **71.** $(x^3 - 2x^2 - 5x + 6) \div (x - 1)$

72. $(x^3 + 4x^2 - x - 4) \div (x + 4)$ **73.** $(x^3 - 4x^2 - 4x - 5) \div (x - 5)$

74. $(13x^2 - 51x - 4) \div (x - 4)$ **75.** $(9x^3 - 18x^2 - x + 2) \div (3x + 1)$

Lesson 3-5

Find the equations of the traces of each graph.

76. $x - y + z = 5$ **77.** $x + y + 4z = -2$ **78.** $3x + 3y - 6z = 24$

79. $x - y + 2z = 8$ **80.** $3x + y + 9z = -18$ **81.** $-2x + y - 5z = 10$

Checkpoint Quiz 1 — Lessons 8-1 through 8-2

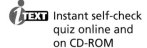

TEXT Instant self-check quiz online and on CD-ROM

Identify each function as modeling either exponential growth or exponential decay. What percent of increase or decrease does the function model?

1. $y = 15(1.45)^x$ **2.** $y = 0.32(0.99)^x$ **3.** $y = 0.1(1.7)^x$ **4.** $y = 7.3(0.8)^x$

Graph each function.

5. $y = 3^x$ **6.** $y = 2^x + 1$ **7.** $y = (0.25)^x$ **8.** $y = 4^x - 5$

9. **Open-Ended** Describe a real-world problem that you could model with an exponential growth function.

10. **Chemistry** An element has a half-life of 30 hours. Write the exponential decay function for a 100-mg sample. Use the function to find the amount of the element remaining after 100 hours.

8-3 Logarithmic Functions as Inverses

North Carolina Objectives

1.01 Simplify and perform operations with rational exponents and logarithms (common and natural) to solve problems.
2.01 Use the inverse of functions to model and solve problems.

Lesson Preview

What You'll Learn

OBJECTIVE 1 To write and evaluate logarithmic expressions

OBJECTIVE 2 To graph logarithmic functions

. . . And Why

To compare the acidities of milk and lemon juice, as in Example 4

Check Skills You'll Need

(For help, go to Lessons 7-1 and 7-7.)

Solve each equation.

1. $8 = x^3$ **2.** $x^{\frac{1}{4}} = 2$ **3.** $27 = 3^x$ **4.** $4^6 = 4^{3x}$

Graph each relation and its inverse on a coordinate plane.

5. $y = 5x$ **6.** $y = 2x^2$ **7.** $y = -x^3$ **8.** $y = \frac{1}{2}x$

New Vocabulary • logarithm • common logarithm • logarithmic function

Interactive lesson includes instant self-check, tutorials, and activities.

OBJECTIVE 1 Writing and Evaluating Logarithmic Expressions

The magnitude of an earthquake is a measure of the amount of energy released at its source. The Richter scale is an exponential measure of earthquake magnitude. An earthquake of magnitude 5 releases about 30 times as much energy as an earthquake of magnitude 4.

The Richter Scale

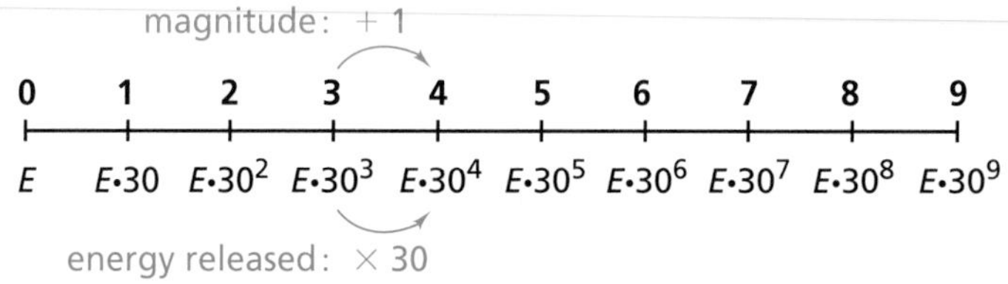

Real-World Connection

The earthquake that struck Washington in 2001 measured 6.8 on the Richter scale.

1 EXAMPLE Real-World Connection

Seismology In 1995, an earthquake in Mexico registered 8.0 on the Richter scale. In 2001, an earthquake of magnitude 6.8 shook Washington state. Compare the amounts of energy released in the two earthquakes.

$\frac{E \cdot 30^{8.0}}{E \cdot 30^{6.8}}$ **Write a ratio.**

$= \frac{30^{8.0}}{30^{6.8}}$ **Simplify.**

$= 30^{8.0 - 6.8}$ **Division Property of Exponents**

$= 30^{1.2}$ **Simplify.**

≈ 59.2 **Use a calculator.**

The earthquake in Mexico released about 59 times as much energy as the earthquake in Washington.

Check Understanding **1** In 1997, an earthquake in Alabama registered 4.9 on the Richter scale. In 1999, one in California registered 7.0. Compare the energy released in the two quakes.

The exponents used by the Richter scale shown in Example 1 are called logarithms, or logs.

Key Concepts

Definition	**Logarithm**
The **logarithm** to the base b of a positive number y is defined as follows: If $y = b^x$, then $\log_b y = x$.	

Reading Math

Read $\log_b y$ as "log base b of y."

The exponent x in the exponential expression b^x is the logarithm in the equation $\log_b y = x$. The base b in b^x is the same as the base b in the logarithm. In both cases, $b \neq 1$ and $b > 0$.

A positive number b raised to any power x cannot equal a number y less than or equal to zero. Therefore, the logarithm of a negative number or zero is undefined.

2 EXAMPLE Writing in Logarithmic Form

Write $25 = 5^2$ in logarithmic form.

If $y = b^x$, then $\log_b y = x$. **Write the definition.**

If $25 = 5^2$, then $\log_5 25 = 2$. **Substitute.**

The logarithmic form of $25 = 5^2$ is $\log_5 25 = 2$.

Check Understanding 2 Write each equation in logarithmic form.

a. $729 = 3^6$ **b.** $\left(\frac{1}{2}\right)^3 = \frac{1}{8}$ **c.** $10^0 = 1$

To evaluate logarithms, you can write them in exponential form.

3 EXAMPLE Evaluating Logarithms

Evaluate $\log_8 16$.

$\log_8 16 = x$ **Write an equation in logarithmic form.**

$16 = 8^x$ **Convert to exponential form.**

$2^4 = (2^3)^x$ **Write each side using base 2.**

$2^4 = 2^{3x}$ **Power Property of Exponents**

$4 = 3x$ **Set the exponents equal to each other.**

$\frac{4}{3} = x$ **Solve for x.**

So $\log_8 16 = \frac{4}{3}$.

Check Understanding 3 Evaluate each logarithm.

a. $\log_{64} \frac{1}{32}$ **b.** $\log_9 27$ **c.** $\log_{10} 100$

A **common logarithm** is a logarithm that uses base 10. You can write the common logarithm $\log_{10} y$ as $\log y$.

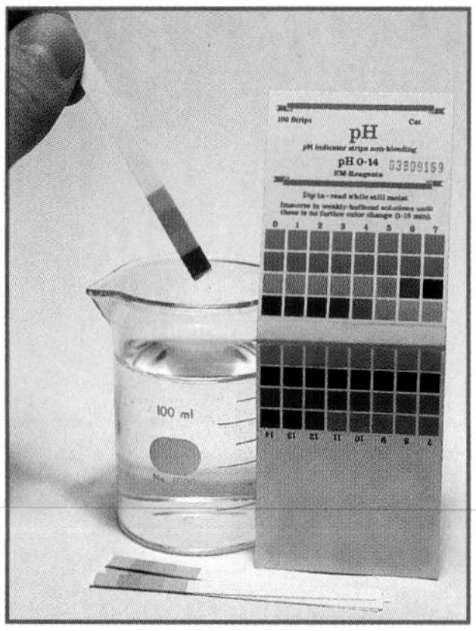

Real-World Connection

You can use pH strips to measure the acidity of a water solution. The pH scale ranges from 0 to 14.

Scientists use common logarithms to measure acidity, which increases as the concentration of hydrogen ions in a substance increases. The pH of a substance equals $-\log[H^+]$, where $[H^+]$ is the concentration of hydrogen ions.

4 EXAMPLE Real-World Connection

Chemistry The pH of lemon juice is 2.3, while the pH of milk is 6.6. Find the concentration of hydrogen ions in each substance. Which substance is more acidic?

Lemon juice	**Milk**
$\text{pH} = -\log[H^+]$	$\text{pH} = -\log[H^+]$
$2.3 = -\log[H^+]$	$6.6 = -\log[H^+]$
$\log[H^+] = -2.3$	$\log[H^+] = -6.6$
$[H^+] = 10^{-2.3}$	$[H^+] = 10^{-6.6}$
$\approx 5.0 \times 10^{-3}$	$\approx 2.5 \times 10^{-7}$

The $[H^+]$ of lemon juice is about 5.0×10^{-3}. The $[H^+]$ of milk is about 2.5×10^{-7}. Lemon juice has a higher concentration of hydrogen ions, so it is more acidic.

Check Understanding **4** Find the concentration of hydrogen ions in seawater of pH 8.5.

OBJECTIVE

2 Graphing Logarithmic Functions

A **logarithmic function** is the inverse of an exponential function. The graph shows $y = 10^x$ and $y = \log x$. Note that (0, 1) and (1, 10) lie on the graph of $y = 10^x$, and that (1, 0), and (10, 1) lie on the graph of $y = \log x$.

Recall that the graph of a function is symmetric to the graph of its inverse over the line $y = x$. You can graph $y = \log_b x$ as the inverse of $y = b^x$.

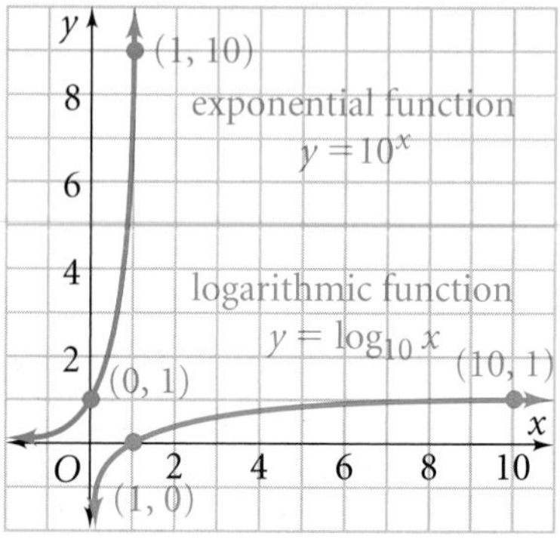

5 EXAMPLE Graphing a Logarithmic Function

Graph $y = \log_2 x$.

By the definition of logarithm, $y = \log_2 x$ is the inverse of $y = 2^x$.

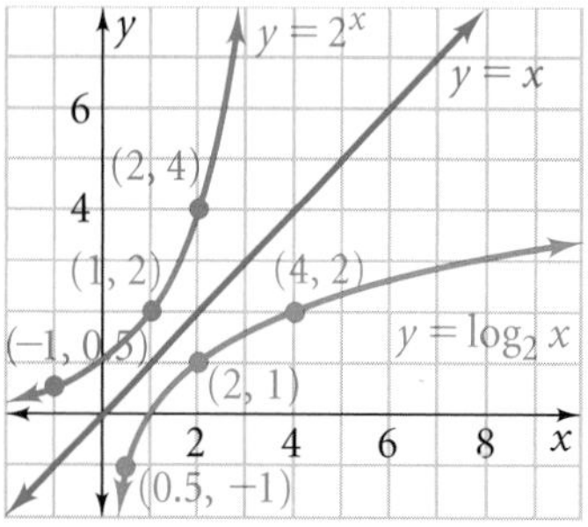

Step 1 Graph $y = 2^x$.

Step 2 Draw $y = x$.

Step 3 Choose a few points on $y = 2^x$. Reverse the coordinates and plot the points of $y = \log_2 x$.

Check Understanding **5** Graph $y = \log_3 x$.

The function $y = \log_b x$ is the inverse of $y = b^x$. Since $(0, 1)$ and $(1, b)$ are points on the graph of $y = b^x$, $(1, 0)$ and $(b, 1)$ are points on the graph of $y = \log_b x$. Since the x-axis is an asymptote of the graph of $y = b^x$, the y-axis is an asymptote of the graph of $y = \log_b x$. Using these facts, you can sketch graphs of $y = \log_b x$.

You can graph $y = \log_b (x - h) + k$ as the translation h units horizontally and k units vertically of $y = \log_b x$.

Key Concepts

Summary **Translations of Logarithmic Functions**

Characteristic	$y = \log_b x$	$y = \log_b (x - h) + k$
Asymptote	$x = 0$	$x - h = 0$, or $x = h$
Domain	$x > 0$	$x > h$
Range	All real numbers	All real numbers

6 EXAMPLE Translating $y = \log_b x$

Graph $y = \log_6 (x - 2) + 3$.

Step 1 Make a table of values for the parent function.

x	$\log_6 x$	y
6	$\log_6 6 = 1$	1
1	$\log_6 1 = 0$	0
$\frac{1}{6}$	$\log_6 \frac{1}{6} = -1$	-1
$\frac{1}{36}$	$\log_6 \frac{1}{36} = -2$	-2
$\frac{1}{216}$	$\log_6 \frac{1}{216} = -3$	-3

Step 2 Graph the function by shifting the points from the table to the right 2 units and up 3 units.

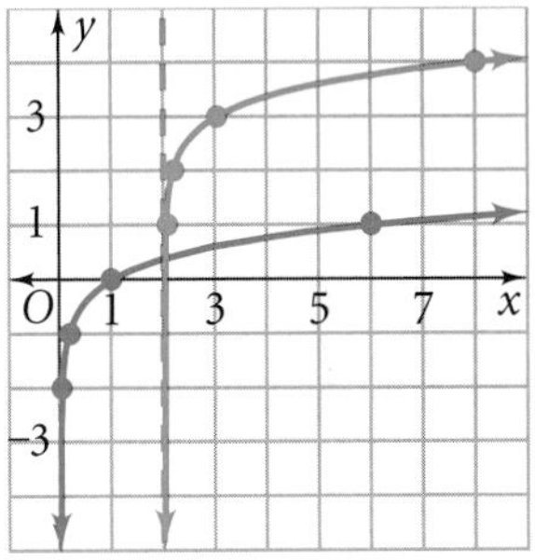

Need Help?
A parent function is the simplest function in a family of functions.

Check Understanding 6 Graph $y = \log_3 (x + 3)$.

EXERCISES

For more practice, see *Extra Practice.*

Practice and Problem Solving

A Practice by Example

Seismology In 1812, an earthquake of magnitude 7.9 shook New Madrid, Missouri. Compare the amount of energy released by that earthquake to the amount of energy released by each earthquake below.

Example 1 (page 438)

1. magnitude 7.7 in San Francisco, California, in 1906
2. magnitude 9.5 in Valdivia, Chile, in 1960
3. magnitude 3.2 in Charlottesville, Virginia, in 2001
4. magnitude 6.9 in Kobe, Japan, in 1995
5. magnitude 9.2 in Prince William Sound, Alaska, in 1964

Example 2 (page 439)

Write each equation in logarithmic form.

6. $49 = 7^2$ **7.** $10^3 = 1000$ **8.** $625 = 5^4$ **9.** $\frac{1}{10} = 10^{-1}$

10. $8^2 = 64$ **11.** $4 = \left(\frac{1}{2}\right)^{-2}$ **12.** $\left(\frac{1}{3}\right)^3 = \frac{1}{27}$ **13.** $10^{-2} = 0.01$

Example 3 (page 439)

Evaluate each logarithm.

14. $\log_2 16$ **15.** $\log_4 2$ **16.** $\log_8 8$ **17.** $\log_4 8$

18. $\log_2 8$ **19.** $\log_{49} 7$ **20.** $\log_5 (-25)$ **21.** $\log_3 9$

22. $\log_2 2^5$ **23.** $\log_{\frac{1}{2}} \frac{1}{2}$ **24.** $\log 10{,}000$ **25.** $\log_5 125$

Example 4 (page 440)

The pH of each food is given. Find the concentration of hydrogen ions $[H^+]$.

26. maple syrup, 5.2 **27.** lime juice, 2.2 **28.** egg white, 8.0

29. cider vinegar, 3.1 **30.** condensed milk, 6.3 **31.** soy sauce, 4.9

32. tomato juice, 4.0 **33.** watermelon, 5.4 **34.** mustard, 3.6

Examples 5 and 6 (pages 440 and 441)

Graph each logarithmic function.

35. $y = \log_4 x$ **36.** $y = \log_5 x$ **37.** $y = \log_8 x$

38. $y = \log_5 x + 1$ **39.** $y = \log_7 (x - 2)$ **40.** $y = \log_3 (x - 5) + 3$

B Apply Your Skills

Use your calculator to evaluate each logarithm to four decimal places. Then find the largest integer that is less than the value of the logarithm.

41. $\log 5$ **42.** $\log (6.1 \times 10^{-5})$ **43.** $\log 0.08$ **44.** $\log 200$

45. $\log \frac{1}{6}$ **46.** $\log 17.52$ **47.** $\log (1.3 \times 10^7)$ **48.** $\log \frac{13}{4}$

Reading Math

For help with reading and solving Exercise 49, see p. 445.

49. Chemistry The pH scale ranges from 0 to 14. A pH level of 7 is neutral. A level greater than 7 is basic, and a level less than 7 is acidic. The table shows the hydrogen ion concentration $[H^+]$ for selected foods. Find the pH of each item. Determine whether it is basic or acidic.

Approximate $[H^+]$ of Foods

Food	$[H^+]$
Apple juice	3.2×10^{-4}
Buttermilk	2.5×10^{-5}
Cream	2.5×10^{-7}
Ketchup	1.3×10^{-4}
Shrimp sauce	7.9×10^{-8}
Strained peas	1.0×10^{-6}

50. Error Analysis Find the error in the following evaluation of $\log_{27} 3$. Then evaluate the logarithm correctly.

$$\log_{27} 3 = x$$
$$27 = x^3$$
$$3 = x$$
$$\log_{27} 3 = 3$$

51. Writing Explain why the base b in $y = \log_b x$ cannot equal 1.

52. Open-Ended Write a logarithmic function of the form $y = \log_b x$. Find its inverse function. Graph both functions on one set of axes.

Write each equation in exponential form.

53. $\log_2 128 = 7$ **54.** $\log 0.0001 = -4$ **55.** $\log_7 16{,}807 = 5$

56. $\log_6 6 = 1$ **57.** $\log_4 1 = 0$ **58.** $\log_3 \frac{1}{9} = -2$

59. $\log_2 \frac{1}{2} = -1$ **60.** $\log 10 = 1$ **61.** $\log_2 8192 = 13$

Real-World Connection

Samples are loaded into a linear accelerator for carbon dating.

62. Archaeology One method of dating artifacts is radiocarbon dating. The artifacts in the table were found at a dig site near Kit Carson, Colorado. An artifact's age t in years is $t = 1.904 \times 10^4 \cdot \log\left(\frac{13.7}{R}\right)$, where R is the number of beta radiation emissions per minute per gram of carbon in the artifact.

Beta Emissions of Artifacts

Object	Mass of Carbon (g)	Beta Emissions per Minute
Buffalo bone	400	1640 ± 30
Bone fragment	15	61.5 ± 1.5
Pottery shard	25	342 ± 7
Charcoal	10	41.0 ± 1.3
Spear shaft	250	1020 ± 30

a. For each artifact, use the range of beta emissions to find the artifact's maximum and minimum ages.

b. Critical Thinking Which artifact is significantly different in age from the others? Give two possible explanations for the difference.

Find the inverse of each function.

63. $y = \log_4 x$ **64.** $y = \log_{0.5} x$ **65.** $y = \log_{10} x$

66. $y = \log_2 2x$ **67.** $y = \log(x + 1)$ **68.** $y = \log 10x$

69. $y = \log(x - 2)$ **70.** $y = \log_5 x^2$ **71.** $y = \log_x 3$

Graph each logarithmic function.

72. $y = \log 2x$ **73.** $y = 2\log_2 x$ **74.** $y = \log_4(2x + 3)$

Find the domain and the range of the graph of each function.

75. $y = \log_5 x$ **76.** $y = 3\log x$ **77.** $y = \log_2(x - 3)$

78. $y = 1 + \log x$ **79.** $y = \log(x - 2) + 1$ **80.** $y = \log_6(x + 1)$

81. $y = \log_8 x - 2$ **82.** $y = \log_2 x + \frac{1}{3}$ **83.** $y = \log(x - t)$

C Challenge **Sound** **The loudness in decibels (dB) of a sound is defined as $10 \log \frac{I}{I_0}$. I is the intensity of the sound. I_0 is 10^{-12}, the intensity of a barely audible sound. Complete the table.**

Loudness of Sounds

	Type of Sound	Intensity (W/m^2)	Loudness (dB)
	Pain-producing	1	120
84.	Jackhammer	10^{-2}	■
85.	Busy street	10^{-5}	■
86.	Conversation	10^{-6}	■
87.	Whisper	10^{-10}	■
88.	Rustle of leaves	10^{-11}	■
	Barely audible sound	10^{-12}	0

89. Match each function with its inverse.

a. $y = \log_{\frac{1}{4}} x$ **b.** $y = \log_4 x$ **c.** $y = -\log_4 x$ **d.** $y = -\log_{\frac{1}{4}} x$

I. $y = 4^x$ **II.** $y = \left(\frac{1}{4}\right)^{-x}$ **III.** $y = \left(\frac{1}{4}\right)^x$ **IV.** $y = 4^{-x}$

90. Match each function with the graph of its inverse.

a. $y = \log_3 x$ **b.** $y = \log_2 4x$ **c.** $y = \log_{\frac{1}{2}} x$

I.
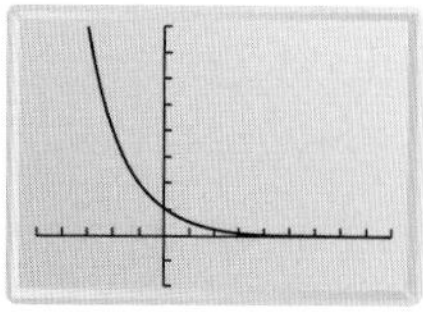
II.
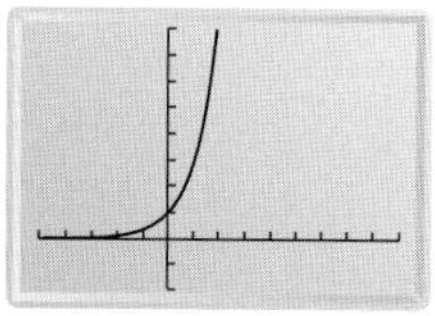
III.
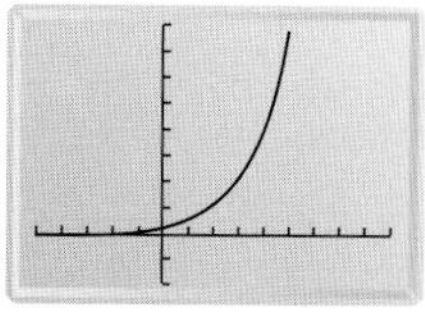

Standardized Test Prep

Multiple Choice

91. What is the ratio of $(65 \cdot 3^{17})$ to $(65 \cdot 3^{14})$?

A. 17 to 14 **B.** 3 to 1 **C.** 9 to 1 **D.** 27 to 1

92. What is the logarithmic form of the exponential equation $2^4 = 16$?

F. $\log_{16} 2 = 4$ **G.** $\log_{16} 4 = 2$ **H.** $\log_4 16 = 2$ **I.** $\log_2 16 = 4$

Quantitative Comparison

Compare the boxed quantity in Column A with the boxed quantity in Column B. Choose the best answer.

A. The quantity in Column A is greater.
B. The quantity in Column B is greater.
C. The two quantities are equal.
D. The relationship cannot be determined from the information given.

Take It to the NET
Online lesson quiz at
www.PHSchool.com
Web Code: aga-0803

	Column A	Column B
93.	the value of x if $4^x = 64$	the value of y if $y = \log_5 125$
94.	$\log_4 1$	$\log_4 \frac{1}{16}$
95.	the value of x if $\log_x 36 = 2$	the value of y if $\log_{10} y = 2$
96.	$\log_{16} 4$	$\log_{81} 9$

Mixed Review

Lesson 8-2 **Sketch the graph of each function. Then locate the asymptote of the curve.**

97. $y = 5^x - 100$ **98.** $y = -10(4)^{x+2}$ **99.** $y = -27(3)^{x-1} + 9$

Lesson 7-4 **Write each expression in radical form.**

100. $t^{\frac{2}{3}}$ **101.** $(16w^3)^{\frac{1}{2}}$ **102.** $z^{\frac{8}{5}}$ **103.** $x^{\frac{p}{n}}$

Lesson 6-4 **Solve each equation by graphing. If necessary, round to the nearest thousandth.**

104. $3x^2 + 18x + 24 = 0$ **105.** $1 - x = x^2 - 7x$ **106.** $x^4 = 7x^3 + 10x^2$

Lesson 5-4 **Factor each expression.**

107. $4x^2 - 8x + 3$ **108.** $\frac{1}{4}b^2 - 4$ **109.** $5x^2 + 13x - 6$

Reading Data

For Use With Page 442, Exercise 49

Read the problem below to see how a table of values represents data. Check your understanding with the exercise at the bottom of the page.

Chemistry The pH scale ranges from 0 to 14. A pH level of 7 is neutral. A level greater than 7 is basic, and a level less than 7 is acidic. The table shows the hydrogen ion concentration $[H^+]$ for selected foods. Find the pH of each item. Determine whether it is basic or acidic.

Approximate [H+] of Selected Foods

Food	[H+]
Apple Juice	3.2×10^{-4}
Buttermilk	2.5×10^{-5}
Cream	2.5×10^{-7}
Ketchup	1.3×10^{-4}
Shrimp Sauce	7.9×10^{-8}
Strained Peas	1.0×10^{-6}

A table is a tool for organizing data.

The title of the table indicates the type of data represented. →

Approximate [H+] of Selected Foods

Food	[H+]
Apple Juice	3.2×10^{-4}
Buttermilk	2.5×10^{-5}

← **Each row represents a different item. Row 1 contains data for apple juice.**

Each column represents a different category of data. Column 2 lists the $[H^+]$ of each food.

Now you can use the table.

$\text{pH} = -\log [H^+]$		**Refer to page 440 for the formula for pH.**
$\text{pH of apple juice} = -\log ([H^+] \text{ of apple juice})$		**Use the formula.**
$= -\log (3.2 \times 10^{-4})$		**Substitute.**
≈ 3.49		**Simplify.**

Since the pH of apple juice is less than 7, it is acidic.

The problem asks you to find the pH and whether the item is basic or acidic. To organize the information, you can add two columns to the table.

Food	[H+]	pH	Acid or Base
Apple Juice	3.2×10^{-4}	3.49	Acid

EXERCISE

Copy and complete the table below.

[H+]	pH	Acid or Base
4.6×10^{-8}	■	■
3.7×10^{-3}	■	■
1.8×10^{-4}	■	■

8-4

Properties of Logarithms

North Carolina Objectives

1.01 Simplify and perform operations with rational exponents and logarithms (common and natural) to solve problems.

Lesson Preview

What You'll Learn

OBJECTIVE 1 To use the properties of logarithms

. . . And Why

To relate sound intensity and decibel level, as in Example 4

Check Skills You'll Need

(For help, go to Lessons 8-3 and 1-2.)

Simplify each expression.

1. $\log_2 4 + \log_2 8$ **2.** $\log_3 9 - \log_3 27$ **3.** $\log_2 16 \div \log_2 64$

Evaluate each expression for $x = 3$.

4. $x^3 - x$ **5.** $x^5 \cdot x^2$ **6.** $\frac{x^6}{x^9}$ **7.** $x^3 + x^2$

Interactive lesson includes instant self-check, tutorials, and activities.

OBJECTIVE

1 Using the Properties of Logarithms

Investigation: Properties of Logarithms

1. Complete the table. Round to the nearest thousandth.

x	1	2	3	4	5	6	7	8	9	10	15	20
log *x*	■	■	■	■	■	■	■	■	■	■	■	■

2. Complete each pair of statements. What do you notice?
   a. log 3 + log 5 = ■ and log (3 · 5) = ■
   b. log 1 + log 7 = ■ and log (1 · 7) = ■
   c. log 2 + log 4 = ■ and log (2 · 4) = ■
   d. log 10 + log 2 = ■ and log (10 · 2) = ■
3. Complete the statement: log *M* + log *N* = ■.
4. a. **Make a Conjecture** How could you rewrite the expression $\log \frac{M}{N}$ using the expressions log *M* and log *N*?
   b. Use your calculator to verify your conjecture for several values of *M* and *N*.

The properties of logarithms are summarized below.

Key Concepts

Properties **Properties of Logarithms**

For any positive numbers, M, N, and b, $b \neq 1$,

$\log_b MN = \log_b M + \log_b N$ **Product Property**

$\log_b \frac{M}{N} = \log_b M - \log_b N$ **Quotient Property**

$\log_b M^x = x \log_b M$ **Power Property**

You can use the properties of logarithms to rewrite logarithmic expressions.

1 EXAMPLE Identifying the Properties of Logarithms

State the property or properties used to rewrite each expression.

a. $\log_2 8 - \log_2 4 = \log_2 2$

Quotient Property: $\log_2 8 - \log_2 4 = \log_2 \frac{8}{4} = \log_2 2$

b. $\log_b x^3y = 3\log_b x + \log_b y$

Product Property: $\log_b x^3y = \log_b x^3 + \log_b y$

Power Property: $\log_b x^3 + \log_b y = 3\log_b x + \log_b y$

Check Understanding 1 State the property or properties used to rewrite each expression.

a. $\log_5 2 + \log_5 6 = \log_5 12$

b. $3\log_b 4 - 3\log_b 2 = \log_b 8$

You can write the sum or difference of logarithms with the same base as a single logarithm.

2 EXAMPLE Simplifying Logarithms

Write each logarithmic expression as a single logarithm.

a. $\log_3 20 - \log_3 4$

$\log_3 20 - \log_3 4 = \log_3 \frac{20}{4}$ **Quotient Property**

$= \log_3 5$ **Simplify.**

b. $3\log_2 x + \log_2 y$

$3\log_2 x + \log_2 y = \log_2 x^3 + \log_2 y$ **Power Property**

$= \log_2 (x^3y)$ **Product Property**

So $\log_3 20 - \log_3 4 = \log_3 5$, and $3\log_2 x + \log_2 y = \log_2 (x^3y)$.

Check Understanding 2 **a.** Write $3\log 2 + \log 4 - \log 16$ as a single logarithm.

b. Critical Thinking Can you write $3\log_2 9 - \log_6 9$ as a single logarithm? Explain.

You can sometimes write a single logarithm as a sum or difference of two or more logarithms.

Reading Math

In mathematics, to expand means "to show the full form of."

3 EXAMPLE Expanding Logarithms

Expand each logarithm.

a. $\log_5 \frac{x}{y}$

$= \log_5 x - \log_5 y$ **Quotient Property**

b. $\log 3r^4$

$= \log 3 + \log r^4$ **Product Property**

$= \log 3 + 4\log r$ **Power Property**

Check Understanding 3 Expand each logarithm.

a. $\log_2 7b$ **b.** $\log \left(\frac{y}{3}\right)^2$ **c.** $\log_7 a^3b^4$

Logarithms are used to model sound. The intensity of a sound is a measure of the energy carried by the sound wave. The greater the intensity of a sound, the louder it seems. This apparent loudness L is measured in decibels. You can use the formula $L = 10 \log \frac{I}{I_0}$, where I is the intensity of the sound in watts per square meter (W/m^2). I_0 is the lowest-intensity sound that the average human ear can detect.

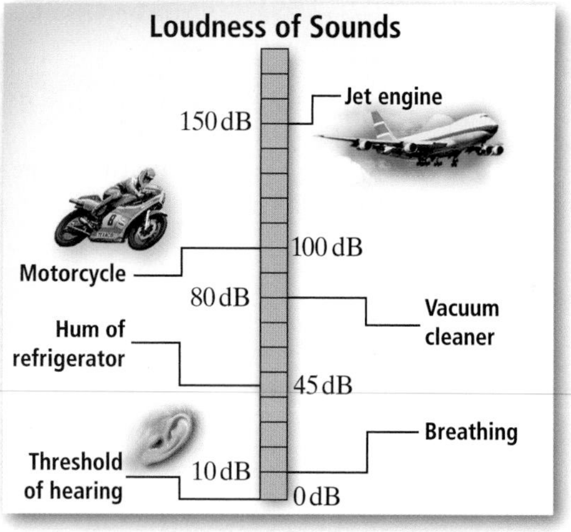

4 EXAMPLE Real-World Connection

Noise Control A shipping company has started flying cargo planes out of the city airport. Residents in a nearby neighborhood have complained that the cargo planes are too loud. Suppose the shipping company hires you to design a way to reduce the intensity of the sound by half. By how many decibels would the loudness of the sound be decreased?

Relate The reduced intensity is one half of the present intensity.

Define Let I_1 = present intensity.
Let I_2 = reduced intensity.
Let L_1 = present loudness.
Let L_2 = reduced loudness.

Write $I_2 = 0.5 I_1$

$$L_1 = 10 \log \frac{I_1}{I_0}$$

$$L_2 = 10 \log \frac{I_2}{I_0}$$

$$L_1 - L_2 = 10 \log \frac{I_1}{I_0} - 10 \log \frac{I_2}{I_0}$$ **Find the decrease in loudness $L_1 - L_2$.**

$$= 10 \log \frac{I_1}{I_0} - 10 \log \frac{0.5 I_1}{I_0}$$ **Substitute $I_2 = 0.5I_1$.**

$$= 10 \log \frac{I_1}{I_0} - 10 \log \left(0.5 \cdot \frac{I_1}{I_0}\right)$$

$$= 10 \log \frac{I_1}{I_0} - 10\left(\log 0.5 + \log \frac{I_1}{I_0}\right)$$ **Product Property**

$$= 10 \log \frac{I_1}{I_0} - 10 \log 0.5 - 10 \log \frac{I_1}{I_0}$$ **Distributive Property**

$$= -10 \log 0.5$$ **Combine like terms.**

$$\approx 3.0$$ **Use a calculator.**

The decrease in loudness would be about three decibels.

Real-World Connection

The workers who direct planes at airports must wear ear protection.

Check Understanding **4** Suppose the shipping company wants you to reduce the sound intensity to 25% of the original intensity. By how many decibels would the loudness be reduced?

EXERCISES

For more practice, see *Extra Practice*.

Practice and Problem Solving

A Practice by Example

Example 1 (page 447)

State the property or properties used to rewrite each expression.

1. $\log 4 + \log 5 = \log 20$

2. $\log_3 32 - \log_3 8 = \log_3 4$

3. $\log z^2 = 2 \log z$

4. $\log_6 \sqrt[n]{x^p} = \frac{p}{n} \log_6 x$

5. $8 \log 2 - 2 \log 8 = \log 4$

6. $\log \sqrt[3]{3x} = \frac{1}{3} \log 3x$

7. $3 \log_4 5 - 3 \log_4 3 = \log_4 \left(\frac{5}{3}\right)^3$

8. $2 \log w + 4 \log z = \log w^2 z^4$

9. $2 \log_2 m - 4 \log_2 n = \log_2 \frac{m^2}{n^4}$

10. $\log_b \frac{1}{8} + 3 \log_b 4 = \log_b 8$

Example 2 (page 447)

Write each logarithmic expression as a single logarithm.

11. $\log 7 + \log 2$

12. $\log_2 9 - \log_2 3$

13. $5 \log 3 + \log 4$

14. $\log 8 - 2 \log 6 + \log 3$

15. $4 \log m - \log n$

16. $\log 5 - k \log 2$

17. $\log_6 5 + \log_6 x$

18. $\log_7 x + \log_7 y - \log_7 z$

Example 3 (page 447)

Expand each logarithm.

19. $\log x^3 y^5$

20. $\log_7 22xyz$

21. $\log_4 5\sqrt{x}$

22. $\log 3m^4 n^{-2}$

23. $\log_5 \frac{r}{s}$

24. $\log_3 (2x)^2$

25. $\log_3 7(2x - 3)^2$

26. $\log \frac{a^2 b^3}{c^4}$

27. $\log \sqrt{\frac{2x}{y}}$

28. $\log_8 8\sqrt{3a^5}$

29. $\log \frac{s\sqrt{7}}{t^2}$

30. $\log_b \frac{1}{x}$

Example 4 (page 448)

31. One brand of ear plugs claims to block the sound of snoring as loud as 22 dB. A second brand claims to block snoring that is eight times as intense. If the claims are true, for how many more decibels is the second brand effective?

32. A sound barrier along a highway reduced the intensity of the noise reaching a community by 95%. By how many decibels was the noise reduced?

B Apply Your Skills

Use the properties of logarithms to evaluate each expression.

33. $\log_2 4 - \log_2 16$

34. $3 \log_2 2 - \log_2 4$

35. $\log_3 3 + 5 \log_3 3$

36. $\log 1 + \log 100$

37. $\log_6 4 + \log_6 9$

38. $2 \log_8 4 - \frac{1}{3} \log_8 8$

39. $2 \log_3 3 - \log_3 3$

40. $\frac{1}{2} \log_5 1 - 2 \log_5 5$

41. $\log_9 \frac{1}{3} + 3 \log_9 3$

42. **Error Analysis** Explain why the expansion below of $\log_4 \sqrt{\frac{t}{s}}$ is incorrect. Then do the expansion correctly.

$$\log_4 \sqrt{\frac{t}{s}} = \frac{1}{2} \log_4 \frac{t}{s}$$
$$= \frac{1}{2} \log_4 t - \log_4 s$$

43. **Open-Ended** Write log 150 as a sum or difference of two logarithms.

Assume that $\log 4 \approx 0.6021$, $\log 5 \approx 0.6990$, and $\log 6 \approx 0.7782$. Use the properties of logarithms to evaluate each expression. Do not use your calculator.

44. $\log 24$ **45.** $\log 30$ **46.** $\log 16$

47. $\log 125$ **48.** $\log 1.5$ **49.** $\log 0.8$

50. $\log \frac{1}{4}$ **51.** $\log \frac{1}{25}$ **52.** $\log 25$

53. $\log \frac{1}{6}$ **54.** $\log 36$ **55.** $\log \sqrt{5}$

Real-World Connection

Decibel meters are used to measure sound levels.

56. Noise Control New components reduce the sound intensity of a certain model of vacuum cleaner from 10^{-4} W/m^2 to 6.31×10^{-6} W/m^2. By how many decibels do these new components reduce the vacuum cleaner's loudness?

57. Reasoning If $\log x = 5$, what is the value of $\frac{1}{x}$?

Write *true* or *false* for each statement. Justify your answer.

58. $\log_2 4 + \log_2 8 = 5$ **59.** $\log_3 \frac{3}{2} = \frac{1}{2}\log_3 3$

60. $\log_3 8 = 3\log_3 2$ **61.** $\log_5 16 - \log 2 = \log_5 8$

62. $\log(x - 2) = \dfrac{\log x}{\log 2}$ **63.** $\dfrac{\log_b x}{\log_b y} = \log_b \dfrac{x}{y}$

64. $(\log x)^2 = \log x^2$ **65.** $\log_4 7 - \log_4 3 = \log_4 4$

66. $\log x + \log(x^2 + 2) = \log(x^3 + 2x)$ **67.** $\log_2 3 + \log_3 2 = \log_6 6$

68. $\log_2 x - 4\log_2 y = \log_2 \dfrac{x}{y^4}$ **69.** $\log_b \frac{1}{8} + 3\log_b 4 = \log_b 8$

70. Construction Suppose you are the supervisor on a road construction job. Your team is blasting rock to make way for a roadbed. One explosion has an intensity of 1.65×10^{-2} W/m^2. What is the loudness of the sound in decibels? (Use $I_0 = 10^{-12}$ W/m^2.)

71. Critical Thinking Can you expand $\log_3(2x + 1)$? Explain.

72. Writing Explain why $\log(5 \cdot 2) \neq \log 5 \cdot \log 2$.

Write each logarithmic expression as a single logarithm.

73. $\frac{1}{4}\log_3 2 + \frac{1}{4}\log_3 x$ **74.** $\frac{1}{2}(\log_x 4 + \log_x y) - 3\log_x z$

75. $2\log 3 - \frac{1}{2}\log 4 + \frac{1}{2}\log 9$ **76.** $x\log_4 m + \frac{1}{y}\log_4 n - \log_4 p$

77. $\left(\dfrac{2\log_b x}{3} + \dfrac{3\log_b y}{4}\right) - 5\log_b z$ **78.** $\dfrac{\log z - \log 3}{4} - 5\,\dfrac{\log x}{2}$

Expand each logarithm.

79. $\log\left(\dfrac{2\sqrt{x}}{5}\right)^3$ **80.** $\log \dfrac{m^3}{n^4 p^{-2}}$ **81.** $\log 2\sqrt{\dfrac{4r}{s^2}}$

82. $\log_b \dfrac{\sqrt{x}\,\sqrt[3]{y^2}}{\sqrt[5]{z^2}}$ **83.** $\log_4 \dfrac{\sqrt{x^5 y^7}}{zw^4}$ **84.** $\log \dfrac{\sqrt{x^2 - 4}}{(x + 3)^2}$

85. $\log\sqrt{\dfrac{x\sqrt{2}}{y^2}}$ **86.** $\log_3\left[(xy)^{\frac{1}{3}} \div z^2\right]^3$ **87.** $\log_7 \dfrac{\sqrt{r + 9}}{s^2 t^{\frac{1}{3}}}$

C Challenge

88. Let $u = \log_b M$, and let $v = \log_b N$. Prove the Product Property of Logarithms by completing the equations below.

Statement	Reason
$u = log_b M$	Given
$b^u = M$	Rewrite in exponential form.
$v = \blacksquare$	Given
$b^v = \blacksquare$	Rewrite in exponential form.
$MN = b^u b^v = b^{\blacksquare}$	Apply the Product Property of Exponents.
$\log_b MN = \blacksquare$	Take the logarithm of each side.
$\log_b MN = \log_b \blacksquare + \log_b \blacksquare$	Substitute $\log_b M$ for u and $\log_b N$ for v.

89. Let $u = \log_b M$. Prove the Power Property of logarithms.

90. Let $u = \log_b M$ and $v = \log_b N$. Prove the Quotient Property of logarithms.

Standardized Test Prep

Multiple Choice

91. Which statement is NOT correct?

A. $\log_2 25 = 2 \cdot \log_2 5$ **B.** $\log_3 16 = 2 \cdot \log_3 8$
C. $\log_5 27 = 3 \cdot \log_5 3$ **D.** $\log_8 10{,}000 = 4 \cdot \log_8 10$

Take It to the NET
Online lesson quiz at **www.PHSchool.com**
Web Code: aga-0804

92. Which expression is equal to $\log_7 5 + \log_7 3$?

F. $\log_7 8$ **G.** $\log_7 15$ **H.** $\log_7 125$ **I.** $\log_{49} 15$

93. Which expression is equal to $\log_5 x + 4 \cdot \log_5 y - 2 \cdot \log_5 z$?

A. $\log_5 (-8xyz)$ **B.** $-\log_5 \frac{4xy}{2z}$ **C.** $\log_5 \frac{(xy)^4}{z^2}$ **D.** $\log_5 \frac{xy^4}{z^2}$

Short Response

94. $\log_5 10 \approx 1.4307$ and $\log_5 20 \approx 1.8614$. Find the value of $\log_5 \left(\frac{1}{2}\right)$ without using a calculator. Explain how you found the value.

Extended Response

95. Use the properties of logarithms to write log 12 in four different ways. Name each property you use.

Mixed Review

Lesson 8-3

Write each equation in logarithmic form.

96. $49 = 7^2$ **97.** $5^3 = 125$ **98.** $\frac{1}{4} = 8^{-\frac{2}{3}}$ **99.** $5^{-3} = \frac{1}{125}$

Lesson 7-5

Solve each equation. Check for extraneous solutions.

100. $\sqrt[3]{y^4} = 16$ **101.** $\sqrt[3]{7x} - 4 = 0$ **102.** $2\sqrt{w - 1} = \sqrt{w + 2}$

Lesson 6-5

A polynomial equation with integer coefficients has the given roots. What additional roots can you identify?

103. $\sqrt{3}, -\sqrt{5}$ **104.** $-i, 4i$ **105.** $2i, -4 + i$

106. $\sqrt{2}, i - 1$ **107.** $-\sqrt{7}, -\sqrt{11}$ **108.** $-2i + 3, i$

Technology

Verifying Properties of Logarithms

For Use With Lesson 8-4

You can verify the properties of logarithms by graphing two equations simultaneously.

Take It to the NET
Graphing Calculator procedures online at **www.PHSchool.com**
Web Code: age-2117

EXAMPLE

Verify the Product Property for logarithms, $\log_b MN = \log_b M + \log_b N$, by graphing equations of the form $y = \log_b MN$ and $y = \log_b M + \log_b N$.

Step 1 Enter $Y_1 = \log(3x)$ and $Y_2 = \log(3) + \log(x)$. Don't forget to enter a closing parenthesis in Y_2.

Step 2 Place the cursor to the left of Y_2 and press ENTER four times. This changes the "path style" so that the second graph can be seen as drawn over the first graph.

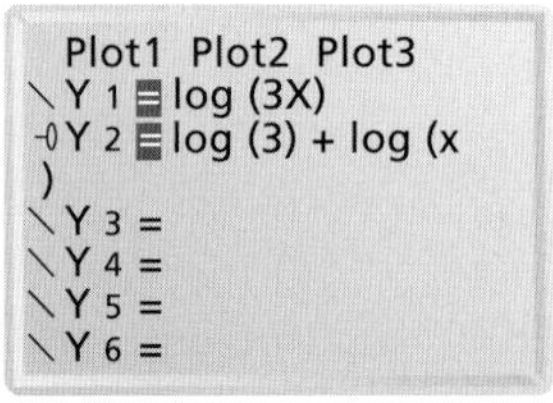

Step 3 Adjust the viewing window.

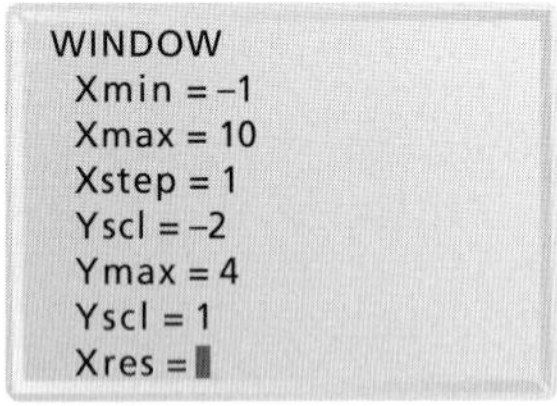

Step 4 Graph the equations. The moving circular cursor shows that the equations have the same graph.

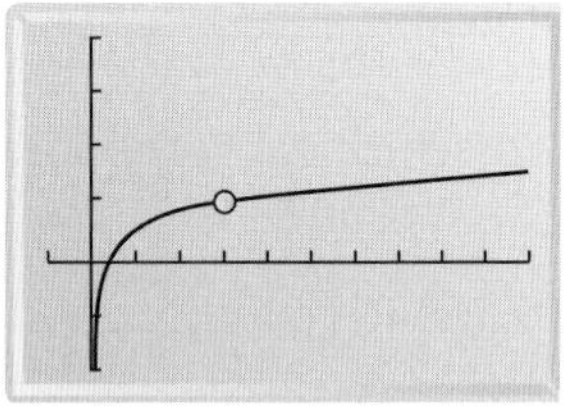

EXERCISES

1. Verify each property.
   a. Quotient Property
   b. Power Property

2. a. Two expressions form an identity if they are always equal, regardless of the values of the variables. Substitute $M = 3$ and $N = x$ to show whether $\log(M + N) = \log M + \log N$ is an identity. Sketch the graph.
   b. For what values of x are the expressions equal?

3. Show whether $\log\left(\frac{x}{x-1} + x\right) = \log\frac{x}{x-1} + \log x$ is an identity. Sketch the graph. For what values of x are the expressions equal?

4. A graphing calculator cannot directly graph logarithmic functions that are not common logarithms or natural logarithms. You can graph equations such as $y = \log_3 x$ by using the Change of Base Formula, $\log_b M = \frac{\log_c M}{\log_c b}$. Graph $y = \log_3 x$ using the Change of Base Formula. Use common logarithms in Y_1 and natural logarithms in Y_2. Sketch your graph.

5. Use your calculator to graph each equation. Sketch your graph.
   a. $y = \log_6 x$
   b. $y = \log_8 x$
   c. $y = \log_{16} x$

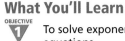

8-5 Exponential and Logarithmic Equations

North Carolina Objectives

1.01 Simplify and perform operations with rational exponents and logarithms (common and natural) to solve problems.
2.01 Use the inverse of functions to model and solve problems.

Lesson Preview

What You'll Learn

OBJECTIVE 1 To solve exponential equations

OBJECTIVE 2 To solve logarithmic equations

. . . And Why

To model animal populations, as in Example 5

Check Skills You'll Need

(For help, go to Lessons 8-3 and 7-4.)

Evaluate each logarithm.

1. $\log_9 81 \cdot \log_9 3$ **2.** $\log 10 \cdot \log_3 9$ **3.** $\log_2 16 \div \log_2 8$

4. Simplify $125^{-\frac{2}{3}}$.

New Vocabulary
- exponential equation
- logarithmic equation
- Change of Base Formula

Interactive lesson includes instant self-check, tutorials, and activities.

OBJECTIVE 1 Solving Exponential Equations

Need Help?
In a general form of an equation, c refers to a constant.

An equation of the form $b^{cx} = a$, where the exponent includes a variable, is an **exponential equation.** If m and n are positive and $m = n$, then $\log m = \log n$. You can therefore solve an exponential equation by taking the logarithm of each side of the equation.

1 EXAMPLE Solving an Exponential Equation

Solve $7^{3x} = 20$.

$7^{3x} = 20$

$\log 7^{3x} = \log 20$ **Take the common logarithm of each side.**

$3x \log 7 = \log 20$ **Use the power property of logarithms.**

$x = \dfrac{\log 20}{3 \log 7}$ **Divide each side by 3 log 7.**

≈ 0.5132 **Use a calculator.**

Check $7^{3x} = 20$

$7^{3(0.5132)} \approx 20.00382 \approx 20$ ✓

Check Understanding **1** Solve each equation. Round to the nearest ten-thousandth. Check your answers.
a. $3^x = 4$ **b.** $6^{2x} = 21$ **c.** $3^{x+4} = 101$

To evaluate a logarithm with any base, you can use the **Change of Base Formula.**

Key Concepts

Property	Change of Base Formula

For any positive numbers, M, b, and c, with $b \neq 1$ and $c \neq 1$,

$$\log_b M = \frac{\log_c M}{\log_c b}$$

2 EXAMPLE Using the Change of Base Formula

Use the Change of Base Formula to evaluate $\log_3 15$. Then convert $\log_3 15$ to a logarithm in base 2.

$\log_3 15 = \frac{\log 15}{\log 3}$	**Use the Change of Base Formula.**
≈ 2.4650	**Use a calculator.**
$\log_3 15 = \log_2 x$	**Write an equation.**
$2.4650 \approx \log_2 x$	**Substitute $\log_3 15 = 2.465$.**
$2.4650 \approx \frac{\log x}{\log 2}$	**Use the Change of Base Formula.**
$2.4650 \cdot \log 2 \approx \log x$	**Multiply each side by log 2.**
$0.7420 \approx \log x$	**Simplify.**
$x \approx 10^{0.7420}$	**Write in exponential form.**
≈ 5.5208	**Use a calculator.**

The expression $\log_3 15$ is approximately equal to 2.4650, or $\log_2 5.5208$.

Check Understanding 2 **a.** Evaluate $\log_5 400$ and convert it to a logarithm in base 8.

b. Critical Thinking Consider the equation $2.465 \approx \log_2 x$ from Example 2. How could you solve the equation without using the Change of Base Formula?

You can use the Change of Base Formula to solve an exponential equation. Take the logarithm of each side using the base of the exponent as the base for the logarithm. Then use the Change of Base Formula.

Need Help?

If $y = b^x$, then $\log_b y = x$.

3 EXAMPLE Solving an Exponential Equation by Changing Bases

Solve $2^{3x} = 172$.

$2^{3x} = 172$	
$\log_2 2^{3x} = \log_2 172$	**Take the base-2 logarithm of each side.**
$3x = \log_2 172$	**Simplify.**
$3x = \frac{\log 172}{\log 2}$	**Use the Change of Base Formula.**
$x \approx 2.4754$	**Use a calculator to solve for x.**

Check Understanding 3 Use the Change of Base Formula to solve $7^{5x} = 3000$. Check your answer.

You can also solve exponential equations by graphing.

4 EXAMPLE Solving an Exponential Equation by Graphing

Solve $6^{2x} = 1500$.

Graph the equations $y = 6^{2x}$ and $y = 1500$. Find the point of intersection.

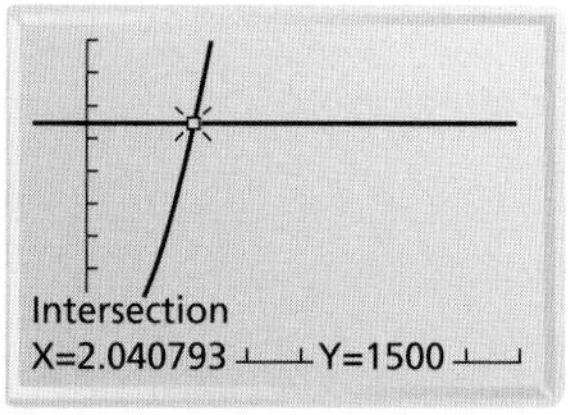

The solution is $x \approx 2.0408$.

Check Understanding 4 Solve $11^{6x} = 786$ by graphing.

5 EXAMPLE Real-World Connection

Real-World Connection

The U.S. population of peninsular bighorn sheep was 1170 in 1971. By 1999, only 335 remained.

Zoology Refer to the photo. Write an exponential equation to model the decline in the population. If the decay rate remains constant, in what year might only five peninsular bighorn sheep remain in the United States?

Step 1 Enter the data into your calculator. Let 0 represent the initial year, 1971.

Step 2 Use the **ExpReg** feature to find the exponential function that fits the data.

```
ExpReg
 y = a*b^x
 a = 1170
 b = .9563175045
```

Step 3 Graph the function and the line $y = 5$.

Step 4 Find the point of intersection.

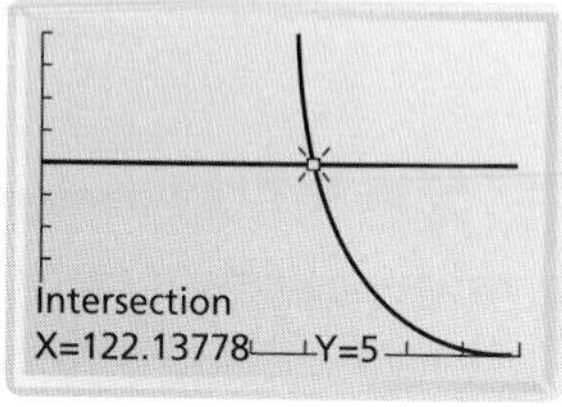

The solution is $x \approx 122$, and $1971 + 122 = 2093$, so there may be only five peninsular bighorn sheep in 2093.

Check Understanding 5 The population of peninsular bighorn sheep in Mexico was approximately 6200 in 1971. By 1999, about 2300 remained. Determine the year by which only 200 peninsular bighorn sheep might remain in Mexico.

OBJECTIVE

2 Solving Logarithmic Equations

An equation that includes a logarithmic expression is called a **logarithmic equation.**

6 EXAMPLE Solving a Logarithmic Equation

Solve $\log (3x + 1) = 5$.

$\log (3x + 1) = 5$

$3x + 1 = 10^5$ **Write in exponential form.**

$3x + 1 = 100{,}000$

$x = 33{,}333$ **Solve for x.**

Check $\log (3x + 1) = 5$

$\log (3 \cdot 33{,}333 + 1) \stackrel{?}{=} 5$

$\log 100{,}000 \stackrel{?}{=} 5$

$\log 10^5 = 5$ ✓

Check Understanding 6 Solve $\log (7 - 2x) = -1$. Check your answer.

In some cases, you must use the properties of logarithms to simplify expressions before solving the equation.

7 EXAMPLE Using Logarithmic Properties to Solve an Equation

Solve $2 \log x - \log 3 = 2$.

$2 \log x - \log 3 = 2$

$\log\left(\frac{x^2}{3}\right) = 2$ **Write as a single logarithm.**

$\frac{x^2}{3} = 10^2$ **Write in exponential form.**

$x^2 = 3(100)$ **Multiply each side by 3.**

$x = \pm 10\sqrt{3}$, or about ± 17.32

Since the logarithm of a negative number is undefined, the only solution is $10\sqrt{3}$, or about 17.32.

Check Understanding 7 Solve $\log 6 - \log 3x = -2$.

EXERCISES

For more practice, see *Extra Practice.*

Practice and Problem Solving

A Practice by Example

Example 1 (page 453)

Solve each equation. Round to the nearest ten-thousandth. Check your answers.

1. $2^x = 3$ **2.** $4^x = 19$ **3.** $5^x = 81.2$ **4.** $3^x = 27.3$

5. $8 + 10^x = 1008$ **6.** $5 - 3^x = -40$ **7.** $9^{2y} = 66$

8. $14^{x+1} = 36$ **9.** $12^{y-2} = 20$ **10.** $25^{2x+1} = 144$

Example 2 (page 454)

Use the Change of Base Formula to evaluate each expression. Then convert it to a logarithm in base 8.

11. $\log_2 9$ **12.** $\log_4 8$ **13.** $\log_3 54$ **14.** $\log_5 62$

15. $\log_3 33$ **16.** $\log_2 7$ **17.** $\log_5 510$ **18.** $\log_4 1.116$

Example 3 (page 454)

Use the Change of Base Formula to solve each equation.

19. $2^x = 5$ **20.** $6^{2x} = 21$ **21.** $7^{x+2} = 54$ **22.** $3^x = 27.3$

23. $4^{2x} = 17$ **24.** $5^{x+1} = 24$ **25.** $3^{x+4} = 101$ **26.** $4^{x-2} = 89$

Examples 4 and 5 (pages 454 and 455)

Solve by graphing.

27. $4^{7x} = 250$ **28.** $5^{3x} = 500$ **29.** $6^x = 4565$ **30.** $1.5^x = 356$

31. An investment of \$2000 earns 5.75% interest, which is compounded quarterly. After approximately how many years will the investment be worth \$3000?

32. The equation $y = 281(1.0124)^x$ models the U.S. population y, in millions of people, x years after the year 2000. Graph the function on your graphing calculator. Estimate when the U.S. population will reach 350 million.

Example 6 (page 455)

Solve each equation. Check your answers.

33. $\log 2x = -1$ **34.** $2 \log x = -1$ **35.** $\log (3x + 1) = 2$

36. $\log x + 4 = 8$ **37.** $\log 6x - 3 = -4$ **38.** $\log (x - 2) = 1$

39. $3 \log x = 1.5$ **40.** $2 \log (x + 1) = 5$ **41.** $\log (5 - 2x) = 0$

Example 7 (page 456)

Solve each equation.

42. $\log x - \log 3 = 8$

43. $\log 2x + \log x = 11$

44. $2 \log x + \log 4 = 2$

45. $\log 5 - \log 2x = 1$

46. $3 \log x - \log 6 + \log 2.4 = 9$

47. $\log (7x + 1) = \log (x - 2) + 1$

B Apply Your Skills

48. Consider the equation $2^{\frac{x}{3}} = 80$.

a. Solve the equation by taking the logarithm in base 10 of each side.

b. Solve the equation by taking the logarithm in base 2 of each side.

c. Writing Compare your result in parts (a) and (b). What are the advantages of either method? Explain.

Real-World Connection

Careers Seismologists use models to determine the source, nature, and size of seismic events.

49. Seismology An earthquake of magnitude 7.9 occurred in 2001 in Gujarat, India. It was 11,600 times as strong as the greatest earthquake ever to hit Pennsylvania. Find the magnitude of the Pennsylvania earthquake. (*Hint*: Refer to the Richter Scale on page 438.)

Write an equation. Then solve the equation without graphing.

50. A parent raises a child's allowance by 20% each year. If the allowance is \$8 now, when will it reach \$20?

51. Protactinium-234*m*, a toxic radioactive metal with no known use, has a half-life of 1.17 minutes. How long does it take for a 10-mg sample to decay to 2 mg?

52. As a town gets smaller, the population of its high school decreases by 12% each year. The student body numbers 125 students now. In how many years will it number about 75 students?

Mental Math **Solve each equation.**

53. $2^x = \frac{1}{2}$

54. $3^x = 27$

55. $\log_9 3 = x$

56. $\log_4 64 = x$

57. $\log_8 2 = x$

58. $10^x = \frac{1}{100}$

59. $\log_7 343 = x$

60. $25^x = \frac{1}{5}$

Population **The table below shows information about the population of the four most populous states in the United States in 2000. Use it for Exercises 61–63.**

Largest States

Rank in 2000	State	2000 Population	Average Annual Percentage Increase Since 1990
1	California	33,871,648	1.30%
2	Texas	20,851,820	2.08%
3	New York	18,976,457	0.54%
4	Florida	15,982,378	2.13%

SOURCE: U.S. Census Bureau. Go to **www.PHSchool.com** for a data update. Web Code: agg-2041

61. a. Determine the growth factors for Florida and New York. Then write an equation to model each state's population growth.

b. Estimate when Florida's population might exceed New York's population.

62. a. Determine the growth factors for Texas and California. Then write an equation to model each state's population growth.

b. Estimate when Texas's population might exceed California's population.

63. Critical Thinking Is it likely that Florida's population will exceed that of Texas? Explain your reasoning.

64. **Error Analysis** What is wrong with the "proof" below that $2 = 1$?

$$2 = \frac{2}{1} = \frac{\log 10^2}{\log 10^1} = \log 10^{2-1} = \log 10^1 = 1$$

65. **Open-Ended** Write and solve a logarithmic equation.

Real-World Connection

Many Florida manatees die after collisions with motorboats.

66. **Zoology** Conservation efforts have increased the endangered Florida manatee population from 1465 in 1991 to 3276 in 2001. If this growth rate continues, when might there be 10,000 manatees? Explain the reasoning behind your choice of a model.

67. Consider the equation $a^x = b$.
   a. Solve the equation by using log base 10.
   b. Solve the equation by using log base a.
   c. Use your results in parts (a) and (b) to justify the Change of Base Formula.

Write each logarithm as the quotient of two common logarithms. Do not simplify the quotient.

68. $\log_7 2$	**69.** $\log_3 8$	**70.** $\log_5 140$	**71.** $\log_9 3.3$
72. $\log_4 3x$	**73.** $\log_6 (1 - x)$	**74.** $\log_x 5$	**75.** $\log_x (x + 1)$

Acoustics **In Exercises 76–78, the loudness measured in decibels (dB) is defined by loudness = $10 \log \frac{I}{I_0}$, where I is the intensity and $I_0 = 10^{-12}$ W/m^2.**

76. The human threshold for pain is 120 dB. Instant perforation of the eardrum occurs at 160 dB.
   a. Find the intensity of each sound.
   b. How many times as intense is the noise that will perforate an eardrum as the noise that causes pain?

77. The noise level inside a convertible driving along the freeway with its top up is 70 dB. With the top down, the noise level is 95 dB.
   a. Find the intensity of the sound with the top up and with the top down.
   b. By what percent does leaving the top up reduce the intensity of the sound?

78. A screaming child can reach 90 dB. A launch of the space shuttle produces sound of 180 dB at the launch pad.
   a. Find the intensity of each sound.
   b. How many times as intense as the noise from a screaming child is the noise from a shuttle launch?

Solve each equation. If necessary, round to the nearest ten-thousandth.

79. $8^x = 444$	**80.** $14^{9x} = 146$
81. $3^{7x} = 120$	**82.** $\frac{1}{2} \log x + \log 4 = 2$
83. $4 \log_3 2 - 2 \log_3 x = 1$	**84.** $\log x^2 = 2$
85. $9^{2x} = 42$	**86.** $\log_8 (2x - 1) = \frac{1}{3}$
87. $1.3^x = 7$	**88.** $\log (5x - 4) = 3$
89. $2.1^x = 9$	**90.** $12^{4-x} = 20$
91. $5^{3x} = 125$	**92.** $\log 4 + 2 \log x = 6$
93. $4^{3x} = 77.2$	**94.** $\log_7 3x = 3$
95. $3^x + 0.7 = 4.9$	**96.** $7^x - 1 = 371$

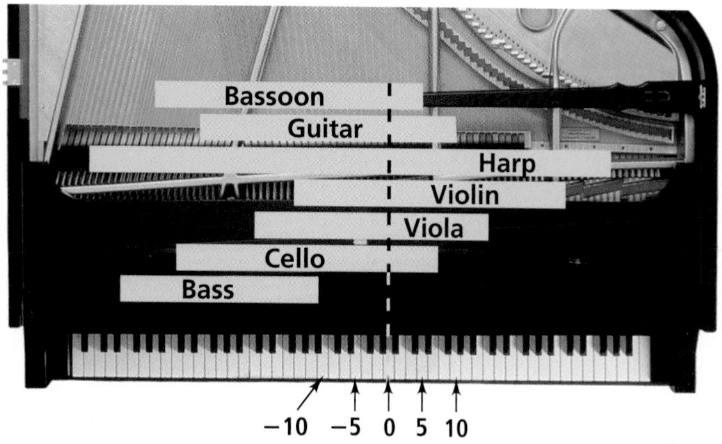

Challenge

97. Music The pitch, or frequency, of a piano note is related to its position on the keyboard by the function $F(n) = 440 \cdot 2^{\frac{n}{12}}$, where F is the frequency of the sound wave in cycles per second and n is the number of piano keys above or below Concert A, as shown above. If $n = 0$ at Concert A, which of the instruments shown in the diagram can sound notes of the given frequency?

a. 590 **b.** 120 **c.** 1440 **d.** 2093

98. Astronomy The brightness of an astronomical object is called its magnitude. A decrease of five magnitudes increases the brightness exactly 100 times. The sun is magnitude -26.7, and the full moon is magnitude -12.5. The sun is about how many times brighter than the moon?

99. Archaeology A scientist carbon-dates a piece of fossilized tree trunk that is thought to be over 5000 years old. The scientist determines that the sample contains 65% of the original amount of carbon-14. The half-life of carbon-14 is 5730 years. Is the reputed age of the tree correct? Explain.

Solve each equation.

100. $\log_7 (2x - 3)^2 = 2$

101. $\log_2 (x^2 + 2x) = 3$

102. $\log_4 (x^2 - 17) = 3$

103. $\frac{3}{2} \log_2 4 - \frac{1}{2} \log_2 x = 3$

104. In the formula $P = P_0\left(\frac{1}{2}\right)^{\frac{h}{4795}}$, P is the atmospheric pressure in millimeters of mercury at elevation h meters above sea level. P_0 is the atmospheric pressure at sea level. If P_0 equals 760 mm, at what elevation is the pressure 42 mm?

105. Chemistry A technician found 12 mg of a radon isotope in a soil sample. After 24 hours, another measurement revealed 10 mg of the isotope.

a. Estimate the length of the isotope's half-life to the nearest hour and to the nearest day.

b. For each estimate, determine the amount of the isotope after two weeks.

c. Compare your answers to part (b). Which is more accurate? Explain.

Standardized Test Prep

Gridded Response

Use a calculator to solve each equation. Enter each answer to the nearest hundredth.

106. $7^{2x} = 75$

107. $11^{x-5} = 250$

108. $1080 = 15^{3x-4}$

Gridded Response Use the Change of Base Formula to solve each equation. Enter the answer to the nearest tenth.

109. $\log_5 x = \log_3 29$

110. $\log_9 x = \log_6 15$

Take It to the NET
Online lesson quiz at www.PHSchool.com
Web Code: aga-0805

Solve each equation.

111. $\log(2 + 4x) = 3$

112. $\log(x - 3) = 2$

Mixed Review

Lesson 8-4 **Expand each logarithm.**

113. $\log 2x^3y^{-2}$

114. $\log_3 \frac{x}{y}$

115. $\log_2 (3x)^3$

116. $\log_3 7(2x - 3)^2$

117. $\log_4 5\sqrt{x}$

118. $\log_2 \left(\frac{5a}{b^2}\right)$

Lesson 7-6 **Evaluate each expression for $f(x) = 3x$ and $g(x) = x^2 - 1$.**

119. $(f + g)(x)$

120. $(g - f)(x)$

121. $(f \cdot g)(x)$

Lesson 6-6 **Find all the zeros of each function.**

122. $y = x^3 - x^2 + x - 1$

123. $f(x) = x^4 - 16$

124. $f(x) = x^4 - 5x^2 + 6$

125. $y = 3x^3 - 21x - 18$

Lesson 1-3 **Write an equation to solve each problem.**

126. A customer at a hardware store mentions that he is buying fencing for a vegetable garden that is 12 ft longer than it is wide. He buys 128 ft of fencing. What is the width of the garden?

127. A bowler has an average of 133. In a set of games one night, her scores are 135, 127, 119, 142, and 156. What score must she bowl in the sixth game to maintain her average?

Checkpoint Quiz 2 — Lessons 8-3 through 8-5

iTEXT Instant self-check quiz online and on CD-ROM

Graph each logarithmic function.

1. $y = \log_6 x$

2. $y = \log(x - 2)$

Expand each logarithm.

3. $\log \frac{s^3}{r^5}$

4. $\log_6 (3xy)^2$

5. $\log_6 4\sqrt{x}$

Solve each equation.

6. $7 - 2^x = -1$

7. $\log 5x = 2$

8. $3 \log x = 9$

9. Evaluate the expressions below and order them from least to greatest.

2^3 $\quad \log_2 3$ $\quad \log_3 2$ $\quad 3^2$ $\quad \log 2$

10. Writing Explain how to use the Change of Base Formula to rewrite $\log_2 10$ as a logarithmic expression with base 3.

Extension Linear and Exponential Models

For Use With Lesson 8-5

You can transform an exponential function into a linear function by taking the logarithm of each side. Since linear models are easy to recognize, you can then determine whether an exponential function is a good model for a set of values.

Take It to the NET
Graphing Calculator procedures online at **www.PHSchool.com**
Web Code: age-2117

$y = ab^x$	**Write the general form of an exponential function.**
$\log y = \log ab^x$	**Take the logarithm of each side.**
$\log y = \log a + x(\log b)$	**Product Property and Power Property**
$\log y = (\log b)x + \log a$	**Rewrite.**

If $\log b$ and $\log a$ are constants, then $\log y = (\log b)x + \log a$ is a linear equation in slope-intercept form. To confirm that $\log b$ is a constant, check that the graph of $\log y = (\log b)x + \log a$ is a line.

EXAMPLE

Determine whether an exponential function is a good model for the values in the table.

x	0	2	4	6	8	10
y	3.0	5.1	8.6	14.5	24.5	41.4

Step 1 Enter the values into STAT lists L_1 and L_2. To enter the values of $\log y$, place the cursor in the heading of L_3 and press LOG L_2 ENTER.

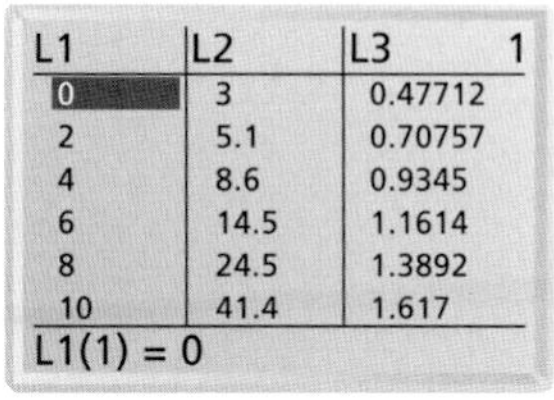

L1	L2	L3 1
0	3	0.47712
2	5.1	0.70757
4	8.6	0.9345
6	14.5	1.1614
8	24.5	1.3892
10	41.4	1.617

L1(1) = 0

Step 2 To graph $\log y$, access the **STAT PLOT** feature and press 1. Then enter L_3 next to Ylist:. Then press ZOOM 9.

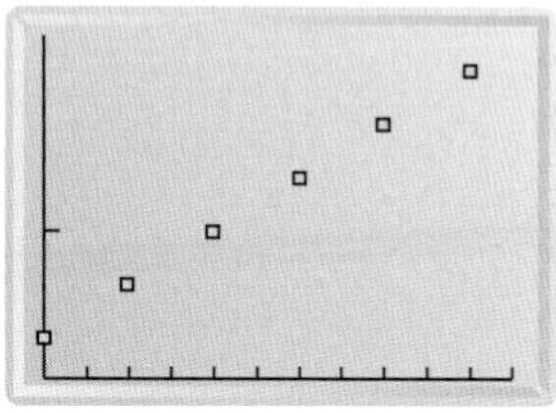

Since the graph of $\log y = (\log b)x + \log a$ is linear, the slope $\log b$ is constant, and b also is constant. An exponential function therefore is a suitable model.

Step 3 Press STAT ▶ 0 ENTER to find the exponential function: $y = 3(1.3)^x$.

EXERCISES

For each set of values, determine whether an exponential function is a good model. If so, find the function.

1.

x	1	3	5	7	9
y	6	22	54	102	145

2.

x	−1	0	1	2	3
y	40.2	19.8	9.9	5.1	2.5

3. Writing Explain how you could determine whether a logarithmic function is a good model for a set of values.

8-6 Natural Logarithms

North Carolina Objectives

1.01 Simplify and perform operations with rational exponents and logarithms (common and natural) to solve problems.
2.01 Use the inverse of functions to model and solve problems.

Lesson Preview

What You'll Learn

OBJECTIVE 1 To evaluate natural logarithmic expressions

OBJECTIVE 2 To solve equations using natural logarithms

. . . And Why

To model the velocity of a rocket, as in Example 2

Check Skills You'll Need

(For help, go to Lessons 8-2 and 8-5.)

Use your calculator to evaluate each expression to the nearest thousandth.

1. e^5 **2.** $2e^3$ **3.** e^{-2} **4.** $\frac{1}{e}$ **5.** $4.2e$

Solve.

6. $\log_3 x = 4$ **7.** $\log_{16} 4 = x$ **8.** $\log_{16} x = 4$

New Vocabulary • natural logarithmic function

Interactive lesson includes instant self-check, tutorials, and activities.

OBJECTIVE 1 Natural Logarithms

In Lesson 8-2, you learned that the number $e \approx 2.71828$ can be used as a base for exponents. The function $y = e^x$ has an inverse, the **natural logarithmic function.**

Key Concepts

Definition **Natural Logarithmic Function**

If $y = e^x$, then $\log_e y = x$, which is commonly written as $\ln y = x$.

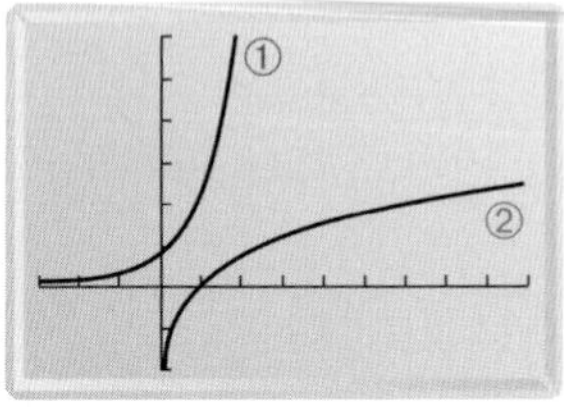

① $y = e^x$

② $y = \ln x$

Reading Math

ln *y* means "the natural logarithm of *y*." The *l* stands for "logarithm" and the *n* stands for "natural."

The properties of common logarithms apply to natural logarithms also.

1 EXAMPLE Simplifying Natural Logarithms

Write $3 \ln 6 - \ln 8$ as a single natural logarithm.

$3 \ln 6 - \ln 8 = \ln 6^3 - \ln 8$ **Power Property**

$= \ln \frac{6^3}{8}$ **Quotient Property**

$= \ln 27$ **Simplify.**

Check Understanding 1 Write each expression as a single natural logarithm.

a. $5 \ln 2 - \ln 4$ **b.** $3 \ln x + \ln y$ **c.** $\frac{1}{4} \ln 3 + \frac{1}{4} \ln x$

Real-World Connection

The space shuttle is launched into orbit.

Natural logarithms are useful because they help express many relationships in the physical world.

2 EXAMPLE **Real-World Connection**

Space A spacecraft can attain a stable orbit 300 km above Earth if it reaches a velocity of 7.7 km/s. The formula for a rocket's maximum velocity v in kilometers per second is $v = -0.0098t + c \ln R$. The booster rocket fires for t seconds and the velocity of the exhaust is c km/s. The ratio of the mass of the rocket with fuel to its mass without fuel is R. Suppose a rocket used to propel a spacecraft has a mass ratio of 25, an exhaust velocity of 2.8 km/s, and a firing time of 100 s. Can the spacecraft attain a stable orbit 300 km above Earth?

Let $R = 25$, $c = 2.8$, and $t = 100$. Find v.

$v = -0.0098t + c \ln R$	**Use the formula.**
$= -0.0098(100) + 2.8 \ln 25$	**Substitute.**
$\approx -0.98 + 2.8(3.219)$	**Use a calculator.**
≈ 8.0	**Simplify.**

The maximum velocity of 8.0 km/s is greater than the 7.7 km/s needed for a stable orbit. Therefore, the spacecraft can attain a stable orbit 300 km above Earth.

Check Understanding **2** **a.** A booster rocket for a spacecraft has a mass ratio of about 15, an exhaust velocity of 2.1 km/s, and a firing time of 30 s. Find the velocity of the spacecraft. Can the spacecraft achieve a stable orbit 300 km above Earth?

b. **Critical Thinking** Suppose a rocket, as designed, cannot provide enough velocity to achieve a stable orbit. Look at the variables in the velocity formula. What alterations could be made to the rocket so that a stable orbit could be achieved?

OBJECTIVE 2

Natural Logarithmic and Exponential Equations

You can use the properties of logarithms to solve natural logarithmic equations.

3 EXAMPLE **Solving a Natural Logarithmic Equation**

Solve $\ln (3x + 5)^2 = 4$.

$\ln (3x + 5)^2 = 4$	
$(3x + 5)^2 = e^4$	**Rewrite in exponential form.**
$(3x + 5)^2 \approx 54.60$	**Use a calculator.**
$3x + 5 \approx \pm\sqrt{54.60}$	**Take the square root of each side.**
$3x + 5 \approx 7.39 \text{ or } -7.39$	**Use a calculator.**
$x \approx 0.797 \text{ or } -4.130$	**Solve for *x*.**

Check $\ln (3 \cdot 0.797 + 5)^2 \stackrel{?}{=} 4$ $\quad$ $\ln (3 \cdot (-4.130) + 5)^2 \stackrel{?}{=} 4$

$\ln 54.6 \stackrel{?}{=} 4$ $\quad$ $\ln 54.6 \stackrel{?}{=} 4$

$4 \approx 4$ ✓ $\quad$ $4 \approx 4$ ✓

Check Understanding **3** Solve each equation. Check your answers.

a. $\ln x = 0.1$ **b.** $\ln (3x - 9) = 21$ **c.** $\ln \left(\frac{x + 2}{3}\right) = 12$

You can use natural logarithms to solve exponential equations.

Need Help?

If $y = e^x$, then $\ln y = x$.

4 EXAMPLE Solving an Exponential Equation

Use natural logarithms to solve $7e^{2x} + 2.5 = 20$.

$7e^{2x} + 2.5 = 20$	
$7e^{2x} = 17.5$	**Subtract 2.5 from each side.**
$e^{2x} = 2.5$	**Divide each side by 7.**
$\ln e^{2x} = \ln 2.5$	**Take the natural logarithm of each side.**
$2x = \ln 2.5$	**Simplify.**
$x = \frac{\ln 2.5}{2}$	**Solve for *x*.**
$x = 0.458$	**Use a calculator.**

Check Understanding 4 Use natural logarithms to solve each equation.

a. $e^{x+1} = 30$ **b.** $e^{\frac{2x}{5}} + 7.2 = 9.1$

5 EXAMPLE Real-World Connection

Investing An initial investment of \$100 is now valued at \$149.18. The interest rate is 8%, compounded continuously. How long has the money been invested?

$A = Pe^{rt}$	**Continuously compounded interest formula**
$149.18 = 100e^{0.08t}$	**Substitute 149.18 for *A*, 100 for *P*, and 0.08 for *r*.**
$1.4918 = e^{0.08t}$	**Divide each side by 100.**
$\ln 1.4918 = \ln e^{0.08t}$	**Take the natural logarithm of each side.**
$\ln 1.4918 = 0.08t$	**Simplify.**
$\frac{\ln 1.4918}{0.08} = t$	**Solve for *t*.**
$5 \approx t$	**Use a calculator.**

The money has been invested for about five years.

Check Understanding 5 An initial investment of \$200 is worth \$315.24 after seven years of continuous compounding. Find the interest rate.

EXERCISES

For more practice, see *Extra Practice.*

Practice and Problem Solving

A Practice by Example

Example 1 (page 462)

Write each expression as a single natural logarithm.

1. $3 \ln 5$

2. $\ln 9 + \ln 2$

3. $\ln 24 - \ln 6$

4. $4 \ln 8 + \ln 10$

5. $\ln 3 - 5 \ln 3$

6. $2 \ln 8 - 3 \ln 4$

7. $5 \ln m - 3 \ln n$

8. $\frac{1}{3}(\ln x + \ln y) - 4 \ln z$

9. $\ln a - 2 \ln b + \frac{1}{2} \ln c$

Example 2 (page 463)

Find the value of *y* for the given value of *x*.

10. $y = 15 + 3 \ln x$, for $x = 7.2$

11. $y = 0.05 - 10 \ln x$, for $x = 0.09$

For Exercises 12 and 13, use $v = -0.0098t + c \ln R$.

12. Space Find the velocity of a spacecraft whose booster rocket has a mass ratio of 20, an exhaust velocity of 2.7 km/s, and a firing time of 30 s. Can the spacecraft achieve a stable orbit 300 km above Earth?

13. A rocket has a mass ratio of 24 and an exhaust velocity of 2.5 km/s. Determine the minimum firing time for a stable orbit 300 km above Earth.

Example 3 (page 463)

Solve each equation. Check your answers.

14. $\ln 3x = 6$

15. $\ln x = -2$

16. $\ln (4x - 1) = 36$

17. $\ln (2m + 3) = 8$

18. $\ln (t - 1)^2 = 3$

19. $1.1 + \ln x^2 = 6$

20. $\ln \frac{x - 1}{2} = 4$

21. $\ln 4r^2 = 3$

22. $2 \ln 2x^2 = 1$

Example 4 (page 464)

Use natural logarithms to solve each equation.

23. $e^x = 18$

24. $e^{2x} = 10$

25. $e^{x + 1} = 30$

26. $e^{\frac{x}{5}} + 4 = 7$

27. $e^{2x} = 12$

28. $e^{\frac{x}{9}} - 8 = 6$

Example 5 (page 464)

29. Investing An initial deposit of \$200 is now worth \$331.07. The account earns 8.4% interest, compounded continuously. Determine how long the money has been in the account.

30. An investor sold 100 shares of stock valued at \$34.50 per share. The stock was purchased at \$7.25 per share two years ago. Find the rate of continuously compounded interest that would be necessary in a banking account for the investor to make the same profit.

B Apply Your Skills

Mental Math **Simplify each expression.**

31. $\ln e$

32. $\ln e^2$

33. $\ln e^{10}$

34. $10 \ln e$

35. $\ln 1$

36. $\frac{\ln e}{4}$

37. $\frac{\ln e^2}{2}$

38. $\ln e^{83}$

39. Space Use the formula for maximum velocity $v = -0.0098t + c \ln R$. Find the mass ratio of a rocket with an exhaust velocity of 3.1 km/s, a firing time of 50 s, and a maximum shuttle velocity of 6.9 km/s.

40. Power The battery power available to run a satellite is given by the formula $P = 50e^{-\frac{t}{250}}$, where P is power in watts and t is time in days. How long can the satellite run if it requires 15 watts? 45 watts?

Determine whether each statement is *always* true, *sometimes* true, or *never* true.

41. $\ln e^x > 1$

42. $\ln e^x = \ln e^x + 1$

43. $\ln t = \log_e t$

Biology **For Exercises 44–46, use the formula $H = \left(\frac{1}{r}\right)(\ln P - \ln A)$. H is the number of hours, r is the rate of decline, P is the initial bacteria population, and A is the reduced bacteria population.**

44. A scientist determines that an antibiotic reduces a population of 20,000 bacteria to 5000 in 24 hours. Find the rate of decline caused by the antibiotic.

45. A laboratory assistant tests an antibiotic that causes a rate of decline of 0.14. How long should it take for a population of 8000 bacteria to shrink to 500?

46. A scientist spilled coffee on the lab report shown at the left. Determine the initial population of the bacteria.

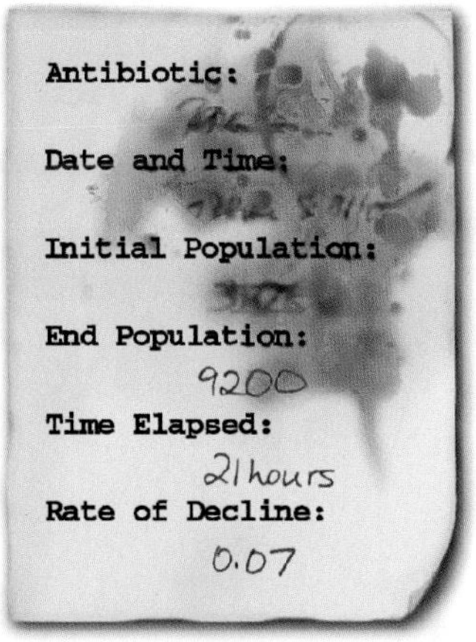

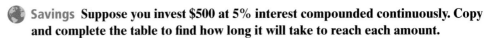

Savings **Suppose you invest $500 at 5% interest compounded continuously. Copy and complete the table to find how long it will take to reach each amount.**

	Amount (A)	Time (years)
47.	$600	■
48.	$700	■
49.	$800	■
50.	$900	■
51.	$1000	■
52.	$1100	■
53.	$1200	■
54.	$1300	■

Solve each equation.

55. $\ln x - 3 \ln 3 = 3$

56. $\ln (2x - 1) = 0$

57. $4e^{x+2} = 32$

58. $\ln (5x - 3)^{\frac{1}{3}} = 2$

59. $2e^{3x-2} + 4 = 16$

60. $2e^{x-2} = e^{x} + 7$

61. $\frac{1}{3} \ln x + \ln 2 - \ln 3 = 3$

62. $\ln (x + 2) - \ln 4 = 3$

C Challenge

63. Critical Thinking Can $\ln 5 + \log_2 10$ be written as a single logarithm? Explain.

64. In 2000, there were about 300 million Internet users. That number is projected to grow to 1 billion in 2005.

a. Let t represent the time, in years, since 2000. Write a function of the form $y = ae^{ct}$ that models the expected growth in the population of Internet users.

b. In what year might there be 500 million Internet users?

c. In what year might there be 1.5 billion Internet users?

d. Solve your equation for t.

e. Writing Explain how you can use your equation from part (d) to verify your answers to parts (b) and (c).

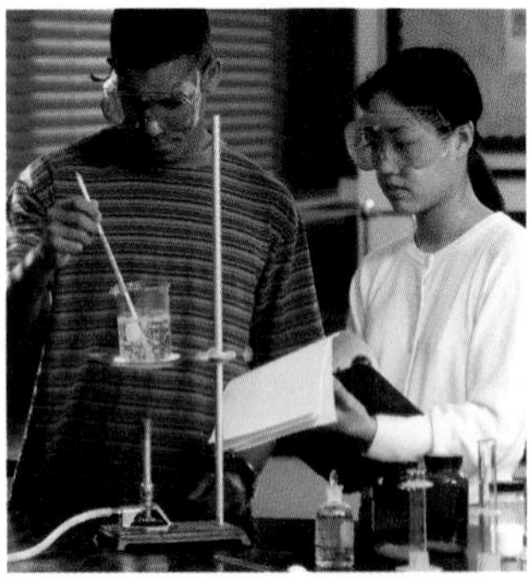

65. Physics The function $T(t) = T_r + (T_i - T_r)e^{kt}$ models Newton's Law of Cooling. $T(t)$ is the temperature of a heated substance t minutes after it has been removed from a heat (or cooling) source. T_i is the substance's initial temperature, k is a constant for that substance, and T_r is room temperature.

a. The initial surface temperature of a beef roast is 236°F and room temperature is 72°F. If $k = -0.041$, how long will it take for this roast to cool to 100°F?

b. Write and graph an equation that you can use to check your answer to part (a). Use your graph to complete the table below.

Temperature (°F)	225	200	175	150	125	100	75
Minutes Later	■	■	■	■	■	■	■

66. Open-Ended Write a real-world problem that you can answer using Newton's Law of Cooling. Then answer it.

Standardized Test Prep

Multiple Choice

67. Which expression is equal to $3 \ln 4 - 5 \ln 2$?

A. $\ln (-18)$ **B.** $\ln \left(\frac{6}{5}\right)$ **C.** $\ln 2$ **D.** $\ln 32$

68. What is the value of x if $17e^{4x} = 85$?

F. $\frac{5}{4}$ G. $\frac{\ln 85}{17 \cdot \ln 4}$ H. $\frac{\ln 5}{4}$ I. $\frac{\ln 85 - \ln 17}{\ln 4}$

Take It to the NET
Online lesson quiz at **www.PHSchool.com**
Web Code: aga-0806

69. An investment of \$750 will be worth \$1500 after 12 years of continuous compounding at a fixed interest rate. What is that interest rate?

A. 2.00% B. 5.78% C. 6.93% D. 200%

Extended Response

70. The table shows the values of an investment after the given number of years of continuously compounded interest.

Years	0	1	2	3	4
Value	\$500.00	\$541.64	\$586.76	\$635.62	\$688.56

a. What is the rate of interest?
b. Write an equation to model the growth of the investment.
c. To the nearest year, when will the investment be worth \$1800?

Mixed Review

Lesson 8-5 **Solve each equation.**

71. $3^{2x} = 6561$ 72. $7^x - 2 = 252$ 73. $25^{2x+1} = 144$

74. $\log 3x = 4$ 75. $\log 5x + 3 = 3.7$ 76. $\log 9 - \log x + 1 = 6$

Lesson 7-7 **Find the inverse of each function. Is the inverse a function?**

77. $y = 5x + 7$ 78. $y = 2x^3 + 10$ 79. $y = -x^2 + 5$

Lesson 6-7

80. The Nut Shop carries 30 different types of nuts. The shop special is the Triple Play, a made-to-order mixture of any three different types of nuts. How many different Triple Plays are possible?

A Point in Time

The first manned moon landing on July 20, 1969, gave scientists a unique opportunity to test their theories about the moon's geologic history.

A logarithmic function was used to date lunar rocks. Radioactive rubidium-87 decays into stable strontium-87 at a fixed rate. The ratio r of the two isotopes in a sample can be measured and used in the equation $T = -h\frac{\ln (r + 1)}{\ln 0.5}$, where T is the age in years and h is the half-life of rubidium-87, 4.7×10^{10} years. For the lunar sample, r was measured at 0.0588, giving an approximate age of 3.87 billion years.

Take It to the NET For more information about space exploration, go to **www.PHSchool.com**.
Web Code: age-2032

Test-Taking Strategies

Testing Multiple Choices

One advantage of multiple-choice tests is that the correct answer is among the choices. A frequently useful strategy is to test a choice in the original problem.

EXAMPLE

What number is the solution to $\left(\frac{1}{4}\right)^x = 8$?

A. -2 **B.** $-\frac{3}{2}$ **C.** 0 **D.** 16

You can answer the question without solving the equation. Substitute each answer choice into the equation until you find the right one.

If $x = -2$, then $\left(\frac{1}{4}\right)^x = \left(\frac{1}{4}\right)^{-2} = 4^2 = 16$. Since $16 \neq 8$, answer A is wrong.

If $x = -\frac{3}{2}$, then $\left(\frac{1}{4}\right)^x = \left(\frac{1}{4}\right)^{-\frac{3}{2}} = 4^{\frac{3}{2}} = 8$. Since $8 = 8$, the correct answer is B.

You don't have to test the two other choices.

When answering a multiple-choice question that involves solving a difficult equation, you often can save time and effort by working backward from the answers to the question.

EXERCISES

1. Refer to the Example. Explain why you can eliminate choices C and D even before trying A and B.
2. Algebraically solve the equation in the Example to show that B is the correct answer.

Answer each question by testing the choices. Then solve each equation algebraically.

3. What is the solution to $\log_x (3x + 2) = x + 1$?
   A. 0 **B.** 2 **C.** 6 **D.** 10
4. What is the solution to $2^{x+1} + 2x + 1 = 0$?
   F. 2 **G.** 0 **H.** $-\frac{1}{2}$ **I.** -1
5. What is the solution to $\ln \sqrt{x + 2} + \ln \sqrt{3x + 4} = \ln 15$?
   A. -1 **B.** 0 **C.** 1 **D.** 7
6. What is the solution to $\log (\log (3x - 2)) = 0$?
   F. $\frac{2}{3}$ **G.** 1 **H.** 4 **I.** 34
7. Use the formula for continuously compounded interest, $A = Pe^{rt}$, to find the annual interest rate for an \$8000 investment that earns \$410.17 in one year.
   A. 7% **B.** 6% **C.** 5% **D.** 4%

Chapter 8

Chapter Review

Vocabulary

- **asymptote** (p. 425)
- **Change of Base Formula** (p. 453)
- **common logarithm** (p. 439)
- **continuously compounded interest formula** (p. 433)
- **decay factor** (p. 425)
- **exponential equation** (p. 453)
- **exponential function** (p. 422)
- **growth factor** (p. 422)
- **logarithm** (p. 439)
- **logarithmic equation** (p. 455)
- **logarithmic function** (p. 440)
- **natural logarithmic function** (p. 462)

Reading Math
Understanding Vocabulary

Take It to the NET
Online vocabulary quiz at **www.PHSchool.com**
Web Code: agj-0851

Choose the correct term to complete each sentence.

1. In the exponential function $y = ab^x$, when $b > 1$, b is the _?_.

2. A _?_ is a logarithm that uses base 10.

3. The line $x = 2$ is a(n) _?_ of the function $f(x) = \frac{2}{x-2}$.

4. The Change of Base Formula can be used to evaluate a _?_ with any base.

5. An _?_ can be solved by taking the logarithm of each side of the equation.

Skills and Concepts

8-1 Objectives

- To model exponential growth (p. 422)
- To model exponential decay (p. 424)

The general form of an **exponential function** is $y = ab^x$, where x is a real number, $a \neq 0, b > 0$, and $b \neq 1$. When $b > 1$, the function models exponential growth, and b is the **growth factor**. When $0 < b < 1$, the function models exponential decay, and b is the **decay factor**.

Determine whether each equation represents exponential growth or exponential decay. Find the rate of increase or decrease for each model. Graph each equation.

6. $y = 5^x$ **7.** $y = 2(4)^x$ **8.** $y = 0.2(3.8)^x$ **9.** $y = 3(0.25)^x$

Write an exponential equation whose graph passes through the given points.

10. $(1, 5), (2, 7)$ **11.** $(3, 1.5), (4, 15)$ **12.** $\left(-1, 6\frac{3}{4}\right), \left(2, \frac{1}{4}\right)$ **13.** $(-2, 9), (0, 1)$

Write an exponential function to model each situation. Find the value of each function after five years, to the nearest dollar.

14. A \$12,500 car depreciates 9% each year.

15. A baseball card bought for \$50 increases 3% in value each year.

Write an exponential equation for each graph. Evaluate the equation for $x = 4$.

16.

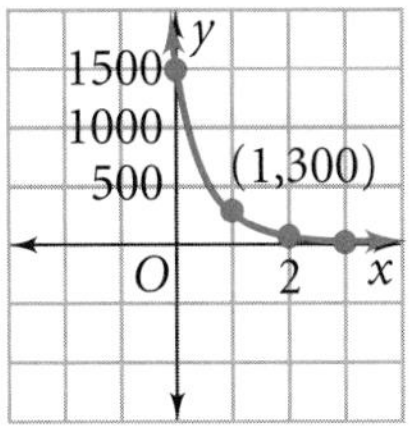

17.

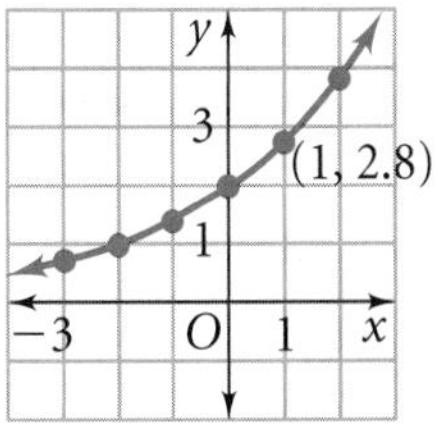

8-2 Objectives

- To identify the role of constants in $y = ab^{cx}$ (p. 431)
- To use e as a base (p. 433)

Exponential functions can be translated and reflected. The graph of $y = ab^{x-h} + k$ is the graph of $y = ab^x$ translated h units horizontally and k units vertically.

The **continuously compounded interest** formula is $A = Pe^{rt}$, where P is the principal, r is the annual rate, and t is time in years.

Describe how the graph of each function relates to the graph of its parent function. Then graph each function.

18. $y = -3^x + 1$

19. $y = 8^x - 1$

20. $y = 2(2)^{x+1} + 3$

21. $y = -2\left(\frac{1}{3}\right)^{x-2}$

Find the amount in a continuously compounded account for the given conditions.

22. principal: \$1000, annual interest rate: 4.8%, time: 2 yr

23. principal: \$250, annual interest rate: 6.2%, time: 2.5 yr

24. principal: \$500, annual interest rate: 8.5%, time: 3 yr

Evaluate to four decimal places.

25. e^1

26. e^{-1}

27. e^5

28. $e^{-\frac{1}{2}}$

29. **Physics** Radium has a half-life of 1620 years. Write the decay function for a 3-mg sample. Find the amount of radium remaining after 50 years.

8-3 Objectives

- To write and evaluate logarithmic expressions (p. 438)
- To graph logarithmic functions (p. 440)

If $y = b^x$, then $\log_b y = x$. The **logarithmic function** is the inverse of the exponential function, so the graphs of the functions are reflections of one another over the line $y = x$. Logarithmic functions can be translated and reflected.

When $b = 10$, the logarithm is called a **common logarithm**, which you can write as $\log y$.

30. **Chemistry** The pH of a substance equals $-\log[H^+]$, where $[H^+]$ is the concentration of hydrogen ions. A sample of well water has a pH of 5.7. Find the concentration of hydrogen ions in the sample.

31. The concentration of hydrogen ions in water is 10^{-7}. Find the pH of water.

Write each equation in logarithmic form.

32. $6^2 = 36$

33. $2^{-3} = 0.125$

34. $3^3 = 27$

35. $10^{-3} = 0.001$

Evaluate each logarithm.

36. $\log_2 64$

37. $\log_3 \frac{1}{9}$

38. $\log 0.00001$

39. $\log_2 1$

Graph each logarithmic function.

40. $y = \log_3 x$

41. $y = \log (x + 2)$

42. $y = \log_2 2x$

43. $y = \log_5 (x + 1)$

8-4 Objective

▼ To use the properties of logarithms (p. 446)

For any positive numbers, M, N, and b, $b \neq 1$, each of the following statements is true. Each can be used to rewrite a logarithmic expression.

- $\log_b MN = \log_b M + \log_b N$, by the Product Property
- $\log_b \frac{M}{N} = \log_b M - \log_b N$, by the Quotient Property
- $\log_b M^x = x \log_b M$, by the Power Property

Write each logarithmic expression as a single logarithm.

44. $\log 8 + \log 3$

45. $\log_2 5 - \log_2 3$

46. $4 \log_3 x + \log_3 7$

47. $\log z - \log y$

Expand each logarithm. State the properties of logarithms that you use.

48. $\log_4 x^2y^3$

49. $\log 4s^4t$

50. $\log_3 \frac{2}{x}$

51. $\log (x + 3)^2$

52. Use the formula $L = 10 \log \frac{I}{I_0}$. Suppose the sound intensity of a fan must be reduced by one third. By how many decibels would the loudness be decreased?

8-5 Objectives

▼ To solve exponential equations (p. 453)

▼ To solve logarithmic equations (p. 455)

An equation in the form $b^{cx} = a$, where the exponent includes a variable, is called an **exponential equation**. You can solve exponential equations by taking the logarithm of each side of the equation. An equation that includes a logarithmic expression is called a **logarithmic equation**.

Solve each equation. Round your answers to the nearest hundredth.

53. $4^x = 27$

54. $3^x = 36$

55. $7^{x-3} = 25$

56. $5^x = 9$

Solve by graphing.

57. $5^{2x} = 25$

58. $3^{7x} = 160$

59. $6^{3x+1} = 215$

60. $0.5^x = 0.12$

Solve each logarithmic equation. Leave your answer in exact form.

61. $\log 3x = 1$

62. $\log_2 4x = 5$

63. $\log x = \log 2x^2 - 2$

64. $2 \log_3 x = 54$

65. Convert $\log_2 7$ to a logarithm in base 5.

66. Biology A culture of 10 bacteria is started, and the number of bacteria will double every hour. In about how many hours will there be 3,000,000 bacteria?

8-6 Objectives

▼ To evaluate natural logarithmic expressions (p. 462)

▼ To solve equations using natural logarithms (p. 463)

The inverse of $y = e^x$ is the **natural logarithmic function** $y = \log_e x = \ln x$. You solve natural logarithm equations in the same way as common logarithm equations.

Solve each equation.

67. $e^{3x} = 12$

68. $\ln x + \ln(x + 1) = 2$

69. $2 \ln x + 3 \ln 2 = 5$

70. $\ln 4 - \ln x = 10$

71. $4e^{(x - 1)} = 64$

72. $3 \ln x + \ln 5 = 7$

73. Savings An initial investment of \$350 is worth \$429.20 after six years of continuous compounding. Find the interest rate.

Chapter 8

Chapter Test

Take It to the NET
Online chapter test at www.PHSchool.com
Web Code: aga-0852

Evaluate each function to the nearest hundredth for for $x = 0, 1, 2, 3, 4, 5$. Graph each function.

1. $y = 3(0.25)^x$
2. $f(x) = -(6)^x$
3. $y = 0.1(10)^x$
4. $f(x) = 100(2)^x$

5. **Open-Ended** Give an example of an exponential function that models exponential growth and an example of an exponential function that models exponential decay.

Write an exponential function of the form $y = ab^x$ that has a graph through the given points.

6. $(1, 1), (2, 3)$
7. $\left(-2, \frac{2}{25}\right), (1, 10)$
8. $\left(-3, \frac{1}{16}\right), (-1, 1)$

9. **Investment** You put \$1500 into an account earning 7% annual interest compounded continuously. How long will it be until you have \$2000 in your account?

Describe how the graph of each function is related to the graph of its parent function.

10. $y = 3^x + 2$
11. $y = 3\left(\frac{1}{2}\right)^{x+1}$
12. $y = 5^{x-2} - 1$
13. $y = -(2)^{x+2}$

Evaluate each logarithm.

14. $\log_2 8$
15. $\log_7 7$
16. $\log_5 25$
17. $\log_3 27$
18. $\log_{11} 1$
19. $\log_4 256$

Graph each logarithmic function.

20. $y = \log_9 x$
21. $y = \log_3 (x - 1)$
22. $y = \frac{1}{2}\log_3 (x + 2)$
23. $y = 1 - \log_2 x$

Use the properties of logarithms to rewrite each logarithmic expression.

24. $\log_2 4 + 3\log_2 9$
25. $3\log a - 2\log b$
26. $\log_7 \frac{a}{b}$
27. $\log 3x^3y^2$

Use the properties of logarithms to evaluate each expression.

28. $\log_3 27 - \log_3 9$
29. $2\log_2 64 + \log_2 2$
30. $-\log_4 \frac{1}{16} - \log_4 64$
31. $2\log 5 + \log 40$

32. **Writing** Show that solving the equation $3^{2x} = 4$ by taking common logarithms of both sides is equivalent to solving it by taking logarithms to the base 3 of both sides.

Solve each equation.

33. $\left(\frac{3}{4}\right)^x = 81$
34. $3^{x-1} = 24$
35. $\log 4x = 3$
36. $2\log x = -4$

Use the Change of Base Formula to rewrite each expression using common logarithms.

37. $\log_3 16$
38. $\log_2 10$
39. $\log_7 8$

Use the properties of logarithms to simplify each equation and solve it. Round to thousandths.

40. $\ln 2 + \ln x = 1$
41. $\ln (x + 1) + \ln (x - 1) = 4$
42. $\ln (2x - 1)^2 = 7$
43. $3\ln x - \ln 2 = 4$

44. **Physics** Seawater absorbs light. In some instances, this relationship is modeled by $\ln I = \ln I_0 - 0.014d$. I_0 is the intensity of the light at the surface of the water, and I is the intensity at a depth of d cm. At what depth will the intensity of the light in the water be 25% of the surface intensity?

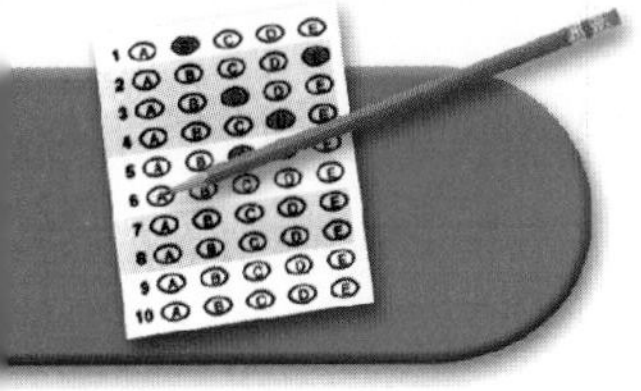

Standardized Test Prep

Multiple Choice

For Exercises 1–7, choose the correct letter.

1. What can you tell about the roots of $3x^2 + 4x - 1 = 0$ from the discriminant?
   A. There are two real roots.
   B. There are two imaginary roots.
   C. There is one real and one imaginary root.
   D. There are no roots.

2. Which expressions are equivalent to $\log a - 3\log b$?
   I. $\log ab^3$ **II.** $\log \frac{a}{b^3}$
   III. $\log a - \log b^3$ **IV.** $\log (ab)^3$
   F. I and II **G.** II and III
   H. III and IV **I.** I and IV

3. What is the factored form of $2x^3 + 5x^2 - 12x$?
   A. $x(2x - 3)(x + 4)$
   B. $(2x^2 - 3)(x + 4)$
   C. $x(2x + 4)(x - 3)$
   D. $(2x - 4)(x + 3)$

4. Which is NOT a solution of the system? $\begin{cases} 2x - y > 3 \\ 2x + y \geq 5 \end{cases}$
   F. $(3, 0)$ **G.** $(4, -1)$
   H. $(6, 1)$ **I.** $(0, -3)$

5. How is the graph of $y = (x - 4)^2 + 1$ translated from the graph of $y = x^2$?
   A. left 1, up 4 **B.** left 4, down 1
   C. right 1, down 4 **D.** right 4, up 1

6. What is the inverse of $\begin{bmatrix} 3 & -5 \\ 1 & 4 \end{bmatrix}$?
   F. $\begin{bmatrix} 4 & 5 \\ -1 & 3 \end{bmatrix}$ **G.** $\begin{bmatrix} -2 & 5 \\ -1 & -3 \end{bmatrix}$
   H. $\begin{bmatrix} -3 & 5 \\ -1 & -4 \end{bmatrix}$ **I.** $\frac{1}{17}\begin{bmatrix} 4 & 5 \\ -1 & 3 \end{bmatrix}$

7. Solve the system. $\begin{cases} 2x + 3y - z = -2 \\ x - 4y + 2z = 18 \\ 5x + 2y - 6z = 8 \end{cases}$
   A. $x = 3, y = 1, z = 2$
   B. $x = -3, y = 2, z = -1$
   C. $x = 4, y = -3, z = 1$
   D. $x = -1, y = 3, z = 2$

Quantitative Comparison

Compare the boxed quantity in Column A with the boxed quantity in Column B. Choose the best answer.

A. The quantity in Column A is greater.
B. The quantity in Column B is greater.
C. The two quantities are equal.
D. The relationship cannot be determined from the information given.

	Column A	Column B
8.	e^2	$2 \ln e$
9.	$\log_3 2$	$\log_2 3$
10.	$\log_a a$	$\log_a 1$

Gridded Response

11. Solve $3^x = 7$. Round your answer to the nearest hundredth.

12. What is the discriminant of $2x^2 - 8x + 8 = 0$?

13. Evaluate $\log_4 8$.

Short Response

14. Write $\log \frac{x^2y^3}{z^6}$ in expanded form.

15. Solve $5^{2x + 1} = 62$. Round your answer to the nearest hundredth. Show your work.

16. Graph the function $y = 10^{x + 1} - 3$ as a translation of its parent function.

Extended Response

17. Suppose you put \$1000 in an account earning 5.5% interest compounded continuously. How much will be in the account after one year? After four years?

18. What is the determinant of $\begin{bmatrix} 1 & 2 & 3 \\ 2 & 1 & 3 \\ 2 & 3 & 1 \end{bmatrix}$?

    Show your work.

A Crowded House

Applying Exponential Functions The number of people in the world has more than tripled since 1900—from less than 2 billion to more than 6 billion. In 2000, an average of about 360,000 babies were born each day. That means that there were four babies born every second.

Old South Meeting House

Historical Site

Old South Meeting House, in Boston, Massachusetts, (left about 1903, right in 2002), was built in 1730. At the time, it was the tallest building in Boston. Note that the time on the clock is 1:43 in both photos.

Proportional Populations

These maps of China, the United States, and Australia are drawn so that their sizes are proportional to their populations.

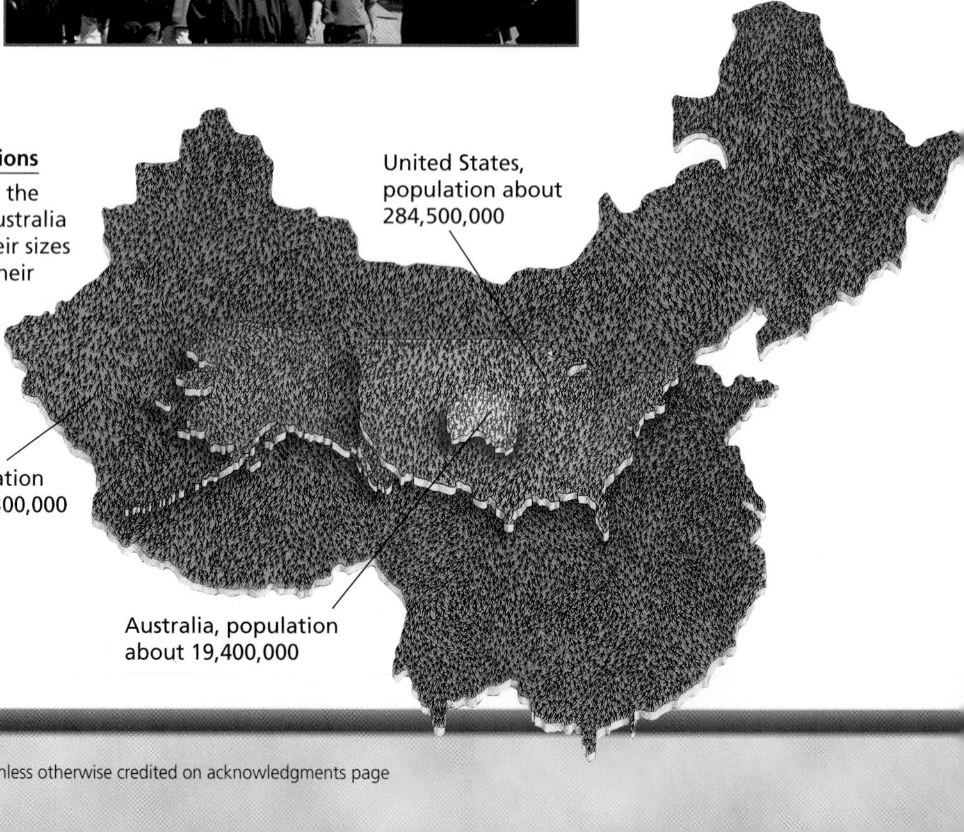

United States, population about 284,500,000

China, population about 1,273,300,000

Australia, population about 19,400,000

About one of every five people in the world lives in China.

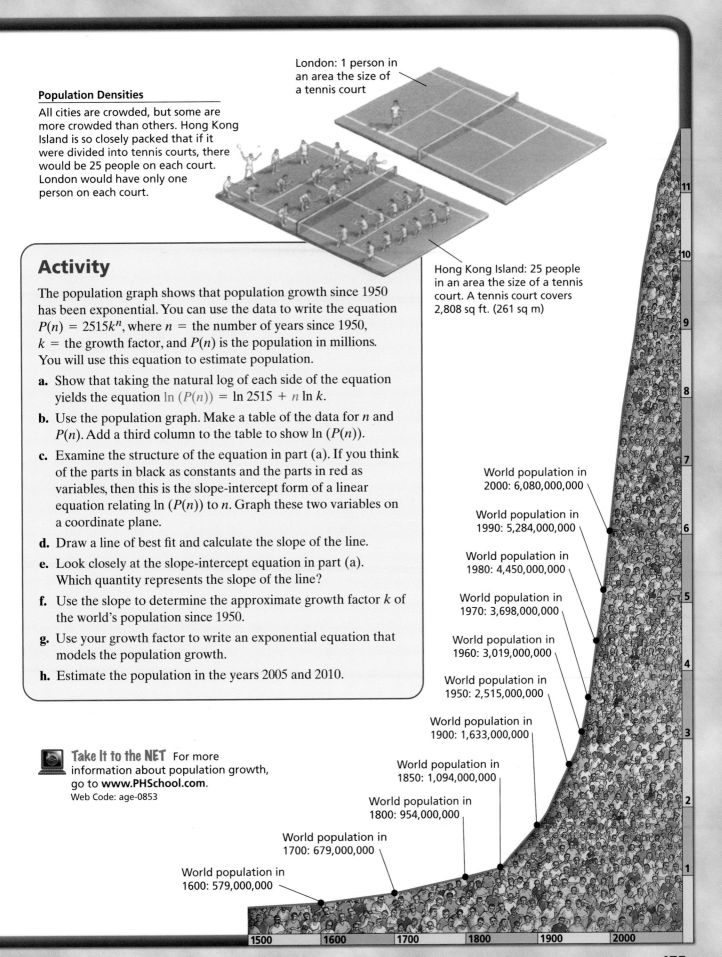

Population Densities

All cities are crowded, but some are more crowded than others. Hong Kong Island is so closely packed that if it were divided into tennis courts, there would be 25 people on each court. London would have only one person on each court.

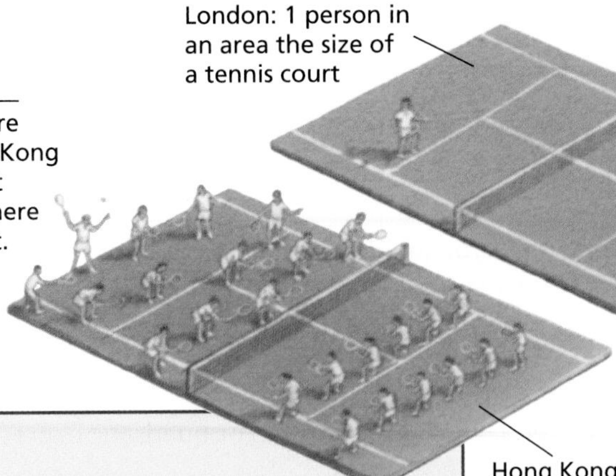

Activity

The population graph shows that population growth since 1950 has been exponential. You can use the data to write the equation $P(n) = 2515k^n$, where n = the number of years since 1950, k = the growth factor, and $P(n)$ is the population in millions. You will use this equation to estimate population.

a. Show that taking the natural log of each side of the equation yields the equation $\ln(P(n)) = \ln 2515 + n \ln k$.

b. Use the population graph. Make a table of the data for n and $P(n)$. Add a third column to the table to show $\ln(P(n))$.

c. Examine the structure of the equation in part (a). If you think of the parts in black as constants and the parts in red as variables, then this is the slope-intercept form of a linear equation relating $\ln(P(n))$ to n. Graph these two variables on a coordinate plane.

d. Draw a line of best fit and calculate the slope of the line.

e. Look closely at the slope-intercept equation in part (a). Which quantity represents the slope of the line?

f. Use the slope to determine the approximate growth factor k of the world's population since 1950.

g. Use your growth factor to write an exponential equation that models the population growth.

h. Estimate the population in the years 2005 and 2010.

Take It to the NET For more information about population growth, go to **www.PHSchool.com**.
Web Code: age-0853

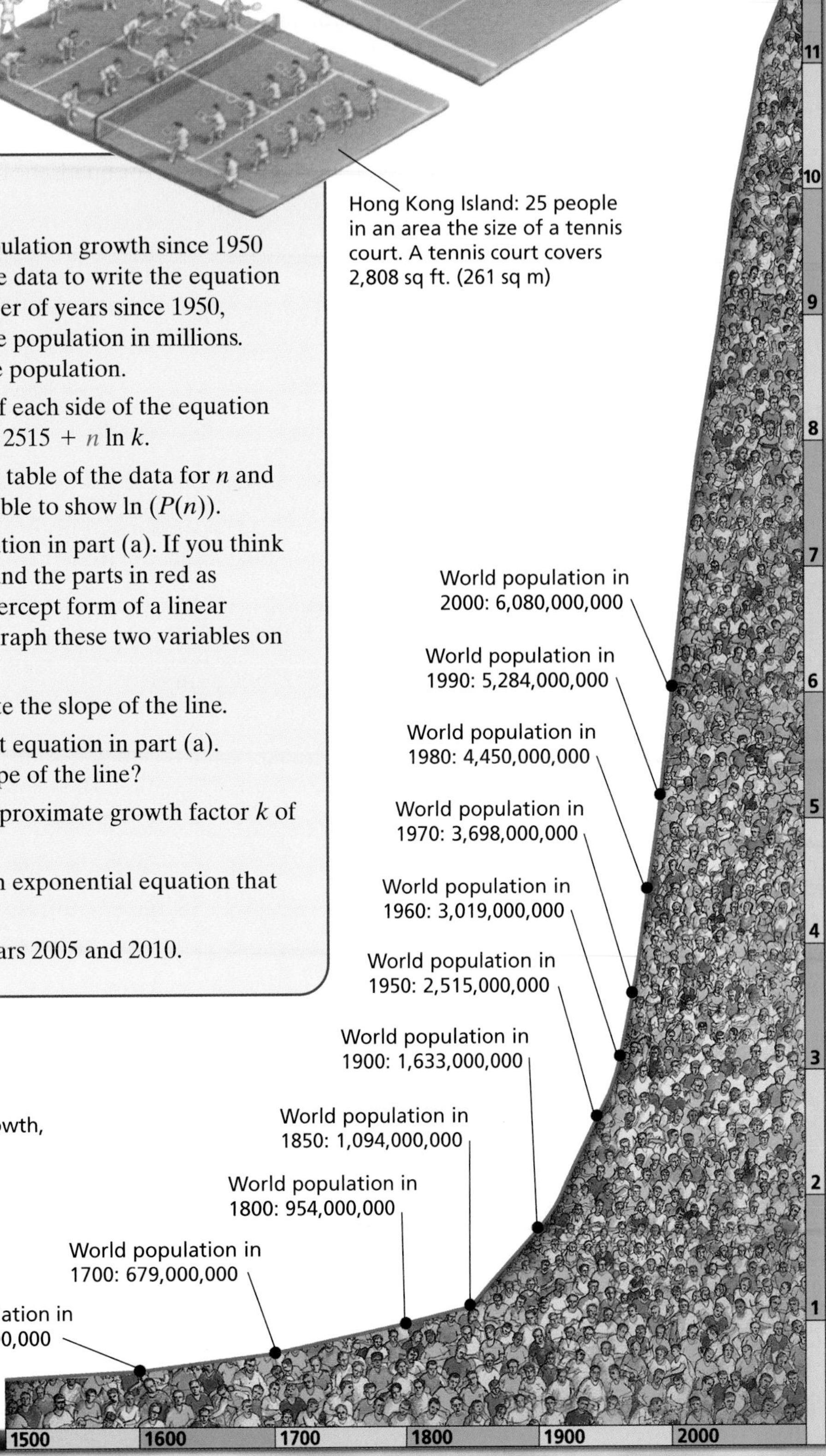

Where You've Been

- In Chapter 1, you learned to find theoretical probabilities for random events.
- In Chapter 2, you learned to write and interpret direct variation equations to solve real-world problems.
- In Chapter 5, you learned to factor quadratic expressions and to solve quadratic equations.

Instant self-check online and on CD-ROM

Diagnosing Readiness

(For help, go to the Lesson in green.)

Finding Theoretical Probabilities (Lesson 1-6)

A bookshelf contains 18 math books, 27 science books, 21 history books, and 15 grammar books. You pick one book at random from the shelf. Find each theoretical probability.

1. P(history)
2. P(science)
3. P(math or science)
4. P(math or science or history)
5. P(not grammar)
6. P(not math and not science)

Using Direct Variation (Lesson 2-3)

For each direct variation, find the constant of variation. Then find the value of y when $x = -3$.

7. $y = 4$ when $x = 3$
8. $y = 1$ when $x = -1.5$
9. $y = -5$ when $x = \frac{3}{2}$
10. $y = -16$ when $x = 7$

Factoring Quadratic Expressions (Lesson 5-4)

Factor each expression.

11. $x^2 + x - 6$
12. $4x^2 + 17x + 15$
13. $9x^2 - 25$
14. $x^2 - 12x + 36$
15. $3x^2 + 10x + 8$
16. $x^2 - 5x + 6$

Solving Quadratic Equations (Lesson 5-5)

Solve each equation.

17. $x^2 + 7x - 8 = 0$
18. $\frac{1}{4}x^2 + \frac{7}{2}x = -12$
19. $3x^2 = 18x - 24$
20. $9x^2 + 6x = 0$
21. $4x^2 + 16 = 34x$
22. $x^2 - 13x - 30 = 0$

Rational Functions

Chapter 9

LESSONS

Key Vocabulary

- branch (p. 485)
- combined variation (p. 480)
- complex fraction (p. 506)
- dependent events (p. 519)
- independent events (p. 519)
- inverse variation (p. 478)
- mutually exclusive events (p. 521)
- point of discontinuity (p. 491)
- rational function (p. 491)
- simplest form (p. 499)

Where You're Going

- In Chapter 9, you will learn to use inverse variation and the graphs of inverse variations to solve real-world problems.
- You will learn to identify properties of rational functions.
- You will learn to simplify rational expressions and to solve rational equations.

Real-World Connection Applying what you learn, on page 505 you will solve a problem involving photography.

9-1 Inverse Variation

North Carolina Objectives

1.05 Model and solve problems using direct, inverse, combined and joint variation.

Lesson Preview

What You'll Learn

OBJECTIVE 1 To use inverse variation

OBJECTIVE 2 To use combined variation

. . . And Why

To find the life spans of mammals, as in Example 3

✓ Check Skills You'll Need

(For help, go to Lesson 2-3.)

In Exercises 1–3, y varies directly with x.

1. Given that $x = 2$ when $y = 4$, find y when $x = 5$.
2. Given that $x = 1$ when $y = 5$, find y when $x = 3$.
3. Given that $x = 10$ when $y = 3$, find y when $x = 4$.

New Vocabulary • inverse variation • combined variation

Interactive lesson includes instant self-check, tutorials, and activities.

OBJECTIVE 1 Using Inverse Variation

In Chapter 2, you studied direct variation. A direct variation is a linear function of the form $y = kx$, where k is the nonzero constant of variation. A function of the form $y = \frac{k}{x}$ or $xy = k$, where $k \neq 0$, is an **inverse variation.**

The table and graph below show the time needed to bike 24 miles pedaling at different rates.

Rate (mi/h)	Time (h)
3	8
6	4
12	2
24	1

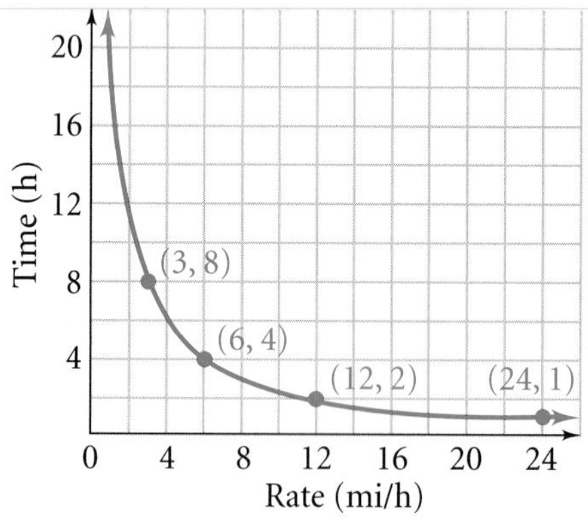

Notice that as the rate increases, the time decreases. Doubling the rate halves the time. The inverse variation $t = \frac{24}{r}$ models this situation.

1 EXAMPLE Modeling Inverse Variation

Suppose that x and y vary inversely, and $x = 3$ when $y = -5$. Write the function that models the inverse variation.

$y = \frac{k}{x}$ — **x and y vary inversely.**

$-5 = \frac{k}{3}$ — **Substitute the given values of x and y.**

$-15 = k$ — **Find k.**

$y = \frac{-15}{x}$ — **Use the value of k to write the function.**

Check Understanding 1 Suppose that x and y vary inversely, and $x = 0.3$ when $y = 1.4$. Write the function that models the inverse variation.

2 EXAMPLE Identifying Direct and Inverse Variations

Is the relationship between the variables in each table a direct variation, an inverse variation, or neither? Write functions to model the direct and inverse variations.

a.

x	0.5	2	6
y	1.5	6	18

As x increases, y increases. Since each y-value is 3 times the corresponding x-value, y varies directly with x, the constant of variation is 3, and the function is $y = 3x$.

b.

x	0.2	0.6	1.2
y	12	4	2

As x increases, y decreases. The product of each pair of x- and y-values is 2.4. y varies inversely with x and the constant of variation is 2.4. So $xy = 2.4$ and the function is $y = \frac{2.4}{x}$.

c.

x	1	2	3
y	2	1	0.5

As x increases, y decreases, but this is not an inverse variation. Not all the products of x and y are the same $(2 \cdot 1 \neq 3 \cdot 0.5)$. This is neither a direct variation nor an inverse variation.

Reading Math

You can describe an inverse variation as "y varies inversely as x" or as "y is inversely proportional to x."

Check Understanding 2 Is the relationship between the values in each table a direct variation, an inverse variation, or neither? Write functions to model the direct and inverse variations.

a.

x	0.8	0.6	0.4
y	0.9	1.2	1.8

b.

x	2	4	6
y	3.2	1.6	1.1

c.

x	1.2	1.4	1.6
y	18	21	24

3 EXAMPLE Real-World Connection

Zoology Heart rates and life spans of most mammals are inversely related. Use the data to write a function that models this inverse variation. Use your function to estimate the average life span of a cat with a heart rate of 126 beats/min.

Heart Rate and Life Span

Mammal	Heart rate (beats/min)	Life span (min)
Mouse	634	1,576,800
Rabbit	158	6,307,200
Lion	76	13,140,000
Horse	63	15,768,000

SOURCE: *The Handy Science Answer Book*

Relate heart rate · life span = a constant

Define Let r = heart rate (beats/min).

Let s = life span (min).

Let k = constant of variation (beats in a life span).

Write $r \quad s = k$

For each of the four mammals in the table, $rs \approx 1{,}000{,}000{,}000$.

$rs = 1{,}000{,}000{,}000$ **Substitute 1,000,000,000 for *k*.**

$126s = 1{,}000{,}000{,}000$ **Substitute 126 for *r*.**

$s \approx 8{,}000{,}000$

A cat's life span is about 8 million minutes, or about 15.2 years.

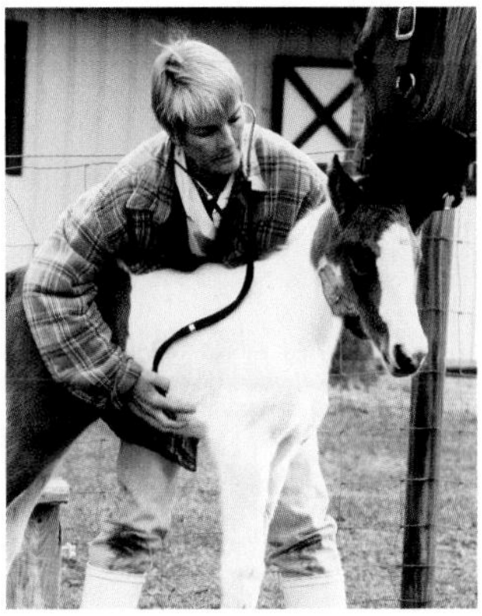

Real-World Connection

Horses have a life span of about 30 years.

Check Understanding 3 **a.** A squirrel's heart rate is 190 beats per minute. Estimate its life span.
b. An elephant's life span is about 70 years. Estimate its average heart rate.

OBJECTIVE

2 Using Combined Variation

A **combined variation** combines direct and inverse variations in more complicated relationships.

> **Reading Math**
> You can write "z varies jointly with x and y" as "z varies directly with the product of x and y."

Examples of Combined Variations

Combined Variation	Equation Form
y varies directly with the square of x.	$y = kx^2$
y varies inversely with the cube of x.	$y = \frac{k}{x^3}$
z varies jointly with x and y.	$z = kxy$
z varies jointly with x and y and inversely with w.	$z = \frac{kxy}{w}$
z varies directly with x and inversely with the product of w and y.	$z = \frac{kx}{wy}$

4 EXAMPLE Real-World Connection

Physics Newton's Law of Universal Gravitation is modeled by the formula $F = \frac{Gm_1m_2}{d^2}$. F is the gravitational force between two objects with masses m_1 and m_2, and d is the distance between the objects. G is the gravitational constant. Describe Newton's law as a combined variation.

$F = \frac{Gm_1m_2}{d^2}$ ← F varies jointly with the masses m_1 and m_2, and
← F varies inversely with the square of the distance d.

Check Understanding 4 **Geometry** The formula for the area of a trapezoid is $A = \frac{1}{2}h(b_1 + b_2)$. Describe this relationship as a combined variation.

5 EXAMPLE Finding a Formula

Geometry The volume of a regular tetrahedron varies directly as the cube of the length of an edge. The volume of a regular tetrahedron with edge length 3 is $\frac{9\sqrt{2}}{4}$. Find the formula for the volume of a regular tetrahedron.

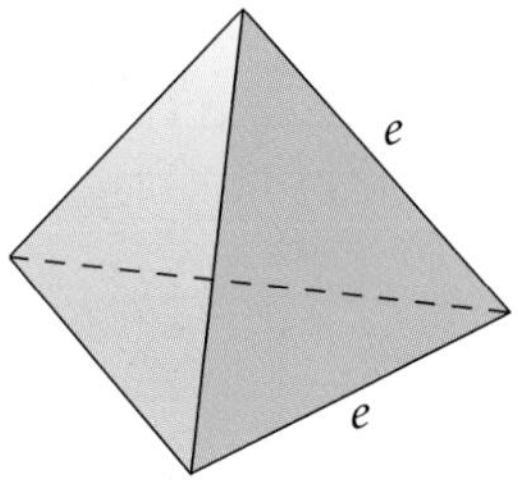

$V = ke^3$ **V varies directly as the cube of e.**

$\frac{9\sqrt{2}}{4} = k(3)^3$ **Substitute the values for V and e.**

$\frac{\sqrt{2}}{12} = k$ **Solve for k.**

$V = \frac{\sqrt{2}}{12}e^3$ **Substitute the value for k.**

Check Understanding 5 The volume of a square pyramid with congruent edges varies directly as the cube of the length of an edge. The volume of a square pyramid with edge length 4 is $\frac{32\sqrt{2}}{3}$. Find the formula for the volume of a square pyramid with congruent edges.

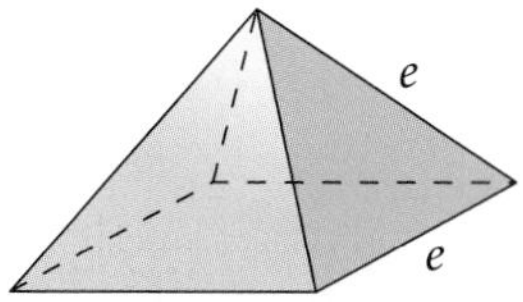

EXERCISES

For more practice, see *Extra Practice.*

Practice and Problem Solving

A Practice by Example

Example 1 (page 478)

Suppose that x and y vary inversely. Write a function that models each inverse variation.

1. $x = 1$ when $y = 11$ **2.** $x = -13$ when $y = 100$ **3.** $x = 1$ when $y = 1$

4. $x = 28$ when $y = -2$ **5.** $x = 1.2$ when $y = 3$ **6.** $x = 2.5$ when $y = 100$

Example 2 (page 479)

Is the relationship between the values in each table a direct variation, an inverse variation, or neither? Write equations to model the direct and inverse variations.

7.

x	3	8	10	22
y	15	40	50	110

8.

x	3	5	7	10.5
y	14	8.4	6	4

9.

x	0.5	2.1	3.5	11
y	1	4.2	7	22

10.

x	0.1	3	6	24
y	3	0.1	0.05	0.0125

11.

x	7	3	1	$\frac{1}{5}$
y	$\frac{1}{7}$	$\frac{1}{3}$	1	5

12.

x	10	12	20	23
y	2	$2\frac{2}{5}$	4	$5\frac{3}{5}$

Example 3 (page 479)

Suppose that x and y vary inversely. Write a function that models each inverse variation and find y when $x = 10$.

13. $x = 20$ when $y = 5$ **14.** $x = 20$ when $y = -4$ **15.** $x = 5$ when $y = -\frac{1}{3}$

Example 4 (page 480)

Describe the combined variation that is modeled by each formula.

16. $A = \pi r^2$ **17.** $A = 0.5bh$ **18.** $h = \frac{2A}{b}$ **19.** $V = \frac{Bh}{3}$

20. $V = \pi r^2 h$ **21.** $h = \frac{V}{\pi r^2}$ **22.** $V = \ell wh$ **23.** $\ell = \frac{V}{wh}$

Example 5 (page 480)

Write the function that models each relationship. Find z when $x = 4$ and $y = 9$.

24. z varies directly with x and inversely with y. When $x = 6$ and $y = 2$, $z = 15$.

25. z varies jointly with x and y. When $x = 2$ and $y = 3$, $z = 60$.

26. z varies directly with the square of x and inversely with y. When $x = 2$ and $y = 4$, $z = 3$.

27. z varies inversely with the product of x and y. When $x = 2$ and $y = 4$, $z = 0.5$.

B Apply Your Skills

28. a. The spreadsheet shows data that could be modeled by an equation of the form $PV = k$. Estimate the value of k.

b. Estimate P when $V = 62$.

	A	B
1	P	V
2	140.00	100
3	147.30	95
4	155.60	90
5	164.70	85
6	175.00	80
7	186.70	75

Each ordered pair is from an inverse variation. Find the constant of variation.

29. $(6, 3)$ **30.** $(0.9, 4)$ **31.** $\left(\frac{3}{8}, \frac{2}{3}\right)$

32. $\left(\sqrt{2}, \sqrt{18}\right)$ **33.** $\left(\sqrt{3}, \sqrt{27}\right)$ **34.** $\left(\sqrt{8}, \sqrt{32}\right)$

35. Mechanics Gear A drives Gear B. Gear A has a teeth and speed r_A in revolutions per minute (rpm). Gear B has b teeth and speed r_B. The quantities are related by the formula $ar_A = br_B$. Gear A has 60 teeth and speed 5400 rpm. Gear B has 45 teeth. Find the speed of Gear B.

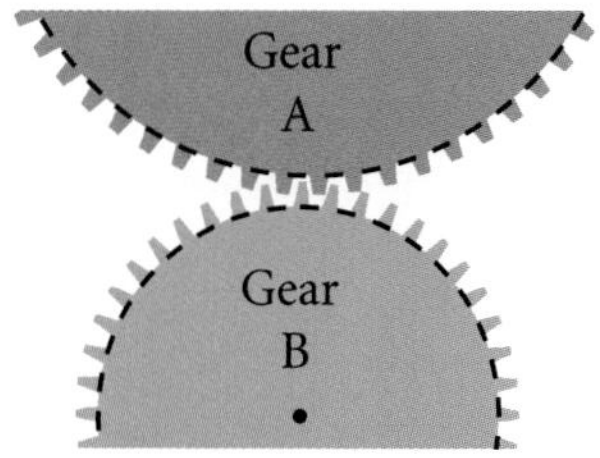

36. Physics The force F of gravity on a rocket varies directly with its mass m and inversely with the square of its distance d from Earth. Write a model for this combined variation.

Each pair of values is from a direct variation. Find the missing value.

37. $(3, 7), (8, y)$ **38.** $(2, 5), (4, y)$ **39.** $(4, 6), (x, 3)$

40. $(9, 5), (x, 3)$ **41.** $(8.3, 7.1), (5, y)$ **42.** $(2.6, 4.5), (x, 6.3)$

Each pair of values is from an inverse variation. Find the missing value.

43. $(3, 7), (8, y)$ **44.** $(2, 5), (4, y)$ **45.** $(4, 6), (x, 3)$

46. $(9, 5), (x, 3)$ **47.** $(8.3, 7.1), (5, y)$ **48.** $(2.6, 4.5), (x, 6.3)$

49. Suppose that y varies inversely with the square of x, and $y = 50$ when $x = 4$. Find y when $x = 5$.

50. Suppose that c varies jointly with d and the square of g, and $c = 30$ when $d = 15$ and $g = 2$. Find d when $c = 6$ and $g = 8$.

51. Suppose that d varies jointly with r and t, and $d = 110$ when $r = 55$ and $t = 2$. Find r when $d = 40$ and $t = 3$.

Exercise 52

52. Construction A concrete supplier sells premixed concrete in 300-ft^3 truckloads. The area A that the concrete will cover is inversely proportional to the depth d of the concrete.

a. Write a model for the relationship between the area and the depth of a truckload of poured concrete.

b. What area will the concrete cover if it is poured to a depth of 0.5 ft? A depth of 1 ft? A depth of 1.5 ft?

c. When the concrete is poured into a circular area, the depth of the concrete is inversely proportional to the square of the radius r. Write a model for this relationship.

53. Suppose that y varies directly with x and inversely with z^2, and $x = 48$ when $y = 8$ and $z = 3$. Find x when $y = 12$ and $z = 2$.

54. Suppose that t varies directly with s and inversely with the square of r. How is the value of t changed when the value of s is doubled? Is tripled?

55. Suppose that x varies directly with the square of y and inversely with z. How is the value of x changed if the value of y is halved? Is quartered?

C Challenge

56. Writing Explain why 0 cannot be in the domain of an inverse variation.

57. Critical Thinking Suppose that (x_1, y_1) and (x_2, y_2) are values from an inverse variation. Show that $\frac{x_1}{x_2} = \frac{y_2}{y_1}$.

58. Open-Ended The height h of a cylinder varies directly with its volume V and inversely with the square of its radius r. Find at least four ways to change the volume and radius of a cylinder so that its height is quadrupled.

59. **Health** Health care professionals use the body mass index (BMI) to establish guidelines for determining any possible risks of their patients and for planning any useful preventative programs. The BMI varies directly with weight and inversely with the square of height. Use this portion of the BMI chart to determine the BMI formula.

Weights and Body Mass Index (BMI)

Height	Range of Weight (pounds)			
	BMI 19–24.9	BMI 25–29.9	BMI 30–39.9	BMI ≥ 40
5′6″	118–154	155–185	186–246	≥247
5′7″	121–158	159–190	191–254	≥255
5′8″	125–163	164–196	197–261	≥262
5′9″	128–168	169–202	203–269	≥270
5′10″	132–173	174–208	209–277	≥278
5′11″	136–178	179–214	215–285	≥286
6′0″	140–183	184–220	221–293	≥294

Standardized Test Prep

Multiple Choice

60. Which equation does NOT represent inverse variation between x and z?

A. $x = \frac{y}{z}$ B. $x = \frac{-15z}{y}$

C. $z = \frac{-15y}{x}$ D. $xz = 5y$

61. If p and q vary inversely, and $p = 10$ when $q = -4$, what is q when $p = -2$?

F. 20 G. $\frac{4}{5}$ H. $-\frac{4}{5}$ I. -20

Take It to the NET
Online lesson quiz at www.PHSchool.com
Web Code: aga-0901

62. Which equation shows that z varies directly with the square of x and inversely with the cube of y?

A. $z = \frac{x^2}{y^3}$ B. $z = \frac{x^3}{y^2}$ C. $z = \frac{y^2}{x^3}$ D. $z = \frac{y^3}{x^2}$

Short Response

63. Describe how the variables A and r vary in the formula for the area of a circle, $A = \pi r^2$.

Extended Response

64. Which data set shows inverse variation: (24.4, 4.8) and (9.6, 12.2), or (24.0, 4.5) and (18.0, 6.5)? Explain.

Mixed Review

Lesson 8-6

Solve each equation.

65. $\ln 4 + \ln x = 5$ 66. $\ln x - \ln 3 = 4$ 67. $2 \ln x + 3 \ln 4 = 4$

Lesson 7-2

Multiply and simplify. Assume that all variables are positive.

68. $-5\sqrt{6x} \cdot 3\sqrt{6x^2}$ 69. $3\sqrt[3]{4x^2} \cdot 7\sqrt[3]{12x^4}$ 70. $\sqrt{5x^3} \cdot \sqrt{40xy^7}$

Lesson 7-1

Simplify each radical expression. Use absolute value bars where they are needed.

71. $\sqrt{x^{10}y^{100}}$ 72. $\sqrt[3]{-64a^3b^6}$ 73. $\sqrt[4]{64m^8n^4}$ 74. $\sqrt[n]{x^n}$

Technology

Graphing Rational Functions

For Use With Lesson 9-2

You can use your graphing calculator to graph rational functions. It is sometimes preferable to use the Dot plotting mode rather than the Connected plotting mode. The Connected mode can join branches of a graph that should be separated. Try both modes to get the best graph.

EXAMPLE

Graph $y = \frac{4}{x - 3} - 1.5$.

Step 1 Press the MODE key. Scroll down to highlight the word Dot. Then press ENTER.

```
Normal  Sci  Eng
Float  0123456789
Radian  Degree
Func  Par  Pol  Seq
Connected  Dot
Sequential  Simul
Real  a+bi  re^θi
Full  Horiz  G–T
```

Step 2 Enter the function. Use parentheses to enter the denominator accurately.

```
Plot1 Plot2 Plot3
\Y1=4/(X – 3) – 1.5
\Y2 =
\Y3 =
\Y4 =
\Y5 =
\Y6 =
\Y7 =
```

Step 3 Graph the function.

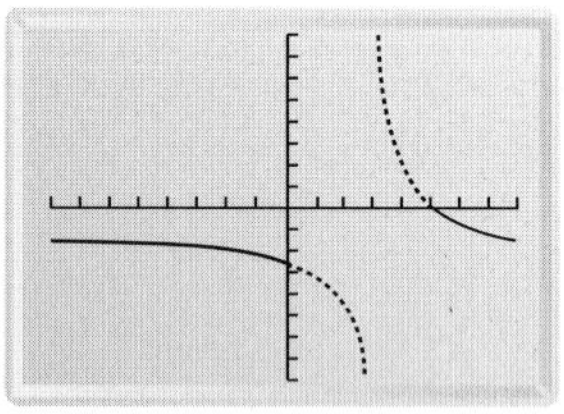

EXERCISES

Use a graphing calculator to graph each function. Then sketch the graph.

1. $y = \frac{7}{x}$

2. $y = \frac{3}{x + 4} - 2$

3. $y = \frac{x + 2}{(x + 1)(x + 3)}$

4. $y = \frac{4x + 1}{x - 3}$

5. $y = \frac{2}{x - 2}$

6. $y = \frac{1}{x + 2} + 3$

7. $y = \frac{2x}{x + 3}$

8. $y = \frac{x^2}{x^2 - 5}$

9. $y = \frac{20}{x^2 + 5}$

10. $y = \frac{1}{x - 3} - 6$

11. $y = \frac{10}{x^2 - 5x - 10}$

12. $y = \frac{x}{x^2 - 1}$

13. a. Graph $y = \frac{1}{x}$. Sketch the graph.

b. Examine both negative and positive values of x. Describe what happens to the y-values as x approaches zero.

c. What happens to the y-values as x increases? As x decreases?

14. a. Change the mode on your graphing calculator to Connected. Graph the function from the example. Sketch the graph.

b. Press the TRACE key and trace the function. What happens between $x \approx 2.9$ and $x \approx 3.2$?

c. **Critical Thinking** How does your graph differ from the graph in the example? Explain the differences.

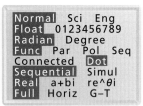

9-2 Graphing Inverse Variations

North Carolina Objectives

1.05 Model and solve problems using inverse variation.
2.05 Use rational equations to solve problems. c) Identify the asymptotes and intercepts graphically and algebraically.

Lesson Preview

What You'll Learn

OBJECTIVE 1 To graph inverse variations

OBJECTIVE 2 To graph translations of inverse variations

. . . And Why

To analyze musical pitch and the size of the instrument, as in Example 4

Check Skills You'll Need

(For help, go to Lesson 2-6.)

Each of the following equations is a translation of $y = |x|$. Describe each translation.

1. $y = |x| + 2$

2. $y = |x + 2|$

3. $y = |x| - 3$

4. $y = |x - 3|$

5. $y = |x + 4| - 5$

6. $y = |x - 10| + 7$

New Vocabulary

- branch

Interactive lesson includes instant self-check, tutorials, and activities.

OBJECTIVE 1 Graphing Inverse Variations

The graphs of inverse variations have two parts.

1 EXAMPLE Graphing an Inverse Variation

Draw a graph of $y = \frac{6}{x}$.

Make a table of values that includes positive and negative values of x. Notice that x cannot be 0.

x	−12	−6	−3	−2	−1	$-\frac{1}{2}$	$\frac{1}{2}$	1	2	3	6	12
y	$-\frac{1}{2}$	−1	−2	−3	−6	−12	12	6	3	2	1	$\frac{1}{2}$

Graph the points and connect them with a smooth curve.

The graph has two parts. Each part is called a **branch.**

The x-axis is a horizontal asymptote.

The y-axis is a vertical asymptote.

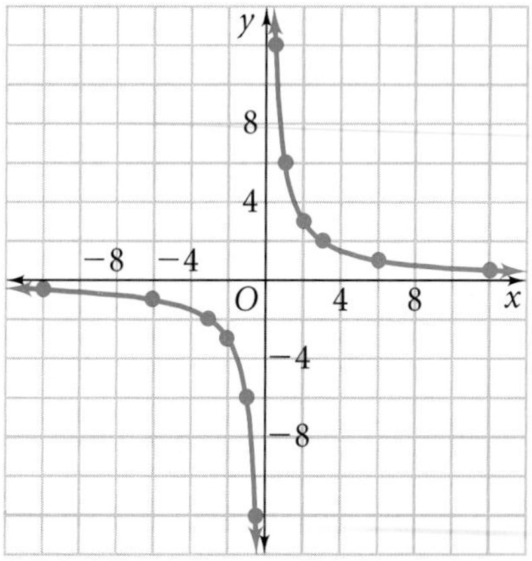

Reading Math

In a graph, a branch is a distinct part of a curve, just as, in nature, a branch is a distinct part of a river.

Check Understanding

1 Draw a graph of $y = \frac{16}{x}$.

A function must be defined for all values of its domain. Since $\frac{k}{x}$ is not defined for $x = 0$, zero is not included in the domain of an inverse variation $y = \frac{k}{x}$. The domain is all nonzero real numbers.

When k is positive, the branches of $y = \frac{k}{x}$ are in Quadrants I and III.

2 EXAMPLE Comparing Graphs of Inverse Variations

Need Help?

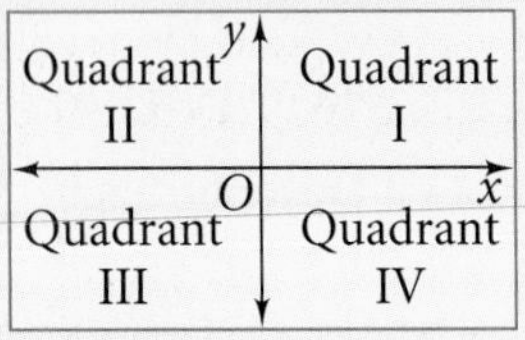

Compare the graphs of $y = \frac{4}{x}$ and $y = \frac{9}{x}$ shown at the right. What points on the graphs are closest to the origin?

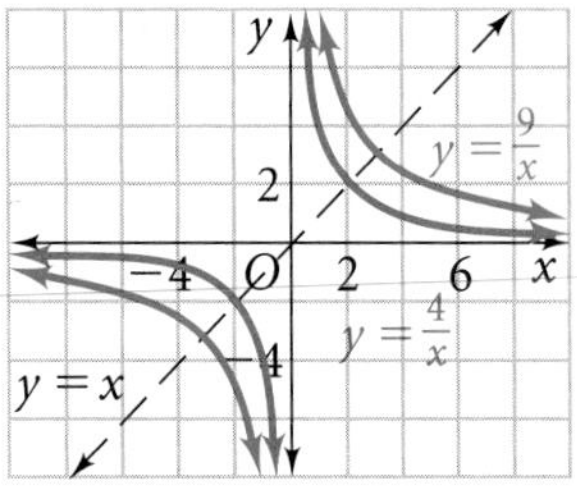

The axes are asymptotes for both graphs. Both graphs are symmetric with respect to $y = x$ and $y = -x$. The branches of $y = \frac{4}{x}$ are closer to the axes than are the branches of $y = \frac{9}{x}$. The intersections of the graphs with $y = x$ are $(\sqrt{k}, \sqrt{k})$ and $(-\sqrt{k}, -\sqrt{k})$, where k is the constant of variation. These points, $(2, 2)$, $(-2, -2)$, $(3, 3)$, and $(-3, -3)$, are closest to the origin.

Check Understanding 2 Use a graphing calculator. Draw and compare the graphs of $y = \frac{25}{x}$ and $y = \frac{100}{x}$. Compare their intersections with the graph of $y = x$.

When k is negative, the branches of $y = \frac{k}{x}$ are in Quadrants II and IV.

3 EXAMPLE Comparing Graphs of Inverse Variations

Compare the graphs of $y = \frac{1}{x}$ and $y = -\frac{1}{x}$ shown at the right.

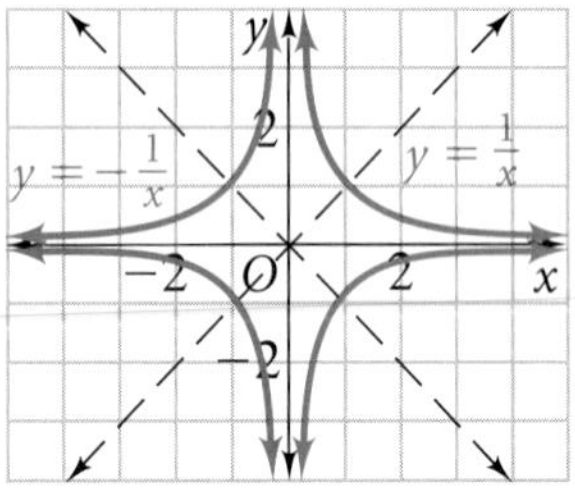

The axes are asymptotes for both graphs. Both graphs are symmetric with respect to $y = x$ and $y = -x$. The x-and y-axes are lines of reflection of the two graphs.

Check Understanding 3 Use a graphing calculator. Compare the graphs of $y = \frac{5}{x}$ and $y = -\frac{5}{x}$.

Real-World Connection

The length, not the diameter, of a panpipe or organ pipe determines its pitch.

4 EXAMPLE Real-World Connection

Music A musical pitch is determined by the frequency of vibration of the sound waves reaching the ear. The greater the frequency, the higher is the pitch. Frequency is measured in vibrations per second, or hertz (Hz).

The pitch y produced by a panpipe varies inversely with the length x of the pipe. The function $y = \frac{564}{x}$ models the inverse variation where x is the length in feet. Find the length of the pipe that produces a pitch of 277 Hz.

Graph the functions $y = \frac{564}{x}$ and $y = 277$. Use the **Intersect** feature.

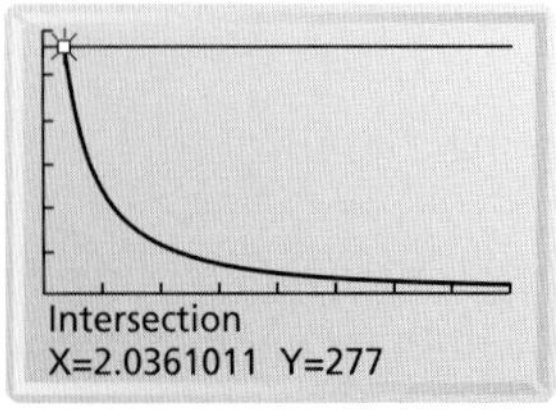

Xmin=0 Ymin=–75
Xmax=40 Ymax=300
Xscl=5 Yscl=50

The pipe should be about 2.0 ft long.

Check Understanding **4** **a.** Pitches of 247 Hz, 311 Hz, and 370 Hz form a musical chord. Find the length of pipe that will produce each pitch.

b. Writing The asymptotes of $y = \frac{564}{x}$ are $x = 0$ and $y = 0$. Explain why this makes sense in terms of the panpipe.

OBJECTIVE 2

Graphing Translations of Inverse Variations

The graphs at the right show the parent function $y = \frac{4}{x}$ and two of its translations, $y = \frac{4}{x - 2}$ and $y = \frac{4}{x + 4}$.

The vertical asymptotes of the graphs are $x = 0$, $x = 2$, and $x = -4$.

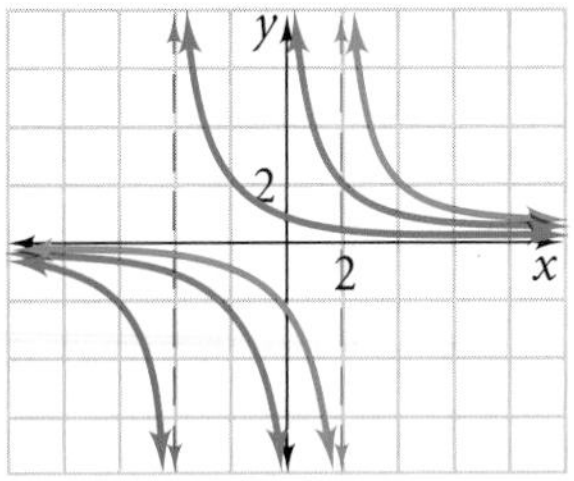

The graphs at the right show the parent function $y = \frac{4}{x}$ and two of its translations, $y = \frac{4}{x} + 2$ and $y = \frac{4}{x} - 4$.

The horizontal asymptotes of the graphs are $y = 0$, $y = 2$, and $y = -4$.

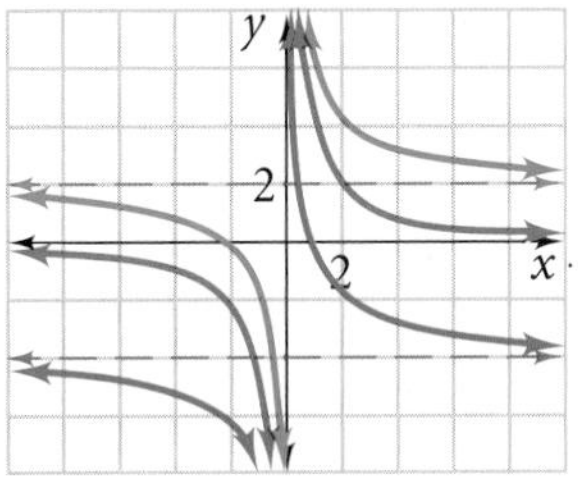

Key Concepts

Properties **Translations of Inverse Variations**

The graph of $y = \frac{k}{x - b} + c$ is a translation of $y = \frac{k}{x}$ by b units horizontally and c units vertically. The vertical asymptote is $x = b$. The horizontal asymptote is $y = c$.

You can use asymptotes to graph translations of inverse variations.

5 EXAMPLE Graphing a Translation

Sketch the graph of $y = \frac{1}{x - 2} - 3$.

Step 1 Draw the asymptotes.

For $y = \frac{1}{x - 2} + (-3)$, $b = 2$ and $c = -3$. The vertical asymptote is $x = 2$. The horizontal asymptote is $y = -3$.

Step 2 Translate $y = \frac{1}{x}$.

The graph of $y = \frac{1}{x}$ includes (1, 1) and (−1, −1). Translate these points 2 units to the right and 3 units down to (3, −2) and (1, −4). Draw the branches through these points.

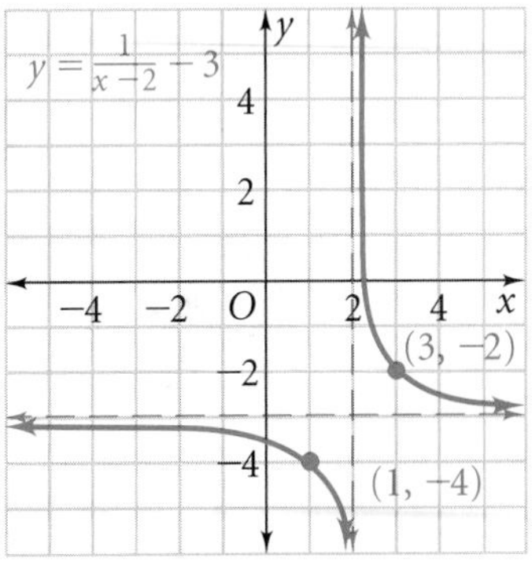

Check Understanding **5** Find the asymptotes and sketch the graph of $y = -\frac{1}{x + 7} - 3$.

If you know the translations or asymptotes of the graph of an inverse variation, you can write its equation.

6 EXAMPLE Writing the Equation of a Translation

Write an equation for the translation of $y = \frac{5}{x}$ that has asymptotes at $x = -2$ and $y = 3$.

$y = \frac{5}{x - b} + c$ **Use the general form of a translation.**

$= \frac{5}{x - (-2)} + 3$ **Substitute −2 for *b* and 3 for *c*.**

$= \frac{5}{x + 2} + 3$ **Simplify.**

An equation for the translation is $y = \frac{5}{x + 2} + 3$.

Check Understanding 6 **a.** Write an equation for the translation of $y = -\frac{1}{x}$ that is 4 units left and 5 units up.
b. Check your work by graphing your solution to part (a).

EXERCISES

For more practice, see *Extra Practice.*

Practice and Problem Solving

A Practice by Example

Example 1 (page 485)

Draw a graph of each inverse variation.

1. $y = \frac{2}{x}$ **2.** $y = \frac{10}{x}$ **3.** $y = -\frac{10}{x}$

Example 2 and 3 (page 486)

Compare the graphs of the inverse variations.

4. $y = \frac{3}{x}$ and $y = \frac{5}{x}$ **5.** $y = \frac{1}{x}$ and $y = \frac{100}{x}$ **6.** $y = \frac{0.2}{x}$ and $y = \frac{0.5}{x}$

7. $y = \frac{8}{x}$ and $y = -\frac{8}{x}$ **8.** $y = -\frac{2}{x}$ and $y = -\frac{3}{x}$ **9.** $y = \frac{12}{x}$ and $y = -\frac{12}{x}$

Example 4 (page 486)

The weight *P* in pounds that a beam can safely carry is inversely proportional to the distance *D* in feet between the supports of the beam. For a certain type of wooden beam, $P = \frac{9200}{D}$. Use a graphing calculator and the Intersect feature to find the distance between supports that is needed to carry each given weight.

10. 500 lb **11.** 1200 lb **12.** 2400 lb **13.** 5000 lb

Example 5 (page 487)

Sketch the asymptotes and the graph of each equation.

14. $y = \frac{1}{x} - 3$ **15.** $y = \frac{-2}{x} - 3$ **16.** $y = \frac{1}{x - 2} + 5$ **17.** $y = \frac{1}{x - 3} + 4$

18. $y = \frac{2}{x + 6} - 1$ **19.** $y = \frac{-10}{x + 1} - 8$ **20.** $y = \frac{1}{x} + 2$ **21.** $y = \frac{-8}{x + 5} - 6$

Example 6 (page 488)

Write an equation for the translation of $y = \frac{2}{x}$ that has the given asymptotes.

22. $x = 0$ and $y = 4$ **23.** $x = -2$ and $y = 3$ **24.** $x = 4$ and $y = -8$

B Apply Your Skills

25. a. **Budgeting** A high school spends $750 each year on student academic achievement awards. The amount spent per award depends on how many awards are given. Write and graph a function of the number *a* of awards given and the cost *c* of each award. Find the asymptotes.
b. Explain how the asymptotes are related to the given facts.

26. **Open-Ended** Write an equation for a horizontal translation of $y = \frac{2}{x}$. Then write an equation for a vertical translation of $y = \frac{2}{x}$. Identify the horizontal and vertical asymptotes of the graph of each function.

Write each equation in the form $y = \frac{k}{x}$.

27. $y = \frac{1}{2x}$
28. $y = \frac{3}{4x}$
29. $y = -\frac{25}{3x}$
30. $xy = -0.01$
31. $3xy = 12$
32. $-7 = 5xy$

Sketch the graph of each function.

33. $xy = 3$
34. $xy + 5 = 0$
35. $3xy = 1$
36. $5xy = 2$
37. $10xy = -4$
38. $3xy = -17$

39. **Writing** Explain how knowing the asymptotes of a translation of $y = \frac{k}{x}$ can help you graph the function. Include an example.

40. **Meteorology** The function $p = \frac{69.1}{a + 2.3}$ relates atmospheric pressure p in inches of mercury to altitude a in miles.
   a. Graph the function.
   b. The photo shows various altitudes on Earth. Find the atmospheric pressure at each altitude.
   c. Is there an altitude at which the atmospheric pressure is 0 in. of mercury? Use your graph to justify your reasoning.

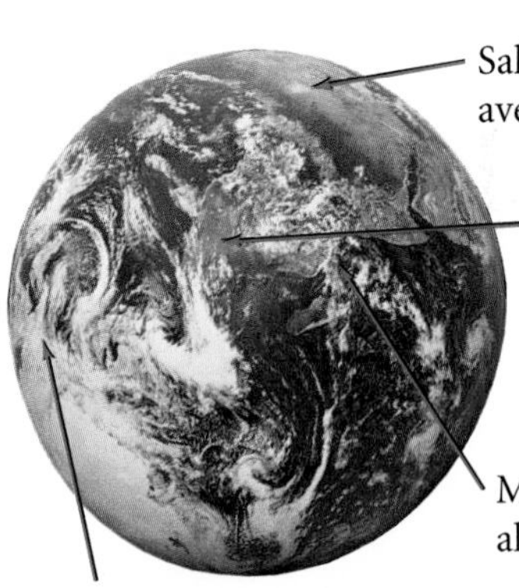

Need Help?
1 mi = 5280 ft

Graph each pair of functions. Find the approximate point(s) of intersection.

41. $y = \frac{6}{x - 2}, y = 6$
42. $y = -\frac{1}{x - 3} - 6, y = 6.2$
43. $y = \frac{3}{x + 1}, y = -4$
44. $y = -\frac{2}{x^2}, y = -10$
45. $y = -\frac{1}{x - 4}, y = 4.2$
46. $y = \frac{4}{x^2} + 2, y = 9$

47. a. **Gasoline Mileage** Suppose you drive an average of 10,000 miles each year. Your gasoline mileage (mi/gal) varies inversely with the number of gallons of gasoline you use each year. Write and graph a model for your average mileage m in terms of the gallons g of gasoline used.
   b. After you begin driving on the highway more often, you use 50 gal less per year. Write and graph a new model to include this information.
   c. Calculate your old and new mileage assuming that you originally used 400 gal of gasoline per year.

C Challenge

Critical Thinking **Compare each pair of graphs and find any points of intersection.**

48. $y = \frac{1}{x}$ and $y = \left|\frac{1}{x}\right|$
49. $y = \frac{1}{x}$ and $y = \frac{1}{x^2}$
50. $y = \left|\frac{1}{x}\right|$ and $y = \frac{1}{x^2}$

51. Find the equations for two inverse variations such that the minimum distance from the origin to the graph of each inverse variation is $4\sqrt{2}$.

52. Write each equation in the form $y = \frac{k}{x - b} + c$, and sketch the graph.

a. $y = \frac{2}{3x - 6}$ b. $y = \frac{1}{2 - 4x}$

c. $xy + 2x = 1$ d. $xy - y = 1$

Standardized Test Prep

Multiple Choice

53. Which point is NOT on the graph of $y = -\frac{2}{x}$?

A. $\left(-\frac{1}{2}, 4\right)$ B. $(-1, 2)$

C. $(2, -1)$ D. $\left(8, -\frac{1}{16}\right)$

54. Which equation is a line of symmetry for $xy = -7$ and does NOT intersect the branches of the graph?

F. $x = 0$ G. $y = 0$

H. $y = x$ I. $y = -x$

55. What are the asymptotes of the graph of $y = \frac{10}{x - 5}$?

A. $x = 0, y = 5$ B. $x = 5, y = 0$

C. $x = 5, y = 10$ D. $x = 10, y = 5$

56. What are the asymptotes of the graph of $y = \frac{10}{x} + 5$?

F. $x = 0, y = 5$ G. $x = 5, y = 5$

H. $x = 5, y = 10$ I. $x = 10, y = 5$

57. What is an equation for the translation of $y = \frac{2}{x}$ that has asymptotes at $x = 3$ and $y = -5$?

A. $y = \frac{2}{x - 3} - 5$ B. $y = \frac{2}{x + 3} + 5$

C. $y = \frac{2}{x + 5} - 3$ D. $y = \frac{2}{x - 5} + 3$

Take It to the NET
Online lesson quiz at
www.PHSchool.com
Web Code: aga-0902

Short Response

58. Explain how to find the asymptotes of $y = -\frac{3}{x - 2} + 11$.

Extended Response

59. Explain how to find an equation for the translation of $y = \frac{-3}{x}$ that has asymptotes at $x = -5$ and $y = -13$.

Mixed Review

Lesson 9-1

Describe the combined variation that is modeled by each formula.

60. $V = \frac{s^2h}{3}$ 61. $h = \frac{3V}{s^2}$ 62. $B = \frac{3V}{h}$ 63. $w = \frac{V}{\ell h}$ 64. $b = \frac{2A}{h}$

Lesson 8-1

Identify each function as exponential growth or decay, and find the growth or decay factor.

65. $y = 3 \cdot 4^x$ 66. $y = 0.1 \cdot 2^x$ 67. $y = 5 \cdot (0.8)^x$ 68. $y = 3 \cdot \left(\frac{1}{2}\right)^x$

Lesson 7-3

Multiply.

69. $(5\sqrt{3} - 2)^2$ 70. $(\sqrt{3} + \sqrt{5})(\sqrt{3} - \sqrt{5})$

71. $(3\sqrt{5} + 2\sqrt{10})(2\sqrt{5} + \sqrt{10})$ 72. $(4 + 2\sqrt{3})(6 - 3\sqrt{3})$

9-3 Rational Functions and Their Graphs

North Carolina Objectives

2.05 Use rational equations to solve problems. b) Interpret the constants and coefficients in the context of the problem. c) Identify the asymptotes and intercepts graphically and algebraically.

Lesson Preview

What You'll Learn

OBJECTIVE 1 To identify properties of rational functions

OBJECTIVE 2 To graph rational functions

. . . And Why

To find the average cost of producing CD-ROMs, as in Example 5

✓ Check Skills You'll Need

(For help, go to Lessons 5-4 and 5-5.)

Factor.

1. $x^2 + 5x + 6$ **2.** $x^2 - 6x + 8$ **3.** $x^2 - 12x + 27$

4. $2x^2 + x - 28$ **5.** $2x^2 - 11x + 15$ **6.** $2x^2 - 19x + 24$

Solve.

7. $x^2 + x - 12 = 0$ **8.** $x^2 - 3x - 28 = 0$ **9.** $x^2 - 9x + 18 = 0$

New Vocabulary

- rational function
- point of discontinuity

Interactive lesson includes instant self-check, tutorials, and activities.

OBJECTIVE 1 Properties of Rational Functions

An inverse variation is an example of a rational function.

Key Concepts

Definition **Rational Function**

A **rational function** $f(x)$ is a function that can be written as

$$f(x) = \frac{P(x)}{Q(x)},$$

where $P(x)$ and $Q(x)$ are polynomial functions and $Q(x) \neq 0$.

Reading Math

A rational function is a ratio of functions, just as a rational number is a ratio of numbers.

The graphs of the rational functions $y = \frac{-2x}{x^2 + 1}$, $y = \frac{1}{x^2 - 4}$, and $y = \frac{(x + 2)(x - 1)}{x + 1}$ are shown below.

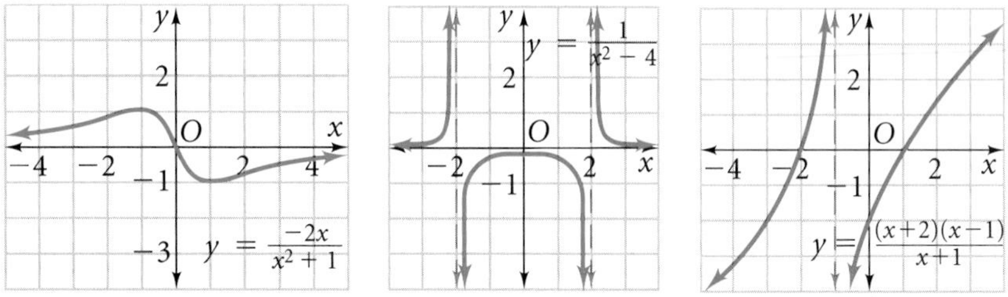

In the first rational function, there is no value of x that makes the denominator 0. The graph is continuous because it has no jumps, breaks, or holes in it. It can be drawn with a pencil that never leaves the paper.

In the second rational function, x cannot be 2 or -2. In the third, x cannot be -1. The last two graphs are discontinuous.

If a is a real number for which the denominator of a rational function f is zero, then a is not in the domain of f. The graph of f is not continuous at $x = a$ and the function has a **point of discontinuity** at $x = a$.

3 EXAMPLE Finding Horizontal Asymptotes

Find the horizontal asymptote of $y = \frac{3x + 5}{x - 2}$.

Divide the numerator by the denominator as shown at the right. The function $y = \frac{3x + 5}{x - 2}$ can be written as $y = \frac{11}{x - 2} + 3$. Its graph is a translation of $y = \frac{11}{x}$. The horizontal asymptote of the graph of $y = \frac{3x + 5}{x - 2}$ is $y = 3$.

$$\begin{array}{r} 3 \\ x - 2\overline{)3x + 5} \\ 3x - 6 \\ \hline 11 \end{array}$$

Check Understanding 3 Find the horizontal asymptote of the graph of each rational function.

a. $y = \frac{-2x + 6}{x - 1}$ **b.** $y = \frac{2x^2 + 5}{x^2 + 1}$

Key Concepts

Properties **Horizontal Asymptotes**

The graph of a rational function has at most one horizontal asymptote.

The graph of a rational function has a horizontal asymptote at $y = 0$ if the degree of the denominator is greater than the degree of the numerator.

If the degrees of the numerator and the denominator are equal, then the graph has a horizontal asymptote at $y = \frac{a}{b}$. a is the coefficient of the term of highest degree in the numerator and b is the coefficient of the term of highest degree in the denominator.

If the degree of the numerator is greater than the degree of the denominator, then the graph has no horizontal asymptote.

OBJECTIVE

2 Graphing Rational Functions

You can use asymptotes to sketch the graphs of rational functions.

4 EXAMPLE Sketching Graphs of Rational Functions

Sketch the graph of $y = \frac{x + 2}{(x + 3)(x - 4)}$.

The degree of the denominator is greater than the degree of the numerator, so the y-axis is the horizontal asymptote. When $x > 4$, y is positive. So as x increases, the graph approaches the y-axis from above. When $x < -3$, y is negative. So as x decreases, the graph approaches the y-axis from below.

Since -2 is the zero of the numerator, the x-intercept is at -2. Since -3 and 4 are the zeros of the denominator, the vertical asymptotes are at $x = -3$ and $x = 4$.

Calculate the values of y for values of x near the asymptotes. Plot those points and sketch the graph.

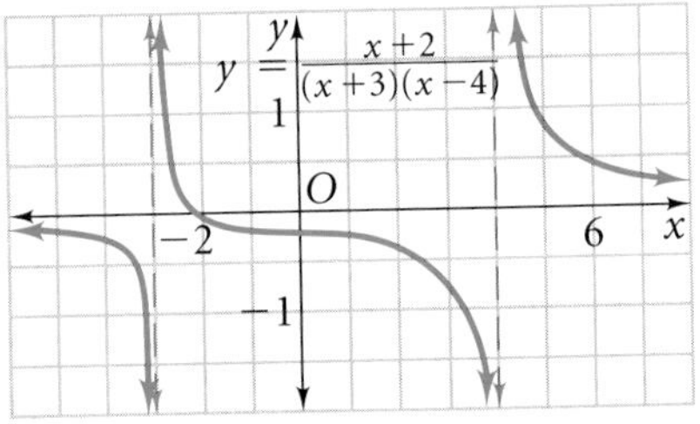

Check Understanding 4 Sketch the graph of $y = \frac{x + 3}{(x - 1)(x - 5)}$.

5 EXAMPLE — Real-World Connection

Business The CD-ROMs for a computer game can be manufactured for \$.25 each. The development cost is \$124,000. The first 100 discs are samples and will not be sold.

Real-World Connection

Careers Video game programmers need a strong background in computer programming.

a. Write a function for the average cost of a salable disc. Graph the function.

Relate average cost $= \dfrac{\text{manufacturing cost of discs} + \text{development cost}}{\text{number of salable discs}}$

Define Let x = number of CD-ROMs produced.
Let y = average cost of one saleable disc.

Write $y = \dfrac{0.25x + 124{,}000}{x - 100}$

Graph the function. Adjust the viewing window.

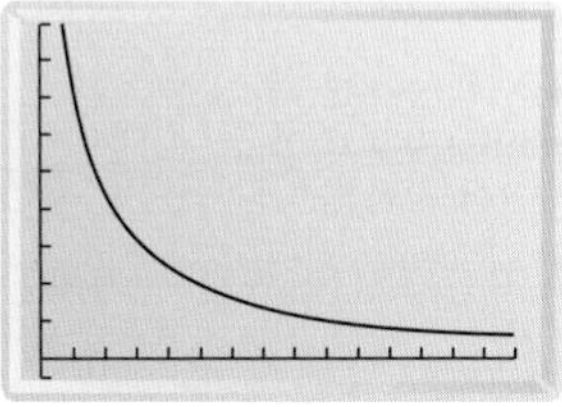

Xmin=0 Ymin=–10
Xmax=15000 Ymax=100
Xscl=1000 Yscl=10

b. What is the average cost if 2000 discs are produced? If 12,800 discs are produced?

Use the **CALC** feature to evaluate the function at $x = 2000$ and at $x = 12{,}800$.
If 2000 discs are produced, the average cost will be about \$65.53.
If 12,800 discs are produced, the average cost will be about \$10.02.

Check Understanding 5 **a. Critical Thinking** How could you find the number of discs that must be produced to bring the average cost under \$8?
b. What is the vertical asymptote of the graph of the function in Example 5? What is the horizontal asymptote?
c. Describe how the asymptotes are related to the information given in Example 5.

EXERCISES

For more practice, see *Extra Practice*.

Practice and Problem Solving

A Practice by Example

Example 1 (page 492)

Find any points of discontinuity for each rational function.

1. $y = \dfrac{2x^2 + 5}{x^2 - 2x}$
2. $y = \dfrac{x^2 + 2x}{x^2 + 2}$
3. $y = \dfrac{3x - 3}{x^2 - 1}$
4. $y = \dfrac{6 - 3x}{x^2 - 5x + 6}$
5. $y = \dfrac{x^2 + 5x + 6}{x^2 + 6x + 9}$
6. $y = \dfrac{x^2 + 4x + 3}{2x^2 + 5x - 7}$
7. $y = \dfrac{x^3 - 8}{x^3 - 8}$
8. $y = \dfrac{x^2}{x^2 + 1}$
9. $y = \dfrac{1}{2x^2 + 3x - 7}$

Example 2 (page 493)

Describe the vertical asymptotes and holes for the graph of each rational function.

10. $y = \dfrac{3}{x + 2}$
11. $y = \dfrac{x + 5}{x + 5}$
12. $y = \dfrac{x + 3}{(2x + 3)(x - 1)}$
13. $y = \dfrac{(x + 3)(x - 2)}{(x - 2)(x + 1)}$
14. $y = \dfrac{x^2 - 4}{x + 2}$
15. $y = \dfrac{x + 5}{x^2 + 9}$
16. $y = \dfrac{9 - x^2}{x^2 - 9}$
17. $y = \dfrac{2x^2}{2x^2 + 2}$
18. $y = \dfrac{6x^2 + x - 2}{3x^2 + 17x + 10}$

Example 3 (page 494)

Find the horizontal asymptote of the graph of each rational function.

19. $y = \frac{5}{x + 6}$ **20.** $y = \frac{x + 2}{2x^2 - 4}$ **21.** $y = \frac{x + 1}{x + 5}$

22. $y = \frac{x^2 + 2}{2x^2 - 1}$ **23.** $y = \frac{5x^3 + 2x}{2x^5 - 4x^3}$ **24.** $y = \frac{3x - 4}{4x + 1}$

Example 4 (page 494)

Sketch the graph of each rational function.

25. $y = \frac{x^2 - 4}{3x - 6}$ **26.** $y = \frac{4x}{x^3 - 4x}$ **27.** $y = \frac{x + 4}{x - 4}$

28. $y = \frac{x(x + 1)}{x + 1}$ **29.** $y = \frac{x + 6}{(x - 2)(x + 3)}$ **30.** $y = \frac{3x}{(x + 2)^2}$

Example 5 (page 495)

31. **Business** CDs can be manufactured for $.19 each. The development cost is $210,000. The first 500 discs are samples and will not be sold.

a. Write a function for the average cost of a salable disc. Graph the function.

b. What is the average cost if 5000 discs are produced? If 15,000 discs are produced?

c. How many discs must be produced to bring the average cost under $10?

d. What are the vertical and horizontal asymptotes of the graph of the function?

B Apply Your Skills

Find the vertical and horizontal asymptotes, if any, of the graph of each rational function.

32. 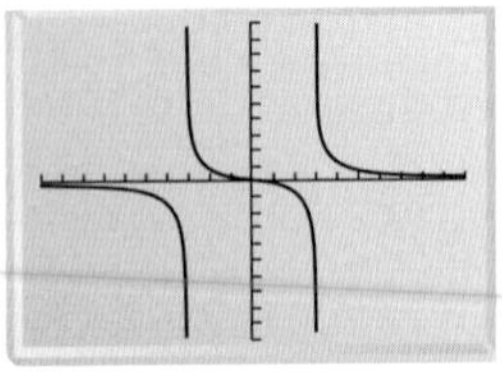

33. 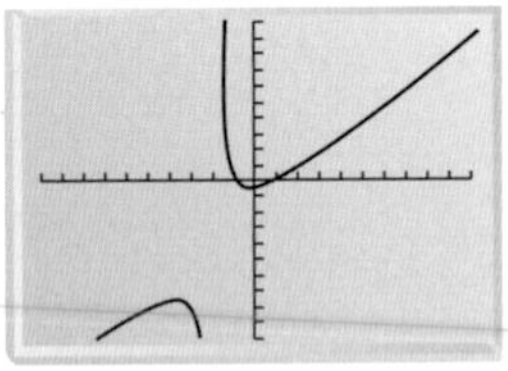

34. 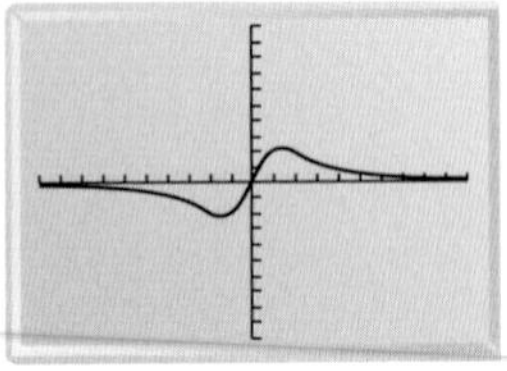

Sketch the graph of each rational function.

35. $y = \frac{2x + 3}{x - 5}$ **36.** $y = \frac{x^2 + 6x + 9}{x + 3}$ **37.** $y = \frac{4x^2 - 100}{2x^2 + x - 15}$

38. $y = -\frac{x}{(x - 1)^2}$ **39.** $y = \frac{2x}{3x - 1}$ **40.** $y = \frac{2}{x^2 - 4}$

41. **Writing** Describe the conditions that will produce a rational function with a graph that has no vertical asymptotes.

42. **Basketball** A basketball player has made 21 of her last 30 free throws—an average of 70%. To model the player's rate of success if she makes x more consecutive free throws, use the function $y = \frac{21 + x}{30 + x}$.

a. Graph the function.

b. Use the graph to find the number of consecutive free throws the player needs to raise her success rate to 75%.

43. **Data Analysis** The president of XYZ Company earns $200,000 a year. Each of the other x employees earns $20,000 a year.

a. Write and graph a function that models the average salary of all employees of XYZ.

b. What is the average salary if there are three employees? If there are 30 employees?

c. **Critical Thinking** Is the average salary the best measure of the workers' pay? Explain. What other measure could you use?

C Challenge

44. Reasoning Look for a pattern in the sequence of shells below.

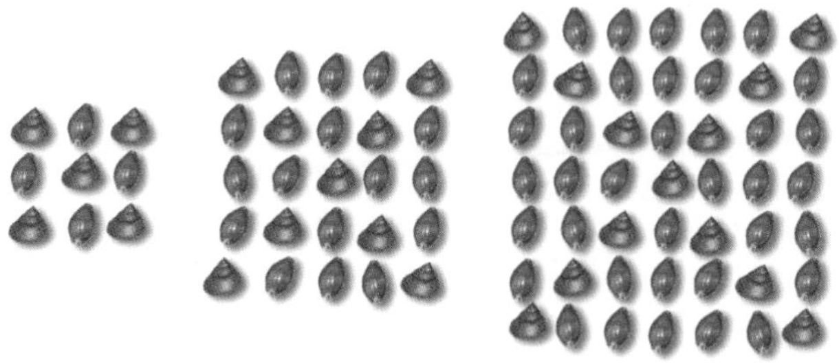

a. Write a model for the number of purple shells $P(n)$ at each step n.
b. Write a model for the number of red shells $R(n)$ at each step n.
c. Write a model for the ratio of $P(n)$ to $R(n)$. Use it to predict the ratio of purple shells to red shells in the next figure. Verify your answer.

45. Wage Policy The graph below compares the average hourly wage for production workers and the minimum hourly wage from 1950 to 2000.

History of the Minimum Wage

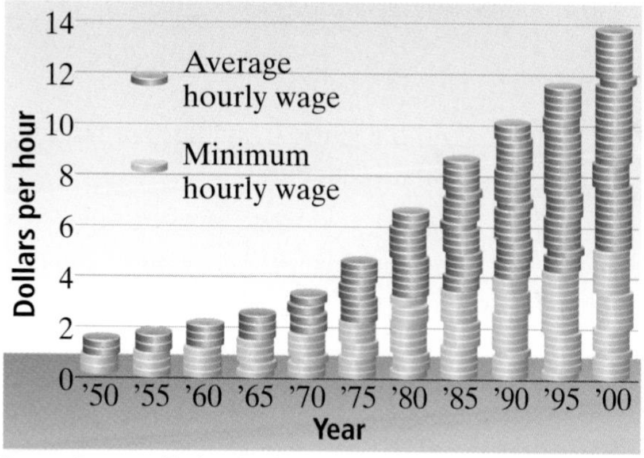

SOURCE: Bureau of Labor Statistics.
Go to **www.PHSchool.com** for a data update.
Web Code: agg-2041

a. How has the comparison of the minimum wage to the production workers' wage changed over the years?
b. If the minimum wage and the production workers' wage are modeled by polynomials, what type of function would model their ratio?
c. The quadratic function $M(x) = 0.00081x^2 + 0.049x + 0.68$ models the minimum wage, where x is the number of years since 1950. The quadratic function $A(x) = 0.0043x^2 + 0.04x + 1.21$ models the average wage. Write a model for the ratio of these two functions.
d. Graph your model. If the present trends continue, when will the minimum wage decrease to 25% of the average wage?

Standardized Test Prep

Multiple Choice

46. What are the points of discontinuity for $y = \frac{(2x + 3)(x - 5)}{(x + 5)(2x - 1)}$?

A. $-5, 1$　**B.** $-\frac{3}{2}, 5$　**C.** $-5, \frac{1}{2}$　**D.** $5, -\frac{1}{2}$

Short Response

47. Find the horizontal asymptote of $y = \frac{5x + 7}{x + 3}$ by dividing the numerator by the denominator. Explain your steps.

Quantitative Comparison Compare the boxed quantity in Column A with the boxed quantity in Column B. Choose the best answer.

A. The quantity in Column A is greater.
B. The quantity in Column B is greater.
C. The two quantities are equal.
D. The relationship cannot be determined from the information given.

	Column A	Column B
48.	the value of the discontinuity of $y = \frac{2x}{3x + 7}$	the value of the discontinuity of $y = \frac{5}{2x}$
49.	the number of points of discontinuity of $y = \frac{2x}{x^2 - 1}$	the number of points of discontinuity of $y = \frac{2x}{x^2 + 1}$
50.	the number of vertical asymptotes of $y = \frac{(x - 3)(x - 5)(x - 4)}{(x - 2)(x - 6)}$	the number of points of discontinuity of $y = \frac{(x - 3)(x - 5)(x - 4)}{(x - 2)(x - 6)}$

Take It to the NET
Online lesson quiz at **www.PHSchool.com**
Web Code: aga-0903

Mixed Review

Lesson 9-2 **Find the asymptotes of the graph of each equation.**

51. $y = \frac{3}{x} + 4$ **52.** $y = \frac{2}{x + 3}$ **53.** $y = \frac{-1}{x + 1} + 1$

54. $y = \frac{5}{x - 7} - 3$ **55.** $y = \frac{5}{2 - x}$ **56.** $y = \frac{-2}{5 - x} - 6$

Lesson 8-2 **Describe how the graph of each function relates to the graph of $y = 4(0.8)^x$.**

57. $y = 4(0.8)^{x-1}$ **58.** $y = 4(0.8)^x + 3$ **59.** $y = 4(0.8)^{x+1} - 5$

Checkpoint Quiz 1 — Lessons 9-1 through 9-3

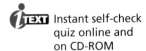

TEXT Instant self-check quiz online and on CD-ROM

If $z = 30$ when $x = 3$ and $y = 2$, write the function that models each relationship.

1. z varies jointly with x and y.

2. z varies directly with x and inversely with y.

3. z varies inversely with the product of x and y.

Compare the graphs of the inverse variations.

4. $y = \frac{4}{x}$ and $y = \frac{9}{x}$ **5.** $y = \frac{1}{x}$ and $y = \frac{1}{x} + 5$

6. $y = \frac{1}{x - 1} + 2$ and $y = \frac{1}{x + 1} - 2$

Sketch the graph of each rational function.

7. $y = \frac{x^2 - 9}{2x + 6}$ **8.** $y = \frac{3x}{x^3 - x}$ **9.** $y = \frac{x + 3}{x - 3}$ **10.** $y = \frac{x^2 - 2x}{x - 2}$

9-4 Rational Expressions

North Carolina Objectives

1.03 Operate with algebraic expressions (polynomial, rational, complex fractions) to solve problems.

Lesson Preview

What You'll Learn

OBJECTIVE 1 To simplify rational expressions

OBJECTIVE 2 To multiply and divide rational expressions

. . . And Why

To compute ratios of volume to surface area, as in Example 2

Check Skills You'll Need

(For help, go to Lesson 5-4 and Skills Handbook page 843.)

Factor.

1. $2x^2 - 3x + 1$ **2.** $4x^2 - 9$

3. $5x^2 + 6x + 1$ **4.** $10x^2 - 10$

Multiply or divide.

5. $\frac{3}{8} \cdot \frac{5}{6}$ **6.** $\frac{1}{2} \cdot \frac{4}{6}$ **7.** $\frac{8}{3} \cdot \frac{2}{16}$ **8.** $\frac{2}{5} \cdot \frac{3}{7}$

9. $\frac{5}{8} \div 4$ **10.** $\frac{3}{4} \div \frac{1}{2}$ **11.** $\frac{9}{16} \div \frac{3}{4}$ **12.** $\frac{5}{4} \div \frac{15}{8}$

New Vocabulary

- simplest form

OBJECTIVE

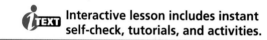

1 Simplifying Rational Expressions

Interactive lesson includes instant self-check, tutorials, and activities.

A rational expression is in **simplest form** when its numerator and denominator are polynomials that have no common divisors.

In simplest form: $\frac{x}{x - 1}$ $\frac{2}{x^2 + 3}$

Not in simplest form: $\frac{x}{x^2}$ $\frac{\frac{1}{x}}{x + 1}$ $\frac{2(x - 3)}{3(x - 3)}$

Need Help?

Restrictions on the variables may be needed to prevent division by 0.

You can simplify some expressions by dividing out common factors.

1 EXAMPLE Simplifying Rational Expressions

Simplify $\frac{x^2 + 10x + 25}{x^2 + 9x + 20}$. State any restrictions on the variable.

$\frac{x^2 + 10x + 25}{x^2 + 9x + 20} = \frac{(x + 5)(x + 5)}{(x + 4)(x + 5)}$ **Factor the polynomials. Notice that $x \neq -4$ or -5.**

$= \frac{\cancel{(x + 5)}^{1}(x + 5)}{(x + 4)\cancel{(x + 5)}_{1}}$ **Divide out common factors.**

$= \frac{x + 5}{x + 4}$

The simplified expression is $\frac{x + 5}{x + 4}$ for $x \neq -4$ or -5. The restrictions on x are needed to prevent the denominator of the original expression from being zero.

Check Understanding

1. Simplify each expression. State any restrictions on the variables.

a. $\frac{-27x^3y}{9x^4y}$ **b.** $\frac{-6 - 3x}{x^2 - 6x + 8}$ **c.** $\frac{2x^2 - 3x - 2}{x^2 - 5x + 6}$

Real-World Connection

Crystal Bridge botanical gardens in Oklahoma City

2 EXAMPLE Real-World Connection

Architecture One factor in designing a structure is the need to maximize the volume (space for working) for a given surface area (material needed for construction). Compare the ratio of the volume to surface area of a cylinder with radius r and height r to a cylinder with radius r and height $2r$.

Use the formulas for volume and surface area of a cylinder.

Volume $(V) = \pi r^2 h$
Surface Area (S.A.) $= 2\pi rh + 2\pi r^2$

Cylinder with height r	Cylinder with height $2r$	
$\frac{V}{\text{S.A.}} = \frac{\pi r^2 h}{2\pi rh + 2\pi r^2}$	$\frac{V}{\text{S.A.}} = \frac{\pi r^2 h}{2\pi rh + 2\pi r^2}$	**Write a ratio.**
$= \frac{\pi r^2(r)}{2\pi r(r) + 2\pi r^2}$	$= \frac{\pi r^2(2r)}{2\pi r(2r) + 2\pi r^2}$	**Substitute for *h*.**
$= \frac{\pi r^3}{2\pi r^2 + 2\pi r^2}$	$= \frac{2\pi r^3}{4\pi r^2 + 2\pi r^2}$	**Simplify.**
$= \frac{\pi r^3}{4\pi r^2}$	$= \frac{2\pi r^3}{6\pi r^2}$	**Combine like terms.**
$= \frac{r}{4}$	$= \frac{r}{3}$	**Simplify.**

For a given radius, the ratio of volume to surface area is greater for the cylinder with a height of $2r$.

Check Understanding 2 **a.** Find the ratio of volume to surface area of a cylinder whose height is $4r$.
b. **Critical Thinking** Let mr be the height of a cylinder of radius r, with m a positive number. Describe how the ratio of volume to surface area changes as m changes.

OBJECTIVE

2 Multiplying and Dividing Rational Expressions

You can use what you know about simplifying rational expressions when you multiply and divide them.

3 EXAMPLE Multiplying Rational Expressions

Multiply $\frac{2x^2 + 7x + 3}{x - 4}$ and $\frac{x^2 - 16}{x^2 + 8x + 15}$. State any restrictions on the variable.

$$\frac{2x^2 + 7x + 3}{x - 4} \cdot \frac{x^2 - 16}{x^2 + 8x + 15} = \frac{(2x + 1)(x + 3)}{x - 4} \cdot \frac{(x - 4)(x + 4)}{(x + 3)(x + 5)} \quad \textbf{Factor.}$$

$$= \frac{(2x + 1)\overset{1}{\cancel{(x + 3)}}}{\underset{1}{\cancel{x - 4}}} \cdot \frac{\overset{1}{\cancel{(x - 4)}}(x + 4)}{\underset{1}{\cancel{(x + 3)}}(x + 5)} \quad \textbf{Divide out common factors.}$$

$$= \frac{(2x + 1)(x + 4)}{x + 5}$$

The product is $\frac{(2x + 1)(x + 4)}{x + 5}$ for $x \neq 4, -3,$ or -5.

Check Understanding 3 Multiply $\frac{a^2 - 4}{a^2 - 1}$ and $\frac{a + 1}{a^2 + 2a}$. State any restrictions on the variable.

To divide rational expressions, remember to multiply by the reciprocal of the divisor, just as you did when dividing rational numbers.

Need Help?
For practice in dividing fractions, go to p. 843.

4 EXAMPLE Dividing Rational Expressions

Divide $\frac{4-x}{(3x+2)(x-2)}$ by $\frac{5(x-4)}{(x-2)(7y-5)}$. State any restrictions on the variables.

$$\frac{4-x}{(3x+2)(x-2)} \div \frac{5(x-4)}{(x-2)(7y-5)}$$

$$= \frac{4-x}{(3x+2)(x-2)} \cdot \frac{(x-2)(7y-5)}{5(x-4)}$$ **Multiply by the reciprocal.**

$$= \frac{-\overset{1}{(x-4)}}{(3x+2)\underset{1}{(x-2)}} \cdot \frac{\overset{1}{(x-2)}(7y-5)}{5\underset{1}{(x-4)}}$$ **Divide out common factors.**

$$= \frac{-1}{3x+2} \cdot \frac{7y-5}{5}$$ **Rewrite the expression.**

$$= \frac{-(7y-5)}{5(3x+2)}$$ **Multiply.**

The quotient is $\frac{-(7y+5)}{5(3x+2)}$ for $x \neq -\frac{2}{3}, 2$, or 4, and $y \neq \frac{5}{7}$.

Check Understanding 4 Divide $\frac{a^2+2a-15}{a^2-16}$ by $\frac{a+1}{3a-12}$. State any restrictions on the variable.

EXERCISES

For more practice, see *Extra Practice.*

Practice and Problem Solving

A Practice by Example

Examples 1 and 2 (pages 499–500)

Simplify each rational expression. State any restrictions on the variable.

1. $\frac{2x}{4x^2-2x}$
2. $\frac{6c^2+9c}{3c}$
3. $\frac{b^2-1}{b-1}$
4. $\frac{z^2-49}{z+7}$
5. $\frac{2x+10}{x^2+10x+25}$
6. $\frac{x^2+8x+16}{x^2-2x-24}$

Example 3 (page 500)

Multiply. State any restrictions on the variables.

7. $\frac{4x^2}{5y} \cdot \frac{7y}{12x^4}$
8. $\frac{2x^4}{10y^2} \cdot \frac{5y^3}{4x^3}$
9. $\frac{8y-4}{10y-5} \cdot \frac{5y-15}{3y-9}$
10. $\frac{2x+12}{3x-9} \cdot \frac{2x-6}{3x+8}$
11. $\frac{x^2-4}{x^2-1} \cdot \frac{x+1}{x^2+2x}$
12. $\frac{x^2-5x+6}{x^2-4} \cdot \frac{x^2+3x+2}{x^2-2x-3}$

Example 4 (page 501)

Divide. State any restrictions on the variables.

13. $\frac{7x}{4y^3} \div \frac{21x^3}{8y}$
14. $\frac{3x^3}{5y^2} \div \frac{6x^5}{5y^3}$
15. $\frac{6x+6y}{x-y} \div \frac{18}{5x-5y}$
16. $\frac{3y-12}{2y+4} \div \frac{6y-24}{4y+8}$
17. $\frac{x^2}{x^2+2x+1} \div \frac{3x}{x^2-1}$
18. $\frac{y^2-5y+6}{y^3} \div \frac{y^2+3y-10}{4y^2}$

B Apply Your Skills

Simplify each rational expression. State any restrictions on the variables.

19. $\frac{x^2 - 5x - 24}{x^2 - 7x - 30}$ **20.** $\frac{2y^2 + 8y - 24}{2y^2 - 8y + 8}$ **21.** $\frac{xy^3 - 9xy}{12xy^2 + 12xy - 144x}$

22. Write an expression for the area of the rectangle at the right.

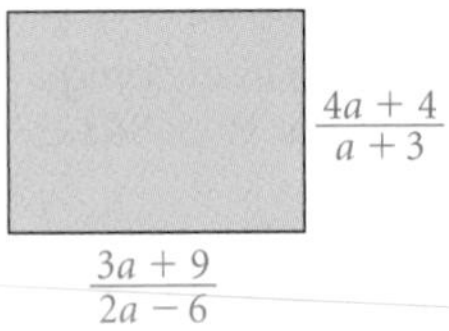

23. Error Analysis A student claims that $x = 2$ is the only solution of the equation $\frac{x}{x - 2} = \frac{1}{2} + \frac{2}{x - 2}$. Is the student correct? Explain.

24. Open-Ended Write three rational expressions that simplify to $\frac{x}{x + 1}$.

25. Writing How can you tell whether a rational expression is in simplest form? Include an example with your explanation.

Exercise 26

26. Industrial Design A storage tank will have a circular base of radius r and a height of r. The tank can be either cylindrical or hemispherical (half a sphere).

a. Write and simplify an expression for the ratio of the volume of the hemispherical tank to its surface area (including the base). For a sphere, $V = \frac{4}{3}\pi r^3$ and S.A. $= 4\pi r^2$.

b. Write and simplify an expression for the ratio of the volume of the cylindrical tank to its surface area (including the bases).

c. Compare the ratios of volume to surface area for the two tanks.

d. Compare the volumes of the two tanks.

Multiply or divide. State any restrictions on the variable.

27. $\frac{a + 3}{a^2 + a - 12} \div \frac{a^2 - 9}{a^2 + 7a + 12}$ **28.** $\frac{b^2 - 25}{(b + 5)^2} \div \frac{2b + 10}{4b + 20}$

29. $\frac{6x^3 - 6x^2}{x^4 + 5x^3} \div \frac{3x^2 - 15x + 12}{2x^2 + 2x - 40}$ **30.** $\frac{2x^2 - 6x}{x^2 + 18x + 81} \cdot \frac{9x + 81}{x^2 - 9}$

31. $\frac{x^2 - x - 2}{2x^2 - 5x + 2} \div \frac{x^2 - x - 12}{2x^2 + 5x - 3}$ **32.** $\frac{2x^2 + 5x + 2}{4x^2 - 1} \cdot \frac{2x^2 + x - 1}{x^2 + x - 2}$

Simplify. State any restrictions on the variables.

33. $\frac{(x^2 - x)^2}{x(x - 1)^{-2}(x^2 + 3x - 4)}$ **34.** $\frac{2x + 6}{(x - 1)^{-1}(x^2 + 2x - 3)}$ **35.** $\frac{54x^3y^{-1}}{3x^{-2}y}$

36. The width of the rectangle at the right is $\frac{a + 10}{3a + 24}$. Write an expression for the length of the rectangle.

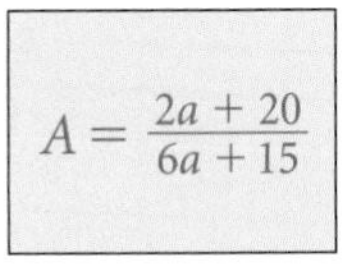

37. Physics The acceleration of an object is a measure of how much its velocity changes in a given period of time.

$$\text{acceleration} = \frac{\text{final velocity} - \text{initial velocity}}{\text{time}}$$

Suppose you are riding a bicycle at 6 m/s. You step hard on the pedals and increase your speed to 12 m/s in about 5 s.

a. Find your acceleration in m/s^2.

b. A sedan can go from 0 to 60 mi/h in about 10 s. What is the acceleration in m/s^2? (*Hints:* 1 mi $\approx$ 1609 m; 1 h = 3600 s.)

C Challenge

38. a. Critical Thinking Simplify $\frac{(2x^n)^2 - 1}{2x^n - 1}$, where x is an integer and n is a positive integer. (*Hint:* Factor the numerator.)

b. Use the result from part (a) to show that the value of the given expression is always an odd integer.

Use the fact that $\dfrac{\frac{a}{b}}{\frac{c}{d}} = \frac{a}{b} \div \frac{c}{d}$ to simplify each rational expression. State any restrictions on the variables.

39. $\dfrac{\frac{8x^2y}{x+1}}{\frac{6xy^2}{x+1}}$ **40.** $\dfrac{\frac{3a^3b^3}{a-b}}{\frac{4ab}{b-a}}$ **41.** $\dfrac{\frac{9m+6n}{m^2n^2}}{\frac{12m+8n}{5m^2}}$

Standardized Test Prep

Multiple Choice

42. Which expression can be simplified to $\frac{x-1}{x-3}$?

A. $\dfrac{x^2-x-6}{x^2-x-2}$ B. $\dfrac{x^2-2x+1}{x^2+2x-3}$

C. $\dfrac{x^2-3x-4}{x^2-7x+12}$ D. $\dfrac{x^2-4x+3}{x^2-6x+9}$

43. Which expression is in simplest form?

F. $\dfrac{x^2-x}{x^2-1}$ G. $\dfrac{x^2-1}{x^2+1}$

H. $\dfrac{x^2-1}{x+1}$ I. $\dfrac{x+3}{x^2+4x+3}$

44. What is the product of $\dfrac{4x^2-1}{2x^2-5x-3}$ and $\dfrac{x^2-6x+9}{2x^2+5x-3}$?

A. 1 B. $x-3$

C. $x+3$ D. $\dfrac{x-3}{x+3}$

45. What are the restrictions on x when $\dfrac{x^2-x-2}{x^2-9}$ is divided by $\dfrac{x-8}{x^2+10x+25}$?

F. $x \neq -3$ or -5 G. $x \neq 3, -3,$ or -5

H. $x \neq 3, -3, -5,$ or 8 I. $x \neq 2, 9, 8,$ or -25

Short Response

46. Let $f(x)$, $g(x)$, $h(x)$, and $k(x)$ be rational expressions. Explain how to find all the restrictions for $\dfrac{f(x)}{g(x)} \div \dfrac{h(x)}{k(x)}$.

47. The product of $\dfrac{x^2-11x+28}{x^2-2x-35}$ and a second rational expression $\dfrac{f(x)}{g(x)}$ is $\dfrac{x+4}{x+5}$. What is the second rational expression? Show each step of your work.

Take It to the NET
Online lesson quiz at
www.PHSchool.com
Web Code: aga-0904

Mixed Review

Lesson 9-3 **Describe the vertical asymptotes and holes for the graph of each rational function.**

48. $y = \dfrac{x-3}{x-3}$ **49.** $y = \dfrac{x-1}{(3x+2)(x+1)}$ **50.** $y = \dfrac{(x-4)(x+5)}{(x+3)(x-4)}$

Lesson 8-3 **Evaluate each logarithm.**

51. $\log_4 64$ **52.** $\log_2 \frac{1}{32}$ **53.** $\log_5 5\sqrt{5}$ **54.** $\log_{16} 8$

Lesson 7-5 **Solve each equation.**

55. $\sqrt{x+3} - 1 = 4$ **56.** $\sqrt{7x+1} - \sqrt{6x+7} = 0$

9-5 Adding and Subtracting Rational Expressions

North Carolina Objectives

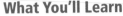

1.03 Operate with algebraic expressions (polynomial, rational, complex fractions) to solve problems.

Lesson Preview

What You'll Learn

OBJECTIVE 1 To add and subtract rational expressions

OBJECTIVE 2 To simplify complex fractions

. . . And Why

To find the focal length of a camera lens, as in Example 1

Check Skills You'll Need

(For help, go to Skills Handbook page 843.)

Find the least common multiple of the two numbers.

1. 7, 21 **2.** 6, 10 **3.** 11, 17 **4.** 30, 105

Add or subtract.

5. $\frac{5}{19} + \frac{7}{38}$ **6.** $\frac{2}{15} + \frac{3}{25}$ **7.** $\frac{7}{24} - \frac{5}{36}$ **8.** $\frac{11}{12} - \frac{7}{45}$

New Vocabulary • complex fraction

Interactive lesson includes instant self-check, tutorials, and activities.

OBJECTIVE 1

Adding and Subtracting Rational Expressions

Investigation: Adding Fractions—Extended

1. Add. Simplify where possible.
   a. $\frac{2}{x} + \frac{3}{x}$ b. $\frac{4}{3x} + \frac{2}{3x}$ c. $\frac{3c}{2c - 1} + \frac{5c + 1}{2c - 1}$
2. Explain the steps you followed in Question 1.
3. How is adding rational expressions similar to adding fractions?

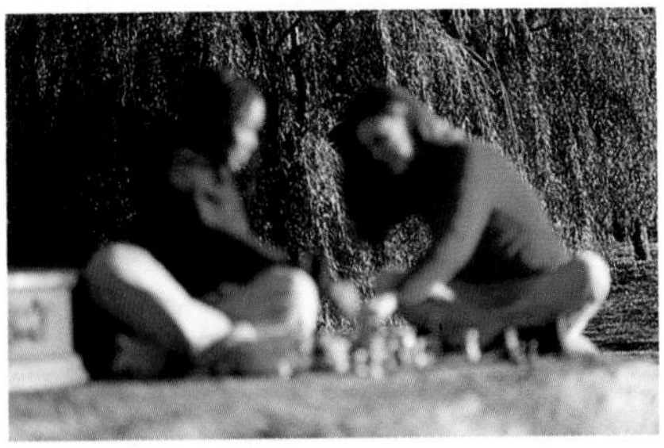

To produce a clear photograph, light rays must be focused on the film. The focal length of a camera lens is the distance from the lens to the point where parallel rays of light are focused.

When you focus a camera, you change the distance from the lens to the film.

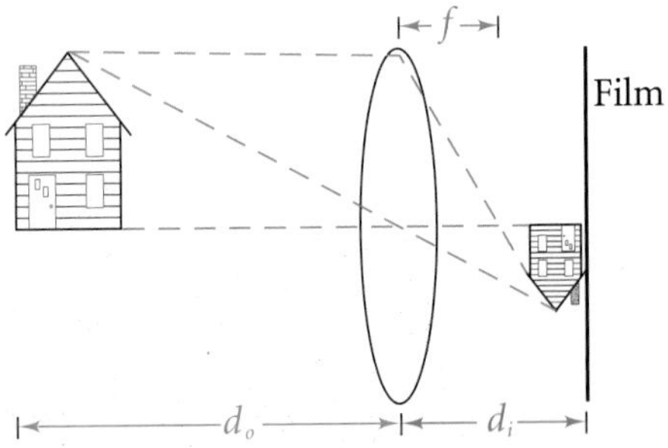

The lens equation is $\frac{1}{f} = \frac{1}{d_i} + \frac{1}{d_o}$.

f = focal length of the lens

d_i = distance from the lens to the film

d_o = distance from the lens to the object

1 EXAMPLE Real-World Connection

Photography An object is 15 cm from a camera lens. The object is in focus on the film when the lens is 10 cm from the film. Find the focal length of the lens.

$\frac{1}{f} = \frac{1}{d_i} + \frac{1}{d_o}$ **Use the lens equation.**

$\frac{1}{f} = \frac{1}{10} + \frac{1}{15}$ **Substitute.**

$= \frac{3}{30} + \frac{2}{30}$ **Write equivalent fractions with the LCD.**

$= \frac{5}{30} = \frac{1}{6}$ **Add and simplify.**

Since $\frac{1}{f} = \frac{1}{6}$, the focal length of the lens is 6 cm.

Check Understanding 1 Suppose an object is 20 cm from a camera lens. When the object is properly focused, the lens is 5 cm from the film. Find the focal length of the lens.

Need Help?
For practice in adding and subtracting fractions, go to p. 843.

To add or subtract rational expressions with different denominators, you must write all the expressions with a common denominator. It is easiest to use the least common denominator (LCD). To do this, find the least common multiple of the denominators.

2 EXAMPLE Finding Least Common Multiples

Find the least common multiple of $4x^2 - 36$ and $6x^2 + 36x + 54$.

Step 1 Find the prime factors of each expression.

$$4x^2 - 36 = 4(x^2 - 9) = (2)(2)(x - 3)(x + 3)$$

$$6x^2 + 36x + 54 = 6(x^2 + 6x + 9) = (2)(3)(x + 3)(x + 3)$$

Step 2 Write each prime factor the greatest number of times it appears in either expression. Simplify where possible.

$$(2)(2)(3)(x - 3)(x + 3)(x + 3) = 12(x - 3)(x + 3)^2$$

The least common multiple is $12(x - 3)(x + 3)^2$.

Check Understanding 2 Find the least common multiple of each pair of expressions.
a. $3x^2 - 9x - 30$ and $6x + 30$ **b.** $5x^2 + 15x + 10$ and $2x^2 - 8$

3 EXAMPLE Adding Rational Expressions

Simplify $\frac{1}{x^2 + 5x + 4} + \frac{5x}{3x + 3}$.

$\frac{1}{x^2 + 5x + 4} + \frac{5x}{3x + 3} = \frac{1}{(x + 1)(x + 4)} + \frac{5x}{3(x + 1)}$ **Factor the denominators.**

$= \frac{1}{(x + 1)(x + 4)} \cdot \frac{3}{3} + \frac{5x}{3(x + 1)} \cdot \frac{x + 4}{x + 4}$ **identity for multiplication**

$= \frac{3}{3(x + 1)(x + 4)} + \frac{5x(x + 4)}{3(x + 1)(x + 4)}$ **Multiply.**

$= \frac{3 + 5x(x + 4)}{3(x + 1)(x + 4)}$ **Add.**

$= \frac{5x^2 + 20x + 3}{3(x + 1)(x + 4)}$ **Simplify the numerator.**

Check Understanding **3** Simplify $\frac{1}{x^2 - 4x - 12} + \frac{3x}{4x + 8}$.

4 EXAMPLE Subtracting Rational Expressions

Simplify $\frac{7y}{5y^2 - 125} - \frac{4}{3y + 15}$.

$$\frac{7y}{5y^2 - 125} - \frac{4}{3y + 15} = \frac{7y}{5(y + 5)(y - 5)} - \frac{4}{3(y + 5)}$$ **Factor the denominators.**

$$= \frac{7y}{5(y + 5)(y - 5)} \cdot \frac{3}{3} - \frac{4}{3(y + 5)} \cdot \frac{5(y - 5)}{5(y - 5)}$$ **identity for multiplication**

$$= \frac{(3)(7y)}{(3)(5)(y + 5)(y - 5)} - \frac{(4)(5)(y - 5)}{(3)(5)(y + 5)(y - 5)}$$ **Multiply.**

$$= \frac{(3)(7y) - (4)(5)(y - 5)}{(3)(5)(y + 5)(y - 5)}$$ **Simplify.**

$$= \frac{y + 100}{15(y + 5)(y - 5)}$$ **Simplify.**

Check Understanding **4** Simplify each expression.

a. $\frac{-2}{3x^2 + 36x + 105} - \frac{3x}{6x + 30}$ **b.** $\frac{x}{3x^2 - 9x + 6} - \frac{2x + 1}{3x^2 + 3x - 6}$

OBJECTIVE 2 Simplifying Complex Fractions

> **Need Help?**
> Note that the complex fractions below are *not* equivalent.
> $\frac{\frac{a}{b}}{c}$ $\frac{a}{\frac{b}{c}}$

A **complex fraction** is a fraction that has a fraction in its numerator or denominator or in both its numerator and denominator. Here are some examples.

$$\frac{\frac{1}{x}}{y} \qquad \frac{3}{1 - \frac{1}{2y}} \qquad \frac{\frac{x - 2}{x} - \frac{2}{x + 1}}{\frac{3}{x - 1} - \frac{1}{x + 1}}$$

To simplify a complex fraction such as $\frac{\frac{a}{b}}{\frac{c}{d}}$ you can multiply the numerator $\frac{a}{b}$ and denominator $\frac{c}{d}$ by their LCD *bd*. Or you can divide the numerator $\frac{a}{b}$ by the denominator $\frac{c}{d}$.

5 EXAMPLE Simplifying Complex Fractions

Simplify $\frac{\frac{1}{x} + 3}{\frac{5}{y} + 4}$.

Method I First find the LCD of all the rational expressions.

$$\frac{\frac{1}{x} + 3}{\frac{5}{y} + 4} = \frac{\left(\frac{1}{x} + 3\right) \cdot xy}{\left(\frac{5}{y} + 4\right) \cdot xy}$$ **The LCD is *xy*. Multiply the numerator and denominator by *xy*.**

$$= \frac{\frac{1}{x} \cdot xy + 3 \cdot xy}{\frac{5}{y} \cdot xy + 4 \cdot xy}$$ **Use the Distributive Property.**

$$= \frac{y + 3xy}{5x + 4xy}$$ **Simplify.**

Investigation

Extraneous Solutions

FOR USE WITH LESSON 9-6

Since division by zero is undefined, strange and illogical things can happen when division by zero sneaks unnoticed into algebraic procedures.

Does 2 = 1? Study the proof below.

① $a = b$

② $a^2 = ab$

③ $a^2 - b^2 = ab - b^2$

④ $(a - b)(a + b) = b(a - b)$

⑤ $\dfrac{(a - b)(a + b)}{a - b} = \dfrac{b(a - b)}{a - b}$

⑥ $a + b = b$

⑦ $b + b = b$

⑧ $2b = b$

⑨ $2 = 1$

1. a. Describe each step of the proof.

b. Check equation ① by replacing a and b with a number such as 3. Do the same for each of the other equations. Which equations are true?

c. Equation ⑤ seems to be derived by using the Division Property of Equality: If $a = b$ and $c \neq 0$, then $\frac{a}{c} = \frac{b}{c}$. Explain why the property is not used correctly.

2. a. Justify each step of the solution to $\frac{1}{x^2} = \frac{2}{x}$.

① $\dfrac{1}{x^2} = \dfrac{2}{x}$

② $2x^2 = x$

③ $2x^2 - x = 0$

④ $x(2x - 1) = 0$

⑤ $x = 0$ or $x = \frac{1}{2}$

b. Check the solution $x = \frac{1}{2}$ in equations ④, ③, ②, and ①.

c. Check the solution $x = 0$ in equations ④, ③, ②, and ①.

d. How are the checks different? Explain.

e. If equations ④ and ① have the same solutions, then you can work backward to derive equation ① from ④. What goes wrong when you try?

f. **Critical Thinking** Explain why equation ③ can be derived from ②, and ② from ③, thereby ensuring that they have the same solutions.

g. Equation ② is derived from equation ① using the Multiplication Property of Equality: If $a = b$ then $ac = bc$. Both sides of equation ① are multiplied by x^3 to obtain equation ②. Is there anything wrong with this step?

h. **Critical Thinking** Explain why equation ② can be derived from ①, but ① cannot be derived from ②.

9-6

Solving Rational Equations

North Carolina Objectives

2.05 Use rational equations to model and solve problems. a) Solve using tables, graphs, and algebraic properties. b) Interpret the constants and coefficients in the context of the problem.

Lesson Preview

What You'll Learn

OBJECTIVE 1 To solve rational equations

OBJECTIVE 2 To use rational equations in solving problems

. . . And Why

To find the average speed of a bicycle trip, as in Example 3

Check Skills You'll Need

(For help, go to Skills Handbook page 843.)

Find the LCD of each pair of fractions.

1. $\frac{1}{3t}, \frac{1}{5t^2}$
2. $\frac{x}{2}, \frac{3x}{8}$
3. $\frac{4}{3h^2}, \frac{2h}{h^3}$
4. $\frac{4}{y+2}, \frac{3}{y-1}$
5. $\frac{z}{2z+1}, \frac{1}{z}$
6. $\frac{1}{k+2}, \frac{3k}{k^2-4}$

Interactive lesson includes instant self-check, tutorials, and activities.

OBJECTIVE 1

Solving Rational Equations

Extraneous solutions can be introduced when you multiply both sides of an equation by the same algebraic expression. An extraneous solution is a solution of the derived equation, but not of the original equation.

You must check all solutions of the derived equation in the original equation to find whether any of them are not solutions of the original equation.

1 EXAMPLE Solving Rational Equations

Solve $\frac{5}{2x-2} = \frac{15}{x^2-1}$. Check each solution.

$$\frac{5}{2x-2} = \frac{15}{x^2-1}$$

$5(x^2-1) = 15(2x-2)$	**Write the cross products.**
$5x^2 - 5 = 30x - 30$	**Distributive Property**
$5x^2 - 30x + 25 = 0$	**Write in standard form.**
$x^2 - 6x + 5 = 0$	**Divide each side by 5.**
$(x-1)(x-5) = 0$	**Factor.**
$x = 1$ or $x = 5$	**Zero-Product Property**

Check When $x = 1$, both denominators in the original equation are zero. The original equation is undefined at $x = 1$. So $x = 1$ is not a solution.

When 5 is substituted for x in the original equation, both sides equal $\frac{5}{8}$.

The solution is $x = 5$.

Need Help?

In a proportion, the cross products are equal.
If $\frac{a}{b} = \frac{c}{d}$, then $ad = cb$ $(b \neq 0, d \neq 0)$.

Check Understanding

1 Solve each equation. Check each solution.

a. $\frac{-4}{5(x+2)} = \frac{3}{x+2}$

b. $\frac{-2}{x^2-2} = \frac{2}{x-4}$

C Challenge

56. **Open-Ended** Write a rational equation that has the following.
 a. one solution **b.** two solutions **c.** no real solution

57. A salesman drove from his home to a nearby city at an average speed of 40 mi/h. He returned home at an average speed of 50 mi/h. What was his average speed for the entire trip?

58. An automatic pitching machine can pitch all its baseballs in $1\frac{1}{4}$ hours. One attendant can retrieve all the baseballs pitched by one machine in $3\frac{1}{2}$ hours. At least how many attendants working at the same rate should be hired so that the baseballs from 10 machines are all retrieved in less than 8 hours?

Standardized Test Prep

Multiple Choice

59. Which value of x would NOT make the equation $\frac{5}{2x - 1} = \frac{7x}{x^2 - 25}$ undefined?
 A. -5 B. 0 C. $\frac{1}{2}$ D. 5

60. What is the solution of $x + \frac{1}{x} = -2$?
 F. 1 or -1 G. 0 only H. $-\frac{1}{2}$ only I. -1 only

61. Which equation has 2 as an extraneous solution?
 A. $\frac{x + 1}{17} = \frac{x + 3}{15}$ B. $\frac{3}{3x + 6} = \frac{4}{x^2 - 4}$
 C. $\frac{3x + 1}{3x} = \frac{5x}{5x + 3}$ D. $\frac{4}{2x - 4} = \frac{1}{x - 2}$

62. Solve $\frac{2}{x + 7} = \frac{x}{x^2 - 49}$.
 F. 14 only G. 7 only H. 7 or -7 I. -7 only

Take It to the NET
Online lesson quiz at
www.PHSchool.com
Web Code: aga-0906

Short Response

63. A large snowplow can clear a parking lot in 4 hours. A small snowplow needs more time to clear the lot. Working together, they can clear the lot in 3 hours. How long would it take the small plow to clear the lot by itself? Show your work.

Extended Response

64. Solve and check the equation $\frac{x}{3x + 9} = \frac{x + 2}{x + 3}$. Show your work.

Mixed Review

Lesson 9-5 **Simplify each difference.**

65. $\frac{3y + 1}{4y + 4} - \frac{2y + 7}{2y + 2}$ 66. $\frac{5x}{2y + 4} - \frac{6}{y^2 + 2y}$ 67. $\frac{x + 1}{2x - 2} - \frac{2x}{x^2 + 2x - 3}$

Lesson 8-5 **Solve each equation.**

68. $\log_{10} 0.001 = x$ 69. $\log_3 27 = 3x + 6$

70. $\log_{0.1} (x + 1) = 3$ 71. $\log_3 \frac{1}{9} = \frac{x}{3}$

Lesson 7-7 **Find the inverse of each function. Is the inverse a function?**

72. $y = 5 - 2x$ 73. $y = x^2 + 1$ 74. $y = x^3 - 4$

Reading Math

Reading for Problem Solving

For Use With Page 515, Exercise 32

Read the problem below. Then follow along with Ahmed as he solves the problem. Check your understanding with the exercise at the bottom of the page.

Anita and Fran have volunteered to contact every member of their organization by phone to inform them of an upcoming event. Fran can complete the calls in six days if she works alone. Anita can complete them in four days. How long will they take to complete the calls working together?

What Ahmed Thinks	What Ahmed Writes
I'll write the information in my own words.	Fran can complete the work in 6 days. Anita can complete the work in 4 days.
Work problems involve rates. Even though I don't know the number of calls Fran and Anita are making, maybe I can just consider the entire job, or total amount of work, being done.	$\text{rate} = \frac{\text{work being done}}{\text{time}}$ $\text{Fran's rate} = \frac{\text{work being done}}{\text{time}} = \frac{\text{total work}}{6}$ $\text{Anita's rate} = \frac{\text{work being done}}{\text{time}} = \frac{\text{total work}}{4}$
I'll define variables, *t* for time and *w* for work.	w = total work t = time working together
Now I can write an equation.	$\text{Fran's rate} + \text{Anita's rate} = \text{combined rate}$ $\frac{\text{total work}}{6} + \frac{\text{total work}}{4} = \frac{\text{total work}}{\text{time together}}$
The variable *w* is going to cancel out of the equation, so I can just solve for *t*.	$\frac{w}{6} + \frac{w}{4} = \frac{w}{t}$ $\frac{1}{6} + \frac{1}{4} = \frac{1}{t}$ $2t + 3t = 12$ $5t = \frac{12}{5} = 2\frac{2}{5}$
I can write my answer in a sentence now.	It will take Anita and Fran, working together, $2\frac{2}{5}$ days to complete all the calls.

EXERCISE

Charlene and Robert are washing cars for a fund-raiser. Charlene can wash a car in 15 minutes, and Robert can wash the same size car in 12 minutes. How long will it take them to wash a car if they work together?

9-7 Probability of Multiple Events

Lesson Preview

What You'll Learn

OBJECTIVE 1 To find the probabilities of events *A* and *B*

OBJECTIVE 2 To find the probabilities of events *A* or *B*

. . . And Why

To solve problems involving radio call-in shows, as in Example 2

Check Skills You'll Need

(For help, go to Lesson 1-6.)

A bag contains 24 green marbles, 22 blue marbles, 14 yellow marbles, and 12 red marbles. Suppose you pick one marble at random. Find each probability.

1. P(yellow) **2.** P(not blue) **3.** P(green or red)

4. Of 300 senior students at Taft High, 150 have taken physics, 192 have taken chemistry, and 30 have taken neither physics nor chemistry. How many students have taken both physics and chemistry?

New Vocabulary
- dependent events
- independent events
- mutually exclusive events

Interactive lesson includes instant self-check, tutorials, and activities.

OBJECTIVE

1 Finding *P*(*A* and *B*)

Investigation: Multiple Events

- Work with a partner to analyze the game Primarily Odd.
- **Partner A:** Roll two standard number cubes. If the sum is either odd *or* a prime number, score a point.
- **Partner B:** Roll two standard number cubes. If the sum is both odd *and* a prime number, score a point.
- Alternate turns rolling the number cubes.

1. **a.** List all the possible outcomes of rolling two number cubes.
   b. How many outcomes result in an odd sum? Calculate the probability of getting an odd sum.
   c. How many outcomes result in a prime sum? Calculate the probability of getting a prime sum.
2. Predict which partner is more likely to score points in Primarily Odd. Justify your reasoning.
3. Play the game with your partner. Take 10 turns each. Keep track of each player's score. How do your results compare with the prediction you made in Question 2?

When the outcome of one event affects the outcome of a second event, the two events are **dependent events.** When the outcome of one event does *not* affect the outcome of a second event, the two events are **independent events.**

1 EXAMPLE Classifying Events

Classify each pair of events as *dependent* or *independent*.

a. Roll a number cube. Then toss a coin.
Since the two events do not affect each other, they are independent.

b. Pick a flower from a garden. Then pick another flower from the same garden.
Picking the first flower affects the possible outcomes of picking the second flower. So the events are dependent.

Check Understanding **1** Suppose you select a marble from a bag of marbles. You replace the marble and then select again. Are your selections dependent or independent events? Explain.

You can find the probability that two independent events will both occur by multiplying probabilities.

Key Concepts

Property	Probability of A and B

If A and B are independent events, then $P(A \text{ and } B) = P(A) \cdot P(B)$.

Example: If $P(A) = \frac{1}{2}$ and $P(B) = \frac{1}{3}$, then $P(A \text{ and } B) = \frac{1}{2} \cdot \frac{1}{3} = \frac{1}{6}$.

2 EXAMPLE Real-World Connection

Radio Suppose your favorite radio station is running a promotional campaign. Every hour, four callers chosen at random get to select two songs each. You call the station once after 7:00 A.M. and again after 3:00 P.M. What is the probability that you will be one of the four callers both times you call?

WKW Radio Statistics

Hour	Calls Received That Hour
7:00 A.M.	125
3:00 P.M.	200

Relate probability of both events is probability of first event times probability of second event

Define Event A = you are one of the four callers after 7:00 A.M. Then $P(A) = \frac{4}{125}$.

Event B = you are one of the four callers after 3:00 P.M. Then $P(B) = \frac{4}{200}$.

Write $P(A \text{ and } B) = P(A) \cdot P(B)$

$$P(A \text{ and } B) = \frac{4}{125} \cdot \frac{4}{200}$$

$$= \frac{16}{25{,}000} \quad \textbf{Multiply.}$$

$$= \frac{2}{3125} \quad \textbf{Simplify.}$$

The probability of being one of the four callers selected at random both times you call is $\frac{2}{3125}$, or 0.064%.

Real-World Connection

Careers Radio broadcasters try to increase the size of their listening audience so they can increase their advertising rates.

Check Understanding **2** Suppose the radio station changes the promotional campaign. Now it chooses five callers at random each hour.
a. What is the probability of being one of the five callers after 7 A.M? After 3 P.M.?
b. Find the probability of being one of the five callers both times you call.

OBJECTIVE 2

Finding P(A or B)

When two events cannot happen at the same time, the events are **mutually exclusive events.** If A and B are mutually exclusive events, then $P(A \text{ and } B) = 0$.

Reading Math

Events that are not mutually exclusive are sometimes called inclusive events, or non-mutually exclusive events.

3 EXAMPLE Mutually Exclusive Events

Are the events mutually exclusive? Explain.

a. rolling a 2 or a 3 on a number cube

Since you cannot roll a 2 and a 3 at the same time, the events are mutually exclusive.

b. rolling an even number or a multiple of 3 on a number cube

By rolling a 6, you can roll an even number and a multiple of 3 at the same time. So the events are not mutually exclusive.

Check Understanding 3 Are the events mutually exclusive? Explain.

a. rolling an even number and rolling a prime number on a number cube

b. rolling an even number and rolling a number less than 2 on a number cube

You need to determine whether events A and B are mutually exclusive before you can find the probability of (A or B).

Key Concepts

Property	Probability of *A or B*

If A and B are mutually exclusive events, then
$P(A \text{ or } B) = P(A) + P(B)$.

If A and B are not mutually exclusive events, then
$P(A \text{ or } B) = P(A) + P(B) - P(A \text{ and } B)$.

Many statistical measures are based on probabilities of the form $P(A \text{ or } B)$.

4 EXAMPLE Real-World Connection

College Enrollment About 53% of U.S. college students are under 25 years old. About 21% of U.S. college students are over 34 years old. What is the probability that a U.S. college student chosen at random is under 25 or over 34?

Since a student cannot be under 25 and over 34, the events are mutually exclusive.

$$P(\text{under 25 or over 34}) = P(\text{under 25}) + P(\text{over 34})$$ **Use the *P*(*A* or *B*) formula for mutually exclusive events.**

$$= 0.53 + 0.21$$

$$= 0.74$$

The probability that a U.S. college student chosen at random is under 25 or over 34 is about 0.74, or about 74%.

Check Understanding 4 A U.S. college student is chosen at random. Find the probability for each age range of the student.

a. 25–34 **b.** 25–34 or over 34 **c.** under 34

When two events are *not* mutually exclusive, you need to subtract the probability of the common outcomes.

5 EXAMPLE Probabilities of Events

Food Suppose you reach into the fruit bowl at the left and select a piece of fruit at random. What is the probability that the piece of fruit is an apple or green?

$$P(\text{apple or green}) = P(\text{apple}) + P(\text{green}) - P(\text{apple and green})$$
$$= \tfrac{5}{9} + \tfrac{3}{9} - \tfrac{2}{9}$$
$$= \tfrac{6}{9}$$

The probability of picking a piece of fruit that is an apple or green is $\frac{6}{9}$, or $\frac{2}{3}$.

Check Understanding 5 Find each probability.

a. P(apple or red) **b.** P(green or citrus fruit)

EXERCISES

For more practice, see *Extra Practice*.

Practice and Problem Solving

A Practice by Example

Example 1 (page 520)

Classify each pair of events as *dependent* or *independent*.

1. A month is selected at random; a number from 1 to 30 is selected at random.

2. A month is selected at random; a day of that month is selected at random.

3. A letter of the alphabet is selected at random; one of the remaining letters is selected at random.

4. The color of a car is selected at random; the type of transmission is selected at random.

Example 2 (page 520)

***Q* and *R* are independent events. Find *P*(*Q* and *R*).**

5. $P(Q) = \frac{1}{4}, P(R) = \frac{2}{3}$

6. $P(Q) = \frac{12}{17}, P(R) = \frac{3}{8}$

7. $P(Q) = 0.6, P(R) = 0.9$

8. $P(Q) = \frac{1}{3}, P(R) = \frac{6}{x}$

9. Suppose you have five books in your book bag. Three are novels, one is a biography, and one is a poetry book. Today you grab one book out of your bag without looking, and return it later. Tomorrow you do the same thing. What is the probability that you grab a novel both days?

Example 3 (page 521)

Two standard number cubes are tossed. State whether the events are mutually exclusive. Explain your reasoning.

10. The sum is a prime number; the sum is less than 4.

11. The numbers are equal; the sum is odd.

12. The product is greater than 20; the product is a multiple of 3.

Example 4 (page 521)

13. **Population** About 30% of the U.S. population is under 20 years old. About 17% of the population is over 60. What is the probability that a person chosen at random is under 20 or over 60?

S and T are mutually exclusive events. Find $P(S \text{ or } T)$.

14. $P(S) = \frac{5}{8}, P(T) = \frac{1}{8}$

15. $P(S) = \frac{3}{5}, P(T) = \frac{1}{3}$

16. $P(S) = 12\%, P(T) = 27\%$

17. $P(S) = \frac{1}{7}, P(T) = 60\%$

Example 5 (page 522)

A standard number cube is tossed. Find each probability.

18. $P(3 \text{ or odd})$

19. $P(4 \text{ or even})$

20. $P(\text{even or less than } 4)$

21. $P(\text{odd or greater than } 2)$

22. $P(\text{odd or prime})$

23. $P(\text{even or prime})$

24. $P(4 \text{ or less than } 6)$

25. $P(\text{greater than 1 or less than } 5)$

B Apply Your Skills

C and D are not mutually exclusive events. Copy and complete the table below to find each missing probability.

	P(C)	P(D)	P(C and D)	P(C or D)
26.	$\frac{4}{9}$	$\frac{4}{9}$	■	$\frac{5}{9}$
27.	$\frac{1}{2}$	$\frac{1}{3}$	$\frac{1}{4}$	■
28.	$\frac{2}{3}$	$\frac{3}{5}$	■	$\frac{13}{15}$
29.	$\frac{3}{7}$	$\frac{1}{4}$	$\frac{1}{8}$	■

30. Suppose a number from 1 to 100 is selected at random.
  a. What is the probability that a multiple of 5 is chosen? That a multiple of 4 is chosen? Are these two events mutually exclusive? Explain.
  b. What is the probability that a multiple of both 5 and 4 is chosen?

Real-World Connection

Careers Support personnel keep business and industry running smoothly.

Statistics The graph at the right shows the types of jobs held by people in the United States. Find each probability.

U.S. Employment, by Occupation

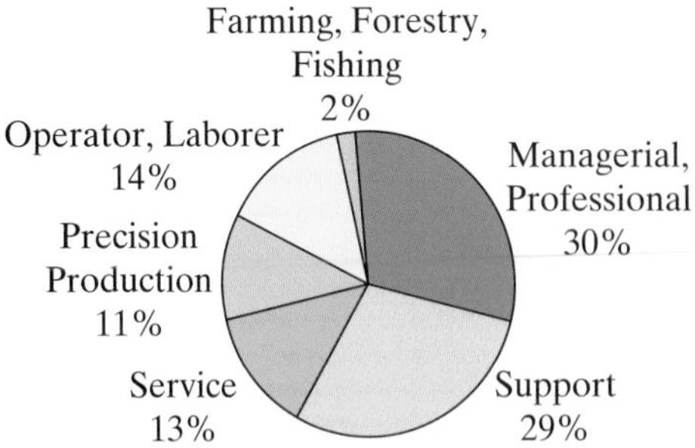

SOURCE: *Statistical Abstract of the United States.* Go to **www.PHSchool.com** for a data update. Web Code: agg-2041

31. A person is in a service occupation.

32. A person is in service or support.

33. A person is not in farming, fishing, or forestry.

34. A person is neither an operator nor a laborer, nor in precision production.

35. A person is neither in service nor in support.

A jar contains four blue marbles and two red marbles. Suppose you choose a marble at random, and do not replace it. Then you choose a second marble. Find the probability of each event.

36. You select a blue marble and then a red marble.

37. You select a red marble and then a blue marble.

38. One of the marbles you select is blue and the other is red.

39. Both of the marbles you select are red.

40. You select two red marbles or two blue marbles.

H and J are not mutually exclusive events. Copy and complete the table below to find each missing probability.

	P(H)	P(J)	P(H and J)	P(H or J)
41.	$\frac{7}{11}$	$\frac{3}{11}$	■	$\frac{9}{11}$
42.	$\frac{1}{2}$	■	$\frac{1}{4}$	$\frac{2}{3}$
43.	■	$\frac{2}{5}$	$\frac{1}{5}$	$\frac{2}{3}$
44.	$\frac{2}{x}$	$\frac{3}{2x}$	$\frac{1}{x}$	■

45. **Tests** A multiple-choice test has four choices for each answer.

a. What is the probability that a random guess on a question will yield the correct answer?

b. Suppose you need to make a random guess on three of the ten test questions. What is the probability that you will answer all three correctly?

46. **Open-Ended** Describe two events that are not mutually exclusive. Estimate the probability of both events occurring.

47. **Error Analysis** Events F and G are mutually exclusive independent events. A student says that $P(F \text{ and } G)$ is greater than $P(F \text{ or } G)$. Explain how you can tell that the student is wrong.

C Challenge

Use the tables below for Exercises 48–50. One student from each school is chosen at random to be on a committee. Find each probability.

School A

Freshman	Sophomore	Junior	Senior
30%	27%	25%	18%

School B

Freshman	Sophomore	Junior	Senior
28%	28%	24%	20%

48. a junior from School A and a senior from School B

49. two juniors

50. a freshman or sophomore from School A and a senior from School B

51. Two number cubes are rolled. What is the probability that the sum is greater than 9 or less than 6?

52. **Critical Thinking** Tatyana has $x + 2$ pens in the pocket of her backpack. Samuel has $2x - 1$ pens in the pocket of his backpack.

a. Tatyana has 2 blue pens. Find the probability that she pulls out a blue pen at random.

b. Samuel has $x - 3$ blue pens. Find the probability that he pulls out a blue pen at random.

c. Find the probability that both Tatyana and Samuel pull out blue pens at random.

d. Find the probability that either Tatyana or Samuel pulls out a blue pen at random.

Standardized Test Prep

Use this information for Exercises 53–58.

Bag 1 contains 7 red marbles, 5 blue marbles, 3 yellow marbles, and 4 green marbles. Bag 2 contains 1 red pencil, 6 red pens, 2 blue pencils, and 10 blue pens.

Gridded Response

53. One marble is drawn from bag 1. What is the probability that the marble is red or yellow?

54. One marble is drawn from bag 1. What is the probability that the marble is blue or not green?

55. One marble is drawn from bag 1. What is the probability that it is blue or yellow or green?

56. One item is drawn from bag 2. What is the probability that it is red?

57. One item is drawn from bag 2. What is the probability that it is a pen or a red pencil?

58. One item is drawn from bag 2. What is the probability that it is blue or a pencil?

Take It to the NET Online lesson quiz at **www.PHSchool.com** Web Code: aga-0907

Mixed Review

Lesson 9-6 **Solve each equation. Check your answer.**

59. $\frac{1}{2} - x = \frac{x}{6}$ **60.** $\frac{2}{2x - 1} = \frac{x}{3}$ **61.** $\frac{3}{2x} - \frac{2}{3x} = 5$

Lesson 8-6 **Solve each equation.**

62. $\ln 2x = 3$ **63.** $\ln x + \ln 2 = 6$ **64.** $\ln x - \ln 4 = 5$

65. $\ln x^2 + 1 = 5$ **66.** $\ln x^2 + \ln x = 6$ **67.** $e^x = 12$

68. $e^{x+1} = 8$ **69.** $e^{x^2} = 3$ **70.** $2e^{2x} + 1 = 5$

Algebra at Work

Economist

Economists study the relationship between the supply of a product and public demand for it. A supply curve shows that the number of units a manufacturer produces will increase as the price of the item increases. A demand curve shows that the number of units sold will decrease as the price increases. The curves cross at a point that establishes a stable equilibrium price.

Take It to the NET For more information about economists, go to **www.PHSchool.com.** Web Code: agb-2031

Test-Taking Strategies

Eliminating Answers

Before you try to find the answer to a problem, you may be able to eliminate some answer choices. Cross out the answers you eliminate in the test booklet, NOT on the answer sheet.

1 EXAMPLE

What is the best approximation to $\sqrt{105} - \frac{3}{2 - \sqrt{27}}$?

A. −5.1 **B.** 8.3 **C.** 11.2 **D.** 28.3

The denominator of $\frac{3}{2 - \sqrt{27}}$ is a negative number, so $\sqrt{105} - \frac{3}{2 - \sqrt{27}}$ is a positive number. Therefore, you can eliminate A.

Since $\sqrt{105}$ is close to 10, and $-\frac{3}{2 - \sqrt{27}}$ is a small positive number, $\sqrt{105} - \frac{3}{2 - \sqrt{27}}$ is a little larger than 10. You can eliminate B and D.

The correct answer must be C.

2 EXAMPLE

Solve $\frac{2x}{x + 2} = 1 + \frac{x}{x - 2}$.

A. $x = \frac{2}{3}, x = -2$, or $x = 2$

B. $x = \frac{2}{3}$

C. $x = 2$ or $x = -2$

D. $x = \frac{3}{2}$

The equation has denominators $x + 2$ and $x - 2$. Since the denominators cannot equal zero, you know that x cannot equal −2 or 2. You can eliminate A and C.

EXERCISES

1. What is the correct answer to Example 2?

Explain how you can eliminate two of the answer choices for each problem.

2. Solve $\frac{x}{x - 4} + 2 = \frac{3x}{x + 1}$.

   A. $x = \frac{8}{7}$ **B.** $x = 4, x = \frac{8}{7}$ **C.** $x = \frac{7}{8}, x = -1$ **D.** $x = \frac{7}{8}$

3. What is the best approximation to $\sqrt{50} + \frac{1}{\sqrt{5} - 3}$?

   A. 5.66 **B.** 5.76 **C.** 7.66 **D.** 7.67

4. A jar contains 3 red, 3 green, and 3 yellow chips. Two chips are drawn at random from the jar, without replacement. What is the probability that one chip is red and the other is green?

   A. 0 **B.** $\frac{1}{9}$ **C.** $\frac{1}{4}$ **D.** 1

Chapter 9

Chapter Review

Vocabulary

branch (p. 485)
combined variation (p. 480)
complex fraction (p. 506)
dependent events (p. 519)
independent events (p. 519)
inverse variation (p. 478)
mutually exclusive events (p. 521)
point of discontinuity (p. 491)
rational function (p. 491)
simplest form (p. 499)

Reading Math
Understanding Vocabulary

Take It to the NET
Online vocabulary quiz at www.PHSchool.com
Web Code: agj-0951

Choose the correct vocabulary term to complete each sentence.

1. Two events are _?_ if they cannot happen at the same time.
2. When the numerator and denominator of a rational expression are polynomials with no common divisors, the rational expression is in _?_.
3. When the outcome of one event does not affect the outcome of a second event, the two events are _?_.
4. A part of the graph of an inverse variation is called a(n) _?_.
5. If a is a zero of the denominator of a function, the function has a(n) _?_ at $x = a$.

Skills and Concepts

9-1 Objectives

- To use inverse variation (p. 478)
- To use combined variation (p. 480)

An equation in two variables of the form $y = \frac{k}{x}$ or $xy = k$, where $k \neq 0$, is an **inverse variation. Combined variation** is an extension of direct and inverse variation to more complicated relationships.

Suppose that *x* and *y* vary inversely. Write a function that models each inverse variation. Find *y* when $x = 5$.

6. $x = 10$ when $y = 15$
7. $x = 30$ when $y = 2$
8. $x = 6$ when $y = 30$

If possible, write direct or inverse variation equations to model each relation.

9.

x	3	4	8
y	24	18	9

10.

x	11	13	15
y	15	13	11

11.

x	5	7	9
y	30	42	54

Write the function that models each relationship. Find *z* when $x = 4$ and $y = 8$.

12. z varies jointly with x and y. When $x = 2$ and $y = 2$, $z = 7$.
13. z varies directly with x and inversely with y. When $x = 5$ and $y = 2$, $z = 10$.
14. z varies directly with the cube of x and inversely with y. When $x = 3$ and $y = 3$, $z = 9$.

Describe the combined variation modeled by each equation.

15. $R = kmn^2$
16. $W = \frac{k}{d^2}$
17. $P = \frac{kx}{y^2z}$

9-2 Objectives

- To graph inverse variations (p. 485)
- To graph translations of inverse variations (p. 487)

The graph of an inverse variation has two parts called **branches**. The graph of $y = \frac{k}{x - b} + c$ is a translation of $y = \frac{k}{x}$ by b units horizontally and c units vertically. It has a vertical asymptote at $x = b$ and a horizontal asymptote at $y = c$.

Sketch the graph of each equation.

18. $y = \frac{1}{x}$ **19.** $y = \frac{-2}{x^2}$ **20.** $y = \frac{-1}{x} - 4$ **21.** $y = \frac{3}{x - 2} + 1$

Write an equation for the translation of $xy = 4$ that has the given asymptotes.

22. $x = 0, y = 3$ **23.** $x = 2, y = 2$ **24.** $x = -3, y = -4$

9-3 Objectives

- To identify properties of rational functions (p. 491)
- To graph rational functions (p. 494)

The rational function $f(x) = \frac{P(x)}{Q(x)}$ has a **point of discontinuity** for each real zero of $Q(x)$. If $P(x)$ and $Q(x)$ have no common factors, then the graph of $f(x)$ has a vertical asymptote when $Q(x) = 0$. If $P(x)$ and $Q(x)$ have a common real zero a, then there is a hole or a vertical asymptote at $x = a$.

If the degree of $Q(x)$ is greater than the degree of $P(x)$, then the graph of $f(x)$ has a horizontal asymptote at $y = 0$.

If $P(x)$ and $Q(x)$ have equal degrees, then there is a horizontal asymptote at $y = \frac{a}{b}$, where a and b are the coefficients of the terms of greatest degree in $P(x)$ and $Q(x)$.

If the degree of $P(x)$ is greater than the degree of $Q(x)$, then there is no horizontal asymptote.

25. A headset can be manufactured for \$.17. The development cost is \$150,000. Graph the function that represents the average cost of a headset. About how many must be manufactured to result in a cost of less than \$5 per headset?

Find any points of discontinuity for each rational function. Sketch the graph. Describe any vertical or horizontal asymptotes and any holes.

26. $y = \frac{2.5}{x + 7}$ **27.** $y = \frac{x - 1}{(x + 2)(x - 1)}$

28. $y = \frac{x^3 - 1}{x^2 - 1}$ **29.** $y = \frac{2x^2 + 3}{x^2 + 2}$

9-4 and 9-5 Objectives

- To simplify rational expressions (p. 499)
- To multiply and divide rational expressions (p. 500)
- To add and subtract rational expressions (p. 504)
- To simplify complex fractions (p. 506)

A rational expression is in **simplest form** when its numerator and denominator are polynomials that have no common divisors. To add or subtract rational expressions with different denominators, write each expression with the least common denominator.

A fraction that has a fraction in its numerator or denominator or in both is called a **complex fraction**. You can simplify a complex fraction by multiplying the numerator and denominator by the LCD of all the rational expressions.

Simplify each rational expression. State any restrictions on the variable.

30. $\frac{x^2 - 2x - 24}{x^2 + 7x + 12} \cdot \frac{x^2 - 1}{x - 6}$ **31.** $\frac{4x^2 - 2x}{x^2 + 5x + 4} \div \frac{2x}{x^2 + 2x + 1}$

Need Help?

$V = \frac{4}{3}\pi r^3$

S.A. $= 4\pi r^2$

$\frac{1}{f} = \frac{1}{d_i} + \frac{1}{d_o}$

32. What is the ratio of the volume of a sphere to its surface area?

33. A camera's focal length is 4 cm. If the lens is 6 cm from the film, what is the distance from the lens to an object that is in focus?

Simplify each expression.

34. $\frac{3x}{x^2 - 4} + \frac{6}{x + 2}$ **35.** $\frac{1}{x^2 - 1} - \frac{2}{x^2 + 3x}$ **36.** $\frac{2 - \frac{2}{3}}{3 - \frac{1}{2}}$ **37.** $\frac{\frac{1}{x + y}}{4}$

9-6 Objectives

- To solve rational equations (p. 512)
- To use rational equations in solving problems (p. 513)

Solving a rational equation often requires multiplying both sides by an algebraic expression. This may introduce an extraneous solution—a solution of a derived equation but not of the original equation. Check all possible solutions in the original equation.

Solve each equation. Check each solution.

38. $\frac{1}{x} = \frac{5}{x - 4}$ **39.** $\frac{2}{x + 3} - \frac{1}{x} = \frac{-6}{x(x + 3)}$ **40.** $\frac{1}{2} + \frac{x}{6} = \frac{18}{x}$

41. One pump can fill a water cistern twice as fast as a second pump. Working together, the two pumps can fill the cistern in 5 hours. Find how long it takes each pump to fill the cistern when working alone.

9-7 Objectives

- To find the probabilities of events *A* and *B* (p. 519)
- To find the probabilities of events *A* or *B* (p. 521)

When the occurrence of one event affects the probability of another event, the two events are **dependent events.** When the occurrence of one event does not affect the probability of another event, the two events are **independent events.** When two events cannot happen at the same time, the events are **mutually exclusive events.**

If A and B are independent, then $P(A \text{ and } B) = P(A) \cdot P(B)$.

If A and B are mutually exclusive, then $P(A \text{ and } B) = 0$.

If A and B are mutually exclusive, then $P(A \text{ or } B) = P(A) + P(B)$.

If A and B are not mutually exclusive, then
$P(A \text{ or } B) = P(A) + P(B) - P(A \text{ and } B)$.

Classify each pair of events as *dependent* or *independent*.

42. A student in your algebra class is selected at random. One of the remaining students is selected at random.

43. A number 1 through 6 is chosen by tossing a standard number cube. The same number cube is tossed again to select a number 1 through 6.

Two standard number cubes are tossed. State whether the events are mutually exclusive.

44. One of the numbers is 1 less than the other. The sum is odd.

45. The sum is greater than 10. Six is one of the numbers.

A standard number cube is tossed. Find each probability.

46. a 5 or a 6 **47.** an even number or a number greater than 4

48. an odd number or a number less than or equal to 5

Chapter 9

Chapter Test

Take It to the NET
Online chapter test at
www.PHSchool.com
Web Code: aga-0952

Write a function that models each variation.

1. $x = 2$ when $y = -8$. y varies inversely with x.
2. $x = 0.2$ and $y = 3$ when $z = 2$. z varies jointly with x and y.
3. $x = \frac{1}{3}$, $y = \frac{1}{5}$, and $r = 3$ when $z = \frac{1}{2}$. z varies directly with x and inversely with the product of r^2 and y.

Is the relationship between the values in each table a direct variation, an inverse variation, or neither? Write an equation to model any direct or inverse variation.

4.

x	3	5	7	9
y	6	8	10	12

5.

x	4	6	8	10
y	10	8	6	4

6.

x	4	8	16	32
y	32	16	8	4

Graph the translation of $y = \frac{7}{x}$ with the given asymptotes. Write the equation of the translation.

7. $x = 1$; $y = 2$
8. $x = -3$; $y = -2$

For each rational function, identify any holes, or horizontal or vertical asymptotes of its graph.

9. $y = \frac{x+1}{x-1}$
10. $y = \frac{x+3}{x+3}$
11. $y = \frac{x-2}{(x+1)(x-2)}$
12. $y = \frac{2x^2}{x^2-4x}$
13. $y = \frac{1}{x+2} - 3$
14. $y = \frac{5}{x-2} + 1$
15. $y = \frac{x^2+5}{x-5}$
16. $y = \frac{x+2}{(x+2)(x-3)}$

Simplify each rational expression. State any restrictions on the variable.

17. $\frac{x^2+7x+12}{x^2-9}$
18. $\frac{(x+3)(2x-1)}{x(x+4)} \div \frac{(-x-3)(2x+1)}{x}$

19. **Open-Ended** Write a function whose graph has a vertical asymptote, a horizontal asymptote, and a hole.

Find the least common multiple of each pair of polynomials.

20. $3x + 5$ and $9x^2 - 25$
21. $5(x+3)(x+1)$ and $2(x+1)(x-3)$

Simplify each sum or difference.

22. $\frac{x+2}{(x-3)(x+1)} + \frac{(x-1)(x+2)}{x-3}$
23. $\frac{x^2-1}{(x-2)(3x-1)} - \frac{x+1}{x+3}$
24. $\frac{x(x+4)}{x-2} + \frac{x-1}{x^2-4}$

Simplify each complex fraction.

25. $\frac{\frac{2}{x}}{1-\frac{1}{y}}$
26. $\frac{3-\frac{3}{4}}{\frac{1}{2}-\frac{1}{4}}$

Solve each equation. Check each solution.

27. $\frac{x}{2} = \frac{x+1}{4}$
28. $\frac{3}{x-1} = \frac{4}{3x+2}$
29. $\frac{3x}{x+1} = 0$
30. $\frac{3}{x+1} = \frac{1}{x^2-1}$
31. $\frac{1}{x} + \frac{1}{3} = \frac{6}{x^2}$
32. $\frac{1}{x} + \frac{x}{x+2} = 1$

33. Almir can seal a driveway in 4 hours. Working together, he and Louis can seal it in 2.3 hours. How long would it take Louis to seal it working alone?

Two standard number cubes are tossed. State whether the events are mutually exclusive. Then find $P(A \text{ or } B)$.

34. A means their sum is 12; B means both are odd
35. A means they are equal; B means their sum is a multiple of 3
36. a. **Writing** Suppose you select a number at random from the set {90, 91, 92, . . . , 99}. Event A is selecting a multiple of 3. Event B is selecting a multiple of 4. Are these two events mutually exclusive? Explain.
    b. Find $P(A \text{ and } B)$.
    c. Find $P(A \text{ or } B)$.

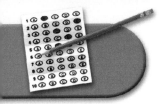

Standardized Test Prep

Reading Comprehension **Read the passage below. Then answer the questions on the basis of what is *stated* or *implied* in the passage.**

Payback Buying a house is the biggest investment most people ever make. So it's important to know how mortgage loans work.

Suppose you borrow $80,000 for a 30-year mortgage with an annual interest rate of 7.8%. The bank calculates a *monthly* interest rate ($7.8\% \div 12 = 0.0065$) and uses it to calculate a monthly payment of $575.90. Each month, the bank adds the monthly interest to the current principal to get the balance, and then subtracts the payment to get the new principal.

End of Month	Current Principal	Amount of Interest	Balance	Payment	New Principal
1	80,000.00	520.00	80,520.00	575.90	79,944.10
2	79,944.10	519.64	80,463.74	575.90	79,887.84
3	79,887.84	519.27	80,407.11	575.90	79,831.21

You can calculate the monthly payment for any mortgage with the formula $P = \dfrac{A \cdot m(1+m)^{12y}}{(1+m)^{12y} - 1}$. P is the monthly payment, A is the amount borrowed, m is the monthly interest rate, and y is the length of the mortgage in years.

If you know the monthly payment you want to make, you can use the formula $A = \dfrac{P\left[(1+m)^{12y} - 1\right]}{m(1+m)^{12y}}$ to find the total amount you can borrow.

1. For the mortgage loan described above, what will be the 4th month's balance after the interest is added to the principal?

A. $518.90 **B.** $575.90
C. $79,744.21 **D.** $80,350.11

2. If the annual interest for a loan is 8.55%, what is the monthly interest rate?

F. 8.8375% **G.** 7.125
H. 0.07125% **I.** 0.007125

3. Consider a 15-year mortgage for $65,000 with an annual interest rate of 6%. Rewrite the formula $P = \dfrac{A \cdot m(1+m)^{12y}}{(1+m)^{12y} - 1}$ by substituting values for A, m, and y.

4. To the nearest cent, what is the monthly payment for a 15-year mortgage loan of $65,000 with an annual interest rate of 6%?

5. To the nearest cent, what is the monthly payment for a 15-year mortgage loan of $65,000 with an annual interest rate of 7.5%?

6. Suppose you want to make a monthly mortgage payment of $675.00. To the nearest hundred dollars, what is the most you can borrow for a 25-yr mortgage with an annual interest rate of 7.2%?

7. Show how to derive the formula

$A = \dfrac{P\left[(1+m)^{12y} - 1\right]}{m(1+m)^{12y}}$ from the

formula $P = \dfrac{A \cdot m(1+m)^{12y}}{(1+m)^{12y} - 1}$.

Where You've Been

- In Chapter 5, you learned to write and graph the equation of a parabola.
- In Chapter 5, you also learned to rewrite a quadratic equation by completing the square.
- In Chapter 8, you learned to locate the asymptote of the graph of an exponential function.

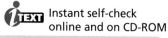

iTEXT Instant self-check online and on CD-ROM

Diagnosing Readiness

(For help, go to the Lesson in green.)

Identifying Quadratic Functions (Lesson 5-1)

Determine whether each function is linear or quadratic. Identify the quadratic, linear, and constant terms.

1. $y = 6x - x^2 + 1$ **2.** $f(x) = -2(3 + x)^2 + 2x^2$ **3.** $y = 2x - y - 13$

4. $y = 4x(7 - 2x)$ **5.** $g(x) = -2x^2 - 3(x - 2)$ **6.** $y = x - 2(x + 5)$

Graphing Quadratic Functions (Lesson 5-2)

Graph each function.

7. $y = -x^2$ **8.** $y = \frac{1}{3}x^2$ **9.** $y = 2x^2 + 5$ **10.** $y = x^2 + 6x + 8$

Completing the Square (Lesson 5-7)

Complete the square.

11. $x^2 + 8x + \blacksquare$ **12.** $x^2 - 5x + \blacksquare$ **13.** $x^2 + 14x + \blacksquare$

Rewrite each function in vertex form. Then graph the function.

14. $y = x^2 + 6x + 7$ **15.** $y = 2x^2 - 4x + 10$ **16.** $y = -3x^2 + x$

Solving Polynomial Equations (Lesson 6-5)

Find all the roots of each polynomial equation.

17. $2x^3 - x^2 + 10x - 5 = 0$ **18.** $2x^3 - 5x^2 + 4x - 1 = 0$

Graphing Exponential Decay (Lesson 8-1)

Sketch the graph for each decay function. Label the asymptote.

19. $y = 8\left(\frac{1}{2}\right)^x$ **20.** $y = 2(0.4)^x$ **21.** $y = \left(\frac{3}{4}\right)^x$

Quadratic Relations

Chapter 10

Where You're Going

- In Chapter 10, you will learn to use conic sections to model real-world problems.
- You will learn to graph parabolas, circles, ellipses, and hyperbolas.
- You will learn to identify the equation of a specific conic section by completing the square.

Applying what you learn, on pages 584–585 you will do activities involving planetary exploration.

LESSONS

Key Vocabulary

- center (p. 549)
- circle (p. 549)
- conic section (p. 535)
- co-vertices (p. 556)
- directrix (p. 543)
- ellipse (p. 556)
- focus of a parabola (p. 543)
- focus of an ellipse (p. 556)
- focus of a hyperbola (p. 563)
- hyperbola (p. 563)
- major axis (p. 556)
- minor axis (p. 556)
- radius (p. 549)
- standard form of an equation of a circle (p. 549)
- transverse axis (p. 563)
- vertices of an ellipse (p. 556)
- vertices of a hyperbola (p. 563)

Investigation

Conic Sections

FOR USE WITH LESSON 10-1

A conic section is a special curve formed by the intersection of a cone and a plane. You can use paper cutouts to investigate conic sections.

Step 1 Draw two circular areas, each one measuring four inches in diameter. Cut out each circular area, and then cut it in half. Roll each half into a cone and secure it with tape.

Step 2 Trace the three templates below onto a sheet of paper. Cut out the parts corresponding to the white areas. The remaining parts corresponding to the blue areas are the templates. Label each one.

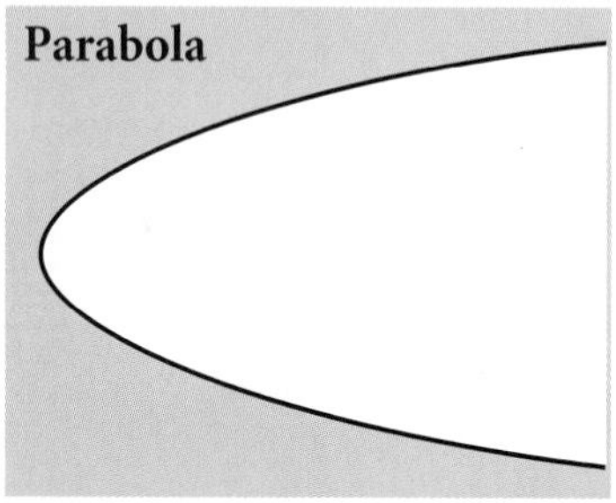

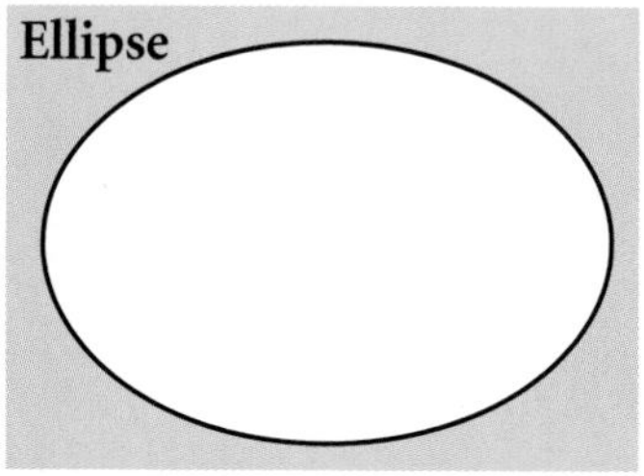

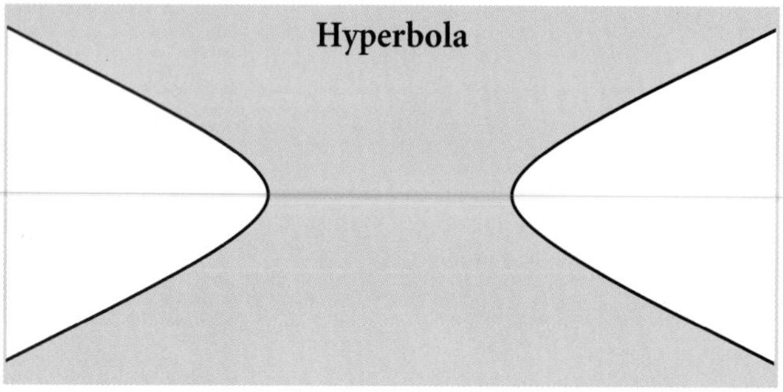

Step 3 Make a fourth template for a circle. Use a compass or a coin of any size to draw the circle.

Step 4 Fit each template around the cones so that the template stays flat, like a plane. The ellipse is shown at the right. Sketch each result.

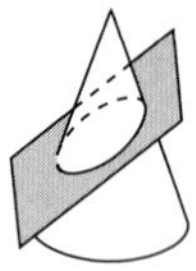

EXERCISES

1. a. The template for a hyperbola has two parts. Explain how you must position the cones to use this template as a model of a hyperbola.

b. Suppose you tried to fit your other three templates around a double cone. Would the results change? Explain.

2. a. Fold the template for each curve so that two halves coincide. In how many ways can you do this for each of the four templates?

b. How many axes of symmetry does each template have?

10-1 Exploring Conic Sections

North Carolina Objectives

2.09 Use the equations of parabolas and circles to model and solve problems. a) Solve using tables, graphs, and algebraic properties. b) Interpret the constants and coefficients in the context of the problem.

Lesson Preview

What You'll Learn

OBJECTIVE 1 To graph conic sections

OBJECTIVE 2 To identify conic sections

. . . And Why

To analyze Moiré patterns, as in Example 5

Check Skills You'll Need

(For help, go to Lessons 2-2, 5-2, and 5-5.)

Find the *x*- and *y*-intercepts of the graph of each function.

1. $y = 3x + 6$ **2.** $2y = -x - 3$

3. $3x - 4y = -12$ **4.** $y = x^2 - 4$

5. $y = (x - 3)^2$ **6.** $y = -4x^2 + 1$

New Vocabulary

- conic section

Interactive lesson includes instant self-check, tutorials, and activities.

OBJECTIVE 1 Graphing Equations of Conic Sections

A **conic section** is a curve formed by the intersection of a plane and a double cone. By changing the inclination of the plane, you can create a circle, a parabola, an ellipse, or a hyperbola. You can use lines of symmetry to graph a conic section.

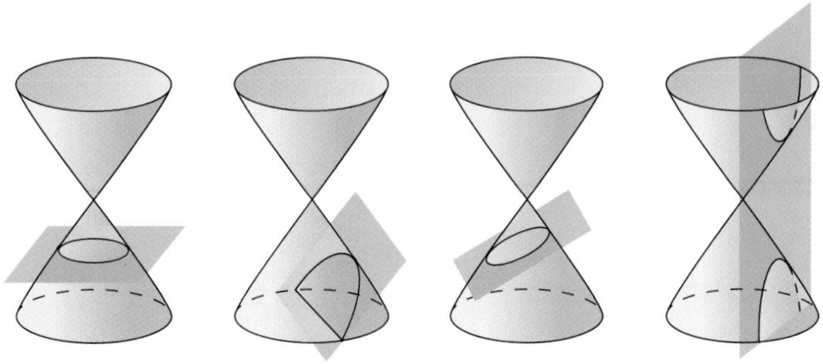

The photograph shows a double cone of illuminated smoke being intersected by a laser to produce a circle.

1 EXAMPLE Graphing a Circle

Graph the equation $x^2 + y^2 = 25$. Describe the graph and its lines of symmetry. Then find the domain and range.

Make a table of values.

x	−5	−4	−3	0	3	4	5
y	0	±3	±4	±5	±4	±3	0

Plot the points and connect them with a smooth curve.

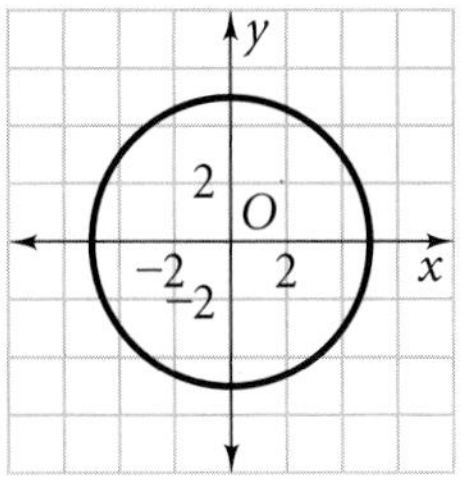

The graph is a circle of radius 5. Its center is at the origin. Every line through the center is a line of symmetry.

Recall from Chapter 2 that you can use set notation to describe a domain or a range. In this example, the domain is $\{x \mid -5 \leq x \leq 5\}$. The range is $\{y \mid -5 \leq y \leq 5\}$.

Check Understanding **1** **a.** Graph the functions $y = \sqrt{25 - x^2}$ and $y = -\sqrt{25 - x^2}$ on the same screen. Compare this graph to the one in Example 1.
b. Explain how you can get the equations in part (a) from $x^2 + y^2 = 25$.
c. **Critical Thinking** Why is there no point on the graph of Example 1 with an x-coordinate of 6?

An ellipse is similar to a circle, but it has only two lines of symmetry.

2 EXAMPLE Graphing an Ellipse

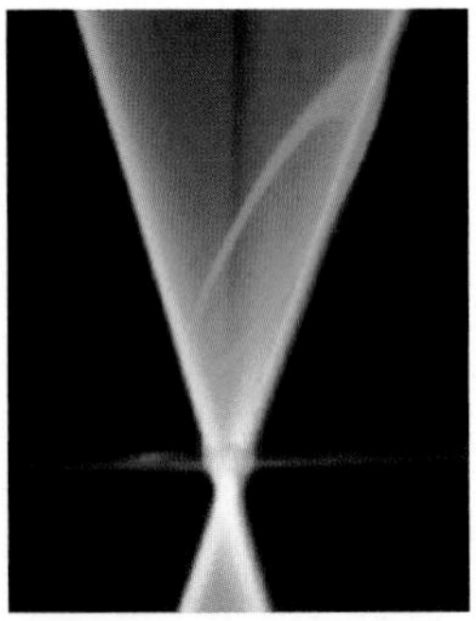
Here the laser intersects the smoke to produce an ellipse.

Graph the equation $9x^2 + 16y^2 = 144$. Describe the graph and the lines of symmetry. Then find the domain and range.

Make a table of values.

x	−4	−3	0	3	4
y	0	±2.0	±3	±2.0	0

Plot the points and connect them with a smooth curve.

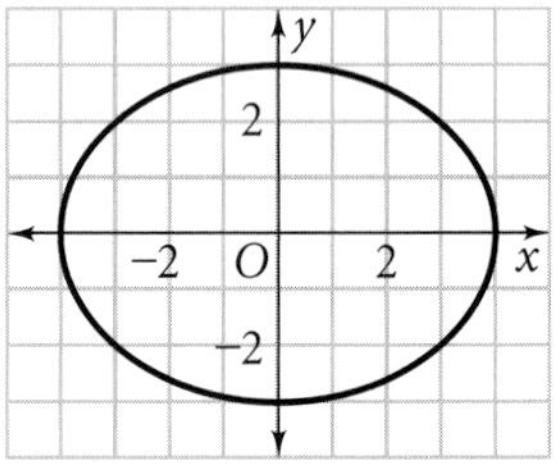

The graph is an ellipse. The center is at the origin. It has two lines of symmetry, the x-axis and the y-axis.

The domain is $\{x \mid -4 \le x \le 4\}$.
The range is $\{y \mid -3 \le y \le 3\}$.

Check Understanding **2** **a.** How far are the x-intercepts from the center of the ellipse? How far are the y-intercepts from the center? Describe how an ellipse differs from a circle.
b. The point (1, 2.9) is an approximation of a point on the graph of Example 2. Use symmetry to find three other approximate points on the ellipse.
c. Graph the equation $2x^2 + y^2 = 18$. Describe the graph and give the coordinates of the x- and y-intercepts.

Not all conic sections consist of one smooth curve. Note the unique shape of the hyperbola.

3 EXAMPLE Graphing a Hyperbola

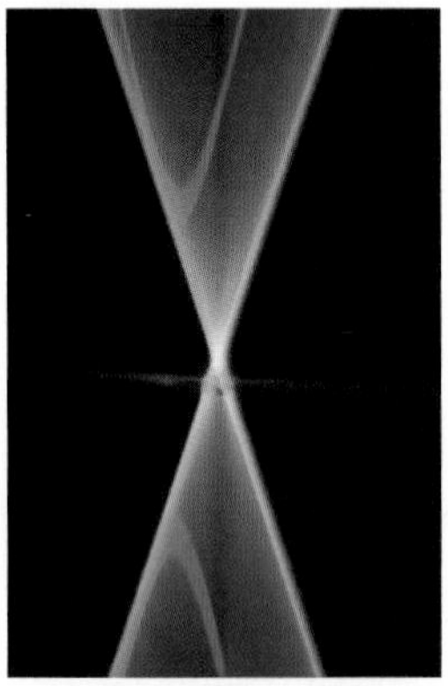
Here the laser intersects the smoke to produce a hyperbola.

Graph the equation $x^2 - y^2 = 9$. Describe the graph and its lines of symmetry. Then find the domain and range.

Make a table of values.

x	−5	−4	−3	−2	−1	0	1	2	3	4	5
y	±4	±2.6	0	–	–	–	–	–	0	±2.6	±4

Plot the points and connect them with smooth curves.

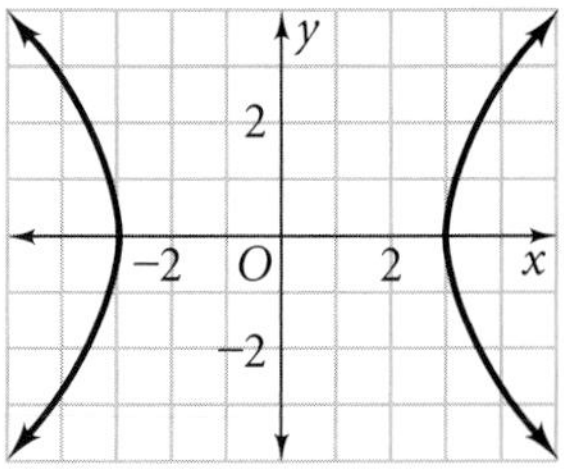

The graph is a hyperbola that consists of two branches. Its center is at the origin. It has two lines of symmetry, the x-axis and the y-axis.

The domain is $\{x \mid x \le -3 \text{ or } x \ge 3\}$. The range is all real numbers.

Check Understanding **3** **a.** Does the graph in Example 3 represent a function? Explain.
b. In the table in Example 3, why is the y-value undefined when $x = -2, -1, 0, 1,$ or 2?
c. **Critical Thinking** What two lines does each branch of this hyperbola get very close to? What are these lines called?

OBJECTIVE

2 Identifying Conic Sections

The center and the intercepts are important points to identify on the graph of some conic sections.

4 EXAMPLE Identifying Graphs of Conic Sections

Identify the center and intercepts of each conic section. Then find the domain and range. In part (b), each interval on the graph represents one unit.

a.

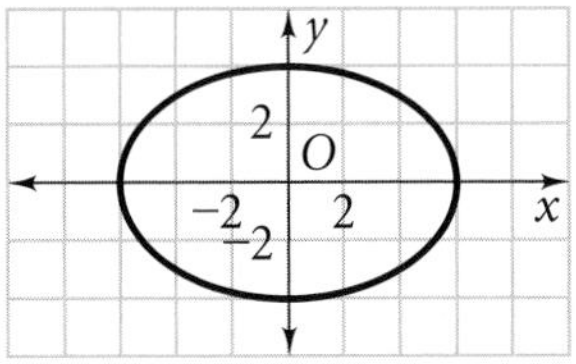

The center of the ellipse is $(0, 0)$. The x-intercepts are $(-6, 0)$ and $(6, 0)$, and the y-intercepts are $(0, -4)$ and $(0, 4)$. The domain is $\{x \mid -6 \leq x \leq 6\}$, and the range is $\{y \mid -4 \leq y \leq 4\}$.

b.

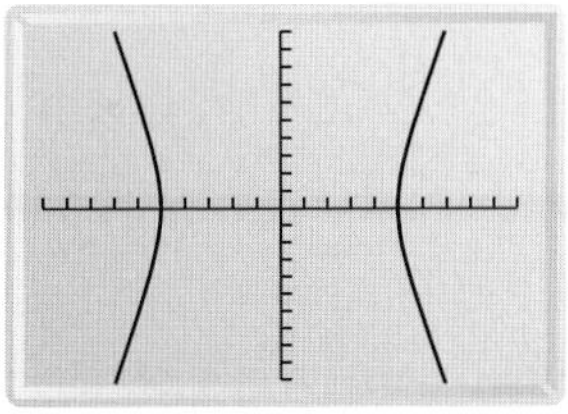

The center of the hyperbola is $(0, 0)$. The x-intercepts are $(-5, 0)$ and $(5, 0)$, and there are no y-intercepts. The domain is $\{x \mid x \geq 5 \text{ and } x \leq -5\}$, and the range is all real numbers.

Check Understanding **4** Identify the center and intercepts of the conic section. Then find the domain and range. Each interval represents one unit.

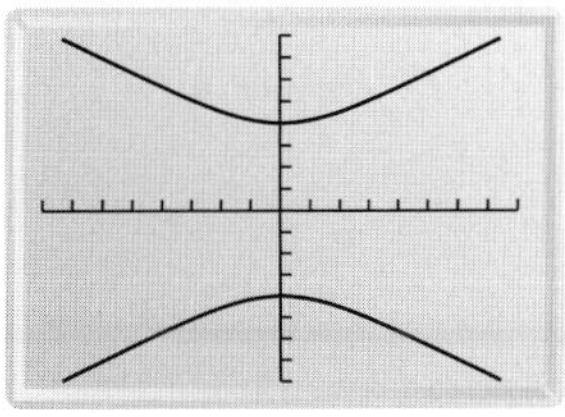

You will study each conic section in detail later in this chapter. Even before you learn the details of the equations of conic sections, you can match the equations with their graphs.

5 EXAMPLE Real-World Connection

Design Moiré patterns are formed when two patterns, such as arrays of dots or lines, overlap to produce a third, unintended pattern. Moiré patterns cause problems for printers and video technicians. Describe each unintended pattern. Match it with one of these possible equations: $x^2 - y^2 = 1$, $x^2 + y^2 = 16$, or $9x^2 + 25y^2 = 225$.

Reading Math

Moiré is a French word meaning "watered" or "wavy."

a.

b.

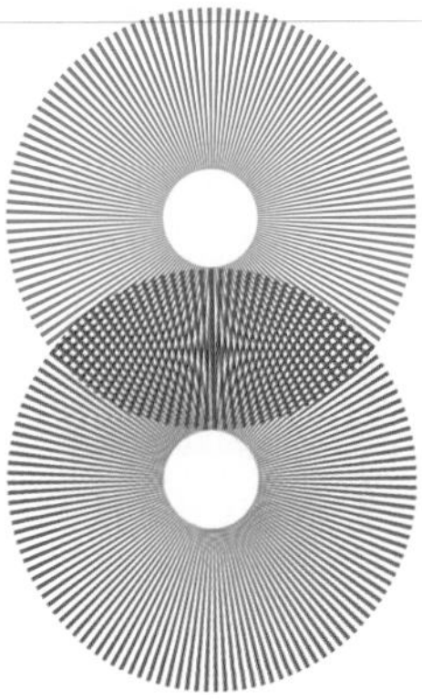

c.

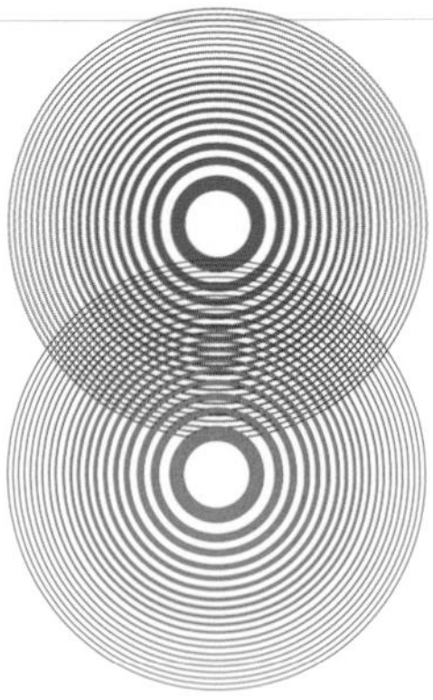

a. Ellipse: The equation $9x^2 + 25y^2 = 225$ represents a conic section with two sets of intercepts, $(\pm5, 0)$ and $(0, \pm3)$. Since the intercepts are not equidistant from the center, the equation models an ellipse.

b. Hyperbola: The equation $x^2 - y^2 = 1$ represents a conic section with one set of intercepts, $(\pm1, 0)$, so the equation must model a hyperbola.

c. Circle: The equation $x^2 + y^2 = 16$ represents a conic section with two sets of intercepts, $(\pm4, 0)$ and $(0, \pm4)$. Since each intercept is 4 units from the center, the equation models a circle.

Check Understanding 5 **a.** **Critical Thinking** What similarities do you notice among the three equations in Example 5?

b. What differences do you notice?

EXERCISES

For more practice, see *Extra Practice.*

Practice and Problem Solving

A Practice by Example

Examples 1, 2, and 3 (pages 535 and 536)

Graph each equation. Identify the conic section and describe the graph and its lines of symmetry. Then find the domain and range.

1. $3y^2 - x^2 = 25$

2. $2x^2 + y^2 = 36$

3. $x^2 + y^2 = 16$

4. $3y^2 - x^2 = 9$

5. $4x^2 + 25y^2 = 100$

6. $x^2 + y^2 = 49$

7. $x^2 - y^2 + 1 = 0$

8. $x^2 - 2y^2 = 4$

9. $6x^2 + 6y^2 = 600$

10. $x^2 + y^2 - 4 = 0$

11. $6x^2 + 24y^2 - 96 = 0$

12. $4x^2 + 4y^2 - 20 = 0$

13. $x^2 + 9y^2 = 1$

14. $4x^2 - 36y^2 = 144$

15. $4y^2 - 36x^2 = 1$

16. $36x^2 + 4y^2 = 144$

Example 4 (page 537) **Identify the center and intercepts of each conic section. Give the domain and range of each graph. On graphing calculator screens, each interval represents one unit.**

17. 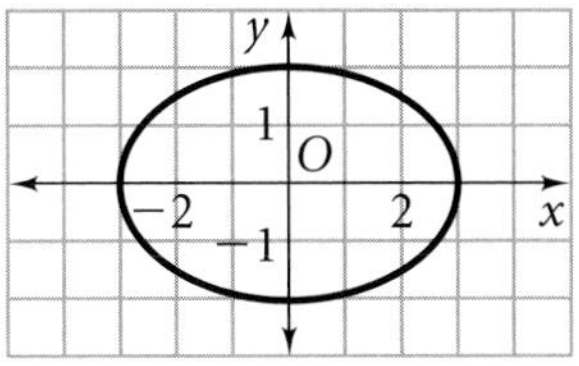

18. 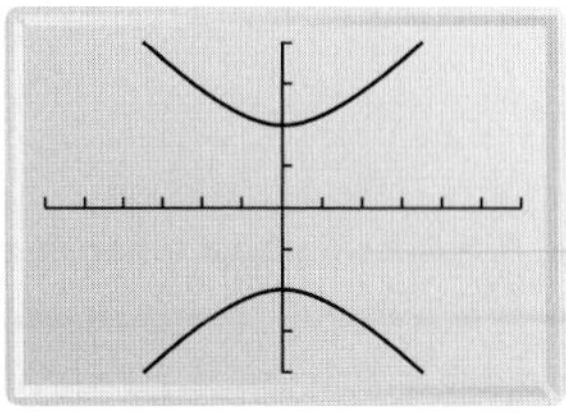

19. 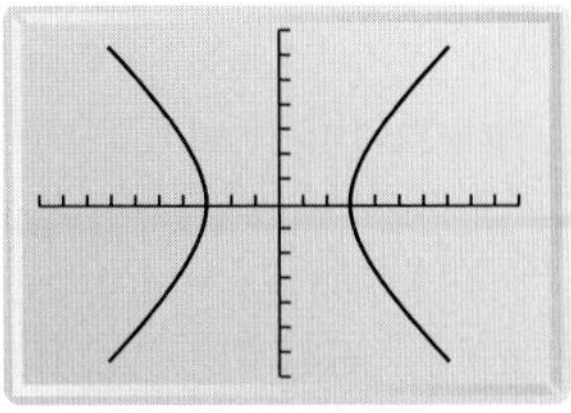

20. 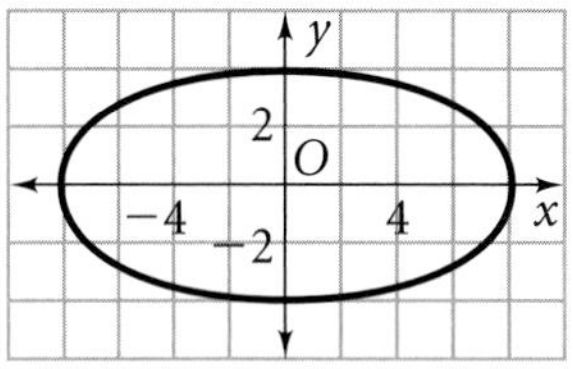

21. 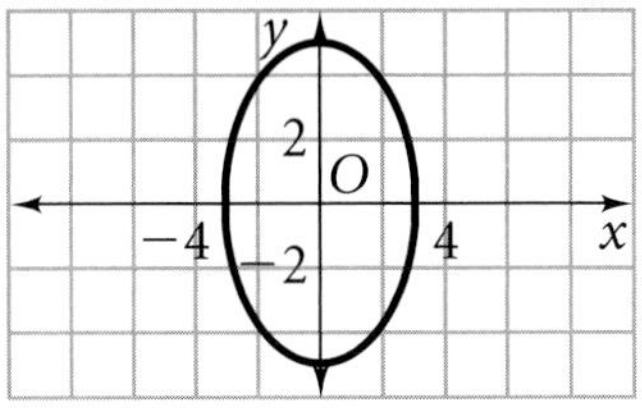

22. 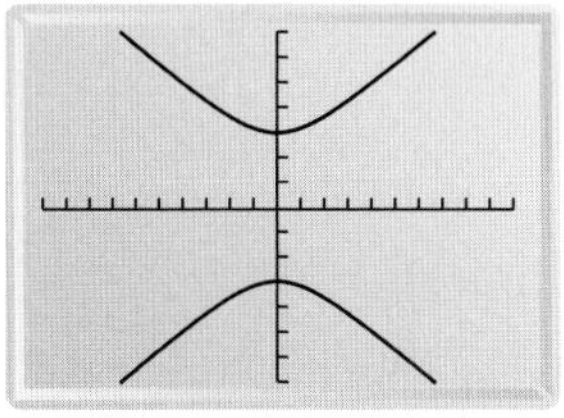

Example 5 (page 538) **Match each equation with a graph in Exercises 17–22.**

23. $x^2 - y^2 = 9$

24. $4x^2 + 9y^2 = 36$

25. $y^2 - x^2 = 4$

26. $x^2 + 4y^2 = 64$

27. $25x^2 + 9y^2 = 225$

28. $y^2 - x^2 = 9$

B Apply Your Skills

Graph each equation. Describe the graph and its lines of symmetry. Then find the domain and range.

29. $9x^2 - y^2 = 144$

30. $11x^2 + 11y^2 = 44$

31. $-8x^2 + 32y^2 - 128 = 0$

32. $25x^2 + 16y^2 - 320 = 0$

33. a. Writing Describe the relationship between the center of a circle and the axes of symmetry of the circle.

b. Make a Conjecture Where is the center of an ellipse or a hyperbola located in relation to the axes of symmetry? Verify your conjectures with examples.

34. Light The light emitted from a lamp with a shade forms a shadow on the wall. Explain how you could turn the lamp in relation to the wall so that the shadow cast by the shade forms each conic section.

a. hyperbola **b.** parabola **c.** ellipse **d.** circle

Mental Math **Each given point is on the graph of the given equation. Use symmetry to find at least one more point on the graph.**

35. $(2, -4), y^2 = 8x$

36. $(-\sqrt{2}, 1), x^2 + y^2 = 3$

37. $(2, 2\sqrt{2}), x^2 + 4y^2 = 36$

38. $(-2, 0), 9x^2 + 9y^2 - 36 = 0$

39. $(-3, -\sqrt{51}), 6y^2 - 9x^2 - 225 = 0$

40. $(0, \sqrt{7}), x^2 + 2y^2 = 14$

Graph each circle so that the center is at the origin. Then write the equation.

41. radius 6 **42.** radius $\frac{1}{2}$ **43.** diameter 8 **44.** diameter 2.5

45. **Open-Ended** Describe any other figures you can imagine that can be formed by the intersection of a plane and other shapes.

C Challenge

46. **a.** Graph the equation $xy = 16$. Use both positive and negative values for x.
b. Which conic section does the equation appear to model?
c. Identify any intercepts and lines of symmetry.
d. Does your graph represent a function? If so, rewrite the equation using function notation.

47. The sharpened portion of the pencil at the right meets each painted side in a curved path. Describe the curve and justify your reasoning.

48. An xy term has an interesting effect on the graph of a conic section. Sketch the graph of each conic section below using your graphing calculator. (*Hint:* To solve for y, you will need to complete a square.)
a. $4x^2 + 2xy + y^2 = 9$
b. $4x^2 + 2xy - y^2 = 9$

Reading Math

Cone comes from the Indo-European word for "sharpen." Section comes from the word for "cut."

49. **Sound** An airplane flying faster than the speed of sound creates a cone-shaped pressure disturbance in the air. This is heard by people on the ground as a sonic boom. What is the shape of the path on the ground?

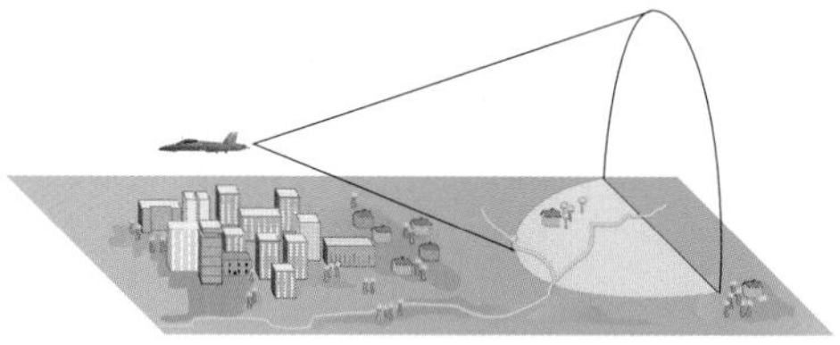

Standardized Test Prep

Multiple Choice

50. The graph of which equation of a circle contains all the points in the table below?

x	−3	0	3
y	0	±3	0

A. $x^2 + y^2 - 4 = 0$ **B.** $x^2 + y^2 = 25$
C. $x^2 + y^2 = 36$ **D.** $6x^2 + 6y^2 = 54$

51. The graph of which ellipse contains all the points in the table below?

x	−4	−2	0	2	4
y	0	$\pm\sqrt{3}$	±2	$\pm\sqrt{3}$	0

F. $x^2 + 4y^2 = 16$ **G.** $4x^2 + 16y^2 = 144$
H. $4x^2 + 25y^2 = 64$ **I.** $9x^2 + y^2 = 81$

52. Which point is NOT on the graph of $4x^2 - y^2 = 4$?
A. $(-2, -2\sqrt{3})$ **B.** $(-1, 0)$ **C.** $(1, 0)$ **D.** $(2, 2)$

Take It to the NET
Online lesson quiz at **www.PHSchool.com**
Web Code: aga-1001

53. Which equation does NOT represent a line of symmetry for the circle with equation $x^2 + y^2 = 100$?
F. $x = 0$ **G.** $y = \frac{1}{2}x$ **H.** $y = x$ **I.** $y = x + 1$

54. Which equation represents a line of symmetry for the ellipse with equation $x^2 + 9y^2 = 9$?
A. $y = -x$ B. $y = 0$ C. $y = x$ D. $xy = 1$

Short Response

55. The graph of the equation $x^2 + y^2 = 121$ is a circle. Describe the graph and its lines of symmetry. Find the domain and the range.

Mixed Review

Lesson 9-7

A standard number cube is tossed. Find each probability.

56. P(5 or greater than 3)
57. P(even or 6)
58. P(even or 7)
59. P(prime or 2)

Lesson 9-1

Suppose z varies jointly with x and y. Write a function that models each relationship. Find the value of z when $x = -2$ and $y = 3$.

60. $z = -5$ when $x = -1$ and $y = -1$
61. $z = 72$ when $x = 3$ and $y = -6$
62. $z = 32$ when $x = 0.1$ and $y = 8$
63. $z = 5$ when $x = -4$ and $y = 2.5$

Lesson 8-1

Write an exponential equation $y = ab^x$ whose graph passes through the given points.

64. $(-1, 2)$ and $(3, 32)$
65. $\left(0, \frac{1}{2}\right)$ and $(2, 8)$
66. $(1, 6)$ and $(2, 12)$
67. $\left(0, \frac{1}{3}\right)$ and $(2, 3)$
68. $\left(-1, \frac{2}{3}\right)$ and $(2, 18)$
69. $\left(-1, \frac{1}{8}\right)$ and $(4, 4)$

Lesson 6-8

Expand each binomial.

70. $(x - y)^3$
71. $(p + q)^6$
72. $(x - 2)^4$
73. $(3 - x)^5$

A Point in Time

Titanic was the largest passenger liner that had yet been built. On its maiden voyage in 1912, it struck an iceberg and sank. More than 1500 people died.

In 1985 a French and American team searched for *Titanic*. Research vessels combed the area with sonar. Transmitters aboard each ship sent out powerful spherical sound waves. Each wave reflected off any object in a half-mile-wide strip of ocean floor and returned to a receiver. The receiver then converted the echo to a picture of the object and calculated its depth. Two months after the search began, *Titanic* was discovered lying in two sections at a depth of some 13,000 feet.

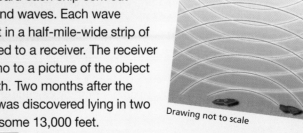

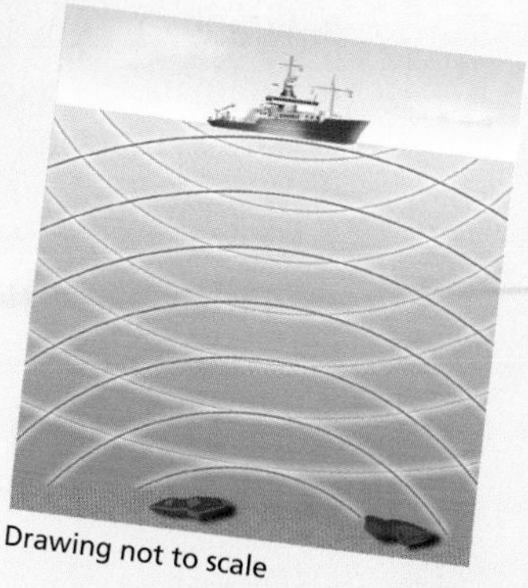

Take It to the NET For more information about *Titanic*, go to **www.PHSchool.com**.
Web Code: age-2032

Technology

Graphing Conic Sections

FOR USE WITH LESSON 10-1

You can use your graphing calculator to graph relations that are not functions.

Take It to the NET
Graphing Calculator procedures online at **www.PHSchool.com**
Web Code: age-2110

EXAMPLE

Graph the ellipse $\frac{x^2}{16} + \frac{y^2}{9} = 1$.

Step 1 Solve the equation for y.

$$\frac{x^2}{16} + \frac{y^2}{9} = 1$$

$$\frac{y^2}{9} = 1 - \frac{x^2}{16}$$

$$y^2 = 9\left(1 - \frac{x^2}{16}\right)$$

$$y = \pm 3\sqrt{1 - \frac{x^2}{16}}$$

Step 2 Enter the equations as Y_1 and Y_2.

Step 3 Select a square window.

Step 4 Graph.

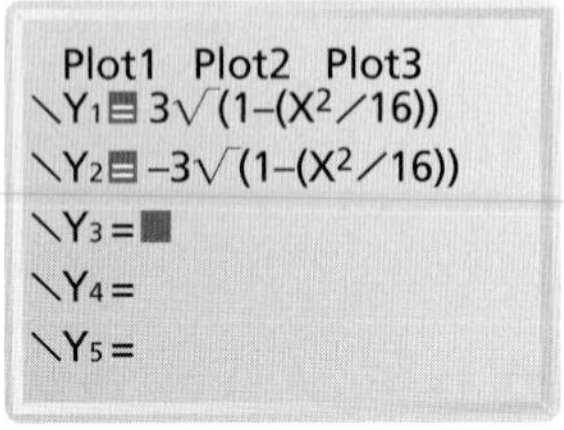

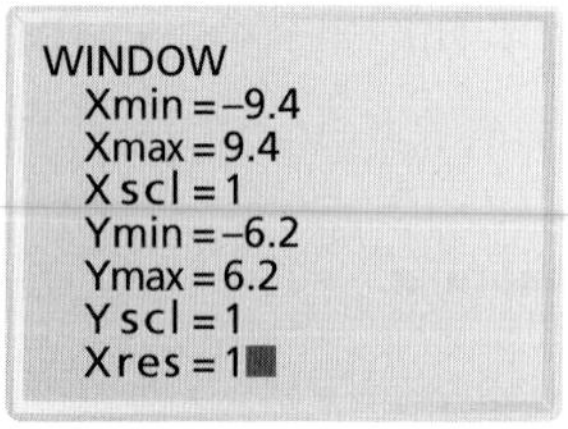

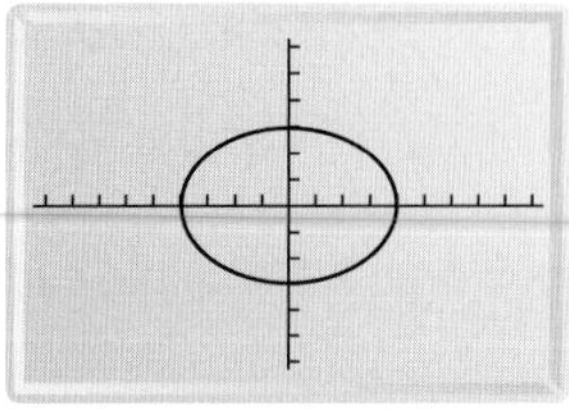

EXERCISES

Graph each conic section.

1. $x^2 + y^2 = 25$

2. $4x^2 + y^2 = 16$

3. $9x^2 - 16y^2 = 144$

4. $x^2 - y^2 = 3$

5. $\frac{x^2}{4} - \frac{y^2}{9} = 1$

6. $x^2 + \frac{y^2}{4} = 16$

7. a. Graph the functions $y = \sqrt{\frac{81}{4} - x^2}$ and $y = -\sqrt{\frac{81}{4} - x^2}$.

b. Estimate the x-intercepts and find the y-intercepts.

c. Adjust the window to $-9.3 \leq x \leq 9.5$. Verify the x-intercepts.

d. What conic section does the graph represent?

Graph each conic section. Find the *x*- and *y*-intercepts.

8. $4x^2 + y^2 = 25$

9. $x^2 + y^2 = 30$

10. $9x^2 - 4y^2 = 72$

11. Writing Explain how to use a graphing calculator to graph the relation $x = |y - 3|$.

10-2 Parabolas

North Carolina Objectives

2.09 Use the equations of parabolas and circles to model and solve problems. a) Solve using tables, graphs, and algebraic properties. b) Interpret the constants and coefficients in the context of the problem.

Lesson Preview

What You'll Learn

OBJECTIVE 1 To write the equation of a parabola

OBJECTIVE 2 To graph parabolas

. . . And Why

To model a solar collector, as in Example 3

Check Skills You'll Need

(For help, go to Skills Handbook pages 844 and 856.)

Solve for *c*.

1. $\frac{1}{8} = \frac{1}{c}$ **2.** $\frac{1}{8} = \frac{1}{2c}$ **3.** $\frac{1}{12} = \frac{1}{4c}$ **4.** $2 = \frac{1}{4c}$

Find the distance between the given points.

5. $(2, 3)$ and $(4, 1)$ **6.** $(4, 6)$ and $(3, -2)$ **7.** $(-1, 5)$ and $(2, -3)$

New Vocabulary • focus of a parabola • directrix

Interactive lesson includes instant self-check, tutorials, and activities.

OBJECTIVE 1 Writing the Equation of a Parabola

In Chapter 5 you learned that a parabola is the graph of a quadratic equation. By definition, a parabola is the set of all points in a plane that are the same distance from a fixed line and a fixed point not on the line. The fixed point is the **focus of a parabola.** The fixed line is the **directrix.** The line through the focus and perpendicular to the directrix is the axis of symmetry.

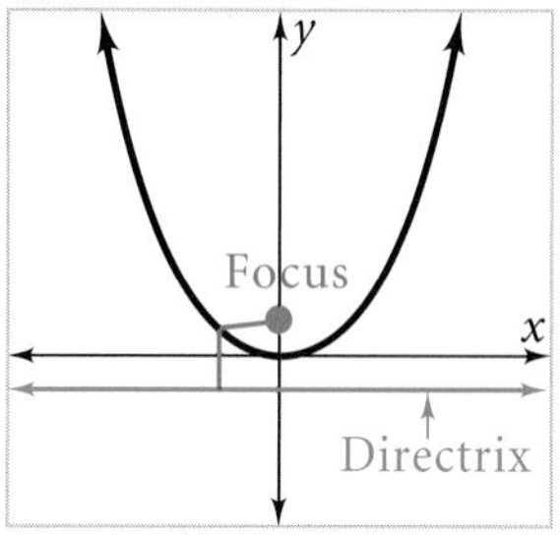

1 EXAMPLE Using the Definition of a Parabola

Write an equation for a graph that is the set of all points in the plane that are equidistant from the point $F(0, 3)$ and the line $y = -3$.

You need to find all points $P(x, y)$ such that FP and the distance from P to the given line are equal.

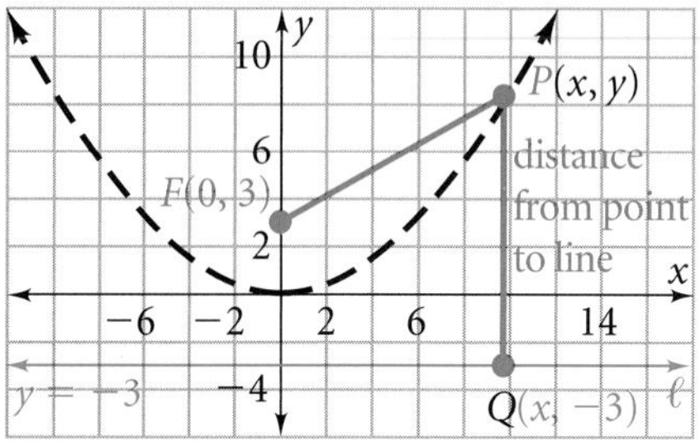

$$FP = PQ$$

$$\sqrt{(x - 0)^2 + (y - 3)^2} = \sqrt{(x - x)^2 + (y - (-3))^2}$$

$$x^2 + (y - 3)^2 = 0^2 + (y + 3)^2$$

$$x^2 + y^2 - 6y + 9 = y^2 + 6y + 9$$

$$x^2 = 12y$$

$$y = \frac{1}{12}x^2$$

An equation of the set of all points equidistant from $F(0, 3)$ and $y = -3$ is $y = \frac{1}{12}x^2$.

Need Help?

The distance between $P_1(x_1, y_1)$ and $P_2(x_2, y_2)$ is $\sqrt{(x_2 - x_1)^2 + (y_2 - y_1)^2}$.

Check Understanding **1** Write an equation for a graph that is the set of all points in the plane that are equidistant from the point $F(2, 0)$ and the line $x = -2$.

In Chapter 5 you learned about the special relationship between the value of a and the graph of a quadratic function in the form $y = ax^2$. Now you will learn about the relationship between the value of a and the graph of a quadratic relation in the form $y = ax^2$ or $x = ay^2$.

If c is the distance from the vertex to the focus of a parabola, then $|a| = \frac{1}{4c}$.

Consider any parabola with equation $y = ax^2$.

Need Help?

To review graphing parabolas, go to Lesson 5-2.

If $a > 0$, then
- the parabola opens upward
- the focus is at $(0, c)$
- the directrix is $y = -c$

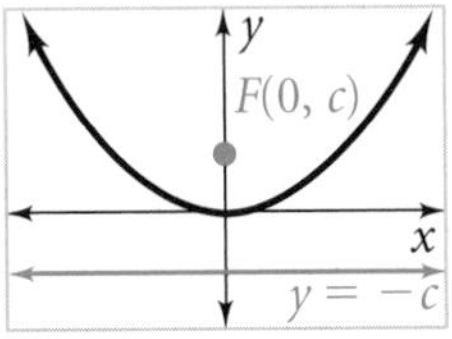

If $a < 0$, then
- the parabola opens downward
- the focus is at $(0, -c)$
- the directrix is at $y = c$

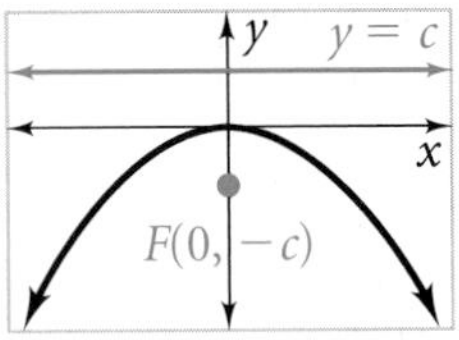

Consider any parabola with equation $x = ay^2$.

If $a > 0$, then
- the parabola opens to the right
- the focus is at $(c, 0)$
- the directrix is at $x = -c$

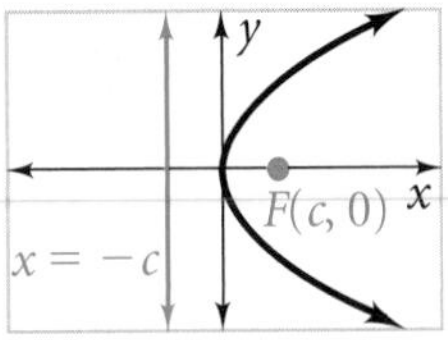

If $a < 0$, then
- the parabola opens to the left
- the focus is at $(-c, 0)$
- the directrix is at $x = c$

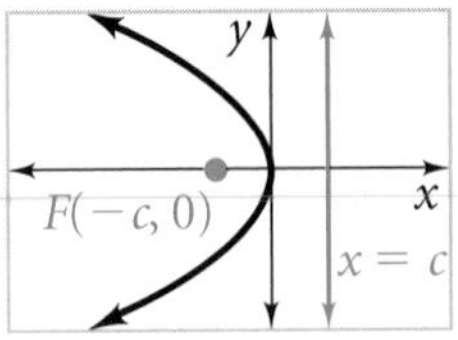

You can use the information above to write an equation of a parabola.

2 EXAMPLE Writing the Equation of a Parabola

Write an equation of a parabola with a vertex at the origin and a focus at $(-5, 0)$.

Step 1 Determine the orientation of the parabola. Make a sketch. Since the focus is located to the left of the vertex, the parabola must open to the left. Use $x = ay^2$.

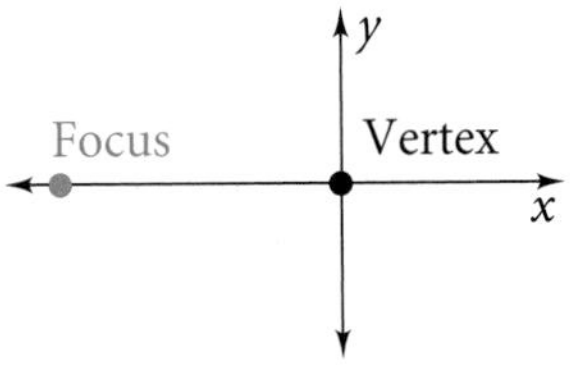

Step 2 Find a.

$|a| = \frac{1}{4c}$

$= \frac{1}{4(5)}$ **Since the focus is a distance of 5 units from the vertex, $c = 5$.**

$= \frac{1}{20}$

Since the parabola opens to the left, a is negative. So $a = -\frac{1}{20}$.

An equation for the parabola is $x = -\frac{1}{20}y^2$.

Check Understanding 2 Write an equation of a parabola with a vertex at the origin and a focus at $\left(\frac{1}{2}, 0\right)$.

You can find the equation of a parabola that models a real-world situation.

3 EXAMPLE Real-World Connection

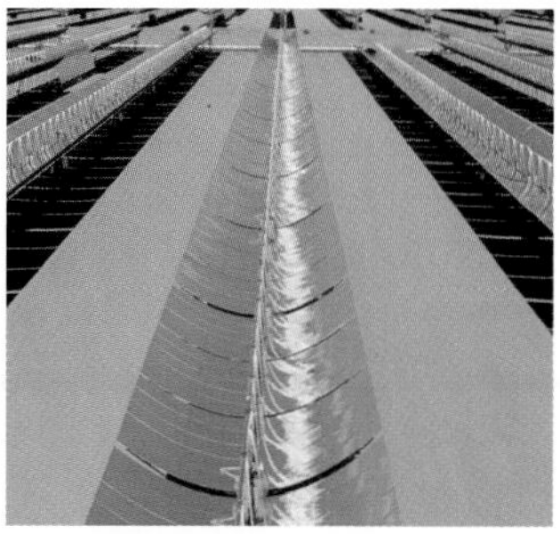

Real-World Connection

Parabolic solar mirrors focus the sun's energy to produce steam that drives electric generators.

Solar Energy In some solar collectors, a mirror with a parabolic cross section is used to concentrate sunlight on a pipe, which is located at the focus of the mirror.

a. Suppose the pipe is located 6 in. from the vertex of the mirror. Write an equation of the parabola that models the cross section of the mirror.

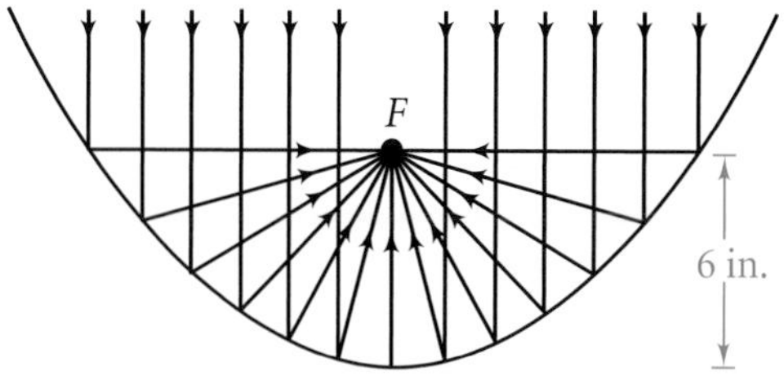

b. The amount of light collected by the mirror is directly proportional to its width. Using this mirror, the pipe receives 30^2, or 900, times more sunlight than it would without the mirror. Suppose the diameter of the pipe is 1 in. What must be the width of the mirror?

a. The distance from the vertex to the focus is 6 in., so $c = 6$. Find the value of a.

$$a = \frac{1}{4c}$$
$$= \frac{1}{4(6)}$$
$$= \frac{1}{24}$$ **Since the parabola opens upward, *a* is positive.**

The equation of the parabola is $y = \frac{1}{24}x^2$.

b. The width of the mirror must be 30 times the diameter of the pipe, or 30 in.

Check Understanding **3** Suppose the pipe is located 8.25 in. from the vertex of the mirror. Write an equation of the parabola to model the cross section of the mirror.

OBJECTIVE

2 Graphing Parabolas

You can use the value of a to identify the focus and directrix of a parabola.

4 EXAMPLE Identifying Focus and Directrix

Identify the focus and the directrix of the graph of the equation $y = -\frac{1}{16}x^2$.

The parabola is of the form $y = ax^2$, so the vertex is at the origin and the parabola has a vertical axis of symmetry. Since $a < 0$, the parabola opens downward.

$$|a| = \frac{1}{4c}$$
$$\left|-\frac{1}{16}\right| = \frac{1}{4c}$$ **Substitute $-\frac{1}{16}$ for *a*.**
$$4c = 16$$ **Solve for *c*.**
$$c = 4$$

The focus is at $(0, -4)$. The equation of the directrix is $y = 4$.

Check Understanding **4** Identify the focus and the directrix of the graph of the equation $y = \frac{1}{12}x^2$.

You can use the focus and directrix to graph the equation of a parabola.

5 EXAMPLE Graphing the Equation of a Parabola

Identify the vertex, the focus, and the directrix of the graph of the equation $y^2 - 4x - 4y + 16 = 0$. Then graph the parabola.

$y^2 - 4x - 4y + 16 = 0$

$4x = y^2 - 4y + 16$ **Solve for *x*, since *x* is in only one term.**

$4x = (y^2 - 4y + 4) + 16 - 4$ **Complete the square in *y*.**

$x = \frac{1}{4}(y^2 - 4y + 4) + 4 - 1$ **Divide both sides of the equation by 4.**

$x = \frac{1}{4}(y - 2)^2 + 3$ **vertex form**

Need Help?
To review completing the square, go to Lesson 5-7.

The parabola is of the form $x = a(y - k)^2 + h$, so the vertex is at (3, 2) and the parabola has a horizontal axis of symmetry. Since $a > 0$, the parabola opens to the right.

$|a| = \frac{1}{4c}$

$\left|\frac{1}{4}\right| = \frac{1}{4c}$ **Substitute $\frac{1}{4}$ for *a*.**

$4c = 4$ **Solve for *c*.**

$c = 1$

The vertex is at (3, 2) and the focus is at (4, 2). The equation of the directrix is $x = 2$.

Locate one or more points on the parabola. Select a value for *y*, such as 4. The point on the parabola with a *y*-value of 4 is (4, 4). Use the symmetric nature of a parabola to find the corresponding point, (4, 0).

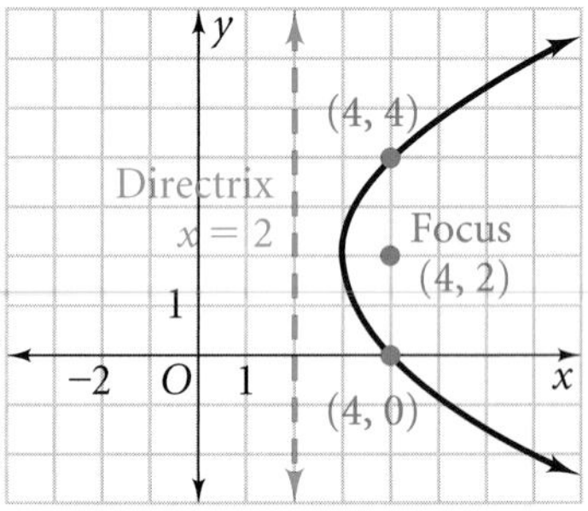

Check Understanding 5 Identify the vertex, the focus, and the directrix of the graph of $x^2 + 6x + 3y + 12 = 0$. Then graph the equation.

EXERCISES

For more practice, see *Extra Practice*.

Practice and Problem Solving

A Practice by Example

Example 1 (page 543)

Write an equation for a graph that is the set of all points in the plane that are equidistant from the given point and the given line.

1. $F(0, 2), y = -2$ **2.** $F(0, -1), y = 1$ **3.** $F(-3, 0), x = 3$

4. $F(0, -8), y = 8$ **5.** $F(0, 4), y = 0$ **6.** $F\left(\frac{1}{2}, 0\right), x = -\frac{1}{2}$

Example 2 (page 544)

Write an equation of a parabola with a vertex at the origin and the given focus.

7. focus at (6, 0) **8.** focus at (0, −4) **9.** focus at (0, 7)

10. focus at (−1, 0) **11.** focus at (2, 0) **12.** focus at (0, −5)

Example 3 (page 545)

Write an equation of a parabola opening upward with a vertex at the origin.

13. focus 1.5 units from vertex **14.** focus $\frac{1}{8}$ of a unit from vertex

15. **Optics** A cross section of a flashlight reflector is a parabola. The bulb is located at the focus. Suppose the bulb is located $\frac{1}{4}$ in. from the vertex of the reflector. You can model the reflector with a parabola that opens upward and has a vertex at the origin.
   a. Write an equation of the parabola to model the cross section of the reflector.
   b. Reasoning Use the properties of parabolas to explain the advantages of this design.

Example 4 (page 545)

Identify the focus and the directrix of the graph of each equation.

16. $y = \frac{1}{4}x^2$ **17.** $y = x^2$ **18.** $y = -\frac{1}{8}x^2$ **19.** $x = \frac{1}{2}y^2$

20. $y = \frac{1}{2}x^2$ **21.** $x = \frac{1}{36}y^2$ **22.** $x = -\frac{1}{18}y^2$ **23.** $y = -2x^2$

Example 5 (page 546)

Identify the vertex, the focus, and the directrix of the graph of each equation. Then sketch the graph.

24. $x = \frac{1}{24}y^2$ **25.** $y = -\frac{1}{4}x^2$ **26.** $x = \frac{1}{12}y^2$

27. $y^2 - 25x = 0$ **28.** $x^2 = 4y$ **29.** $x^2 = -4y$

30. $(x - 2)^2 = 4y$ **31.** $-8x = y^2$ **32.** $(x + 2)^2 = y - 4$

33. $y^2 - 6x = 18$ **34.** $x^2 + 24y - 8x = -16$ **35.** $y^2 - 12x + 2y = -37$

B Apply Your Skills

Write an equation of a parabola with a vertex at the origin.

36. directrix $x = -3$ **37.** focus at $(0, 100)$ **38.** directrix $y = 5$

39. focus at $(-7, 0)$ **40.** directrix $x = 9$ **41.** directrix $y = 2.8$

Real-World Connection

Tsunamis are ocean waves that result from an undersea earthquake. As the waves approach shallow water, their height increases and their speed decreases.

42. **Earth Science** The equation $d = \frac{1}{10}s^2$ relates the depth d (in meters) of the ocean to the speed s (in meters per second) at which tsunamis travel. Graph the equation.

Use the information in each graph to write the equation for the graph.

43.

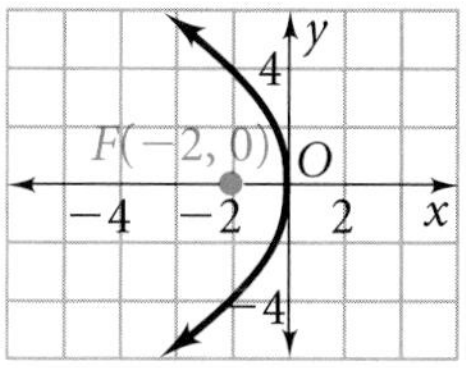

44.

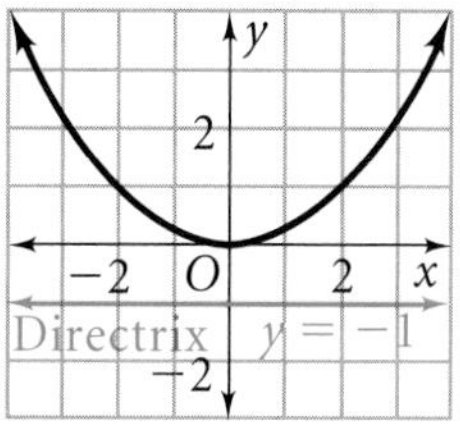

45.

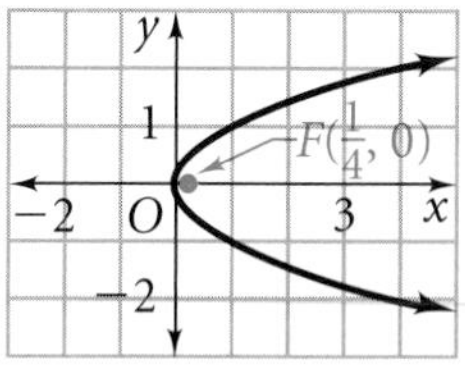

Graph each equation.

46. $y^2 - 8x = 0$ **47.** $y^2 - 8y + 8x = -16$ **48.** $2x^2 - y + 20x = -53$

49. $x^2 = 12y$ **50.** $y = 4(x - 3)^2 - 2$ **51.** $(y - 2)^2 = 4(x + 3)$

Write an equation of a parabola with a vertex at (1, 1).

52. directrix $y = -\frac{1}{2}$ **53.** directrix $x = \frac{3}{2}$ **54.** focus at $(1, 0)$

55. **Open-Ended** Write an equation for a parabola that opens to the left. Give the focus and directrix of the parabola.

56. **Writing** Explain how to find the distance from the focus to the directrix of the parabola $x = 2y^2$.

C Challenge

57. **Critical Thinking** Use the definition of a parabola to show that the parabola with vertex (h, k) and focus $(h, k + c)$ has the equation $(x - h)^2 = 4c(y - k)$.

58. **Modeling** Draw a cross section of a parabolic mirror modeled by the equation $y = 0.002323x^2$.

59. **a.** What part of a parabola is modeled by the function $y = -\sqrt{x}$?
 b. State the domain and range for the function in part (a).

60. The directrix of a parabola is the line $y = -2$. The focus is the point $(0, 2)$.
 a. Suppose the directrix remains fixed, but the focus is shifted along the y-axis farther away from the directrix. Explain what happens to the vertex and the shape of the parabola.
 b. Suppose the focus moves along the y-axis toward the directrix. Explain what happens to the vertex and the shape of the parabola.
 c. What would happen if the focus moved down all the way to the directrix?

Standardized Test Prep

Multiple Choice

61. What is the distance from $P(2, -5)$ to the line $y = -8$?
 A. -6 B. 3 C. 5 D. 10

62. Which point is equidistant from $F(0, 5)$ and the line $y = -5$?
 F. $(-10, 5)$ G. $(-5, 0)$ H. $(0, 1)$ I. $(10, 10)$

63. Which equation represents a parabola that opens to the left?
 A. $x = -2y^2$ B. $x = 2y^2$ C. $y = -2x^2$ D. $y = 2x^2$

Take It to the NET
Online lesson quiz at www.PHSchool.com
Web Code: aga-1002

64. Which equation represents a parabola that opens downward?
 F. $x = -2y^2$ G. $x = 2y^2$ H. $y = -2x^2$ I. $y = 2x^2$

Short Response

65. What is the equation of a parabola that is the set of all points that are equidistant from $F(0, 4)$ and the line $y = -4$?

66. Find the focus and the directrix of the parabola with equation $y = \frac{1}{36}x^2$.

Mixed Review

Lesson 10-1 **Graph each equation.**

67. $x^2 + y^2 = 64$ 68. $x^2 + 9y^2 = 9$ 69. $4x^2 - 9y^2 = 36$

Lesson 9-2 **Find the asymptotes of the graph of each equation.**

70. $y = \frac{3}{x}$ 71. $y = \frac{1}{x} + 4$ 72. $y = \frac{4}{x + 1}$

73. $y = -\frac{1}{x - 1}$ 74. $y = \frac{5}{x + 5} + 2$ 75. $y = \frac{2}{x - 3} - 1$

Lesson 8-2 76. **Investing** Suppose you have a continuously compounding account with a beginning principal of \$3,800 and an interest rate of 8.1%. What is the balance after 4 years?

10-3 Circles

North Carolina Objectives

2.09 Use the equations of parabolas and circles to model and solve problems. a) Solve using tables, graphs, and algebraic properties. b) Interpret the constants and coefficients in the context of the problem.

Lesson Preview

What You'll Learn

OBJECTIVE 1 To write and graph the equation of a circle

OBJECTIVE 2 To find the center and radius of a circle and use it to graph the circle

. . . And Why

To model gears in machinery, as in Example 3

Check Skills You'll Need

(For help, go to Lesson 5-7 and Skills Handbook page 855.)

Simplify.

1. $\sqrt{16}$ **2.** $\sqrt{49}$ **3.** $\sqrt{20}$ **4.** $\sqrt{48}$ **5.** $\sqrt{72}$

Find the missing value to complete the square.

6. $x^2 - 2x + ■$ **7.** $x^2 + 4x + ■$ **8.** $x^2 - 6x + ■$

New Vocabulary

- circle
- center
- radius
- standard form of an equation of a circle

Interactive lesson includes instant self-check, tutorials, and activities.

OBJECTIVE 1 Writing the Equation of a Circle

Real-World Connection

People of many cultures use circular dwellings, like those shown above in Mali, to maximize volume for a given surface area.

A **circle** is the set of all points in a plane that are a distance r from a given point, called the **center.** The distance r is the **radius** of the circle.

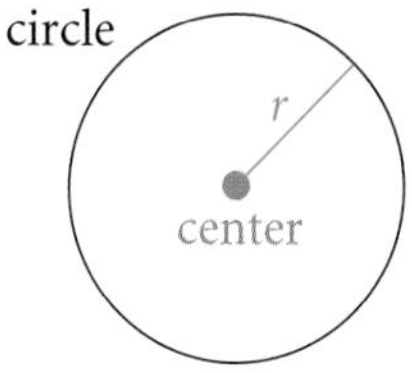

If r is the radius of a circle with a center at the origin, then the equation of the circle can be written in the form $x^2 + y^2 = r^2$.

Not every circle has its center at the origin. You can use the distance formula to find an equation of a circle with a radius r and a center at the point (h, k).

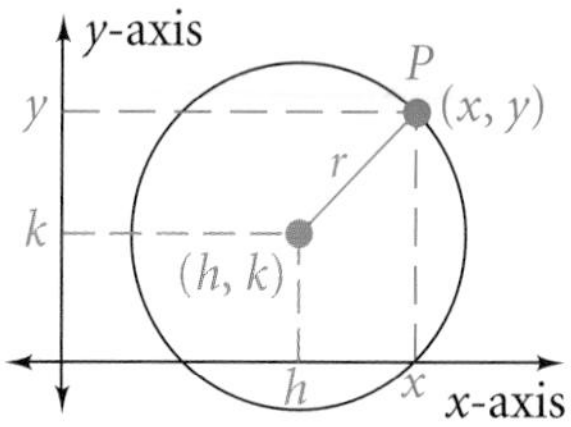

Let (x, y) be any point on the circle. The distance from (h, k) to (x, y) is the radius.

$d = \sqrt{(x_2 - x_2)^2 + (y_2 - y_1)^2}$ **Distance Formula**

$r = \sqrt{(x - h)^2 + (y - k)^2}$ **Substitute r for d, (h, k) for (x_1, y_1), and (x, y) for (x_2, y_2).**

$r^2 = (x - h)^2 + (y - k)^2$ **Square each side.**

The above proof leads to a definition.

Key Concepts

Definition	**Standard Form of an Equation of a Circle**

The standard form of an equation of a circle with center (h, k) and radius r is

$$(x - h)^2 + (y - k)^2 = r^2.$$

You can use the center and the radius of a circle to write an equation for a circle.

1 EXAMPLE Writing the Equation of a Circle

Write an equation of a circle with center $(-4, 3)$ and radius 4.

$(x - h)^2 + (y - k)^2 = r^2$	**Use the standard form of the equation of a circle.**
$(x - (-4))^2 + (y - 3)^2 = 4^2$	**Substitute −4 for *h*, 3 for *k*, and 4 for *r*.**
$(x + 4)^2 + (y - 3)^2 = 16$	**Simplify.**

An equation for the circle is $(x + 4)^2 + (y - 3)^2 = 16$.

Check Solve the equation for y and enter both functions into your graphing calculator.

$$(x + 4)^2 + (y - 3)^2 = 16$$
$$(y - 3)^2 = 16 - (x + 4)^2$$
$$y - 3 = \pm\sqrt{16 - (x + 4)^2}$$
$$y = 3 \pm \sqrt{16 - (x + 4)^2}$$

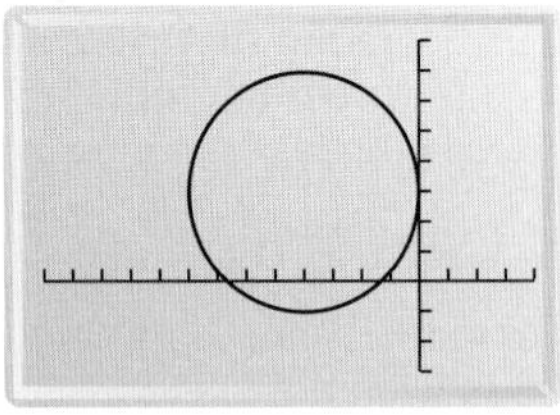

Graphing Calculator Hint

When graphing a conic section, press ZOOM 5 to select a square window. The standard window makes a circle look like an ellipse.

Check Understanding 1 Write an equation for a circle with center at $(5, -2)$ and radius 8. Check your answer.

The graph of the equation $(x - h)^2 + (y - k)^2 = r^2$ is the graph of $x^2 + y^2 = r^2$ translated h units horizontally and k units vertically. When h is positive the graph shifts right; when h is negative the graph shifts left. When k is positive the graph shifts up; when k is negative the graph shifts down.

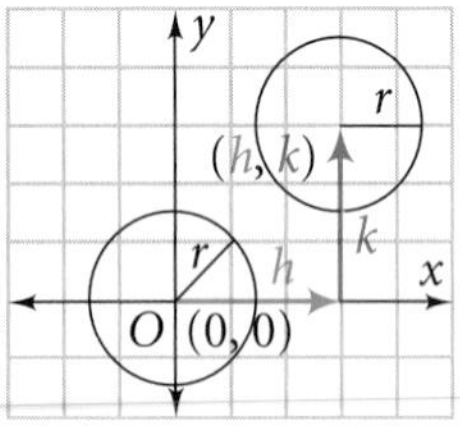

You can use translations to write an equation of a circle.

2 EXAMPLE Using Translations to Write an Equation

Write an equation for the translation of $x^2 + y^2 = 9$ four units left and three units up. Then graph the translation.

$(x - h)^2 + (y - k)^2 = r^2$	**Use standard form.**
$(x - (-4))^2 + (y - 3)^2 = 9$	**Substitute −4 for *h*, 3 for *k*, and 9 for r^2.**
$(x + 4)^2 + (y - 3)^2 = 9$	**Simplify.**

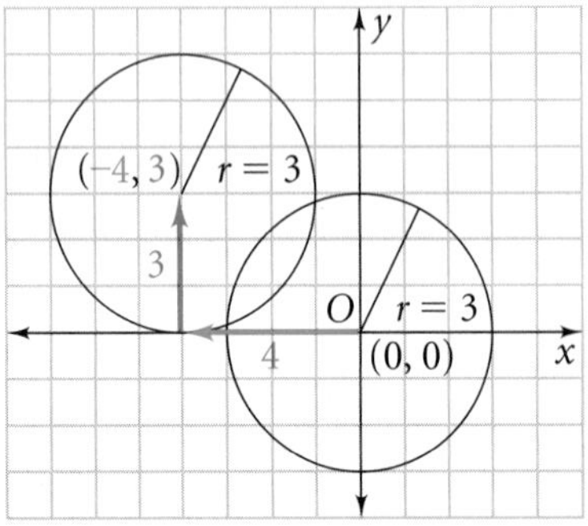

Check Understanding 2 Write an equation for each translation.

a. $x^2 + y^2 = 1$; left 5 and down 3

b. $x^2 + y^2 = 9$; right 2 and up 3

Example 5 (page 552)

Use the center and the radius to graph each circle.

27. $(x + 9)^2 + (y + 2)^2 = 100$

28. $(x + 4)^2 + (y - 4)^2 = 4$

29. $(x - 6)^2 + y^2 = 64$

30. $(x - 1)^2 + (y + 3)^2 = 16$

31. $x^2 + y^2 = 9$

32. $(x + 3)^2 + (y - 9)^2 = 49$

33. $(x - 7)^2 + (y - 1)^2 = 100$

34. $x^2 + (y + 4)^2 = 144$

B Apply Your Skills

Write the equation of the circle that passes through the given point and has a center at the origin. (*Hint:* You can use the distance formula to find the radius.)

35. $(0, 4)$ **36.** $(0, -3)$ **37.** $(-5, 0)$ **38.** $(\sqrt{3}, 0)$ **39.** $(4, -3)$

40. $(-5, -12)$ **41.** $(12, -5)$ **42.** $(-2, 3)$ **43.** $(1, -5)$ **44.** $(-6, -4)$

Use the given information to write an equation of the circle.

45. radius 7, center $(-6, 13)$

46. area 78.54, center $(5, -3)$

47. center $(-2, 7.5)$, circumference 3π

48. center $(1, -2)$, through $(0, 1)$

49. center $(2, 1)$, through $(6, 4)$

50. center $(6, 4)$, through $(2, 1)$

51. translation of $(x - 1)^2 + (y + 3)^2 = 36$, 2 units left and 4 units down

52. Recreation Write the equation of the circular fountain at the right.

53. Open-Ended Write two functions that together represent a circle.

54. Error Analysis A student claims that the circle $(x + 7)^2 + (y - 7)^2 = 8$ is a translation of the circle $x^2 + y^2 = 8$, 7 right and 7 down. What is the student's mistake?

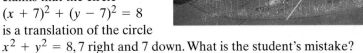

Find the center and the radius of each circle.

55. $x^2 + y^2 = 2$

56. $x^2 + (y + 1)^2 = 5$

57. $x^2 + y^2 = 14$

58. $x^2 + (y - 4)^2 = 11$

59. $(x + 5)^2 + y^2 = 18$

60. $(x + 2)^2 + (y + 4)^2 = 50$

61. $(x + 3)^2 + (y - 5)^2 = 38$

62. $x^2 + 2x + 1 + y^2 = 4$

63. $x^2 + y^2 - 6x - 2y + 4 = 0$

64. $x^2 + y^2 - 4y - 16 = 0$

Graph each pair of equations. Identify the conic section represented by the graph. Then write the equation of the conic section.

65. $y = 3 + \sqrt{16 - (x - 4)^2}$
$y = 3 - \sqrt{16 - (x - 4)^2}$

66. $y = -2 + \sqrt{x - 3}$
$y = -2 - \sqrt{x - 3}$

C Challenge

67. Reasoning Let $P(x, y)$ be any point on the circle with center $(0, 0)$ and radius r. Choose a method for proving that $x^2 + y^2 = r^2$.

68. a. Writing Explain why $x^2 + y^2 = 0$ does not represent a circle.
b. Critical Thinking What does the equation represent?

69. The table gives the diameters of four planets.
   a. Use a center of (0, 0) to graph a circle that represents the size of each planet.
   b. Write an equation representing the circular cross section through the center of each planet.

Planet	Diameter (miles)
Pluto	1430
Mercury	3031
Mars	4222
Earth	7926

70. a. A circle contains (0, 0), (6, 8), and (7, 7). Find its equation by solving a system of three equations.
   b. Several parabolas contain the three points of part (a), but only one is described by a quadratic function. Find that function.

Standardized Test Prep

Gridded Response

71. What is the radius of the circle with equation $(x + 5)^2 + (y - 3)^2 = 144$?

72. What is the radius of the circle with equation $(x - 2)^2 + 3 + (y + 1)^2 = 7$?

73. Circle *A* has equation $(x + 5)^2 + y^2 = 169$. The diameter of circle *B* is one fourth as long as the diameter of circle *A*. What is the radius of circle *B*?

74. What is the distance between $T(9, -5)$ and the center of the circle with equation $(x - 6)^2 + (y + 1)^2 = 10$?

75. Find the distance between the centers of the circles with equations $(x - 5)^2 + (y - 1)^2 = 16$ and $(x + 1)^2 + (y - 9)^2 = 49$.

76. What is the area of the circle whose equation is $(x + 1)^2 + (y + 1)^2 = 1$? Round your answer to the nearest hundredth.

Take It to the NET
Online lesson quiz at
www.PHSchool.com
Web Code: aga-1003

Mixed Review

Lesson 10-2

77. Write an equation of a parabola opening left with vertex (0, 0) and focus (–3, 0).

Lesson 9-3

For each rational function, find any points of discontinuity.

78. $y = \frac{2}{x + 1}$

79. $y = \frac{1}{x^2 - 5x + 6}$

80. $y = \frac{2x - 1}{x^2 + 4}$

Lesson 8-3

Evaluate each logarithm.

81. $\log_2 16$

82. $\log_5 25$

83. $\log_3 \frac{1}{27}$

84. $\log 10{,}000$

85. $\log_3 81$

86. $\log_{36} 6$

87. $\log_4 256$

88. $\log_2 \frac{1}{4}$

89. $\log_{100} 100$

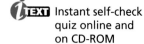

Checkpoint Quiz 1

Lessons 10-1 through 10-3

iTEXT Instant self-check quiz online and on CD-ROM

Identify the vertex, focus, and directrix of each parabola. Then graph the parabola.

1. $y = 3x^2$

2. $x = 4(y + 2)^2$

3. $y + 1 = (x - 3)^2$

4. Write an equation in standard form of the circle with center $(-6, 3)$ and radius 8.

5. What translation of $x^2 + y^2 = 18$ results in $(x + 4)^2 + (y - 6)^2 = 18$?

Extension

Using Parametric Form

For Use With Lesson 10-3

The graphing calculator program below uses parametric forms to graph a circle. To enter the program, use the PRGM **NEW** menu. Name your program **CIRCLE**.

Note that you find the **Disp**, **Prompt**, and **DispGraph** features in the PRGM **I/O** menu, and $\mathbf{X_{1T}}$ and $\mathbf{Y_{1T}}$ in the VARS **Y-Vars Parametric** menu. You can find **Par** and **Radian** under MODE, and **Tmin**, **Tmax**, and **Tstep** in the VARS **Window T/θ** menu.

Use ALPHA keys to enter words, quotation marks, and variables H, K, R, and T.

```
PROGRAM:CIRCLE
:Disp "CENTER (H,K)"
:Disp "RADIUS R"
:Prompt H,K,R
:"Rcos(T)+H"→X1T
■
```

```
PROGRAM:CIRCLE
:"Rsin(T)+K"→Y1T
:Param
:Radian
:0→Tmin
:2π→Tmax
:.05→Tstep
:DispGraph■
```

The next screens show the program being run for a circle with a center at $(-2, 3)$ and a radius of 5. Enter appropriate square-window values with the calculator in function mode. Then choose the program from the PRGM **EXEC** menu.

```
WINDOW
  Xmin=-12
  Xmax=12
  Xscl=1
  Ymin=-8
  Ymax=8
  Yscl=1
  Xres=1■
```

```
prgmCIRCLE
CENTER (H,K)
RADIUS R
H=?-2
K=?3
R=?5■
```

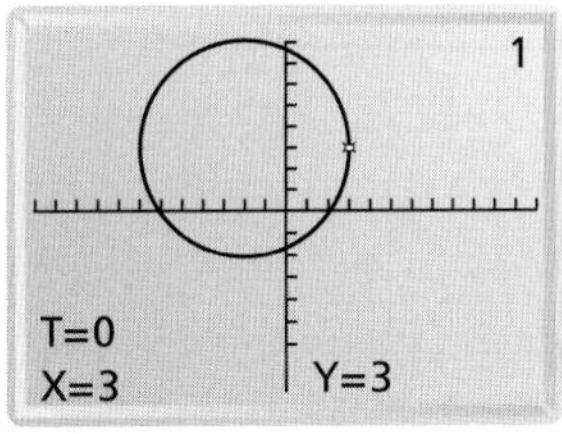

Note that you can trace to find the coordinates of points on the circle.

EXERCISES

Use your program to graph each circle. Use an appropriate square window for each graph.

1. center $(0, 2)$, radius 4

2. center $(5, -2)$, radius 5

3. center $(-1, 3)$, radius 8

4. $(x - 2)^2 + (y + 1)^2 = 25$

5. $(x + 4)^2 + (y - 3)^2 = 100$

6. $x^2 + (y + 2)^2 = 49$

7. $(x - 1)^2 + (y + 2)^2 = 36$

8. $(x - 6)^2 + y^2 = 100$

9. Open-Ended Use TRACE to find four points in Quadrant III that lie on the circle described by the equation $(x + 5)^2 + (y - 2)^2 = 16$.

10. Writing Describe how to change your program to work in degrees and plot a point every 5° of rotation.

10-4 Ellipses

Lesson Preview

What You'll Learn

OBJECTIVE 1 To write the equation of an ellipse

OBJECTIVE 2 To find the foci of an ellipse and to graph an ellipse

. . . And Why

To model NASA's Transonic Tunnel, as in Example 2

Check Skills You'll Need

(For help, go to Lesson 5-5 and Skills Handbook page 846.)

Solve each equation.

1. $27 = x^2 + 11$ **2.** $x^2 = 48$ **3.** $84 = 120 - x^2$

Evaluate each expression for $a = 3$ and $b = 5$.

4. $a^2 + b^2$ **5.** $a^2 - b^2$ **6.** $b^2 - 2a^2$

New Vocabulary
- ellipse
- focus of an ellipse
- major axis
- vertices of an ellipse
- minor axis
- co-vertices

Interactive lesson includes instant self-check, tutorials, and activities.

OBJECTIVE 1 Writing the Equation of an Ellipse

Ellipses play an important role in science. For example, the planets follow elliptical, not circular, orbits around the sun.

Key Concepts

Definition **Ellipse**

An **ellipse** is a set of points P in a plane such that the sum of the distances from P to two fixed points F_1 and F_2 is a given constant k.

$$PF_1 + PF_2 = k, \text{ where } k > F_1F_2$$

Reading Math

Ellipse comes from a Greek word for "smaller." The cutting plane of an ellipse makes a smaller angle with the base than does the side of the cone. See p. 535.

Each fixed point F is a **focus of an ellipse** (plural: foci). The **major axis** is the segment that contains the foci and has its endpoints on the ellipse. The endpoints of the major axis are **vertices of an ellipse.** The midpoint of the major axis is the center of the ellipse. The **minor axis** is perpendicular to the major axis at the center. The endpoints of the minor axis are **co-vertices.**

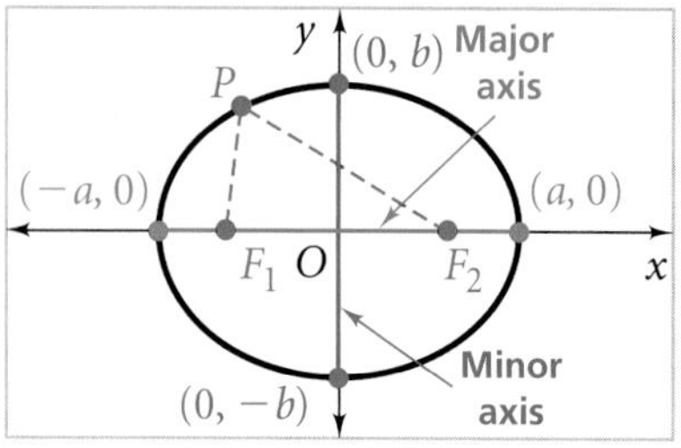

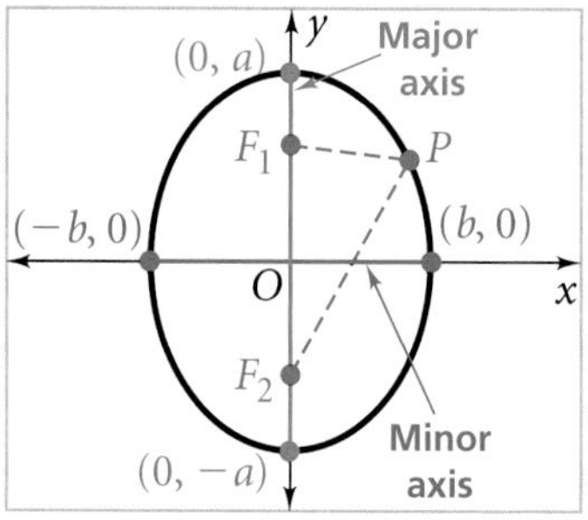

$\frac{x^2}{a^2} + \frac{y^2}{b^2} = 1$ ⟵ **standard forms of an equation of an ellipse, with center at the origin and $a > b > 0$** ⟶ $\frac{x^2}{b^2} + \frac{y^2}{a^2} = 1$

major axis: horizontal
vertices: $(\pm a, 0)$
co-vertices: $(0, \pm b)$

major axis: vertical
vertices: $(0, \pm a)$
co-vertices: $(\pm b, 0)$

You can write the equation of an ellipse with a center at the origin if you know an x-intercept and a y-intercept.

1 EXAMPLE Writing the Equation of an Ellipse

Write an equation in standard form of an ellipse that has a vertex at (0, 5), a co-vertex at (2, 0), and a center at the origin.

Since (0, 5) is a vertex of the ellipse, the other vertex is at (0, −5), and the major axis is vertical. Since (2, 0) is a co-vertex, the other co-vertex is at (−2, 0), and the minor axis is horizontal. So $a = 5, b = 2, a^2 = 25$, and $b^2 = 4$.

$\frac{x^2}{b^2} + \frac{y^2}{a^2} = 1$ **standard form of an equation of an ellipse with a vertical major axis**

$\frac{x^2}{4} + \frac{y^2}{25} = 1$ **Substitute 4 for b^2 and 25 for a^2.**

An equation of the ellipse is $\frac{x^2}{4} + \frac{y^2}{25} = 1$.

Check Understanding 1 Write an equation in standard form for an ellipse that has a vertex at (0, −6), a co-vertex at (3, 0), and a center at the origin.

You can write an equation for an ellipse with a center at the origin if you know the length of both axes.

2 EXAMPLE Real-World Connection

Architecture The Transonic Tunnel at NASA Langley Research Center, Virginia, is used to study the dynamics of air flow. The elliptical opening of the Transonic Tunnel is 82 ft wide and 58 ft high. Find an equation of the ellipse.

Real-World Connection

The guide vanes in the elliptical opening of the Transonic Tunnel allow a smooth flow of air through the passageway.

Imagine a large coordinate grid placed over the elliptical opening. Since the widest part of the ellipse is horizontal and the width is 82 ft, place the vertices at (±41, 0). Place the co-vertices at (0, ±29).

So $a = 41, b = 29, a^2 = 1681$, and $b^2 = 841$.

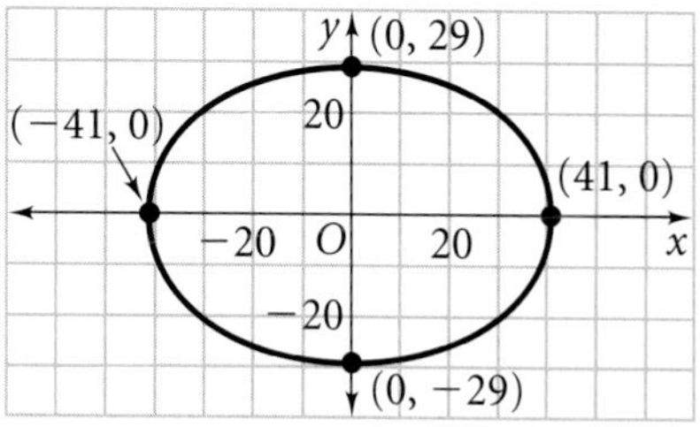

$\frac{x^2}{a^2} + \frac{y^2}{b^2} = 1$ **standard form for an ellipse with a horizontal major axis**

$\frac{x^2}{1681} + \frac{y^2}{841} = 1$ **Substitute 1681 for a^2 and 841 for b^2.**

An equation of the ellipse is $\frac{x^2}{1681} + \frac{y^2}{841} = 1$.

Check Understanding 2 Find an equation of an ellipse centered at the origin that is 12 units wide and 30 units high.

OBJECTIVE 2

Finding and Using the Foci of an Ellipse

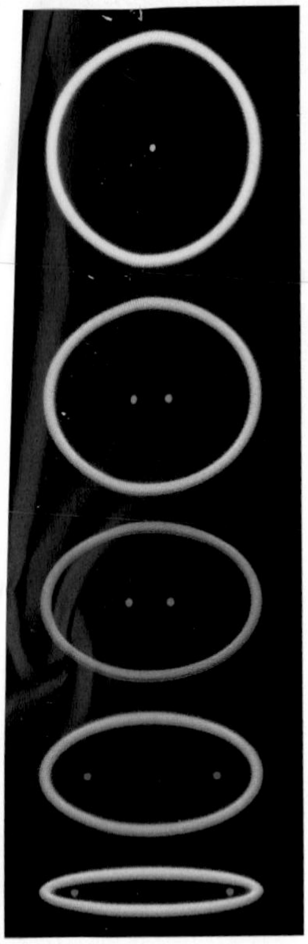

The figure above shows the relationship between the center of a circle and the foci of an ellipse.

The foci are important points in an ellipse. For example, the sun is at a focus, not at the center, of Earth's orbit around the sun.

The foci of an ellipse are always on the major axis at c units from the center.

There is an important and useful relationship among a, b, and c: $c^2 = a^2 - b^2$.

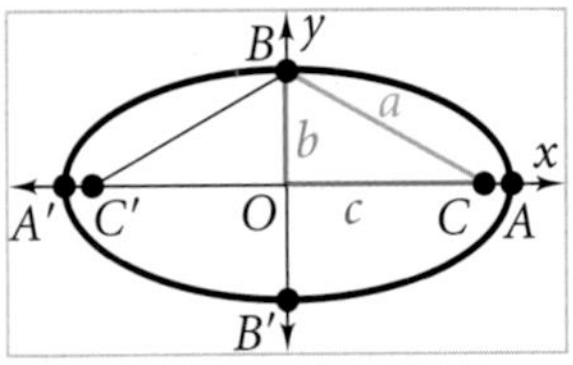

You can use the relationship to find the foci of an ellipse.

3 EXAMPLE Finding the Foci of an Ellipse

Find the foci of the ellipse with the equation $25x^2 + 9y^2 = 225$. Graph the ellipse.

$25x^2 + 9y^2 = 225$

$\frac{x^2}{9} + \frac{y^2}{25} = 1$ **Write in standard form.**

Since $25 > 9$ and 25 is with y^2, the major axis is vertical, $a^2 = 25$, and $b^2 = 9$.

$c^2 = a^2 - b^2$ **Find c.**

$= 25 - 9$ **Substitute 25 for a^2 and 9 for b^2.**

$= 16$

$c = 4$

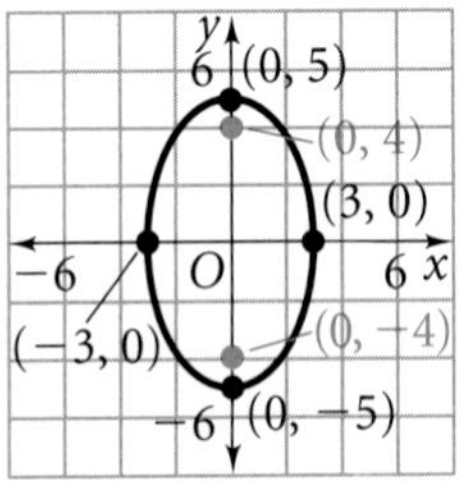

The major axis is vertical, so the coordinates of the foci are $(0, \pm c)$. The foci are $(0, 4)$ and $(0, -4)$.

The vertices are $(0, \pm 5)$. The co-vertices are $(\pm 3, 0)$.

Check Understanding 3 Find the foci of the ellipse with the equation $x^2 + 9y^2 = 9$. Graph the ellipse.

You can use the relationship among a, b, and c to write the equation of an ellipse.

4 EXAMPLE Using the Foci of an Ellipse

Write an equation of the ellipse with foci at $(\pm 7, 0)$ and co-vertices at $(0, \pm 6)$.

Since the foci have coordinates $(\pm 7, 0)$, the major axis is horizontal.

Since $c = 7$ and $b = 6$, $c^2 = 49$ and $b^2 = 36$.

$c^2 = a^2 - b^2$ **Use the equation to find a^2.**

$49 = a^2 - 36$ **Substitute 49 for c^2 and 36 for b^2.**

$a^2 = 85$ **Simplify.**

$\frac{x^2}{85} + \frac{y^2}{36} = 1$ **Substitute 85 for a^2 and 36 for b^2.**

An equation of the ellipse is $\frac{x^2}{85} + \frac{y^2}{36} = 1$.

Check Understanding 4 Write an equation of the ellipse with foci at $(0, \pm\sqrt{17})$ and co-vertices at $(\pm 8, 0)$.

EXERCISES

For more practice, see *Extra Practice*.

Practice and Problem Solving

A Practice by Example

Example 1 (page 557)

Write an equation of an ellipse in standard form with center at the origin and with the given vertex and co-vertex.

1. $(4, 0), (0, 3)$ **2.** $(0, 1), (2, 0)$ **3.** $(3, 0), (0, -1)$ **4.** $(0, 6), (1, 0)$

5. $(0, -7), (4, 0)$ **6.** $(-6, 0), (0, 5)$ **7.** $(-9, 0), (0, -2)$ **8.** $(0, 5), (-3, 0)$

Example 2 (page 557)

Find an equation of an ellipse for each given height and width. Assume that the center of the ellipse is (0, 0).

9. $h = 1$ m, $w = 3$ m **10.** $h = 32$ ft, $w = 16$ ft **11.** $h = 20$ ft, $w = 12$ ft

12. $h = 10$ cm, $w = 7$ cm **13.** $h = 14$ yd, $w = 28$ yd **14.** $h = 8$ ft, $w = 2$ ft

15. $h = 15$ ft, $w = 32$ ft **16.** $h = 40$ mi, $w = 60$ mi **17.** $h = 5$ m, $w = 2$ m

Example 3 (page 558)

Find the foci for each equation of an ellipse. Then graph the ellipse.

18. $\frac{x^2}{4} + \frac{y^2}{9} = 1$ **19.** $\frac{x^2}{9} + \frac{y^2}{25} = 1$ **20.** $\frac{x^2}{81} + \frac{y^2}{49} = 1$

21. $\frac{x^2}{100} + \frac{y^2}{36} = 1$ **22.** $\frac{x^2}{64} + \frac{y^2}{100} = 1$ **23.** $3x^2 + y^2 = 9$

24. $x^2 + 4y^2 = 16$ **25.** $\frac{x^2}{225} + \frac{y^2}{144} = 1$ **26.** $\frac{x^2}{256} + \frac{y^2}{121} = 1$

Example 4 (page 558)

Write an equation of an ellipse for the given foci and co-vertices.

27. foci $(\pm 6, 0)$, co-vertices $(0, \pm 8)$ **28.** foci $(0, \pm 8)$, co-vertices $(\pm 8, 0)$

29. foci $(\pm 5, 0)$, co-vertices $(0, \pm 8)$ **30.** foci $(0, \pm 4)$, co-vertices $(\pm 2, 0)$

31. foci $(\pm 14, 0)$, co-vertices $(0, \pm 7)$ **32.** foci $(\pm 17, 0)$, co-vertices $(0, \pm 15)$

B Apply Your Skills

Find the foci for each equation of an ellipse.

33. $4x^2 + 9y^2 = 36$ **34.** $16x^2 + 4y^2 = 64$ **35.** $36x^2 + 4y^2 = 144$

36. $25x^2 + 4y^2 = 100$ **37.** $36x^2 + 8y^2 = 288$ **38.** $25x^2 + 24y^2 = 600$

39. $25x^2 + 16y^2 + 150x = 160y - 225$ **40.** $2x^2 + 8x + y^2 + 4 = 0$

Reading Math

Eccentric means "out of center."

41. The eccentricity of an ellipse is a measure of how nearly circular it is. Eccentricity is defined as $\frac{c}{a}$, where c is the distance from the center to a focus and a is the distance from the center to a vertex.

a. Find the eccentricity of an ellipse with foci $(\pm 9, 0)$ and vertices $(\pm 10, 0)$. Sketch the graph.

b. Find the eccentricity of an ellipse with foci $(\pm 1, 0)$ and vertices $(\pm 10, 0)$. Sketch the graph.

c. Describe the shape of an ellipse that has an eccentricity close to 0.

d. Describe the shape of an ellipse that has an eccentricity close to 1.

42. Find the equation of the ellipse with foci on the x-axis, major axis 9 units long, minor axis 4 units long, and center at the origin.

43. a. **Critical Thinking** Suppose the foci of an ellipse are near the center of the ellipse. Will the shape of the ellipse be nearly a circle? Explain.

b. Is a circle also an ellipse? Explain.

Write an equation for each ellipse.

44.

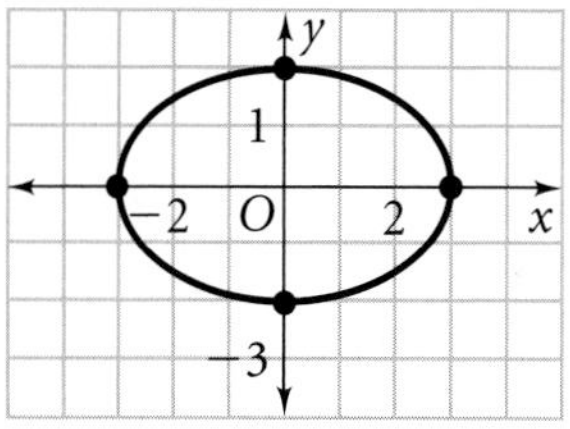

45.

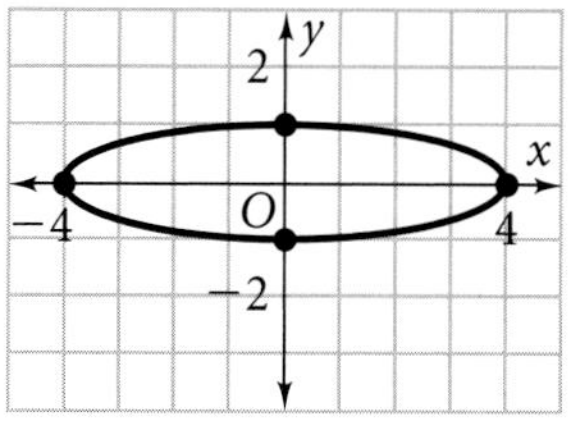

46.

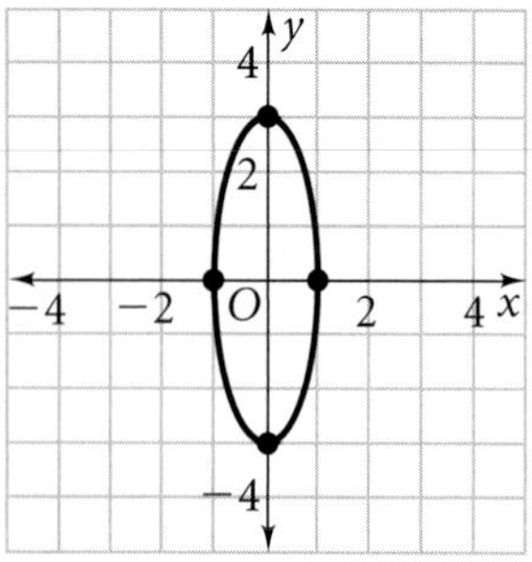

47.

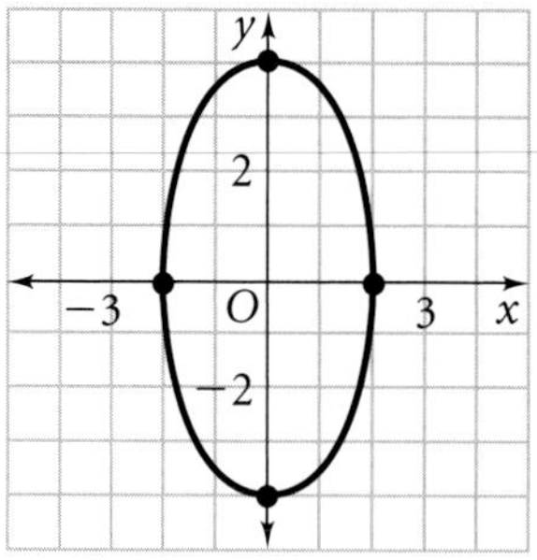

48. **Error Analysis** A student claims that an ellipse has vertices at $(\pm 3, 0)$ and co-vertices at $(0, \pm 7)$. What is the student's error?

49. **Open-Ended** Find a real-world design that uses ellipses. Place a coordinate grid over the design and write an equation of the ellipse.

Write an equation of an ellipse in standard form with center at the origin and with the given characteristics.

50. focus $(1, 0)$, width 4

51. $a = 5$, $b = 2$, width 10

52. vertex $(-11, 0)$, co-vertex $(0, 9)$

53. height 29, width 53

54. focus $(-5, 0)$, co-vertex $(0, -12)$

55. $c^2 = 68$, vertex $(0, -18)$

56. focus $(0, 3\sqrt{2})$, height 19

57. focus $(10\sqrt{3}, 0)$, width 40

58. focus $(2, 0)$, x-intercept 4

59. focus $(0, 3)$, y-intercept 5

60. focus $(0, -5)$, y-intercept 8

61. focus $(3, 0)$, x-intercept -6

62. $a = 3$, $b = 2$, width 4

63. $a = 2\sqrt{5}$, $b = 3\sqrt{2}$, width $6\sqrt{2}$

64. Draw an ellipse by placing two tacks in a piece of graph paper laid over a piece of cardboard. Place a loop of string around the tacks. With your pencil keeping the string taut, draw around the tacks. Mark the center of your ellipse $(0, 0)$ and draw the x- and y-axes.

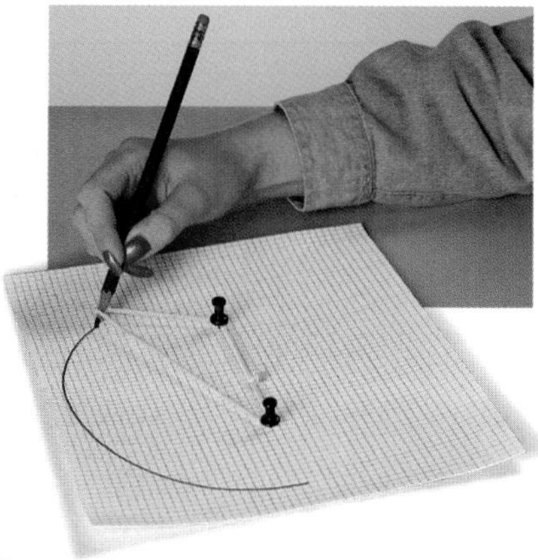

a. Where are the vertices and co-vertices of your ellipse?

b. Where are the foci?

c. Write the equation of your ellipse.

C Challenge

65. **Writing** The area of a circle is πr^2. The area of an ellipse is πab. Explain the connection.

66. **Astronomy** The sun is at a focus of Earth's elliptical orbit.

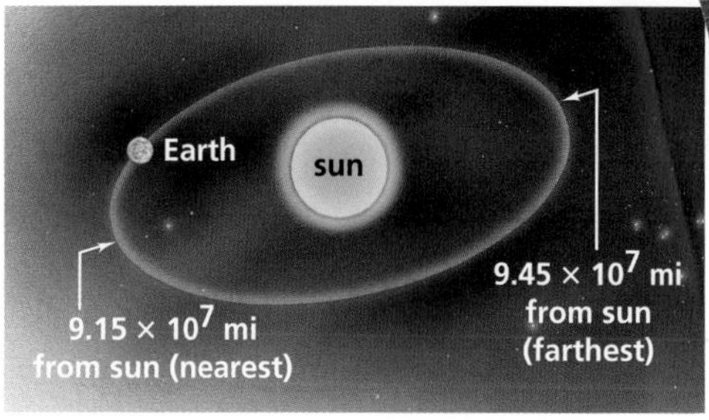

a. Find the distance from the sun to the other focus.
b. Refer to Exercise 41 for the definition of eccentricity. What is the eccentricity of the orbit?
c. Write an equation of Earth's orbit. Assume that the major axis is horizontal.

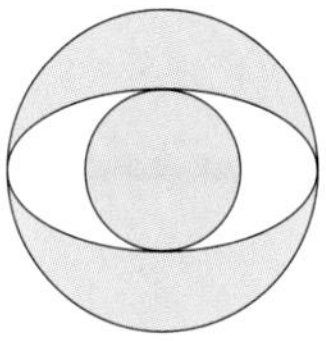

67. An ellipse and two circles share a center. The major axis of the ellipse is twice as long as its minor axis. The diameter of the larger circle is the same length as the major axis of the ellipse. The diameter of the smaller circle is the same length as the minor axis of the ellipse. The area of an ellipse is πab. Compare the areas of the blue and white regions at the left.

68. **Acoustics** In "whispering galleries" a sound made at one focus can be clearly heard at the other focus, even though very little can be heard by someone in between. Suppose an elliptical room measures 320 ft long and 150 ft wide. How far would the listener have to be from the source of the sound in order to hear it?

Standardized Test Prep

Multiple Choice

69. The point $A(-10, 0)$ is on the ellipse with equation $\frac{x^2}{100} + \frac{y^2}{64} = 1$. What is the sum of the distances $AF_1 + AF_2$, where F_1 and F_2 are the foci?
A. 10 **B.** 12 **C.** 14 **D.** 20

70. What is the length of the major axis on the graph of $\frac{x^2}{100} + \frac{y^2}{64} = 1$?
F. 12 **G.** $2\sqrt{41}$ **H.** 16 **I.** 20

Take It to the NET
Online lesson quiz at **www.PHSchool.com**
Web Code: aga-1004

71. What is the length of the minor axis of the graph of $\frac{x^2}{100} + \frac{y^2}{64} = 1$?
A. 12 **B.** $2\sqrt{41}$ **C.** 16 **D.** 20

Short Response

72. Explain how to find an equation for the ellipse, centered at the origin, that is 50 units wide and 40 units high.

Mixed Review

Lesson 10-3 **Write an equation of a circle with the given center and radius.**

73. center $(2, -3)$, radius 6
74. center $(-4, 7)$, radius 11

Lesson 9-4 **Simplify each expression. What are the restrictions on the variables?**

75. $\frac{3x}{6x^2 - 9x^5}$
76. $\frac{x^2 - 36}{x^2 + 5x - 6}$
77. $\frac{x^2 - 3x - 10}{x^3 + 8}$

Lesson 8-4 **Write each logarithmic expression as a single logarithm.**

78. $\log 3 + \log 5$
79. $\log_3 12 - \log_3 2$
80. $3 \log 2 - \log 4$
81. $5 \log 2 + \log 10$
82. $\log x - \log y$
83. $k \log 5 - \log 4$

10-5 Hyperbolas

Lesson Preview

What You'll Learn

OBJECTIVE 1 To graph hyperbolas

OBJECTIVE 2 To find and use the foci of a hyperbola

. . . And Why

To write an equation that models the path of Voyager 2 around Saturn, as in Example 3

Check Skills You'll Need

(For help, go to Lesson 2-2 and Skills Handbook page 846.)

Write an equation of a line in slope-intercept form using the given information.

1. rise -5, run 2, through the origin

2. through (3, 1) and (9, 3)

Solve each equation for *y*.

3. $\frac{x^2}{4} - \frac{y^2}{16} = 1$

4. $\frac{y^2}{9} - \frac{x^2}{25} = 1$

5. $\frac{x^2}{36} - \frac{y^2}{81} = 1$

New Vocabulary

- hyperbola
- transverse axis
- focus of a hyperbola
- vertices of a hyperbola

Interactive lesson includes instant self-check, tutorials, and activities.

OBJECTIVE 1

Graphing Hyperbolas Centered at the Origin

Reading Math

Hyperbola comes from a Greek word for "greater." The cutting plane of a hyperbola makes a greater angle with the base than does the side of the cone. See p. 535.

Investigation: Analyzing Hyperbolas

1. The diagram below shows the shape of a hyperbola. Measure the distances to the nearest millimeter to complete the table.

2. **Make a Conjecture** What is the relationship between the distances from the points F_1 and F_2 to any point on the hyperbola?

Distance	P_1	P_2	P_3	...
Distance From F_1	■	■	■	■
Distance From F_2	■	■	■	■
$\lvert PF_1 - PF_2 \rvert$	■	■	■	■

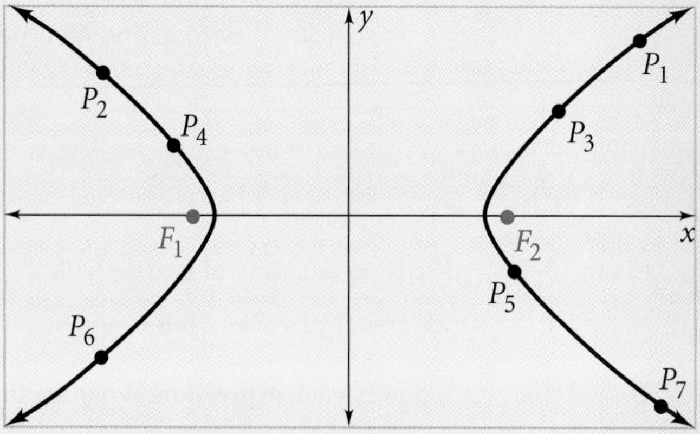

Hyperbolas play an important role in science and navigation. Some comets follow hyperbolic paths.

Key Concepts

Definition | **Hyperbola**

A **hyperbola** is a set of points P in a plane such that the difference between the distances from P to two fixed points F_1 and F_2 is a given constant k.

$$|PF_1 - PF_2| = k, \text{ where } k < F_1F_2$$

Each fixed point F is a **focus of a hyperbola.** The segment that lies on the line containing the foci and has endpoints on a hyperbola is the **transverse axis.** The endpoints are the **vertices of a hyperbola.** The midpoint of the segment is the center of a hyperbola.

Below are the standard forms of the equation of a hyperbola centered at (0, 0).

$$\frac{x^2}{a^2} - \frac{y^2}{b^2} = 1$$ **standard form of an equation of a hyperbola with a horizontal transverse axis**

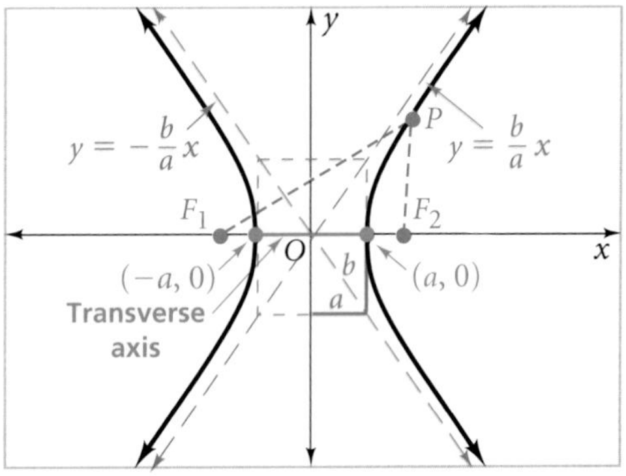

foci: F_1, F_2

vertices: $(\pm a, 0)$

asymptotes: $y = \pm\frac{b}{a}x$

x-intercepts: $\pm a$

y-intercepts: none

Need Help?
An asymptote is a line that a graph approaches.

$$\frac{y^2}{a^2} - \frac{x^2}{b^2} = 1$$ **standard form of an equation of a hyperbola with a vertical transverse axis**

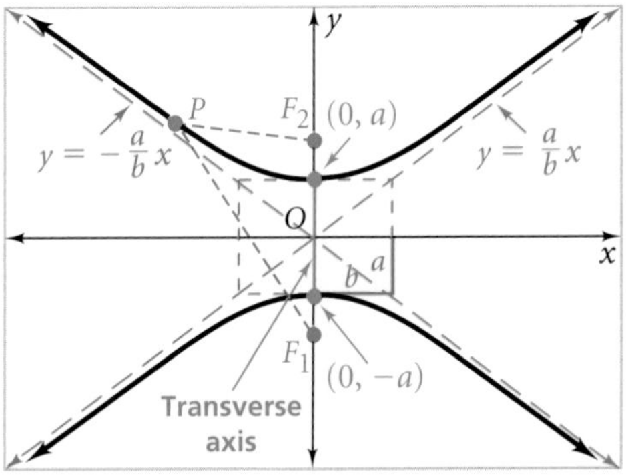

foci: F_1, F_2

vertices: $(0, \pm a)$

asymptotes: $y = \pm\frac{a}{b}x$

x-intercepts: none

y-intercepts: $\pm a$

To graph a hyperbola, use the standard form of the equation to find the values of a and b. You can use a and b to find and graph the vertices and to draw a central rectangle that is used to guide the graph.

Draw the asymptotes through the diagonals of the central rectangle. Then draw the branches of the hyperbola through the vertices so they approach the asymptotes.

1 EXAMPLE Graphing a Hyperbola

Graph $9x^2 - 25y^2 = 225$.

$9x^2 - 25y^2 = 225$

$\frac{x^2}{25} - \frac{y^2}{9} = 1$ **Rewrite the equation in standard form.**

The equation is of the form $\frac{x^2}{a^2} - \frac{y^2}{b^2} = 1$, so the transverse axis is horizontal. Since $a^2 = 25$ and $b^2 = 9$, $a = 5$ and $b = 3$.

Step 1 Graph the vertices. Since the transverse axis is horizontal, the vertices lie on the x-axis. The coordinates are $(\pm a, 0)$, or $(\pm 5, 0)$.

Step 2 Use the values of a and b to draw the central rectangle. The lengths of its sides are $2a$ and $2b$, or 10 and 6.

Step 3 Draw the asymptotes. The equations of the asymptotes are $y = \pm\frac{b}{a}x$ or $y = \pm\frac{3}{5}x$. The asymptotes contain the diagonals of the central rectangle.

Step 4 Sketch the branches of the hyperbola through the vertices so they approach the asymptotes.

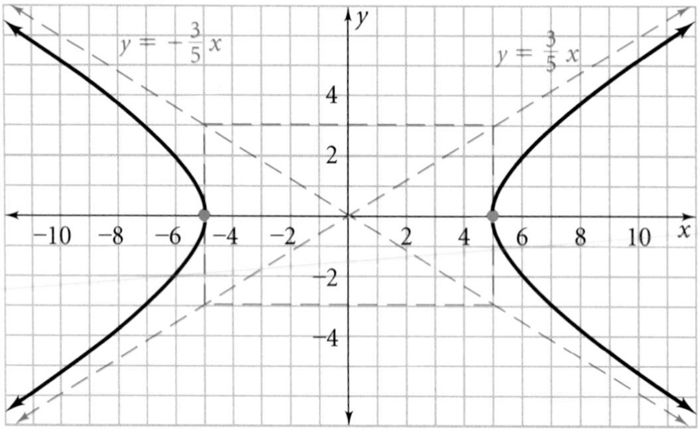

Check Understanding 1 Graph the hyperbola with equation $\frac{y^2}{16} - \frac{x^2}{9} = 1$.

OBJECTIVE 2 Using the Foci of a Hyperbola

Use $(\pm c, 0)$ for the coordinates of the foci if the transverse axis is horizontal or $(0, \pm c)$ if it is vertical.

The distance between the foci, $2c$, is also the length of the diagonal of the central rectangle.

You can find the value of c using the Pythagorean Theorem.

$c^2 = a^2 + b^2$

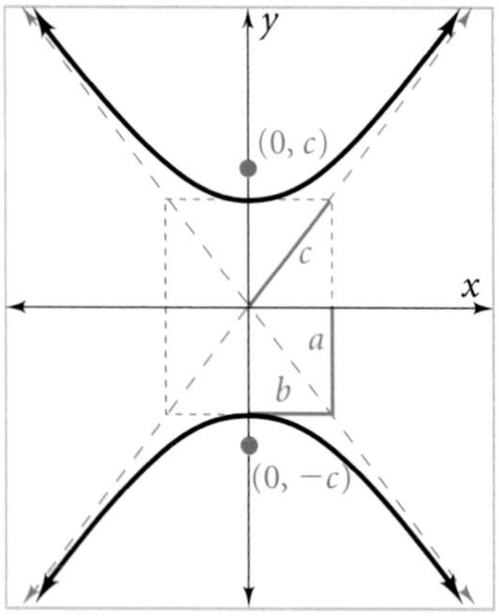

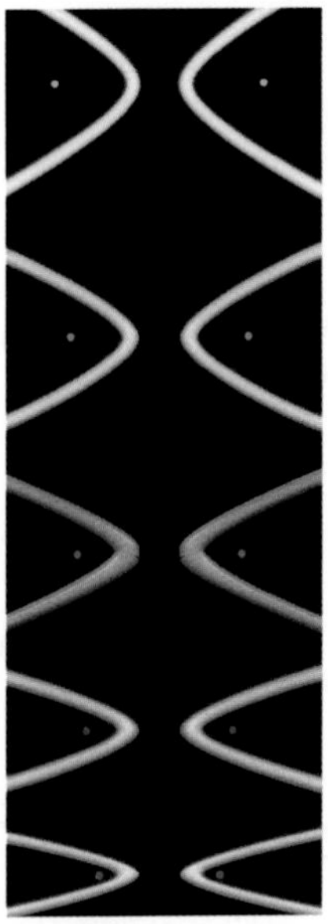

The figures above show how the shape of a hyperbola changes with decreased distances between the foci and the vertices.

2 EXAMPLE Finding the Foci of a Hyperbola

Find the foci of the graph $\frac{x^2}{36} - \frac{y^2}{4} = 1$. Draw the graph.

The equation is in the form $\frac{x^2}{a^2} - \frac{y^2}{b^2} = 1$, so the transverse axis is horizontal; $a^2 = 36$ and $b^2 = 4$.

$c^2 = a^2 + b^2$ **Use the Pythagorean Theorem.**

$= 36 + 4$ **Substitute 36 for a^2 and 4 for b^2.**

$c = \sqrt{40} \approx 6.3$ **Find the square root of each side of the equation.**

The foci $(\pm c, 0)$ are approximately $(-6.3, 0)$ and $(6.3, 0)$. The vertices $(\pm a, 0)$ are $(6, 0)$ and $(-6, 0)$. The asymptotes are the lines $y = \pm\frac{b}{a}x$, or $y = \pm\frac{1}{3}x$.

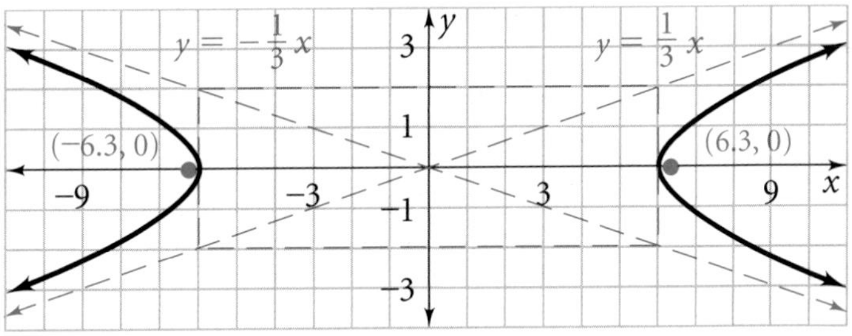

Check Understanding **2** Find the foci of $\frac{x^2}{25} - \frac{y^2}{9} = 1$. Draw the graph.

You can use the value of c to write the equation of a hyperbola.

3 EXAMPLE Real-World Connection

Space As a spacecraft approaches a planet, the gravitational pull of the planet changes the spacecraft's path to a hyperbola that diverges from its asymptote. Find an equation that models the path of Voyager 2 around Saturn, given that $a = 332{,}965$ km and $c = 492{,}788.2$ km.

Assume that the center of the hyperbola is at the origin and that the transverse axis is horizontal. The equation will be in the form $\frac{x^2}{a^2} - \frac{y^2}{b^2} = 1$.

$c^2 = a^2 + b^2$ **Use the Pythagorean Theorem.**

$(492{,}788.2)^2 = (332{,}965)^2 + b^2$ **Substitute.**

$2.428 \times 10^{11} = 1.109 \times 10^{11} + b^2$ **Use a calculator.**

$b^2 = 2.428 \times 10^{11} - 1.109 \times 10^{11}$ **Solve for b^2.**

$= 1.320 \times 10^{11}$

$\frac{x^2}{1.109 \times 10^{11}} - \frac{y^2}{1.320 \times 10^{11}} = 1$ **Substitute a^2 and b^2.**

The path of Voyager 2 around Saturn can be modeled by

$$\frac{x^2}{1.109 \times 10^{11}} - \frac{y^2}{1.320 \times 10^{11}} = 1.$$

Check Understanding **3** Find an equation that models the path of Voyager 2 around Jupiter, given that $a = 2{,}184{,}140$ km and $c = 2{,}904{,}906.2$ km.

EXERCISES

For more practice, see *Extra Practice*.

Practice and Problem Solving

A Practice by Example

Example 1 (page 564)

Graph each equation.

1. $\frac{x^2}{16} - \frac{y^2}{4} = 1$
2. $\frac{y^2}{169} - \frac{x^2}{16} = 1$
3. $\frac{x^2}{25} - \frac{y^2}{36} = 1$
4. $x^2 - 4y^2 = 4$
5. $36y^2 - 9x^2 = 324$
6. $25x^2 - 16y^2 = 400$
7. $9x^2 - 49y^2 = 441$
8. $25x^2 - 35y^2 = 875$
9. $81y^2 - 9x^2 = 729$

Example 2 (page 565)

Find the foci of each hyperbola. Then draw the graph.

10. $\frac{y^2}{81} - \frac{x^2}{16} = 1$
11. $\frac{y^2}{49} - \frac{x^2}{64} = 1$
12. $\frac{x^2}{121} - \frac{y^2}{144} = 1$
13. $\frac{x^2}{64} - \frac{y^2}{36} = 1$
14. $\frac{y^2}{25} - \frac{x^2}{100} = 1$
15. $\frac{x^2}{36} - \frac{y^2}{169} = 1$
16. $4y^2 - 25x^2 = 100$
17. $36x^2 - 8y^2 = 288$
18. $14y^2 - 28x^2 = 448$

Example 3 (page 565)

For Exercises 19–21, find the equation of a hyperbola with the given values. Assume that the transverse axis is horizontal.

19. $a = 263, c = 407$
20. $b = 100, c = 500$
21. $a = 13{,}872, c = 19{,}043$

22. Find an equation that models the path of Voyager 2 around Jupiter, given that $a = 1{,}362{,}450$ km and $c = 1{,}543{,}781$ km.

B Apply Your Skills

Write the equation of a hyperbola with the given foci and vertices.

23. foci $(\pm 5, 0)$, vertices $(\pm 3, 0)$
24. foci $(0, \pm 13)$, vertices $(0, \pm 5)$
25. foci $(0, \pm 2)$, vertices $(0, \pm 1)$
26. foci $(\pm\sqrt{5}, 0)$, vertices $(\pm 2, 0)$

Graph each equation.

27. $5x^2 - 12y^2 = 120$
28. $16x^2 - 20y^2 = 560$
29. $\frac{y^2}{20} - \frac{x^2}{5} = 1$

Write the equation of a hyperbola from the given information. Graph the equation. Place the center of each hyperbola at the origin of the coordinate plane.

30. Transverse axis is vertical and is 9 units; central rectangle is 9 units by 4 units.
31. Perimeter of central rectangle is 16 units; vertices are at $(0, 3)$ and $(0, -3)$.
32. (Distance from the center of a hyperbola to a focus)$^2 = 96$; endpoints of the transverse axis are at $(-\sqrt{32}, 0)$ and $(\sqrt{32}, 0)$.

Reading Math

For help with reading and solving Exercise 32, see p. 569.

Solve each equation for *y*. Graph each relation on your graphing calculator. Use the TRACE feature to locate the vertices.

33. $x^2 - 2y^2 = 4$
34. $x^2 - y^2 = 1$
35. $3x^2 - y^2 = 2$

36. **Open-Ended** Choose two points on an axis to be the vertices of a hyperbola. Choose two other points on the same axis to be the foci. Write the equation of your hyperbola and draw its graph.
37. **Writing** Describe the similarities and differences between hyperbolas and ellipses.
38. List all the properties of a hyperbola that allow you to sketch its graph.

Find the vertices and the asymptotes of each hyperbola.

39. $y^2 - x^2 = 1$ **40.** $x^2 - 9y^2 = 1$ **41.** $y^2 - 4x^2 = 64$

42. $16x^2 - 25y^2 = 400$ **43.** $9y^2 - 36x^2 = 144$ **44.** $25x^2 - 49y^2 = 1225$

C Challenge

45. Recall what you have learned about translating graphs. Rewrite the equation $4x^2 - 9y^2 = 36$ in standard form for a translation right 3 units and down 5 units.

Real-World Connection

Careers Air traffic controllers coordinate the flow of air traffic by the use of radar and visual observation.

46. Air Traffic Control Suppose you are an air traffic controller directing the pilot of a plane on a hyperbolic flight path. You and another air traffic controller from a different airport send radio signals to the pilot simultaneously. The two airports are 48 km apart. The pilot's instrument panel tells him that the signal from your airport always arrives 100 μs (microseconds) before the signal from the other airport.

a. To which airport is the plane closer?

b. If the signals travel at a rate of 300 m/μs, what is the difference in distances from the plane to the two airports?

c. Write the equation of the flight path. (*Hint:* $k = 2a$)

d. Draw the hyperbola. Which branch represents the flight path?

47. The function $y = \sqrt{x^2 - 9}$ represents part of a hyperbola. The tables at the right show the coordinates of several points on the graph.

a. Explain why ERROR appears for some entries.

b. Describe the relationship between the x- and y-coordinates as x gets larger.

c. Critical Thinking Do you think that the x- and y-coordinates will ever be equal? Explain.

d. Make a Conjecture What are the equations of the asymptotes of this hyperbola? Verify your answer by drawing the complete graph.

X	Y1
0	ERROR
1	ERROR
2	ERROR
3	0
4	2.6458
5	4
6	5.1962
X=0	

X	Y1
10	9.5394
20	19.774
30	29.85
40	39.887
50	49.91
60	59.925
70	69.936
X=10	

48. a. Prove that the hyperbola $\frac{y^2}{a^2} - \frac{x^2}{b^2} = 1$ never intersects its asymptotes.

b. Is $\frac{y^2}{16} - \frac{x^2}{9} = 4$ a hyperbola? Is $\frac{y^2}{16} - \frac{x^2}{9} = -1$ a hyperbola? Explain.

Standardized Test Prep

Multiple Choice

49. Which hyperbola has $(\pm 6, 0)$ as its x-intercepts?

A. $y^2 - x^2 = 36$ B. $\frac{y^2}{36} - \frac{x^2}{49} = 1$ C. $\frac{x^2}{25} - \frac{y^2}{36} = 1$ D. $\frac{x^2}{36} - \frac{y^2}{4} = 1$

50. Which hyperbola does NOT have $(0, \pm 4)$ as its y-intercepts?

F. $y^2 - x^2 = 16$ G. $4y^2 - 16x^2 = 64$

H. $\frac{x^2}{25} - \frac{y^2}{16} = 1$ I. $\frac{y^2}{16} - \frac{x^2}{9} = 1$

51. What are the x-intercepts of $\frac{y^2}{25} - \frac{x^2}{49} = 1$?

A. $(\pm 7, 0)$ B. $(\pm 5, 0)$ C. $(0, \pm 5)$ D. none

Short Response

52. What is the standard form of an equation of a hyperbola? Explain how to rewrite $25x^2 - 49y^2 = 1225$ in standard form.

Reading Comprehension

53. Read the article below. Then complete the exercises.

Jupiter Bound: Voyager on its Way . . .

Voyager 1 explored the outer planets of our solar system. Its path was a hyperbola that depended on the planet that was closest.

The table below gives the distance c from each planet to the center of the hyperbola and the distance a from the vertex of the hyperbola to the center of the hyperbola. At each vertex, Voyager 1's path was directly between a planet and the center of the hyperbola.

	Jupiter	Saturn
a	1,092,356 km	166,152 km
c	1,441,909.92 km	219,320.64 km

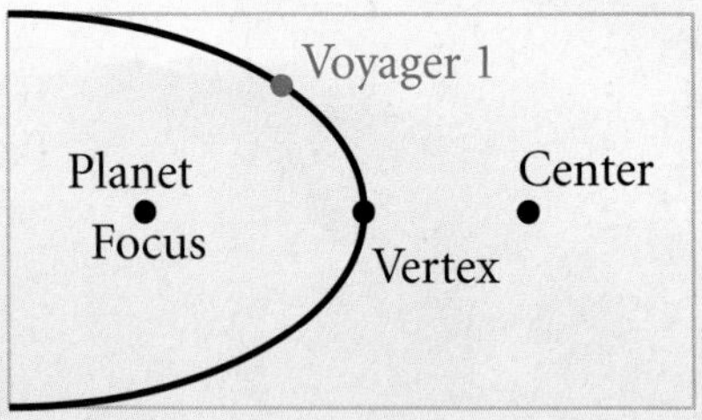

a. Write an equation of the path taken by Voyager 1 around Jupiter.
b. Write an equation of the path taken by Voyager 1 around Saturn.

Take It to the NET
Online lesson quiz at **www.PHSchool.com**
Web Code: aga-1005

Mixed Review

Lesson 10-4

Find the vertices and co-vertices of each ellipse.

54. $\frac{x^2}{34} + \frac{y^2}{25} = 1$ **55.** $3x^2 + 2y^2 = 6$ **56.** $25x^2 + 16y^2 = 1600$

Lesson 9-5

Simplify each expression.

57. $\frac{1}{5x} + \frac{1}{10x}$ **58.** $\frac{2x}{x^2 - 2x - 3} - \frac{7}{x^2 - 9}$ **59.** $\frac{4}{2x - 6} + \frac{x + 1}{x - 3}$

Lesson 8-5

Solve each equation.

60. $8^{2x} = 4$ **61.** $\log 8x = 3$ **62.** $2 \log_3 x - \log_3 4 = 2$

Checkpoint Quiz 2 — Lessons 10-4 through 10-5

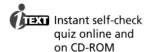

Instant self-check quiz online and on CD-ROM

Write an equation for each ellipse with the given foci and co-vertices.

1. foci $(\pm 3, 0)$ co-vertices $(0, \pm 4)$
2. foci $(0, \pm 2)$ co-vertices $(\pm 5, 0)$
3. foci $(0, \pm 7)$ co-vertices $(\pm 10, 0)$

Find the foci for each conic section. Then draw the graph.

4. $\frac{x^2}{16} - \frac{y^2}{49} = 1$ **5.** $\frac{y^2}{100} - \frac{x^2}{36} = 1$ **6.** $\frac{x^2}{4} - \frac{y^2}{81} = 1$ **7.** $\frac{y^2}{25} - \frac{x^2}{64} = 1$

Write an equation for a hyperbola centered at the origin with the given characteristics.

8. horizontal transverse axis, $a = 11, c = 15$

9. vertices $(\pm 4, 0)$, perimeter of central rectangle 28 units

10. Transverse axis is vertical, 16 units long; central rectangle is 16 units by 7 units.

Reading Math

Reading for Problem Solving

For Use With Page 566, Exercise 32

Read the problem below. Then follow along with Michelle as she solves the problem. Check your understanding with the exercise at the bottom of the page.

Write the equation of a hyperbola from the given information. Graph the equation. Place the center of the hyperbola at the origin of the coordinate plane.

32. (Distance from the center of a hyperbola to a focus)^2 = 96; endpoints of the transverse axis are at $\left(-\sqrt{32}, 0\right)$ and $\left(\sqrt{32}, 0\right)$.

What Michelle Thinks	What Michelle Writes
There is a lot of information here. I'll start with the second part. The endpoints of the transverse axis of a hyperbola are its vertices.	Vertices: $(-\sqrt{32}, 0)$ and $(\sqrt{32}, 0)$
I know that the hyperbola opens horizontally, because the transverse axis lies on the *x*-axis. The vertices are at $(-a, 0)$ and $(a, 0)$, so I know the value of a^2.	The transverse axis is horizontal, so the equation will look like $\frac{x^2}{a^2} - \frac{y^2}{b^2} = 1$.
Now I'll work on the first part of the given information. The distance from the center to the focus is *c*, which is also half the length of the diagonal of the central rectangle. I'll draw what I know so far.	$a = \sqrt{32}$, so $a^2 = 32$. c = distance from center to focus = half length of diagonal $c^2 = 96$, so $c = \sqrt{96}$
Knowing *c* will help me find *b*! I can use the Pythagorean Theorem.	$b^2 = c^2 - a^2 = 96 - 32 = 64$
I'm ready to fill in the rest of the standard form of the equation for the hyperbola. Then I'll graph the hyperbola.	Equation: $\frac{x^2}{32} - \frac{y^2}{64} = 1$

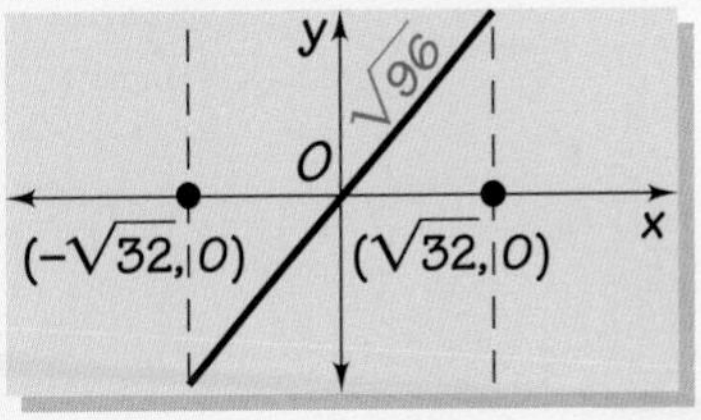

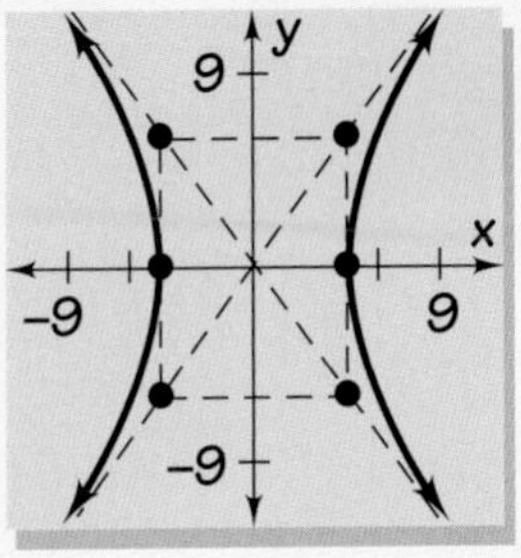

EXERCISE

Write the equation of a hyperbola from the given information. Graph the equation. Place the center of the hyperbola at the origin of the coordinate plane.

(Distance from the center of a hyperbola to a focus)^2 = 40; endpoints of the transverse axis are at $(-4, 0)$ and $(4, 0)$.

10-6 Translating Conic Sections

North Carolina Objectives

2.09 Use the equations of parabolas and circles to model and solve problems. a) Solve using tables, graphs, and algebraic properties. b) Interpret the constants and coefficients in the context of the problem.

Lesson Preview

What You'll Learn

OBJECTIVE 1 To write the equation of a translated conic section

OBJECTIVE 2 To identify the equation of a translated conic section

. . . And Why

To explore the LORAN navigation system, as in Example 3

Check Skills You'll Need

(For help, go to Lesson 5-3.)

Name the parent function for the equations in Exercises 1–4. Describe each equation as a translation of the parent function.

1. $y = x^2 + 4$

2. $y = (x - 3)^2 - 2$

3. $y - 1 = x^2$

4. $y = (x + 5)^2 + 6$

Rewrite each equation in vertex form.

5. $y = x^2 - 6x + 1$

6. $y = x^2 + 10x - 7$

7. $y = 2x^2 + 8x + 5$

8. $y = 4x^2 - 12x + 3$

Interactive lesson includes instant self-check, tutorials, and activities.

OBJECTIVE 1 Writing Equations of Translated Conic Sections

Investigation: Translating Conic Sections

1. Examine the calculator screen at the right. Describe the relationship between the two ellipses. How are they similar? How are they different?

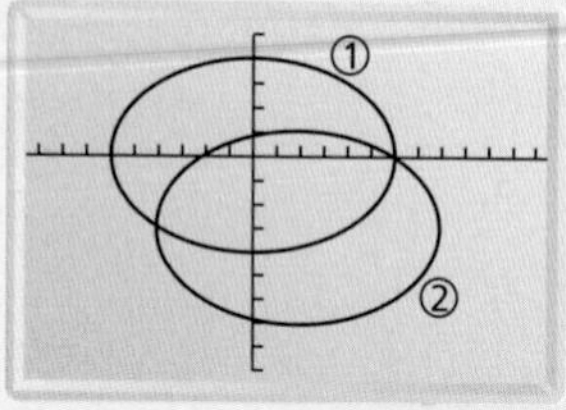

Xmin=–9 Ymin=–9
Xmax=12 Ymax=5
Xscl=1 Yscl=1

2. The equation of ellipse ① is $\frac{x^2}{36} + \frac{y^2}{16} = 1$. Use what you know about translations to write the equation of ellipse ②.

3. The graph at the right shows the hyperbola with equation $\frac{x^2}{9} - \frac{y^2}{4} = 1$. Write the equation of the hyperbola that has been shifted four units left and one unit up.

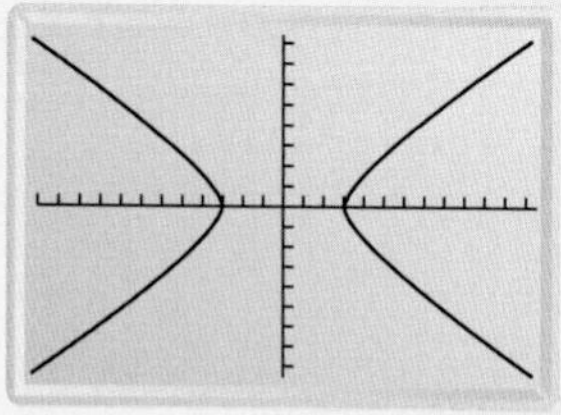

Xmin=–12 Ymin=–8
Xmax=12 Ymax=8
Xscl=1 Yscl=1

Need Help?

A translation is an operation that shifts a graph horizontally, vertically, or both.

Just as you have translated parabolas in Chapter 5 and circles in Lesson 10-3, you can also translate ellipses and hyperbolas. A translated ellipse or hyperbola has center (h, k).

Key Concepts

Summary — **Equations of Conic Sections**

Conic Section	Standard Form of Equation	
Parabola	Vertex (0, 0) $y = ax^2$ $x = ay^2$	Vertex (h, k) $y - k = a(x - h)^2$ or $y = a(x - h)^2 + k$ $x - h = a(y - k)^2$ or $x = a(y - k)^2 + h$
Circle	Center (0, 0) $x^2 + y^2 = r^2$	Center (h, k) $(x - h)^2 + (y - k)^2 = r^2$
Ellipse	Center (0, 0) $\frac{x^2}{a^2} + \frac{y^2}{b^2} = 1$ $\frac{x^2}{b^2} + \frac{y^2}{a^2} = 1$	Center (h, k) $\frac{(x-h)^2}{a^2} + \frac{(y-k)^2}{b^2} = 1$ $\frac{(x-h)^2}{b^2} + \frac{(y-k)^2}{a^2} = 1$
Hyperbola	Center (0, 0) $\frac{x^2}{a^2} - \frac{y^2}{b^2} = 1$ $\frac{y^2}{a^2} - \frac{x^2}{b^2} = 1$	Center (h, k) $\frac{(x-h)^2}{a^2} - \frac{(y-k)^2}{b^2} = 1$ $\frac{(y-k)^2}{a^2} - \frac{(x-h)^2}{b^2} = 1$

1 EXAMPLE Writing the Equation of a Translated Ellipse

Write an equation of an ellipse with center $(-3, -2)$, vertical major axis of length 8, and minor axis of length 6.

The length of the major axis is $2a$. So $2a = 8$ and $a = 4$. The length of the minor axis is $2b$. So $2b = 6$ and $b = 3$. Since the center is $(-3, -2)$, $h = -3$ and $k = -2$.

The major axis is vertical, so the equation has the form $\frac{(x-h)^2}{b^2} + \frac{(y-k)^2}{a^2} = 1$.

$\frac{(x-(-3))^2}{3^2} + \frac{(y-(-2))^2}{4^2} = 1$ **Substitute −3 for *h* and −2 for *k*.**

The equation of the ellipse is $\frac{(x+3)^2}{9} + \frac{(y+2)^2}{16} = 1$.

Check Solve the equation for y and graph both equations.

$$\frac{(x+3)^2}{9} + \frac{(y+2)^2}{16} = 1$$
$$16(x+3)^2 + 9(y+2)^2 = 144$$
$$9(y+2)^2 = 144 - 16(x+3)^2$$
$$(y+2)^2 = \tfrac{1}{9}(144 - 16(x+3)^2)$$
$$y + 2 = \pm\sqrt{\tfrac{1}{9}\left(144 - 16(x+3)^2\right)}$$
$$y = -2 \pm \tfrac{1}{3}\sqrt{144 - 16(x+3)^2}$$

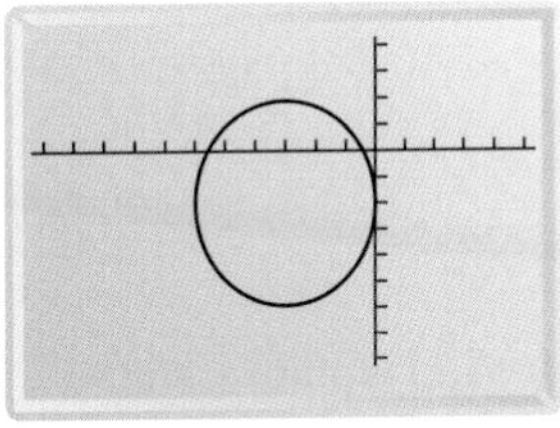

Check Understanding 1 Write an equation of an ellipse with center $(1, -4)$, horizontal major axis of length 10, and minor axis of length 4. Check your answer.

2 EXAMPLE Writing the Equation of a Translated Hyperbola

Write an equation of a hyperbola with vertices $(0, 1)$ and $(6, 1)$, and foci $(-1, 1)$ and $(7, 1)$.

Need Help?

The midpoint of the segment joining (x_1, y_1) and (x_2, y_2) is $\left(\frac{x_1 + x_2}{2}, \frac{y_1 + y_2}{2}\right)$.

Draw a sketch. The center is the midpoint of the line joining the vertices. Its coordinates are $(3, 1)$.

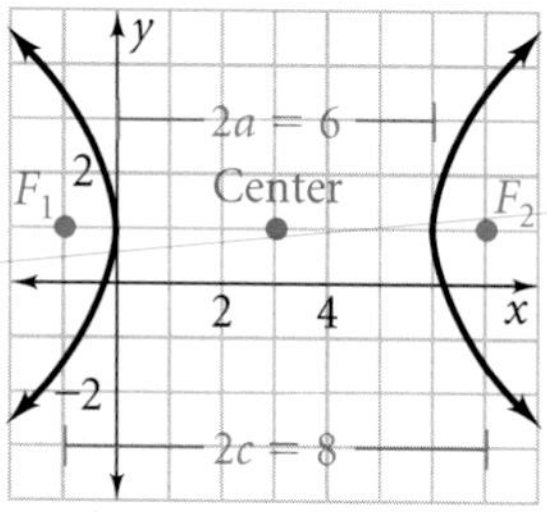

The distance between the vertices is $2a$ and the distance between the foci is $2c$. $2a = 6$, so $a = 3$; $2c = 8$, so $c = 4$.

Find b^2 using the Pythagorean Theorem.

$c^2 = a^2 + b^2$

$16 = 9 + b^2$

$b^2 = 7$

The transverse axis is horizontal. The equation has form $\frac{(x-h)^2}{a^2} - \frac{(y-k)^2}{b^2} = 1$.

The equation of the hyperbola is $\frac{(x-3)^2}{9} - \frac{(y-1)^2}{7} = 1$.

Check Understanding **2** Write an equation of a hyperbola with vertices $(2, -1)$ and $(2, 7)$, and foci $(2, 10)$ and $(2, -4)$.

3 EXAMPLE Real-World Connection

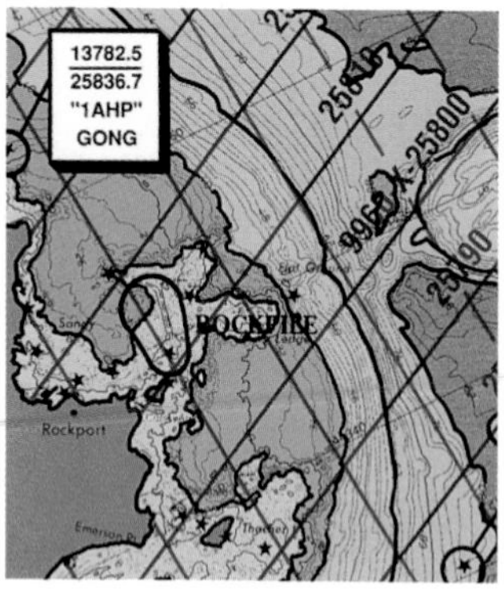

Real-World Connection

LORAN stands for *lo*ng *r*ange *n*avigation. It uses simultaneously broadcast radio signals from three transmitters to locate the ship's position at the intersection of the red and the blue hyperbolas.

Navigation Some ships navigate using LORAN. The ship's equipment calculates the difference between the arrival times of simultaneously broadcast radio signals. The difference in arrival times indicates how much closer the ship is to one transmitter than to the other. The navigator then locates the ship on a hyperbola shown in red. The process is repeated using a second pair of transmitters to locate the ship on a hyperbola shown in blue.

All points on hyperbola #25800 as shown in the diagram are 48 mi closer to one transmitter than the other. The transmitters, at the foci, are 200 mi apart and are located at $(0, 0)$ and $(200, 0)$. Find the equation of hyperbola #25800.

Step 1 Find c. Since the foci are 200 mi apart, $2c = 200$, $c = 100$, and the center of the hyperbola is at $(100, 0)$.

Step 2 Find a by calculating the difference in the distances from the vertex at $(a + 100, 0)$ to the two foci.

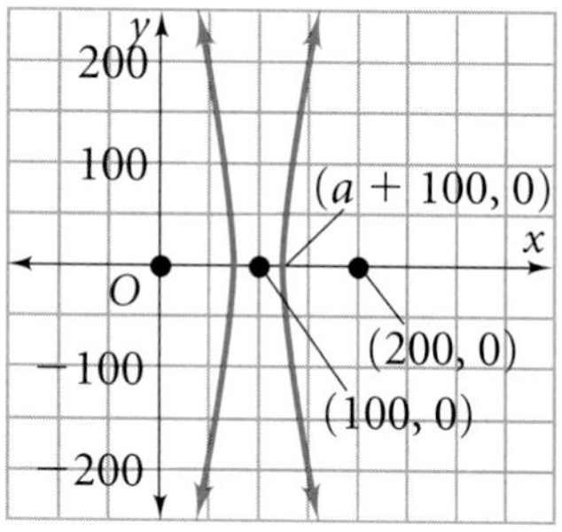

$48 = (a + 100) - [200 - (a + 100)]$

$= 2a$

$24 = a$

Step 3 Find b^2.

$c^2 = a^2 + b^2$

$(100)^2 = (24)^2 + b^2$

$10{,}000 = 576 + b^2$

$b^2 = 9424$

The equation of the hyperbola is $\frac{(x-100)^2}{24^2} - \frac{y^2}{9424} = 1$ or $\frac{(x-100)^2}{576} - \frac{y^2}{9424} = 1$.

Check Understanding **3** Use the information from Example 3. Find the equation of the hyperbola with all points 56 mi closer to one transmitter than the other.

OBJECTIVE

2 Identifying Translated Conic Sections

The equation $Ax^2 + Bxy + Cy^2 + Dx + Ey + F = 0$ is the general equation for all conic sections, where A and C are not both equal to zero. To determine which conic section the equation represents, write the equation in standard form by completing the square for the x- and y-terms.

4 EXAMPLE Identifying a Translated Conic Section

Identify the conic section with equation $4x^2 + y^2 - 24x + 6y + 9 = 0$. If it is a parabola, give the vertex. If it is a circle, give the center and radius. If it is an ellipse or a hyperbola, give the center and foci. Sketch the graph.

Complete the square for the x- and y-terms to write the equation in standard form.

$$4x^2 + y^2 - 24x + 6y + 9 = 0$$

$$4x^2 - 24x + y^2 + 6y = -9 \qquad \textbf{Group the } x\textbf{- and } y\textbf{-terms.}$$

$$4(x^2 - 6x + \blacksquare) + (y^2 + 6y + \blacksquare) = -9 \qquad \textbf{Complete the square.}$$

$$4(x^2 - 6x + (-3)^2) + (y^2 + 6y + 3^2) = -9 + 4(-3)^2 + 3^2 \qquad \textbf{Add } 4(-3)^2 \textbf{ and } 3^2 \textbf{ to each side.}$$

$$4(x^2 - 6x + 9) + (y^2 + 6y + 9) = -9 + 36 + 9 \qquad \textbf{Simplify.}$$

$$4(x - 3)^2 + (y + 3)^2 = 36 \qquad \textbf{Write the trinomials as binomials squared.}$$

$$\frac{4(x - 3)^2}{36} + \frac{(y + 3)^2}{36} = 1 \qquad \textbf{Divide each side by 36.}$$

$$\frac{(x - 3)^2}{9} + \frac{(y + 3)^2}{36} = 1 \qquad \textbf{Simplify.}$$

The equation represents an ellipse. The center is $(3, -3)$. The major axis is vertical. Since $b^2 = 9, b = 3$. Since $a^2 = 36, a = 6$.

$$c^2 = a^2 - b^2 = 36 - 9$$
$$= 27$$
$$c = 3\sqrt{3}$$

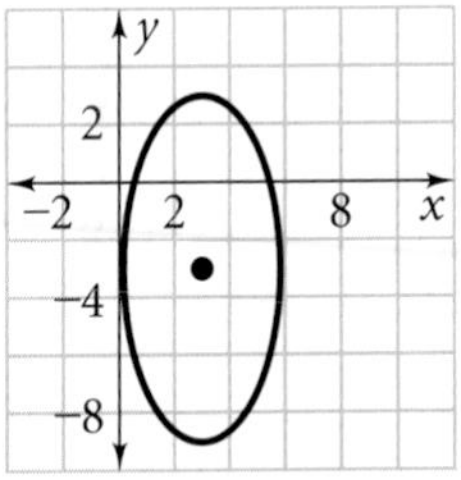

The distance from the center of the ellipse to the foci is $3\sqrt{3}$. Since the ellipse is centered at $(3, -3)$ and the major axis is vertical, the foci are located $3\sqrt{3}$ above and below this center. The foci are at $(3, -3 + 3\sqrt{3})$ and $(3, -3 - 3\sqrt{3})$.

Check Understanding 4 Identify the conic section represented by $x^2 + y^2 - 12x + 4y = 8$. Sketch the graph.

EXERCISES

For more practice, see *Extra Practice*.

Practice and Problem Solving

A Practice by Example

Example 1 (page 571)

Write an equation of an ellipse with the given characteristics. Check your answers.

1. center $(-2, 1)$, horizontal major axis of length 6, minor axis of length 4

2. center $(5, 3)$, vertical major axis of length 12, minor axis of length 8

3. center $(0, -4)$, horizontal major axis of length 12, minor axis of length 10

4. center $(3, -6)$, vertical major axis of length 14, minor axis of length 6

Example 2 (page 572)

Write an equation of a hyperbola with the given characteristics.

5. vertices $(1, -3)$ and $(-7, -3)$, foci $(2, -3)$ and $(-8, -3)$

6. vertices $(4, -1)$ and $(4, -5)$, foci $(4, 3)$ and $(4, -9)$

7. vertices $(2, 2)$ and $(-4, 2)$, foci $(6, 2)$ and $(-8, 2)$

8. vertices $(-1, 4)$ and $(-1, -6)$, foci $(-1, 8)$ and $(-1, -10)$

9. vertices $(0, -2)$ and $(0, 4)$, foci $(0, 6)$ and $(0, -4)$

Example 3 (page 572)

For Exercises 10–11, find the equation of each hyperbola described.

10. All points on the hyperbola are 72 units closer to one focus than the other. The foci are located at $(0, 0)$ and $(300, 0)$.

11. All points on the hyperbola are 88 units closer to one focus than the other. The foci are located at $(0, 0)$ and $(350, 0)$.

Example 4 (page 573)

Identify the conic section represented by each equation by writing the equation in standard form. For a parabola, give the vertex. For a circle, give the center and the radius. For an ellipse or a hyperbola, give the center and the foci. Sketch the graph.

12. $x^2 - 8x - y + 19 = 0$

13. $x^2 + y^2 + 12x = 45$

14. $3x^2 + 6x + y^2 - 6y = -3$

15. $x^2 + y^2 - 2x + 6y = 3$

16. $y^2 - x^2 + 6x - 4y = 6$

17. $x^2 - 4y^2 - 2x - 8y = 7$

18. $x^2 + y^2 + 14y = -13$

19. $y^2 - 2x - 4y = -10$

20. $4x^2 + 9y^2 + 16x - 54y = -61$

21. $x^2 - y^2 + 6x + 10y = 17$

22. $x^2 + 4y^2 - 2x - 15 = 0$

23. $9x^2 - 4y^2 - 24y = 72$

B Apply Your Skills

24. A conic section centered at the origin is translated. Describe the translation that would produce the equation $x^2 - 2y^2 + 6x - 7 = 0$.

25. Critical Thinking Use the equation $Ax^2 + Bxy + Cy^2 + Dx + Ey + F = 0$ to identify the shape of the graph that results in each case.
a. $A = C = D = E = 0, B \neq 0, F \neq 0$
b. $A = B = C = 0, D \neq 0, E \neq 0, F \neq 0$

26. a. How does the translation of an ellipse or hyperbola from center $(0, 0)$ to center (h, k) affect the coordinates of the vertices and foci?
b. How does the translation of an ellipse affect the length of its major and minor axes? Justify your answer.

27. Writing Describe how the translation of a hyperbola affects the equations of its asymptotes.

28. Error Analysis Your friend claims that the equation $\frac{x^2}{16} + \frac{y^2}{16} = 1$ represents an ellipse. Explain why your friend is wrong.

Write an equation for each conic section. Then sketch the graph.

29. circle with center $(-6, 9)$ and radius 9

30. ellipse with center $(3, 2)$, vertices $(9, 2)$ and $(-3, 2)$, and co-vertices $(3, 5)$ and $(3, -1)$

31. parabola with vertex $(2, -3)$ and focus $(2, 5)$

32. hyperbola with center $(6, -3)$, one focus $(6, 0)$, and one vertex $(6, -1)$

Write the equation of each graph. In Exercise 35, each interval represents one unit.

33.

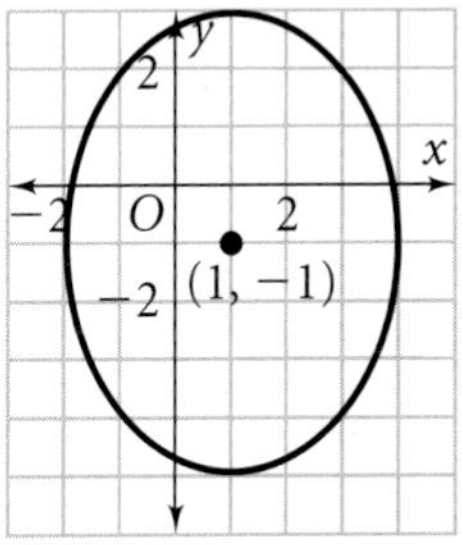

34.

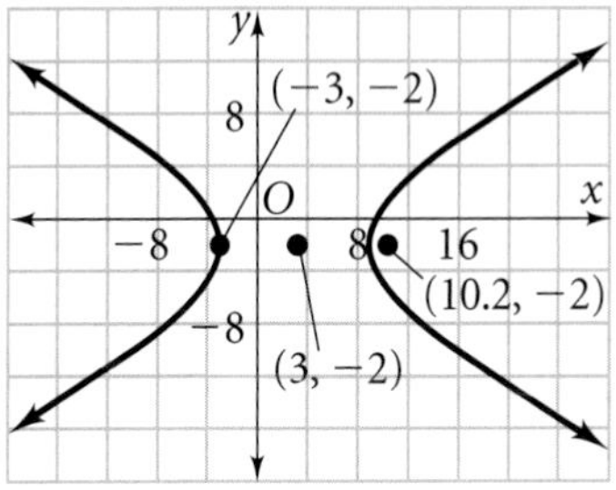

35.

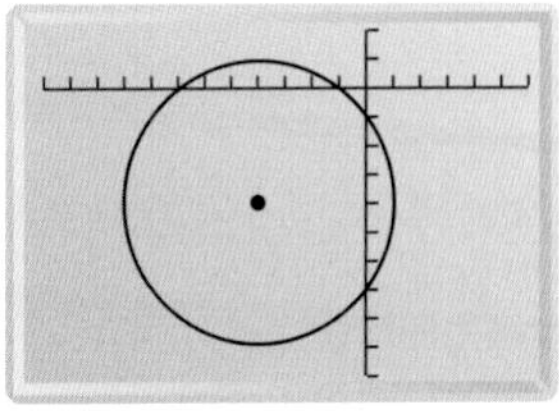

36.

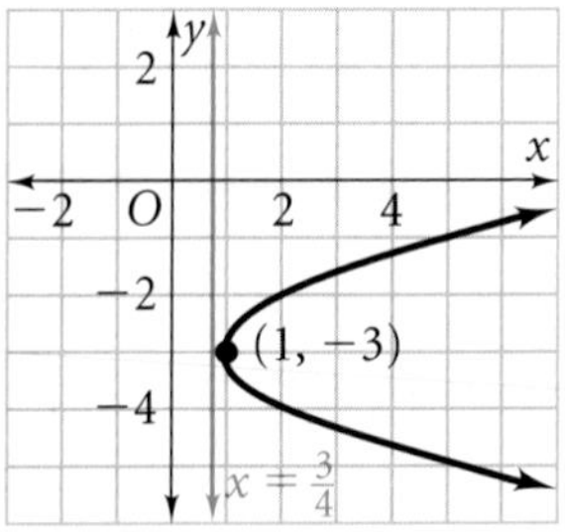

The graph of each equation is to be translated 3 units right and 5 units up. Write each new equation.

37. $(x-5)^2+(y+3)^2=4$

38. $\dfrac{(x-3)^2}{64}+\dfrac{(y+3)^2}{36}=1$

39. $y=4x^2$

40. $9x^2+3x+10=16y^2+154+3x$

41. $\dfrac{(x-2)^2}{36}-\dfrac{(y-3)^2}{25}=1$

42. $\dfrac{(x-3)^2}{4}+\dfrac{(y-4)^2}{9}=1$

43. $9x^2+16y^2+18x=64y+71$

44. $x^2+4y^2+6x-7=0$

45. $x^2-16y^2-2x+128y=271$

46. $(x-5)^2=12(y-6)$

47. $25x^2+16y^2+150x=160y-225$

48. $x^2-y^2+6x+10y=17$

Graph each pair of functions. Identify the conic section represented by the graph and write each equation in standard form.

49. $y=\sqrt{36-4x^2}$
$y=-\sqrt{36-4x^2}$

50. $y=\sqrt{4x^2-36}$
$y=-\sqrt{4x^2-36}$

51. $y=\sqrt{4x^2+36}$
$y=-\sqrt{4x^2+36}$

52. $y=\sqrt{36-x^2}$
$y=-\sqrt{36-x^2}$

53. $y=0.5\sqrt{36-x^2}$
$y=-0.5\sqrt{36-x^2}$

54. $y=\sqrt{x-4}$
$y=-\sqrt{x-4}$

C Challenge

55. Open-Ended On a graphing calculator, create a design using three translated quadratic relations.

56. History Some symbols of the writing system of the Ejagham, people who lived in Nigeria and Cameroon, are shown. The symbol for marriage consists of two parabolic shapes. Reproduce this symbol on a graphing calculator. What equations did you use?

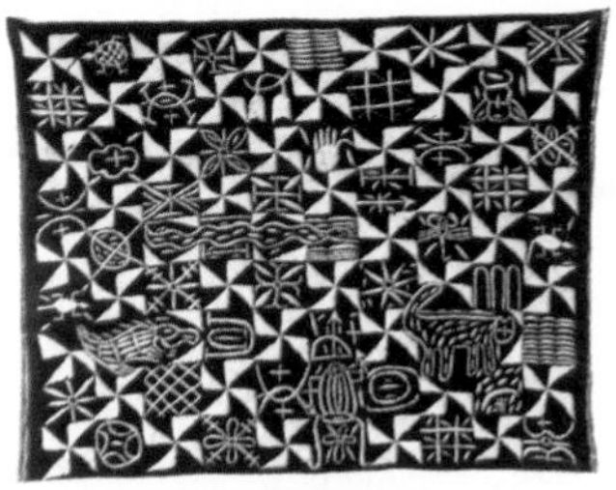

Real-World Connection

This Nigerian cloth combines writing symbols and patterns.

57. Consider equations of the form $Ax^2+By^2+Cx+Dy+E=0$.

a. What must be true about A and B for the graph of the equation to be a circle? To be an ellipse? To be a hyperbola? To be a parabola?

b. Suppose $A=1$ and $B=1$. Must the graph be a circle? Explain.

c. Suppose $A=1, B=-1$, and $C=D=E=0$. Describe the graph.

58. **Astronomy** The dimensions of the elliptical orbits of three planets are given in millions of kilometers in the table. The sun is at one focus. The other focus is on the positive x-axis.

Planet	a	b
Earth	149.60	149.58
Mars	227.9	226.9
Mercury	57.9	56.6

a. Write an equation for each orbit and draw the curves on your graphing calculator. (Remember to adjust the viewing window.)

b. **Reasoning** Which orbit is most circular? Justify your reasoning.

Standardized Test Prep

Quantitative Comparison

Compare the boxed quantity in Column A with the boxed quantity in Column B. Choose the best answer.

A. The quantity in Column A is greater.
B. The quantity in Column B is greater.
C. The two quantities are equal.
D. The relationship cannot be determined from the information given.

	Column A	Column B
59.	distance from a focus to the center on the graph of $3x^2 + 4y^2 - 12x + 8y = 32$	distance from a focus to the nearest vertex on the graph of $3x^2 + 4y^2 - 12x + 8y = 32$
60.	length of the major axis on the graph of $4x^2 - 24x = 64 - 25y^2$	length of the minor axis on the graph of $4x^2 - 24x = 64 - 25y^2$
61.	number of horizontal units shifted in translating from $x^2 - 4y^2 = 16$ to $x^2 - 2x - 4y^2 = 15$	number of vertical units shifted in translating from $x^2 - 4y^2 = 16$ to $x^2 - 2x - 4y^2 = 15$

Take It to the NET
Online lesson quiz at
www.PHSchool.com
Web Code: aga-1006

Multiple Choice

62. Which conic section is represented by the equation $x^2 + y^2 = 6x - 14y - 9$?
F. circle **G.** ellipse **H.** parabola **I.** hyperbola

Extended Response

63. Explain how you can tell which conic section is represented by the equation $x^2 + y^2 - 26 = 14x - 10y$. Describe the conic section.

Mixed Review

Lesson 10-5

Find the foci of each hyperbola. Draw the graph.

64. $\frac{x^2}{49} - \frac{y^2}{36} = 1$ **65.** $8y^2 - 6x^2 = 72$ **66.** $4y^2 - 100x^2 = 400$

Lesson 9-6

Solve each equation. Check your answers.

67. $\frac{1}{3x + 1} = \frac{1}{x^2 - 3}$ **68.** $\frac{2}{x + 2} = \frac{6}{x^2 - 4}$ **69.** $\frac{5}{x^2 - x} + \frac{3}{x - 1} = 6$

Lesson 8-6

Simplify each expression.

70. $\ln e$ **71.** $2 \ln e$ **72.** $\ln e^3$ **73.** $4 \ln e^2$

Extension

Solving Quadratic Systems

FOR USE WITH LESSON 10-6

In Chapter 3 you solved systems of linear equations algebraically and graphically. You can use the same methods to solve systems that include quadratic equations.

1 EXAMPLE Solving Algebraically

Solve the system algebraically. $\begin{cases} x^2 - y^2 = 9 \\ x^2 + 9y^2 = 169 \end{cases}$

$$\begin{aligned} x^2 - y^2 &= 9 \\ x^2 + 9y^2 &= 169 \\ \hline -10y^2 &= -160 \end{aligned}$$

Subtract like terms to eliminate the x^2 terms.

$y = 4$ or $y = -4$ **Solve for y.**

$x^2 - (4)^2 = 9$ **Substitute the values of y into one of the original equations.** $x^2 - (-4)^2 = 9$

$x^2 = 25$ $\qquad$ $x^2 = 25$

$x = 5$ or $x = -5$ **Solve for x.** $x = 5$ or $x = -5$

The ordered pairs $(5, 4)$, $(-5, 4)$, $(5, -4)$, and $(-5, -4)$ are solutions to the system.

2 EXAMPLE Solving Graphically

Solve the system by graphing. $\begin{cases} x^2 + y^2 = 36 \\ y = (x - 2)^2 - 3 \end{cases}$

$x^2 + y^2 = 36$

$y = \pm\sqrt{36 - x^2}$ **Solve the first equation for y.**

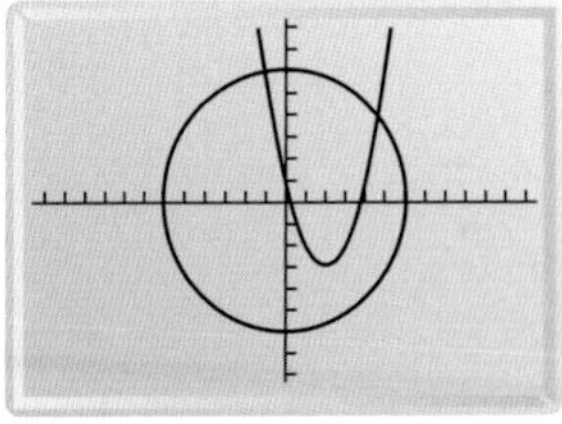

Graph the equations and find the point(s) of intersection.
The solutions are approximately $(-1, 6)$ and $(4.6, 3.8)$.

EXERCISES

Solve each quadratic system.

1. $\begin{cases} x^2 + 64y^2 = 64 \\ x^2 + y^2 = 64 \end{cases}$ **2.** $\begin{cases} 2x^2 - y^2 = 2 \\ x^2 + y^2 = 25 \end{cases}$ **3.** $\begin{cases} 9x^2 + 25y^2 = 225 \\ y = -x^2 + 5 \end{cases}$ **4.** $\begin{cases} 4x^2 + 4y^2 = 100 \\ 3x^2 + 3y^2 = 27 \end{cases}$

5. a. Writing The system that consists of $y = -3x + 6$ and $y = x^2 - 4x$ is a linear-quadratic system. How would you solve the system algebraically? Graphically?

b. Solve the system in part (a).

Identify each system as linear-quadratic or quadratic-quadratic. Then solve.

6. $\begin{cases} y = x - 1 \\ x^2 + y^2 = 25 \end{cases}$ **7.** $\begin{cases} 9x^2 + 4y^2 = 36 \\ x^2 - y^2 = 4 \end{cases}$ **8.** $\begin{cases} -x + y = 4 \\ y = x^2 - 4x + 2 \end{cases}$ **9.** $\begin{cases} 4x^2 + 25y^2 = 100 \\ y = x + 2 \end{cases}$

Test-Taking Strategies

Choosing *Cannot Be Determined*

Some multiple-choice questions cannot be answered. If so, then one of the answer choices will be *cannot be determined*. Be careful, however. Sometimes the answer choice *cannot be determined* is included as a distractor.

1 EXAMPLE

Find an equation of a circle that passes through the points $(0, 0)$, $(1, 0)$ and $(2, 0)$.

A. $(x - 1)^2 + y^2 = 1$

B. $\left(x - \frac{1}{2}\right)^2 + y^2 = \frac{1}{4}$

C. $\left(x - \frac{3}{2}\right)^2 + y^2 = \frac{1}{4}$

D. cannot be determined

Since the y-coordinates of all three points are zero, the points are collinear. A circle cannot pass through three collinear points. The correct answer is D.

2 EXAMPLE

Which of the following completely describes the graphs of $(x - r)^2 + (y - r)^2 = 2r^2$?

A. circles of radius r with centers on the line $y = x$
B. circles with centers (r, r)
C. circles with centers on the line $y = x$ and passing through $(0, 0)$
D. cannot be determined

The standard form of an equation of a circle is $(x - h)^2 + (y - k)^2 = r^2$, where (h, k) is the center of the circle. So the equation in Example 2 describes circles that have centers at (r, r) and have radius $\sqrt{2r^2}$, or $r\sqrt{2}$.

Eliminate choice A, since the radius is incorrect. Since the centers of the circles are (r, r), they all lie on the line $y = x$. Choices B and C could be correct. Test choice C by substituting $x = 0$ and $y = 0$.

$(0 - r)^2 + (0 - r)^2 \stackrel{?}{=} 2r^2$ **Substitute (0, 0) for *x* and *y*.**

$(r)^2 + (r)^2 \stackrel{?}{=} 2r^2$ **Simplify.**

$2r^2 = 2r^2$

The circles pass through the point $(0, 0)$. The correct answer is C. Choice D is a distractor.

EXERCISES

If the answer to an exercise can be determined, write the answer. If not, write *cannot be determined* and explain your reasoning.

1. Find the radius of the circle defined by $x^2 + y^2 - 4x - 2y + 14 = 0$.
2. Find the number of points of intersection of the graphs of $y = x^2$ and $y = 2ax - a^2$.
3. Given that $x^2 - y^2 = 12$, find y when $x = 3$.
4. The focus of a parabola is $(0, 3)$. Find the equation of the directrix.

Chapter Review

Chapter 10

Vocabulary

center (p. 549)
circle (p. 549)
conic section (p. 535)
co-vertices (p. 556)
directrix (p. 543)
ellipse (p. 556)
focus of a parabola (p. 543)
focus of an ellipse (p. 556)
focus of a hyperbola (p. 563)
hyperbola (p. 563)
major axis (p. 556)
minor axis (p. 556)
radius (p. 549)
standard form of an equation of a circle (p. 549)
transverse axis (p. 563)
vertices of an ellipse (p. 556)
vertices of a hyperbola (p. 563)

Reading Math
Understanding Vocabulary

Take It to the NET
Online vocabulary quiz at **www.PHSchool.com**
Web Code: agj-1051

Choose the correct vocabulary term to complete each sentence.

1. In the definition of a parabola, the fixed line is the __?__ .

2. The vertices of an ellipse are on its __?__.

3. $(x - h)^2 + (y - k)^2 = r^2$ is the __?__.

4. The distance from a point on a circle to its center is the __?__ of the circle.

5. The vertices of a hyperbola are on its __?__.

Skills and Concepts

10-1 Objectives

- To graph conic sections (p. 535)
- To identify conic sections (p. 537)

A **conic section** is a curve formed by the intersection of a plane and a double cone. Circles, ellipses, parabolas, and hyperbolas are all conic sections.

Graph each equation. Identify the conic section and describe the graph and its lines of symmetry. Then find the domain and range.

6. $\frac{x^2}{49} + \frac{y^2}{121} = 1$ **7.** $x^2 + y^2 = 4$ **8.** $\frac{x^2}{25} - \frac{y^2}{4} = 1$ **9.** $x = 2y^2 + 5$

Identify the center, the intercepts, and the domain and range of each graph.

10.

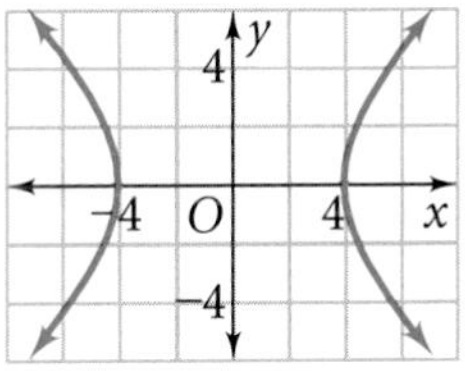

11.

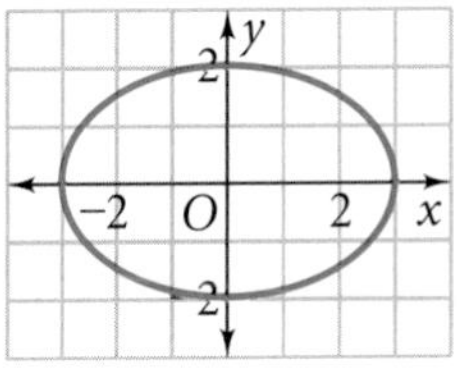

10-2 Objectives

- To write the equation of a parabola (p. 543)
- To graph parabolas (p. 545)

In a plane, a parabola is the set of all points that are the same distance c from a fixed line, the **directrix,** and a fixed point not on the line, the **focus.**

For $y = ax^2$ when $a > 0$, the parabola opens upward. The focus is $(0, c)$ and the directrix is $y = -c$. When $a < 0$, the parabola opens downward. The focus is $(0, -c)$ and the directrix is $y = c$. For $x = ay^2$, when $a > 0$, the parabola opens to the right. The focus is $(c, 0)$ and directrix is $x = -c$. When $a < 0$, the parabola opens to the left. The focus is $(-c, 0)$ and the directrix is $x = c$. Always, $|a| = \frac{1}{4c}$.

Write an equation for a graph that is the set of all points in the plane that are equidistant from the given point and the given line.

12. $F(0, 3), y = -1$ **13.** $F(-2, 0), x = 4$

Write an equation of a parabola with a vertex at the origin and the given focus.

14. focus at $(5, 0)$ **15.** focus at $(0, -5)$ **16.** focus at $(0, 6)$

Write an equation of a parabola opening upward with a vertex at the origin.

17. focus is 2.5 units from the vertex **18.** focus is $\frac{1}{12}$ of a unit from the vertex

Find the focus and the directrix of the graph of each equation. Sketch the graph.

19. $y = 5x^2$ **20.** $x = 2y^2$ **21.** $x = -\frac{1}{8}y^2$

10-3 Objectives

- To write and graph the equation of a circle (p. 549)
- To find the center and radius of a circle and use it to graph the circle (p. 551)

In a plane, a **circle** is the set of all points at a given distance, the **radius** r, from a given point, the **center** (h, k). The **standard form of an equation of a circle** is $(x - h)^2 + (y - k)^2 = r^2$.

Write an equation in standard form of the circle with the given center and radius.

22. center $(0, 0)$, radius 4 **23.** center $(8, 1)$, radius 5

Write an equation for each translation of $x^2 + y^2 = r^2$ with the given radius.

24. left 3 units, up 2 units; radius 10 **25.** right 5 units, down 3 units; radius 8

Write an equation for each circle. Each interval represents one unit.

26.

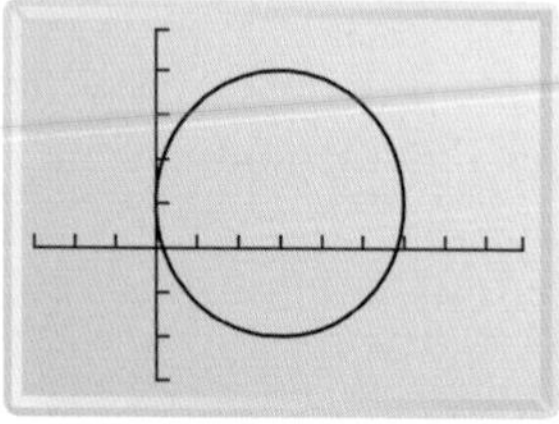

27.

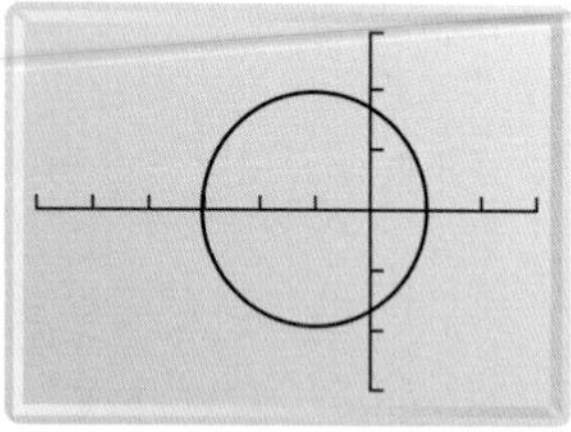

Find the center and the radius of each circle. Sketch the graph.

28. $(x - 1)^2 + y^2 = 64$ **29.** $(x + 7)^2 + (y + 3)^2 = 49$

10-4 Objectives

- To write the equation of an ellipse (p. 556)
- To find the foci of an ellipse, and to graph an ellipse (p. 558)

In a plane, an **ellipse** is the set of all points P, the sum of whose distances to two fixed points, the **foci,** is constant. The **major axis** is the segment that contains the foci and has endpoints called the **vertices of an ellipse.** The **minor axis** is perpendicular to the major axis and has endpoints called the **co-vertices.**

There are two standard forms of an ellipse centered at the origin. If $\frac{x^2}{a^2} + \frac{y^2}{b^2} = 1$, the major axis is horizontal with vertices $(\pm a, 0)$ and co-vertices $(0, \pm b)$, where $a > b > 0$.

If $\frac{x^2}{b^2} + \frac{y^2}{a^2} = 1$, the major axis is vertical with vertices $(0, \pm a)$ and co-vertices $(\pm b, 0)$. In either case, you can find the foci c using the relationship $c^2 = a^2 - b^2$.

Write an equation of an ellipse in standard form with a center at the origin and with the given characteristics.

30. foci $(\pm 1, 0)$, co-vertices $(0, \pm 4)$

31. vertex $(0, \sqrt{29})$, co-vertex $(-5, 0)$

32. focus $(0, 1)$, vertex $(0, \sqrt{10})$

33. foci $(\pm 2, 0)$, co-vertices $(0, \pm 6)$

34. Write the equation of an ellipse centered at the origin with height 8 units and width 16 units.

35. Graph $\frac{x^2}{4} + \frac{y^2}{9} = 1$. Identify the foci.

10-5 Objectives

- To graph hyperbolas (p. 562)
- To find and use the foci of a hyperbola (p. 564)

In a plane, a **hyperbola** is the set of all points P such that difference between the distances from P to two fixed points, the **foci,** is constant. The foci lie on the line containing the **transverse axis**. Each branch of a hyperbola intersects the transverse axis at a **vertex of the hyperbola**. Each branch approaches the two asymptotes, which contain the diagonals of the central rectangle.

There are two standard forms of hyperbolas centered at the origin. If $\frac{x^2}{a^2} - \frac{y^2}{b^2} = 1$, the asymptotes are $y = \pm\frac{b}{a}x$, the transverse axis is horizontal with vertices $(\pm a, 0)$, and the foci are $(\pm c, 0)$. If $\frac{y^2}{a^2} - \frac{x^2}{b^2} = 1$, the asymptotes are $y = \pm\frac{a}{b}x$, the transverse axis is vertical with vertices $(0, \pm a)$, and the foci are $(0, \pm c)$. In either case, you can find the value of b using the relationship $c^2 = a^2 + b^2$.

Find the foci of each hyperbola. Draw the graph.

36. $\frac{x^2}{36} - \frac{y^2}{225} = 1$

37. $\frac{y^2}{400} - \frac{x^2}{169} = 1$

38. $\frac{x^2}{121} - \frac{y^2}{81} = 1$

39. Find an equation that models the path of a spacecraft around a planet if $a = 107{,}124$ and $c = 213{,}125.9$.

10-6 Objectives

- To write the equation of a translated conic section (p. 570)
- To identify the equation of a translated conic section (p. 573)

You can substitute $(x - h)$ for x and $(y - k)$ for y to translate graphs of an ellipse or a hyperbola. A translated ellipse or hyperbola has center (h, k).

Write an equation of a conic section with the given characteristics.

40. an ellipse with center $(3, -2)$, vertical major axis of length 6; minor axis of length 4

41. a hyperbola with vertices $(3, 3)$ and $(9, 3)$, foci $(1, 3)$ and $(11, 3)$

42. All points on the hyperbola are 81 units closer to one focus than the other. The foci are at $(0, 0)$ and $(155, 0)$.

Identify the conic section represented by each equation by writing the equation in standard form. For a parabola, give the vertex. For a circle, give the center and the radius. For an ellipse or a hyperbola, give the center and the foci. Sketch the graph.

43. $-x^2 + y^2 + 4y - 16 = 0$

44. $x^2 + y^2 + 3x - 4y - 9 = 0$

45. $x^2 + x - y - 42 = 0$

46. $2x^2 + 3y^2 - 4x + 12y - 20 = 0$

Chapter 10

Chapter Test

Take It to the NET
Online chapter test at
www.PHSchool.com
Web Code: aga-1052

Identify the center and intercepts of each conic section. Give the domain and range of each graph.

1.

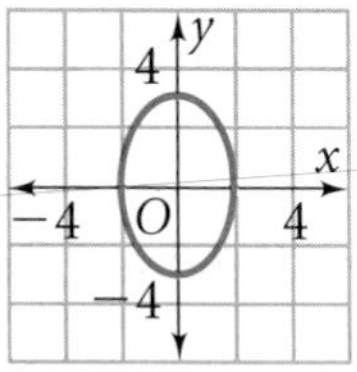

2.

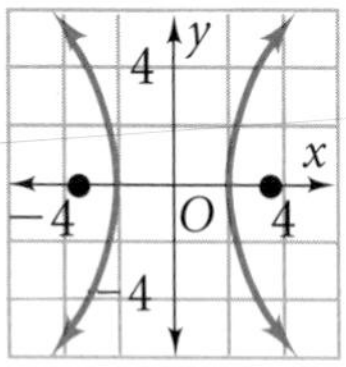

3.

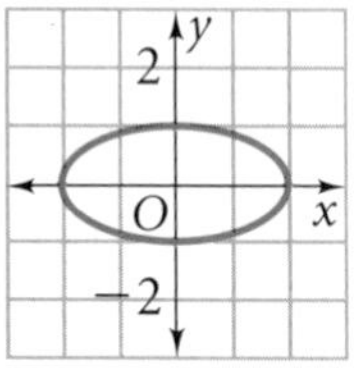

4.

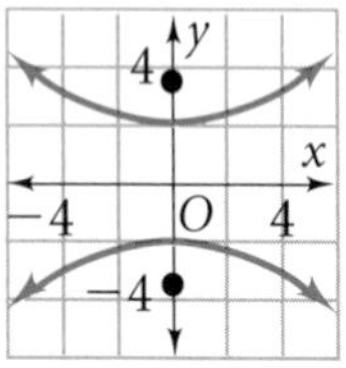

5. **Writing** Explain how you can tell what kind of conic section a quadratic equation describes without graphing the equation.

Identify the focus and the directrix of the graph of each equation.

6. $y = 3x^2$

7. $x = -2y^2$

8. $x + 5y^2 = 0$

9. $9x^2 - 2y = 0$

Write an equation of a parabola with a vertex at the origin and the given characteristic.

10. focus at $(0, -2)$

11. focus at $(3, 0)$

12. directrix $x = 7$

13. directrix $y = -1$

Find the center and radius of the circle. Sketch the circle.

14. $(x - 2)^2 + (y - 3)^2 = 36$

15. $(x + 5)^2 + (y + 8)^2 = 100$

16. $(x - 1)^2 + (y + 7)^2 = 81$

17. $(x + 4)^2 + (y - 10)^2 = 121$

Find an equation of an ellipse for each given height and width. Assume that the center of the ellipse is (0, 0).

18. height 10 units, width 16 units

19. height 2 units, width 12 units

20. height 9 units, width 5 units

Find the foci for each ellipse. Sketch the ellipse.

21. $\frac{x^2}{81} + \frac{y^2}{36} = 1$

22. $\frac{x^2}{25} + \frac{y^2}{121} = 1$

23. $x^2 + \frac{y^2}{49} = 1$

24. $4x^2 + y^2 = 4$

25. **Critical Thinking** What is the shape of an ellipse whose height and width are equal?

Find the foci for each hyperbola. Sketch the hyperbola.

26. $\frac{x^2}{144} - \frac{y^2}{100} = 1$

27. $\frac{y^2}{169} - \frac{x^2}{400} = 1$

28. $\frac{x^2}{64} - \frac{y^2}{4} = 1$

29. $y^2 - \frac{x^2}{225} = 1$

30. **Open-Ended** Write the equation of a hyperbola with a transverse axis on the x-axis.

Write an equation of an ellipse with the given characteristics.

31. center $(0, 0)$, vertex $(4, 0)$, co-vertex $(0, -3)$

32. center $(-2, 7)$, horizontal major axis of length 8, minor axis of length 6

33. center $(3, -2)$, vertical major axis of length 12, minor axis of length 10

Write an equation of a hyperbola with the given characteristics.

34. vertices $(\pm 3, 7)$, foci $(\pm 5, 7)$

35. vertices $(2, \pm 5)$, foci $(2, -7), (2, 7)$

36. vertices $(-3, -1), (-5, -1)$, foci $(0, -1), (-8, -1)$

Identify the conic section represented by each equation. If it is a parabola, give the vertex. If it is a circle, give the center and radius. If it is an ellipse or a hyperbola, give the center and foci. Sketch the graph.

37. $3y^2 - x - 6y + 5 = 0$

38. $x^2 + y^2 - 4x - 6y + 4 = 0$

39. $4x^2 + y^2 - 16x - 6y + 9 = 0$

40. $4x^2 - y^2 - 16x + 6y - 9 = 0$

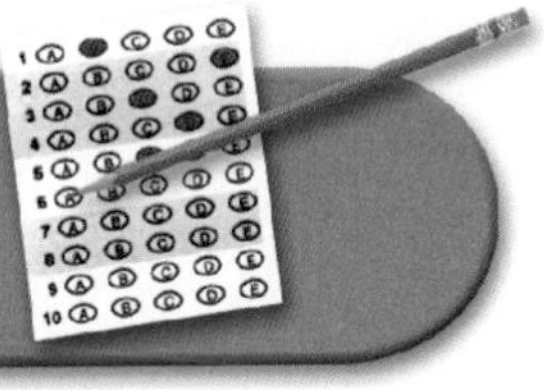

Standardized Test Prep

Multiple Choice

For Exercises 1–7, choose the correct letter.

1. Which equation represents a circle with center (−3, 8) and radius 12?
   A. $(x-8)^2+(y+3)^2=144$
   B. $(x-8)^2-(y+3)^2=144$
   C. $(x+3)^2+(y-8)^2=144$
   D. $(x-3)^2-(y-8)^2=144$

2. Which function has a growth factor of 1.25?
   F. $y=1.25x$
   G. $y=4.1(1.25)^x$
   H. $y=1.25(3.7)^x$
   I. $y=1.25(0.9)^x$

3. What is the product $\frac{x^2(x-2)}{x+4}\cdot\frac{2(2x+8)}{x^3-x^2}$?
   A. $\frac{x^4(x-1)(x-2)-4(x+4)^2}{x^2(x-1)(x+4)}$
   B. $\frac{12x^4+14x^3-32x^2}{x^4+2x^3-4x^2}$
   C. $\frac{x^4(x-1)(x-2)}{4(x+4)^2}$
   D. $\frac{4(x-2)}{x-1}$

4. The equation $y=(x-4)^2$ represents which conic section?
   F. circle
   G. ellipse
   H. parabola
   I. hyperbola

5. Which events are dependent?
   I. spinning a spinner three times
   II. choosing three students from a class
   III. tossing two coins and a number cube
   A. I only B. II only C. III only D. I and II

6. The graph below represents which function?

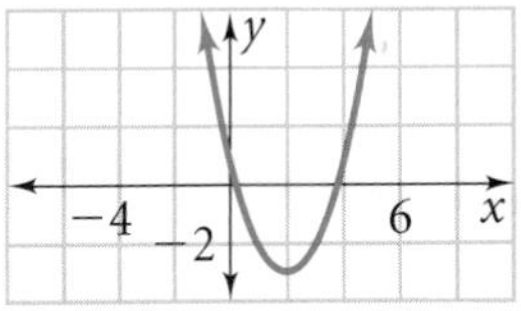

   F. $y=\frac{x^2-4}{x+4}$
   G. $y=x^2-4x+1$
   H. $y=|x+4|$
   I. $y=x^3+x^2-4$

7. Which equation has roots −3, 0, 1, and 2?
   A. $x^4-7x^2+6x=0$
   B. $x^4-6x^3+11x-6x=0$
   C. $x^4-4x^3+x^2-6x=0$
   D. $x^4-7x^2-6=0$

Quantitative Comparison

Compare the boxed quantity in Column A with the boxed quantity in Column B. Choose the best answer.

F. The quantity in Column A is greater.
G. The quantity in Column B is greater.
H. The two quantities are equal.
I. The relationship cannot be determined from the information given.

	Column A	Column B
8.	the radius of the circle $x^2+(y-1)^2=34$	the radius of the circle $(x-4)^2+y^2=48$
9.	${}_7C_2$	${}_7C_5$
10.	$4^{-\frac{2}{3}}$	$4^{-\frac{3}{2}}$

Gridded Response

11. Simplify $\frac{1-\frac{1}{8}}{2-\frac{3}{4}}$.

12. *A* and *B* are not mutually exclusive events. $P(A)=\frac{1}{4}$ and $P(B)=\frac{1}{5}$. Find $P(A \text{ or } B)$.

Short Response

13. $\begin{bmatrix}1 & 0\\0 & 2\\1 & 3\end{bmatrix}+\begin{bmatrix}2 & 1\\1 & 3\\0 & 0\end{bmatrix}$

14. Find the zeros of the function $y=x^2-2x$. Show your work.

Extended Response

15. a. Write an equation of a line perpendicular to $y=3x+2$.
    b. Write an equation of a line parallel to $y=3x+2$.

16. Find $\frac{x+4}{x^2+6x+8}\div\frac{x^2-16}{x^2+8x+12}$.
    What are the restrictions on the variable?

Real-World Snapshots

Martian Math

Applying Conic Sections Even though we haven't discovered life on Mars, we know a lot of other things about the planet. Mars has a day about 25 hours long, a pattern of seasons similar to Earth's, and polar icecaps. Mars also has surface temperatures that rarely rise above freezing and almost no oxygen in its atmosphere. Mars is often called the Red Planet because red deserts cover its surface.

Activity 1

a. Mars travels in an elliptical orbit with the sun at one of its foci. Use the data from the diagram to calculate a, b, and c of this elliptical orbit.

b. Point P is the midpoint between Mars' closest and farthest distances to the sun. Use your values of a and b to write an equation of the elliptical orbit of Mars relative to a coordinate system drawn through point P (y-axis in gray). Use distances in millions of kilometers.

c. It is also useful to define Mars' motion relative to the sun. Imagine a new coordinate system (y-axis in black) with its origin at the center of the sun. Rewrite your equation for the ellipse in this new coordinate system.

d. **Critical Thinking** Explain how the eccentricity of a planet's orbit can affect its annual weather cycle.

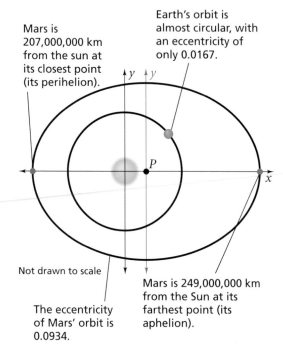

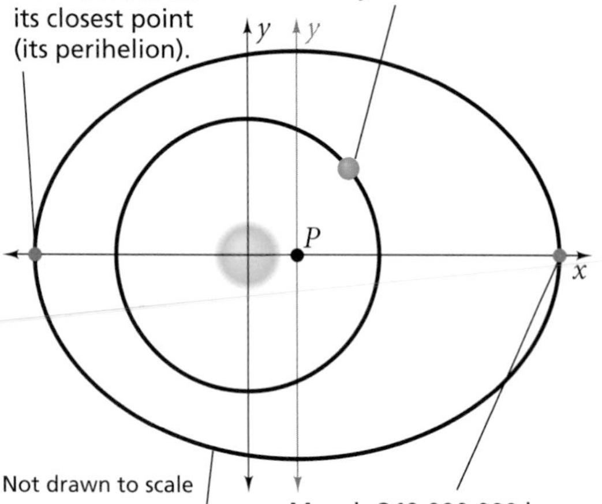
Mars is 207,000,000 km from the sun at its closest point (its perihelion).
Earth's orbit is almost circular, with an eccentricity of only 0.0167.
y
y
P
x
Not drawn to scale
The eccentricity of Mars' orbit is 0.0934.
Mars is 249,000,000 km from the Sun at its farthest point (its aphelion).

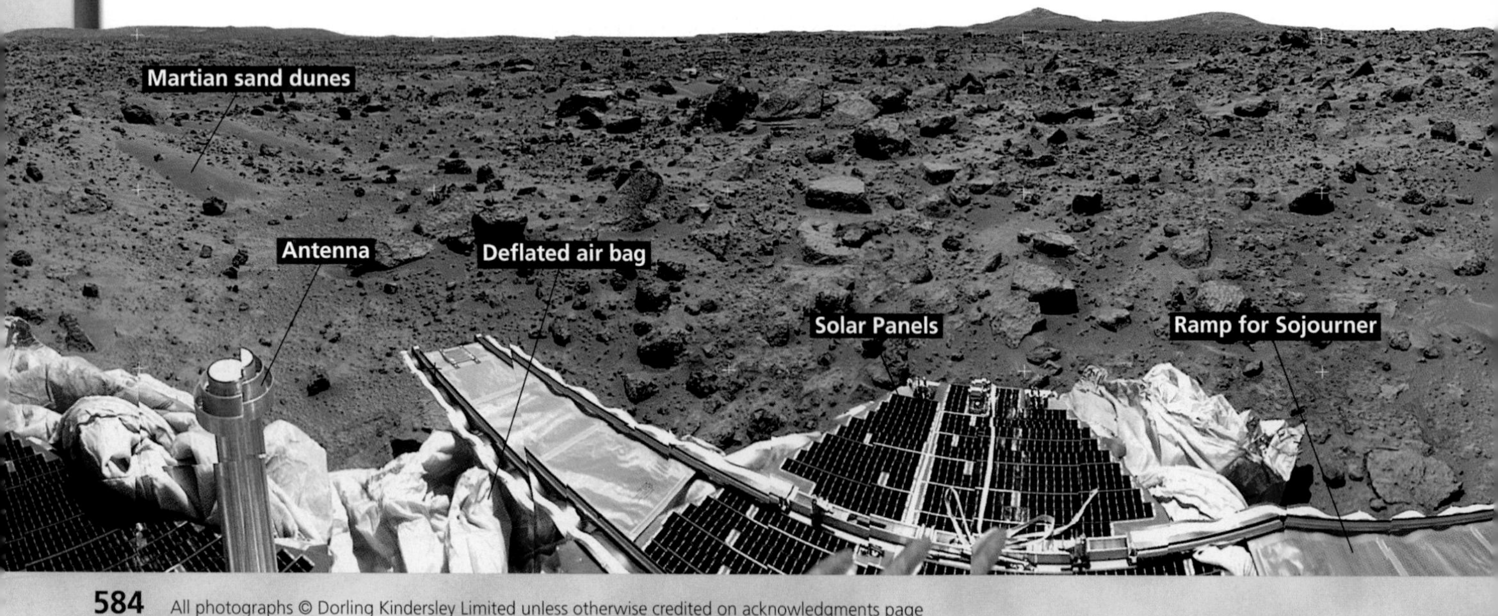
Martian sand dunes
Antenna
Deflated air bag
Solar Panels
Ramp for Sojourner

Activity 2

Astronauts who walked on the moon felt as if they weighed about one sixth of their weight on Earth. This is because the weight of an object is determined by the gravitational attraction between the object and the planet (or moon) it's on. You can use the following formula to estimate the weight of an object on the surface of any of the planets: gravitational force $= \frac{GmM}{r^2}$, where G = universal gravitational constant, m = mass of the object, M = mass of the planet, and r = radius of the planet. For a given object, G and m remain constant, so the force of gravity depends only on the variables M and r.

a. Use the data below. Write a ratio to determine the factor by which you would multiply the weight of a 150-lb person on Earth to find his or her weight on Mars.

b. Find the person's weight on Mars.

c. Repeat parts (a) and (b) for two other planets.

Man on the Moon

On July 20, 1969, U.S. astronauts first set foot on the moon.

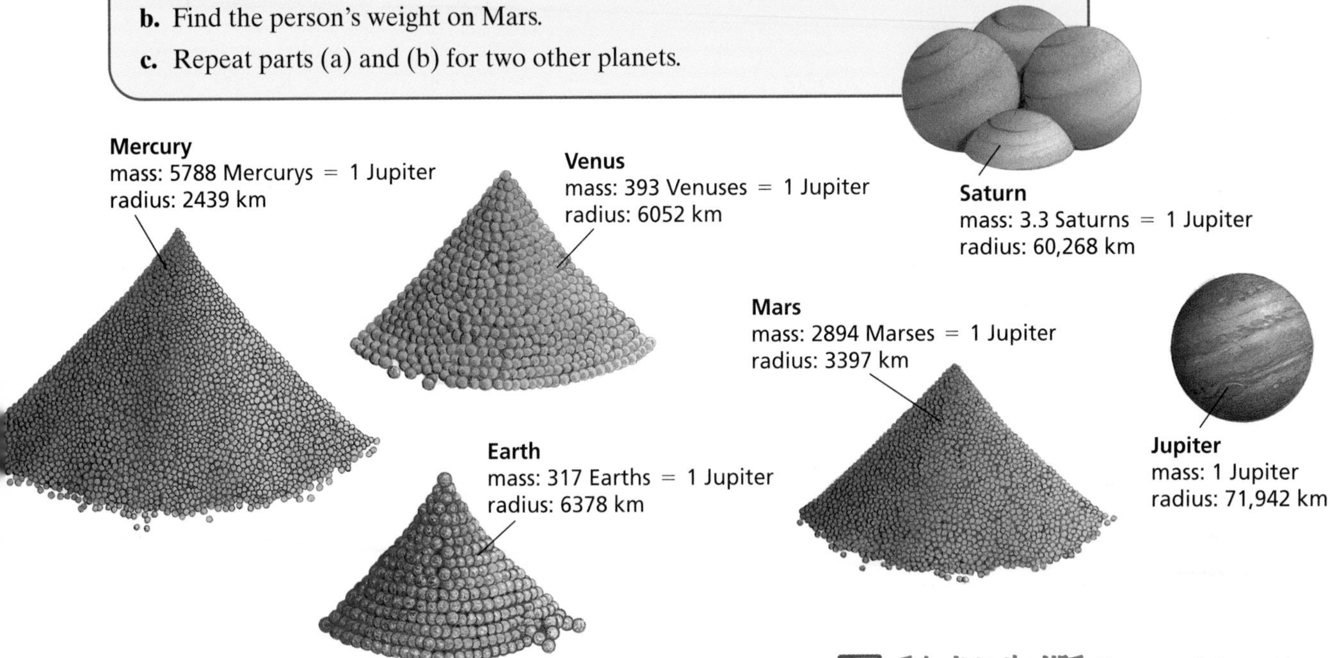

Take It to the NET For more information about Mars, go to **www.PHSchool.com**.
Web Code: age-1053

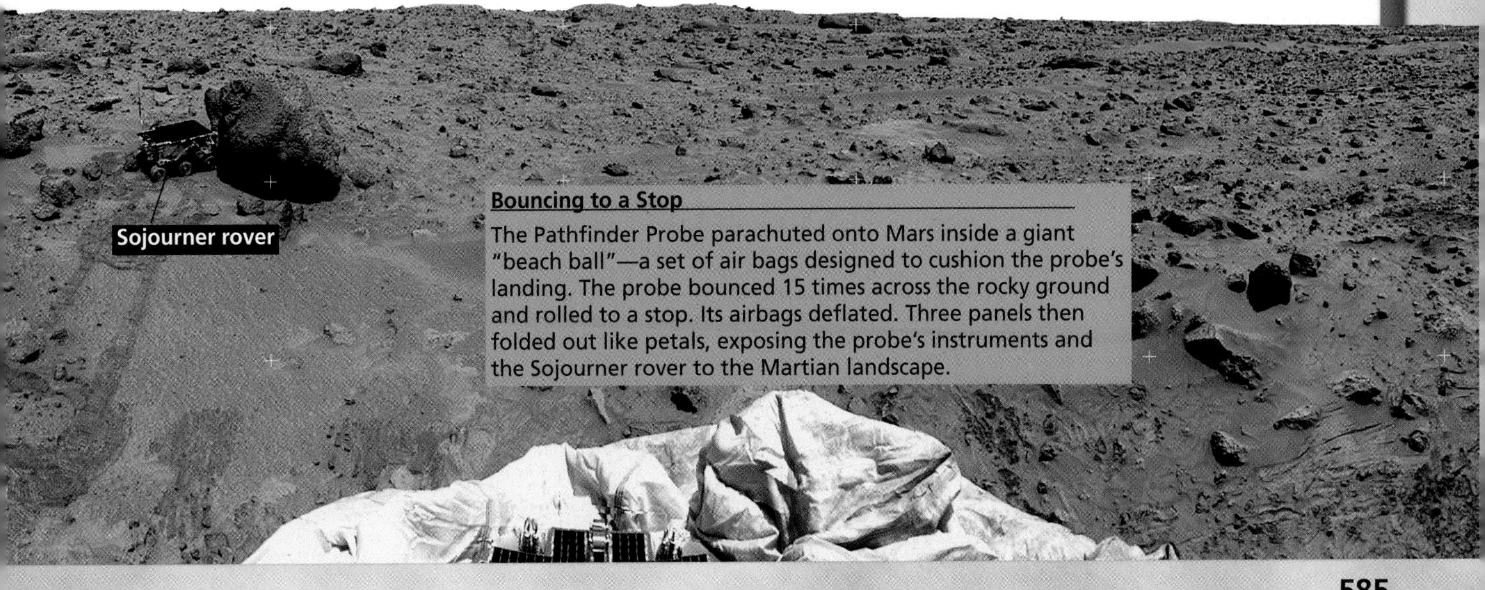

Bouncing to a Stop

The Pathfinder Probe parachuted onto Mars inside a giant "beach ball"—a set of air bags designed to cushion the probe's landing. The probe bounced 15 times across the rocky ground and rolled to a stop. Its airbags deflated. Three panels then folded out like petals, exposing the probe's instruments and the Sojourner rover to the Martian landscape.

Where You've Been

- In Chapter 2, you learned to evaluate functions in function notation.
- In Chapter 5, you learned to use parabolas for graphing quadratic functions.
- In Chapter 7, you learned to evaluate radical expressions.
- In Chapter 9, you learned to simplify complex fractions, which are fractions that have fractions in the numerator or denominator or in both the numerator and denominator.

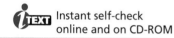

Instant self-check online and on CD-ROM

Diagnosing Readiness

(For help, go to the Lesson in green.)

Evaluating Functions (Lesson 2-1)

For each function, find $f(1), f(2), f(3)$, and $f(4)$.

1. $f(x) = 2x + 7$ **2.** $f(x) = 5x - 4$ **3.** $f(x) = 0.2x + 0.7$

4. $f(x) = -5x + 3$ **5.** $f(x) = 4x - \frac{2}{3}$ **6.** $f(x) = -3x - 9$

Graphing Quadratic Functions (Lesson 5-2)

Graph each function.

7. $y = x^2 + 3$ **8.** $y = -\frac{1}{2}x^2 + 2$ **9.** $y = 4x^2 - 1$

10. $y = 2x^2 - 7x + 3$ **11.** $y = -4x^2 + 8x + 5$ **12.** $y = x^2 + 3x + 4$

Evaluating Radical Expressions (Lesson 7-1)

Find each real-number root.

13. $\sqrt{16}$ **14.** $-\sqrt{16}$ **15.** $\sqrt{0.16}$ **16.** $\sqrt{2500}$

Simplify each radical expression. Use absolute value symbols as needed.

17. $\sqrt{25x^4}$ **18.** $-\sqrt{0.09y^8}$ **19.** $\sqrt{x^6y^{10}}$ **20.** $\sqrt{121y^{24}}$

Simplifying Complex Fractions (Lesson 9-5)

Simplify each complex fraction.

21. $\dfrac{1 - \frac{1}{3}}{\frac{1}{2}}$ **22.** $\dfrac{\frac{1}{3} + \frac{1}{6}}{\frac{2}{3}}$ **23.** $\dfrac{1}{1 - \frac{2}{5}}$ **24.** $\dfrac{1 - \frac{3}{8}}{2 + \frac{1}{4}}$

Sequences and Series

Chapter 11

Where You're Going

- In Chapter 11, you will learn to identify and generate arithmetic sequences and geometric sequences.
- You will learn to evaluate arithmetic series and geometric series.
- You will use rectangles to approximate the area under a curve.

Real-World Connection Applying what you learn, on page 623 you will solve a problem involving the speed of a falcon.

LESSONS

Key Vocabulary

- arithmetic mean (p. 595)
- arithmetic sequence (p. 594)
- arithmetic series (p. 608)
- circumscribed rectangles (p. 623)
- common difference (p. 594)
- common ratio (p. 600)
- converge (p. 615)
- diverge (p. 615)
- explicit formula (p. 590)
- geometric mean (p. 602)
- geometric sequence (p. 600)
- geometric series (p. 614)
- inscribed rectangles (p. 623)
- limit (p. 609)
- recursive formula (p. 590)
- sequence (p. 588)
- series (p. 607)
- term (p. 588)

11-1 Mathematical Patterns

Lesson Preview

What You'll Learn

OBJECTIVE 1 To identify mathematical patterns

OBJECTIVE 2 To use a formula for finding the *n*th term of a sequence

. . . And Why

To predict the height of a bouncing ball, as in Example 2

✓ Check Skills You'll Need

(For help, see Skills Handbook p. 838.)

Find the next two numbers of each pattern. Then write a rule to describe the pattern.

1. 1, 3, 5, 7, 9, 11, . . .

2. −2, −4, −6, −8, −10, −12, . . .

3. 0.2, 1, 5, 25, 125, 625, . . .

4. 50, 45, 40, 35, 30, 25, . . .

5. 512, 256, 128, 64, 32, 16, . . .

6. 2, 5, 8, 11, 14, 17, . . .

7. 16, 32, 64, . . .

8. −3, −7, −11, −15, . . .

New Vocabulary • sequence • term • recursive formula • explicit formula

Interactive lesson includes instant self-check, tutorials, and activities.

OBJECTIVE 1 Identifying Mathematical Patterns

Investigation: Generating a Pattern

Suppose each student in your math class has a phone conversation with every other member of the class. What is the minimum number of calls required?

Instead of actually making the calls, you can represent telephone conversations by drawing diagrams like the ones below.

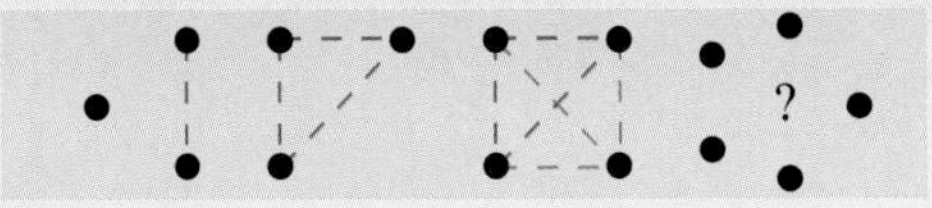

1. How many calls are necessary for two people to have a conversation?
2. How many calls are necessary for everyone to talk to everyone else in a group of three people? In a group of four people?
3. Use a diagram to find the number of calls needed for five people.
4. **Reasoning** Which of the following formulas can you use to find the pattern for the telephone calls?
   A. $2n - 3$ **B.** $n(n - 1) - 5$ **C.** $\frac{n(n-1)}{2}$
5. Use the formula from Question 4 to find the number of calls needed for a group of seven students.
6. How many calls would be needed for your class?

Sometimes steps in a process form a pattern. You can describe some patterns with a **sequence,** or ordered list of numbers. Each number in a sequence is a **term.**

When you apply the construction from Example 1 to an equilateral triangle, you form the Koch snowflake.

1 EXAMPLE Generating a Sequence

a. To create one side of the Koch snowflake, replace each ___ with _/_. Draw the first four figures of the pattern.

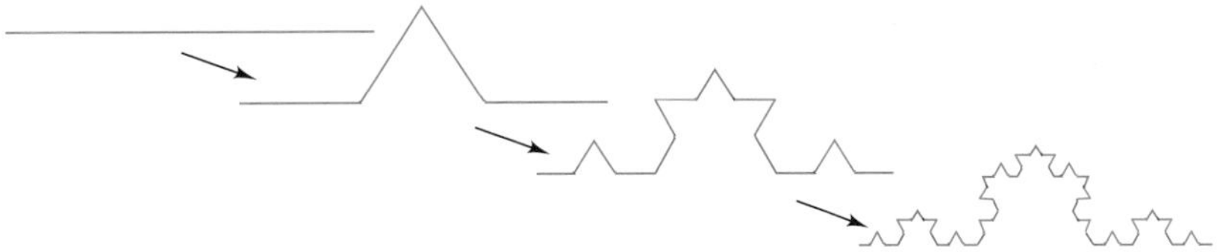

b. Write the number of segments in each figure above as a sequence.

1, 4, 16, 64, . . .

c. Predict the next term of the sequence. Explain your choice.

Each term is 4 times the preceding term. The next term is $64 \cdot 4$, or 256. There will be 256 segments in the next figure in the pattern.

Check Understanding **1** Describe the pattern formed. Find the next three terms.

a. 27, 34, 41, 48, . . .

b. 243, 81, 27, 9, . . .

Sometimes you can find the next term in a sequence by using a pattern from the terms that come before it.

2 EXAMPLE Real-World Connection

Physics Suppose you drop a handball from a height of 10 ft. After the ball hits the floor, it rebounds to 85% of its previous height. How high will the ball rebound after its fourth bounce?

Original height of ball: 10 ft →

After 1st bounce: 85% of 10 = $0.85(10) = 8.5$ →

After 2nd bounce: $0.85(8.5) = 7.225$ →

After 3rd bounce: $0.85(7.225) \approx 6.141$ →

After 4th bounce: $0.85(6.141) \approx 5.220$ →

The ball will rebound about 5.2 ft after the fourth bounce.

Check Understanding **2** **a.** About how high will the ball rebound after the seventh bounce?
b. After what bounce will the rebound height be less than 2 ft?

You can use a variable, such as a, with positive integer subscripts to represent the terms in a sequence.

1st term	2nd term	3rd term	. . .	$n - 1$ term	nth term	$n + 1$ term	. . .
↓	↓	↓		↓	↓	↓	
a_1	a_2	a_3	. . .	a_{n-1}	a_n	a_{n+1}	. . .

OBJECTIVE

2 Using Formulas to Generate Mathematical Patterns

A **recursive formula** defines the terms in a sequence by relating each term to the ones before it. The pattern in Example 2 was recursive because the height of the ball after each bounce was 85% of its previous height. The recursive formula that describes the ball's height is $a_n = 0.85a_{n-1}$, where $a_1 = 10$.

3 EXAMPLE Using a Recursive Formula

a. Describe the pattern that allows you to find the next term in the sequence 2, 4, 6, 8, 10, . . . Write a recursive formula for the sequence.

The terms of the sequence are the even numbers. Add 2 to a term to find the next term. A recursive formula is $a_n = a_{n-1} + 2$, where $a_1 = 2$.

b. Find the sixth and seventh terms in the sequence.

Since $a_5 = 10$, $a_6 = 10 + 2 = 12$, and $a_7 = 12 + 2 = 14$.

c. Find the value of term a_9 in the sequence.

Term a_9 is the ninth term. $a_9 = a_8 + 2 = (a_7 + 2) + 2 = (14 + 2) + 2 = 18$

Check Understanding 3 Find terms a_{11} and a_{15} in the sequence.

Need Help?
Many explicit formulas are proved by mathematical induction (p. 620).

Sometimes you can find the value of a term of a sequence without knowing the preceding term. Instead, you can use the number of the term to calculate its value. A formula that expresses the nth term in terms of n is an **explicit formula.**

4 EXAMPLE Real-World Connection

Geometry The spreadsheet below shows the perimeters of squares with sides from 1 to 6 units long. The numbers in each row form a sequence.

	A	B	C	D	E	F	G	H
1		a1	a2	a3	a4	a5	a6	. . .
2	Length of a Side	1	2	3	4	5	6	. . .
3	Perimeter	4	8	12	16	20	24	. . .

a. For each sequence, find the next term (a_7) and the twenty-fifth term (a_{25}).

In the sequence in row 2, each term is the same as its subscript. Therefore, $a_7 = 7$ and $a_{25} = 25$.
In the sequence in row 3, each term is 4 times its subscript. Therefore, $a_7 = 4(7) = 28$ and $a_{25} = 4(25) = 100$.

b. Write an explicit formula for each sequence.

The explicit formula for the sequence in row 2 is $a_n = n$. The explicit formula for the sequence in row 3 is $a_n = 4n$.

Check Understanding 4 **a.** Write the first six terms in the sequence showing the areas of the squares in Example 4. Then find a_{20}.
b. Write an explicit formula for the sequence from part (a).
c. **Critical Thinking** Given the recursive formula $a_n = a_{n-1} + 3$, can you find the fourth term in the sequence? Explain.

EXERCISES

For more practice, see *Extra Practice.*

Practice and Problem Solving

A Practice by Example

Examples 1 and 2 (page 589)

Describe each pattern formed. Find the next three terms.

1. 80, 77, 74, 71, 68, . . . **2.** 4, 8, 16, 32, 64, . . . **3.** 0, 3, 7, 12, 18, . . .

4. 1, 4, 7, 10, 13, . . . **5.** 100, 10, 1, 0.1, 0.01, . . . **6.** $\frac{1}{2}, \frac{1}{4}, \frac{1}{8}, \frac{1}{16}, \frac{1}{32}, \ldots$

7. 4, −8, 16, −32, 64, . . . **8.** 1, 2, 6, 24, 120, . . . **9.** $0, 1, 0, \frac{1}{3}, 0, \frac{1}{5}, \ldots$

Fractal Geometry **Draw the first four figures of the sequence described.**

10.  is replaced by .

11. 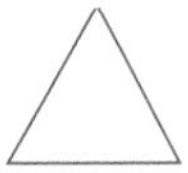 is replaced by 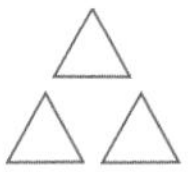.

Example 3 (page 590)

Write a recursive formula for each sequence. Then find the next term.

12. −2, −1, 0, 1, 2, . . . **13.** 43, 41, 39, 37, 35, . . . **14.** $40, 20, 10, 5, \frac{5}{2}, \ldots$

15. 6, 1, −4, −9, . . . **16.** $144, 36, 9, \frac{9}{4}, \ldots$ **17.** $\frac{1}{2}, \frac{1}{4}, \frac{1}{8}, \frac{1}{16}, \frac{1}{32}, \ldots$

Example 4 (page 590)

Write an explicit formula for each sequence. Then find a_{12}.

18. 4, 5, 6, 7, 8, . . . **19.** $\frac{1}{2}, \frac{1}{3}, \frac{1}{4}, \frac{1}{5}, \frac{1}{6}, \ldots$ **20.** 4, 7, 10, 13, 16, . . .

21. 3, 7, 11, 15, 19, . . . **22.** $-2\frac{1}{2}, -2, -1\frac{1}{2}, -1, \ldots$ **23.** 2, 5, 10, 17, 26, . . .

B Apply Your Skills

Decide whether each formula is *explicit* or *recursive*. Then find the first five terms of each sequence.

24. $a_n = 2a_{n-1} + 3$, where $a_1 = 3$ **25.** $a_n = \frac{1}{2}(n)(n-1)$

26. $(n-5)(n+5) = a_n$ **27.** $a_n = -3a_{n-1}$, where $a_1 = -2$

28. $a_n = -4n^2 - 2$ **29.** $a_n = 2n^2 + 1$

30. $a_n = 5n$ **31.** $a_n = a_{n-1} - 17$, where $a_1 = 340$

32. Entertainment Suppose you are building a tower of cards with levels as displayed below. Complete the table, assuming the pattern continues.

Levels	1	2	3	4	5
Cards Needed	2	7	■	■	■

Real-World Connection

Bryan Berg built a 24-ft 4-in. 127-story freestanding house of cards.

Find the next two terms in each sequence. Write a formula for the *n*th term. Identify each formula as *explicit* or *recursive.*

33. 5, 8, 11, 14, 17, . . . **34.** 3, 6, 12, 24, 48, . . . **35.** 1, 8, 27, 64, 125, . . .

36. 4, 16, 64, 256, 1024, . . . **37.** 49, 64, 81, 100, 121, . . . **38.** −1, 1, −1, 1, −1, 1, . . .

39. −16, −8, −4, −2, . . . **40.** −75, −68, −61, −54, . . . **41.** 21, 13, 5, −3, . . .

42. Suppose the cartoon at the right included one sheep to the left and another sheep to the right of the three shown. What "names" would you give these sheep?

WHEN MATHEMATICIANS CAN'T SLEEP

43. **Writing** Explain the difference between a recursive formula and an explicit formula.

44. a. **Open-Ended** Write four terms of a sequence of numbers that you can describe both recursively and explicitly.
 b. Write a recursive formula and an explicit formula for your sequence.
 c. Find the 20th term of the sequence by evaluating one of your formulas. Use the other formula to check your work.

Use the given rule to write the 4th, 5th, 6th, and 7th terms of each sequence.

45. $a_1 = -1, a_n = (a_{n-1})^2 + 1$ **46.** $a_1 = -2, a_n = 3(a_{n-1} + 2)$

47. $a_n = (n + 1)^2$ **48.** $a_n = 2\,(n - 1)^3$

49. $a_n = \frac{n^2}{n + 1}$ **50.** $a_n = \frac{n + 1}{n + 2}$

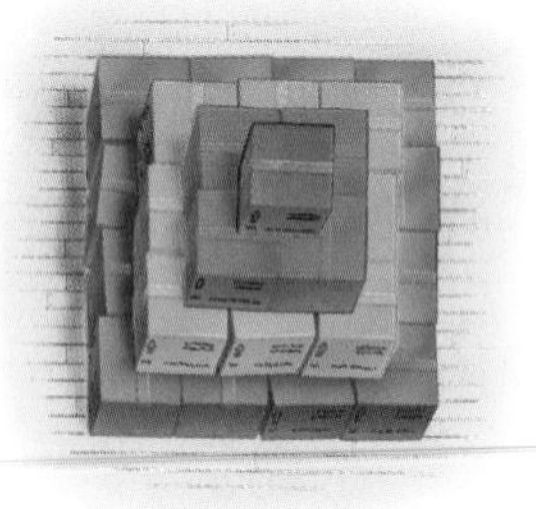

51. Geometry Suppose you are stacking boxes in levels that form squares. The numbers of boxes in successive levels form a sequence. The figure at the left shows the top four levels as viewed from above.
 a. How many boxes of equal size would you need for the next lower level?
 b. How many boxes of equal size would you need to add three levels?
 c. Suppose you are stacking a total of 285 boxes. How many levels will you have?

C Challenge

Use each recursive formula to write an explicit formula for the sequence.

52. $a_1 = 10, a_n = 2a_{n-1}$ **53.** $a_1 = -5, a_n = a_{n-1} - 1$

54. $a_1 = -2, a_n = \frac{1}{2}a_{n-1}$ **55.** $a_1 = 1, a_n = a_{n-1} + 4$

56. Finance Use the information in the ad.
 a. Suppose you start a savings account at Mun e-Bank. Write both a recursive formula and an explicit formula for the amount of money you would have in the bank at the end of any week.
 b. How much money would you have in the bank after four weeks?
 c. Assume the bank pays interest every four weeks. To calculate your interest, multiply the balance at the end of the four weeks by 0.005. Then add that much to your account on the last day of the four-week period. Write a recursive formula for the amount of money you have after each interest payment.
 d. **Critical Thinking** What is the bank's annual interest rate?

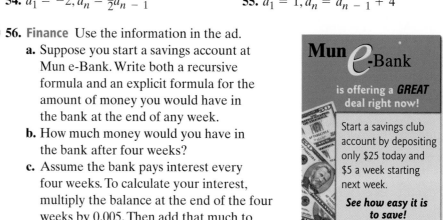

57. Geometry The triangular numbers form a sequence. The diagram represents the first three triangular numbers: 1, 3, and 6.

a. Find the fifth and sixth triangular numbers.

b. Write a recursive formula for the *n*th triangular number.

c. Is the explicit formula $a_n = \frac{1}{2}(n^2 + n)$ the correct formula for this sequence? How do you know?

Standardized Test Prep

Multiple Choice

58. What is the difference between the third term in the sequence whose recursive formula is $a_1 = -5$, $a_n = 2a_{n-1} + 1$ and the third term in the sequence whose recursive formula is $a_1 = -3$, $a_n = -a_{n-1} + 3$?

A. 2 **B.** 14 **C.** 20 **D.** 32

59. What is a recursive formula for the sequence whose explicit formula is $a_n = (n + 1)^2$?

F. $a_1 = 1$, $a_n = (a_{n-1} + 1)^2$ **G.** $a_1 = 4$, $a_n = \left(\sqrt{a_{n-1}} + 1\right)^2$

H. $a_1 = n$, $a_n = a_{n-1} + n$ **I.** $a_1 = n^2$, $a_n = (a_{n-1})^2 + 1$

Use the figure below for Exercises 60–62.

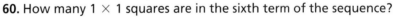

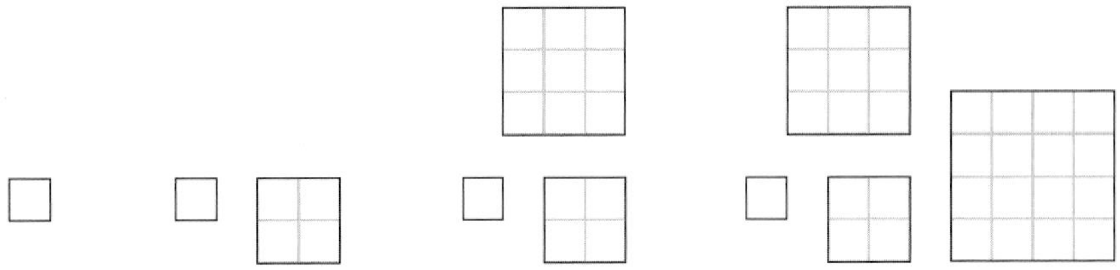

60. How many 1×1 squares are in the sixth term of the sequence?

A. 21 **B.** 36 **C.** 91 **D.** 441

Take It to the NET
Online lesson quiz at **www.PHSchool.com**
Web Code: aga-1101

61. Which expressions represent the first three terms of the sequence?

F. $1^2, 2^2, 3^2, \ldots$ **G.** $1, 1 + 2, 1 + 2 + 3, \ldots$

H. $1^2, (1 + 2)^2, (1 + 2 + 3)^2, \ldots$ **I.** $1^2, 1^2 + 2^2, 1^2 + 2^2 + 3^2, \ldots$

Short Response

62. Write a recursive formula for the sequence in the figure above. Explain your reasoning.

Mixed Review

Lesson 10-6

The graph of each equation is translated 2 units left and 3 units down. Write each new equation.

63. $(x + 2)^2 + (y - 1)^2 = 5$

64. $\frac{(x - 1)^2}{36} + \frac{(y - 1)^2}{36} = 1$

Lesson 9-1

Each point is from an inverse variation. Write an equation to model the data.

65. $(1, 20)$ **66.** $(5, 2)$ **67.** $(9, 13)$ **68.** $(-3, -9)$

69. $(2, 5)$ **70.** $(-6, -12)$ **71.** $\left(\frac{1}{2}, -\frac{1}{2}\right)$ **72.** $(-10, -10)$

11-2 Arithmetic Sequences

Lesson Preview

What You'll Learn

OBJECTIVE 1 To identify and generate arithmetic sequences

. . . And Why

To determine the amount of money raised during a fund-raiser, as in Example 2

Check Skills You'll Need

(For help, see Skills Handbook p. 838)

Describe the pattern in each sequence. Use at least one of the words *add*, *subtract*, or *difference*.

1. 10, 8, 6, 4, 2, 0, . . .

2. 100, 117, 134, 151, 168, . . .

3. $\frac{5}{7}, \frac{8}{7}, \frac{11}{7}, 2, \ldots$

4. $-\frac{1}{4}, -\frac{1}{2}, -\frac{3}{4}, -1, -\frac{5}{4}, -\frac{3}{2}, \ldots$

New Vocabulary • arithmetic sequence • common difference • arithmetic mean

Interactive lesson includes instant self-check, tutorials, and activities.

OBJECTIVE 1 Identifying and Generating Arithmetic Sequences

Reading Math

The stress in the noun *arithmetic* is on the second syllable (uh RITH muh tik). The stress in the adjective *arithmetic* is on the third syllable (ar ith MET ik).

In an **arithmetic sequence,** the difference between consecutive terms is constant. This difference is called the **common difference.** The common difference can be positive (the terms of the sequence are increasing in value) or negative (the terms of the sequence are decreasing in value).

1 EXAMPLE Identifying an Arithmetic Sequence

Is the given sequence arithmetic?

a. 2, 4, 8, 16, . . .

$$2, \xrightarrow{+2} 4, \xrightarrow{+4} 8, \xrightarrow{+8} 16, \ldots$$

$4 - 2 = 2$ $\quad 8 - 4 = 4$ $\quad 16 - 8 = 8$

There is no common difference. This is *not* an arithmetic sequence.

b. the golf ball pattern at the right

$$6, \xrightarrow{+6} 12, \xrightarrow{+6} 18, \ldots$$

$12 - 6 = 6$ $\quad 18 - 12 = 6$

The common difference is 6. The dots on the golf ball form an arithmetic sequence.

Check Understanding **1** Is the given sequence arithmetic? If so, identify the common difference.

a. 2, 5, 7, 12, . . . **b.** 48, 45, 42, 39, . . .

You can use an explicit formula to find the value of the *n*th term of an arithmetic sequence when the previous term is unknown.

Key Concepts

Property | **Arithmetic Sequence Formulas**

Recursive Formula	**Explicit Formula**
a_1 = a given value, $a_n = a_{n-1} + d$	$a_n = a_1 + (n - 1)d$

In these formulas, a_n is the nth term, a_1 is the first term, n is the number of the term, and d is the common difference.

Real-World Connection

The AIDSRide raises money for AIDS services in locations across the United States.

2 EXAMPLE Real-World Connection

Fund-Raising Suppose you participate in a bike-a-thon for charity. The charity starts with \$1100 in donations. Each participant must raise at least \$35 in pledges. What is the minimum amount of money raised if there are 75 participants?

Find the 76th term of the sequence 1100, 1135, 1170, . . .

$a_n = a_1 + (n - 1)d$	**Use the explicit formula.**
$a_{76} = 1100 + (76 - 1)(35)$	**Substitute $a_1 = 1100$, $n = 76$, and $d = 35$.**
$= 1100 + (75)(35)$	**Subtract within parentheses.**
$= 3725$	**Simplify.**

With 75 participants, the bike-a-thon will raise a minimum of \$3725.

Check Understanding **2** **a.** **Critical Thinking** In Example 2, why find the value of the 76th term, not the 75th term?

b. Use the explicit formula to find the 25th term in the sequence 5, 11, 17, 23, 29, . . .

The **arithmetic mean** of any two numbers is the average of the two numbers.

$$\text{arithmetic mean} = \frac{\text{sum of two numbers}}{2}$$

For any three sequential terms in an arithmetic sequence, the middle term is the arithmetic mean of the first and third terms.

Graphs of arithmetic sequences are linear. Two terms of an arithmetic sequence and their arithmetic mean lie on the same line.

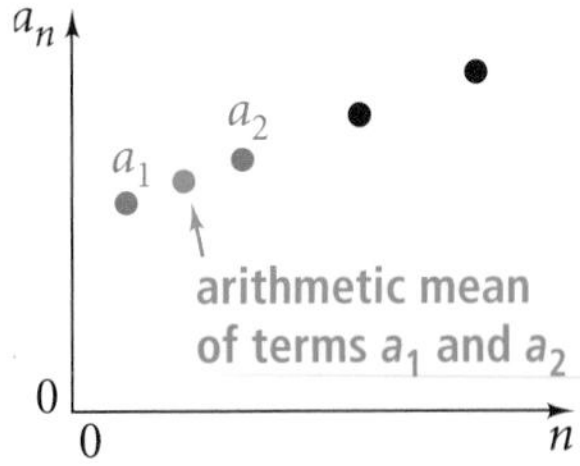

You can use the arithmetic mean to find a missing term of an arithmetic sequence.

3 EXAMPLE Using the Arithmetic Mean

Find the missing term of the arithmetic sequence 84, ■, 110.

arithmetic mean $= \frac{84 + 110}{2}$	**Write the average.**
$= 97$	**Simplify.**

The missing term is 97.

Check Understanding **3** **a.** Find the missing term of the arithmetic sequence 24, ■, 57.

b. Write an expression for the arithmetic mean of a_6 and a_7.

EXERCISES

For more practice, see *Extra Practice.*

Practice and Problem Solving

A Practice by Example

Example 1 (page 594)

Is the given sequence arithmetic? If so, identify the common difference.

1. $1, 4, 9, 16, \dots$

2. $10, 20, 30, 40, \dots$

3. $1, 1, 2, 3, 5, 8, \dots$

4. $0, 1, 3, 6, 10, \dots$

5. $-21, -18, -15, -12, \dots$

6. $97, 86, 75, 64, \dots$

7. $3, 7, 11, 15, \dots$

8. $100, 10, 1, 0.1, \dots$

9. $\frac{1}{2}, \frac{1}{4}, \frac{1}{8}, \frac{1}{16}, \dots$

10. $-5, 5, -5, 5, -5, \dots$

Example 2 (page 595)

Find the 32nd term of each sequence.

11. $34, 37, 40, 43, \dots$

12. $-9, -8.7, -8.4, \dots$

13. $0.1, 0.5, 0.9, 1.3, \dots$

14. $0.0023, 0.0025, 0.0027, \dots$

15. $101, 105, 109, 113, \dots$

16. $213, 201, 189, 177, \dots$

17. $3, 1, -1, -3, \dots$

18. $23, 30, 37, 44, \dots$

19. $9, 4, -1, -6, -11, \dots$

20. $13, 17, 21, 25, \dots$

Example 3 (page 595)

Find the missing term of each arithmetic sequence.

21. $-16, ■, 1, \dots$

22. $14, ■, 28, \dots$

23. $\dots 5, ■, 21, \dots$

24. $\frac{13}{2}, ■, \frac{51}{2}, \dots$

25. $101, ■, -115, \dots$

26. $203, ■, 1117, \dots$

27. $25, ■, -10, \dots$

28. $\dots 65, ■, -60, \dots$

29. $\dots a_{10}, ■, a_{12}, \dots$

30. $\dots 99, ■, 66, \dots$

B Apply Your Skills

Find the arithmetic mean a_n of the given terms.

31. $a_{n-1} = 7, a_{n+1} = 1$

32. $a_{n-1} = 4, a_{n+1} = -3$

33. $a_{n-1} = 21, a_{n+1} = 5$

34. $a_{n-1} = 100, a_{n+1} = 140$

35. $a_{n-1} = -18, a_{n+1} = -21$

36. $a_{n-1} = 0.3, a_{n+1} = 1.9$

37. $a_{n-1} = 9, a_{n+1} = -11$

38. $a_{n-1} = \frac{3}{5}, a_{n+1} = 1$

39. $a_{n-1} = r, a_{n+1} = s$

40. $a_{n-1} = r, a_{n+1} = r + s$

41. $a_{n-1} = -2x, a_{n+1} = 2x$

42. $a_{n-1} = x + 3, a_{n+1} = 3x - 1$

43. **Error Analysis** A student claims that the next term of the arithmetic sequence $0, 2, 4, \dots$ is 8. What error did the student make?

44. **a.** **Open-Ended** Use your calculator to generate an arithmetic sequence with a common difference of -7. How could you use a calculator to find the 6th term? The 8th term? The 20th term?

b. **Critical Thinking** Explain how your answer to part (a) relates to the explicit formula $a_n = a_1 + (n - 1)d$.

45. **Writing** Describe some advantages and some disadvantages of a recursive formula and an explicit formula.

Find the 17th term of each sequence.

46. $a_{16} = 18, d = 5$

47. $a_{16} = 18, d = -3$

48. $a_{16} = 18, d = \frac{1}{2}$

49. $a_{18} = 18, d = -4$

50. $a_{18} = 18, d = 12$

51. $a_{18} = 18, d = -11$

Write an explicit and a recursive formula for each sequence.

52. $2, 4, 6, 8, 10, \dots$

53. $0, 6, 12, 18, 24, \dots$

54. $-5, -4, -3, -2, -1, \dots$

55. $-4, -8, -12, -16, -20, \dots$

56. $-2, 5, 12, 19, 26, 33, \dots$

57. $27, 15, 3, -9, -21, \dots$

58. $-5, -3.5, -2, -0.5, 1, \dots$

59. $-32, -20, -8, 4, 16, \dots$

60. $1, 1\frac{1}{3}, 1\frac{2}{3}, 2, \dots$

61. $0, \frac{1}{8}, \frac{1}{4}, \frac{3}{8}, \dots$

Real-World Connection

San Francisco's historic cable cars move by gripping and releasing a moving steel cable under the street.

62. Transportation Suppose a trolley stops at a certain intersection every 14 min. The first trolley of the day gets to the stop at 6:43 A.M. How long do you have to wait for a trolley if you get to the stop at 8:15 A.M.? At 3:20 P.M.?

Find the missing terms of each arithmetic sequence. (*Hint:* The arithmetic mean of the first and fifth terms is the third term.)

63. 2, ■, ■, ■, −22, . . .

64. 10, ■, ■, ■, −11.6, . . .

65. 1, ■, ■, ■, −35, . . .

66. . . . $\frac{13}{5}$, ■, ■, ■, $\frac{37}{5}$, . . .

67. 17, ■, ■, ■, 17, . . .

68. 660, ■, ■, ■, 744, . . .

69. . . . −17, ■, ■, ■, 1, . . .

70. . . . $a + 1$, ■, ■, ■, $a + 17$, . . .

71. Savings In February you start a holiday savings account with a deposit of $20. You increase each monthly deposit by five dollars until the end of the year.

a. Write the amount in the account after each deposit.

b. Write a recursive formula for the sequence of balances.

c. How much money will you have saved by the end of the year?

Graph the arithmetic sequence generated by each formula over the domain $1 \le n \le 10$.

72. $a_1 = -60, a_n = a_{n-1} + 9$

73. $a_n = 50 - 7n$

74. Critical Thinking Suppose you turn the water on in an empty bathtub with vertical sides. After 20 s, the water has reached a level of 1.15 in. You then leave the room. You want to turn the water off when the level in the bathtub is 8.5 in. How many minutes later should you return? (*Hint:* Begin by identifying two terms of an arithmetic sequence.)

C Challenge

75. The arithmetic mean of two terms in an arithmetic sequence is 42. One term is 30. Find the other term.

76. The arithmetic mean of two terms in an arithmetic sequence is −6. One term is −20. Find the other term.

77. In an arithmetic sequence with $a_1 = 4$ and $d = 9$, which term is 184?

78. In an arithmetic sequence with $a_1 = 2$ and $d = -2$, which term is −82?

Given two terms of each arithmetic sequence, find a_1 and d.

79. $a_3 = 5$ and $a_5 = 11$

80. $a_4 = 8$ and $a_7 = 20$

81. $a_3 = 32$ and $a_7 = -8$

82. $a_{10} = 17$ and $a_{14} = 34$

83. $a_4 = -34.5$ and $a_5 = -12.5$

84. $a_4 = -2.4$ and $a_6 = 2$

Find the indicated term of each arithmetic series.

85. $a_1 = k, d = k + 4; a_9$

86. $a_1 = k + 7, d = 2k - 5; a_{11}$

Standardized Test Prep

Multiple Choice

87. Which arithmetic sequence DOES NOT include the term 33?

A. 1, 5, 9, 13, . . .
B. 1, 11, 21, . . .
C. 3, 9, 15, . . .
D. 85, 72, 59, . . .

88. Which arithmetic sequence includes the term 27?

I. $a_1 = 7$, $a_n = a_{n-1} + 5$ **II.** $a_n = 3 + (n - 1)4$ **III.** $a_n = 57 - 6n$

F. I only
G. I and II only
H. II and III only
I. I, II, and III

Take It to the NET
Online lesson quiz at
www.PHSchool.com
Web Code: aga-1102

89. The arithmetic mean of the monthly salaries of two people is \$2955. One person earns \$2760 per month. What is the monthly salary of the other person?

A. \$2857.50
B. \$3150
C. \$5520
D. \$5715

90. What is the 30th term of the sequence 7, 16, 25, 34, . . . ?

F. 277
G. 270
H. 268
I. 261

Short Response

91. Explain how to use the arithmetic mean to find the missing terms in the arithmetic sequence 15, ■, ■, ■, 47, . . .

Extended Response

92. Find the 100th term of the arithmetic sequence 3, 10, 17, 24, 31, . . . Explain your steps.

Mixed Review

Lesson 11-1

Decide whether each formula is *explicit* or *recursive*. Then find the first five terms of each sequence.

93. $a_1 = -2, a_n = a_{n-1} - 5$

94. $a_n = 3n(n + 1)$

95. $a_n = n^2 - 1$

96. $a_1 = -121, a_n = a_{n-1} + 13$

Lesson 10-6

Find the foci of each ellipse.

97. $\frac{x^2}{4} + \frac{y^2}{9} = 1$

98. $\frac{x^2}{36} + \frac{y^2}{4} = 1$

99. $\frac{(x-1)^2}{121} + \frac{y^2}{100} = 1$

100. $\frac{(x-1)^2}{64} + \frac{(y-3)^2}{25} = 1$

Lesson 7-2

101. Geometry The formula for volume V of a sphere with radius r is $V = \frac{4}{3}\pi r^3$. Find the radius of a sphere as a function of its volume. Rationalize the denominator.

Extension The Fibonacci Sequence

For Use With Lesson 11-2

One famous mathematical sequence is the Fibonacci sequence. You can find each term of the sequence using addition, but the sequence is not arithmetic.

EXAMPLE Generating the Fibonacci Sequence

The recursive formula for the Fibonacci sequence is $F_n = F_{n-2} + F_{n-1}$, with $F_1 = 1$ and $F_2 = 1$. Use the formula to generate the first five terms of the sequence.

$$F_1 = 1$$
$$F_2 = 1$$
$$F_3 = F_1 + F_2 = 1 + 1 = 2$$
$$F_4 = F_2 + F_3 = 1 + 2 = 3$$
$$F_5 = F_3 + F_4 = 2 + 3 = 5$$

The first five terms of the Fibonacci sequence are 1, 1, 2, 3, 5.

EXERCISES

1. **Nature** The numbers of the Fibonacci sequence are often found in other areas, especially in nature. Which term of the Fibonacci sequence does each picture represent?

a.

b.

c.

d.

2. **Critical Thinking** Study Pascal's Triangle (at the right). How is it similar to the Fibonacci sequence?

```
          1
         1 1
        1 2 1
       1 3 3 1
      1 4 6 4 1
    1 5 10 10 5 1
  1 ■  ■  ■  ■  ■  ■
```

3. **a.** Generate the first ten terms of the Fibonacci sequence.
   b. Find the sum of the first ten terms of the Fibonacci sequence. Divide the sum by 11. What do you notice?
   c. **Open-Ended** Choose two numbers other than 1 and 1. Generate a Fibonacci-like sequence from them. Write the first ten terms of your sequence, find the sum, and divide the sum by 11. What do you notice?
   d. **Make a Conjecture** What is the sum of the first ten terms of any Fibonacci-like sequence?

4. **a.** Study the pattern at the right. Write the next line.
   b. Without calculating, use the pattern to predict the sum of squares of the first ten terms of the Fibonacci sequence.
   c. Verify the prediction you made in part (b).

$$1^2 + 1^2 = 2 = 1 \cdot 2$$
$$1^2 + 1^2 + 2^2 = 6 = 2 \cdot 3$$
$$1^2 + 1^2 + 2^2 + 3^2 = 15 = 3 \cdot 5$$
$$1^2 + 1^2 + 2^2 + 3^2 + 5^2 = 40 = 5 \cdot 8$$

11-3 Geometric Sequences

Lesson Preview

What You'll Learn

OBJECTIVE 1 To identify and generate geometric sequences

. . . And Why

To find the size of a reduced logo, as in Example 2

✓ Check Skills You'll Need

(For help, go to Lesson 11-1.)

Find the next term in each sequence.

1. 1, 2, 4, 8, . . .

2. 336, 168, 84, 42, . . .

3. 0.1, 1, 10, 100, . . .

4. 900, 300, 100, . . .

New Vocabulary • geometric sequence • common ratio • geometric mean

Interactive lesson includes instant self-check, tutorials, and activities.

OBJECTIVE 1 Identifying and Generating Geometric Sequences

Investigation: Geometric Sequences

- Make a large right isosceles triangle out of colored paper.
- Cut the triangle into two congruent isosceles triangles.
- Place one triangle on top of the other and repeat the previous step.

1. Copy and complete the sequence below.

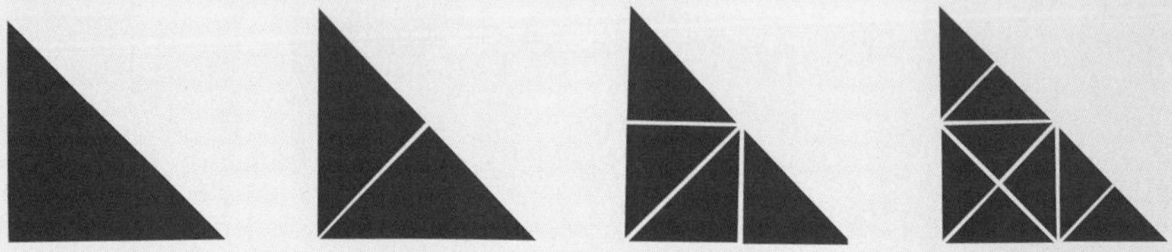

$a_1 =$ ■ $a_2 =$ ■ $a_3 =$ ■ $a_4 =$ ■

2. Is the sequence in Question 1 arithmetic? Explain why or why not.
3. a. Find the sixth term, a_6, of the sequence.
   b. Write a formula for a_6 in terms of a_5.
   c. Write a general formula for a_n in terms of a_{n-1}.
4. a. **Open-Ended** Generate two sequences by multiplying by a constant factor. Write each sequence.
   b. Write a recursive formula for each sequence. What do these formulas and the formula for a_n from Question 3 have in common?
   c. Graph all three sequences. Then sketch each graph.
   d. Compare all three graphs. Write a description of the pattern.

Graphing Calculator Hint

Enter the values of n and a_n into lists. Then use the STAT and 2nd STAT PLOT features to graph the sequences.

In a **geometric sequence,** the ratio between consecutive terms is constant. This ratio is called the **common ratio.** Unlike in an arithmetic sequence, the difference between consecutive terms varies.

1 EXAMPLE Identifying a Geometric Sequence

Is the given sequence geometric? If so, identify the common ratio.

a. 5, 15, 45, 135, . . .

5, → 15, → 45, → 135, . . .

$\times 3$ $\times 3$ $\times 3$

$15 \div 5 = 3$ $45 \div 15 = 3$ $135 \div 45 = 3$

There is a common ratio of 3. This is a geometric sequence.

b. 15, 30, 45, 60, . . .

15, → 30, → 45, → 60, . . .

$\times 2$ $\times 1\frac{1}{2}$ $\times 1\frac{1}{3}$

$30 \div 15 = 2$ $45 \div 30 = 1\frac{1}{2}$ $60 \div 45 = 1\frac{1}{3}$

There is no common ratio. This is *not* a geometric sequence.

Check Understanding 1 **a.** Write the first ten terms of the geometric sequence from Example 1. Explain how you found the tenth term in the sequence, a_{10}.

b. Is the sequence 6, −24, 96, −384, . . . *arithmetic, geometric,* or *neither?* Explain.

c. Is the sequence 8, 20, 32, 44, . . . *arithmetic, geometric,* or *neither?* Explain.

Key Concepts

Property **Geometric Sequence Formulas**

Recursive Formula

a_1 = a given value, $a_n = a_{n-1} \cdot r$

Explicit Formula

$a_n = a_1 \cdot r^{n-1}$

In these formulas, a_n is the nth term, a_1 is the first term, n is the number of the term, and r is the common ratio.

Real-World Connection

Careers Graphic designers use math to lay out pages of books and magazines.

As with an arithmetic sequence, you can use an explicit formula to find the value of the nth term when the previous term is unknown.

2 EXAMPLE Real-World Connection

Design Suppose you want a reduced copy of a photograph. The actual length of the photograph is 10 in. The smallest size the copier can make is 64% of the original. Find the length of the photograph after five reductions at 64%.

For five reductions, you need to find the 6th term of the geometric sequence 10, 6.4, . . .

$a_n = a_1 \cdot r^{n-1}$ **Use the explicit formula.**

$a_6 = 10 \cdot 0.64^{6-1}$ **Substitute $a_1 = 10$, $n = 6$, and $r = 0.64$.**

$= 10 \cdot 0.64^5$ **Simplify the exponent.**

≈ 1.07 **Use a calculator.**

After five reductions of 64%, the photograph is about 1 in. long.

Check Understanding 2 Find the 19th term in each sequence.

a. 11, 33, 99, 297, . . .

b. 20, 17, 14, 11, 8, . . .

The graphs of arithmetic and geometric sequences have different shapes.

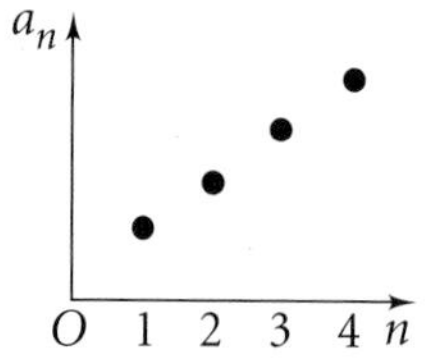

Arithmetic graphs are linear.

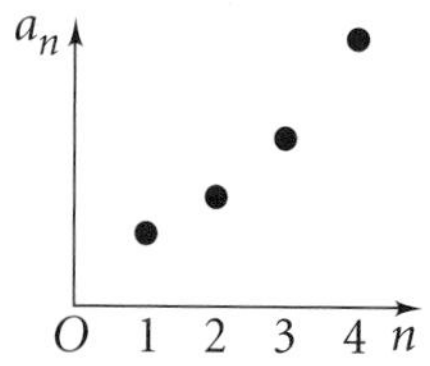

Geometric graphs are exponential.

Need Help?
To review exponential curves, go to Lesson 8–2.

You can find the **geometric mean** of any two positive numbers by taking the positive square root of the product of the two numbers.

$$\text{geometric mean} = \sqrt{\text{product of the two numbers}}$$

You can use the geometric mean to find a missing term of a geometric sequence.

3 EXAMPLE Real-World Connection

Physics When a child swings without being pushed, air resistance causes the length of the arc of the swing to decrease geometrically. Find the missing arc length.

Find the geometric mean of the two arc lengths.

$$\begin{aligned}\text{geometric mean} &= \sqrt{8 \cdot 6\tfrac{1}{8}}\\ &= \sqrt{49}\\ &= 7\end{aligned}$$

On the second swing, the length of the arc is 7 ft.

Check Understanding **3** Find the missing term of each geometric sequence.

a. 20, ■, 80, . . . **b.** 3, ■, 18.75, . . . **c.** 28, ■, 5103, . . .

EXERCISES

For more practice, see *Extra Practice*.

Practice and Problem Solving

A Practice by Example

Example 1 (page 601)

Is the given sequence geometric? If so, identify the common ratio and find the next two terms.

1. 1, 2, 4, 8, . . .

2. 1, 2, 3, 4, . . .

3. $1, -2, 4, -8, \ldots$

4. $-1, 1, -1, 1, \ldots$

5. 10, 4, 1.6, 0.64, . . .

6. 7, 0.7, 0.07, 0.007, . . .

7. $18, -6, 2, -\frac{2}{3}, \ldots$

8. $1, \frac{1}{2}, \frac{1}{3}, \frac{1}{4}, \ldots$

9. 10, 15, 22.5, 33.75, . . .

10. $2, -10, 50, -250, \ldots$

11. $-1, -6, -36, -216, \ldots$

12. $\frac{1}{2}, \frac{1}{4}, \frac{1}{6}, \frac{1}{8}, \ldots$

Example 2
(page 601)

Write the explicit formula for each sequence. Then generate the first five terms.

13. $a_1 = 5, r = -3$
14. $a_1 = 0.0237, r = 10$
15. $a_1 = \frac{1}{2}, r = \frac{2}{3}$
16. $a_1 = 1, r = 0.5$
17. $a_1 = 100, r = -20$
18. $a_1 = 7, r = 1$
19. $a_1 = 1024, r = 0.5$
20. $a_1 = 4, r = 0.1$
21. $a_1 = 10, r = -1$

Example 3
(page 602)

Find the missing term of each geometric sequence.

22. 5, ■, 911.25, . . .
23. 9180, ■, 255, . . .
24. $\frac{2}{5}$, ■, $\frac{8}{45}$, . . .
25. 3, ■, 0.75, . . .
26. 5, ■, 2.8125, . . .
27. 12, ■, 3, . . .

B Apply Your Skills

Identify each sequence as *arithmetic, geometric,* or *neither.* Then find the next two terms.

28. 45, 90, 180, 360, . . .
29. 25, 50, 75, 100, . . .
30. 3, −3, 3, −3, . . .
31. 30, 35, 40, 45, . . .
32. −5, 10, −20, 40, . . .
33. 2, 1, 0.5, 0.25, . . .
34. 5, 6, 8, 11, 15, . . .
35. 2, 2, 2, 2, . . .
36. 1, 4, 9, 16, . . .

Find the missing terms of each geometric sequence. (*Hint:* The geometric mean of the first and fifth terms is the third term.)

37. 19,683; ■; ■; ■; 243; . . .
38. 2.5, ■, ■, ■, 202.5, . . .
39. 12.5, ■, ■, ■, 5.12, . . .
40. −4, ■, ■, ■, $-30\frac{3}{8}$, . . .

Reading Math
For help with reading and solving Exercise 37, see p. 606.

41. a. Open-Ended Choose two positive numbers. Find their geometric mean.
b. Find the common ratio for a geometric sequence that includes the terms from part (a) in order from least to greatest or from greatest to least.
c. Find the 9th term of the geometric sequence from part (b).
d. Find the geometric mean of the term from part (c) and the first term of your sequence. What term of the sequence have you just found?

For the geometric sequence 3, 12, 48, 192, . . . , find the indicated term.

42. 5th term
43. 7th term
44. 10th term
45. 14th term
46. 17th term
47. *n*th term

Find the 10th term of each sequence.

48. $a_9 = 8, r = \frac{1}{2}$
49. $a_{11} = 8, r = \frac{1}{2}$
50. $a_9 = -5, r = -\frac{1}{2}$
51. $a_{11} = -5, r = -\frac{1}{2}$
52. $a_9 = -\frac{1}{3}, r = \frac{1}{2}$
53. $a_{11} = -\frac{1}{3}, r = \frac{1}{2}$

54. Writing Describe the similarities and differences between a common difference and a common ratio.

C Challenge

55. Banking Copy and complete the table below. Use the geometric mean. Assume compound interest is earned and no withdrawals are made.

Period 1	\$140.00	\$600.00	\$25.00	\$57.50	\$100.00	\$250.00
Period 2	■	■	■	■	■	■
Period 3	\$145.64	\$627.49	\$32.76	\$60.37	\$111.98	\$276.55

56. **Golf** Each of the putts misses the hole and continues past it for half the distance.

a. Write a sequence to represent the ball's distance from the hole before each of his first six putts.
b. Is this sequence geometric? Explain your reasoning.
c. Write a recursive formula for the sequence.

57. **Critical Thinking** How are the formulas for a geometric sequence similar to the formulas for an arithmetic sequence?

58. Suppose a balloon loses one fourth of its helium each day. The balloon starts with a volume of 5000 cm^3.
a. Write the geometric sequence that shows the amount of helium in the balloon at the start of each day for five days.
b. What is the common ratio of the sequence?
c. How much helium will be left in the balloon at the start of the tenth day?
d. Graph the sequence. Then sketch the graph.
e. **Critical Thinking** How does the common ratio affect the shape of the graph?

Find a_1 for a geometric sequence with the given terms.

59. $a_5 = 112$ and $a_7 = 448$

60. $a_9 = \frac{1}{2}$ and $a_{12} = \frac{1}{16}$

Standardized Test Prep

Multiple Choice

61. Which geometric sequence DOES NOT include the term 100?
A. 5, 10, 20, . . .
B. 337.5, 225, 150, . . .
C. $a_1 = 25$, $a_n = 2a_{n-1}$
D. $a_n = 4 \cdot 5^n$

62. What is the product of the geometric mean of 2 and 32 and the geometric mean of 1 and 4?
F. 16 **G.** 19 **H.** 32 **I.** 256

Take It to the NET
Online lesson quiz at
www.PHSchool.com
Web Code: aga-1103

Quantitative Comparison

Compare the boxed quantity in Column A with the boxed quantity in Column B. Choose the best answer.
A. The quantity in Column A is greater.
B. The quantity in Column B is greater.
C. The two quantities are equal.
D. The relationship cannot be determined from the information given.

Each group of three terms represents a geometric sequence.

	Column A	Column B
63.	the missing term in 5, ■, 125	the missing term in 5, 10, ■
64.	the missing term in 10, 100, ■	the missing term in ■, 200, 40
65.	the missing term in 15, 45, ■	the missing term in ■, 280, 560

Short Response

66. Which is greater, the geometric mean of 4 and 16 or the arithmetic mean of 4 and 16? Show your work.

Extended Response

67. In a geometric sequence, $a_1 = 3$ and $a_4 = 192$. Explain how to find a_2 and a_3.

Mixed Review

Lesson 11-2 **Write an explicit and a recursive formula for each arithmetic sequence.**

68. $-3, 0, 3, 6, \ldots$ **69.** $17, 8, -1, \ldots$ **70.** $-2, -13, -24, \ldots$

Lesson 10-3 **Write an equation of the circle with the given center and radius. Graph the circle.**

71. center $(0, 0)$, radius 3 **72.** center $(-3, 1)$, radius 5 **73.** center $(1, 1)$, radius 2

Lesson 9-3 **Find the vertical asymptotes of each function.**

74. $y = \frac{x - 3}{x + 3}$ **75.** $y = \frac{x - 3}{x + 1}$ **76.** $y = \frac{x - 3}{x(x - 1)}$

Checkpoint Quiz 1 — Lessons 11-1 through 11-3

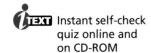

iTEXT Instant self-check quiz online and on CD-ROM

Identify each sequence as *arithmetic* or *geometric*. Then find the common difference or common ratio.

1. $15, 30, 45, 60, \ldots$ **2.** $2, 6, 18, 54, \ldots$ **3.** $37, 34, 31, 28, 25, \ldots$

4. $700, 350, 175, 87.5, \ldots$ **5.** $8, -4, 2, -1, 0.5, \ldots$ **6.** $4, 2, 0, -2, -4, \ldots$

Find the fifth term of each sequence.

7. $a_1 = 100, a_n = \frac{1}{2}a_{n-1}$ **8.** $a_1 = 2, a_n = 3a_{n-1} - 2$ **9.** $a_n = -n + 6$

10. Writing Explain how to compute the arithmetic mean and the geometric mean of two terms of a sequence.

A Point in Time

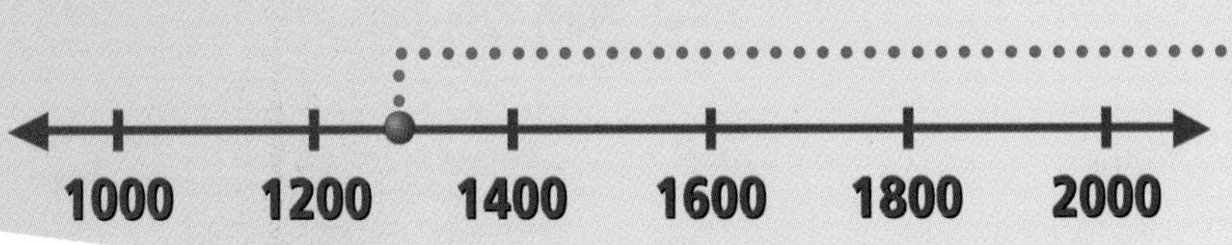

In 1276, the Chinese astronomer Guo Shoujing built a device to study the sun. A hole in the tower of his observatory faced due south. At noon, a horizontal pole in the tower cast a shadow on a low wall that extended north from the building. Guo Shou jing learned about the sun's movements by studying the geometric pattern of the shadows on the wall.

Take It to the NET For more information about techniques for measuring the sun's position, go to **www.PHSchool.com**.
Web Code: age-2032

Reading Math

Reading for Problem Solving

For Use With Page 603, Exercise 37

Read the problem below. Then follow along with Wanda as she solves the problem. Check your understanding with the exercise at the bottom of the page.

Find the missing terms of the geometric sequence. (*Hint:* The geometric mean of the first and fifth terms is the third term.

19,683; ■; ■; ■; 243; ...

What Wanda Thinks	What Wanda Writes
In this geometric sequence, the numbers decrease.	19,683; ■; ■; ■; 243; . . .
The hint tells me information about terms in the sequence. I'll label the terms.	1st term = 19,683 2nd term = ■ 3rd term = ■ 4th term = ■ 5th term = 243
The hint says that the geometric mean of the first and fifth terms is the third term. That makes sense, because the third term is the middle term. I'll write that relationship and substitute.	Geometric mean of 1st and 5th terms is 3rd term 3rd term $= \sqrt{19{,}683 \cdot 243}$ 3rd term $= \sqrt{4{,}782{,}969}$
Perfect. I have the third term in the sequence.	3rd term = 2187
I can rewrite the sequence to include the third term.	19,683; ■; 2187; ■; 243; . . .
Now I can find the 2nd and 4th terms in the same way, because they are between terms I know.	2nd term $= \sqrt{19{,}683 \cdot 2187} = 6561$ 4th term $= \sqrt{2187 \cdot 243} = 729$
I'll rewrite the sequence with the missing terms filled in.	The sequence is 19,683; 6561; 2187; 729; 243; . . .

EXERCISES

Find the missing terms of each geometric sequence.

1. 12,312; ■; ■; ■; 152; . . .

2. 1.7; ■; ■; ■; 1239.3; . . .

11-4 Arithmetic Series

Lesson Preview

What You'll Learn

OBJECTIVE 1 To write and evaluate arithmetic series

OBJECTIVE 2 To use summation notation

. . . And Why

To find the number of stitches in a cross-stitch pattern, as in Example 2

✓ Check Skills You'll Need

(For help, go to Lesson 11-1.)

Find each sum.

1. $2 + 3.5 + 5 + 6.5 + 8$
2. $-17 + (-13) + (-9) + (-5) + (-1) + 3$

Write an explicit formula for each sequence.

3. $4, 6, 8, 10, 12, \ldots$
4. $1, 4, 7, 10, 13, 16, \ldots$
5. $-17, -23, -29, -35, \ldots$
6. $10, 1, -8, -17, \ldots$

New Vocabulary • series • arithmetic series • limit

Interactive lesson includes instant self-check, tutorials, and activities.

OBJECTIVE 1 Writing and Evaluating Arithmetic Series

Investigation: Arithmetic Series

Use the sequence 1, 2, 3, 4, . . . 97, 98, 99, 100 to answer each question.

1. Is it *arithmetic, geometric,* or *neither?* Justify your reasoning.
2. a. Add the first and last terms of the sequence and write down the answer. Then add the second and next-to-last terms. Continue adding terms until you get to the middle of the sequence.
   b. **Reasoning** What patterns do you notice in your answers to part (a)?
3. Use your answer to Question 2 to find the sum of the terms of the sequence.
4. a. Describe a short method for finding the following sum.
   $5 + 10 + 15 + 20 + 25 + 30 + 35 + 40 + 45 + 50$
   b. Find the sum.

Reading Math

Ellipsis points are three dots indicating a missing part of a statement.

A **series** is the expression for the sum of the terms of a sequence. Finite sequences and series have terms that you can count individually from 1 to a final whole number n. Infinite sequences and series continue without end. You indicate an infinite sequence or series with ellipsis points.

Finite sequence	Finite series
$6, 9, 12, 15, 18$	$6 + 9 + 12 + 15 + 18$
Infinite sequence	**Infinite series**
$3, 7, 11, 15, \ldots$	$3 + 7 + 11 + 15 + \ldots$

1 EXAMPLE Writing and Evaluating a Series

Use the finite sequence 2, 11, 20, 29, 38, 47. Write the related series. Then evaluate the series.

Related series → $2 + 11 + 20 + 29 + 38 + 47 = 147$ ← **Add to evaluate.**

The sum of the terms of the sequence is 147.

Check Understanding

1 Write the related series for each finite sequence. Then evaluate the series.
a. 0.3, 0.6, 0.9, 1.2, 1.5, 1.8, 2.1, 2.4, 2.7, 3.0 **b.** 100, 125, 150, 175, 200, 225

An **arithmetic series** is a series whose terms form an arithmetic sequence. When a sequence has many terms, or when you know only the first and last terms of the sequence, you can use a formula to evaluate the related series quickly.

Key Concepts

Property **Sum of a Finite Arithmetic Series**

The sum S_n of a finite arithmetic series $a_1 + a_2 + a_3 + \dots + a_n$ is

$$S_n = \frac{n}{2}(a_1 + a_n)$$

where a_1 is the first term, a_n is the nth term, and n is the number of terms.

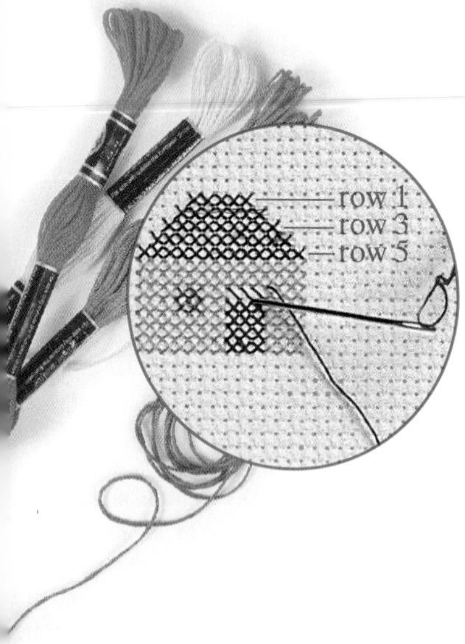

2 EXAMPLE Real-World Connection

Crafts Embroidery such as cross-stitch frequently decorates table linens and clothing, although it was originally used to strengthen and repair woven fabric.

Several rows of cross-stitches make up the green roof. Find the total number of green cross-stitches in the roof.

Relate sum of the series is $\frac{\text{number of terms}}{2}$ times (the first term plus the last term)

Define Let S_n = total number of cross-stitches,

and let n = the number of rows.

Then a_1 = the number of cross-stitches in the first row,

and a_n = the number of cross-stitches in the last row.

Write $S_n = \frac{n}{2}(a_1 + a_n)$ **Use the formula.**

$= \frac{5}{2}(5 + 13)$ **Substitute $n = 5$, $a_1 = 5$, and $a_n = 13$.**

$= 2.5(18)$ **Simplify.**

$= 45$ **Multiply.**

There are 45 cross-stitches in the green roof.

Check Understanding

2 Suppose the pattern from Example 2 extends to 14 rows of cross-stitches.
a. Find the 14th term of the sequence.
b. Use the formula to find the value of the series to the 14th term.

OBJECTIVE

2 Using Summation Notation

Reading Math

Σ is the Greek letter sigma, the equivalent of the English letter S (for summation).

You can use the summation symbol Σ to write a series. Then you can use limits to indicate how many terms you are adding. **Limits** are the least and greatest integral values of n.

upper limit, greatest value of n

explicit formula for the sequence

$$\sum_{n=1}^{3} (5n + 1)$$

lower limit, least value of n

3 EXAMPLE Writing a Series in Summation Notation

Use summation notation to write the series $3 + 6 + 9 + \ldots$ for 33 terms.

$3 \cdot 1 = 3, 3 \cdot 2 = 6, 3 \cdot 3 = 9, \ldots$ **The explicit formula for the sequence is 3*n*.**

$3 + 6 + 9 + \ldots + 99 = \sum_{n=1}^{33} 3n$ **The lower limit is 1 and the upper limit is 33.**

Check Understanding 3 Use summation notation to write each series for the specified number of terms.

a. $1 + 2 + 3 + \ldots; n = 6$

b. $3 + 8 + 13 + 18 + \ldots; n = 9$

To expand a series from summation notation, you can substitute each value of n into the explicit formula and add the results.

4 EXAMPLE Finding the Sum of a Series

Use the series $\sum_{n=1}^{3} (5n + 1)$.

a. Find the number of terms in the series.
Since the values of n are 1, 2, and 3, there are three terms in the series.

b. Find the first and last terms of the series.
The first term of the series is $5n + 1 = 5(1) + 1 = 6$.
The last term of the series is $5n + 1 = 5(3) + 1 = 16$.

c. Evaluate the series.

$\sum_{n=1}^{3} (5n + 1) = (5(1) + 1) + (5(2) + 1) + (5(3) + 1)$ **Substitute.**

$= 6 + 11 + 16$ **Simplify within parentheses.**

$= 33$ **Add.**

The sum of the series is 33.

Check Understanding 4 For each sum, find the number of terms, the first term, and the last term. Then evaluate the series.

a. $\sum_{n=1}^{10} (n - 3)$ **b.** $\sum_{n=1}^{4} \left(\frac{1}{2}n + 1\right)$ **c.** $\sum_{n=2}^{5} n^2$

EXERCISES

For more practice, see *Extra Practice.*

Practice and Problem Solving

A Practice by Example

Example 1 (page 608)

Write the related series for each finite sequence. Then evaluate each series.

1. 21, 18, 15, 12, 9, 6, 3

2. −5, −15, −25, −35, −45

3. 100, 99, 98, . . . , 95

4. 0.5, 0.25, 0, . . . , −0.75

5. 17.3, 19.6, 21.9, 24.2, 26.5

6. 4.5, 5.6, 6.7, . . . , 11.1

Example 2 (page 608)

Each sequence has eight terms. Evaluate each related series.

7. $\frac{1}{2}, \frac{3}{2}, \frac{5}{2}, \ldots, \frac{15}{2}$

8. 1, −1, −3, . . . , −13

9. 5, 13, 21, . . . , 61

10. −3.5, −1.25, 1, . . . , 12.25

11. 1765, 1414, 1063, . . . , −692

12. −13, −14.5, −16, . . . , −23.5

Example 3 (page 609)

Use summation notation to write each arithmetic series for the specified number of terms.

13. $2 + 4 + 6 + \ldots; n = 4$

14. $8 + 9 + 10 + \ldots; n = 8$

15. $5 + 6 + 7 + \ldots; n = 7$

16. $1 + 4 + 7 + 10 + \ldots; n = 11$

17. $7 + 14 + 21 + \ldots; n = 15$

18. $(-3) + (-6) + (-9) + \ldots; n = 5$

Example 4 (page 609)

For each sum, find the number of terms, the first term, and the last term. Then evaluate the series.

19. $\sum_{n=1}^{5} (2n - 1)$

20. $\sum_{n=1}^{5} (-2n - 1)$

21. $\sum_{n=3}^{8} (7 - n)$

22. $\sum_{n=1}^{5} (0.2n - 0.2)$

23. $\sum_{n=2}^{10} \frac{4n}{3}$

24. $\sum_{n=5}^{10} (20 - n)$

B Apply Your Skills

Tell whether each list is a *sequence* or a *series*. Then tell whether it is *finite* or *infinite*.

25. 1, 2, 4, 8, 16, 32, . . .

26. 1, 0.5, 0.25, 0.125, 0.0625

27. $5 + 10 + \ldots + 25$

28. $-0.5 - 0.25 - 0.125 - \ldots$

29. $\frac{4}{3}, \frac{7}{3}, \frac{10}{3}, \frac{13}{3}, \frac{16}{3}, \ldots$

30. $2.3 + 4.6 + 9.2 + 18.4$

Real-World Connection

The seats in a theater are staggered so people don't block the view of those in the row behind them.

31. Architecture A 20-row theater has two aisles. The two side sections have four chairs in the first row and one more chair in each succeeding row. The middle section has 10 chairs in the first row and one more chair in each succeeding row.

a. Find the total number of chairs in each section. Then find the total seating capacity of the theater.

b. Write an arithmetic series to represent each section.

c. After every five rows, the ticket price goes down by \$5. Front-row tickets cost \$60. What is the total amount of money generated by a full house?

32. a. Consider the finite arithmetic series $10 + 13 + 16 + \ldots + 31$. How many terms are in it? Explain.

b. Evaluate the series.

33. Education Luis has taken three math tests so far this semester. The spreadsheet shows his grades.

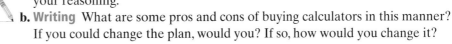

	A	B	C	D
1	Student Name	Test 1	Test 2	Test 3
2	Luis Ortez	75	79	83
3	Marie Bova	78	85	84
4	Lasheha Brown	87	82	91

a. Suppose his test grades continue to improve at the same rate. What will be his grade on the fifth (and final) test?

b. What will his test average be for this grading period? (Assume each test is worth 100 points.)

34. a. A supermarket displays cans in a triangle. Write an explicit formula for the sequence of the number of cans.

b. Use summation notation to write the related series for a triangle with 10 cans in the bottom row.

c. Suppose the triangle had 17 rows. How many cans would be in the 17th row?

d. Critical Thinking Could the triangle have 110 cans? 140 cans? Justify your reasoning.

Evaluate each series to the given term.

35. $2 + 4 + 6 + 8 + \ldots$; 10th term

36. $-5 - 25 - 45 - \ldots$; 9th term

37. $2 + 3 + 4 + 5 + \ldots$; 100th term

38. $\frac{5}{2} + 1 - \frac{1}{2} - 2 - \ldots$; 8th term

39. $0.17 + 0.13 + 0.09 + 0.05 + \ldots$; 12th term

40. $1500 + 1499 + 1498 + 1497 + \ldots$; 1000th term

41. Technology A school committee has decided to spend a large portion of its annual technology budget on graphing calculators. This year, the technology coordinator bought 75 calculators, and plans to buy 25 new calculators each year from now on.

a. Suppose the school committee has decided that each student in the school should have access to a graphing calculator within seven years. The school population is 500. Will the technology coordinator meet this goal? Explain your reasoning.

b. Writing What are some pros and cons of buying calculators in this manner? If you could change the plan, would you? If so, how would you change it?

42. a. Open-Ended Write two explicit formulas for arithmetic sequences.

b. Write the first five terms of each related series.

c. Use summation notation to rewrite each series.

d. Evaluate each series.

C Challenge

Use the values of a_1 and S_n to find the value of a_n.

43. $a_1 = 4$ and $S_{40} = 6080$; a_{40}

44. $a_1 = -6$ and $S_{50} = -5150$; a_{50}

Find a_1 for each arithmetic series.

45. $S_8 = 440$ and $d = 6$

46. $S_{30} = 240$ and $d = -2$

47. Evaluate S_{10} for the series $x + (x + y) + (x + 2y) + \ldots$

48. Evaluate S_{15} for the series $3x + (3x - 2y) + (3x - 4y) + \ldots$

Standardized Test Prep

Multiple Choice

49. Which expression represents the sum of the finite series $10 + 20 + 30 + 40$?

I. $\sum_{n=1}^{4} 10n$ **II.** $\sum_{n=10}^{40} 10n$ **III.** $10\left(\sum_{n=1}^{4} n\right)$

A. I and II only **B.** I and III only **C.** II and III only **D.** I, II, and III

50. What is the value of $\sum_{n=1}^{5} (2n - 3)$?

F. 6 **G.** 15 **H.** 17 **I.** $10n - 15$

51. Which expression defines the series $14 + 20 + 26 + 32 + 38 + 44 + 50$?

A. $\sum_{n=2}^{8} (7n - 1)$ **B.** $\sum_{n=3}^{8} (6n - 4)$ **C.** $\sum_{n=3}^{9} (6n - 4)$ **D.** $\sum_{n=8}^{14} (n + 6)$

Quantitative Comparison

Compare the boxed quantity in Column A with the boxed quantity in Column B. Choose the best answer.

A. The quantity in Column A is greater.
B. The quantity in Column B is greater.
C. The two quantities are equal.
D. The relationship cannot be determined from the information given.

	Column A	Column B
52.	$\sum_{n=1}^{10} n$	$\sum_{n=1}^{10} (n - 1)$
53.	$\sum_{n=1}^{5} (2n + 12)$	$\sum_{n=2}^{4} 10n$
54.	$\sum_{n=1}^{4} n^2$	$\sum_{n=5}^{8} 2n$

Take It to the NET
Online lesson quiz at
www.PHSchool.com
Web Code: aga-1104

Mixed Review

Lesson 11-3

Write the explicit formula for each geometric sequence. Then generate the first three terms.

55. $a_1 = 1, r = 2$ **56.** $a_1 = 1, r = 5$ **57.** $a_1 = -1, r = -1$

58. $a_1 = 3, r = \frac{3}{2}$ **59.** $a_1 = -7, r = 0.1$ **60.** $a_1 = 20, r = -0.5$

Lesson 10-1

Graph each equation. Describe each graph and its lines of symmetry. Give the domain and range for each graph.

61. $x^2 + 3y^2 = 36$ **62.** $x^2 - y^2 = 25$ **63.** $x^2 + y^2 = 4$

Lesson 9-4

Simplify each rational expression.

64. $\frac{x^2 + 4x + 3}{x^2 - 3x - 4}$ **65.** $\frac{c^2 - 8c + 12}{c^2 - 11c + 30}$ **66.** $\frac{3z^4 + 36z^3 + 60z^2}{3z^3 - 3z^2}$

Investigation

Geometry and Infinite Series

For Use With Lesson 11-5

You can use geometric figures to model some infinite series.

1 EXAMPLE Modeling an Infinite Series

Geometry Draw a geometric figure to model the series.

$\frac{1}{2} + \left(\frac{1}{2}\right)^2 + \left(\frac{1}{2}\right)^3 + \ldots + \left(\frac{1}{2}\right)^n + \ldots$

Use a square grid. Shade one half of the grid. Then shade one half of the remaining area. Continue until the grid is full.

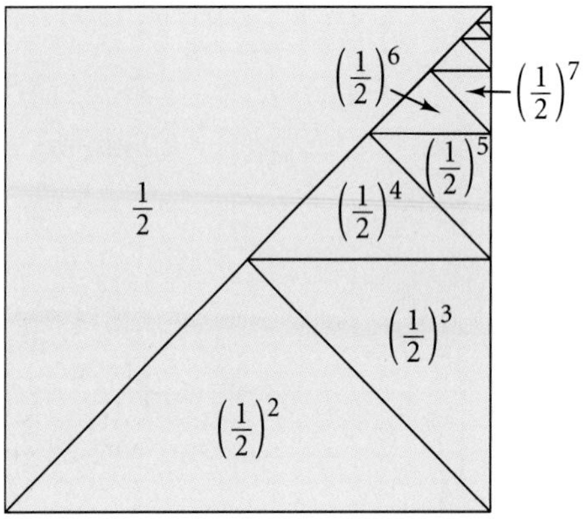

So the series

$\frac{1}{2} + \left(\frac{1}{2}\right)^2 + \left(\frac{1}{2}\right)^3 + \ldots + \left(\frac{1}{2}\right)^n + \ldots$

appears to have a sum of 1.

You can write an infinite series from a geometric model.

2 EXAMPLE Writing an Infinite Series

Geometry Write the series modeled by the trapezoids. Estimate the sum of the series. Explain your reasoning.

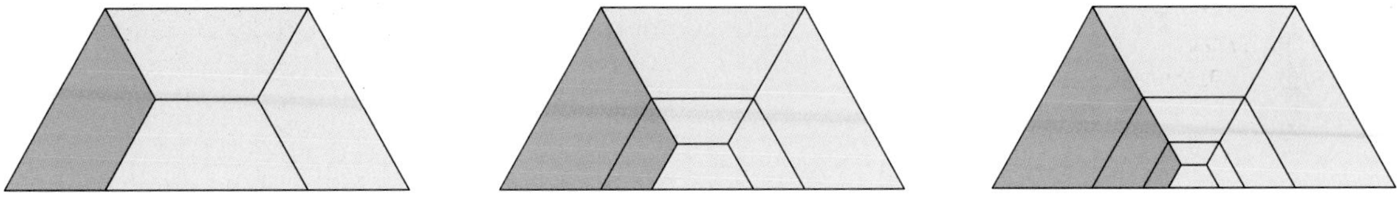

$\frac{1}{4} \quad + \quad \left(\frac{1}{4}\right)^2 \quad + \quad \left(\frac{1}{4}\right)^3 \quad + \ldots$

The red area approaches one third of the figure.

So the series $\frac{1}{4} + \left(\frac{1}{4}\right)^2 + \left(\frac{1}{4}\right)^3 + \ldots + \left(\frac{1}{4}\right)^n + \ldots$ appears to have a sum of $\frac{1}{3}$.

EXERCISES

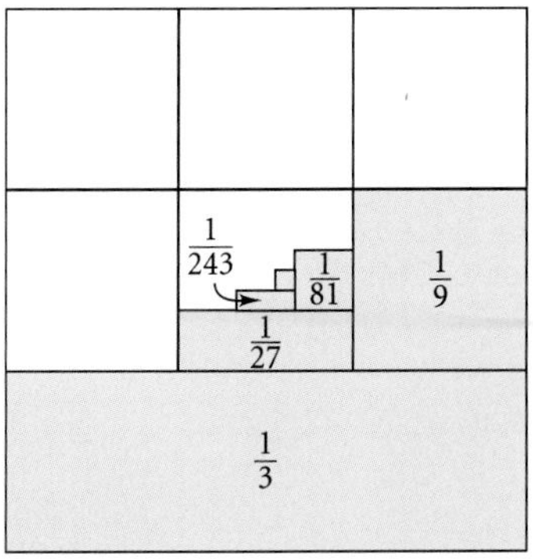

1. **a.** Write the series modeled by the figure at the right.
   b. Evaluate the series. Explain your reasoning.
2. Draw a figure to model the series. Begin with a 10×10 square.
   $\frac{1}{5} + \left(\frac{1}{5}\right)^2 + \left(\frac{1}{5}\right)^3 + \ldots + \left(\frac{1}{5}\right)^n + \ldots$
3. **Make a Conjecture** Consider the series
   $\frac{1}{c} + \left(\frac{1}{c}\right)^2 + \left(\frac{1}{c}\right)^3 + \ldots + \left(\frac{1}{c}\right)^n + \ldots$
   What is the sum of the series? Explain your reasoning.

11-5

Geometric Series

Lesson Preview

What You'll Learn

OBJECTIVE 1 To evaluate a finite geometric series

OBJECTIVE 2 To evaluate an infinite geometric series

. . . And Why

To find the length of a chambered nautilus shell, as in Example 4

✓ Check Skills You'll Need

(For help, go to Lesson 9-5.)

Find each sum or difference.

1. $100 + 50 + 25 + \frac{25}{2} + \frac{25}{4}$
2. $3 + 9 + 27 + 81$
3. $-2 + 4 - 8 + 16 - 32$
4. $-5 - 10 - 20 - 40$

Simplify each fraction.

5. $\dfrac{1 - \frac{1}{5}}{\frac{1}{3}}$
6. $\dfrac{1}{1 - \frac{1}{4}}$
7. $\dfrac{\frac{1}{2} - \frac{1}{3}}{\frac{1}{4}}$
8. $\dfrac{2 + \frac{1}{16}}{\frac{1}{3}}$

New Vocabulary • geometric series • converges • diverges

Interactive lesson includes instant self-check, tutorials, and activities.

OBJECTIVE 1 Evaluating a Finite Geometric Series

A **geometric series** is the expression for the sum of the terms of a geometric sequence. As with arithmetic series, you can use a formula to evaluate a finite geometric series.

Key Concepts

Property — **Sum of a Finite Geometric Series**

The sum S_n of a finite geometric series $a_1 + a_2 + a_3 + \ldots + a_n, r \neq 1$, is

$$S_n = \frac{a_1(1 - r^n)}{1 - r}$$

where a_1 is the first term, r is the common ratio, and n is the number of terms.

1 EXAMPLE Using the Geometric Series Formula

Use the formula to evaluate the series $3 + 6 + 12 + 24 + 48 + 96$.

The first term is 3, and there are six terms in the series.

The common ratio is $\frac{6}{3} = \frac{12}{6} = \frac{24}{12} = \frac{48}{24} = \frac{96}{48} = 2$.

So $a_1 = 3, r = 2$, and $n = 6$.

$S_n = \dfrac{a_1(1 - r^n)}{1 - r}$ **Write the formula.**

$S_6 = \dfrac{3(1 - 2^6)}{1 - 2}$ **Substitute $a_1 = 3$, $r = 2$, and $n = 6$.**

$= \dfrac{-189}{-1} = 189$ **Simplify.**

The sum of the series is 189.

Need Help?

For more practice with ratios, see Skills Handbook p. 844.

Check Understanding 1 Identify a_1, r, and n for each series. Then evaluate each series.

a. $-45 + 135 - 405 + 1215 - 3645$ **b.** $\frac{1}{3} + \frac{1}{9} + \frac{1}{27} + \frac{1}{81}$

You can use the formula to solve problems involving geometric series.

2 EXAMPLE Real-World Connection

Real-World Connection

Careers Financial planners use math to help families plan savings for college, retirement, and vacations.

Financial Planning In March, the Floyd family starts saving for a vacation in August. The Floyds expect the vacation to cost \$1375. They start with \$125. Each month they plan to deposit 20% more than the previous month. Will they have enough money for their trip?

Relate $S_n = \frac{a_1(1 - r^n)}{1 - r}$ **Write the formula for the sum of a geometric series.**

Define S_n = total amount saved

$a_1 = 125$ **initial amount**

$r = 1.2$ **common ratio**

$n = 6$ **number of months (March through August)**

Write $S_6 = \frac{125(1 - 1.2^6)}{1 - 1.2}$ **Substitute.**

$= 1241.24$ **Simplify.**

The final balance will be \$1241.24. The Floyds will *not* have enough money for their trip in August.

Check Understanding 2 **a.** **Reasoning** Explain how the common ratio 1.2 was found.

b. Suppose each month the Floyds deposit 25% more than the previous month. Describe how this changes the problem.

c. At this rate of saving, will they have enough money for their trip? Explain.

OBJECTIVE

2 Evaluating an Infinite Geometric Series

In some cases you can evaluate an infinite geometric series. When $|r| < 1$, the series **converges,** or gets closer and closer, to the sum S. When $|r| \geq 1$, the series **diverges,** or approaches no limit.

3 EXAMPLE Determining Divergence and Convergence

Decide whether each infinite geometric series *diverges* or *converges*. State whether the series has a sum.

a. $1 - \frac{1}{3} + \frac{1}{9} - \dots$

$a_1 = 1, a_2 = -\frac{1}{3}$

$r = -\frac{1}{3} \div 1 = -\frac{1}{3}$

Since $|r| < 1$, the series converges, and the series has a sum.

b. $\sum_{n=1}^{\infty} 5(2)^{n-1}$

$a_1 = 5(2^0) = 5, a_2 = 5(2^1) = 10$

$r = 10 \div 5 = 2$

Since $|r| \geq 1$, the series diverges, and the series does not have a sum.

Check Understanding 3 Determine whether each series has a sum.

a. $1 + \frac{1}{5} + \frac{1}{25} + \dots$ **b.** $4 + 8 + 16 + \dots$

Key Concepts

Definition — **Sum of an Infinite Geometric Series**

An infinite geometric series with $|r| < 1$ converges to the sum

$$S = \frac{a_1}{1 - r}$$

where a_1 is the first term and r is the common ratio.

You can use the sum formula to evaluate some infinite geometric series.

4 EXAMPLE — Real-World Connection

Biology The length of the outside shell of each closed chamber of a chambered nautilus is 0.9 times the length of the larger chamber next to it. Estimate the total length of the outside shell for the enclosed chambers.

The outside edge of the largest enclosed chamber is 27 mm long, so $a_1 = 27$.

$S = \frac{a_1}{1 - r}$ **Use the formula.**

$= \frac{27}{1 - 0.9}$ **Substitute.**

$= 270$ **Simplify.**

The total length of the outside shell for the enclosed chambers is about 270 mm.

Check Understanding 4 Evaluate each infinite geometric series.

a. $1 + \frac{1}{2} + \frac{1}{4} + \frac{1}{8} + \ldots$

b. $3 - \frac{3}{2} + \frac{3}{4} - \frac{3}{8} + \ldots$

EXERCISES

For more practice, see *Extra Practice*.

Practice and Problem Solving

A Practice by Example

Examples 1 and 2 (pages 614 and 615)

Evaluate the series to the given term.

1. $1 + 2 + 4 + \ldots; S_8$

2. $4 + 12 + 36 + \ldots; S_6$

3. $3 + 6 + 12 + \ldots; S_7$

4. $7 - 35 + 175 - \ldots; S_5$

5. $-5 - 10 - 20 - \ldots; S_{11}$

6. $-\frac{1}{6} + 1 - 6 + 36 - \ldots; S_5$

7. $\frac{1}{2} + \frac{1}{4} + \frac{1}{8} + \ldots; S_8$

8. $1 - 3 + 9 - 27 + \ldots; S_8$

Example 3 (page 615)

Decide whether each infinite geometric series *diverges* or *converges*. State whether each series has a sum.

9. $1 + \frac{1}{4} + \frac{1}{16} + \ldots$

10. $1 - \frac{1}{2} + \frac{1}{4} - \ldots$

11. $4 + 2 + 1 + \ldots$

12. $1 + 2 + 4 + \ldots$

13. $6 + 18 + 54 + \ldots$

14. $-54 - 18 - 6 - \ldots$

15. $1 - 1 + 1 - \ldots$

16. $1 + \frac{1}{5} + \frac{1}{25} + \ldots$

17. $\frac{1}{4} + \frac{1}{2} + 1 + 2 + \ldots$

Example 4 (page 616)

Evaluate each infinite geometric series.

18. $1.1 + 0.11 + 0.011 + \dots$

19. $1.1 - 0.11 + 0.011 - \dots$

20. $1 - \frac{1}{5} + \frac{1}{25} - \frac{1}{125} + \dots$

21. $3 + 1 + \frac{1}{3} + \frac{1}{9} + \dots$

22. $3 + 2 + \frac{4}{3} + \frac{8}{9} + \dots$

23. $3 - 2 + \frac{4}{3} - \frac{8}{9} + \dots$

B Apply Your Skills

Determine whether each series is *arithmetic* or *geometric*. Then evaluate the series to the given term.

24. $2 + 4 + 8 + 16 + \dots; S_{10}$

25. $2 + 4 + 6 + 8 + \dots; S_{20}$

26. $-5 + 25 - 125 + 625 - \dots; S_9$

27. $6.4 + 8 + 10 + 12.5 + \dots; S_7$

28. $1 + 2 + 3 + 4 + \dots; S_{1000}$

29. $81 + 27 + 9 + 3 + \dots; S_{200}$

30. Communications Many companies use a telephone chain to notify employees of a closing due to bad weather. Suppose the first person in the chain calls four people. Then each of these people calls four others, and so on.

a. Make a tree diagram to show the first three stages in the telephone chain. How many calls are made at each stage?

b. Write the series that represents the total number of calls made through the first six stages.

c. How many employees have been notified after stage six?

31. The graph shows the sum of the first n terms in the series with $a_1 = 20$ and $r = 0.9$.

a. Write the first four terms of the series.

b. Use the graph to evaluate the series to the 47th term.

c. Write and evaluate the formula for the sum of the series.

d. Graph the sum using the window values shown. Use the graph to verify your answer to part (c).

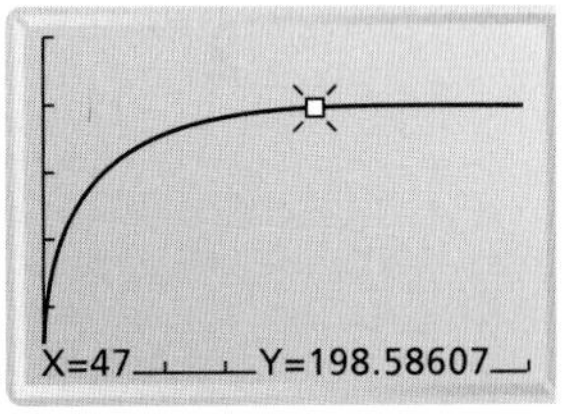

Xmin=0 Ymin=0
Xmax=94 Ymax=250
Xscl=10 Yscl=50

Evaluate each infinite series that has a sum.

32. $\sum_{n=1}^{\infty} \left(\frac{1}{5}\right)^{n-1}$

33. $\sum_{n=1}^{\infty} 3\left(\frac{1}{4}\right)^{n-1}$

34. $\sum_{n=1}^{\infty} \left(-\frac{1}{3}\right)^{n-1}$

35. $\sum_{n=1}^{\infty} 7(2)^{n-1}$

36. $\sum_{n=1}^{\infty} (-0.2)^{n-1}$

37. $\sum_{n=1}^{\infty} 2(1.2)^{n-1}$

Reading Math

In $\sum_{n=1}^{\infty}$, the symbol for infinity ∞ indicates that the series continues without end.

38. A bouncing ball reaches heights of 16 cm, 12.8 cm, and 10.24 cm on three consecutive bounces.

a. If the ball started at a height of 25 cm, how many times has it bounced when it reaches a height of 16 cm?

b. Write a geometric series for the downward distances the ball travels from its release at 25 cm.

c. Write a geometric series for the upward distances the ball travels from its first bounce.

d. Find the total vertical distance the ball travels before it comes to rest.

39. Open-Ended Write an infinite geometric series that converges to 3. Use the formula to evaluate the series.

40. **a.** A classmate uses the formula for the sum of an infinite geometric series to evaluate $1 + 1.1 + 1.21 + 1.331 + \ldots$ and gets -10. Is your classmate's answer reasonable? Explain.
b. **Error Analysis** What did your classmate fail to check before using the formula?

Critical Thinking **Find the specified value for each infinite geometric series.**

41. $a_1 = 12, S = 96$; find r.

42. $S = 12, r = \frac{1}{6}$; find a_1.

43. **Writing** Suppose you are to receive an allowance each week for the next 26 weeks. Would you rather receive (a) \$1000 per week or (b) 2¢ the first week, 4¢ the second week, 8¢ the third week, and so on for the 26 weeks? Justify your answer.

44. The sum of an infinite geometric series is twice its first term.
a. **Error Analysis** A student says the common ratio of the series is $\frac{3}{2}$. What is the student's error?
b. Find the common ratio of the series.

C Challenge

Technology **Create a spreadsheet to evaluate the first n terms of each series. Determine whether each infinite series converges to a sum. If so, estimate the sum.**

45. $\sum_{n=1}^{\infty} \frac{1}{2^n}$

46. $\sum_{n=1}^{\infty} \frac{100}{n}$

47. $\sum_{n=1}^{\infty} \frac{1}{(n-1)!}$

48. **Physics** Because of friction and air resistance, each swing of a pendulum is a little shorter than the previous one. The lengths of the swings form a geometric sequence. Suppose the first swing of a pendulum has a length of 100 cm and the return swing is 99 cm.
a. On which swing will the arc first have a length less than 50 cm?
b. Find the total distance traveled by the pendulum until it comes to rest.

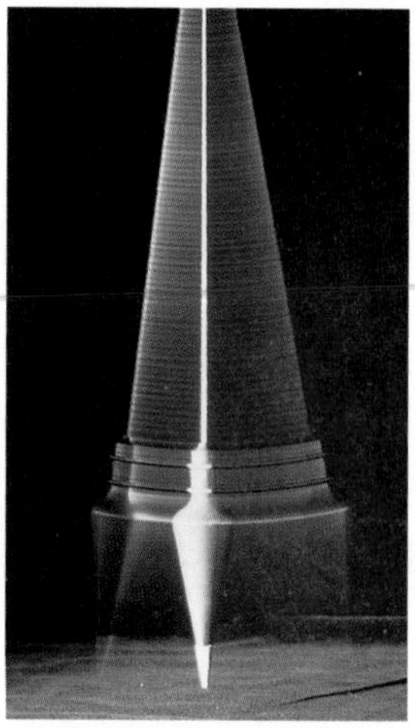

49. **a.** Show that the infinite geometric series $0.142857 + 0.000000142857 + \ldots$ has a sum of $\frac{1}{7}$.
b. Find the fraction form of the repeating decimal $0.428571428571\ldots$.

50. The function $S(n) = \frac{10(1 - 0.8^n)}{0.2}$ represents the sum of the first n terms of an infinite geometric series.
a. What is the domain of the function?
b. Find $S(n)$ for $n = 1, 2, 3, \ldots, 10$. Sketch the graph of the function.
c. Find the sum S of the infinite geometric series.

Standardized Test Prep

Gridded Response

51. What is the common ratio for the geometric series $\sum_{n=1}^{10} 7\left(\frac{4}{7}\right)^{n-1}$? Enter your answer as a fraction.

52. What is the common ratio in a geometric series if $a_2 = \frac{2}{5}$ and $a_5 = \frac{16}{135}$? Enter your answer as a fraction.

Take It to the NET
Online lesson quiz at www.PHSchool.com
Web Code: aga-1105

53. Evaluate the infinite geometric series $\frac{2}{5} + \frac{4}{25} + \frac{8}{125} + \ldots$ Enter your answer as a fraction.

54. Find the sum of the two infinite series $\sum_{n=1}^{\infty} \left(\frac{2}{3}\right)^{n-1}$ and $\sum_{n=1}^{\infty} \left(\frac{2}{3}\right)^{n}$.

55. Evaluate the sum $\sum_{n=1}^{3} \left(\frac{1}{n+1}\right)^2$. Round to the nearest thousandth.

56. Car 1 cost $22,600 when new and depreciated 14% each year for 5 years. The same year, Car 2 cost $17,500 when new and depreciated 7% each year for 5 years. To the nearest dollar, what was the difference in the values of the two cars after 5 years?

Mixed Review

Lesson 11-4

Evaluate each series to the given term.

57. $12.5 + 15 + 17.5 + 20 + 22.5 + \ldots$; 7th term

58. $-100 - 95 - 90 - 85 - \ldots$; 11th term

59. $-17 - 11 - 5 + 1 + 7 + 13 + \ldots$; 25th term

Lesson 10-2

Identify the focus and directrix of each parabola. Then graph the parabola.

60. $y = \frac{1}{16}x^2$

61. $x = -\frac{1}{4}y^2$

62. $x^2 = -9y$

Lesson 9-5

Add or subtract. Simplify where possible.

63. $\frac{7}{2c} - \frac{2}{c^2}$

64. $\frac{5}{y+3} + \frac{15}{y-3}$

65. $\frac{4}{x^2-36} + \frac{x}{x-6}$

66. $\frac{15}{3-d} - \frac{-3}{9-d^2}$

Checkpoint Quiz 2 — Lessons 11-4 through 11-5

Instant self-check quiz online and on CD-ROM

Determine whether each series is *arithmetic* or *geometric*. Then evaluate the series to the given term.

1. $1 + 3 + 5 + 7 + \ldots; S_{30}$

2. $1 + 3 + 9 + 27 + \ldots; S_{10}$

3. $-4 - 2 - 1 - 0.5 - \ldots; S_7$

4. $500 + 380 + 260 + 140 + \ldots; S_6$

5. $120 + 60 + 30 + 15 + \ldots; S_8$

6. $-175 - 50 + 75 + 200 + \ldots; S_{12}$

Evaluate each infinite geometric series.

7. $\sum_{n=1}^{\infty} \left(\frac{1}{15}\right)^{n-1}$

8. $\sum_{n=1}^{\infty} 2(0.5)^{n-1}$

9. **Open-Ended** Write a finite geometric series with a sum less than 1.

10. **Critical Thinking** Can an infinite arithmetic series converge? Explain. Do not consider the series $0 + 0 + \ldots = 0$.

Extension Mathematical Induction

For Use with Lesson 11-5

Consider the pattern in the following statements.

$$\begin{aligned} 1 &= 1 \\ 1 + 3 &= 4 \\ 1 + 3 + 5 &= 9 \\ 1 + 3 + 5 + 7 &= 16 \\ 1 + 3 + 5 + 7 + 9 &= 25 \end{aligned}$$

If this pattern continues without end, then the statement

$$1 + 3 + 5 + 7 + \dots + (2n - 1) = n^2$$

is true for all positive integers n.

The general statement above is true for the first several values of n. There is, however, no number of examples that would prove it true for all positive integers. To prove such a statement true for all positive integers, you can use a method called mathematical induction.

Theorem **Principle of Mathematical Induction**

Let S be a statement involving a positive integer n.

Then S is true for all positive integers if the following two conditions hold.

1. S is true for $n = 1$.
2. For any positive integer k, if S is true for k, then S is true for $k + 1$.

The principle of mathematical induction is like a chain reaction in an infinite line of dominoes. Proving that a statement is true for $n = 1$ is like knocking over the first domino. Knowing that if the statement is true for any value of k then it will be true for $k + 1$ is like knowing that if any domino is knocked over the one after it will be knocked over also.

EXAMPLE Using Mathematical Induction

Prove that the following statement is true for all positive integers n.

$1 + 3 + 5 + \dots + (2n - 1) = n^2$

Proof First show that the statement is true for $n = 1$.

$2n - 1 = n^2$	**Use the statement.**
$2(1) - 1 \stackrel{?}{=} 1^2$	**Substitute 1 for n.**
$2 - 1 \stackrel{?}{=} 1^2$	**Multiply.**
$1 = 1$ ✓	**Simplify.**

The statement is true for $n = 1$.

Next, assume that the statement is true for k.

$1 + 3 + 5 + \ldots + (2k - 1) = k^2$

From this assumption, prove that the statement is true for $k + 1$.

$1 + 3 + 5 + \ldots + [2(k + 1) - 1] \stackrel{?}{=} (k + 1)^2$	**Write the statement for $k + 1$.**
$1 + 3 + 5 + \ldots + (2k + 1) \stackrel{?}{=} (k + 1)^2$	**Simplify the left side.**
$1 + 3 + 5 + \ldots + (2k - 1) + (2k + 1) \stackrel{?}{=} (k + 1)^2$	**Rewrite to show the odd number preceding (2k + 1).**
$k^2 + (2k + 1) \stackrel{?}{=} (k + 1)^2$	**Substitute from the assumption.**
$(k + 1)^2 = (k + 1)^2$ ✓	**Factor the left side.**

The proof shows that conditions 1 and 2 of the principle of mathematical induction are true. By the principle, then, $1 + 3 + 5 + \ldots + (2n - 1) = n^2$ is true for all positive integers, which is what we wanted to prove.

EXERCISES

1. Test the statement from the example to verify that it is true for $n = 6, 7$, and 8.

2. Complete the mathematical induction steps below to prove that
$2 + 4 + 6 + \ldots + 2n = n(n + 1)$
is true for all positive integers n.
 a. Show that the statement is true for $n = 1$.
 b. What statement will you assume to be true?
 c. What statement will you prove true using the assumption from part (b)?
 d. Express the sum in your statement from part (c) in terms of what you assumed. Then substitute and simplify to complete the proof.

Use mathematical induction to prove that each statement is true for all positive integers *n*.

3. $\frac{1}{1 \cdot 2} + \frac{1}{2 \cdot 3} + \frac{1}{3 \cdot 4} + \ldots + \frac{1}{n(n + 1)} = \frac{n}{n + 1}$

4. $1 + 2 + 3 + \ldots + n = \frac{n(n + 1)}{2}$

5. $1 + 4 + 7 + \ldots + (3n - 2) = \frac{n(3n - 1)}{2}$

6. $\frac{1}{2} + \left(\frac{1}{2}\right)^2 + \left(\frac{1}{2}\right)^3 + \left(\frac{1}{2}\right)^4 + \ldots + \left(\frac{1}{2}\right)^n = 1 - \left(\frac{1}{2}\right)^n$

7. $n^2 + n$ is divisible by 2.

8. $1 \cdot 2 + 2 \cdot 3 + 3 \cdot 4 + \ldots + n(n + 1) = \frac{n(n + 1)(n + 2)}{3}$

9. $1^2 + 2^2 + 3^2 + \ldots + n^2 = \frac{n(n + 1)(2n + 1)}{6}$

10. $a_1 + a_1r + a_1r^2 + a_1r^3 + \ldots + a_1r^{n-1} = \frac{a_1(1 - r^n)}{1 - r}, r \neq 1$

(This is the formula for the sum of a finite geometric series, page 614.)

Technology

Evaluating Series

For Use With Lesson 11-5

You can use a graphing calculator to evaluate series with limits.

1 EXAMPLE Using the Sum Feature

Find the sum of the terms of the sequence: 15, 30, 45, 60, 75, 90, 105.

Step 1 Enter the sequence in a list. Exit using **QUIT**.

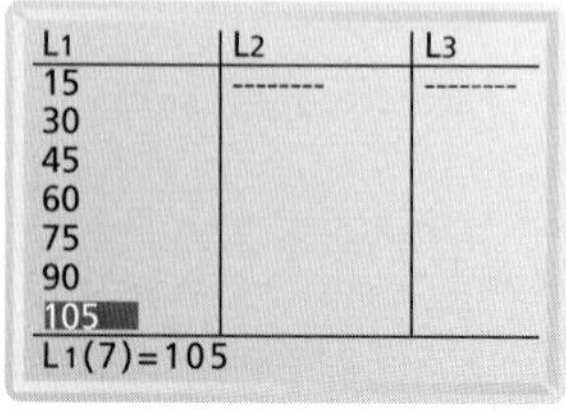

Step 2 Select 5 from the **MATH** menu of the **LIST** feature.

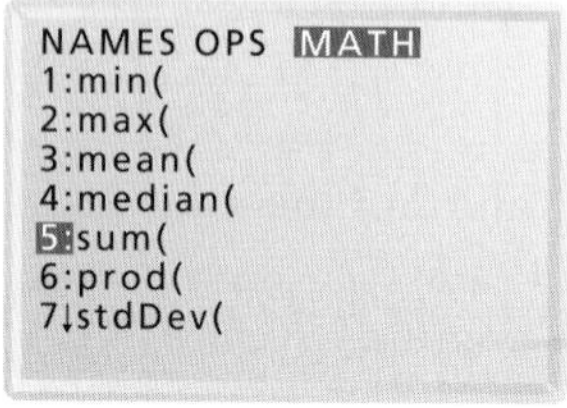

Step 3 Enter the list number. Press ENTER.

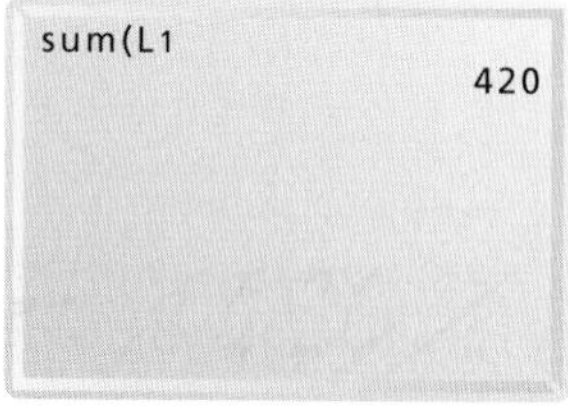

The sum of the series 15 + 30 + 45 + . . . + 105 is 420.

2 EXAMPLE Evaluating a Sum

Use your graphing calculator to evaluate $\sum_{n=1}^{5} \frac{n^2}{2}$.

Step 1 Access the **SUM** feature (Step 2 above).

Step 2 Select 5 from the **OPS** menu of the **LIST** feature.

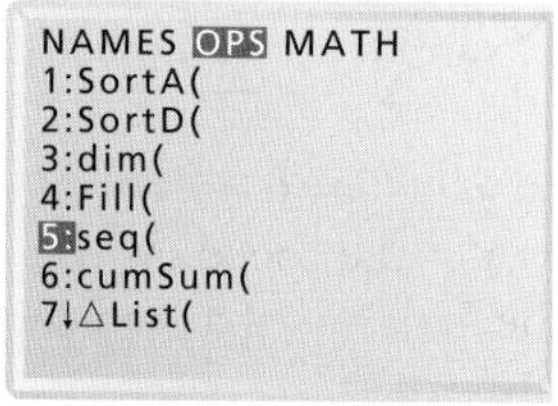

Step 3 Enter the explicit formula, N, the lower limit, the upper limit, and 1 (because n increases by 1 each time). Press ENTER.

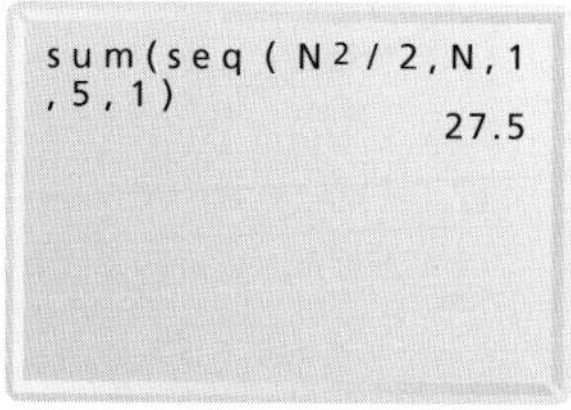

The value of $\sum_{n=1}^{5} \frac{n^2}{2}$ is 27.5.

EXERCISES

Evaluate each series.

1. 595 + 495 + 395 + 295

2. 3 + 9 + 27 + 81

3. $4 + 2 + 1 + \dots + \frac{1}{8}$

4. $\sum_{n=1}^{5} (2n^2 - 5)$

5. $\sum_{x=1}^{5} 2^x$

6. $\sum_{n=1}^{5} -\sqrt{n^2}$

7. **Writing** Compare the examples. When would you use the method from Example 1? When would you use the method from Example 2? Explain.

11-6 Area Under a Curve

Lesson Preview

What You'll Learn

OBJECTIVE 1 To find area under a curve

. . . And Why

To estimate the distance traveled by a peregrine falcon, as in Example 1

Check Skills You'll Need

(For help, go to Skills Handbook page 847.)

Find the area of a rectangle with the given length and width.

1. $\ell = 4$ ft, $w = 1$ ft
2. $\ell = 5.5$ m, $w = 0.5$ m
3. $\ell = 6.2$ cm, $w = 0.1$ cm
4. $\ell = 9\frac{1}{2}$ in., $w = 3\frac{5}{8}$ in.

New Vocabulary • inscribed rectangles • circumscribed rectangles

Interactive lesson includes instant self-check, tutorials, and activities.

OBJECTIVE 1 Finding Area Under a Curve

You can easily calculate the exact area under part of a line parallel to the x-axis, but it is not so easy to calculate the exact area under part of a curve. You can use rectangles to estimate the area under a curve and analyze data.

Inscribed rectangles are completely under the curve. The approximation is less than the area.

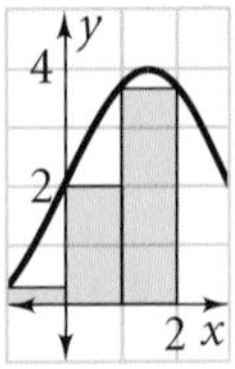

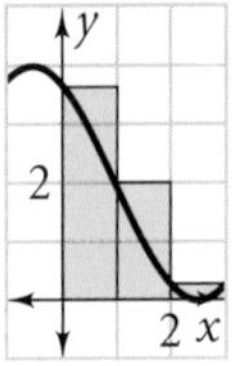

Circumscribed rectangles are partially above the curve. The approximation is greater than the area.

Real-World Connection

Adult peregrine falcons can reach speeds of 200 mi/h in a dive.

1 EXAMPLE Real-World Connection

Data Analysis The curve at the right approximates the speed of a peregrine falcon during the first 20 s of a high-speed dive.

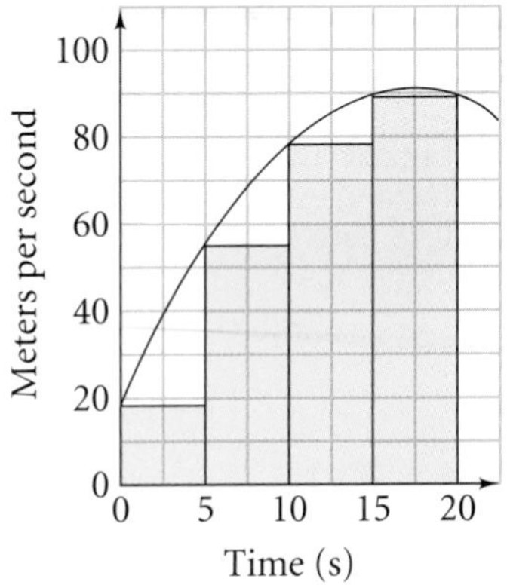

a. What does the area under the curve represent?

$$\text{area} = \frac{\text{meters}}{\cancel{\text{second}}} \cdot \cancel{\text{seconds}}$$ **Use dimensional analysis.**

$$= \text{meters}$$ **Simplify.**

The area under the curve approximates the total distance traveled by the peregrine falcon.

b. Use inscribed rectangles 5 units wide to estimate the area under the curve.

Width of each rectangle — **Total area**

$$5(18) + 5(54) + 5(78) + 5(88) = 1190$$

Value of curve at upper edge of each rectangle

The area under the curve is about 1190 units^2. The peregrine falcon traveled about 1190 m during the first 20 s of its dive. The estimate is low because inscribed rectangles were used.

Check Understanding **1** The graph at the right shows the curve from Example 1, but it shows circumscribed rectangles.

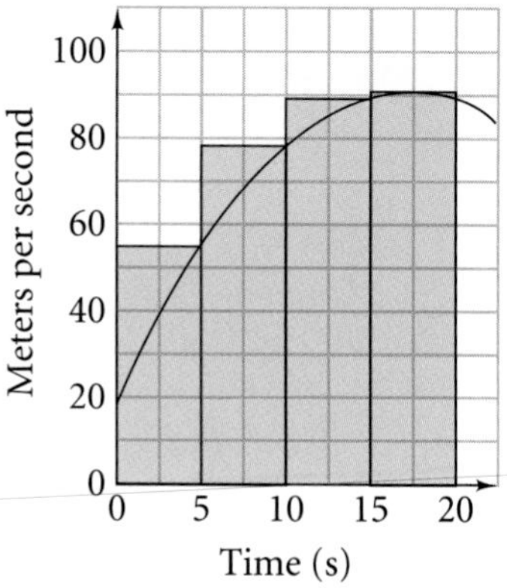

a. Estimate the area under the curve using circumscribed rectangles. How does your answer differ from the answer to Example 1?

b. Critical Thinking Find the mean of the answer using inscribed rectangles and the answer using circumscribed rectangles. Of the three answers, which is the most accurate? Explain.

You can use summation notation to represent the area of a series of rectangles and to approximate the area under the curve $f(x)$. Let a_n represent a point on the base of the nth rectangle.

$$A = \sum_{n=1}^{b} (w)f(a_n)$$

b ← number of rectangles; w: width of each rectangle; $f(a_n)$: function value at a_n

The expression $f(a_n)$ gives the height of the nth rectangle.

2 EXAMPLE Using a Sum to Estimate Area Under a Curve

Estimate the area under the curve $f(x) = -x^2 + 5$ for the domain $0 \le x \le 2$ by evaluating the sum A.

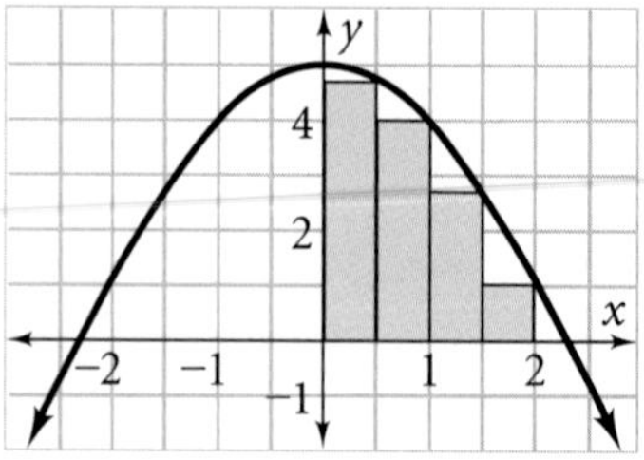

$$A = \sum_{n=1}^{4} (0.5)f(a_n)$$

Evaluate the function at the right side of each rectangle.

$a_1 = 0.5, a_2 = 1, a_3 = 1.5, a_4 = 2$ **Use an endpoint on the *x*-axis and on the right side of each rectangle.**

$A = 0.5f(0.5) + 0.5f(1) + 0.5f(1.5) + 0.5f(2)$ **Add the areas of the rectangles.**

$= 0.5(4.75 + 4 + 2.75 + 1)$ **total area = width of each rectangle · sum of the heights**

$= 0.5(12.5)$ **Add within parentheses.**

$= 6.25$ **Simplify.**

The indicated area is about 6.25 units^2.

Need Help?

The area could also be estimated by evaluating $\sum_{n=1}^{8} (0.25)f(a_n)$ because there are 8 rectangles of width 0.25 between 0 and 2.

Check Understanding **2** **a.** Sketch the graph from Example 2 and draw circumscribed rectangles for the domain $0 \le x \le 2$.

b. Critical Thinking To find the area using these rectangles, you should evaluate the function at the left side of each rectangle. Explain why.

c. Use the circumscribed rectangles to write and evaluate a sum that approximates the area under the curve for the domain $0 \le x \le 2$. Compare your answer to the answer in Example 2.

You can use a graphing calculator to find the exact area under a curve.

3 EXAMPLE Using a Graphing Calculator

Graph the function $f(x) = -2x^2 + 5$. Find the area under the curve for the domain $-1 \le x \le 1.5$.

Step 1 Input the equation. Adjust the window values.

Step 2 Access the $\int f(x)dx$ feature from the CALC menu.

Step 3 Use the lower limit of $x = -1$.

Step 4 Use the upper limit of $x = 1.5$.

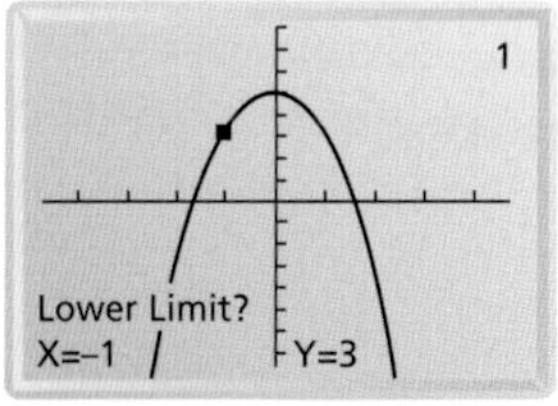

Xmin=-4.7 Ymin=-7
Xmax=4.7 Ymax=8
Xscl=1 Yscl=1

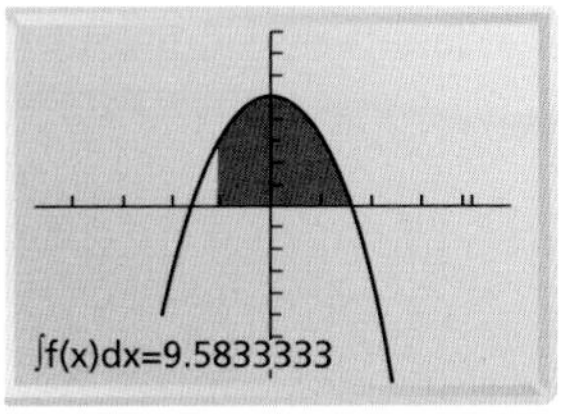

The area under the curve between $x = -1$ and $x = 1.5$ is $9.58\overline{3}$ units^2.

Check Understanding **3** Use the equation from Example 3 and a graphing calculator. Find the area under the curve for each domain.

a. $0 \le x \le 1$ **b.** $-1 \le x \le 1$ **c.** $-1.5 \le x \le 0$

EXERCISES

For more practice, see *Extra Practice.*

Practice and Problem Solving

A Practice by Example

Example 1 (page 623)

Given each set of axes, what does the area under the curve represent?

1. y-axis: production rate, x-axis: time

2. y-axis: rate of growth, x-axis: time

3. y-axis: miles per gallon, x-axis: gallons

4. y-axis: distance traveled per year, x-axis: years

5. y-axis: price per pound of gold, x-axis: pounds of gold

Use the given rectangles to estimate each area.

6.

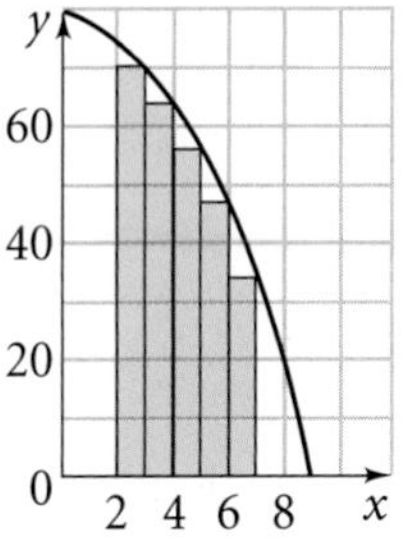

7.

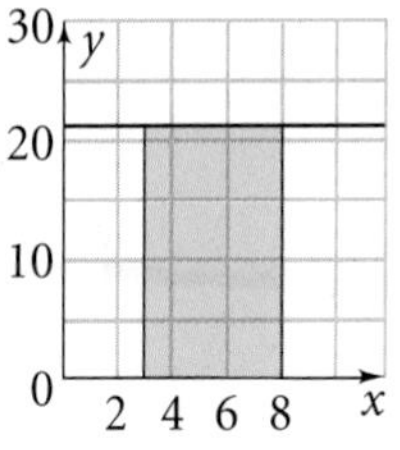

8.

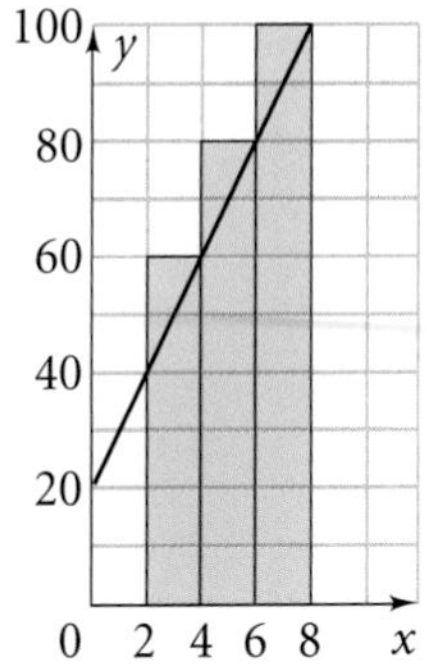

Example 2 (page 624)

Write and evaluate a sum to approximate the area under each curve for the domain $0 \le x \le 2$.
a. Use inscribed rectangles 1 unit wide.
b. Use circumscribed rectangles 1 unit wide.

9. $f(x) = \frac{1}{2}x^2$ **10.** $y = -x^2 + 5$ **11.** $g(x) = x^2 + 1$

12. $y = -x^2 + 4$ **13.** $y = \frac{2}{3}x^2 + 5$ **14.** $h(x) = 5x^2$

15. $y = 4 - \frac{1}{4}x^2$ **16.** $h(x) = -(x - 2)^2 + 5$ **17.** $y = (x - 2)^2 + 2$

Example 3 (page 625)

Find the area under each curve for the domain $0 \le x \le 1$.

18. $y = -x^2 + 2$ **19.** $f(x) = x + 2$ **20.** $y = x^3$

21. $y = -x^4 + 2x^3 + 3$ **22.** $y = x^5 - x^2 + 2.5$ **23.** $y = -(x - 1)^3 + 3$

B Apply Your Skills

Graph each curve. Use inscribed rectangles to approximate the area under the curve for the interval and rectangle width given.

24. $y = x^2 + 1, 1 \le x \le 3, 0.5$ **25.** $y = 3x^2 + 2, 2 \le x \le 4, 1$

26. $y = x^2, 3 \le x \le 5, 0.5$ **27.** $y = 2x^2, 3 \le x \le 5, 1$

28. $y = x^3, 1 \le x \le 3, 0.25$ **29.** $y = x^2 + 4, -2 \le x \le 2, 0.5$

30. a. Graph the curve $y = \frac{1}{3}x^3$.
b. Use inscribed rectangles to approximate the area under the curve for the interval $0 \le x \le 3$ and rectangle width of 1 unit.
c. Repeat part (b) using circumscribed rectangles.
d. Find the mean of the areas you found in parts (b) and (c). Of the three estimates, which best approximates the area for the interval? Explain.

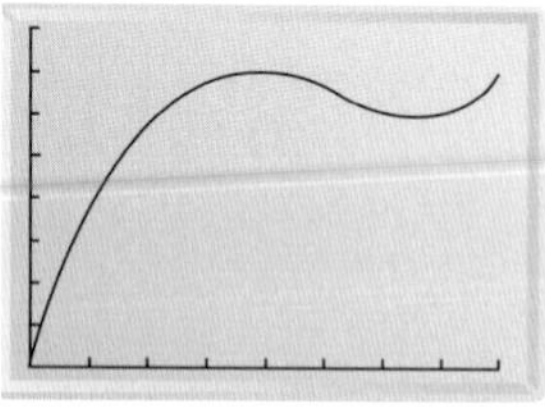

Xmin: 0 Ymin: 0
Xmax: 200 Ymax: 70
Xscl: 25 Yscl: 10

31. The graph at the left approximates the speed of a car as it enters a highway from a stopped position and merges with traffic. The x-axis represents time in seconds, and the y-axis represents miles per hour.
a. Copy the graph. Use inscribed rectangles half the width of a grid square to estimate the total distance the car traveled in 50 s.
b. Writing How does your choice of inscribed or circumscribed rectangles in part (a) affect your area estimate?

Evaluate the area under each curve for $-1 \le x \le 2$.

32. $f(x) = -x^2 + 4$ **33.** $y = (x - 0.5)^2 + 1.75$ **34.** $g(x) = 2 + 3x^2$

35. $y = \sqrt{1 + x}$ **36.** $g(x) = 2^x + 1$ **37.** $y = x^3 + 2$

38. $y = -(x - 1)^2 + 4\frac{1}{3}$ **39.** $h(x) = \sqrt{x^2}$ **40.** $f(x) = -x^4 + 2x^3 + 3$

41. Open-Ended Write equations for three curves that are positive for $1 \le x \le 3$. Use your graphing calculator to find the area under each curve for this domain.

C Challenge

42. Approximate the area under the curve $f(x) = x^2$ for the interval $0 \le x \le 4$ by evaluating each sum. Use inscribed rectangles.

a. $\sum_{n=1}^{8} (0.5)f(a_n)$ **b.** $\sum_{n=1}^{4} (1)f(a_n)$

c. Which estimate is closer to the actual area under the curve? Explain.

43. a. Graph $y = \frac{1}{4}x^3 + 1$ and $y = 1$ over the domain $-4.7 \le x \le 4.7$.
b. Critical Thinking Evaluate the area under each curve for the interval $-1.5 \le x \le 1.5$. What do you notice? Explain.

44. **Critical Thinking** Use your graphing calculator to find the area of the triangle with vertices $(-3, 0)$, $(-1, 3)$, and $(1, 0)$. (*Hint:* First find the function whose graph makes a peak at $(-1, 3)$.)

45. **a.** Write the equation $\frac{x^2}{25} + \frac{y^2}{9} = 1$ in calculator-ready form.
b. Graph the top half of the ellipse. Calculate the area under the curve for the interval $-5 \le x \le 5$.
c. Use symmetry to find the area of the entire ellipse.
d. **Open-Ended** Find the area of another symmetric shape by graphing part of it. Sketch your graph and show your calculations.

Standardized Test Prep

Multiple Choice

Use the graph of $f(x) = \sqrt{x} + 2$ for Exercises 46–49.

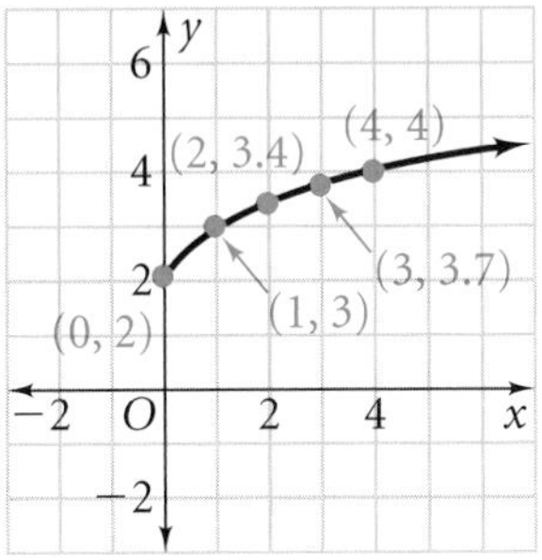

46. Which series represents the area of four inscribed rectangles?
A. (1)(2) + (1)(3) + (1)(3.4) + (1)(3.7)
B. (1)(3) + (1)(3.4) + (1)(3.7) + (1)(4)
C. (1 + 2 + 3 + 4)(0 + 1 + 2 + 3)
D. (1 + 2 + 3 + 4)(3 + 3.4 + 3.7 + 4)

47. Which series represents the area of four circumscribed rectangles?
F. (1)(2) + (1)(3) + (1)(3.4) + (1)(3.7)
G. (1)(3) + (1)(3.4) + (1)(3.7) + (1)(4)
H. (1 + 2 + 3 + 4)(0 + 1 + 2 + 3)
I. (1 + 2 + 3 + 4)(3 + 3.4 + 3.7 + 4)

48. Which of the following is the most accurate value of the area under $f(x) = \sqrt{x} + 2$ for $0 \le x \le 4$?
A. 12.1 **B.** 14.1 **C.** 16.1 **D.** 24.0

Take It to the NET
Online lesson quiz at
www.PHSchool.com
Web Code: aga-1106

49. Which expression does NOT represent a reasonable estimate of the area under $f(x) = \sqrt{x} + 2$ for $0 \le x \le 4$?
F. $\sum_{n=1}^{4} f(a_n)$ **G.** $\sum_{n=1}^{5} (0.2)f(a_n)$ **H.** $\sum_{n=1}^{8} (0.5)f(a_n)$ **I.** $\sum_{n=1}^{10} (0.4)f(a_n)$

Short Response

50. The area under a curve is estimated using inscribed rectangles and circumscribed rectangles. Explain why the mean of these two values might be a more accurate estimate than either one.

Mixed Review

Lesson 11-5

Determine whether the sum of each infinite geometric series exists.

51. $4 + 2 + 1 + \frac{1}{2} + \frac{1}{4} + \ldots$ **52.** $-972 - 324 - 108 - \ldots$

Lesson 10-5

Write the equation of each hyperbola in standard form. Sketch the graph.

53. $9x^2 - 16y^2 = 144$ **54.** $x^2 - 25y^2 = 25$ **55.** $16x^2 - 10y^2 = 160$

Lesson 9-6

Solve each equation. Check your solution.

56. $\frac{x}{4} = \frac{x - 3}{8}$ **57.** $\frac{5}{2 - x} = \frac{4}{2x + 1}$ **58.** $\frac{x}{x + 1} - \frac{x}{x - 3} = 9$

Test-Taking Strategies

Using Estimation

Estimating the answer to a test question may help you eliminate one or more answers, find the answer, or check your answer.

1 EXAMPLE

A ball drops from a height of 2 m. After it hits the floor, it rebounds to 60% of its previous height. Find the total distance the ball travels before it comes to rest.

A. 3 m **B.** 3.5 m **C.** 5 m **D.** 10 m

Estimate the distance the ball travels before the second bounce. The ball rebounds about one-half its previous height, so it travels down 2 m, then up about 1 m, and then down about 1 m. Since $2 + 1 + 1 = 4$, the ball travels about 4 m before the second bounce. You can eliminate answer choices A and B.

Since the distance the ball travels on each bounce models a geometric sequence with $r < 1$, the final answer will be closer to 4 than to 10. The answer is C.

2 EXAMPLE

A student jogs 3.8 mi around a local reservoir five afternoons a week. The student claims to have run about 990 mi around the reservoir last year. Is the student correct? Explain.

$3.8 \cdot 5 \cdot 52 \approx 4 \cdot 5 \cdot 50$	**distance · days per week · weeks per year**
$= 20 \cdot 50 = 1000$	**Simplify and multiply.**

The student ran about 1000 mi around the reservoir last year. The student is correct.

EXERCISES

Choose the best estimate.

1. A square is inscribed in a circle. The square has side length 4 cm. Find the approximate area of the circle.

A. 25 cm^2 **B.** 16 cm^2 **C.** 15 cm^2 **D.** 12 cm^2

2. Find the approximate area of the region between the function $y = (x - 1)^2$, the x-axis, and the y-axis.

A. 2 $units^2$ **B.** 1.5 $units^2$ **C.** 1 $units^2$ **D.** 0.5 $units^2$

Estimate the answer to each problem.

3. Suppose your aunt gives you \$100 on your birthday, along with a promise to give you one half the previous year's amount each year until the amount reaches 1¢. What is the total amount of money that your aunt will give you?

4. If two numbers a and b are approximately equal, their arithmetic mean and their geometric mean are approximately equal. Use this fact to estimate the value of $\sqrt{56}$.

Chapter 11

Chapter Review

Vocabulary

arithmetic mean (p. 595)
arithmetic sequence (p. 594)
arithmetic series (p. 608)
circumscribed rectangles (p. 623)
common difference (p. 594)
common ratio (p. 600)
converge (p. 615)
diverge (p. 615)
explicit formula (p. 590)
geometric mean (p. 602)
geometric sequence (p. 600)
geometric series (p. 614)
inscribed rectangles (p. 623)
limit (p. 609)
recursive formula (p. 590)
sequence (p. 588)
series (p. 607)
term (p. 588)

Reading Math
Understanding Vocabulary

Take It to the NET
Online vocabulary quiz at **www.PHSchool.com**
Web Code: agj-1151

Choose the correct vocabulary term to complete each sentence.

1. When using Σ to write a series, you can use _?_ to indicate how many terms you are adding.

2. Using _?_ to approximate the area under a curve will result in an approximation that is greater than the area.

3. An ordered list of terms is a _?_.

4. If an infinite geometric series _?_, then it must have a sum.

5. There is a _?_ between consecutive terms in a geometric sequence.

Skills and Concepts

11-1 Objectives

- To identify mathematical patterns (p. 588)
- To use a formula for finding the *n*th term of a sequence (p. 590)

A **sequence** is an ordered list of numbers called **terms.** A **recursive formula** gives the first term and defines the other terms in a sequence by relating each term to the one before it. An **explicit formula** expresses the *n*th term in a sequence in terms of n, where n is a positive integer.

Write a recursive formula for each sequence. Then find the next three terms.

6. $5, 22, 39, 56, \ldots$ **7.** $1, -7, 49, -343, \ldots$ **8.** $-2, 7, 16, 25, \ldots$

Write an explicit formula for each sequence. Then find a_{12}.

9. $1, 4, 7, 10, \ldots$ **10.** $2, 4, 8, 16, \ldots$ **11.** $-24, -6, 24, 66, \ldots$

12. Writing Explain how you decide whether a formula is explicit or recursive.

11-2 Objectives

- To identify and generate arithmetic sequences (p. 594)

In an **arithmetic sequence,** the difference between consecutive terms is constant. The difference is the **common difference.** A recursive formula for an arithmetic sequence is $a_n = a_{n-1} + d$, given a_1. An explicit formula for an arithmetic sequence is $a_n = a_1 + (n - 1)d$. In each case, a_n is the nth term, a_1 is the first term, n is the number of the term, and d is the common difference. The **arithmetic mean** of any two numbers (or terms in a sequence) is the average of the two numbers.

$$\text{arithmetic mean} = \frac{\text{sum of two numbers}}{2}$$

Is each given sequence arithmetic? If so, identify the common difference and find the 32nd term of the sequence.

13. 2, 4, 7, 10, 13, . . . **14.** 3, 18, 33, 48, . . . **15.** 7, 10, 13, 16, . . .

Find the missing term(s) of each arithmetic sequence.

16. 1, ■, 9, . . . **17.** 104, ■, 99, . . . **18.** −4.6, ■, −5.2, . . .

19. −1, ■, 11, . . . **20.** −13, ■, ■, ■, −3, . . . **21.** 2, ■, ■, ■, −0.4, . . .

Find a_n, the arithmetic mean of the given terms.

22. $a_{n-1} = 7, a_{n+1} = 15$ **23.** $a_{n-1} = -2, a_{n+1} = 3$

24. Writing Explain how you can determine if a sequence is arithmetic.

11-3 Objectives

- To identify and generate geometric sequences (p. 600)

In a **geometric sequence,** the ratio of consecutive terms is constant. The ratio is the **common ratio.** You can use recursive or explicit formulas to express a geometric sequence.

A recursive formula for a geometric sequence is $a_n = a_{n-1} \cdot r$, given a_1. An explicit formula for a geometric sequence is $a_n = a_1 \cdot r^{n-1}$. In each case, a_n is the nth term, a_1 is the first term, n is the number of the term, and r is the common ratio.

You can find the geometric mean of two positive numbers by taking the positive square root of the product of the two numbers.

$$\text{geometric mean} = \sqrt{\text{product of two numbers}}$$

The middle term of any three consecutive terms in a geometric sequence is the geometric mean of the first and third terms.

Is the given sequence geometric? If so, identify the common ratio, write the explicit formula for the sequence, and find the next two terms.

25. $1, \frac{1}{2}, \frac{1}{4}, \frac{1}{8}, \ldots$ **26.** 1, 3, 5, 7, . . . **27.** 3, 3.6, 4.32, 5.184, . . .

Find the missing term(s) of each geometric sequence.

28. 3, ■, 12, . . . **29.** 60, ■, $\frac{20}{3}$, . . . **30.** 0.004, ■, 0.4, . . .

31. −20, ■, ■, ■, −1.25, . . . **32.** $-\frac{1}{6}$, ■, ■, ■, $-2\frac{2}{3}$, . . . **33.** 1, ■, ■, ■, $150\frac{1}{16}$, . . .

11-4 Objectives

- To write and evaluate arithmetic series (p. 607)
- To evaluate a given number of terms of a series (p. 609)

A **series** is the expression for the sum of the terms of a sequence. Whether the sequence is finite or infinite determines whether the series is finite or infinite.

An **arithmetic series** is the expression for the sum of the terms of an arithmetic sequence. The sum S_n of the first n terms of an arithmetic series is $S_n = \frac{n}{2}(a_1 + a_n)$.

You can use a summation symbol, Σ, and **limits** to write a series. Limits are the least and greatest integral values of n.

Use summation notation to write each arithmetic series for the specified number of terms. Then evaluate the sum.

34. $10 + 7 + 4 + \ldots; n = 5$ **35.** $50 + 55 + 60 + \ldots; n = 7$

36. $6 + 7.4 + 8.8 + \ldots; n = 11$ **37.** $21 + 19 + 17 + \ldots; n = 8$

Find the number of terms in each series, the first term, and the last term. Then evaluate the sum.

38. $\sum_{n=1}^{3}(17n - 25)$

39. $\sum_{n=2}^{10}\left(\frac{1}{2}n + 3\right)$

40. $\sum_{n=5}^{15}\left(-\frac{2}{3}n\right)$

41. Business Deanna Jones opened a video rental store this year with 400 tapes. She plans to buy 150 new tapes each year from now on. Deanna expects to have 1300 tapes available during her fifth year in business. At her current purchasing rate, will she reach her goal? Explain.

11-5 Objectives

- To evaluate a finite geometric series (p. 614)
- To evaluate an infinite geometric series (p. 615)

A **geometric series** is the sum of the terms of a geometric sequence. The sum S_n of the first n terms of a geometric series is $S_n = \frac{a_1(1 - r^n)}{1 - r}$.

You can find the sum of some infinite geometric series. When $|r| < 1$, the series gets closer and closer, or **converges,** to $S = \frac{a_1}{1 - r}$. When $|r| \geq 1$, the series **diverges,** or approaches no limit.

Find the sum of the series to the given term.

42. $3 + 1 + \frac{1}{3} + \ldots; S_7$

43. $1 + 2 + 4 + \ldots; S_5$

44. $80 - 40 + 20 - \ldots; S_8$

45. $12 + 2 + \frac{1}{3} + \ldots; S_4$

Decide whether each infinite geometric series *converges* or *diverges*. Then state whether each series has a sum, and if it does, find the sum.

46. $150 + 30 + 6 + \ldots$

47. $2.2 + 2.42 + 2.662 + \ldots$

48. $-10 - 20 - 40 - \ldots$

49. $\frac{2}{3} + \frac{4}{9} + \frac{8}{27} + \ldots$

11-6 Objective

- To find the area under a curve (p. 623)

You can approximate the area under a curve by using **inscribed rectangles** or **circumscribed rectangles.** If you use inscribed rectangles, the approximation is less than the area under the curve. If you use circumscribed rectangles, the approximation is greater than the area under the curve. You can use summation notation to represent the area of a series of rectangles and the approximate area under a curve $f(x)$:

$$A = \sum_{n=1}^{b}(w)f(a_n),$$

where b is the number of rectangles, w is the width of each rectangle, a_n is a point on the base of the nth rectangle, and $f(a_n)$ is the function value at a_n.

Write and evaluate a sum to approximate the area under each curve for the domain $0 \leq x \leq 2$.

a. Use inscribed rectangles 1 unit wide.
b. Use circumscribed rectangles 1 unit wide.
c. Use a graphing calculator to find the exact area under the curve.

50. $y = x^2$

51. $y = x^3 + 1$

52. $y = -2x^2 + 8$

53. $y = -x + 5$

54. $y = x^3 + 4$

55. $y = x^2 + 3$

Chapter 11

Chapter Test

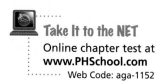

Take It to the NET
Online chapter test at www.PHSchool.com
Web Code: aga-1152

Write a recursive and an explicit formula for each sequence. Then find a_{12}.

1. 7, 13, 19, 25, 31, . . .
2. 10, 20, 40, 80, 160, . . .

3. After one month at a new job, you have saved \$50. You decide to save \$5 more each month.
   a. Write an explicit formula to model the amounts you save each month.
   b. How much will you save in the sixth month?

Determine whether each sequence is *arithmetic*, *geometric*, or *neither*. Then find the tenth term.

4. 23, 27, 31, 35, 39, . . .
5. −12, −5, 2, 9, 16, . . .
6. −5, 15, −45, 135, −405, . . .

Find the arithmetic mean a_n of the given terms.

7. $a_{n-1} = 4, a_{n+1} = 12$
8. $a_{n-1} = -11, a_{n+1} = 23$
9. **Open-Ended** Write an arithmetic sequence. Then write an explicit formula for it.

Determine whether each sequence is *arithmetic* or *geometric*. Then identify the common difference or the common ratio.

10. 1620, 540, 180, 60, 20, . . .
11. 78, 75, 72, 69, 66, 63, 60, . . .
12. $\frac{3}{32}, \frac{3}{16}, \frac{3}{8}, \frac{3}{4}, \frac{3}{2}, 3, 6, \dots$

In Exercises 13–16, a_1 is the first term of a sequence, r is a common ratio, and d is a common difference. Write the first five terms.

13. $a_1 = 2, r = -2$
14. $a_1 = 3, d = 7$
15. $a_1 = -100, r = \frac{1}{5}$
16. $a_1 = 19, d = -4$

Find the missing term of each geometric sequence.

17. 2, ■, 0.5, . . .
18. 2, ■, 8, . . .

Find the sum of each infinite geometric series.

19. $0.5 + 0.05 + 0.005 + \dots$
20. $1 - \frac{1}{2} + \frac{1}{4} - \dots$
21. $6 + 5 + \frac{25}{6} + \dots$

Determine whether each series is *arithmetic* or *geometric*. Then find the sum to the given term.

22. $2 + 7 + 12 + \dots; S_8$
23. $5000 + 1000 + 200 + \dots; S_{15}$
24. $1 + 0.01 - 0.98 - \dots; S_5$

For each sum, find the number of terms, the first term, and the last term. Then evaluate the sum.

25. $\sum_{n=1}^{5} (3n + 1)$
26. $\sum_{n=1}^{8} \frac{2n}{3}$
27. $\sum_{n=4}^{10} (0.8n - 0.4)$
28. $\sum_{n=2}^{6} (-2)^{n-1}$
29. **Critical Thinking** How can you tell whether or not a geometric series converges? Include examples of both types of series. Evaluate the series that converges.
30. **Investments** A diamond is purchased for \$2500. Suppose its value increases 5% each year. Find the value of the diamond after 8 years.
31. **Physics** A ball on a pendulum moves 40 cm on its first swing. On each succeeding swing back or forth it moves 90% of the distance of the previous swing. Write the first four terms of the sequence of swing lengths.

Given each set of axes, what does the area under the curve represent?

32. y-axis: miles per hour, x-axis: hours
33. y-axis: pounds per in.^{2}, x-axis: in.^{2}
34. y-axis: dollars per gallon, x-axis: gallons

Use left endpoints in the given interval and inscribed rectangles 1 unit wide to approximate the area under the curve $y = f(x)$.

35. $y = 2x^2; 0 \le x \le 2$
36. $y = x^2 + 1; -1 \le x \le 2$
37. $y = x^3; 1 \le x \le 3$
38. **Writing** Explain how you could use circumscribed and inscribed rectangles to estimate the area under a curve.

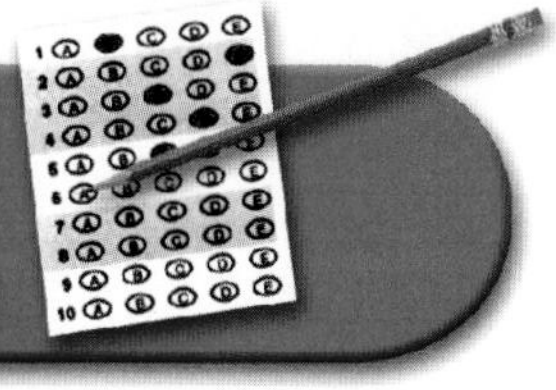

Standardized Test Prep

Reading Comprehension **Read the passage below. Then answer the questions on the basis of what is *stated* or *implied* in the passage.**

Arcs To cut an arc-topped shape from a rectangular board, carpenters may choose a circular arc or an elliptical arc.

Suppose the length of the board is $2m$ and the height is n.

For a circular arc, the carpenter can find the radius of the circle by using the formula $r = \frac{m^2 + n^2}{2n}$. Using a tack at the center C, and a piece of string of length r, the carpenter can draw a circular arc through points P, T, and Q.

For an elliptical arc, the carpenter can find points A and B on $\overline{PQ}$ that are $\sqrt{m^2 - n^2}$ units from point Z. Using tacks at A and B and a piece of string of length $2m$, the carpenter can draw an elliptical arc through points P, T, and Q.

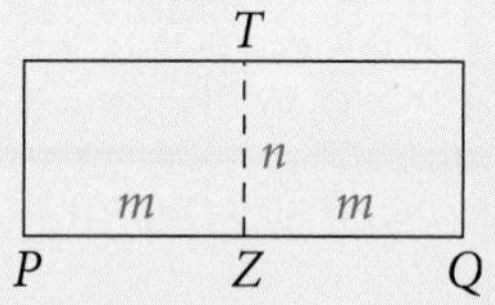

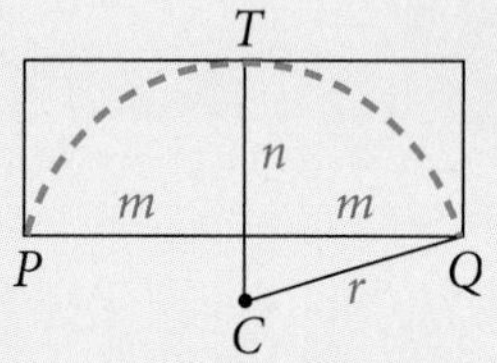

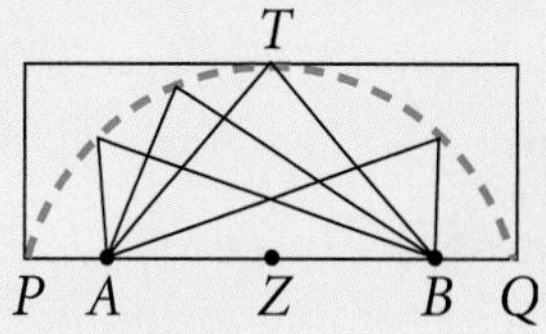

1. What is the value of PQ?
   A. $m + n$ B. $2n$
   C. $2m$ D. $\sqrt{m^2 + n^2}$

2. For a circular arc, what is the distance from point C to point Z?
   F. r G. $r - n$
   H. $r - m$ I. $\frac{m^2 + n^2}{2n}$

3. Suppose $m = 21$ in. and $n = 7$ in. For a circular arc, what length of string should the carpenter use?
   A. 19.8 in. B. 22.1 in.
   C. 28 in. D. 35 in.

4. Suppose $\overline{PQ}$ is on the x-axis of a coordinate system and $\overline{TZ}$ is on the y-axis. What are the coordinates of the foci of the ellipse needed to draw an elliptical arc?
   F. $(m, 0)$ and $(-m, 0)$
   G. $(0, n)$ and $(0, -n)$
   H. $(\sqrt{m^2 + n^2}, 0)$ and $(-\sqrt{m^2 + n^2}, 0)$
   I. $(\sqrt{m^2 - n^2}, 0)$ and $(-\sqrt{m^2 - n^2}, 0)$

5. Suppose $m = 70$ cm and $n = 9$ cm. For an elliptical arc, what length of string should the carpenter use?
   A. 18 cm B. 70.58 cm
   C. 140 cm D. 276.72 cm

6. Use the Pythagorean Theorem and a diagram of a circular arc to derive the formula $r = \frac{m^2 + n^2}{2n}$.

7. A carpenter wants to cut the largest possible circular arc-topped shape from a board that is 40 in. by 12 in. Find the length of string the carpenter should use.

8. Using a board the same size as the one in Question 7, a carpenter wants to cut the largest possible elliptical arc-topped shape. What length of string should the carpenter use? Where should the carpenter attach the string?

9. A board is 30 in. by 15 in. Compare the largest circular and elliptical arc-topped shapes that can be cut from the board.

Where You've Been

- In Chapter 1, you learned to find theoretical and experimental probabilities.
- In Chapter 6, you learned to use the Binomial Theorem.
- In Chapter 9, you learned to find the probability of multiple events.

Instant self-check online and on CD-ROM

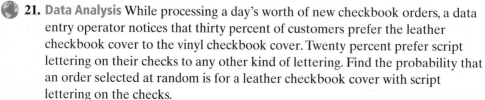

Diagnosing Readiness

(For help, go to the Lesson in green.)

Evaluating Expressions (Lesson 6-7)

Evaluate each expression.

1. $5!$ **2.** $6!$ **3.** $4! \cdot 3!$

4. ${}_5C_5$ **5.** ${}_6C_1$ **6.** ${}_7C_4$

Expanding Binomials (Lesson 6-8)

Use Pascal's Triangle or the Binomial Theorem to expand each binomial.

7. $(a + b)^5$ **8.** $(j + 3k)^3$ **9.** $(m + 0.7)^2$ **10.** $(0.2 + t)^6$

Finding Real Roots (Lesson 7-1)

Find the real square roots of each number. Round to the nearest thousandth.

11. $\frac{1}{100}$ **12.** $\frac{1}{200}$ **13.** $\frac{1}{250}$

14. $\frac{1}{391}$ **15.** $\frac{1}{435}$ **16.** $\frac{1}{757}$

Finding Probability (Lesson 9-7)

A and B are independent events. Find $P(A \text{ and } B)$.

17. $P(A) = 0.4, P(B) = 0.2$ **18.** $P(A) = 0.25, P(B) = 0.5$ **19.** $P(A) = 0.85, P(B) = 0.10$

20. Find $P(A \text{ or } B)$ for the events in Exercise 19.

21. Data Analysis While processing a day's worth of new checkbook orders, a data entry operator notices that thirty percent of customers prefer the leather checkbook cover to the vinyl checkbook cover. Twenty percent prefer script lettering on their checks to any other kind of lettering. Find the probability that an order selected at random is for a leather checkbook cover with script lettering on the checks.

Probability and Statistics

Chapter 12

LESSONS

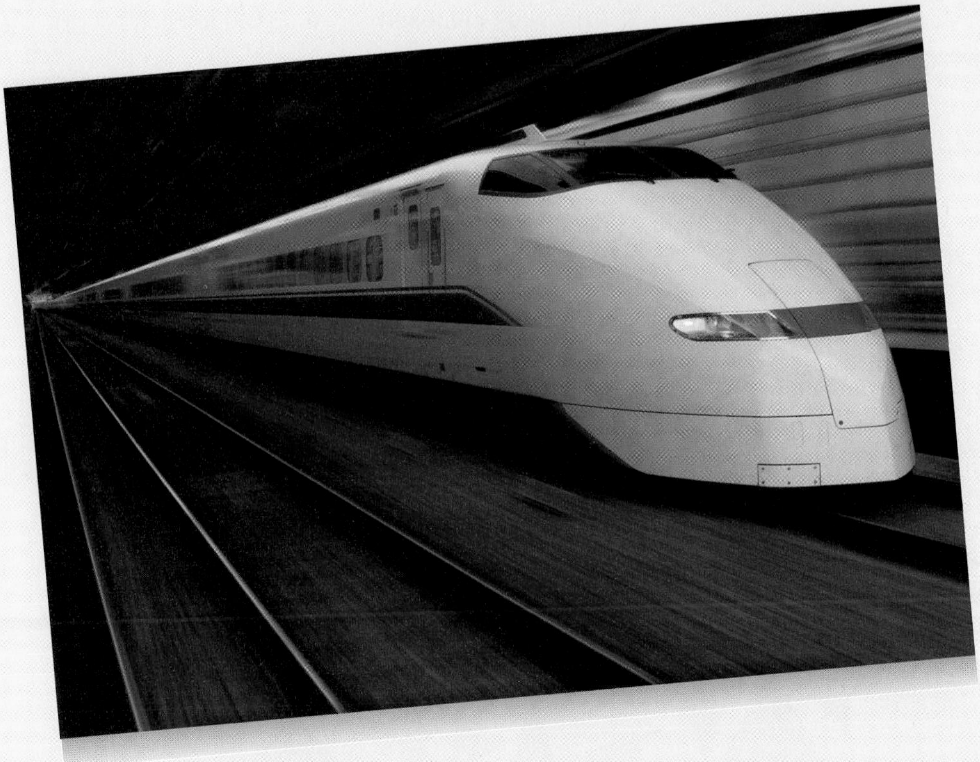

Key Vocabulary

- binomial probability (p. 673)
- box-and-whisker plot (p. 650)
- conditional probability (p. 642)
- cumulative probability (p. 636)
- interquartile range (p. 657)
- margin of error (p. 665)
- measures of central tendency (p. 648)
- measures of variation (p. 657)
- normal distribution (p. 678)
- outlier (p. 652)
- percentile (p. 651)
- probability distribution (p. 637)
- quartiles (p. 650)
- sample (p. 663)
- sample proportion (p. 663)
- standard deviation (p. 657)
- standard normal curve (p. 679)
- *z*-score (p. 659)

Where You're Going

- In Chapter 12, you will learn to make and use a probability distribution to conduct a simulation.
- You will learn to use formulas, tree diagrams, and normal distributions to find the probability of an event.
- You will learn to use measures of central tendency and measures of variation to compare data in real-world problems.

Applying what you learn, on pages 692–693 you will do activities involving trains.

12-1 Probability Distributions

Lesson Preview

What You'll Learn

OBJECTIVE 1 To make a probability distribution

OBJECTIVE 2 To use a probability distribution in conducting a simulation

... And Why

To conduct market research, as in Example 5

Check Skills You'll Need

(For help, go to Lesson 1-6.)

Suppose you roll a standard number cube. State whether each set represents a sample space for the outcomes.

1. {1, 2, 3, 4, 5, 6} **2.** {less than 3, 4, 5, 6} **3.** {even, prime}

Find each probability for two tosses of a number cube.

4. P(4 and 3) **5.** P(two odd numbers) **6.** P(two integers)

New Vocabulary
- frequency table
- cumulative probability
- probability distribution

Interactive lesson includes instant self-check, tutorials, and activities.

OBJECTIVE 1 Making a Probability Distribution

A **frequency table** is a list of the outcomes in a sample space and the number of times each outcome occurs.

1 EXAMPLE Making a Frequency Table

Reading Math

Scalene comes from the Latin word for uneven.

Below are three types of triangles: equilateral, isosceles, and scalene. Make a frequency table. For isosceles, use triangles with exactly two congruent sides.

Step 1 Count the number of each type.

Equilateral 卌 |
Isosceles 卌 卌 |
Scalene 卌 |||
Total number of triangles: 25

Step 2 Make a table.

Type	Number
Equilateral	6
Isosceles	11
Scalene	8
Total	25

Check Understanding 1 The triangles in Example 1 can also be described as acute, right, and obtuse. Make a frequency table using those categories.

Probability over a continuous range of events is **cumulative probability.** You can use a frequency table to find cumulative probability.

2 EXAMPLE Real-World Connection

Need Help?

The experimental probability of an event is the ratio of the number of times the event occurs to the number of trials.

Social Science Use the frequency table. Find the probability that an elderly person living alone will have contact with his or her children more than once a week.

Contact Between Children and Elderly Who Live Alone

How Often Contact Is Made	Number of Elderly
7 times per week	680
2–6 times per week	276
1 time per week	236
Less than 1 time per week	199
Total	1391

SOURCE: *Statistical Handbook on the American Family*

$P(7 \text{ times per week}) = \frac{680}{1391}$

$P(2-6 \text{ times per week}) = \frac{276}{1391}$

Find the experimental probability for each event in the table that represents contact more than once a week.

$\frac{680}{1391} + \frac{276}{1391} = \frac{956}{1391} \approx 0.687$ **Add to find cumulative probability.**

The probability of contact more than once a week is about 0.687, or 68.7%.

Check Understanding 2 Find P(once a week or more).

A **probability distribution** is a function that gives the probability of each event in a sample space. You can use a table or a graph to show a probability distribution.

3 EXAMPLE Probability Distributions

Suppose you roll two number cubes. Show the probability distribution for the sum of the numbers.

Method 1 Make a frequency table. Then extend the table to include probabilities.

Rolling Two Number Cubes

Sum	2	3	4	5	6	7	8	9	10	11	12
Frequency	1	2	3	4	5	6	5	4	3	2	1
Probability	$\frac{1}{36}$	$\frac{2}{36}$	$\frac{3}{36}$	$\frac{4}{36}$	$\frac{5}{36}$	$\frac{6}{36}$	$\frac{5}{36}$	$\frac{4}{36}$	$\frac{3}{36}$	$\frac{2}{36}$	$\frac{1}{36}$

There are 36 possible outcomes.

Divide to find the probability.

Method 2 Draw a graph.

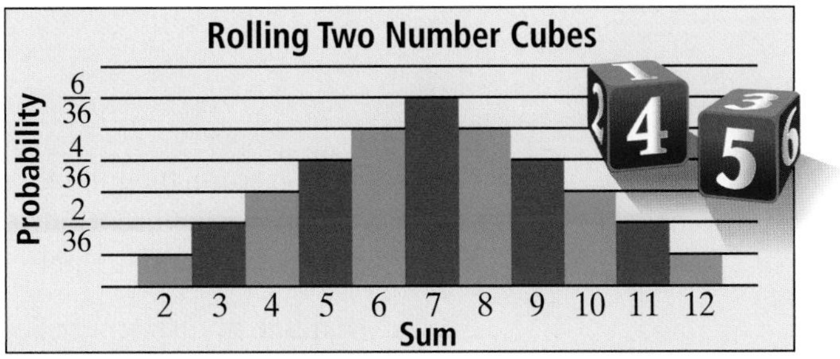

Check Understanding 3 Use a table or a graph to show the probability distribution for the roll of one number cube.

A situation may be described by more than one sample space. In that case, each sample space has its own probability distribution.

Real-World Connection

Careers Agriculturists experiment to grow different types of crops.

4 EXAMPLE Real-World Connection

Genetics Use the information in the chart of inherited gene pairs. Graph the probability distribution for each sample space.

Inherited Gene Pairs From Two Hybrid Corn Plants

		Parent Plant	
		G	w
Parent Plant	G	GG	Gw
	w	Gw	ww

GG = dominant gene pair (green plant)
Gw = hybrid gene pair (green plant)
ww = recessive gene pair (white plant)

a. Genotype Distribution
{GG, Gw, ww}

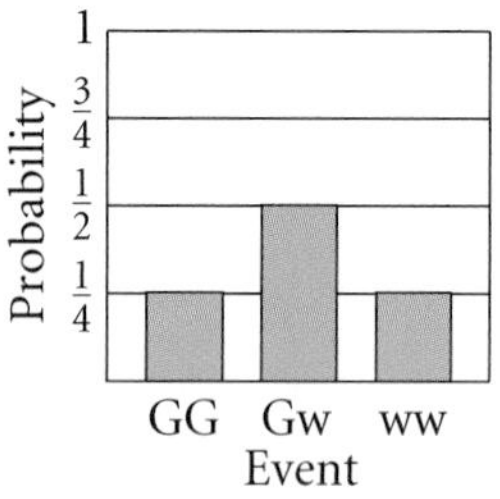

b. Plant Color Distribution
{green, white}

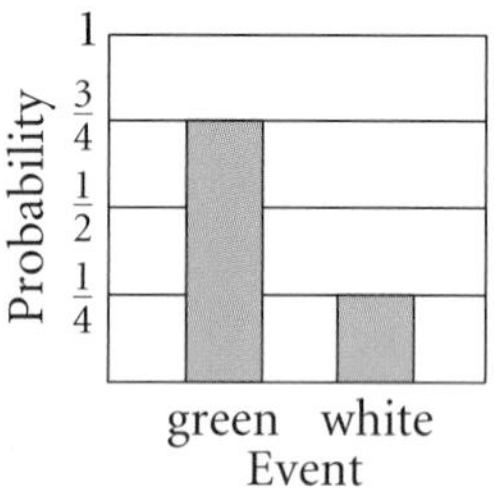

Check Understanding 4 **a.** **Critical Thinking** Which probability distribution would be more useful to a farmer who wants to avoid raising white corn plants? Explain.
b. Make a probability distribution table for each sample space in Example 4.

OBJECTIVE

2 Using a Probability Distribution

You can design a simulation based on a probability distribution. First, use the probabilities to assign numbers to each event in the sample space. For example, if $P(\text{event}) = 0.15$, assign 15 out of 100 numbers to that event. Then you can conduct trials by generating random numbers.

5 EXAMPLE Real-World Connection

Market Research At a certain store, the number of customers c who arrive at the checkout counters each minute varies according to the distribution below. Simulate the number of customers over a ten-minute period.

Number of Customers Each Minute

c	0	1	2	3	4	5	6
P(c)	0.15	0.24	0.28	0.17	0.09	0.05	0.02

Graphing Calculator Hint

Use the command int(100*rand) + 1 to generate random numbers from 1 to 100. Press MATH and use the int option under the NUM menu and the rand option under the PRB menu.

Step 1 Define how the simulation will be done. Use random numbers. Assign numbers from 1 to 100 to the events, based on the probability of each event. Use cumulative probabilities to help you assign the numbers.

Event	Probability	Cumulative Probability	Assigned Numbers
0	0.15	0.15	01–15
1	0.24	0.39	16–39
2	0.28	0.67	40–67
3	0.17	0.84	68–84
4	0.09	0.93	85–93
5	0.05	0.98	94–98
6	0.02	1.00	99–100

Since $P(0) = 0.15$, assign 15 numbers to this outcome.

There are 17 numbers from 68 to 84.

Step 2 Conduct the simulation. Model a ten-minute period by generating ten random numbers from 1 to 100.

Minute →	1st	2nd	3rd	4th	5th	6th	7th	8th	9th	10th
Random numbers →	81	29	83	93	18	9	40	97	47	16
Number of customers →	3	1	3	4	1	0	2	5	2	1

The random number 9 is assigned to the outcome 0 customers.

Step 3 Interpret the simulation. Based on this simulation, a total of 22 customers would arrive at checkout counters over a ten-minute period.

Check Understanding 5 Conduct a simulation for Example 5 over a 20-minute period.

EXERCISES

For more practice, see *Extra Practice.*

Practice and Problem Solving

A Practice by Example

Example 1 (page 636)

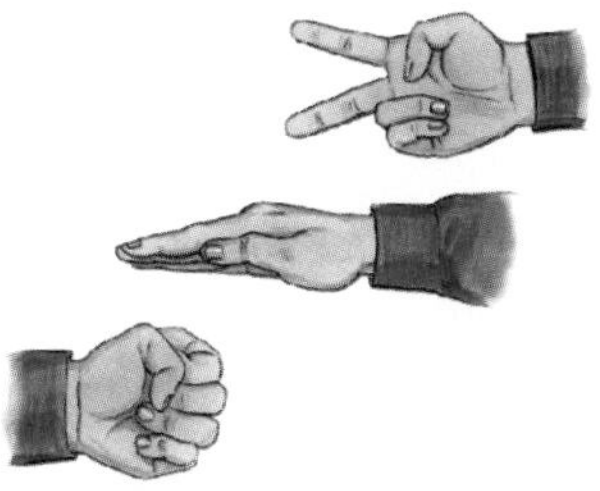

In the game Rock-Paper-Scissors, the scissors cut the paper, the rock dulls the scissors, and the paper covers the rock. Use the results below for Exercises 1 and 2.

Rock-Paper-Scissors

Player 1	**R**	**S**	**P**	P	**S**	R	S	S	R	P	S	S	R	**S**	**P**	P	**R**	S
Player 2	S	P	R	**S**	P	**P**	**R**	S	R	**S**	**R**	**R**	**P**	P	R	**S**	S	S

R = Rock P = Paper S = Scissors **Bold** = Winner

1. Make a frequency table for the objects played: rock, paper, or scissors.
2. Make a frequency table for the winning players: Player 1, Player 2, or tie.

Example 2 (page 637)

The table shows the frequency of responses to editorials. Find each probability.

Number of Responses	0	1	2	3	4	5	6 or more	Total
Number of Editorials	20	30	56	38	34	16	6	200

3. P(5 or more responses) 4. P(at most 4 responses) 5. P(0–2 responses)

Example 3 (page 637)

6. Use a table and a graph to show the probability distribution for the spinner {red, green, blue, yellow}.

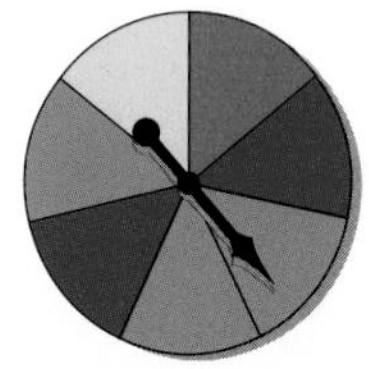

7. Use a table and a graph to show the probability distribution for the number of days {28, 29, 30, 31} in each of 48 consecutive months.

Example 4 (page 638)

Suppose you roll two number cubes. Graph the probability distribution for each sample space.

8. {sum of numbers even, sum of numbers odd}

9. {both numbers even, both numbers odd, one number even and the other odd}

Example 5 (pages 638–639)

10. Design and conduct a simulation to determine the ages of 20 licensed drivers chosen at random in the United States.

Licensed Drivers in the United States, by Age

a	< 20	20–29	30–39	40–49	50–59	60–69	70–79	≥ 80
$P(a)$	0.051	0.176	0.211	0.211	0.156	0.096	0.070	0.029

SOURCE: U.S. Department of Transportation. Go to **www.PHSchool.com** for a data update. Web Code: agg-2041

11. Design and conduct a simulation to determine the size and type of 30 cars purchased from U.S. car dealerships.

U.S. Car Sales by Vehicle Size and Type

t	Luxury	Large	Midsize	Small
$P(t)$	0.165	0.076	0.527	0.232

SOURCE: Ward's Communications

B Apply Your Skills

Graph the probability distribution described by each function.

12. $P(x) = \frac{x}{10}$ for $x = 1, 2, 3,$ and 4

13. $P(x) = \frac{2x + 1}{15}$ for $x = 1, 2,$ and 3

Weather Conditions in Dayton, Ohio

Type of Weather	Days Per Year
Clear	82
Partly Cloudy	118
Mostly Cloudy	34
Rain	75
Light Snow (< 1.5 in.)	45
Snow (≥ 1.5 in.)	11
Total	365

SOURCE: *The USA Today Weather Almanac*

14. **Weather** Refer to the table at the left.
 a. Make a table showing the probability distribution for weather in Dayton.
 b. Define the independent and dependent variables.
 c. Find the probability that a day in Dayton will include rain or snow.

15. **Data Collection** Find weather data for a city near you. Draw a graph to show the probability distribution of weather conditions.

16. a. **Transportation** Sometimes a probability distribution is shown as a circle graph. Define the independent and dependent variables in the distribution at the right.
 b. Draw the distribution as a bar graph.
 c. Find P(the tank is at least half full when a driver buys gas).

SOURCE: *The First Really Important Survey of American Habits*

17. **Writing** In a simulation, how do equally likely outcomes help you represent the probability distribution?

18. **Odds** The odds in favor of an event equal the ratio of the number of times the event occurs to the number of times the event does not occur. The odds in favor of event A are 1 : 4. The odds in favor of event B are 2 : 3. The odds in favor of event C are 1 : 3. The odds in favor of event D are 3 : 17. Graph the probability distribution of events A, B, C, and D.

C Challenge

19. **Safety** The table shows data for 911 calls in a town.
   a. Conduct a simulation for the number of 911 calls over a 24-hour period.
   b. If there are two response teams available, and each response takes about an hour, how many callers in your simulation have to wait?
   c. Find P(caller will have to wait).
   d. **Critical Thinking** Use your simulation to determine whether additional response teams are needed for this town. Explain your reasoning.

Probability Distribution for Number of 911 Calls Each Hour

c	$P(c)$
0	0.21
1	0.30
2	0.18
3	0.13
4	0.09
5	0.05
6	0.03
7	0.01

Real-World Connection

More than 93% of the U.S. population is covered by 911 service.

20. **Marketing** A company includes instant-win tickets with 10,000,000 of its products. Of the prizes offered, one is a large cash prize, 1,600,000 are small cash prizes, and the other prizes are free samples of the company's products.
   a. Find the theoretical probability of winning each type of prize.
   b. Design and conduct a simulation to determine the prizes for 100 products.
   c. Find the experimental probability for winning each type of prize.

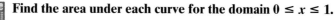

Standardized Test Prep

Multiple Choice

The table shows the number of cities in a region of the U.S. that are served by the given number of airlines. Use the table for Exercises 21–22.

Number of Airlines	Number of Cities
1	27
2	14
3	15
4	18
5	14
6	11

Take It to the NET
Online lesson quiz at **www.PHSchool.com**
Web Code: aga-1201

21. What is the probability that a city chosen at random is served by exactly 4 airlines?
   A. $\frac{1}{18}$ B. $\frac{4}{21}$ C. $\frac{2}{11}$ D. $\frac{2}{9}$

22. What is the probability that a city chosen at random is served by at least 1 airline?
   F. 0 G. $\frac{1}{99}$ H. $\frac{3}{11}$ I. 1

Extended Response

23. A spinner has 4 sections labeled A, B, C, and D. Can the spinner be designed so $P(A) = \frac{1}{12}$, $P(B) = \frac{1}{6}$, $P(C) = \frac{1}{3}$, and $P(D) = \frac{5}{12}$? If so, explain how.

Mixed Review

Lesson 11-6

Find the area under each curve for the domain $0 \le x \le 1$.

24. $y = 3$
25. $y = 4x + 2$
26. $y = 4x^3 + 1$

Lesson 10-6

Sketch the graph of each equation.

27. $x^2 - 4y^2 + 2x + 24y = 51$
28. $20y^2 - 40y - x = -25$

Lesson 9-7

Classify each pair of events as *dependent* or *independent*.

29. Choose one item from a buffet. Then choose a different item from the buffet.

30. Choose a size for your drink. Then select a flavor.

12-2 Conditional Probability

Lesson Preview

What You'll Learn

OBJECTIVE 1 To find conditional probabilities

OBJECTIVE 2 To use formulas and tree diagrams

... And Why

To find the probability of school closings after snowfall, as in Example 4

Check Skills You'll Need

(For help, go to Lesson 9-7.)

A spinner has four equal sections that are red, blue, green, and yellow. Find each probability for two spins.

1. P(blue, then blue)
2. P(red, then yellow)
3. P(not yellow, then green)
4. P(not blue, then not red)
5. P(at least one green)
6. P(neither spin red)

New Vocabulary • conditional probability

Interactive lesson includes instant self-check, tutorials, and activities.

OBJECTIVE 1 Finding Conditional Probabilities

A **conditional probability** contains a condition that may limit the sample space for an event. You can write a conditional probability using the notation $P(B \mid A)$, read "the probability of event B, given event A."

1 EXAMPLE Finding Conditional Probability

The table shows the results of a class survey. Find P(did a chore | male).

Did you do a household chore last night?

	Yes	No	
Male	7	8	← 15 males
Female	7	6	← 13 females

The condition *male* limits the sample space to 15 possible outcomes. Of the 15 males, 7 did a chore. Therefore, P(did a chore | male) equals $\frac{7}{15}$.

Check Understanding 1 Use the data in Example 1 to find P(female | did a chore).

2 EXAMPLE Real-World Connection

Recycling Americans recycle more and more material through municipal waste collection each year. Use the information in the table, based on a recent year, to find the probability that a sample of recycled waste was paper.

Municipal Waste Collected in the U.S. (millions of tons)

Material	Recycled	Not Recycled
Paper	34.9	48.9
Metal	6.5	10.1
Glass	2.9	9.1
Plastic	1.1	20.4
Other	15.3	67.8

SOURCE: U.S. Environmental Protection Agency. Go to www.PHSchool.com for a data update. Web Code: agg-2041

The given condition limits the sample space to *recycled* waste. A favorable outcome is recycled paper.

$$P(\text{paper} \mid \text{recycled}) = \frac{34.9}{34.9 + 6.5 + 2.9 + 1.1 + 15.3}$$
$$\approx 0.57$$

The probability that the recycled waste was paper is about 57%.

Check Understanding 2 Find the probability that a sample of recycled waste was plastic.

OBJECTIVE 2

Using Formulas and Tree Diagrams

You can use a formula to find conditional probability.

Key Concepts

Property	Conditional Probability Formula

For any two events A and B from a sample space with $P(A) \neq 0$,

$$P(B \mid A) = \frac{P(A \text{ and } B)}{P(A)}$$

Using the formula, you can calculate a conditional probability from other probabilities.

3 EXAMPLE Real-World Connection

Market Research Researchers asked shampoo users whether they apply shampoo directly to the head, or indirectly using a hand. Find the probability that a respondent applies shampoo directly to the head, given that the respondent is female.

Applying Shampoo

	Directly Onto Head	Into Hand First
Male	2	18
Female	6	24

Relate $P(\text{female}) = \frac{30}{50}$

$P(\text{female } \textit{and} \text{ applies directly to head}) = \frac{6}{50}$

Define Let A = female.

Let B = applies directly to head.

Write $P(B \mid A) = \frac{P(A \text{ and } B)}{P(A)}$

$= \frac{\frac{6}{50}}{\frac{30}{50}}$ **Substitute.**

$= \frac{6}{30} = \frac{1}{5}$ **Simplify.**

The probability that a respondent applies shampoo directly to the head, given that the respondondent is female, is $\frac{1}{5}$, or 20%.

Check Understanding 3 Eighty percent of an airline's flights depart on schedule. Seventy-two percent of its flights depart and arrive on schedule. Find the probability that a flight that departs on time also arrives on time.

You can use tree diagrams to solve problems involving conditional probabilities.

Real-World Connection

During some winters, Buffalo gets more than 100 inches of snow.

4 EXAMPLE Making a Tree Diagram

A student in Buffalo, New York, made the observations below.

- Of all snowfalls, 5% are heavy (at least 6 in.).
- After a heavy snowfall, schools are closed 67% of the time.
- After a light (less than 6 in.) snowfall, schools are closed 3% of the time.

Find the probability that the snowfall is light and the schools are open.

Make a tree diagram. Use H for heavy snowfall, L for light snowfall, C for schools closed, and O for schools open. Find $P(L \text{ and } O)$.

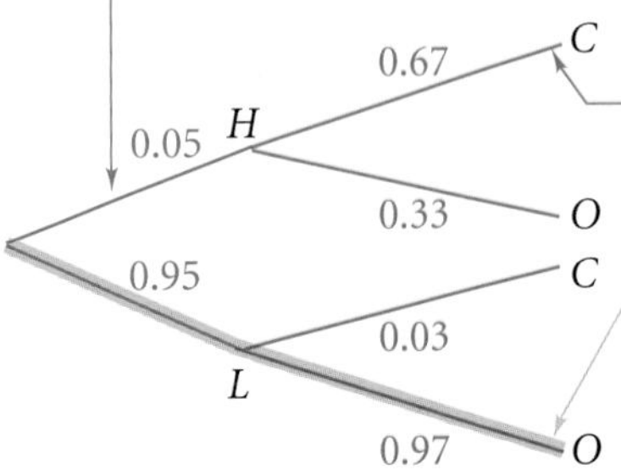

Each first branch represents a simple probability. $P(H) = 0.05$

Each second branch represents a conditional probability. $P(C|H) = 0.67$

The highlighted path represents $P(L \text{ and } O)$.

$$P(L \text{ and } O) = P(L) \cdot P(O|L) = 0.95 \cdot 0.97 = 0.92$$

The probability that the snowfall is light and the schools are open is about 92%.

Check Understanding 4 Find P(schools open, given heavy snow).

EXERCISES

For more practice, see *Extra Practice.*

Practice and Problem Solving

A Practice by Example

Example 1 (page 642)

Use the table to find each probability.

1. P(has diploma)
2. P(has diploma and experience)
3. P(has experience | has diploma)
4. P(has no diploma | has experience)

Characteristics of Job Applicants

		Has Experience	
		Yes	**No**
Has High School Diploma	**Yes**	54	27
	No	5	4

Example 2 (pages 642–643)

Use the table below to find each probability.

5. P(The recipient is male.)
6. P(The degree is a bachelor's.)
7. P(The recipient is female, given that the degree is advanced.)
8. P(The degree is *not* an associate's, given that the recipient is male.)

Projected Number of Degree Recipients in 2010 (thousands)

Degree	Male	Female
Associate's	224	387
Bachelor's	547	776
Advanced	245	322

SOURCE: U.S. National Center for Education Statistics

Example 3 (page 643)

Use the survey results below for Exercises 9 and 10.

> 39% have a pet now and have had a pet.
> 61% do not have a pet now.
> 86% have had a pet.
> 14% do not have a pet now and have never had a pet.

9. Find the probability that a respondent has a pet, given that the respondent has had a pet.

10. Find the probability that a respondent has never had a pet, given that the respondent does not have a pet now.

Example 4 (page 644)

11. Make a tree diagram based on the survey results below. Then find P(a female respondent is left-handed) and P(a respondent is both male and right-handed).
- Of all the respondents, 17% are male.
- Of the male respondents, 33% are left-handed.
- Of female respondents, 90% are right-handed.

12. A football team has a 70% chance of winning when it doesn't snow, but only a 40% chance of winning when it snows. Suppose there is a 50% chance of snow. Make a tree diagram to find the probability that the team will win.

B Apply Your Skills

13. Suppose A and B are independent events, with $P(A) = 0.60$ and $P(B) = 0.25$. Find each probability.
a. $P(A \text{ and } B)$
b. $P(A \mid B)$
c. What do you notice about $P(A)$ and $P(A \mid B)$?
d. **Critical Thinking** One way to describe A and B as independent events is *The occurrence of B has no effect on the probability of A*. Explain how the answer to part (c) illustrates this relationship.

Surveys **Conduct a survey in your class. Then find each probability.**

14. P(left-handed | left shoe)

15. P(left-handed | not the right shoe)

16. P(left shoe | right-handed)

17. P(first shoe picked up | right-handed)

18. P(don't know)

Which Shoe Do You Put on First?		Dominant Hand: Right	Dominant Hand: Left
First Shoe Put On	Right	■	■
	Left	■	■
	First One Grabbed	■	■
	Don't Know	■	■

Weather **Use probability notation to describe the chance of each event. Let *S*, *C*, *W*, and *R* represent sunny, cloudy, windy, and rainy weather, respectively.**

19. cloudy weather

20. sunny and windy weather

21. rainy weather if it is windy

22. windy weather if it is sunny

C Challenge

23. a. **Writing** Explain which branches of the tree diagram at the right represent conditional probabilities. Give a specific example.
b. Are the event of having a license and the event of being an adult independent events? Justify your answer.
c. **Open-Ended** Estimate probabilities for each branch of the tree diagram for your city or town. Then find $P(L)$.

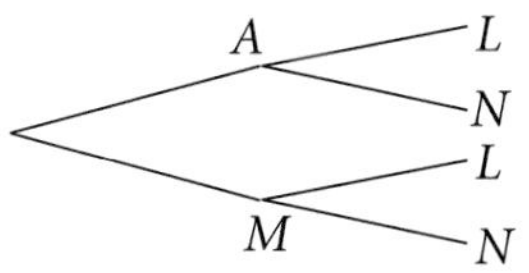

A = adult (21 or older)
M = minor (under 21)
L = licensed driver
N = not licensed to drive

24. **Critical Thinking** Sixty percent of a company's sales representatives have completed training seminars. Of these, 80% have had increased sales. Overall, 56% of the representatives (whether trained or not) have had increased sales. Use a tree diagram to find the probability of increased sales, given that a representative has not been trained.

Standardized Test Prep

Multiple Choice

A school library classifies its books as hardback or paperback, fiction or nonfiction, and illustrated or nonillustrated. Use the table at the right for Exercises 25–27.

		Illustrated	Non-illustrated
Hardback	Fiction	420	780
	Nonfiction	590	250
Paperback	Fiction	150	430
	Nonfiction	110	880

Take It to the NET
Online lesson quiz at
www.PHSchool.com
Web Code: aga-1202

25. What is the probability that a book selected at random is a paperback, given that it is illustrated?

A. $\frac{260}{3610}$ B. $\frac{150}{1270}$ C. $\frac{260}{1270}$ D. $\frac{110}{150}$

26. What is the probability that a book selected at random is nonfiction, given that it is a nonillustrated hardback?

F. $\frac{250}{2040}$ G. $\frac{780}{1030}$ H. $\frac{250}{1030}$ I. $\frac{250}{780}$

27. What is the probability that a book selected at random is a paperback?

A. $\frac{1}{1570}$ B. $\frac{260}{1310}$ C. $\frac{1570}{2040}$ D. $\frac{1570}{3610}$

Short Response

28. In another library, the probability that a book is a hardback, given that it is illustrated, is 0.40. The probability that the book is hardback *and* illustrated is 0.20. Find the probability that a book is illustrated.

Mixed Review

Lesson 12-1

29. Consider a February that is not in a leap year. Graph the probability distribution for the sample space {weekdays, weekend days}.

Lesson 11-1

30. **Construction** An earthmover purchased for $600,000 loses 18% of its value each year. What is the value of the earthmover after one year? After three years?

Lesson 10-1

31. Identify the center and intercepts of the conic section at the right. Then find the domain and range.

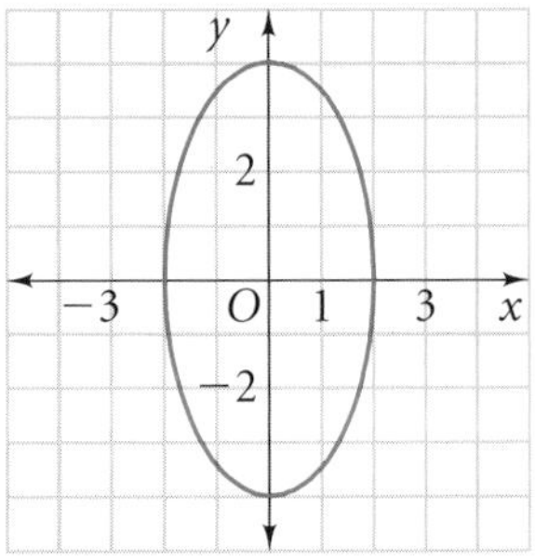

Lesson 8-5

Solve each equation. If necessary, round to the nearest thousandth.

32. $2^x = 4$ **33.** $4^{2x} = 10$ **34.** $4^{x+1} = 28$

35. $7 - 3^x = -38$ **36.** $\log x = -1$

37. $2 \log x = 1$ **38.** $\log (2x + 2) = 2$

Extension Comparing Conditional Probabilities

For Use With Lesson 12-2

You can use a tree diagram like the one at the right to find the conditional probability $P(P \mid D)$, which is the probability that a person with a disease will test positive for it. In this case, $P(P \mid D) = 0.99$.

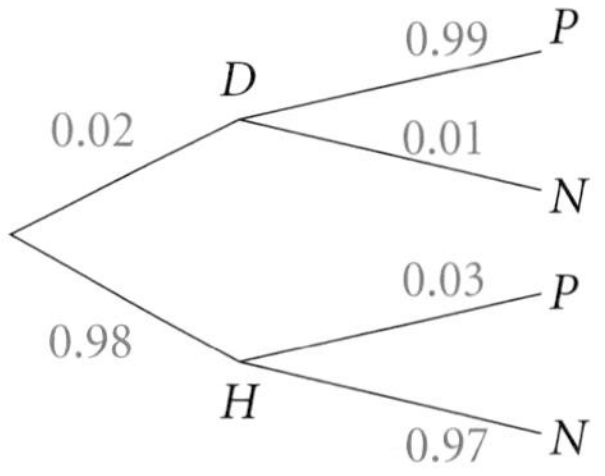

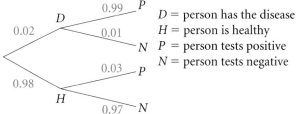

D = person has the disease
H = person is healthy
P = person tests positive
N = person tests negative

Scientists also look at $P(H \mid P)$, the probability of a "false positive," which is the probability that a person who tests positive is actually healthy. Since this probability is not found on a branch in the diagram, you must use the formula for conditional probability.

EXAMPLE

Use the tree diagram above to find $P(H \mid P)$.

Since $P(H \mid P) = \frac{P(H \text{ and } P)}{P(P)}$, find $P(H \text{ and } P)$ and $P(P)$.

$$P(H \text{ and } P) = 0.98 \cdot 0.03 = 0.0294$$

$$P(P) = P(D \text{ and } P) \text{ or } P(H \text{ and } P) = 0.02 \cdot 0.99 + 0.98 \cdot 0.03 = 0.0492$$

So $P(H \mid P) = \frac{P(H \text{ and } P)}{P(P)}$

$= \frac{0.0294}{0.0492}$ **Substitute.**

≈ 0.598 **Simplify.**

About 60% of the people who test positive do not actually have the disease.

EXERCISES

Use the tree diagram in the Example to find each probability.

1. $P(N)$ **2.** $P(H \text{ and } N)$ **3.** $P(H \mid N)$ **4.** $P(D \mid N)$

5. **Writing** Explain the difference in meaning between $P(P \mid D)$ and $P(D \mid P)$ for the test in the Example. Compare the values of $P(P \mid D)$ and $P(D \mid P)$. What is the best use for this test? Explain.

The tree diagram relates snowfall and school closings. Find each probability.

6. $P(C)$ **7.** $P(H \text{ and } O)$

8. $P(H \mid C)$ **9.** $P(L \mid O)$

10. $P(L \mid C)$ **11.** $P(H \mid O)$

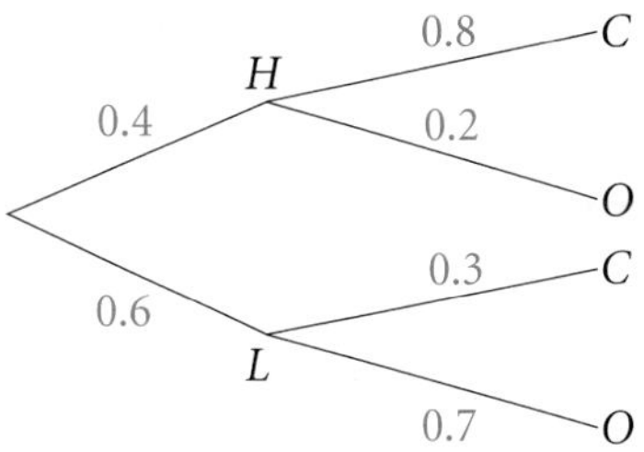

H = heavy snowfall
L = light snowfall
C = schools closed
O = schools open

12-3 Analyzing Data

Lesson Preview

What You'll Learn

OBJECTIVE 1 To calculate measures of central tendency

OBJECTIVE 2 To draw and interpret box-and-whisker plots

. . . And Why

To analyze a set of water temperatures, as in Example 2

Check Skills You'll Need

(For help, go to Lesson 1-1.)

Order each set of values from least to greatest. Then find the middle value.

1. 0.2 0.3 0.6 1.2 0.7 0.9 0.8

2. 11 23 15 17 21 18 21

3. 7.8 2.6 3.9 15.6 9.1 11.7 10.4

4. 76 89 80 82 86 84 86

New Vocabulary

- measures of central tendency
- mean
- median
- mode
- bimodal
- quartiles
- box-and-whisker plot
- percentiles
- outlier

Interactive lesson includes instant self-check, tutorials, and activities.

OBJECTIVE 1 Measures of Central Tendency

Statistics is the study of data analysis and interpretation. The mean, the median, and the mode are single, central values that help describe a set of data. They are called **measures of central tendency.**

Key Concepts

Definition Measures of Central Tendency

Measure	Definition	Example, using {1, 2, 2, 3, 5, 5}
Mean	$\frac{\text{sum of the data values}}{\text{number of data values}}$	$\frac{1+2+2+3+5+5}{6} = \frac{18}{6} = 3$
Median	middle value *or* mean of the two middle values	$\frac{2+3}{2} = 2.5$
Mode	most frequently occurring value	2 and 5

A **bimodal** data set has two modes. If a data set has more than two modes, then the modes are probably not statistically useful. If no value occurs more frequently than any other, then there is no mode.

1 EXAMPLE Finding Measures of Central Tendency

Find the mean, median, and mode for these values: 98, 95, 99, 97, 89, 92, 97, 62, 90.

$$\bar{x} = \frac{98+95+99+97+89+92+97+62+90}{9} = \frac{819}{9} = 91$$

Use the symbol $\bar{x}$ to designate the mean.

62 89 90 92 95 97 97 98 99

(95 ↑ Median; 97 97 ↑ Mode)

Find the median and the mode by ordering the values numerically.

The mean is 91, the median is 95, and the mode is 97.

Reading Math

Read $\bar{x}$ as "the mean of x" or "x bar."

Check Understanding 1 Find the mean, median, and mode for these values: 2.4, 4.3, 3.7, 3.9, 2.8, 5.4, 2.8.

You can use a graphing calculator to find the measures of central tendency.

2 EXAMPLE Real-World Connection

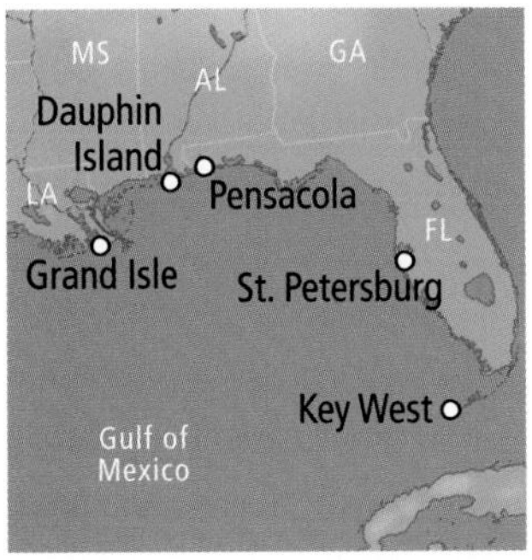

Oceanography Find the mean, the median, and the mode of all the water temperatures listed for the eastern coast of the Gulf of Mexico.

Gulf of Mexico Eastern Coast Water Temperatures (°F)

Location	J	F	M	A	M	J	J	A	S	O	N	D
Pensacola, Florida	56	58	63	71	78	84	85	86	82	74	65	58
St. Petersburg, Florida	62	64	68	74	80	84	86	86	84	78	70	64
Key West, Florida	69	70	75	78	82	85	87	87	86	82	76	72
Dauphin Island, Alabama	51	53	60	70	75	82	84	84	80	72	62	56
Grand Isle, Louisiana	61	61	64	70	77	83	85	85	83	77	70	65

Step 1 Use the STAT feature to enter the data as L1 in your graphing calculator.

Step 2 Use the LIST feature to access the MATH menu. Find the mean.

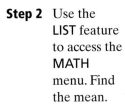

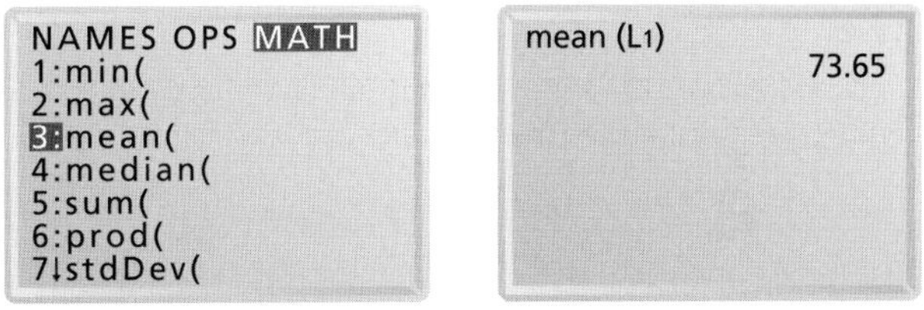

Step 3 Return to the same menu to find the median.

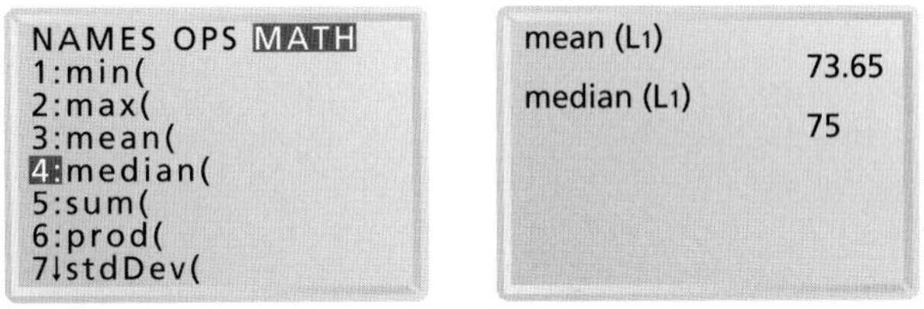

Step 4 Use the STAT PLOT feature to access Plot 1. Choose the histogram, L1, and Frequency 1 options. Then enter an appropriate viewing window.

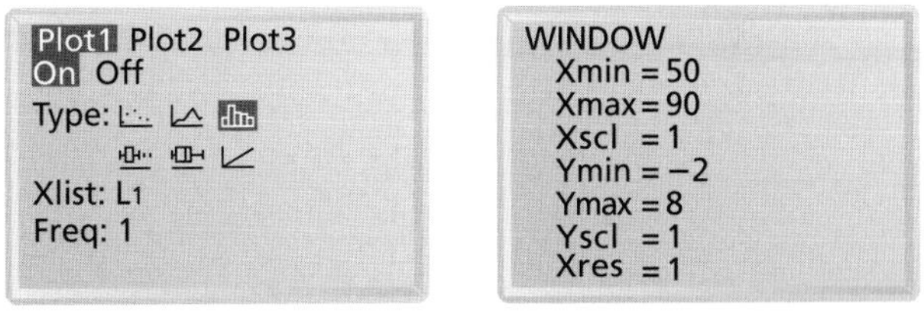

Step 5 Graph the data. Use the TRACE feature to move the cursor to the highest points of the graph.

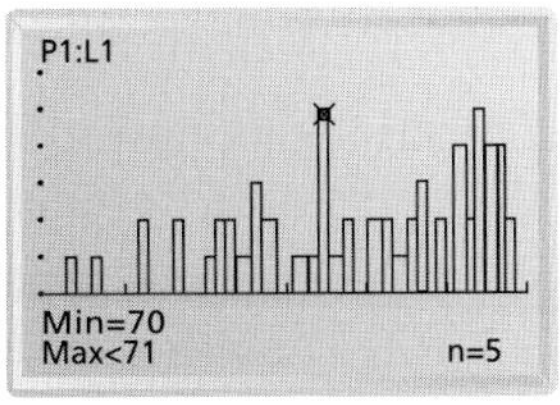

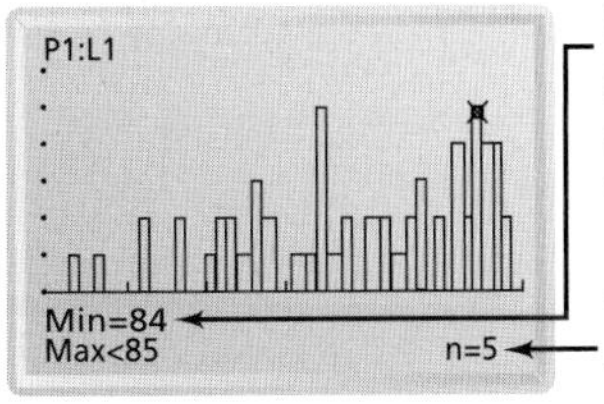

On the screen, the mode appears as the minimum value for the cursor. The modes are 70 and 84.

The modes both occur five times in the data.

The mean is 73.65°F, the median is 75°F, and the modes are 70°F and 84°F.

Check Understanding 2 Find the mean, median, and mode for the water temperatures in Grand Isle, Louisiana.

OBJECTIVE 2

Box-and-Whisker Plots

If you arrange data in increasing order, then the median divides the data set into two equal parts. You can use the median of each of the parts to divide the set further, into four equal parts. The values separating the four parts are called **quartiles.** Quartiles are shown below for the 12 water temperatures from Pensacola in Example 2.

Median of lower part (Q_1) = 60.5 Median of upper part (Q_3) = 83

56 58 58 ↓ 63 65 71 ↑ 74 78 82 ↓ 84 85 86

Median of data set (Q_2) = 72.5

> **Reading Math**
> Quartiles are sometimes called "hinges."

The values Q_1, Q_2, and Q_3 are the first, second, and third quartiles. A **box-and-whisker plot** is a method of displaying data that uses quartiles to form the center box and the minimum and maximum values to form the whiskers.

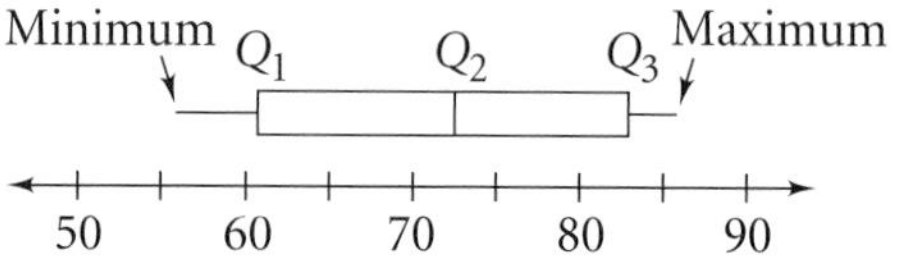

3 EXAMPLE Making a Box-and-Whisker Plot

Make a box-and-whisker plot for these values: 84, 79, 90, 73, 95, 88, 92, 81, 67.

Step 1 Find the quartile values, the minimum value, and the maximum value.

67 73 79 81 84 88 90 92 95

Q_2 = median = 84

When the median is a value of the data set, it is removed for the calculation of Q_1 and Q_3.

67 73 79 81 88 90 92 95

$Q_1 = \frac{73 + 79}{2} = 76$ $Q_3 = \frac{90 + 92}{2} = 91$

The minimum value is 67, and the maximum value is 95.

Step 2 Draw a number line for the base of your box-and-whisker plot. Above the number line, plot the three quartiles, the minimum value, and the maximum value.

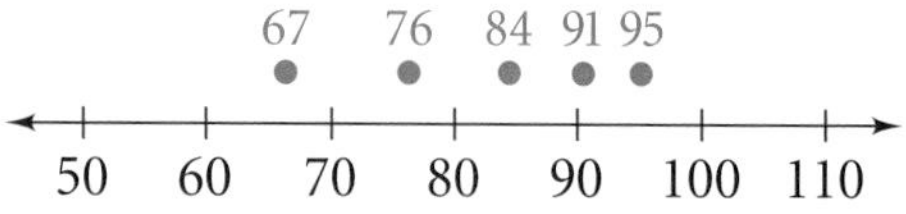

Step 3 Finish your box-and-whisker plot by drawing a box through Q_1 and Q_3, a vertical line through the median, and line segments from the box outward to the minimum and maximum values.

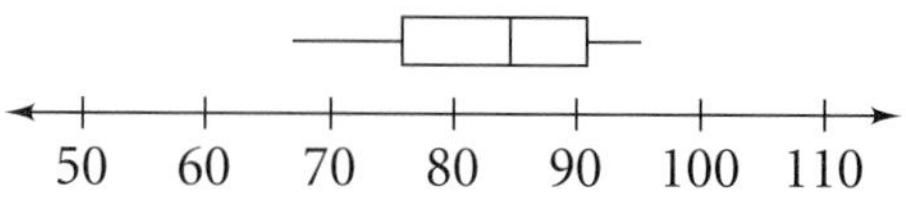

Check Understanding 3 Make a box-and-whisker plot for these values: 34, 36, 47, 45, 28, 31, 29, 40.

4 EXAMPLE Real-World Connection

Oceanography Use a graphing calculator to find the quartiles of the water temperature data in Example 2.

Use the STAT PLOT feature to select a box-and-whisker plot. Enter the window values. Graph the box-and-whisker plot.

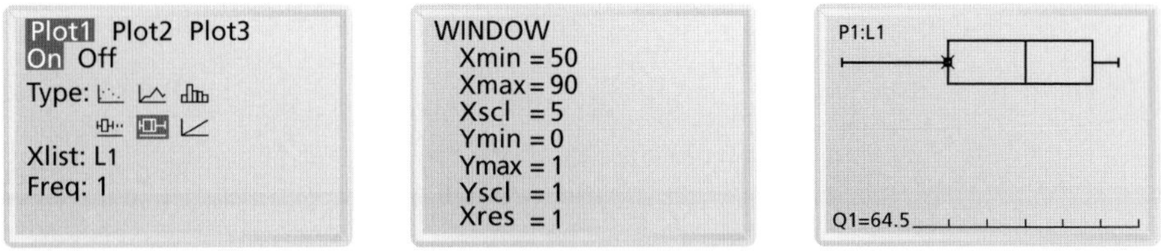

Use the TRACE feature to find the quartiles: $Q_1 = 64.5$, $Q_2 = 75$, and $Q_3 = 83.5$.

Check Understanding 4 Use the data for just the summer months, as shown in the graph below. Find the quartiles by graphing the box-and-whisker plot.

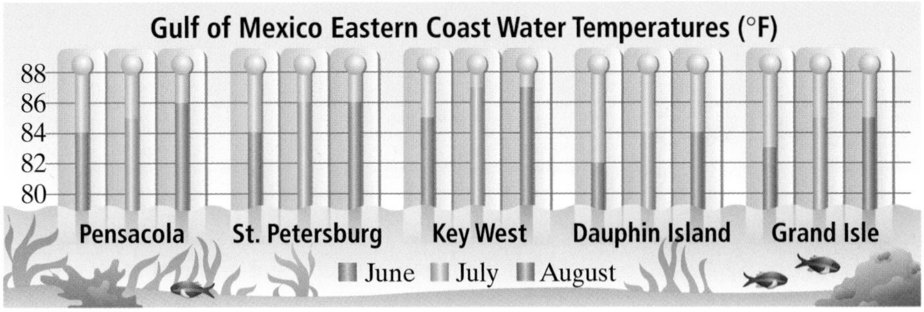

A **percentile** is a value that divides the range of a data set into two parts such that the part below the percentile contains a given percent of the data. If a number x is at the 63rd percentile in a data set, then about 63% of the data are less than x.

5 EXAMPLE Using Percentiles

Find the values at the 20th and 65th percentiles for the values below.

54 98 45 87 98 64 21 61 71 82 93 65 62 98 87 24 65 97 31 47

Step 1 Order the values.

21 24 31 45 47 54 61 62 64 65 65 71 82 87 87 93 97 98 98 98

Step 2 Find the number of values that fall below the 20th percentile and the number that fall below the 65th percentile.

Of the 20 values, 20% should fall below the 20th percentile and 65% should fall below the 65th percentile.

$20 \cdot 20\% = 20 \cdot 0.20 = 4$

Since 47 is greater than 4 values, 47 is at the 20th percentile.

$20 \cdot 65\% = 20 \cdot 0.65 = 13$

Since 87 is greater than 13 values, 87 is at the 65th percentile.

The value at the 20th percentile is 47 and the value at the 65th percentile is 87.

Check Understanding 5 Find the value at each percentile for the data in Example 5.

a. 0th percentile **b.** 45th percentile **c.** 55th percentile

An **outlier** is an item of data with a value substantially different from the rest of the items in the data set. Sometimes an outlier is an important part of the data. At other times it can represent a false reading. When you think an outlier has resulted from an error, you may remove it from the data set.

6 EXAMPLE Identifying an Outlier

Identify an outlier for this set of values: 56 65 73 59 98 65 59.

56 59 59 65 65 73 98 — **Order the data.**

3 0 6 0 8 25 — **Find the differences between adjacent values.**

98 is substantially different, so 98 is an outlier.

Check Understanding 6 **a.** Suppose the values in Example 6 are measurements of the water temperature of a lake. Would you discard the outlier? Explain.

b. Suppose the data represent the number of customers in a small restaurant each night during one week. Would you discard the outlier? Explain.

EXERCISES

For more practice, see *Extra Practice*.

Practice and Problem Solving

A Practice by Example

Examples 1 and 2 (pages 648 and 649)

Find the mean, median, and mode of each set of values.

1. 5 9 1 2 7 3 1 8 8 1 3

2. 307 309 323 304 390 398

3. 475 722 499 572 402 809 499 828 405 499 800 422 672 800

Examples 3 and 4 (pages 650 and 651)

Make a box-and-whisker plot for each set of values.

4. 12 11 15 12 19 20 19

5. 120 145 133 105 117 150

6. 49 57.5 58 49.2 62 22.2 67 52.1 77 99.9 80 51.7 64

7. Weather The table shows the high temperatures for one day at different locations on the island of Maui, Hawaii. Make a box-and whisker plot of the data.

High Temperatures on Maui

Location	Temperature
Kahului	88°F
Kihei	85°F
Lahaina	86°F
Hana	82°F
Haleakala	66°F
Kula	75°F

Example 5 (page 651)

Find the values at the 30th and 90th percentiles for each set of values.

8. 6283 5700 6381 6274 5700 5896 5972 6075 5993 5581

9. 7 12 3 14 17 20 5 3 17 4 13 2 15 9 15 18 16 9 1 6

Example 6 (page 652)

Identify the outlier of each set of values.

10. 3.4 4.5 2.3 5.9 9.8 3.3 2.1 3.0 2.9

11. 17 21 19 10 15 19 14 0 11 16

Dilbert

B Apply Your Skills

12. a. What percent of the customers in the cartoon are exactly the median age?
 b. Must one item from a data set fall exactly at the median? Explain.
 c. Can the company do anything about the shocking discovery? Explain.

Major Tornadoes in Oklahoma, May 3, 1999	
Length of Path (miles)	Intensity
6	F3
9	F3
4	F2
38	F5
7	F2
12	F3
8	F2
7	F2
15	F4
20	F4
1	F5
22	F3
16	F3
8	F2
13	F3
2	F2

SOURCE: National Oceanic & Atmospheric Administration

13. **Meteorology** On May 3, 1999, 59 tornadoes hit Oklahoma in the largest tornado outbreak ever recorded in the state. Sixteen of these were classified as strong (F2 or F3) or violent (F4 or F5).
 a. Make a box-and-whisker plot of the data.
 b. Identify the outlier. Remove it from the data set and make a revised box-and-whisker plot.
 c. **Writing** How does the removal of the outlier affect the box-and-whisker plot? How does it affect the median of the data set?

Identify the outlier of each set of values. Then describe how its value affects the mean of the data.

14. 947 757 103 619 661 582 626 900 869 728 1001 596 515

15. 87 104 381 215 174 199 233 186 142 228 9 53 117 129

For Exercises 16–18, use the set of values below.

1 1 1 1 1 1 2 3 5 8 13 21 34 55 89 89 89 89 89 89

16. At what percentile is 1?

17. At what percentile is 34?

18. **Error Analysis** A student claims that 89 is at the 100th percentile. Explain the student's error.

19. **Geology** The table below shows the number of major earthquakes (magnitude 7.0 or greater) worldwide in the ten-year period from 1991 through 2000.

Major Earthquakes Worldwide (Magnitude 7.0 and Greater)

Year	1991	1992	1993	1994	1995	1996	1997	1998	1999	2000
Earthquakes	11	23	16	15	25	22	20	16	23	18

SOURCE: U.S. Geological Survey National Earthquake Information Center

 a. Find the mean and the median of the numbers of annual earthquakes.
 b. Do the data include an outlier that you should discard? Explain.
 c. Compare the box-and-whisker plots at the right. One shows the data above. The other shows worldwide earthquake data from 1900 through 2000. What conclusions can you draw about recent earthquakes? Justify your reasoning.

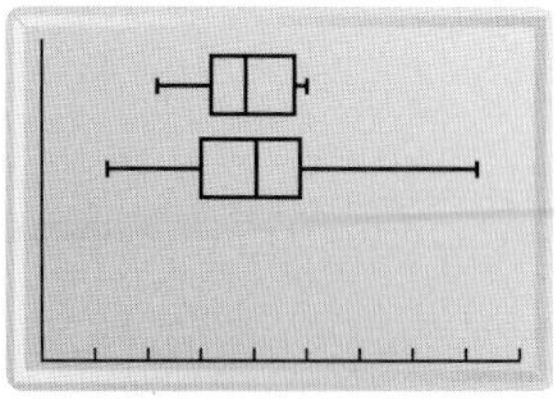

Xmin = 0 Ymin = 0
Xmax = 45 Ymax = 1
Xscl = 5 Yscl = 1

20. **Critical Thinking** Which measure better represents a data set with several outliers—the mean or the median? Justify your answer.

Challenge

21. **Track and Field** The table shows the qualifying distances for the shot put events for both men and women during the 1996 Olympics in Atlanta, Georgia.

Real-World Connection

The "shot" in shot put refers to cannonballs. For centuries, soldiers used them in throwing contests.

1996 Olympic Qualifying Distances for Shot Put (meters)

Men	20.43	20.42	19.81	19.61	19.57	19.40	19.12	19.07	19.05
	19.01	18.98	18.48	18.39	18.37	18.21	13.02	NM	NM
	20.58	20.54	20.23	19.95	19.45	19.39	19.39	19.37	18.96
	18.69	18.67	18.53	18.29	18.23	18.22	17.98	17.29	16.51
Women	19.93	19.08	19.04	18.92	18.55	18.39	18.23	18.16	17.69
	17.14	16.40	15.91	DNS	19.36	19.29	19.22	19.03	19.02
	18.61	18.56	18.55	17.48	16.92	16.49	15.28	13.74	DNS

NM = No Measure DNS = Did Not Show

a. Identify and remove any outliers from the men's results and from the women's results.

b. Using the same number line base for both plots, make a box-and-whisker plot for the men's results and another for the women's results.

c. **Writing** Compare your box-and-whisker plots. Describe any conclusions you can draw about Olympic-level male and female shot-putters.

22. a. **Government** Make a box-and-whisker plot for the data from each of the three types of elections shown in the table below.

Voter Turnout (percent of voting-age population)

Presidential Year	1972	1976	1980	1984	1988	1992	1996
Voting for President	55.2	53.5	52.8	53.3	50.3	55.1	49.0
Voting for Representatives	50.7	48.9	47.6	47.8	44.9	50.8	45.8
Non-Presidential Year	**1974**	**1978**	**1982**	**1986**	**1990**	**1994**	**1998**
Voting for Representatives	35.9	34.9	38.0	33.5	33.1	36.6	32.9

SOURCE: U.S. Census Bureau. Go to **www.PHSchool.com** for a data update.
Web Code: agg-2041

b. **Writing** How does a Presidential election in the United States affect the voter turnout rate in elections for the House of Representatives? Use your box-and-whisker plots to describe any effect that you see.

Standardized Test Prep

Multiple Choice

A person checked for e-mail four times each day. The table shows the number of new e-mails she received each time she checked during 5 days.

Day 1	Day 2	Day 3	Day 4	Day 5
6, 3, 1, 5	5, 3, 7, 2	6, 7, 3, 2	8, 2, 6, 9	7, 7, 6, 11

23. Which value is the greatest?
A. the mean number of e-mails for checks made on days 1–3
B. the mean number of e-mails for checks made on days 2–4
C. the mean number of e-mails for checks made on days 2–3
D. the median number of e-mails for checks made on days 3–4

Take It to the NET

Online lesson quiz at **www.PHSchool.com**

Web Code: aga-1203

24. Which statement(s) is (are) true?

I. The mean number of e-mails for checks made over the 5 days was 5.3.
II. The mean number of e-mails for checks made on day 5 was 7.75.
III. The median number of e-mails for checks made over the 5 days was 6.5.

F. I only **G.** I and II only **H.** II and III only **I.** I, II, and III

Short Response

25. Describe how you could find the scores at the 20th and 60th percentiles in a set of 80 scores.

Extended Response

26. Draw a box-and-whisker plot for this set of values: 123, 127, 127, 142, 118, 131, 137, 125, 131.

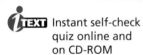

Mixed Review

Lesson 12-2

Of all the respondents to a survey, 59% are girls. Of the girls, 61% read horror stories. Of the boys, 49% read horror stories.

27. Find P(boy and reads horror stories). **28.** Find P(reads horror stories).

Lesson 11-2

Is the sequence arithmetic? If so, identify the common difference.

29. $16, 7, -2, \dots$ **30.** $34, 51, 68, \dots$ **31.** $2, 2.2, 2.22, \dots$ **32.** $1, 1, 1, \dots$

Lesson 10-2

Graph each equation.

33. $y^2 - x - 2y + 1 = 0$ **34.** $x^2 + 4x + 144y + 4 = 0$

Checkpoint Quiz 1 — Lessons 12-1 through 12-3

iTEXT Instant self-check quiz online and on CD-ROM

In a poll, gymnasts were asked, "How many seconds long was your longest handstand on the balance beam?" Use the results below for Exercises 1 and 2.

Longest Handstand

Duration (seconds)	0–2	3–5	6–10	11–20	21–30	31–60	>60	Total
Number of Respondents	14	27	19	18	13	15	24	130

1. Graph the probability distribution. **2.** Find P(6–30 seconds).

3. Writing Could the function $P(x) = \frac{x-2}{2}$ for $x = 1, 2, 3,$ or 4, represent a probability distribution? Explain.

Use the table at the right to find each probability.

4. $P(\text{teacher} \mid \text{yes})$ **5.** $P(\text{no} \mid \text{teacher})$

6. $P(\text{student} \mid \text{no})$ **7.** $P(\text{yes} \mid \text{student})$

Did You Eat Breakfast Today?

	Yes	No
Teachers	12	20
Students	45	23

Find the mean, median, and mode of each data set.

8. 7 4 9 3 5 4 4 7 9 10 3 1 8

9. 1.2 2.1 4.6 2.5 9.7 6.2 2.6 2.4 3.1 3.8

10. Open-Ended Write a data set that includes an outlier. Make a box-and-whisker plot of your data set with and without the outlier.

12-4 Standard Deviation

Lesson Preview

What You'll Learn

OBJECTIVE 1 To find the standard deviation of a set of values

OBJECTIVE 2 To use standard deviation in real-world situations

. . . And Why

To analyze energy demand, as in Example 3

Check Skills You'll Need

(For help, go to Skills Handbook page 845.)

Simplify each expression. If necessary, round to the nearest hundredth.

1. $\frac{34.3}{7}$

2. $\frac{6}{2.4}$

3. $8.4 \cdot 1.25$

4. $12 - 6 \cdot 0.5$

5. $\frac{1}{3}[(2-6)^2 + (7-6)^2 + (8-6)^2]$

6. $\sqrt{\frac{1}{2}(4-3)^2 + (5+3)^2}$

New Vocabulary

- measures of variation
- range of a set of data
- interquartile range
- standard deviation
- *z*-score

OBJECTIVE 1 Finding Standard Deviation

Interactive lesson includes instant self-check, tutorials, and activities.

Investigation: Analyzing Data Spread

1. a. Find the mean, the median, and the mode of each set of data.

Set 1	77	78	79	80	80	81	82	83
Set 2	20	60	70	80	80	90	100	140
Set 3	50	60	70	80	80	90	100	110
Set 4	20	30	40	80	80	120	130	140

b. Are the sets the same? Explain.

2. Find the difference between the greatest and least values in each set of data. What do these differences tell you about each set of data?

3. Find the quartiles of each set of data.

4. For each set, half of the data lie between Q_1 and Q_3. The value $Q_3 - Q_1$ gives you an idea of how the data are spread out. Find $Q_3 - Q_1$ for each set of data.

5. a. Give an example of two sets of data that are spread out differently, though the differences between their extreme values are the same.

b. Give an example of two sets of data that are spread out differently, though their values of $Q_3 - Q_1$ are the same.

6. a. Summarize the similarities and differences among the four sets in terms of central tendency and spread. Which is the most spread-out set? Which is the least? Explain.

b. Make box-and-whisker plots of the four sets of data. Do the plots support your conclusions from part (a)?

Real-World Connection

By age 29, skier Paul Casey Puckett had made the U.S. Olympic teams of 1992, 1994, 1998, and 2002.

Statisticians use several **measures of variation** to describe how the data in a data set are spread out.

The **range of a set of data** is the difference between the greatest and least values. The **interquartile range** is the difference between the third and first quartiles.

1 EXAMPLE Real-World Connection

Thirteen men qualified for the 2002 U.S. Men's Alpine Ski Team. Find the range and the interquartile range of their ages at the time of qualification: 27, 28, 29, 23, 25, 26, 26, 28, 22, 23, 23, 21, 25.

greatest value − least value $= 29 - 21$ **Find the range.**

$= 8$

Median ↓ **Find the median.**

21 22 23 23 23 25 25 26 26 27 28 28 29

$Q_1 = 23$ $\quad Q_3 = \frac{27 + 28}{2} = 27.5$ **Find Q_1 and Q_3.**

$Q_3 - Q_1 = 27.5 - 23$ **Find the interquartile range.**

$= 4.5$

The range is 8 years. The interquartile range is 4.5 years.

Check Understanding 1

a. Seventeen women qualified for the 2002 U.S. Women's Alpine Ski Team. Find the range and the interquartile range of their ages: 24, 30, 29, 21, 22, 22, 28, 21, 16, 17, 25, 22, 21, 18, 19, 18, 19.

b. **Critical Thinking** Can the variation, or spread, in two sets of data be different, even though they have the same range? Give an example.

c. Can the variation in two sets of data be different, even though they have the same interquartile range? Give an example.

Reading Math

The lower case Greek letter σ corresponds to the English letter *s*.

Another measure of variation is the **standard deviation,** a measure of how each value in a data set varies, or deviates, from the mean. The Greek letter σ (sigma) represents standard deviation.

You can use the following procedure to calculate standard deviation.

Key Concepts

Summary **Finding Standard Deviation**

- Find the mean of the data set: $\overline{x}$.
- Find the difference between each value and the mean: $x - \overline{x}$.
- Square each difference: $(x - \overline{x})^2$.
- Find the average (mean) of these squares: $\frac{\sum(x - \overline{x})^2}{n}$.
- Take the square root to find the standard deviation:

$$\sigma = \sqrt{\frac{\sum(x - \overline{x})^2}{n}}.$$

Need Help?

Σ means summation.

2 EXAMPLE Finding the Standard Deviation

Find the mean and the standard deviation for the values: 48.0, 53.2, 52.3, 46.6, 49.9.

$$\bar{x} = \frac{48.0 + 53.2 + 52.3 + 46.6 + 49.9}{5} = 50.0$$

Find the mean.

Organize the next steps in a table.

x	$\bar{x}$	$x - \bar{x}$	$(x - \bar{x})^2$
48.0	50.0	−2.0	4.00
53.2	50.0	3.2	10.24
52.3	50.0	2.3	5.29
46.6	50.0	−3.4	11.56
49.9	50.0	−0.1	0.01

Sum: 31.1

$$\sigma = \sqrt{\frac{\sum (x - \bar{x})^2}{n}}$$

Find the standard deviation.

$$= \sqrt{\frac{31.1}{5}} \approx 2.5$$

The mean is 50.0, and the standard deviation is about 2.5.

Check Understanding **2** Find the mean and the standard deviation for these values: 50, 60, 70, 80, 80, 90, 100, 110.

Standard deviation is like a custom-made measuring stick for the variation in a set of data. A small standard deviation (compared to actual data values) indicates that the data are clustered tightly around the mean. As the data become more spread out, the standard deviation increases.

3 EXAMPLE Real-World Connection

Energy Find the mean and the standard deviation of the data for daily energy demand in a small town during August.

Reading Math

The watt is the metric unit of measurement for power. One million watts of power delivered for one hour results in one megawatt-hour (MWh).

Daily Energy Demand During August (MWh)

Sun.	Mon.	Tues.	Wed.	Thurs.	Fri.	Sat.
		53	52	47	50	39
33	40	41	44	47	49	43
39	47	49	54	53	46	36
33	45	45	42	43	39	33
33	40	40	41	42		

Step 1 Use the STAT feature to enter the data as L1.

Step 2 Use the CALC menu of STAT to access the 1-Var Stats option.

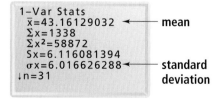

```
1-Var Stats
 x̄=43.16129032      ← mean
 Σx=1338
 Σx²=58872
 Sx=6.116081394
 σx=6.016626288     ← standard deviation
↓n=31
```

The mean is about 43.2 MWh; the standard deviation is about 6.0 MWh.

Check Understanding **3** Find the mean and standard deviation for this data set: 2 mm, 3 mm, 4 mm, 6 mm, 7 mm, 9 mm, 10 mm, 12 mm, 13 mm, 14 mm.

OBJECTIVE

2 Using Standard Deviation

In a data list, every value falls within some number of standard deviations of the mean. When a value falls within one standard deviation of the mean, it is in the range of values from one standard deviation below the mean to one standard deviation above. For example, if the mean is 50 and the standard deviation is 10, then a value x within one standard deviation of the mean must be in the range $40 \leq x \leq 60$.

4 EXAMPLE Real-World Connection

Real-World Connection

Careers Dispatchers coordinate a utility's power supply and demand.

Energy Use the energy demand data from Example 3. Within how many standard deviations of the mean do all of the values fall? How might the company supplying power to the town use this information?

Step 1 Draw a number line. Plot the data values and the mean.

Step 2 Mark off intervals of 6.0 on either side of the mean.

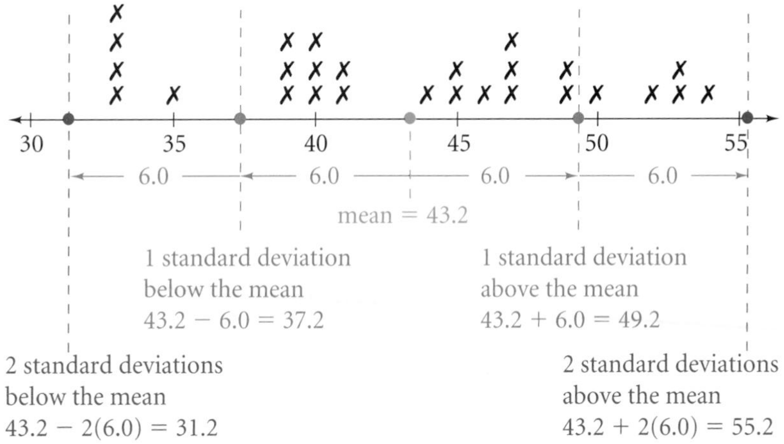

All of the values fall within two standard deviations of the mean. Therefore, the power company can expect that the daily demand on most days in August will fall within two standard deviations of the mean.

Check Understanding **4** **a.** Within how many standard deviations of the mean for August is a demand of 38.5 MWh?

b. In May, the mean daily energy demand is 35.8 MWh, with a standard deviation of 3.5 MWh. The power company prepares for any demand within three standard deviations of the mean. Are they prepared for a demand of 48 MWh? Explain.

The **z-score** is the number of standard deviations that a value is from the mean. In Example 4, the value 49.2 is one standard deviation above the mean, so it has a z-score of 1. The value 37.2, which is one standard deviation below the mean, has a z-score of -1.

5 EXAMPLE Finding the z-score

A set of values has a mean of 85 and a standard deviation of 6. Find the z-score of the value 76.

$$z\text{-score} = \frac{\text{value} - \text{mean}}{\text{standard deviation}}$$

$$= \frac{76 - 85}{6} \quad \textbf{Substitute.}$$

$$= \frac{-9}{6} \quad \textbf{Simplify.}$$

$$= -1.5$$

Check Understanding 5 Use the mean and standard deviation from Example 5. Find the value that has a z-score of 2.5.

EXERCISES

For more practice, see *Extra Practice.*

Practice and Problem Solving

A Practice by Example

Example 1 (page 657)

Find the range and the interquartile range of each set of values.

1. 5 6 7 3 4 5 6 7 8

2. 56 78 125 34 67 91 20

3. 724 786 670 760 300 187 190 345 456 732 891 879 324

Examples 2 and 3 (page 658)

Find the mean and the standard deviation for each set of values.

4. 78 90 456 673 111 381 21

5. 13 15 17 18 12 21 10

6. The Dow Jones Industrial average for the first 24 weeks of 1991:

2501.50	2646.80	2659.40	2730.70	2830.70	2934.70
2889.40	2909.90	2955.20	2948.30	2558.90	2913.90
2896.80	2920.80	2965.60	2912.40	2938.90	2920.20
2886.60	2913.90	3027.50	2976.70	3000.50	2965.60

7. The Dow Jones Industrial average for the first 24 weeks of 2001:

10662.01	10525.38	10587.59	10659.98	10864.10	10781.45
10799.82	10441.90	10466.31	10644.62	9823.41	9504.78
9878.78	9791.09	10126.94	10579.85	10810.05	10951.24
10821.31	11301.74	11005.37	10990.41	10977.00	10623.64

Example 4 (page 659)

Determine the whole number of standard deviations that includes all data values.

8. The mean price of the nonfiction books on a best-sellers list is \$25.07; the standard deviation is \$2.62.
\$26.95, \$22.95, \$24.00, \$24.95, \$29.95, \$19.95, \$24.95, \$24.00, \$27.95, \$25.00

9. The mean length of Beethoven's nine symphonies is 37 minutes; the standard deviation is 12 minutes.
27 min, 30 min, 47 min, 35 min, 30 min, 40 min, 35 min, 22 min, 65 min

Example 5 (page 660)

A data set has mean 25 and standard deviation 5. Find the z-score of each value.

10. 39 **11.** 18 **12.** 125 **13.** 25 **14.** 11

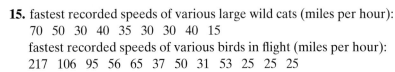

B Apply Your Skills **Find the standard deviation for each data set. Use the standard deviations to compare each pair of data sets.**

15. fastest recorded speeds of various large wild cats (miles per hour):
70 50 30 40 35 30 30 40 15
fastest recorded speeds of various birds in flight (miles per hour):
217 106 95 56 65 37 50 31 53 25 25 25

16. the number of buttons on selected outfits:
11 5 12 8 3 12 10 10 0 5 0 2 7 10
the number of pockets in the same outfits:
5 5 5 2 2 5 3 2 0 2 0 0 5 5

Real-World Connection

The fastest wild cat is the cheetah, which can run as fast as 70 mi/h.

Income **Use the chart at the right for Exercises 17–20.**

17. Find the mean income for each year.

18. Writing Use the range of the data for each year to describe how farm income varied from 1998 to 1999.

19. Find the standard deviation for each year. In which year did farm income cluster more tightly around the mean?

20. Which state's 1998 income has a z-score of about 1.6?

Farm Income in Midwestern States (millions of dollars)

State	1998	1999
Iowa	12,153	10,812
Kansas	8688	8565
Minnesota	8971	8010
Missouri	5464	4902
Nebraska	9827	9429
North Dakota	3664	2921
South Dakota	4264	3974

21. a. Energy Find the mean and the standard deviation for daily energy usage during ten days in June: 51.8 MWh, 53.6 MWh, 54.7 MWh, 51.9 MWh, 49.3 MWh, 52.0 MWh, 53.5 MWh, 51.2 MWh, 60.7 MWh, 59.3 MWh.

b. How many items in the data set fall within one standard deviation of the mean? Within two standard deviations? Within three standard deviations?

Another measure of variation is *variance*, which equals σ^2. Find the variance and the standard deviation of each data set.

22. 12 h 3 h 2 h 4 h 5 h 7 h

23. 60 m 40 m 35 m 45 m 39 m

24. \$6.99 \$5.50 \$7.10 \$9.22 \$8.99

25. 0.7 g 0.84 g 0.9 g 0.8 g 0.69 g

26. Critical Thinking From your results in Exercises 22–25, which do you think is a better measure of variation—variance or standard deviation? Explain.

27. Error Analysis Minh says that the data below fall within three standard deviations of the mean. Marsha disagrees, saying that the data fall within six standard deviations of the mean. With whom do you agree? Explain.

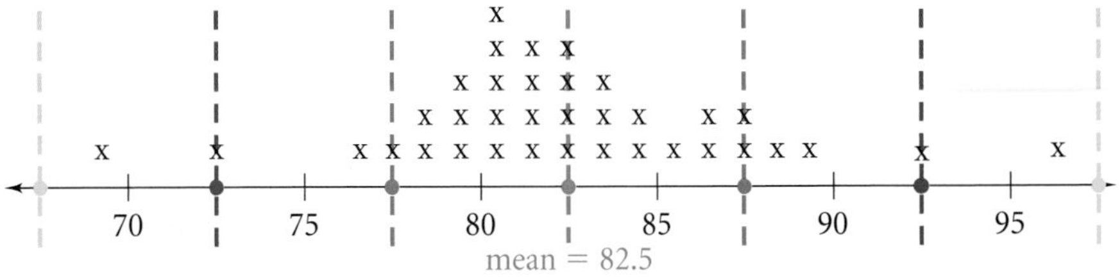

28. a. **Data Collection** Make a table showing the number of siblings of each student in the class.
   b. Find the mean and standard deviation of the data.

Challenge

29. a. Use the table at the left to find the range, the mean, and the standard deviation of the ages for each team.
   b. **Critical Thinking** For two data sets, does the set with the larger range necessarily have the larger standard deviation? Support your answer with your results from part (a).

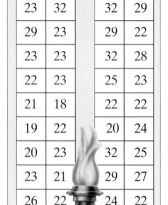

Ages of the Members of the 2000 U.S. Olympic Soccer Teams

Men		Women	
23	32	32	29
29	23	29	22
23	23	32	28
22	23	25	23
21	18	22	22
19	22	20	24
20	23	32	25
23	21	29	27
26	22	24	22

30. **Earnings** The table at the right shows the median weekly earnings of union and nonunion workers in various occupations.
   a. Find the mean and the range of the data for union workers and for nonunion workers.
   b. Find the standard deviation for each set of data.
   c. Within how many standard deviations of the mean are earnings of $395 for union workers? For nonunion workers?
   d. **Writing** Compare the wages of union and nonunion workers. Use your results from parts (a) through (c).

Worker's Median Weekly Earnings, 1999

Occupation	Union	Nonunion
Construction	$778	$509
Transportation and public utilities	$748	$613
Trade	$499	$418
Manufacturing	$614	$561
Services	$554	$515
Finance, insurance, and real estate	$582	$599
Mining	$710	$735

SOURCE: U.S. Bureau of Labor Statistics.
Go to **www.PHSchool.com** for a data update.
Web Code: agg-2041

Standardized Test Prep

Gridded Response

For Exercises 31–32, use the following bowling scores for six members of a bowling team: 175, 210, 180, 195, 208, 196.

31. What is the mean of the scores?

32. What is the standard deviation of the scores?

33. At a second bowling tournament, the mean of all the scores was 205, with a standard deviation of 14. What was the *z*-score for a score of 282?

34. At the second tournament, a participant had a *z*-score of −2.5. What was the participant's bowling score?

Take It to the NET
Online lesson quiz at **www.PHSchool.com**
Web Code: aga-1204

Mixed Review

Lesson 12-3

Make a box-and-whisker plot for each set of values.

35. 25, 25, 30, 35, 45, 45, 50, 55, 60, 60

36. 20, 23, 25, 36, 37, 38, 39, 50, 52, 55

Lesson 11-3

Find the missing positive term in each geometric sequence.

37. 64, ■, 4, . . .

38. 20, ■, 0.05, . . .

39. 29, ■, 65.25, . . .

Lesson 10-3

Graph each circle.

40. $(x - 2)^2 + (y + 1)^2 = 36$

41. $(x - 1)^2 + (y - 1)^2 = 4$

12-5 Working With Samples

Lesson Preview

What You'll Learn

OBJECTIVE 1 To find sample proportions

OBJECTIVE 2 To find the margin of error

. . . And Why

To analyze data from a poll, as in Example 5

✓ Check Skills You'll Need

(For help, go to Lesson 7-1.)

Simplify each expression.

1. $\frac{1}{\sqrt{4}}$ **2.** $-\frac{1}{\sqrt{9}}$ **3.** $\frac{1}{\sqrt{36}}$

4. $-\frac{1}{\sqrt{121}}$ **5.** $\frac{1}{\sqrt{50}}$ **6.** $-\frac{1}{\sqrt{81}}$

New Vocabulary

- sample
- sample proportion
- random sample
- margin of error

Interactive lesson includes instant self-check, tutorials, and activities.

OBJECTIVE 1 Sampling Without Bias

Suppose you want to know what percent of all teenagers recognize the word that means "to pass the summer in a state of slumber." Since it is too costly and time consuming to ask every teenager, use a sample. A **sample** gathers information from only part of a population.

Using any sample, you can find a sample proportion. The **sample proportion** is the ratio $\frac{x}{n}$, where x is the number of times an event occurs in a sample of size n.

Word Wise

Which word means "to pass the summer in a state of slumber"?

A. stridulate
B. ruminate
C. estivate
D. somnambulate

1 EXAMPLE Finding the Sample Proportion

In a sample of 350 teenagers, 294 have never made a snow sculpture. Find the sample proportion for those who have never made a snow sculpture. Write the answer as a percent.

sample proportion	$= \frac{x}{n}$	**Write the formula.**
	$= \frac{294}{350}$	**Substitute 294 for x and 350 for n.**
	$= 0.84$	**Simplify.**

The sample proportion is 84%.

✓ Check Understanding

1 In a poll of 1085 voters, 564 favor Candidate A. Find the sample proportion for those who favor Candidate A.

Samples vary in how well they reflect the entire population. In a **random sample,** all members of the population are equally likely to be chosen.

When a part of a population is overrepresented or underrepresented in a sample, the sample is biased. A random sample can help avoid bias in gathering data.

Reading Math

Bias means "slant."

2 EXAMPLE Real-World Connection

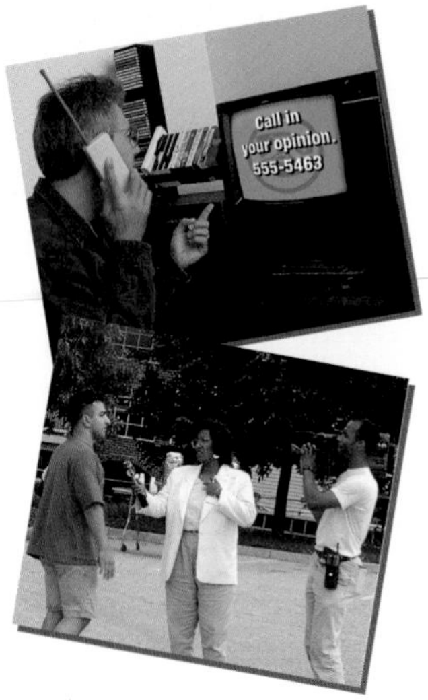

Public Opinion A news program reports on a proposed school dress code. The purpose of the program is to find out what percent of the population in its viewing area favors the dress code. Identify any bias in each sampling method.

a. Viewers are invited to call the program and express their preferences.

The people who decide to call in may over- or underrepresent some views. For example, members of a group favoring the new dress code might encourage its members to call in. This type of sample is called a "self-selected" sample.

b. A reporter interviews people on the street near the local high school.

This is a "convenience" sample, since it is convenient for the reporter to stay in one place. Because the location is near the school, students may be overrepresented in the sample and the results will be biased.

c. During the program, 300 people are selected at random from the viewing area. Then each person is contacted.

This sampling method contains the least bias. It is a random sample.

Check Understanding 2 **a.** Suppose the 350 teenagers in Example 1 all live in Florida. Is there bias in this sample? Explain.

b. **Critical Thinking** The only way to know a true population proportion is to poll every person in the population. Such a poll is no longer a sample, but a census. Describe a situation in which a sample is unsatisfactory and a census is required.

OBJECTIVE

2 Sample Size

The size of a sample affects its reliability. With a small sample size, you are likely to get a wide range of sample proportions. For example, in some samples, no one will recognize the word that means "to pass the summer in a state of slumber." In other samples, everyone will recognize *estivate*. With larger sample sizes, you are less likely to have a sample containing an "all or nothing" result.

The Law of Large Numbers states that the variation in a data set decreases as the sample size increases. By comparing the variation in samples, you can get an idea of their relative sizes.

3 EXAMPLE Comparing Sample Sizes

Each graph below shows the sample proportions for 20 samples. Match each graph to the most likely sample size.

a. 20 people per sample

b. 5 people per sample

Distributions of Sample Proportions

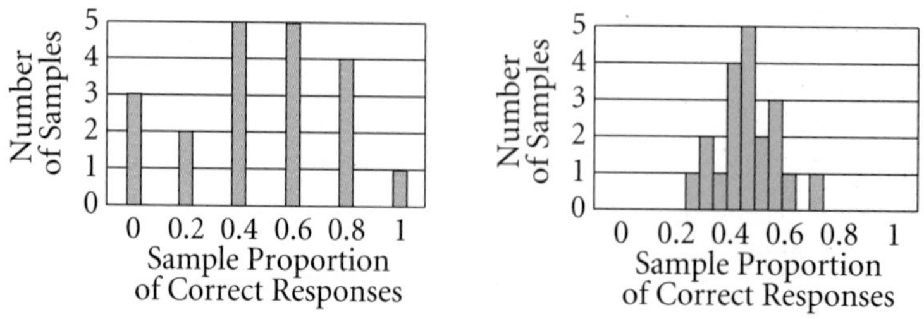

a. The graph on the right shows less variation, so it is more likely to be based on samples of a larger size, 20 people per sample.

b. The graph on the left shows more variation, so it is more likely be based on 5 people per sample.

Check Understanding **3** A science class measured the heights of blades of grass behind the school. The class took three samples. Use the information in the table below to decide which sample most likely was the greatest in size. Explain your reasoning.

Sample	Standard Deviation (in.)
A	1.45
B	1.09
C	1.26

A sample proportion should be reported with an estimate of error, called the **margin of error.** The margin of error is based on the standard deviation in graphs like those in Example 3. The larger the sample size, the smaller the margin of error.

Key Concepts

Property **Margin of Error Formula**

When a random sample of size n is taken from a large population, the sample proportion has a margin of error of approximately $\pm\frac{1}{\sqrt{n}}$.

4 EXAMPLE Using the Margin of Error

A poll reports that 56% of voters favor Candidate B, with a margin of error of ±3%. Estimate the number of voters in the poll.

$\text{margin of error} = \pm\frac{1}{\sqrt{n}}$	**Write the formula.**
$\pm\sqrt{n} = \frac{1}{\text{margin of error}}$	**Rewrite the equation.**
$= \frac{1}{0.03}$	**Substitute 0.03 for margin of error.**
≈ 33.33	**Simplify.**
$n \approx 1111$	**Square each side.**

The poll included about 1100 voters.

Check Understanding **4** Estimate the sample size for each margin of error.

a. ±10% **b.** ±4% **c.** ±2%

You can use the margin of error to determine the likely range for the true population proportion. The graph below shows the range for the population in Example 4.

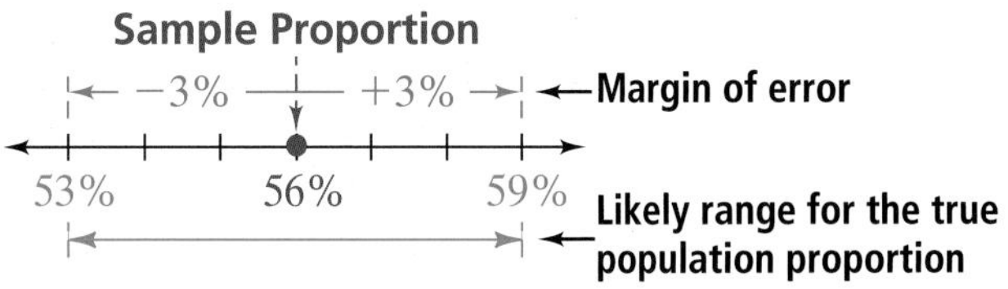

Real-World Connection

Some retail businesses cater to left-handers.

5 EXAMPLE — Real-World Connection

Genetics A survey of 2580 students found that 9% are left-handed.

a. Find the margin of error for the sample.

margin of error	$= \pm\frac{1}{\sqrt{n}}$	**Use the formula.**
	$= \pm\frac{1}{\sqrt{2580}}$	**Substitute.**
	$\approx \pm 0.0197$	**Use a calculator.**

The margin of error is about $\pm 2\%$.

b. Use the margin of error to find an interval that is likely to contain the true population proportion.

The margin of error forms an interval with the sample proportion at its midpoint.

Sample Proportion

$|\leftarrow -2\% \rightarrow|\leftarrow +2\% \rightarrow|$

7% 9% 11%

The proportion of students who are left-handed is likely to be from 7% to 11%.

Check Understanding **5** In a poll of 123 students, 87 have never ridden a ferry. Find the sample proportion, the margin of error, and the interval likely to contain the true population proportion.

EXERCISES

For more practice, see *Extra Practice*.

Practice and Problem Solving

A Practice by Example

Example 1 (page 663)

For each sample, find the sample proportion. Write it as a percent.

1. 837 out of 1150 insurance applicants have no citations on their driving record.
2. 27 out of 60 shoppers prefer generic brands when available.
3. 532 out of 580 households own a color television set.

Example 2 (page 664)

Identify any bias in each sampling method.

4. A supermarket wants to find the proportion of shoppers who use reduced-price coupons. A manager interviews every shopper entering the greeting card aisle.
5. A maintenance crew wants to estimate how many of 3000 air filters in an office building need replacing. The crew examines five filters chosen at random on each floor of the building.
6. The student government wants to find out how many students have after-school jobs. A pollster interviews students selected at random as they board buses at the end of the school day.

Example 3 (pages 664–665)

7. In a survey, teenagers were asked the importance of "making your own things." The response scale ranged from 1 to 5, with 5 being extremely important. Which sample most likely was largest? Explain.

Sample	Score	Standard Deviation
A	3.6	1.2
B	3.8	1.0
C	3.8	0.5

8. The table below shows the results of a poll asking students, "How many hours a week would you say you spend doing academic homework?" Which sample most likely was smaller? Explain.

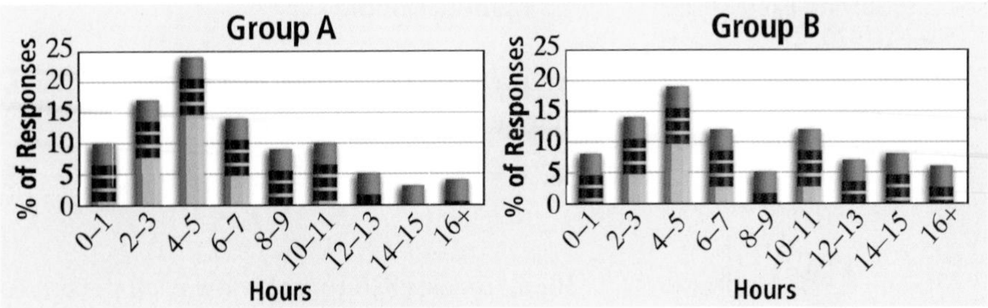

Example 4 (page 665)

Find the margin of error for the sample proportion, given each sample of size *n*.

9. $n = 200$ **10.** $n = 800$ **11.** $n = 1200$

Find the sample size that produces each margin of error.

12. $\pm 8\%$ **13.** $\pm 5\%$ **14.** $\pm 1\%$

Example 5 (page 666)

For each situation, find the margin of error for the sample. Then find an interval likely to contain the true population proportion.

15. Of 750 teenagers polled, 59% think boys and girls are portrayed as equals on television.

16. Of 400 teenagers surveyed, 62% do not plan to stay in their community after finishing their education.

B Apply Your Skills

Surveys **For each sample, find (a) the sample proportion, (b) the margin of error, and (c) the interval likely to contain the true population proportion.**

17. In a random sample of 408 grocery shoppers, 258 prefer one large trip per week to several smaller ones.

18. Of 500 teenagers surveyed, 460 would like to see adults in their community do more to solve drug problems.

19. In a survey of 32 people, 30 return a milk carton to the refrigerator immediately after using it.

20. In a survey of 16 people, one person never locks his car.

21. Writing Write a news article describing the sample proportion and margin of error for the poll results shown at the right.

dailypoll
Do you save more than 5% of your income?
yes
no
dailypoll
Results:
yes 370
no 583

22. Reasoning How is the margin of error affected if you double the sample size? Explain.

23. a. Data Collection Write a survey question to find out the number of students at your school who plan to continue their education after high school

b. Describe the sampling method you would use.

c. Conduct your survey.

24. Critical Thinking A sample proportion provides an estimate for the percent of an entire population that favors an event. Is a sample proportion an experimental or a theoretical probability? Explain.

Reading Math

For help with reading and solving Exercise 25, see p. 670.

25. **Computer Use** An online advertisement asks you to participate in a survey. The survey asks how much time you spend online each week. Identify any bias in this method. If appropriate, suggest a method more likely to produce a random sample.

An event occurs x times in a sample of size n. Find its sample proportion and margin of error.

26. $x = 96$, $n = 900$
27. $x = 20$, $n = 64$
28. $x = 100$, $n = 250$
29. $x = 273$, $n = 435$

C Challenge

30. a. It costs \$20 to interview each person for a survey. Find the cost to obtain a $\pm3\%$ margin of error.
    b. **Critical Thinking** Find the cost to obtain a $\pm2\%$ margin of error. Why do you think polls with smaller margins of error are rare?

31. a. **Elections** A poll of 150 voters shows that a candidate is preferred by 56% of the voters while 44% prefer the opponent. Should the candidate be concerned? Explain.
    b. A later poll of 600 voters shows the candidate is preferred by 55% of the voters. Should this candidate feel more or less confident, given the results of the second poll? Explain.

Exercise 32

32. **Wildlife** Wild animal populations are often estimated through the use of the capture–tag–recapture method. Several animals are captured, tagged, and released back into the wild. The animals continue to roam freely. Then, some time later at the same site, several more animals are captured, and the number of tagged animals is recorded. An estimate of the population can then be calculated. This method of estimation assumes that the fraction of tagged animals in the second sample is equivalent to the fraction of tagged animals in the entire population.

$$\frac{\text{tagged animals in second sample}}{\text{animals in second sample}} = \frac{\text{tagged animals in population}}{\text{population } (P)}$$

Use the formula above to predict the black bear population of the northern coastal plain of South Carolina. Researchers tagged fourteen black bears in the fall and captured eleven bears the following summer. Of the eleven bears, three were tagged.

Standardized Test Prep

Multiple Choice

33. In a sample of 625 airline travelers, 485 collected "airline miles" toward free trips. What does the number $\frac{140}{625}$ represent?
    A. the probability that a passenger collects airline miles
    B. the sample proportion of the travelers who do not collect airline miles
    C. the sample proportion of the travelers who collect airline miles
    D. the margin of error for the sample

34. A random sample of people answered the question "Do you collect airline miles?" The margin of error for the sample was $\pm2\%$. The sample proportion of people who answered no was $\frac{3}{10}$. How many people in the sample answered no?
    F. 15 **G.** 225 **H.** 750 **I.** 2500

Take It to the NET
Online lesson quiz at **www.PHSchool.com**
Web Code: aga-1205

35. A research group had a stack of survey responses. The number of respondents was more than 5000 and fewer than 5500. When the researchers divided the respondents into 13 equal groups, there were no extra respondents. Similarly, there were no extra respondents when they divided the responses into 7 equal groups or 11 equal groups. How many respondents were there?
A. 1001 **B.** 5005 **C.** 5031 **D.** 500,500

Short Response

36. What is the margin of error for a random sample of size 3600? Show your work.

Extended Response

37. In a poll of 2750 airline travelers, 138 said they never check their luggage when they fly. Find the sample proportion, the margin of error, and the interval likely to contain the true population proportion.

Mixed Review

Lesson 12-4

Find the mean and the standard deviation for each data set.

38. 0 km, 1 km, 1 km, 1 km, 2 km, 2 km, 2 km, 3 km, 3 km, 4 km, 5 km, 10 km

39. 1 oz, 1 oz, 2 oz, 2 oz, 3 oz, 4 oz, 5 oz, 6 oz, 8 oz, 9 oz, 10 oz, 10 oz, 12 oz, 20 oz

Lesson 11-4

Use summation notation to write each arithmetic series for the specified number of terms.

40. $3 + 8 + 13 + \ldots; n = 5$

41. $41 + 33 + 25 + \ldots; n = 8$

42. $-14 + (-8) + (-2) + \ldots; n = 6$

43. $-27 + (-21) + (-15) + \ldots; n = 10$

Lesson 10-4

Find the equation of each ellipse centered at the origin.

44. height: 20 units
width: 6 units

45. height: 12 units
width: 10 units

46. height: 24 units
width: 36 units

Algebra at Work

Market Researcher

When questions arise about consumer products or services, a market researcher gathers statistical information to help answer the questions. The information a market researcher collects and analyzes helps companies improve their products and make decisions about their customer base. Quantitative research allows a market researcher to analyze data from a large population of potential customers. Market research strategies for gathering information include the following.

- mail surveys
- focus groups
- telephone surveys
- in-person interviews

Take It to the NET For more information about market research, go to **www.PHSchool.com**.
Web Code: agb-2031

Reading Math

Reading Math Vocabulary

For Use With Page 668, Exercise 25

Read the problem below. Notice that the mathematical meaning of a word may differ from the English meaning. Check your understanding with the exercise at the bottom of the page.

Computer Use An online advertisement asks you to participate in a survey. The survey asks how much time you spend online each week. Identify any bias in this method. If appropriate, suggest a method more likely to produce a random sample.

The table below shows both English and mathematical meanings for the words *sample, bias,* and *random.* In mathematics, an English word can be used either

- in a way that makes use of its common English meaning and applies that meaning to mathematical concepts, or
- in a way that differs from its common English meaning.

WORD	ENGLISH MEANING	MATHEMATICAL MEANING
Sample	an example (noun); or to test or try out (verb)	a part of a group or population
Bias	a tendency to prejudge (noun); or to influence in a way that would cause prejudgment (verb)	A sample is *biased* if it does not represent the population.
Random	by chance or without planning (adjective)	A *random sample* is a part of a population chosen in such a way that all members have an equal chance of being chosen.

If you have questions about the meaning of a word, look it up in the dictionary before you begin working. A good dictionary includes mathematical meanings.

Take a look at Exercise 25.

What bias is there in asking you how much time you spend online each week?

The advertisement was posted online, so only people online would be able to see and take the survey. This automatically excludes people who rarely go online, which would bias the sample by overrepresenting people who go online.

If appropriate, suggest a method more likely to produce a random sample.

One way would be to conduct a survey by phone of a specific number of households, chosen at random throughout a given geographical area.

EXERCISE

Think of another way the sample might be biased.

12-6 Binomial Distributions

Lesson Preview

What You'll Learn

OBJECTIVE 1 To find binomial probabilities

OBJECTIVE 2 To use binomial distributions

. . . And Why

To find the probability of winning a prize, as in Example 2

✓ Check Skills You'll Need

(For help, go to Lessons 6-7 and 6-8.)

Evaluate each expression.

1. ${}_4C_2$ **2.** ${}_3C_3$ **3.** ${}_5C_2$

Use the binomial theorem to expand each binomial.

4. $(x + 2)^3$ **5.** $(w - y)^4$

6. $(m + n)^3$ **7.** $(t + 3s)^4$

8. $(a + 2b)^5$ **9.** $(p + q)^6$

New Vocabulary • binomial experiment • binomial probability

Interactive lesson includes instant self-check, tutorials, and activities.

OBJECTIVE 1 Finding Binomial Probabilities

Investigation: Binomial Probability

1. Examine the situations described in the chart below. What do the situations printed in blue have in common?

receive a numerical grade
receive a pass/fail grade
wear soccer, running, basketball, or street shoes
wear shoes with cleats or no cleats
guess on a matching test
guess on a true/false test

2. Suppose you guess each answer on a ten-question true-or-false test. Are you likely to get 70% or more right?
   a. Design and conduct a simulation for this situation.
   b. Run your simulation 10 times. Make a frequency table of the scores.
   c. Find P(70% or more right).

Need Help?

You can use a coin, a number cube, or random numbers to conduct a simulation.

A **binomial experiment** has three important features:

- The situation involves repeated trials.
- Each trial has two possible outcomes (success or failure).
- The probability of success is constant throughout the trials. (The trials are independent.)

1 EXAMPLE Designing a Binomial Experiment

Suppose that you guess the answers to three questions of a multiple-choice test. Each question has five choices, with one correct choice.

a. Describe a trial for this situation. How many trials are there?

Each guess is a trial. Since you are guessing three times, there are three trials.

b. Describe a success. What is the probability of success on any single trial?

Each correct answer is a success. Since there are five possible answers, all of them equally likely, the probability of success on any single trial is 0.2.

c. Design and conduct a simulation to determine the probability of getting at least two answers correct. Run the simulation 10 times.

Assign each number from 1 to 5 to an outcome, based on each outcome's probability. Let 1 represent a correct response. Let 2–5 represent incorrect responses. Generate random numbers from 1 to 5.

Simulation	1	2	3	4	5	6	7	8	9	10
Number Generated, Trial 1	2	4	2	5	5	2	1	5	1	2
Number Generated, Trial 2	1	1	5	4	4	5	1	4	5	1
Number Generated, Trial 3	1	3	1	2	2	5	4	2	3	2
Number of Correct Guesses	2	1	1	0	0	0	2	0	1	1

Two of the simulations result in two or more correct guesses. So the experimental probability of getting at least two answers correct is $\frac{2}{10}$, or 20%.

Check Understanding 1 Run the simulation an additional 15 times. Use the results of all 25 simulations to find the experimental probability of getting at least two answers correct.

You can use a tree diagram to analyze binomial probabilities.

2 EXAMPLE Real-World Connection

Merchandising As part of a promotion, a store is giving away scratch-off cards. Prizes are awarded on 40% of the game cards. Suppose you have three cards. Find the probability that exactly two of the three cards will reveal a prize.

Each card represents a trial with a probability of success of 0.4. The probability of failure is 0.6. The tree diagram below shows the probabilities along each path.

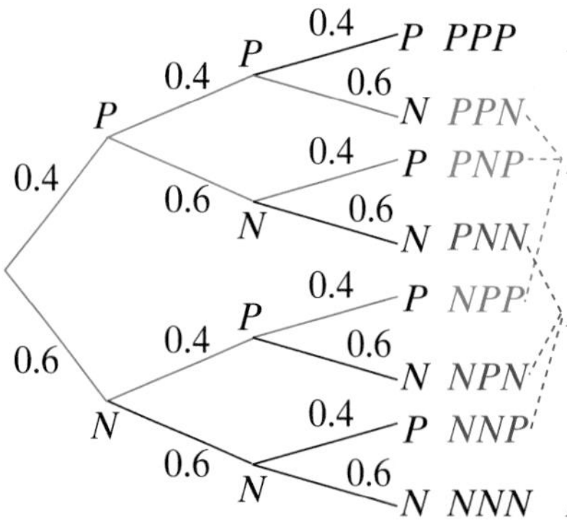

$P(\text{three prizes}) = 1(0.4)^3 = 0.064$

Number of paths

$P(\text{two prizes}) = 3(0.4)^2(0.6) = 0.288$

$P(\text{one prize}) = \blacksquare(0.4)^{\blacksquare}(0.6)^{\blacksquare} = \blacksquare$

$P(\text{no prize}) = \blacksquare(0.6)^{\blacksquare} = \blacksquare$

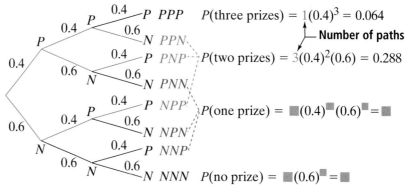

The probability that exactly two of three cards will reveal a prize is 0.288.

Check Understanding **2** **a.** Complete the tree diagram in Example 2 by finding the probability of receiving one prize and the probability of receiving no prize.
b. Verify your work by adding the probabilities for three, two, one, and no prizes. What answer should you get?

The relationships you have seen are summarized in the following formula.

Key Concepts

Need Help?

$$_nC_r = \frac{n!}{r!(n-r)!}$$

Definition **Binomial Probability**

Suppose you have repeated independent trials, each with a probability of success p and a probability of failure q (with $p + q = 1$). Then the probability of x successes in n trials is the following product.

$$_nC_x p^x q^{n-x}$$

3 EXAMPLE **Real-World Connection**

Quality Control A calculator contains four batteries. With normal use, each battery has a 90% chance of lasting for one year. What is the probability that all four batteries will last a year?

Relate This is a binomial experiment.

- There are four batteries.
- Each battery may succeed or fail.
- The probability of success is 0.9 for each battery.

Define Let $n = 4$. Let $x = 4$.
Let $p = 0.9$. Let $q = 0.1$.

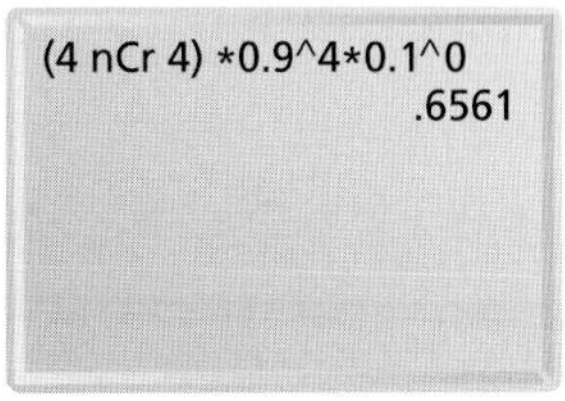

Write

$$\begin{aligned} {}_nC_x p^x q^{n-x} &= {}_4C_4(0.9)^4(0.1)^0 && \textbf{Substitute.} \\ &= (1)(0.9)^4(1) && \textbf{Simplify.} \\ &= 0.6561 && \textbf{Simplify.} \end{aligned}$$

The probability that all four batteries will last one year is about 66%.

Check Understanding **3** Find the probability of x successes in n trials for the given probability of success p on each trial.

a. $x = 2, n = 5, p = 0.25$ **b.** $x = 8, n = 10, p = 0.7$

OBJECTIVE 2

Using a Binomial Distribution

To find the full probability distribution for a binomial experiment, expand the binomial $(p + q)^n$. For example, suppose you guess on four questions of a five-choice multiple choice test. For four questions, $n = 4, p = 0.2$, and $q = 0.8$.

$$\begin{array}{rcccccccccc} & & \text{4 correct} & & \text{3 correct} & & \text{2 correct} & & \text{1 correct} & & \text{0 correct} \\ (p+q)^4 & = & 1p^4 & + & 4p^3q & + & 6p^2q^2 & + & 4pq^3 & + & 1q^4 \\ & = & (0.2)^4 & + & 4(0.2)^3(0.8) & + & 6(0.2)^2(0.8)^2 & + & 4(0.2)(0.8)^3 & + & (0.8)^4 \\ & = & 0.0016 & + & 0.0256 & + & 0.1536 & + & 0.4096 & + & 0.4096 \end{array}$$

Of course, you can display a binomial distribution as a graph.

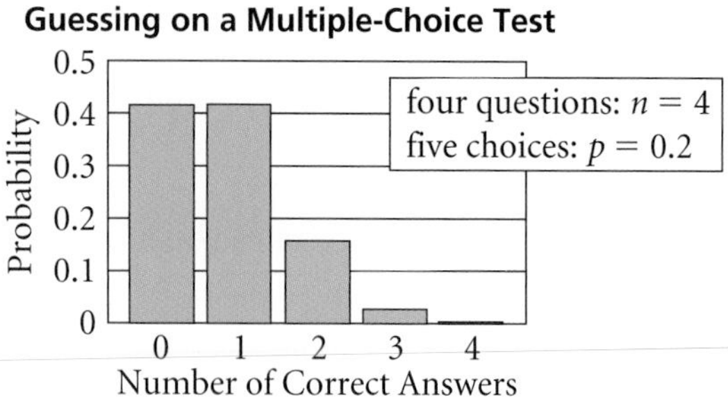

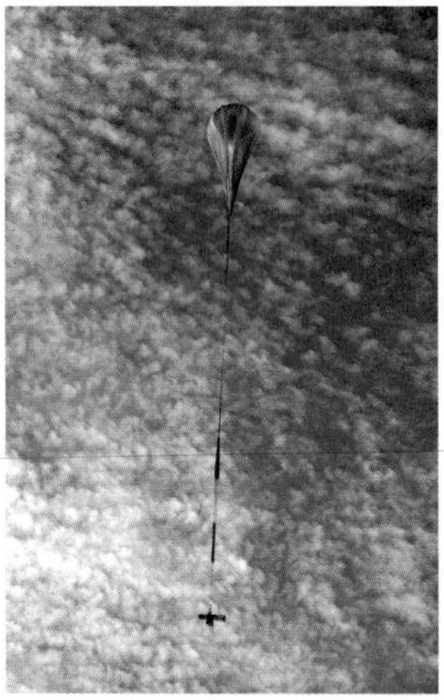

Real-World Connection

The air pressure inside a teardrop-shaped weather balloon remains constant as the balloon rises. Lower outside air pressure at higher altitudes causes the balloon to expand.

4 EXAMPLE **Real-World Connection**

Weather A scientist hopes to launch a weather balloon on one of the next three mornings. For each morning, there is a 40% chance of suitable weather. What is the probability that there will be at least one morning with suitable weather?

Use the expansion for $(p + q)^n$, with $n = 3, p = 0.4$, and $q = 0.6$.

		3 successes		2 successes		1 success		0 successes
$(p+q)^3$	=	$1p^3$	+	$3p^2q$	+	$3pq^2$	+	$1q^3$
	=	$(0.4)^3$	+	$3(0.4)^2(0.6)$	+	$3(0.4)(0.6)^2$	+	$(0.6)^3$
	=	0.064	+	0.288	+	0.432	+	0.216

$$P(\text{at least 1 success}) = P(\text{1 success}) + P(\text{2 successes}) + P(\text{3 successes})$$
$$= 0.432 + 0.288 + 0.064$$
$$= 0.784$$

The probability of at least one morning with suitable weather is about 78%.

Check Understanding **4** One survey found that 80% of respondents eat corn on the cob in circles rather than from side to side. Assume that this sample accurately represents the population. What is the probability that, out of five people you know, at least two of them eat corn on the cob in circles?

EXERCISES

For more practice, see *Extra Practice*.

Practice and Problem Solving

A Practice by Example

For each situation, describe a trial and a success. Then design and run a simulation to find the probability.

Example 1 (page 672)

1. On a true-or-false test, you guess the answers to five questions. Find the probability of guessing the correct answers to exactly three of the five questions.

2. A poll shows that 40% of the voters in a city favor passage of a bond issue to finance park improvements. If ten voters are selected at random, find the probability that exactly four of them will vote in favor of it.

3. A plant production line has a 90% probability of not experiencing a breakdown during an eight-hour shift. Find the probability that three successive shifts will not have a breakdown.

Example 2 (page 672)

Suppose you guess on a true-or-false test. Use a tree diagram to find each probability.

4. P(4 correct in 4 guesses)

5. P(1 correct in 4 guesses)

6. P(3 correct in 4 guesses)

7. P(6 correct in 4 guesses)

Example 3 (page 673)

Find the probability of x successes in n trials for the given probability of success p on each trial.

8. $x = 3, n = 8, p = 0.3$

9. $x = 4, n = 8, p = 0.3$

10. $x = 5, n = 10, p = 0.5$

11. $x = 5, n = 10, p = 0.1$

Example 4 (page 674)

Use the binomial expansion of $(p + q)^n$ to calculate and graph each binomial distribution.

12. $n = 6, p = 0.3$

13. $n = 6, p = 0.5$

14. $n = 6, p = 0.9$

B Apply Your Skills

Marketing **A fruit company guarantees that 90% of the pineapples it ships will be ripe within four days. Find each probability for a case containing 12 pineapples.**

15. All 12 are ripe within four days.

16. At least 10 are ripe within four days.

17. No more than 9 are ripe within four days.

Sociology **A study shows that 50% of the families in a community watch television during dinner. Suppose you select 10 families at random from this population. Find each probability.**

18. P(5 of the 10 families watch television during dinner)

19. P(6 of the 10 families watch television during dinner)

20. P(at least 5 of the 10 families watch television during dinner)

21. Writing Explain how a binomial experiment is related to a binomial expansion.

Real-World Connection

Manufacturers ensure the quality of their products by inspecting raw materials, machinery, and procedures, as well as finished products.

22. Quality Control A company claims that 99% of its cereal boxes have at least as much cereal by weight as the amount stated on the box.
a. At a quality control checkpoint, one box out of a random sample of ten boxes falls short of its stated weight. What is the probability of this happening due to chance variation in box weights?
b. Suppose three of ten boxes fail to have the claimed weight. What would you conclude? Explain why.

23. Data Collection Use the current winning percentage of a local sports team as its probability of success. Find the team's probability of winning at least three of any five games.

24. Genetics About 11% of the general population is left-handed. At a school with an average class size of 30, each classroom contains four left-handed desks. Does this seem adequate? Justify your answer.

25. For a group of 40 people, what is the probability that exactly three people in the group will celebrate their birthdays on a Wednesday this year?
a. Find the probability by using the binomial probability formula.
b. Find the probability by designing and running a simulation.
c. Compare your results for parts (a) and (b). Explain any discrepancy.

26. Open-Ended Describe a binomial experiment that can be solved using the expression ${}_7C_2(0.6)^2(0.4)^5$.

C Challenge

27. **Statistics** A multiple-choice test has ten questions. Each question has five choices, with only one correct.
    a. Statisticians consider a "rare" event to have less than a 5% chance of occurring. According to this standard, what grades would be rare on this test if you guess? Justify your answer.
    b. Design and conduct a simulation to model this situation. Gather results of simulations from your classmates. Do these results confirm the grades you identified as rare in part (a)? Explain.

28. Enter the binomial probability formula as shown. Set the window and table shown. (To get integer values of x, you may need to adjust your window.)

```
Plot1  Plot2  Plot3
\Y1= (7 nCr X) * 0.5^X*
0.5^(7–X)
\Y2=
\Y3=
\Y4=
\Y5=
\Y6=
```

```
WINDOW
 Xmin =–1.7
 Xmax =7.7
 Xscl =1
 Ymin =–.2
 Ymax =.5
 Yscl =.1
 Xres =1
```

```
TABLE SETUP
 TblStart = 0
 ΔTbl = 1
Indpnt: Auto Ask
Depend: Auto Ask
```

a. Examine the graph of $y = {}_7C_x(0.5)^x(0.5)^{7-x}$. Describe any symmetry you see in the graph.
b. Verify the symmetry by displaying values of the function in table form.
c. Change the graph to $y = {}_7C_x(0.6)^x(0.4)^{7-x}$. Does this graph have any symmetry? Explain.

Standardized Test Prep

Quantitative Comparison

Compare the boxed quantity in Column A with the boxed quantity in Column B. Choose the best answer.

A. The quantity in Column A is greater.
B. The quantity in Column B is greater.
C. The two quantities are equal.
D. The relationship cannot be determined from the information given.

	Column A	Column B
29.	${}_3C_2(0.6)^2(0.4)^1$	${}_6C_4(0.6)^4(0.4)^2$

A survey shows that 60% of the adults in a community floss their teeth every day. Consider a sample of 10 adults.

	Column A	Column B
30.	*P*(at least 4 of the 10 adults floss every day)	*P*(at most 7 of the 10 adults floss every day)

Take It to the NET
Online lesson quiz at
www.PHSchool.com
Web Code: aga-1206

Short Response

31. Evaluate ${}_nC_xp^xq^{n-x}$ for $n = 7$, $x = 4$, $p = 0.2$, and $q = 0.8$. Round your answer to the nearest thousandth.

Extended Response

32. A bank of track lights contains several bulbs. The chance that some number of the bulbs will last for at least 2 years is given by the expression ${}_5C_2(0.15)^2\,(0.85)^3$.
    a. What is the number of bulbs in the track?
    b. How many bulbs should last at least 2 years?
    c. What is the probability that all the bulbs will last at least 2 years?

Mixed Review

Lesson 12-5

33. The table contains information from a study of the prices of comparable airline tickets. Which sample most likely was greater in size, A or B? Explain.

Sample	Standard Deviation
A	\$10.81
B	\$3.97

Lesson 11-5

Find the sum of each geometric series to the given term.

34. $8 + 12 + 18 + \dots; n = 8$

35. $20 + (-2) + 0.2 + \dots; n = 12$

36. $729 + 243 + 81 + \dots; n = 9$

37. $\frac{1}{16} + \frac{1}{4} + 1 + \dots; n = 6$

Lesson 10-5

Find the equation of a hyperbola with horizontal transverse axis, centered at the origin, for the given *a* and *c* values.

38. $a = 897$ units, $c = 1024$ units

39. $a = 20$ units, $c = 29$ units

Lesson 5-4

Factor each expression.

40. $x^2 + 6x + 9$

41. $x^2 + x - 6$

42. $x^2 - 7x + 10$

43. $3x^2 + 12x + 9$

44. $2x^2 - x - 6$

45. $5x^2 + 5x - 10$

Checkpoint Quiz 2 — Lessons 12-4 through 12-6

TEXT Instant self-check quiz online and on CD-ROM

Calculate the mean, range, and standard deviation for each set of data.

1. 34 36 29 45 34 25

2. 12 9 10 11 14 10

3. 1 5 2 1 4 1 3 2

4. A set of values has a mean of 300 and a standard deviation of 60. What value has a z-score of -1.2?

5. A survey on the Web site of an online CD store includes the question, "Who is your favorite singer?"

a. Explain why the results of the survey may be biased.

b. **Open-Ended** Suggest a way to make the survey an unbiased representation of the population of your high school.

6. **Consumer Spending** In a survey of 683 car owners selected at random, 235 reported paying cash for their first car.

a. Find the sample proportion.

b. Find the margin of error.

c. Find an interval likely to contain the true population proportion.

7. Determine the sample size that produces a margin of error of $\pm 20\%$.

8. Seventy percent of the time, a friend of yours is more than 10 minutes late to meet you for a movie. What is the probability that your friend will be more than 10 minutes late to meet you for all of the next three movies you see?

Each trial of an experiment has a probability of success *p*. Find the probability of *x* successes in *n* trials.

9. $p = 0.8, x = 4, n = 5$

10. $p = 0.4, x = 4, n = 5$

12-7 Normal Distributions

Lesson Preview

What You'll Learn

OBJECTIVE 1 To use a normal distribution

OBJECTIVE 2 To use the standard normal curve

... And Why

To describe the jaws of great white sharks, as in Example 2

Check Skills You'll Need

(For help, go to Lesson 12-4.)

Find the numbers that are one and two standard deviations above and below each given mean. Write these numbers from least to greatest.

1. $\bar{x} = 12, \sigma = 2$ **2.** $\bar{x} = 16.7, \sigma = 1$ **3.** $\bar{x} = 7, \sigma = 1.5$

4. $\bar{x} = 22, \sigma = 1.7$ **5.** $\bar{x} = 17.5, \sigma = 0.9$ **6.** $\bar{x} = 33.1, \sigma = 1.2$

New Vocabulary • normal distribution • standard normal curve

Interactive lesson includes instant self-check, tutorials, and activities.

OBJECTIVE 1 Using a Normal Distribution

A **normal distribution** shows data that vary randomly from the mean. The pattern the data form is a bell-shaped curve called a normal curve.

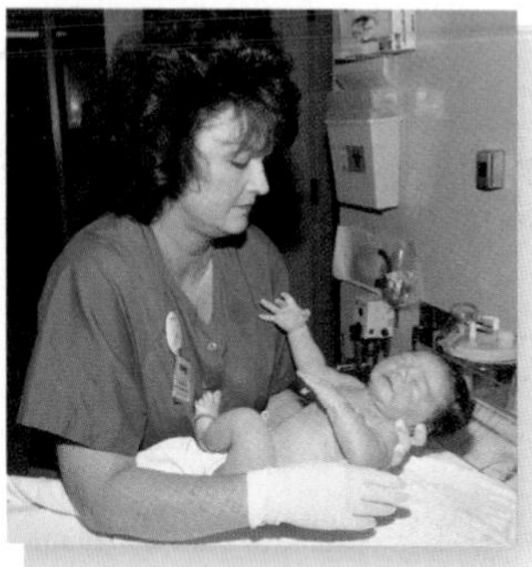

Real-World Connection

Careers Neonatal nurses specialize in the nursing care of newborns and babies up to 30 days old.

1 EXAMPLE Real-World Connection

Medicine The bar graph below gives the birth weights of a population of 100 babies. The red curve shows how the weights are normally distributed about the mean, 3250 g. Estimate the percent of babies weighing 2500–3999 g.

Full-Term Birth Weight Distribution for a Population

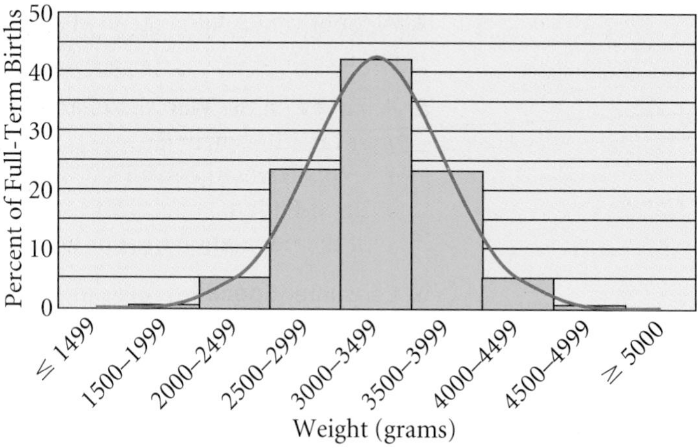

Estimate and add the percents for 2500–2999, 3000–3499, and 3500–3999.

$23\% + 42\% + 23\% = 88\%$

About 88% of the babies weigh 2500–3999 g.

Check Understanding

1 **a.** Estimate the percent of babies weighing less than 3500 g.

b. The standard deviation in birth weights is about 500 g. Estimate the percent of babies whose birth weights are within 1.5 standard deviations of the mean.

Every normal curve has a symmetric bell shape. When outcomes are normally distributed, you can sketch the graph of the distribution.

2 EXAMPLE Real-World Connection

Real-World Connection

The jaw widths of a population of great white sharks are normally distributed about a mean of 15.7 inches.

Biology Refer to the photo. For the given population of sharks, the standard deviation of the jaw widths is 2.8 inches. Sketch a normal curve showing the jaw widths at one, two, and three standard deviations from the mean.

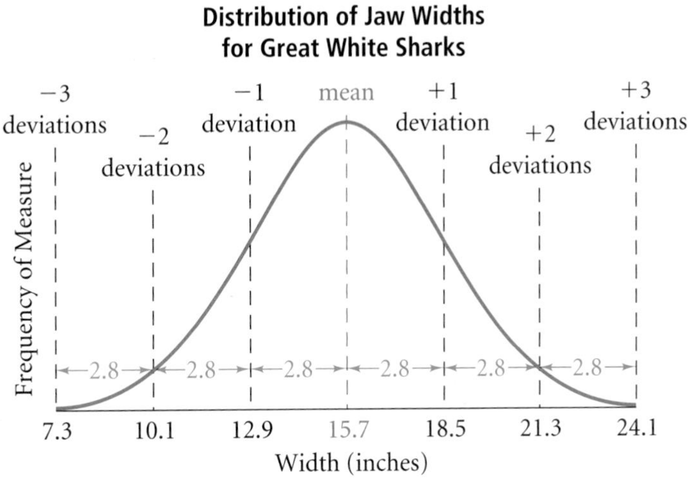

Check Understanding 2 Suppose the mean in Example 2 is 15.4 inches and the standard deviation is 3.1 inches. Sketch a normal curve showing the jaw widths at one, two, and three standard deviations from the mean.

OBJECTIVE 2

Using the Standard Normal Curve

When you show a probability distribution as a bar graph, the height of the bar for each outcome indicates the probability. For a normal curve, however, the area between the curve and the x-axis represents the probability.

The **standard normal curve** is a normal distribution centered on the y-axis. The mean of the standard normal curve is 0. The standard deviation is 1.

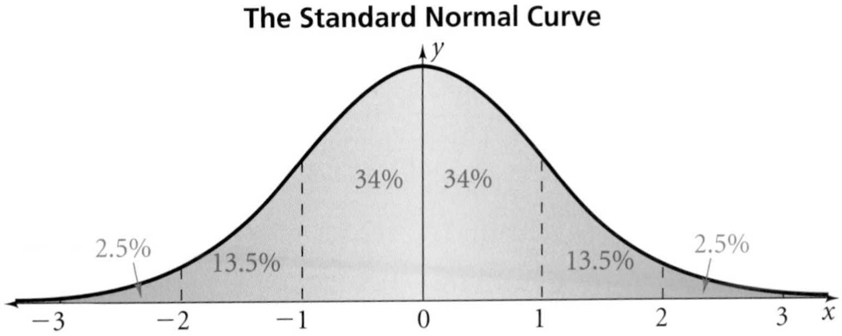

Need Help?

The z-score of a value is the number of standard deviations that the value is from the mean.

Every normal curve contains the same probability distribution. When a data set is normally distributed, about 68% of the data fall within one standard deviation of the mean. About 95% of the data fall within two standard deviations of the mean. To find the values that are two standard deviations away from the mean, find the values that have z-scores of −2 and 2.

3 EXAMPLE Using the Standard Normal Curve

In a survey, the responses to the question "How much time do you spend at meals in one week?" were normally distributed. The mean was 13 h; the standard deviation was 3 h.

a. What values are one standard deviation from the mean?

Values that are one standard deviation from the mean have z-scores of -1 and 1.

$$z\text{-score} = \frac{\text{value} - \text{mean}}{\text{standard deviation}}$$

$$-1 = \frac{v - 13}{3} \qquad 1 = \frac{u - 13}{3}$$

$$v = 10 \qquad u = 16$$

The values 10 h and 16 h are one standard deviation away from the mean.

b. What percent of the responses would you expect to find from 10 h to 16 h?

The responses are normally distributed, and 10 h and 16 h are the values that are one standard deviation from the mean. Since 68% of the data are within one standard deviation of the mean, 68% should be values from 10 h to 16 h.

Check Understanding 3 **a.** Suppose there were 100 responses to the survey question. How many responses would you expect to be values from 10 h to 16 h?
b. Of 100 responses, how many would you expect to be values from 16 h to 19 h?

4 EXAMPLE Real-World Connection

Education In a university lecture class with 174 students, the final exam scores have a mean of 68.5 and a standard deviation of 7.3. The grades on the exams are all whole numbers, and the grade pattern follows a normal curve.

a. Find the number of students who receive grades from one to two standard deviations above the mean.

Use the normal curve. About 13.5% of the students receive grades from one to two standard deviations above the mean.

Distribution of Final Exam Scores

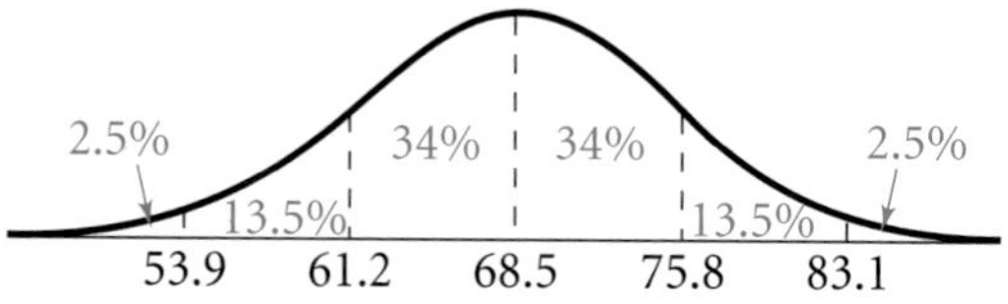

$0.135(174) = 23.49$ **Find the number of students that corresponds to 13.5%.**

About 23 or 24 students receive grades from one to two standard deviations above the mean.

b. Find the number of students who receive grades of 61 or below.

Use the normal curve from part (a). A grade of 61 is about one standard deviation below the mean.

$13.5\% + 2.5\% = 16\%$ **Find the % at least 1 standard deviation below the mean.**

$0.16(174) = 27.84$ **Find the number of students.**

About 28 students receive grades of 61 or below.

Check Understanding 4 **a.** Suppose there are 140 students in the class in Example 4. About how many would receive grades from 69 to 75?
b. Writing How do you know that in a class of 140 students, about 22 students receive grades of 76 or higher?

EXERCISES

For more practice, see *Extra Practice.*

Practice and Problem Solving

A Practice by Example

Example 1 (page 678)

Biology **The heights of men in a survey are distributed normally about the mean. Use the graph for Exercises 1–4.**

Heights of Men Ages 25–34

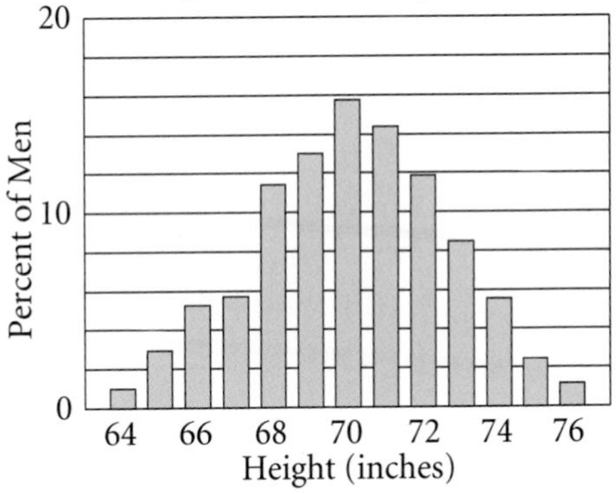

1. About what percent of men aged 25 to 34 are 69–71 inches tall?

2. About what percent of men aged 25 to 34 are less than 70 inches tall?

3. Suppose the survey included data on 100 men. About how many would you expect to be 69–71 inches tall?

4. The mean of the data is 70, and the standard deviation is 2.5. About what percent of men are within one standard deviation of the mean in height?

Example 2 (page 679)

Sketch a normal curve for each distribution. Label the *x*-axis values at one, two, and three standard deviations from the mean.

5. mean = 45, standard deviation = 5

6. mean = 45, standard deviation = 10

7. mean = 45, standard deviation = 2

8. mean = 45, standard deviation = 3.5

Examples 3 and 4 (page 680)

A set of data with a mean of 62 and a standard deviation of 5.7 is normally distributed. Find each value, given its distance from the mean.

9. +3 standard deviations

10. −1 standard deviation

A set of data has a normal distribution with a mean of 50 and a standard deviation of 8. Find the percent of data within each interval.

11. from 42 to 58

12. greater than 34

13. less than 50

14. Test Scores The scores on an exam are normally distributed, with a mean of 85 and a standard deviation of 5. What percent of the scores are from 85 to 95?

B Apply Your Skills

15. The numbers of paper clips in a truckload of boxes are normally distributed, with a mean of 100 and a standard deviation of 5. Find the probability that a box will *not* contain from 95 to 105 clips.

16. Writing In a class of 25, one student receives a grade of 100 on a test. The grades are distributed approximately normally, with a mean of 78 and a standard deviation of 5. Do you think the student's grade is an outlier? Explain.

17. **a.** From the table at the right, select the set of values that appears to be distributed normally.
b. Using the set you chose in part (a), make a histogram of the values.
c. Sketch a normal curve over your graph.

Set 1	Set 2	Set 3
1	5	5
10	7	6
5	7	9
19	7	1
2	4	1
7	11	5
1	7	11
7	7	1
2	7	10
10	9	4
6	7	2
9	7	8

18. **Track** To qualify as a contestant in a race, a runner has to be in the fastest 16% of all applicants. The running times are normally distributed, with a mean of 63 min and a standard deviation of 4 min. To the nearest minute, what is the qualifying time for the race?

19. **Agriculture** To win a prize, a tomato must be greater than 4 in. in diameter. The diameters of a crop of tomatoes grown in a special soil are normally distributed, with a mean of 3.2 in. and a standard deviation of 0.4 in. Find the probability that the crop will contain a winning tomato.

A normal distribution has a mean of 100 and a standard deviation of 10. Find the probability that a value selected at random is in the given interval.

20. from 80 to 100
21. from 70 to 130
22. from 90 to 120
23. at least 100
24. at most 110
25. at least 80

26. Two tomato plants were chosen from two groups of plants grown in different soils. Each sample plant produced 23 tomatoes. The mean number of tomatoes for plants in the first soil was 17, with a standard deviation of 5. The mean number of tomatoes for plants in the second soil was 18, with a standard deviation of 6. Determine which plant, if either, is in the top 16% of its group.

27. In a set of data, the value that is -3 standard deviations from the mean is 86. The value that is $+1$ standard deviation from the mean is 250.
a. Find the mean.
b. Find the standard deviation.
c. Find an interval with an end value of 250 that contains about 81.5% of the data.

28. **Seismology** The table below shows the number of earthquakes worldwide in 2000.
a. Draw a histogram to represent the data.
b. Does the histogram approximate a normal curve? Explain.

Worldwide Earthquakes in 2000

Magnitude	Number	Magnitude	Number
0.1–0.9	6	5.0–5.9	1318
1.0–1.9	1028	6.0–6.9	157
2.0–2.9	3728	7.0–7.9	14
3.0–3.9	4741	8.0–8.9	4
4.0–4.9	8114	≥ 9.0	0

SOURCE: U.S. Geological Survey

29. Critical Thinking Jake and Elena took the same standardized test, but with different groups of students. They both received a score of 87. In Jake's group, the mean was 80 and the standard deviation was 6. In Elena's group, the mean was 76 and the standard deviation was 4. Did either student score in the top 10% of his or her group? Explain.

C Challenge

30. Quality Control Tubs of Better Butter weigh 1.0 lb each, with a standard deviation of 0.06 lb. At a quality control checkpoint, 12 of the tubs taken as samples weighed less than 0.88 lb. Assume that the weights of the samples were normally distributed. How many tubs of butter were taken as samples?

31. Games In the Japanese game pachinko, a player launches small steel balls from the bottom of a playing frame to the top. The balls then fall through pins and bounce around haphazardly. They land in slots at the bottom of the game and form a normal distribution. If a ball falls into a specially marked slot, the player wins additional balls with which to play again in the next round. If a ball does not fall into a marked slot, the player loses that ball.

a. Suppose that all slots between one and two standard deviations from the center are marked. When a ball lands in one of the marked slots, you win the ball back along with two others. If you begin with 200 balls, how many balls should you have after one round?

b. Suppose that there are two sets of marked slots. One set is within one standard deviation of the center and the other set is more than two standard deviations from the center. When a ball lands in one of the slots in the first set, you win the ball back. When a ball lands in one of the slots in the second set, you win the ball back, along with four others. If you begin with 1000 balls, how many balls should you have after one round?

c. Open-Ended Using your knowledge of normal distributions, design a pachinko game with both winning and losing slots in which you would theoretically have the same number of balls after each round as when you started. You can adjust the number of balls at the beginning of the game, the placement of the winning slots, and the number balls won per slot.

Standardized Test Prep

Multiple Choice

For a daily airline flight between two cities, the number of pieces of checked luggage has a mean of 380 and a standard deviation of 20. Use this information for Exercises 32–33.

32. On what percent of the flights would you expect from 340 to 420 pieces of checked luggage?

A. 34% **B.** 47.5% **C.** 68% **D.** 95%

33. What number of pieces of checked luggage is 3 standard deviations above the mean?

F. 60 **G.** 97.5 **H.** 440 **I.** 1140

34. A set of data is normally distributed with a mean of 44 and a standard deviation of 3.2. Which statements are NOT true?

I. 68% of the values are between 37.6 and 50.4
II. 13.5% of the values are less than 40.8
III. 5% of the values are lower than 37.6 or higher than 50.4.

A. I and II only **B.** I and III only **C.** II and III only **D.** I, II, and III

Short Response

35. Distribution A has 50 data values with mean 40 and standard deviation 2.4. Distribution B has 30 data values with mean 40 and standard deviation 2.8. Which distribution has more data values at or below 40? Show your work.

Reading Comprehension

Read the article below. Then answer Exercises 36–38.

College Entrance Exam Results for 2000

In 2000, over 1.2 million students across the country took college entrance exams. The average score on the verbal section showed no improvement over the average scores of the previous four years. The average score on the mathematics section was three points higher than the previous year's average.

Section	Mean	Standard Deviation
Math	505	111
Verbal	514	113

36. What is the probability that a student's score on the verbal section is from 401 to 514?

37. What is the probability that a student's score on the math section is greater than 727?

38. Both Susanna's math score and her verbal score were more than one standard deviation above the mean, but less than two standard deviations above the mean. What are the lower and upper limits of Susanna's combined score?

Take It to the NET
Online lesson quiz at
www.PHSchool.com
Web Code: aga-1207

Mixed Review

Lesson 12-6

39. Production A plant production line has a 95% probability of not experiencing a breakdown during a six-hour shift. The plant managers want to know the probability that four successive shifts will not have a breakdown. Design and run a simulation to find the probability. Include an explanation of what constitutes a trial and a success.

Lesson 11-6

For each set of axes, what does the area under the curve represent?

40. y-axis: tons of garbage generated per year, x-axis: years

41. y-axis: bus passengers per hour, x-axis: hours

Lesson 10-6

42. Coordinate Geometry Write the equation of a circle centered at $(4, -5)$ with radius 7.

Open-Ended **Write the equation of a conic section with the given characteristics.**

43. an ellipse with a major axis 8 units long

44. a hyperbola with an asymptote at $y = -x$

Lesson 9-1

Suppose that x and y vary inversely. Write a function to model inverse variation.

45. $x = 1$ when $y = 5$

46. $x = -1$ when $y = 10$

47. $x = -3$ when $y = 3$

48. $x = 25$ when $y = -5$

49. $x = 1.8$ when $y = -6$

50. $x = 7.5$ when $y = 50$

Technology

Area Under a Curve

For Use With Lesson 12-7

Statisticians use the function $f(x) = \frac{1}{\sqrt{2\pi}}e^{-\frac{x^2}{2}}$ to model data such as height or birth weight. You can use the area under the graph of the function to find probabilities.

EXAMPLE

In a population of 100 babies, the weights are normally distributed about the mean, 3250 g. The standard deviation is 500 g. Find the probability that a baby chosen at random weighs from 2250 g to 4250 g.

Step 1 Find the z-scores of the lower and upper limits.

$$z\text{-score} = \frac{\text{value} - \text{mean}}{\text{standard deviation}}$$

$$z_1 = \frac{2250 - 3250}{500} = \frac{-1000}{500} = -2$$

$$z_2 = \frac{4250 - 3250}{500} = \frac{1000}{500} = 2$$

Step 2 Enter $f(x) = \frac{1}{\sqrt{2\pi}}e^{-\frac{x^2}{2}}$ as Y_1. Adjust the window values.

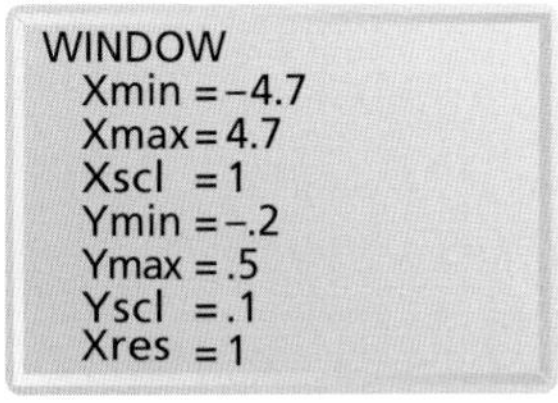

Step 3 Use the CALC feature and press 7 to access the $\int f(x)dx$ feature. Move the cursor until the lower limit is $x = -2$. Press ENTER. Move the cursor until the upper limit is $x = 2$. Press ENTER.

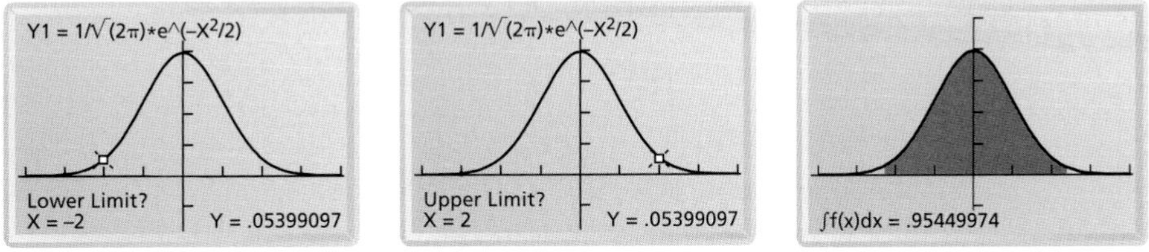

The area under the curve from $x = -2$ to $x = 2$ is about 0.95. So the probability that a baby weighs from 2250 g to 4250 g is about 95%.

EXERCISES

Use the data and the function in the example. Find the probability that the weight of a baby chosen at random falls within each interval.

1. 3150–4150 g

2. 4300–4500 g

3. less than 1800 g

4. more than 4550 g

5. Manufacturing A battery company manufactures batteries having life spans that are normally distributed, with a mean of 45 months and a standard deviation of 5 months. Find the probability that a battery chosen at random will have each life span.

a. 45–52 months

b. 48–50 months

Test-Taking Strategies

Answering the Question Asked

When answering a question, be sure to answer the question that is asked. Read the question carefully and identify the quantity that you are asked to find. Some answer choices are answers to related questions, so you have to be careful that you are answering the right question.

EXAMPLE

There are five puppies in a litter. If the probability that a puppy is male is 0.5, what is the probability that at most one puppy in the litter is male?

A. 0.15625 **B.** 0.1875 **C.** 0.5 **D.** 0.96875

The problem is asking for the probability of "at most" one male puppy. Do not confuse this with "exactly" or "at least" one male puppy.

$$\begin{aligned} P(\text{at most one male puppy}) &= P(\text{no male puppies}) + P(\text{exactly 1 male puppy}) \\ &= {}_5C_0(0.5)^0(0.5)^5 + {}_5C_1(0.5)^1(0.5)^4 \\ &= 0.03125 + 0.15625 = 0.1875 \end{aligned}$$

The correct answer is B.

Choices A and D are answers to related, but different, questions.

$$P(\text{exactly one male puppy}) = {}_5C_1(0.5)^1(0.5)^4 = 0.15625$$

$$\begin{aligned} P\text{ (at least one male puppy)} &= P(\text{exactly 1 male}) + \dots + P(\text{exactly 5 males}) \\ &= {}_5C_1(0.5)^1(0.5)^4 + \dots + {}_5C_5(0.5)^5(0.5)^0 \\ &= 0.15625 + \dots + 0.03125 \\ &= 0.96875 \end{aligned}$$

EXERCISES

Identify the quantity that is being asked for. Then answer the question.

1. A box contains four quarters. Exactly two of the quarters have the American eagle on the back. Suppose you draw two quarters with replacement at random from the box.
   a. What is the probability that both have the American eagle on the back?
   b. What is the probability that neither has the American eagle on the back?
   c. What is the probability that at least one has the American eagle on the back?

2. In a survey, 28% of respondents say they are left-handed, 64% say they are right-handed, and 8% say they are ambidextrous. If the ambidextrous people are omitted, about what percent of those remaining are left-handed?
A. 28% **B.** 30% **C.** 32% **D.** 34%

3. A student conducted a survey at school and found that 75% of the boys and 65% of the girls like to watch hockey games. There are an equal number of boys and girls in the school. If someone does not like to watch hockey games, what is the approximate probability that the person is a boy?
A. 25% **B.** 42% **C.** 55% **D.** 75%

Chapter 12

Chapter Review

Vocabulary

bimodal (p. 648)
binomial experiment (p. 671)
binomial probability (p. 673)
box-and-whisker plot (p. 650)
conditional probability (p. 642)
cumulative probability (p. 636)
frequency table (p. 636)
interquartile range (p. 657)
margin of error (p. 665)
mean (p. 648)
measures of central tendency (p. 648)
measures of variation (p. 657)
median (p. 648)
mode (p. 648)
normal distribution (p. 678)
outlier (p. 652)
percentile (p. 651)
probability distribution (p. 637)
quartiles (p. 650)
random sample (p. 663)
range of a set of data (p. 657)
sample (p. 663)
sample proportion (p. 663)
standard deviation (p. 657)
standard normal curve (p. 679)
***z*-score** (p. 659)

Reading Math
Understanding Vocabulary

Choose the correct term to complete each sentence.

1. A(n) _?_ is part of a population.

2. A(n) _?_ has a value substantially different from other data in a set.

3. A function that gives the probability of each event in a sample space is a(n) _?_.

4. A(n) _?_ involves repeated trials, each of which has two possible outcomes whose probabilities are constant throughout the trials.

5. Dispersion of data in a data set can be measured by _?_.

Take It to the NET
Online vocabulary quiz at **www.PHSchool.com**
Web Code: agj-1251

Skills and Concepts

12-1 and 12-2 Objectives

- To make a probability distribution (p. 636)
- To use a probability distribution in conducting a simulation (p. 638)
- To find conditional probabilities (p. 642)
- To use formulas and tree diagrams (p. 643)

A **probability distribution** is a function that gives the probability of each event in a sample space. A **frequency table** lists outcomes and the number of times each occurs. A frequency table can be used to find **cumulative probability**, which is the probability of a range of events.

A **conditional probability** limits the sample space to a given event. The probability of event A, given event B, is written $P(A|B)$. You can find a conditional probability from a table, a tree diagram, or by the conditional probability formula.

$$P(A|B) = \frac{P(A \text{ and } B)}{P(B)}$$

6. Use the results in the table below for the Rock-Paper-Scissors game.

a. Make a frequency table for the winner: Player 1, Player 2, or tie.

b. Find *P*(Player 2 wins).

Rock-Paper-Scissors

Player 1	**S**	**P**	P	**R**	R	P	**P**	**P**	P	**S**	R	S	**P**	**S**	R
Player 2	P	R	**S**	S	**P**	**S**	R	R	P	P	R	S	R	P	**P**

R = Rock P = Paper S = Scissors **Bold** = Winner

7. Two number cubes are rolled. Use a table to show the probability distribution for the product of the two numbers.

8. At a bank, the number of customers c who arrive at the teller counters each minute varies according to the distribution below. Simulate the number of customers over a ten-minute period.

Number of Customers Each Minute

c	0	1	2	3	4	5	6	7
$P(c)$	0.16	0.28	0.25	0.18	0.09	0.02	0.01	0.01

Use the frequency table below for Exercises 9 and 10.

Birthday Months of Respondents to a Survey

Month	J	F	M	A	M	J	J	A	S	O	N	D
Male	0	1	2	1	1	3	2	0	1	1	0	2
Female	0	1	0	1	0	2	1	3	1	0	4	1

9. Find P(birthday in August | female respondent).

10. Find P(male respondent | birthday in June).

Use these survey results for Exercises 11–13.

- Of all respondents, 60% have 1 sibling and 20% have 2 or more siblings.
- Of the respondents with 0 siblings, 90% have their own room.
- Of the respondents with 1 sibling, 20% do not have their own room.
- Of the respondents with 2 or more siblings, 50% have their own room.

11. Make a tree diagram that reflects the results of the survey.

12. Find P(own room | 0 siblings).

13. Find P(share room | 1 sibling).

12-3 Objectives

- To calculate measures of central tendency (p. 648)
- To draw and interpret box-and-whisker plots (p. 650)

You can use **measures of central tendency** to analyze data. The **mean** $\bar{x}$ equals the sum of the values divided by the number of values. The **median** is the middle value of a data set in numerical order. If the set has an even number of values, then the median is the mean of the middle two values. The **mode** is the most frequently occurring value. There can be more than one mode or no mode. A **bimodal** distribution has 2 modes. The second quartile is the median of the whole set. The first and third **quartiles** are, respectively, the medians of the values less than and greater than the median. A **box-and-whisker plot** displays data by using the quartiles to form a box and the minimum and maximum values to form whiskers. A **percentile** divides the range of a data set into two parts such that the part lying below the value contains a given percentage of the data. An **outlier** is a data value substantially different from the rest of the data.

Use the following set of values for Exercises 14–19.

13 12 15 18 14 16 18 12 13 14 14 17 15 8 17
16 12 16 14 15 13 13 17 15 14 18 16 12 12 13

14. Find the mean, median, and mode.

15. Make a box-and-whisker plot.

16. Find the 20th and 90th percentiles.

17. At what percentile is 15?

18. Identify the outlier.

19. Find the range without the outlier.

12-4 Objectives

- To find the standard deviation of a set of values (p. 656)
- To use standard deviation in real-world situations (p. 659)

You can use **measures of variation** to describe the spread of data. The **range of a set of data** is the difference between the maximum and minimum values. The **interquartile range** is the difference between the third and first quartiles. The **standard deviation** is a measure of how the data values vary from the mean. To find the standard deviation, (1) find the mean, (2) find the difference between each data value and the mean, (3) square each difference, (4) find the mean of the squares, and (5) take the square root of this mean. The ***z*-score** of a value is the number of standard deviations that value is from the mean.

Use the following set of values for Exercises 20–22.

$1.95 $1.27 $1.81 $1.33 $1.30 $.99 $1.63 $1.49 $1.39 $1.25 $1.50

20. Find the standard deviation.

21. Within how many standard deviations of the mean do all of the values fall?

22. Find the z-score of the value $1.85, to the nearest hundredth.

12-5 Objectives

- To find sample proportions (p. 663)
- To find the margin of error (p. 664)

A **sample** is part of a population. For a **random sample**, all members of the population are equally likely to be chosen for the sample. When an event occurs x times in a sample of size n, the **sample proportion** is the ratio $\frac{x}{n}$. When a random sample of size n is taken from a large population, the sample proportion has a **margin of error** of approximately $\pm\frac{1}{\sqrt{n}}$.

23. Of 50 people who rented clubs at a golf course, 38 were right-handed.
  a. Find the sample proportion as a percent.
  b. Find the margin of error.
  c. Find an interval likely to contain the true population proportion.

12-6 and 12-7 Objectives

- To find binomial probabilities (p. 671)
- To use binomial distributions (p. 673)
- To use a normal distribution (p. 678)
- To use the standard normal curve (p. 679)

A **binomial experiment** has repeated independent trials, each trial having two possible outcomes. In a binomial experiment with probability of success p and of failure $q (p + q = 1)$, the probability of x successes in n trials is ${}_nC_x p^x q^{n-x}$. This value is the **binomial probability**.

A **normal distribution** shows data that vary from the mean in a random manner. The pattern they form is a bell-shaped curve called a normal curve. The **standard normal curve** is a normal distribution centered on the y-axis. The mean is 0 and the standard deviation is 1. When a data set follows the normal curve, about 68% of the data fall within one standard deviation of the mean. About 95% of the data fall within two standard deviations of the mean.

24. A true-or-false quiz contains four questions. Design and describe a simulation you could use to find the probability of guessing three questions correctly.

25. Find the probability of 13 successes in 24 trials, given that the probability of success is 0.6 for each trial.

26. Use the binomial expansion of $(p + q)^n$ to write the binomial distribution for $n = 5$ and $p = 0.7$.

27. Sketch a curve for a normal distribution with mean 10 and standard deviation 4. Label the x-axis at one, two, and three standard deviations from the mean.

Chapter 12

Chapter Test

Take It to the NET
Online chapter test at
www.PHSchool.com
Web Code: aga-1252

Graph the probability distribution for each sample space when two number cubes are rolled.

1. {both cubes the same number, each cube a different number}
2. {prime sum, composite sum}
3. **Writing** Describe how a situation can have more than one sample space. Include an example.

Use the table below for Exercises 4–8.

How Many Current Music Groups Can You Name?

Age of Respondent	Number of Groups	
	0 – 4	5 or more
< 30	7	18
≥ 30	13	12

4. Make a frequency table for the ages of the respondents.
5. Make a frequency table for the number of groups named.
6. Find $P(5 \text{ or more})$.
7. Find $P(5 \text{ or more} \mid \text{age} < 30)$.
8. Find $P(\text{age} \geq 30 \mid 0\text{–}4)$.
9. Find the mean, median, and mode for this set of values: 8, 9, 11, 12, 13, 15, 16, 18, 20.
10. Make a box-and-whisker plot for this set of values: 36, 36, 48, 65, 75, 82, 92, 101.
11. Find the 20th and 60th percentiles for this set of values: 36, 38, 42, 47, 51, 56, 62, 69, 70, 74.
12. Given the set of values below, at what percentiles are 78 and 81?
43 58 64 78 78 81 89 89 91 93
13. Identify the outlier of this set of values: 17, 15, 16, 15, 9, 18, 16.
14. **Open-Ended** Write a set of values that has a range of 10, a mean of 86, and a mode of 85.
15. Find the mean and the standard deviation for this set of values: 15, 17, 19, 20, 14, 23, 12.
16. A data set has a mean 30 and a standard deviation of 3. Find the z-score of the value 38.

Find the margin of error for each sample. Then find an interval likely to contain the true population proportion.

17. 15% of 457 teachers
18. 47% of 296 teens
19. 56% of 87 musicians
20. 23% of 100 bakers

A newspaper wants to take a poll about which candidate voters prefer for President. Identify any bias in each sampling method.

21. The newspaper interviews people at a political debate.
22. The newspaper publishes a number for people to call and express their opinion.
23. The newspaper calls people selected at random from the local telephone book.

Find the probability of x successes in n trials for the given probability of success p on each trial.

24. $x = 4, n = 10, p = 0.2$
25. $x = 3, n = 8, p = 0.6$
26. At a high school, 30% of the students buy class rings. You select five students at random. Find $P(\text{exactly two buy rings})$ and $P(\text{at least two buy rings})$.
27. A student guesses the answers to three questions on a true-or-false test. Design and describe a simulation to find the probability that the student guesses at least one of the questions correctly.

A set of data has a normal distribution with a mean of 29 and a standard deviation of 4. Find the percent of data within each interval.

28. from 25 to 33
29. from 21 to 25
30. greater than 29
31. less than 21
32. A data set is normally distributed with a mean of 37 and a standard deviation of 8.1. Sketch a normal curve for the distribution. Label the x-axis values at one, two, and three standard deviations from the mean.

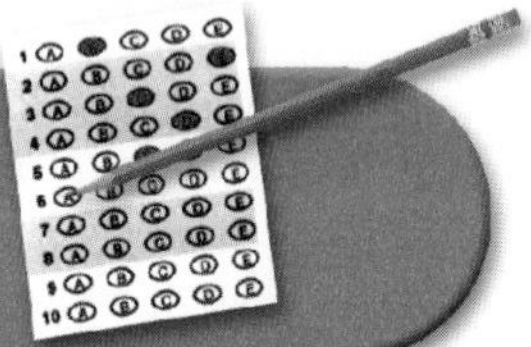

Standardized Test Prep

Multiple Choice

For Exercises 1–8, choose the correct letter.

1. Which polynomial has $(x - 1)$ as a factor?
A. $x^2 + 3x + 2$
B. $x^2 + 2x + 1$
C. $x^3 - x^2 - x + 1$
D. $x^3 - 3x - 2$

2. Which is the equation of an inverse variation for which $x = 5$ when $y = -28$?
F. $y = \frac{-x}{140}$ **G.** $y = \frac{-130}{x}$
H. $y = \frac{-x}{130}$ **I.** $y = \frac{-140}{x}$

3. Which parabola has focus (3, 0) and directrix $x = -3$?
A. $y = \frac{1}{12}x^2$ **B.** $y = -\frac{1}{3}x^2$
C. $x = \frac{1}{12}y^2$ **D.** $x = \frac{1}{3}y^2$

4. Which is greatest for these data?
9 10 10 10 11 12 12 13 15
F. mean **G.** median
H. range **I.** mode

5. What are the quartiles of these data?
18 19 20 20 22 23 25 28 32
A. $Q_1 = 19.5, Q_2 = 22, Q_3 = 26.5$
B. $Q_1 = 20, Q_2 = 21, Q_3 = 26.5$
C. $Q_1 = 20, Q_2 = 22, Q_3 = 25$
D. $Q_1 = 19, Q_2 = 22.5, Q_3 = 28$

6. In which interval is the area above the x-axis and under the curve $y = 4x^2 + 1$ greatest?
F. $-5 \leq x \leq 1$ **G.** $1 \leq x \leq 3$
H. $1 \leq x \leq 4$ **I.** $2 \leq x \leq 5$

7. What are the foci of $\frac{x^2}{64} + \frac{y^2}{36} = 1$?
A. $(0, \pm 10)$ **B.** $(\pm 2\sqrt{7}, 0)$
C. $(\pm 10, 0)$ **D.** $(0, \pm 2\sqrt{7})$

8. Which graph has an asymptote at $x = 3$?
F. $y = \frac{1}{x + 3}$
G. $y = \frac{3}{x - 1}$
H. $y = \frac{x - 3}{x + 3}$
I. $y = \frac{3}{x - 3}$

Quantitative Comparison

Compare the boxed quantity in Column A with the boxed quantity in Column B. Choose the best answer.

A. The quantity in Column A is greater.
B. The quantity in Column B is greater.
C. The two quantities are equal.
D. The relationship cannot be determined from the information given.

	Column A	Column B
	$P(A) = \frac{1}{2}$, $P(A \text{ and } B) = \frac{1}{3}$	
9.	$P(A)$	$P(B \mid A)$
10.	the value that is three standard deviations above the mean, for mean 18 and standard deviation 2.8	the value that is two standard deviations below the mean, for mean 27 and standard deviation 1.5

Gridded Response

11. Evaluate $\sum_{n=1}^{8} \frac{3n}{2}$.

12. Write the sum of the infinite geometric series as a fraction. $1 - 0.2 + 0.04 - \ldots$

Short Response

13. Solve the equation $\frac{x}{6} = \frac{x + 4}{9}$. Check your solution. Show your work.

14. State the property or properties used to justify the identity $9 \log 3 - 3 \log 9 = \log 27$.

Extended Response

15. Find the vertices, intercepts, asymptotes, and foci of the hyperbola $\frac{x^2}{16} - \frac{y^2}{9} = 1$.

16. Determine whether the series below is *arithmetic* or *geometric*. Then find the sum of the first eight terms.
$10{,}000 + 1000 + 100 + 10 + \ldots$

Real-World Snapshots

Training Day

Applying Sequences The world is three-dimensional, but drawings are done on a two-dimensional surface. We know that railroad tracks are parallel, but to create a feeling of depth in a drawing, tracks are often drawn as though they meet. The point where they seem to meet is called a vanishing point. This technique is called perspective drawing.

Strong-Armed Laborer

To build the track of the Canadian Pacific railroad, a freight car loaded with crossties was hauled to the end of the trails. Workers carried the crossties farther down the roadbed to extend the rails.

Legendary Locomotive

During the Civil War, this engine was hijacked by Union soldiers who planned to blow up a bridge. Confederate troops pursued them, and after an 18-hour, 139-km (87-mile) chase, caught up with the engine and recaptured it.

Spanning Three Generations

These three trains represent more than 25 years of development. The original "Bullet Train" (on the right) was built in 1964. Series 300 (on the left) was built in 1992. It has a top speed of 168 mi/h.

Activity 1

Materials: paper and pencil, ruler

a. Draw a set of railroad tracks such that the lengths of the horizontal ties form a geometric sequence.

b. Write the first four terms of the sequence.

c. Write a recursive formula for the sequence.

d. Write an explicit formula for the sequence.

Energy for Trains

Before the invention of the steam engine, heavy loads were transported along railroads using human or animal power. Steam locomotives have nearly disappeared in America. Locomotives are now diesel or electric.

Activity 2

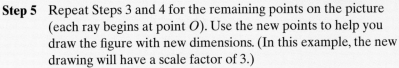

Find a small picture or drawing you want to enlarge. Follow the steps below to enlarge the drawing. Use the diagram below as a guide.

Step 1 Choose a point O to the right of the drawing.

Step 2 Choose and label some key points on the drawing as A, B, C, etc.

Step 3 Lightly draw $\overrightarrow{OA}$.

Step 4 To make a drawing with dimensions that are *three times* the size of the original picture, locate point A' on $\overrightarrow{OA}$ so that $OA' = 3 \cdot OA$.

Step 5 Repeat Steps 3 and 4 for the remaining points on the picture (each ray begins at point O). Use the new points to help you draw the figure with new dimensions. (In this example, the new drawing will have a scale factor of 3.)

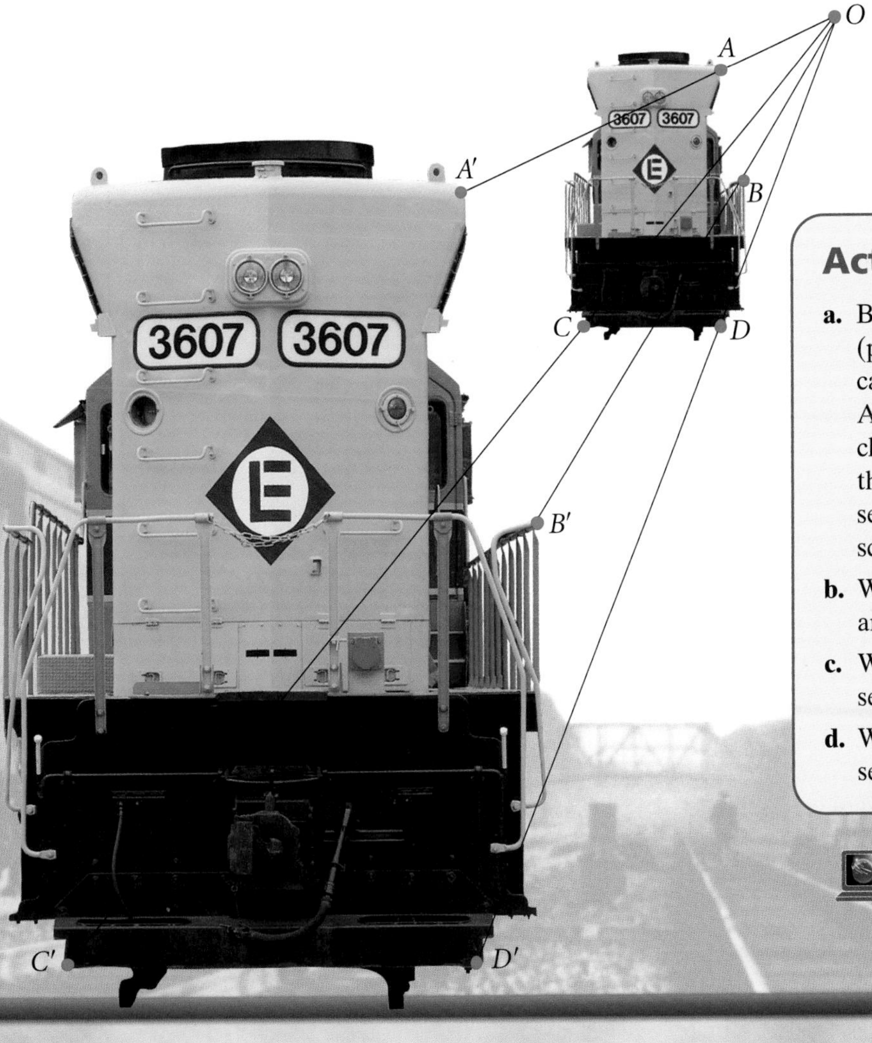

Activity 3

a. Begin with a small, simple drawing (perhaps one of your own or a cartoon). Use the method from Activity 2 to create at least two size changes of the original drawing so that the scale factors form an arithmetic sequence. (The original drawing has a scale factor of 1.)

b. Write the first four terms of the arithmetic sequence of scale factors.

c. Write a recursive formula for the sequence.

d. Write an explicit formula for the sequence.

Take It to the NET For more information about trains, go to **www.PHSchool.com**.
Web Code: age-1253

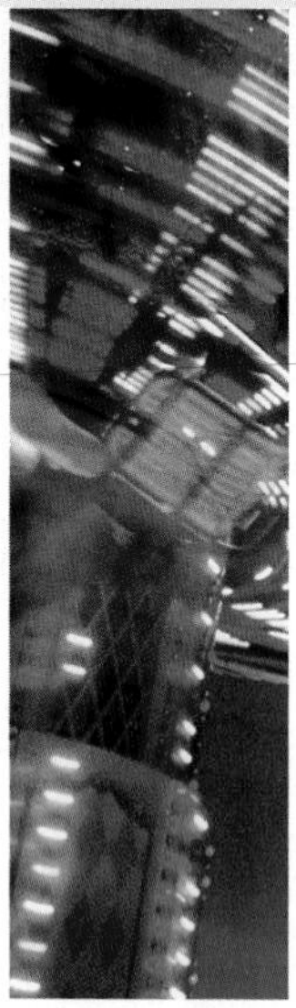

Where You've Been

- In Chapter 9, you learned to graph rational functions, some of which have graphs that are discontinuous in the coordinate plane.
- In Chapter 10, you learned to write and graph equations representing circles, ellipses, hyperbolas, and parabolas.
- In Chapters 11 and 12, you learned about patterns and probability.

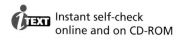

Instant self-check online and on CD-ROM

Diagnosing Readiness

(For help, go to the Lesson in green.)

Analyzing Graphs of Rational Functions (Lesson 9-3)

Describe the vertical asymptotes and holes for each rational function.

1. $y = \frac{2}{x - 3}$ **2.** $y = \frac{(x - 5)(x - 1)}{x - 1}$ **3.** $y = \frac{x + 2}{(2x + 1)(x - 4)}$

Simplifying Complex Fractions (Lesson 9-5)

Simplify each complex fraction.

4. $\frac{\frac{2}{a}}{\frac{1}{b}}$ **5.** $\frac{5 + \frac{1}{2}}{2 - \frac{1}{5}}$ **6.** $\frac{\frac{3}{c + d}}{2}$ **7.** $\frac{\frac{1}{4}}{\frac{4}{c}}$

8. $\frac{\frac{2}{3}}{\frac{6}{c + 4}}$ **9.** $\frac{\frac{4}{x}}{\frac{2}{8}}$ **10.** $\frac{3 - \frac{1}{2}}{\frac{7}{6}}$ **11.** $\frac{\frac{9}{m - n}}{\frac{3}{2m - 2n}}$

Translating Conic Sections (Lesson 10-6)

Write an equation for each conic section. Then sketch the graph.

12. circle with center at $(1, -4)$ and radius 4

13. ellipse with center at $(2, 5)$, vertices at $(5, 5)$ and $(-1, 5)$, and co-vertices at $(2, 3)$ and $(2, 7)$

14. parabola with vertex at $(0, -3)$ and focus at $(0, 5)$

15. hyperbola with center at $(6, 1)$, one focus at $(6, 6)$, and one vertex at $(6, -2)$

Writing Formulas for Sequences (Lesson 11-1)

Find the next two terms in each sequence. Write a formula for the *n*th term. Identify each formula as *explicit* or *recursive*.

16. 16, 13, 10, 7, . . . **17.** $-1, -8, -27, -64, -125, \ldots$ **18.** $9, 3, 1, \frac{1}{3}, \ldots$

Periodic Functions and Trigonometry

Chapter 13

Where You're Going

- In Chapter 13, you will learn how geometric measurement relates to trigonometry.
- You will learn to use radian measure.
- You will learn how to write and graph functions that describe periodic data.

Real-World Connection Applying what you learn, on page 715 you will solve a problem involving a satellite's orbit.

LESSONS

Key Vocabulary

- amplitude (p. 698)
- central angle (p. 712)
- cosecant (p. 749)
- cosine function (p. 729)
- cosine of θ (p. 706)
- cotangent (p. 749)
- coterminal angles (p. 705)
- cycle (p. 697)
- initial side (p. 704)
- intercepted arc (p. 712)
- period (p. 697)
- periodic function (p. 697)
- phase shift (p. 742)
- radian (p. 712)
- secant (p. 749)
- sine curve (p. 721)
- sine function (p. 720)
- sine of θ (p. 706)
- standard position (p. 704)
- tangent function (p. 735)
- tangent of θ (p. 735)
- terminal side (p. 704)
- unit circle (p. 706)

13-1 Exploring Periodic Data

Lesson Preview

What You'll Learn

OBJECTIVE 1 To identify cycles and periods of periodic functions

OBJECTIVE 2 To find the amplitude of periodic functions

. . . And Why

To make predictions about sound waves, as in Example 4

✓ Check Skills You'll Need

(For help, go to Lesson 2-1.)

Determine whether each relation is a function.

1. $\{(2, 4), (1, 3), (-3, -1), (4, 6)\}$

2. $\{(2, 6), (-3, 1), (-2, 2)\}$

3. $\{(x, y) \mid x = 3\}$

4. $\{(x, y) \mid y = 8\}$

5. $\{(x, y) \mid x = y^2\}$

6. $\{(x, y) \mid x^2 + y^2 = 36\}$

7. $\{(a, b) \mid a = b^3\}$

8. $\{(w, z) \mid w = z - 36\}$

New Vocabulary • periodic function • cycle • period • amplitude

Interactive lesson includes instant self-check, tutorials, and activities.

OBJECTIVE 1 Identifying Periodic Functions

Investigation: Periodic Cycles

Use the diagram below. Suppose you and a friend are the last two people seated on a Ferris wheel. Once the ride begins, the wheel moves at a constant speed. It takes 36 seconds to complete one revolution.

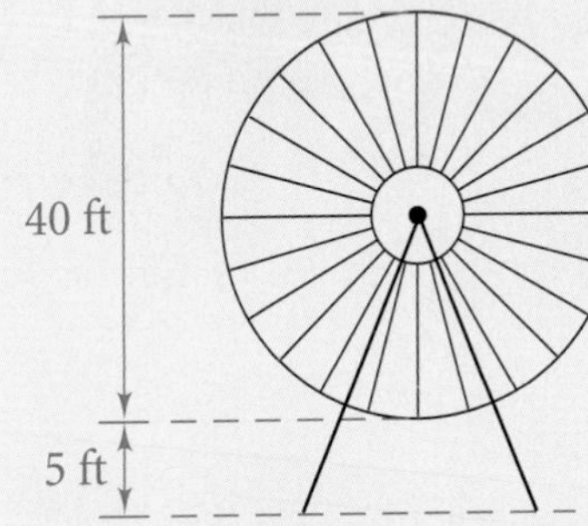

1. a. At 0 seconds, when the ride starts, how high above the ground are you?
   b. At what height are you at 9 seconds? At 18 seconds? At 27 seconds?
   c. At what height are you at 126 seconds? How many revolutions have you made?
   d. Predict where you will be at 3 minutes.
2. Sketch a graph showing the relationship between your height above the ground and the time since the ride began. Use $0 \le t \le 144$ for the domain, where $t = 0$ is the time at which the ride starts.
3. **Critical Thinking** How far (in feet) have you traveled after one revolution of the wheel? How far have you traveled at 144 seconds?

A **periodic function** repeats a pattern of y-values (outputs) at regular intervals. One complete pattern is a **cycle.** A cycle may begin at any point on the graph of the function. The **period** of a function is the horizontal length of one cycle.

1 EXAMPLE Identifying Cycles and Periods

Analyze the periodic function below. Identify one cycle in two different ways. Then determine the period of the function.

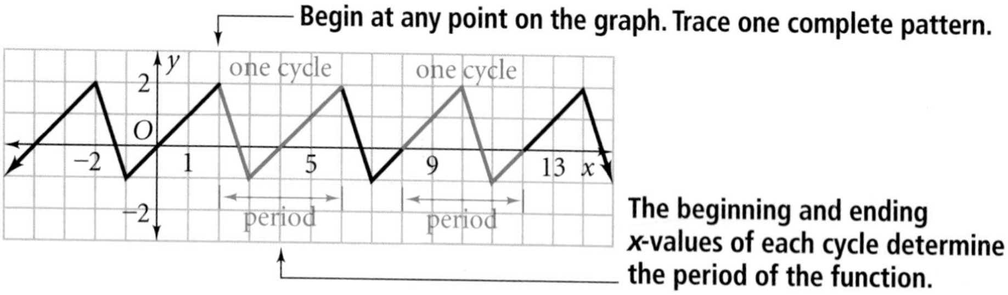

Each cycle is 4 units long. The period of the function is 4.

Check Understanding 1 For each function, identify one cycle in two different ways. Then determine the period of the function.

a.

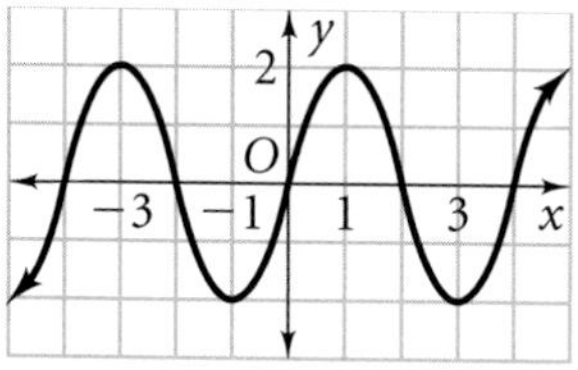

b.

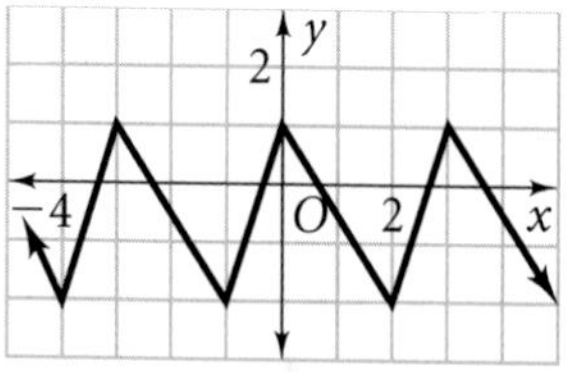

You can determine whether a function is periodic by analyzing its graph.

2 EXAMPLE Identifying Periodic Functions

Determine whether each function *is* or *is not* periodic. If it is, find the period.

a.

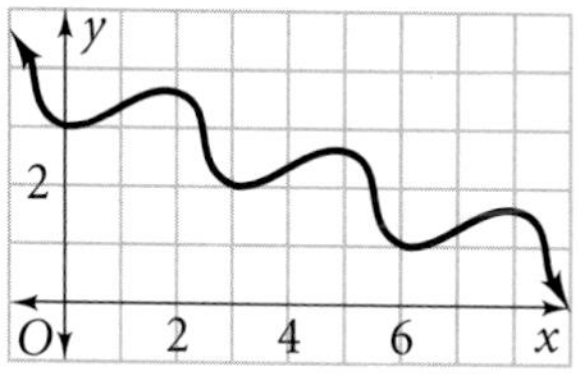

Although the graph shows similar curves, the y-values from one section do not repeat in other sections. The function *is not* periodic.

b.

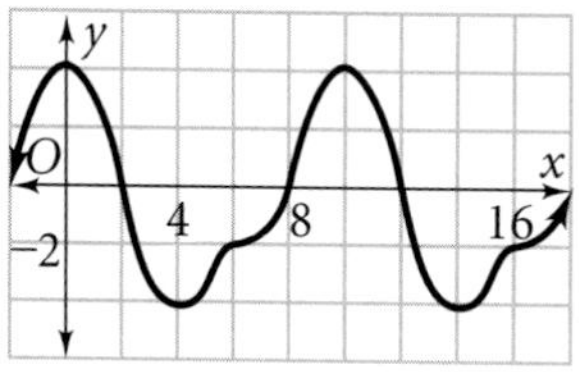

The pattern of y-values in one section repeats exactly in other sections. The function *is* periodic.

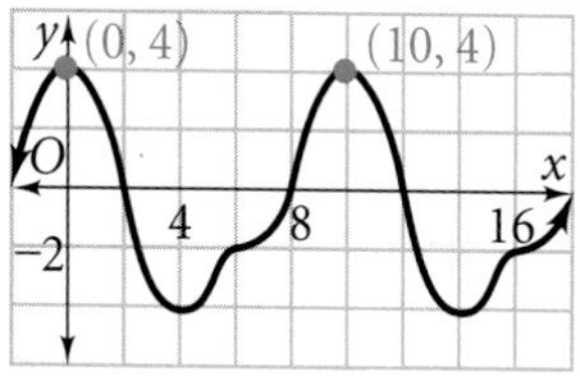

Find points at the beginning and end of one cycle. Subtract the x values of the points: $10 - 0 = 10$. The pattern in the graph repeats every 10 units, so the period is 10.

Check Understanding **2** Determine whether each function *is* or *is not* periodic. If it is, find the period.

a.

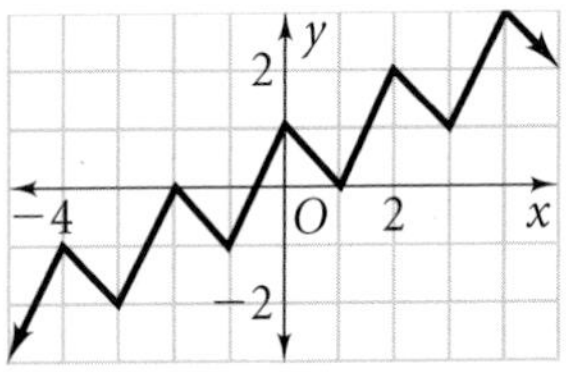

b.

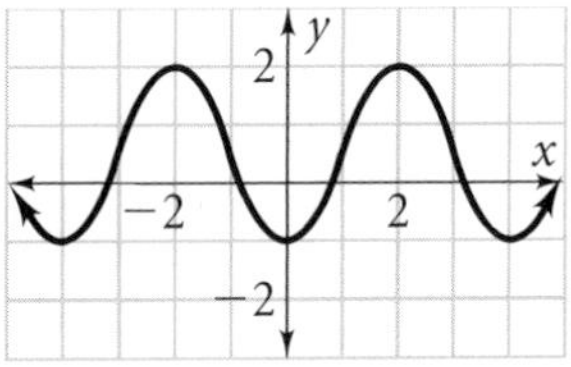

OBJECTIVE

2 Finding the Amplitude of a Periodic Function

Reading Math

Amplitude modulation (AM) radio works by varying the amplitude of radio waves.

The amplitude of a periodic function measures the amount of variation in the function values.

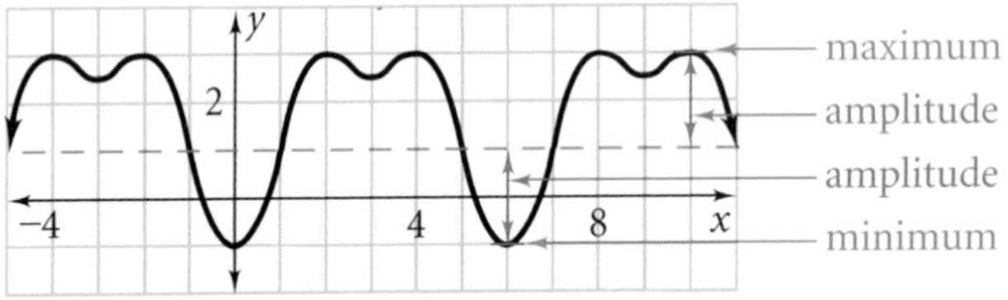

Key Concepts

Definition	**Amplitude of a Periodic Function**
The **amplitude** of a periodic function is half the difference between the maximum and minimum values of the function.	

3 EXAMPLE Finding Amplitude of a Periodic Function

Find the amplitude of the periodic function at the right.

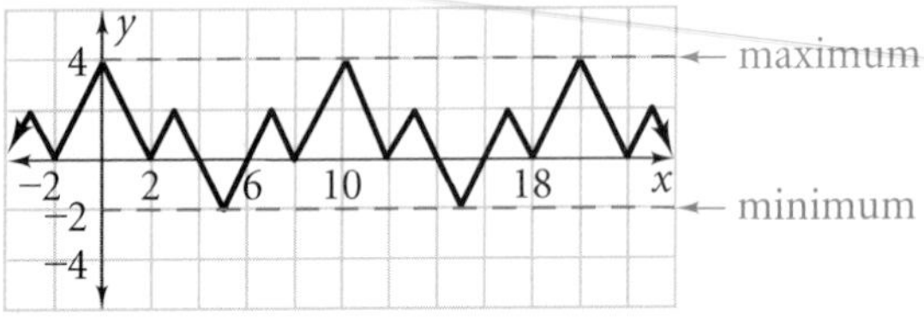

amplitude $= \frac{1}{2}(\text{maximum value} - \text{minimum value})$ **Use the definition of amplitude.**

$= \frac{1}{2}[4 - (-2)]$ **Substitute.**

$= \frac{1}{2}(6) = 3$ **Subtract within parentheses and simplify.**

The amplitude of the function is 3.

Check Understanding **3** Find the amplitude of each function.

a.

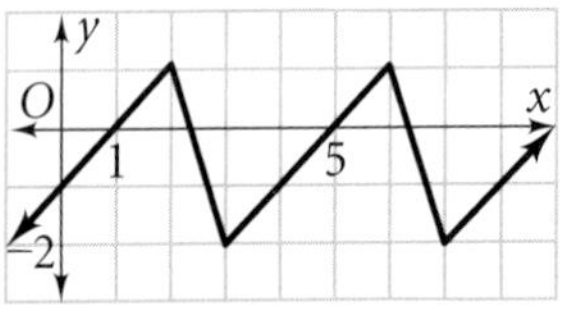

b.

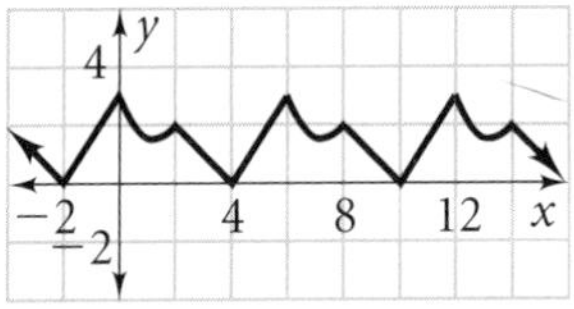

You can model some data with periodic functions. The rotation of a Ferris wheel, the beating of a heart, and the movement of sound waves are all examples of real-world events that generate periodic data.

4 EXAMPLE Real-World Connection

Real-World Connection

A microphone converts sound waves into an electrical signal, which can be shown as a graph on an oscilliscope.

Sound Waves Sound is produced by periodic changes in air pressure called sound waves. The oscilloscope at the right shows the graph of a pure tone from a tuning fork. Find the period and the amplitude of the sound wave.

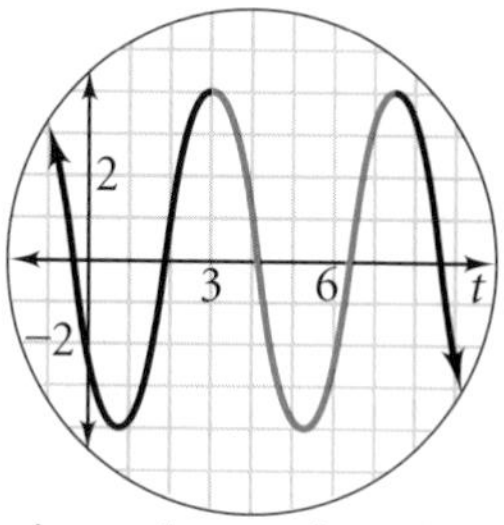

1 unit on the t-axis = 0.001 s

One cycle of the sound wave occurs from 0.003 s to 0.0075 s. The maximum value of the function is 4, and the minimum value is −4.

period $= 0.0075 - 0.003$ **Use the definitions.** amplitude $= \frac{1}{2}[4 - (-4)]$

$= 0.0045$ **Simplify.** $= \frac{1}{2}(8) = 4$

The period of the sound wave is 0.0045 s. The amplitude is 4.

Check Understanding 4 Sketch the graph of a sound wave with a period of 0.004 s and an amplitude of 2.

EXERCISES

For more practice, see *Extra Practice.*

Practice and Problem Solving

A Practice by Example

Example 1 (page 697)

Identify one cycle in two different ways. Then determine the period of the function.

1.

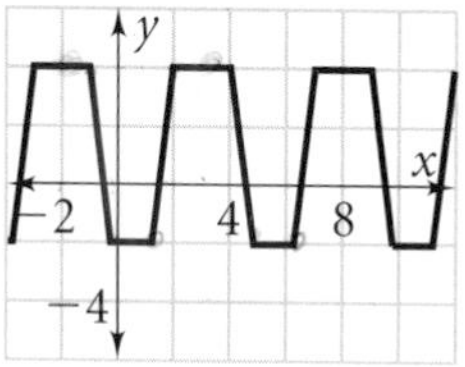

2.

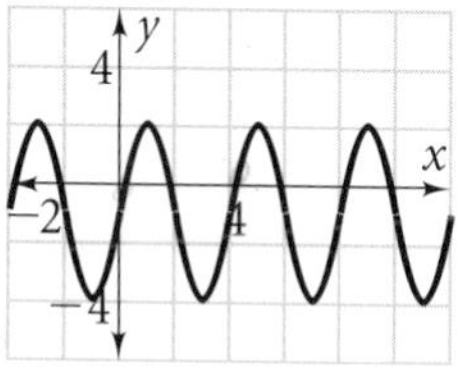

3.

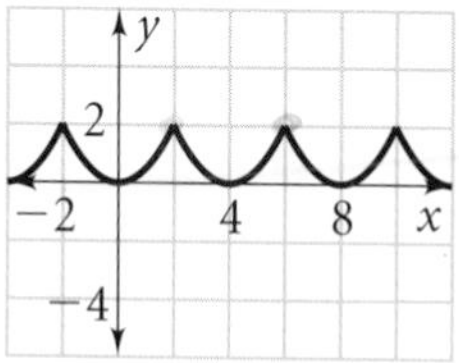

Example 2 (page 697)

Determine whether each function *is* or *is not* periodic. If it is, find the period.

4.

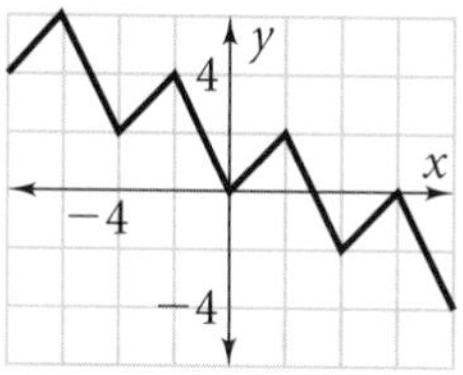

5.

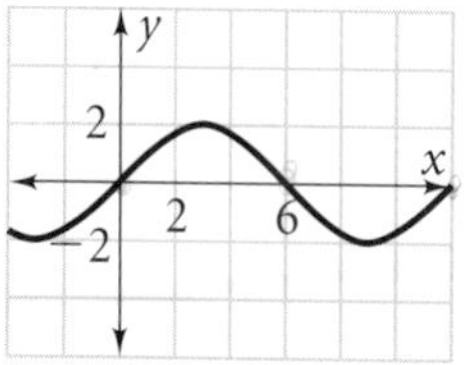

6.

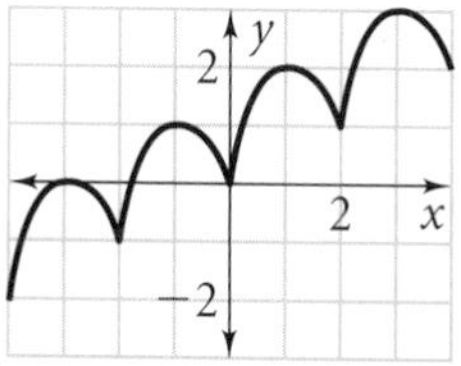

7.

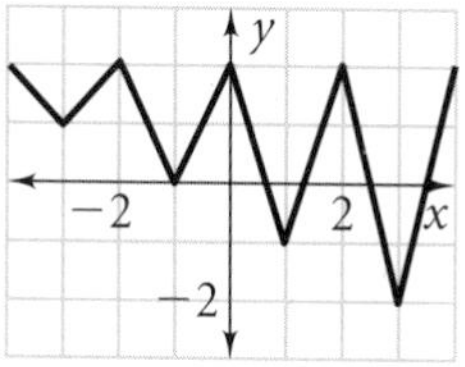

8.

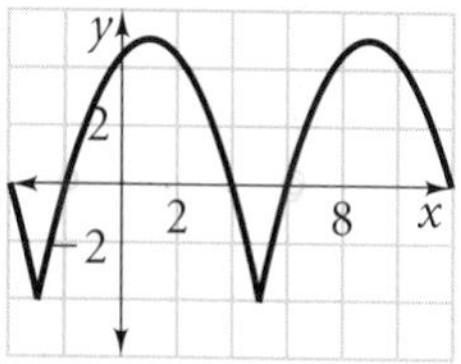

9.

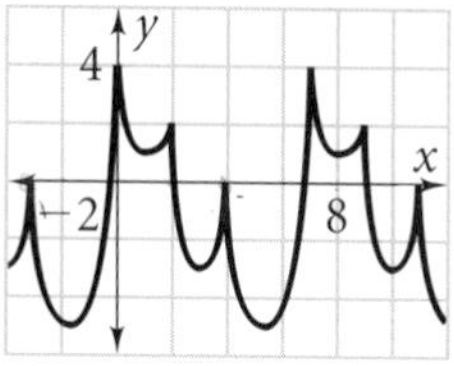

Find the amplitude of each periodic function.

10.

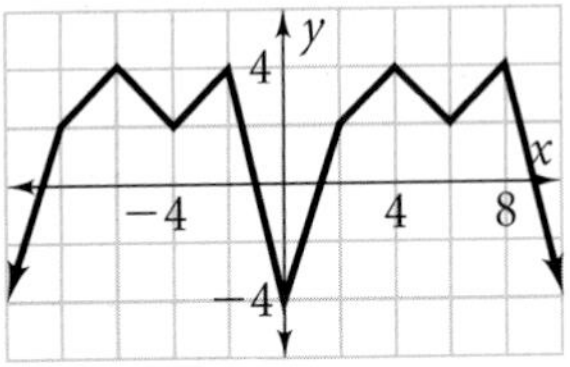

11.

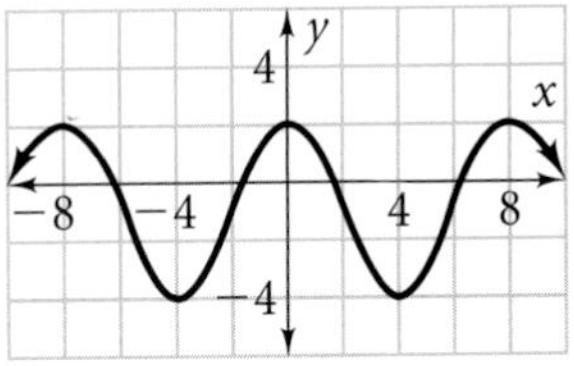

12.

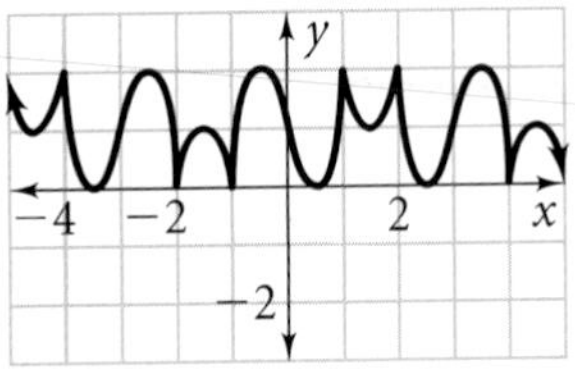

13.

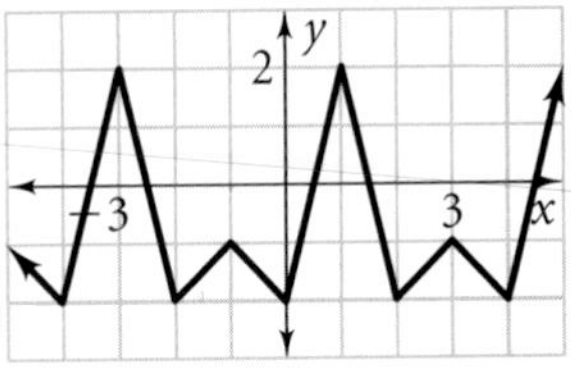

B Apply Your Skills

Sketch the graph of a sound wave with the given period and amplitude.

14. period 0.02, amplitude 4

15. period 0.005, amplitude 9

16. Complete each statement with x or y.

a. You use ■-values to compute the amplitude of a function.

b. You use ■-values to compute the period of a function.

Writing **Could you use a periodic function to represent each situation described below? Explain.**

17. the average monthly temperature in your community, recorded every month for three years

18. the population in your community, recorded every year for the last 50 years

19. the number of cars per hour that pass through an intersection near where you live, recorded for two consecutive work days

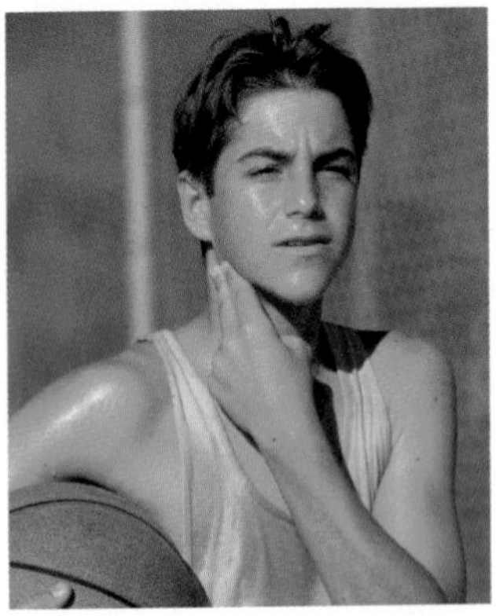

Real-World Connection

The carotid artery of the neck is a commonly used pulse point.

Health **Use the graph below for Exercises 20 and 21.**

20. A person's pulse rate is the number of times his or her heart beats in one minute. Each cycle in the graph represents one heartbeat. Find the pulse rate.

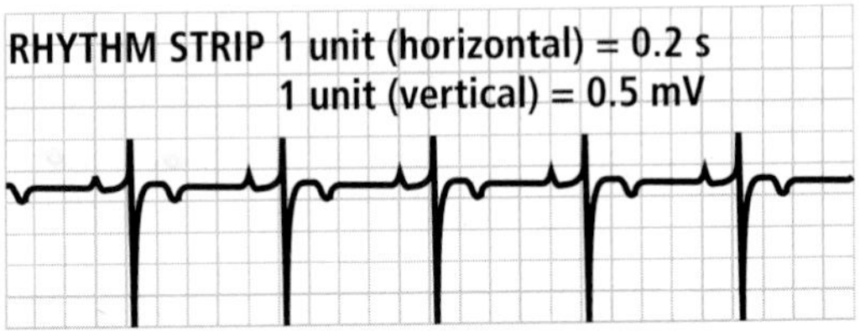

21. An electrocardiogram (EKG or ECG) measures the electrical activity of a person's heart in millivolts over time.

a. What is the period of the EKG shown above?

b. What is the amplitude of the EKG?

22. **Open-Ended** Sketch a graph of a periodic function that has a period of 3 and an amplitude of 2.

Find the maximum, minimum, and period of each periodic function. Then copy the graph and sketch two more cycles.

23.

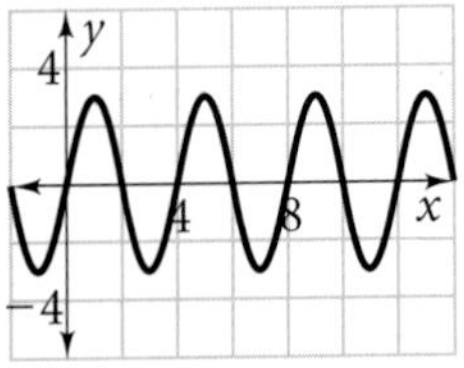

24.

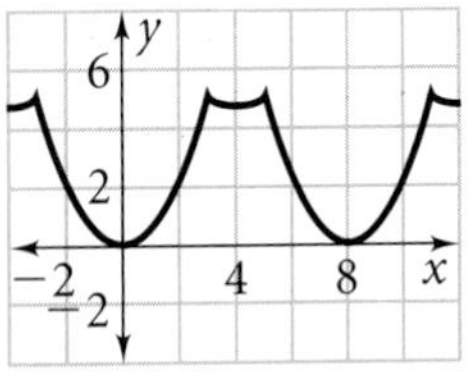

25.

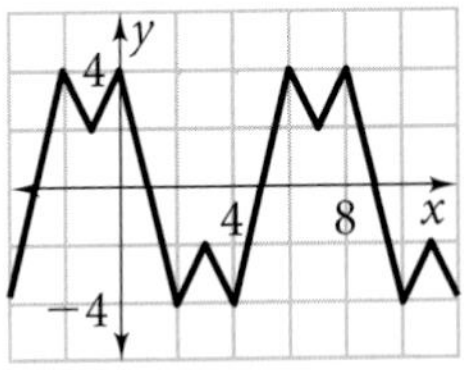

Language Arts **Functions that repeat over time are common in everyday life. The English language has many words that stand for common periods of time. State the period of time from which each term derives.**

26. annual **27.** biweekly **28.** quarterly **29.** hourly **30.** circadian

C Challenge

31. Suppose f is a periodic function. The period of f is 5 and $f(1) = 2$. Find $f(6)$, $f(11)$, and $f(-4)$.

32. Suppose g is a periodic function. The period of g is 24, $g(3) = 67$, and $g(8) = 70$. Find each function value.

a. $g(27)$ **b.** $g(80)$ **c.** $g(-16)$ **d.** $g(51)$

Real-World Connection

Coast Guard rescue jumpers time their pickups for the crests of the waves.

33. Motion You are sitting on a pier watching the waves when you notice a bottle in the water. The bottle bobs so that it is between 2.5 ft and 4.5 ft below the pier. You know you can reach 3 ft below the pier. Suppose the bottle reaches its highest point every 5 s.

a. Sketch a graph of the bottle's distance below the pier for 15 s. Assume that at $t = 0$, the bottle is closest to the pier.

b. Find the period and the amplitude of the function.

c. Estimation Use your graph to estimate the length of time the bottle is within reach during each cycle.

34. Calendar A day—the time Earth takes to rotate from one noon to the next—is a basic measure of time. A solar year is about 365.2422 days. We try to keep our calendar in step with the solar year.

a. If every calendar year has 365 days, by how many days would the calendar year and the solar year differ after 100 years?

b. If every fourth year has an extra "leap" day added, by how many days would the two systems differ after 100 years?

c. If every hundred years the "leap" day is omitted, by how many days would the two systems differ after 100 years?

d. Critical Thinking Why is it important for the difference between the calendar year and the solar year to be zero?

Standardized Test Prep

Multiple Choice

35. A periodic function goes through 5 complete cycles in 4 min. What is the period of the function?

A. $\frac{1}{5}$ min **B.** $\frac{1}{4}$ min **C.** 48 s **D.** 75 s

36. The period of a periodic function is 8 s. How many cycles does it go through in 30 s?

F. $\frac{4}{15}$ cycle **G.** 3.75 cycles **H.** 22 cycles **I.** 240 cycles

37. Which graph is NOT the graph of a periodic function?

I.

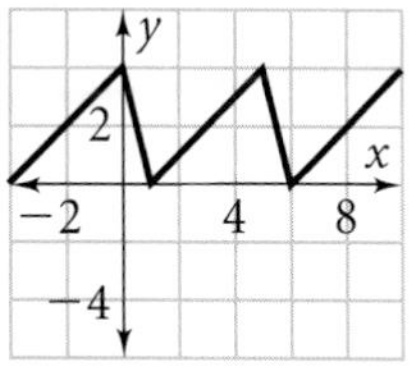

II.

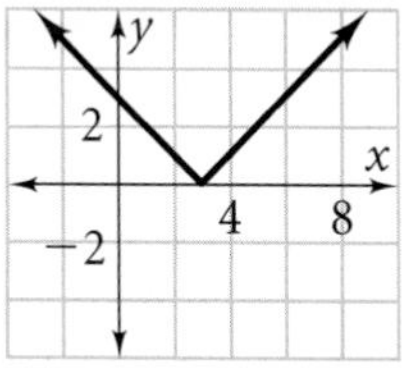

III.

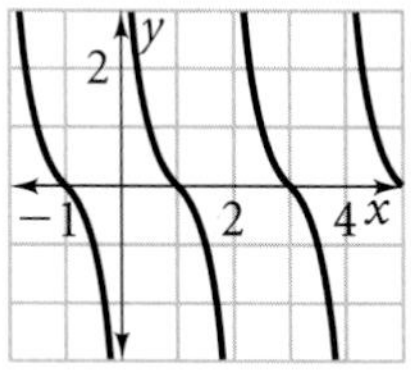

A. I only **B.** II only **C.** III only **D.** II and III

38. The amplitude of a periodic function is 2.5 and its minimum value is 0. What is the function's maximum value?

A. −2.5 **B.** 0 **C.** 2.5 **D.** 5.0

Short Response

39. A periodic function completes *m* cycles in *n* seconds. What is the period of the function? Show your work.

Extended Response

40. A machine begins recording two periodic functions at the same time. The first has a period of 6 s. The second has a period of 7 s. After 20 s, the machine begins recording a third periodic function, with a period of 8 s. How many seconds after the machine begins recording the third function are all three functions at the beginning of their periods? Explain.

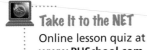

Take It to the NET
Online lesson quiz at **www.PHSchool.com**
Web Code: aga-1301

Mixed Review

Lesson 12-7

41. Sketch a normal curve for a distribution that has mean 57 and standard deviation 12. Label the x-axis values at one, two, and three standard deviations from the mean.

Lesson 11-1

Find the next two terms in each sequence. Write a formula for the *n*th term. Identify each formula as *explicit* or *recursive*.

42. 1, 3, 5, 7, 9, . . .

43. 4, 6, 8, 10, 12, . . .

44. 3, 6, 11, 18, 27, . . .

Lesson 10-6

Write an equation for each conic section. Then sketch the graph.

45. parabola with vertex $(-3, 2)$ and focus $(-3, 7)$

46. hyperbola with center $(5, -3)$, one focus at $(5, 0)$, and one vertex at $(5, -1)$

47. ellipse with center $(-2, 1)$, vertices at $(-6, 1)$ and $(2, 1)$, and co-vertices at $(-2, 3)$ and $(-2, -1)$

A Point in Time

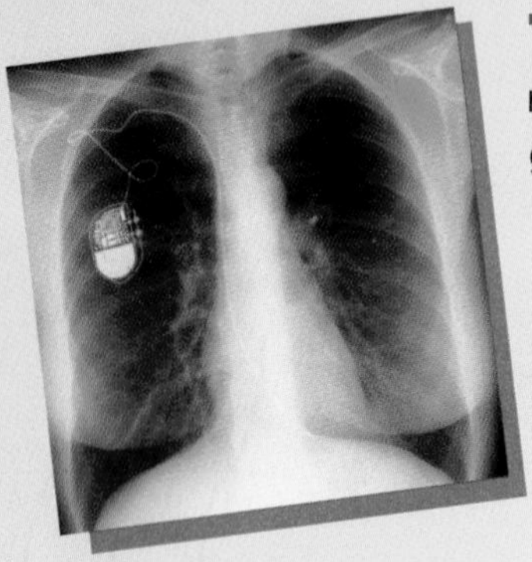

To human beings, the most important periodic function is the rhythm of the heart. About once per second, a nerve in the heart generates an electrical signal. This causes the heart to contract and force blood through the body.

In 1958, doctors placed the first pacemaker in a patient with a malfunctioning nerve. The creator of the device's control unit was Otis Boykin, an inventor from Dallas, Texas. He began his career testing automatic airplane controls. Today, more than a million pacemakers are helping people worldwide enjoy the normal rhythms of the human heart.

Take It to the NET For more information about pacemakers, go to **www.PHSchool.com**.
Web Code: age-2032